ENGINEERING DRAWING

THE

FRENCH DRAWING SERIES

FRENCH, REVISED BY VIERCK

ENGINEERING DRAWING
Seventh Edition
694 pages, 6 x 9, 1278 illustrations

McGRAW-HILL TEXT-FILMS
FOR ENGINEERING DRAWING

A Series of Directly Correlated
Motion Pictures and Filmstrips

FRENCH AND McCULLY—

ENGINEERING DRAWING SHEETS
Series D

FRENCH AND TURNBULL—

LESSONS IN LETTERING
Book I—Vertical Single Stroke Lettering
40 pages, 9 x 6
Book II—Inclined Single Stroke Lettering
40 pages, 9 x 6

FRENCH AND SVENSEN

MECHANICAL DRAWING
Fourth Edition
300 pages, 6 x 9, 618 illustrations

McGRAW-HILL TEXT-FILMS
FOR MECHANICAL DRAWING

A Series of Directly Correlated
Motion Pictures and Filmstrips

FRENCH AND MEIKLEJOHN

ESSENTIALS OF LETTERING
Third Edition
94 pages, 9 x 6, 120 illustrations

A MANUAL OF

ENGINEERING DRAWING

FOR STUDENTS AND DRAFTSMEN

by Thomas E. French

Late Professor of Engineering Drawing, The Ohio State University

REVISED BY

Charles J. Vierck

Professor of Engineering Drawing, The Ohio State University

WITH THE ASSISTANCE OF

Professor Charles D. Cooper, Associate Professor Paul E. Machovina,
Professor Ralph S. Paffenbarger & Associate Professor Hollie W. Shupe
of the Department of Engineering Drawing, The Ohio State University

SEVENTH EDITION
FOURTH IMPRESSION

NEW YORK AND LONDON

McGRAW-HILL BOOK COMPANY, INC.

1947

ENGINEERING DRAWING

FIRST EDITION (August 1911)
Ten Printings, 35,000 copies

SECOND EDITION (July 1918)
Twelve Printings, 108,000 copies

THIRD EDITION (May 1924)
Ten Printings, 96,000 copies

FOURTH EDITION (June 1929)
Ten Printings, 106,000 copies

FIFTH EDITION (April 1935)
Sixteen Printings, 148,000 copies

SIXTH EDITION (May 1941)
Fourteen Printings, 439,700 copies

SEVENTH EDITION (August 1947)
Four Printings, 225,000 copies

Total Issue, 1,157,700 copies

PRINTED IN THE UNITED STATES OF AMERICA

PREFACE TO THE SEVENTH EDITION

As in the previous editions of this book, the aim has again been to keep abreast of modern engineering practice by eliminating the obsolete, revising the old, and adding new material in text and problems. As indicated in the preface to the first edition, the value of a course in drawing lies in the selection, method of presentation, and correlation of the problems with assigned study of the text. In this edition many of the favorite problems of the previous edition have been retained and many new ones representing current design have been added. Some new problems have been arranged in a progressive series and many of the older ones rearranged to make for greater flexibility in their choice.

Since the date of the preceding edition there has been a great deal of emphasis on pictorial drawing and on new standards and practices in dimensioning. It is believed, therefore, that the new chapter on illustration will be appreciated, as will the complete rewriting of the chapter on perspective and the expansion of the chapter on dimensioning into two chapters. Several new projective methods and explanations have also been included. It is hoped that the new material in the text and the rearrangement and expansion of the appendix will make not only a better book for class use but also a more valuable book for the engineer's technical library.

Available with this edition are the McGraw-Hill Text-Films, designed especially for, and correlated with, the text and problems. These visual materials, consisting of motion pictures and filmstrips, have a very high teaching value and illustrate certain features more effectively than is possible by the use of a textbook alone. Thus, these films, added to the previously available series of textbooks, problem books, and lettering books, further extend the coverage of teaching needs.

The undersigned and his colleagues who assisted in this revision are grateful to the scores of teachers of drawing and engineers in industry throughout the country, many of whom are personal friends, for helpful suggestions, encouraging comment, and valuable ideas. The interest and assistance of the author's other colleagues in the department of engineering drawing is recorded with appreciation, as is also the help of A. J. Philby and F. E. Watkins on the drawings.

C. J. V.

COLUMBUS, OHIO
July, 1947.

PREFACE TO THE FIRST EDITION

There is a wide diversity of method in the teaching of engineering drawing, and perhaps less uniformity in the courses in different schools than would be found in most subjects taught in technical schools and colleges. In some well-known instances the attempt is made to teach the subject by giving a series of plates to be copied by the student. Some give all the time to laboratory work; others depend principally upon recitations and homework. Some begin immediately on the theory of descriptive geometry, working in all the angles; others discard theory and commence with a course in machine detailing. Some advocate the extensive use of models; some condemn their use entirely.

Different courses have been designed for different purposes, and criticism is not intended, but it would seem that better unity of method might result if there were a better recognition of the conception that drawing is a real language, to be studied and taught in the same way as any other language. With this conception it may be seen that except for the practice in the handling and use of instruments, and for showing certain standards of execution, copying drawings does little more in the study as an art of expression of thought than copying paragraphs from a foreign book would do in beginning the study of a foreign language.

And it would appear equally true that good pedagogy would not advise taking up composition in a new language before the simple structure of the sentence is understood and appreciated; that is, "working drawings" would not be considered until after the theory of projection has been explained.

After a knowledge of the technic of expression, the "penmanship and orthography," the whole energy should be directed toward training in constructive imagination, the perceptive ability which enables one to think in three dimensions, to visualize quickly and accurately, to build up a clear mental image, a requirement absolutely necessary for the designer who is to represent his thoughts on paper. That this may be accomplished more readily by taking up solids before points and lines has been demonstrated beyond dispute.

It is then upon this plan, regarding drawing as a language, the universal graphical language of the industrial world, with its varied forms of expression, its grammar and its styles, that this book has been built. It is not a "course in drawing," but a textbook, with exercises and problems in some variety from which selections may be made.

Machine parts furnish the best illustrations of principles, and have been used freely, but the book is intended for all engineering students. Chapters on architectural drawing and map drawing have been added, as in the interrelation of the professions every engineer should be able to read and work from such drawings.

In teaching the subject, part of the time, at least one hour per week, may profitably be scheduled for class lectures, recitations, and blackboard work, at which time there may be distributed "study sheets" or home plates of problems on the assigned lesson, to be drawn in pencil and returned at the next corresponding period. In the drawing-room period, specifications for plates, to be approved in pencil and some finished by inking or tracing, should be assigned, all to be done under the careful supervision of the instructor.

The judicious use of models is of great aid, both in technical sketching and, particularly, in drawing to scale, in aiding the student to feel the sense of proportion between the drawing and the structure, so that in reading a drawing he may have the ability to visualize not only the shape but the size of the object represented.

In beginning drawing it is not advisable to use large plates. One set of commercial drafting-room sizes is based on the division of a 36″ × 48″ sheet into 24″ × 36″, 18″ × 24″, 12″ × 18″, and 9″ × 12″. The size 12″ × 18″ is sufficiently large for first year work, while 9″ × 12″ is not too small for earlier plates.

Grateful acknowledgment is made of the assistance of Messrs. Robert Meiklejohn, O. E. Williams, A. C. Harper, Cree Sheets, F. W. Ives, W. D. Turnbull, and W. J. Norris of the staff of the Department of Engineering Drawing, The Ohio State University, not only in the preparation of the drawings, but in advice and suggestion on the text. Other members of the faculty of this University have aided by helpful criticism.

The aim has been to conform to modern engineering practice, and it is hoped that the practical consideration of the draftsman's needs will give the book permanent value as a reference book in the student's library.

The author will be glad to cooperate with teachers using it as a textbook.

T.E.F.

Columbus, Ohio
June 6, 1911.

CONTENTS

TEXT-FILMS

A brief description of each McGraw-Hill Text-Film available for use with this textbook is given at the end of the chapter with which the film is correlated.

The following Text-Film is designed as an orientation film to be used in conjunction with Chap. 1:

According to Plan: Introduction to Engineering Drawing (10-min. sound motion picture).

This film is designed for use at the beginning of the course to introduce the student to the subject of engineering drawing. It shows that engineering drawing is the working language of the engineer, indicates why it is important, and gives an insight into the relation between modern methods of production and engineering drawing.

Chapter 1

INTRODUCTORY

1·1 Engineering drawing is the graphic language used in the industrial world by engineers and designers to express and record the ideas and information necessary for the building of machines and structures.

As distinguished from drawing as a fine art, practiced by artists in pictorial representation, engineering drawing is a descriptive graphical language, whereas drawing as a fine art is a means of aesthetic expression. The artist strives to produce, from either the model or landscape before him or through his creative imagination, a picture which will impart to the observer the same mental impression as that produced by the object itself, or the object's visualization in the artist's mind. By employing color, gradation of tone in monotone light and shade, or line combinations in black and white, he is able to suggest his meanings and to depend upon the observer's imagination to visualize the effect of perspective foreshortening and to supply the lack of complete detail.

The engineering draftsman has a more exacting task. Limited usually to outline alone (shading is not often used, except for illustrations), he may not depend upon suggested meanings but must give precise and positive information regarding every detail of the machine or structure existing in his imagination. Thus drawing to him is more than pictorial representation; it is a complete graphical language, by whose aid he may describe minutely every operation necessary and may keep a complete record of the work for duplication and repairs.

By a logical system of related "views," intricate and complicated shapes are clearly shown; exact and detailed sizes are given without ambiguity; individual parts are identified for assembly and are located in the machine in their correct functional position. In addition, descriptive notes and specifications give materials, finishes, and directions for manufacture and assembly.

In the artist's case, the result can be understood in greater or less degree by anyone. The draftsman's result does not show the object as it would appear to the eye when finished; consequently his drawing can be read and understood only by one trained in the language.

Thus, as the foundation upon which all designing and subsequent manufacture are based, engineering drawing becomes, with the possible exception of mathematics, the most important single branch of study in a technical school. Every engineering student must know how to make and how to read drawings. The subject is essential in all types of engineering practice.

The drafting room is often the entering gateway into industry, but even one who may never have to make drawings must be able to interpret them and to know whether or not a drawing is correct. An engineer without a working knowledge of the engineer's language would be professionally illiterate.

1·2 To write this language easily and accurately the aid of drawing instruments is required. When these implements are used it is called "mechanical drawing"[1] or "instrument drawing." When done with the unaided hand, without the assistance of instruments or appliances, it is known as "freehand drawing" or "technical sketching." Training in both of these methods is necessary for the engineer, the first to develop accuracy and manual dexterity, the second to develop comprehensive observation and to give control and mastery of form and proportion.

Our object, then, is to study this language so that we may write it, express ourselves clearly to one familiar with it, and read it readily when written by another. To do this we must know its basic theory, its composition, and be familiar with its accepted conventions and abbreviations. This language is universal, as its principles are essentially the same throughout the world, and one trained in the practices of one nation can readily adapt himself to the practices of another.

This new language is entirely a graphical or written one. It cannot be read aloud, but must be interpreted by acquiring a visual knowledge of the subject represented; and the student's success in it will be indicated not alone by his skill in execution, but also by his ability to interpret his impressions and to visualize clearly in space.

It is not a language to be learned only by the comparatively few draftsmen who will be professional writers of it, but, as already indicated, should be understood by all connected with, or interested in, technical industry. The training its study gives in quick, accurate observation and the power of reading description from lines is of a value quite unappreciated by those not familiar with it.

In this study we must first of all become familiar with the technique of expression, and, as instruments are used for accurate work, an important requirement is the ability to use these instruments correctly. Continued practice will develop a facility in their use that will free the mind from any thought of the means of expression. Under technique is included the study of lettering, usually the first work taken up in a technical course.

[1] The term "mechanical drawing" is often applied to all industrial graphics and, although an unfortunate misnomer, has the sanction of long usage.

Chapter 2

THE SELECTION OF INSTRUMENTS

2·1 In the selection of instruments and materials for drawing, the only general advice that can be given is to secure the *best* that can be afforded. For one who expects to do work of professional grade, it is a great mistake to buy inferior instruments. Sometimes a beginner is tempted by the suggestion that he get cheap instruments for learning, with the expectation of getting better ones later. With reasonable care a set of good instruments will last a lifetime, while poor ones will be an annoyance from the start and will be worthless after short usage. As poor instruments look so much like good ones that an amateur is unable to distinguish them, trustworthy advice should be sought before buying.

This chapter will be devoted to a short description of the instruments usually necessary for drawing. Mention of some others not in everyday use, but convenient for special work, will be found in Chap. 30.

2·2 Check list of instruments and materials.

1. Set of drawing instruments, including at least: 6″ compasses with fixed needle-point leg, removable pencil and pen legs, and lengthening bar; 6″ hairspring dividers; 3½″ bow pencil, bow pen, and bow dividers; two ruling pens; box of leads.
2. Drawing board.
3. T square.
4. 45° and 30°-60° triangles.
5. Three mechanical engineer's scales of proportional feet and inches, flat pattern, or the equivalent triangular scale.
6. Lettering instrument or triangle.
7. French curves.
8. Drawing pencils, 6H, 4H, 2H, H, and F.
9. Pocketknife or pencil sharpener.
10. Pencil pointer (file or sandpaper).
11. Pencil eraser (Ruby).
12. Artgum or cleaning rubber.
13. Penholder, pens for lettering, and penwiper.
14. Bottle of drawing ink and bottleholder.
15. Thumbtacks or scotch drafting tape.
16. Drawing paper to suit.
17. Tracing paper and cloth.
18. Dusting cloth or brush.

To these may be added:

19. Civil engineer's scale.
20. Protractor.
21. Erasing shield.
22. Slide rule.
23. 2′ folding or 6′ flexible rule.
24. Sketchbook.
25. Hard Arkansas oilstone.
26. Piece of soapstone.

The student should mark all his instruments and materials plainly with initials or name as soon as purchased and approved.

2·3 Instrument joints. Modern high-grade instruments are made with some form of pivot joint, originally patented by Theodore Alteneder in

1850 and again in 1871. Older instruments, and some cheap modern ones, made with tongue joints and a through bolt or pin, are unsatisfactory as wear of the tongue and pin results in lost motion which, after a time, renders the instrument unfit for use. In the pivot joint, however, the wear is on adjustable conical or spherical surfaces. The Alteneder joint and several modifications of it are shown in Fig. 2·1.

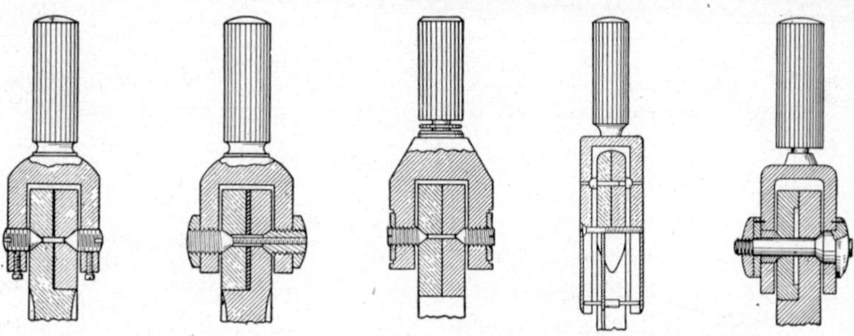

FIG. 2·1—Sections of pivot joints.

The handle attached to the yoke, although not essential to the working of the joint, is very convenient. Not all instruments with handles, however, are pivot-joint instruments. Several straightener devices for keeping the handle erect have been made, but some designs are not good, as pressure upon the handle may change the setting of the instrument.

2·4 Instrument patterns. There are three different patterns or shapes in which modern instruments are made, the beveled, or American (*A*), the round (*B*), and the flat (*C*), Fig. 2·2. The choice of shapes is entirely a matter of personal preference. After one has become accustomed to the balance and feel of a certain instrument he will not wish to exchange it for another shape.

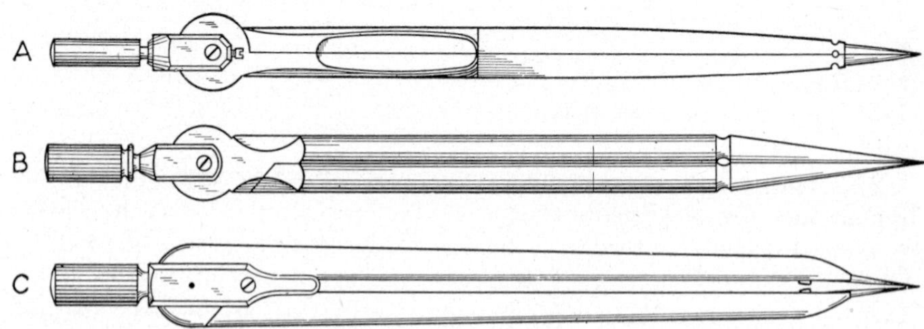

FIG. 2·2—The three patterns.

2·5 Compasses. Compasses are usually preferred in combination style, 6 inches long, with fixed needle-point leg, removable pen and pencil legs, and lengthening bar, Fig. 2·3. A favorite additional instrument with some draftsmen is the 4-inch size with fixed pencil leg, and its companion with fixed pen leg. Compasses may be tested for accuracy by bending the knuckle joints and bringing the points together as in Fig. 2·4. If out of alignment, they should not be accepted.

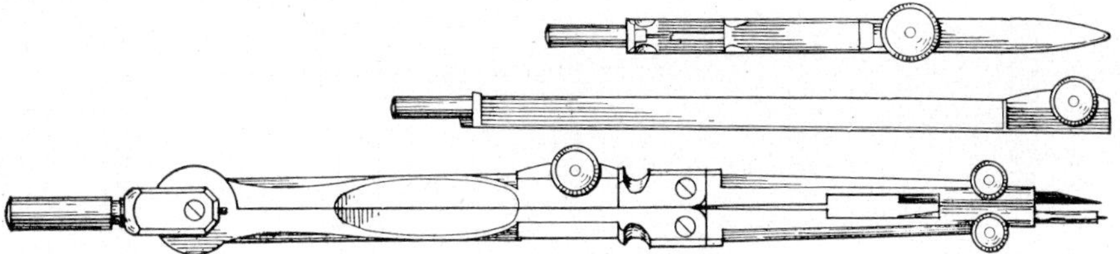

FIG. 2·3—The large compasses.

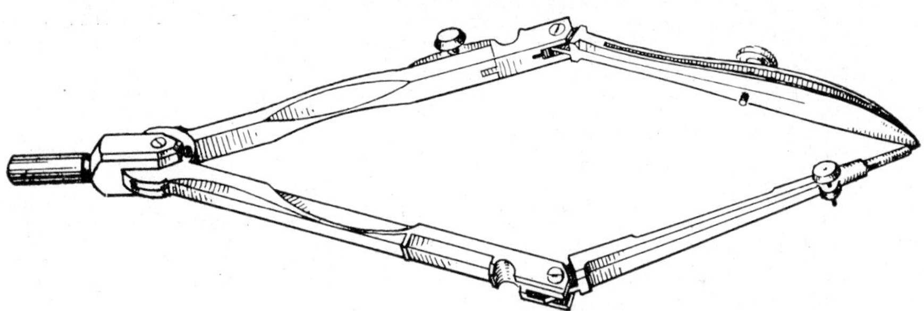

FIG. 2·4—Test for alignment.

2·6 Dividers. Dividers are made either "plain," as those in Fig. 2·2, or "hairspring," as shown in Fig. 2·5. The latter form, having a screw for fine adjustment, is occasionally convenient and is to be preferred. Compasses may also be had with hairspring attachment on the needle-point leg.

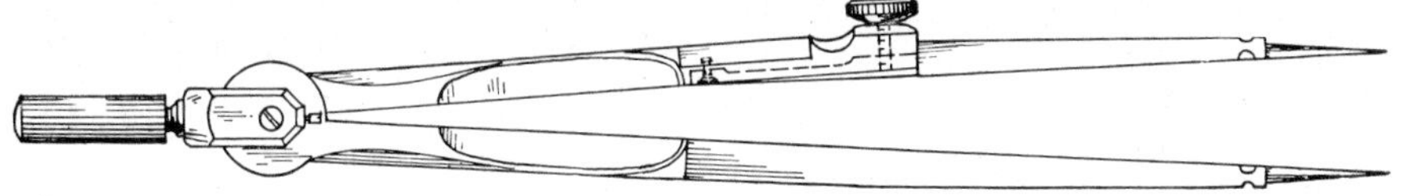

FIG. 2·5—Hairspring dividers.

2·7 Spring bow instruments. The smaller variety of compasses and dividers includes bow points or spacers, bow pencil, and bow pen. There are several designs and sizes. The standard pattern, illustrated at *A*, *B*, *C*, and *E*, Fig. 2·6, has a steel spring as an integral part of the legs and is essentially one-piece construction. At *D* is illustrated the hook or ring-spring type, sometimes called "Richter" bows. Both standard and Richter types are available as side-screw bows, *A*, *B*, *C*, *D*, and also as center-screw instruments illustrated by the center-screw bow pen *E*. Both types are equally popular among draftsmen. The springs of bow instruments should be strong enough to open to the full length of the screw but not so stiff as to be difficult to pinch together.

2·8 Ruling pens. Ruling pens are made in a variety of forms, Fig. 2·7. The two most popular ones are the spring blade (*A*), which opens sufficiently wide for cleaning, and the jackknife (*E*), which may be cleaned

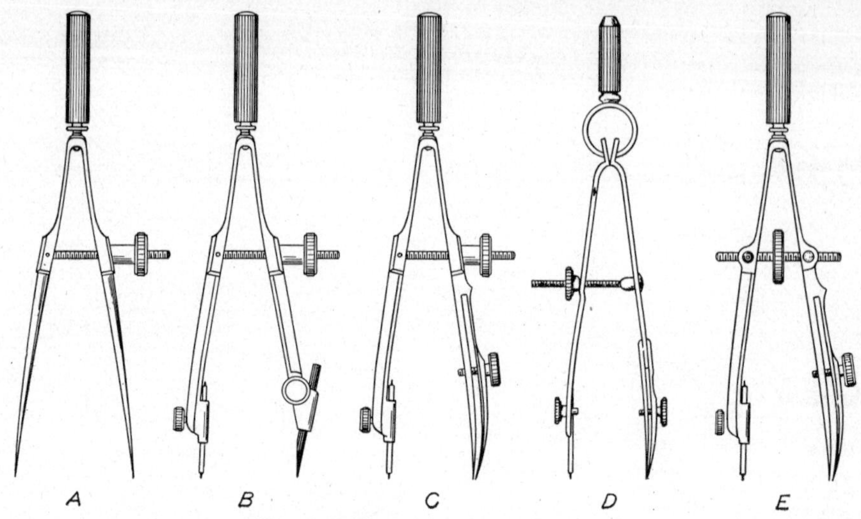

FIG. 2·6—Spring bow instruments.

without changing the setting. The types shown at *B*, *C*, and *D* have special devices to allow the pen to be opened for cleaning. The form shown at *F* is known as a "detail pen" or "Swede pen," which is a very desirable

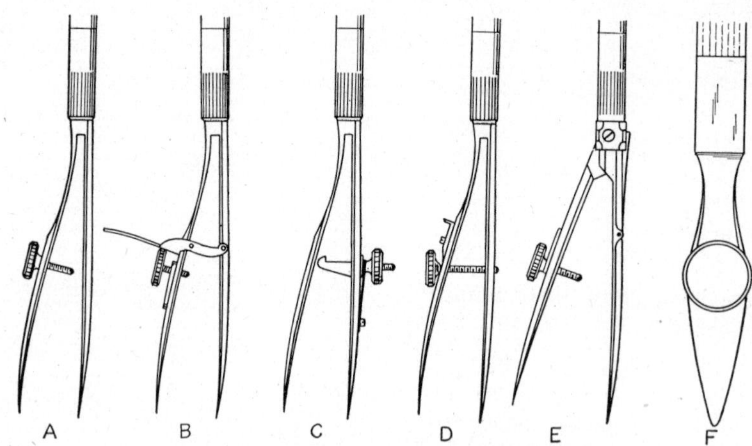

FIG. 2·7—Ruling pens, opened for cleaning.

instrument for large work or long lines. The nibs of pens should be shaped as shown in Fig. 3·21. Pens sometimes come from the factory poorly sharpened and must be dressed as described on page 25 before they can be used.

2·9 Detailer's set. A comparatively new combination of drawing instruments that has been received favorably, particularly in the automotive industry, is shown in Fig. 2·8. It consists of a large sturdy bow instrument, sometimes with interchangeable pen, pencil, and spacer points, along with a tubular beam compass for large circles. The compass pen inserted in a handle provides a ruling pen.

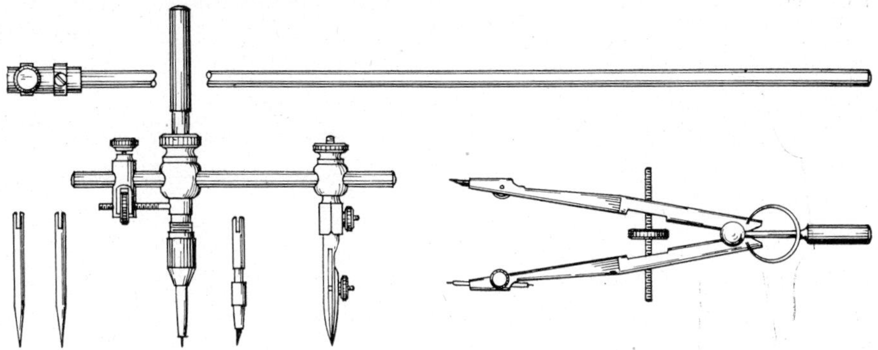

FIG. 2·8—Detailer's set.

2·10 Drawing boards. The drawing surface may be either the tabletop itself or a separate board. In either case, the working surface should be made of clear white pine, cleated to prevent warping. The working edge must be straight and should be tested with a steel straightedge. Some boards and tabletops are supplied with a hardwood edge or a steel insert on the working edge, thus ensuring a better wearing surface.

2·11 The T square. The fixed-head T square, Fig. 2·9*A*, is used for all ordinary work. It should be of hardwood, and the blade should be

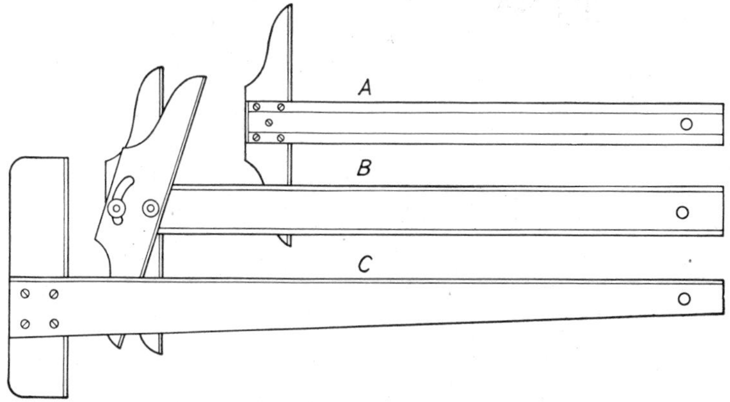

FIG. 2·9—T squares: fixed head, adjustable head, and English forms.

perfectly straight. The transparent-edged blade is much the best. A draftsman will have several fixed-head squares of different lengths and will find an adjustable-head square (*B*) of occasional use. The form shown at *C* is the English type with tapered blade and beveled edge. As a long square, it has an advantage in balance and rigidity but has the objection that the lower edge is apt to disturb the draftsman's sense of perpendicularity. A T-square blade may be tested for straightness by drawing a sharp line through two points and then turning the square over and with the same edge drawing another line through the points, as shown in Fig. 2·10.

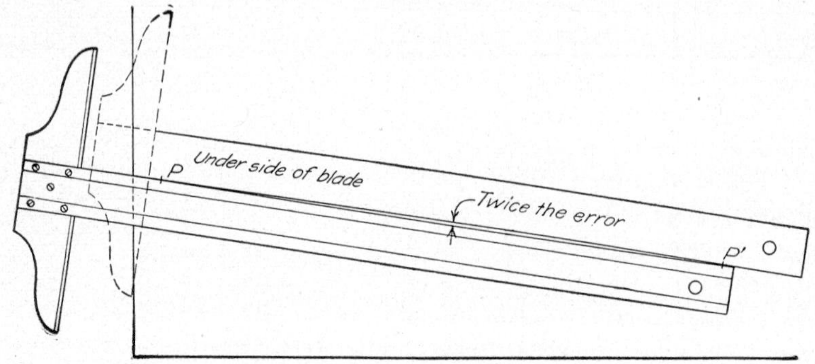

FIG. 2·10—To test a T square.

2·12 Triangles. Transparent celluloid (fiberloid) triangles are much to be preferred over wooden ones. Through internal strains they sometimes lose their accuracy. They should therefore be tested periodically by drawing a perpendicular line, then reversing the triangle and drawing another perpendicular, as shown in Fig. 2·11. For ordinary work, a 6″ or 8″ 45-degree and a 10″ 60-degree are good sizes. Triangles should always be kept flat to prevent warping.

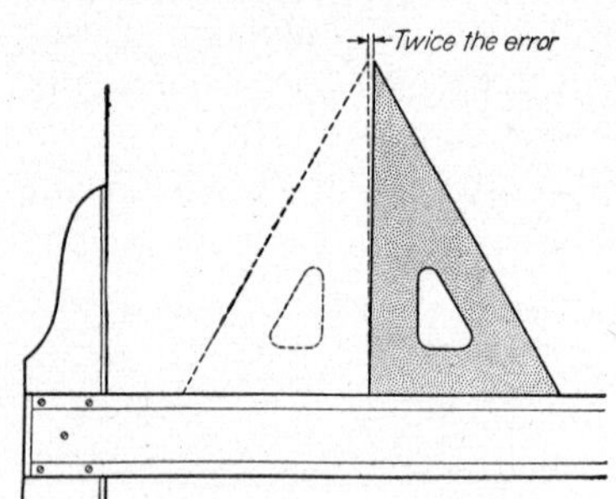

FIG. 2·11—To test a triangle.

2·13 Scales. There are two general classes of scales, (1) the mechanical engineer's and architect's scales, Fig. 2·12, with lengths on the scale representing one foot (12, 6, 3, 1½, etc., *inches to the foot*); and (2) civil engineer's scales divided in decimals, Fig. 2·13, with divisions of 10, 20, 30, 40, 50,

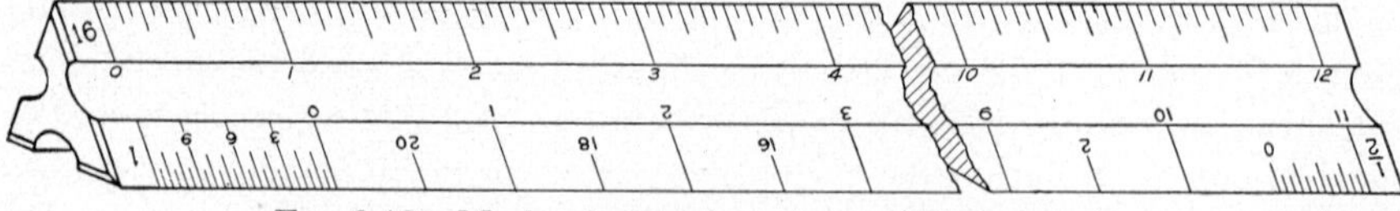

FIG. 2·12—Mechanical engineer's or architect's scale.

and 60 *feet to the inch*. Trade names for these two types are apt to confuse beginning students, as the dealers call the first type "architect's scales," and the second type "engineer's scales," whereas the first type is used not only by architects, but by all engineers—mechanical, electrical, industrial, chemical, mine, and civil—for drawings of machines and structures; the second type is used principally by civil engineers for plotting, map drawing, and the graphic solution of problems.

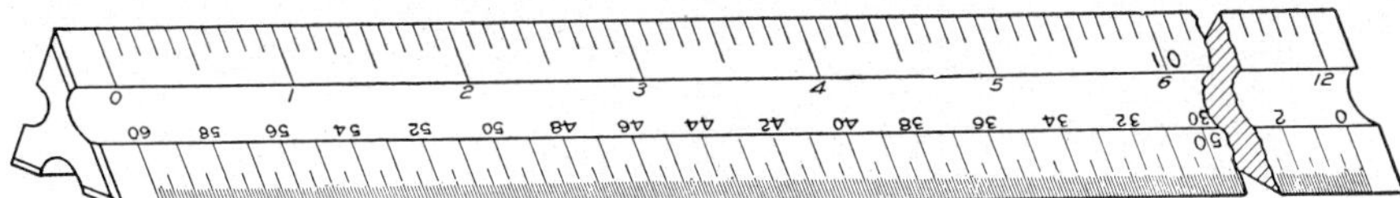

FIG. 2·13—Civil engineer's scale.

Scales are usually made of boxwood, sometimes of metal, plastic, or paper. The triangular form shown in cross section at *A* and *B*, Fig. 2·14, is the commonest. Its only advantage is that it has more scales on one stick than the others, but this is offset by the delay in finding the scale wanted. Three double-edged flat scales are the equivalent of one triangular scale. The "single-bevel" scale *C* and "double-bevel" *D* are common forms of flat scales. The "opposite-bevel" *E* and the "beveled-both-sides" scale *F* are easier to pick up than the regular forms *C* and *D*. Many professional draftsmen use a set of six or eight scales, each graduated in one division only. A very popular scale among machine draftsmen is the opposite-bevel "full-divided" flat scale with full size on one edge and half size on the other, Fig. 2·15, and a second with quarter and eighth sizes.

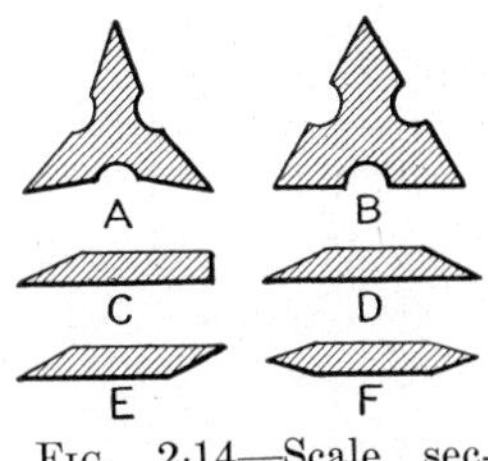

FIG. 2·14—Scale sections.

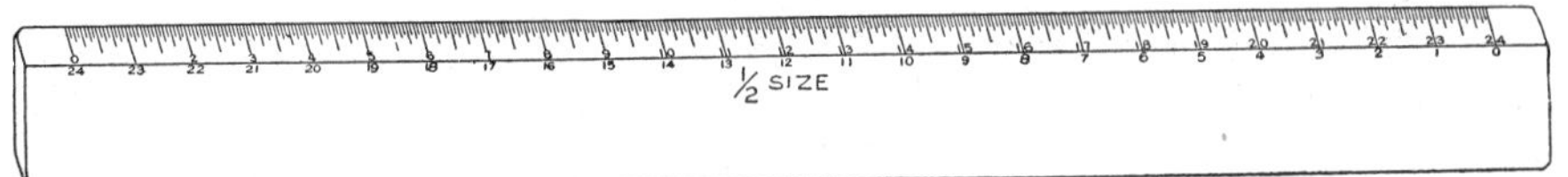

FIG. 2·15—A full- and half-size scale.

2·14 Lettering devices. The Ames lettering instrument and the Braddock-Rowe triangle, Figs. 4·3 and 4·2, are convenient devices used in drawing guide lines for lettering.

2·15 Curves. Curved rulers, called "irregular curves" or "french curves," are used for curved lines other than circle arcs. The patterns for these curves are laid out in parts of ellipses and spirals or other mathematical curves in various combinations. For the student, one ellipse curve of the general shape of Fig. 2·16 *A* or *D*, and one spiral, either a log spiral *B* or one similar to the one used in Fig. 3·34, will be sufficient. *C* is a useful small curve.

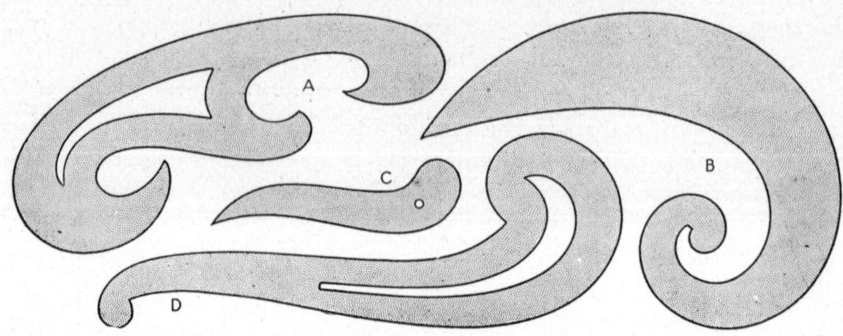

Fig. 2·16—Irregular curves.

2·16 Drawing pencils. The manufacturers grade drawing pencils by numbers and letters from 6B, very soft and black, through 5B, 4B, 3B, 2B, B, and HB to F, the medium grade; then H, 2H, 3H, 4H, 5H, 6H, 7H, and 8H to 9H, the hardest. The soft (B) grades are used primarily for sketching and rendered drawings, and the hard (H) grades for instrument drawings. Some draftsmen prefer a holder using standard-size drawing-lead fillers.

2·17 Pencil pointer. After the wood of the ordinary pencil is cut away with a pocketknife or mechanical sharpener, the lead must be formed to a long conical point. A lance-tooth file about six inches long is fine for the purpose. Some draftsmen prefer the standard sandpaper pencil-pointer pad, Fig. 3·1.

2·18 Erasers. The Ruby pencil eraser, large size with beveled ends, is the standard. This eraser not only removes pencil lines effectively but is much better for ink than the so-called ink eraser, as it will remove the ink perfectly without seriously damaging the surface of paper or cloth. A good metal erasing shield aids in getting clean erasures.

Artgum or a *soft* rubber eraser is useful for cleaning paper and cloth of finger marks and smears that spoil the appearance of the completed drawing.

2·19 Penholders and pens. The penholder should have a grip of medium size, small enough to enter the mouth of a drawing ink bottle easily, yet not so small as to cramp the fingers while in use. A size slightly larger than the diameter of a pencil is good.

An assortment of pens for lettering, grading from course to fine, may be chosen from those listed in Chap. 4.

A penwiper of lintless cloth or thin chamois skin should always be at hand for both lettering and ruling pens.

2·20 Drawing ink. Drawing ink is finely ground carbon in suspension, with natural or synthetic gum added to render the mixture waterproof. Nonwaterproof ink flows more freely but smudges very easily. Drawing ink diluted with distilled water, or Chinese ink in stick form rubbed up with water in a slate slab, is used in making wash drawings and for very fine line work.

Bottleholders prevent the possibility of ruining the drawing, table, or floor by ink from an upset bottle. They are made in various patterns, one of which is illustrated in Fig. 2·17. As a temporary substitute, the lower half of the paper container in which the ink was sold may be fastened to the table with a thumbtack, or a strip of paper or cloth with a hole for the neck of the bottle may be tacked down over the bottle.

2·21 Thumbtacks. The best thumbtacks have thin heads with steel points screwed into them. Cheaper one are made by stamping. Tacks with tapering pins of small diameter should be chosen. Flat-headed (often colored) map pins should not be used, as the heads are too thick and the pins rather large.

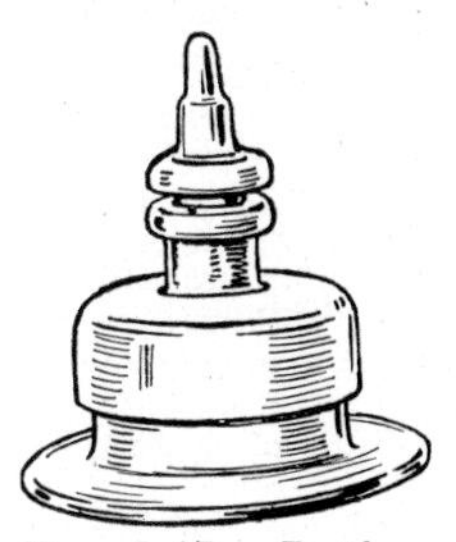

FIG. 2·17 — Bottleholder.

2·22 Drafting tape. Scotch drafting tape is popular as a means of fastening paper to the drawing board. It may be used either by sticking a short piece across each corner or by taping the entire edge of the paper. There is a distinction between "drafting tape" and "masking tape" (made by the same company) in that the latter has a heavier coating of adhesive and does not come off the drawing paper so cleanly as the former.

2·23 Drawing paper. Paper for drawing purposes is made in a variety of qualities with varying prices and may be had in either sheets or rolls. White drawing papers that will not turn yellow with age or exposure are used for finished drawings, maps, charts, and drawings for photographic reproduction. For pencil layouts and working drawings, cream or buff detail papers are easier on the eyes, do not show soil so quickly as white papers, and are therefore preferred. In general, paper should have sufficient grain or "tooth" to take the pencil, be agreeable to the eye, have a hard surface not easily "grooved" by the pencil, with good erasing qualities. Formerly, imported papers were considered superior to American-made products, but our mills are now making practically all the paper used in this country. The cheap manila papers should be avoided. A few cents more per yard is well spent in the increased satisfaction gained from working on good paper.

2·24 Tracing papers. Tracing papers are thin papers, either *natural* or *transparentized,* through which drawings are traced, either in pencil or ink, and from which blueprints or similar contact prints can be made. In many drafting rooms, original drawings are being penciled on tracing papers, and blueprints made directly from these drawings, a practice increasingly successful because of the improvements both in papers and in printing. Tracing papers vary widely in color, thickness, surface, etc., and the grade of pencil and the technique must be adjusted to suit the paper. With the proper combination, however, good resulting prints may be obtained.

2·25 Tracing cloth. Finely woven cloth coated with a special starch or plastic is used for making drawings in either pencil or ink. The standard tracing cloth is used for inked tracings, and specially made pencil cloth for pencil drawings or tracings. The advantage of cloth is that it will stand more handling than paper and is thus more permanent. Tracing and duplicating processes are described in Chap. 15.

2·26 The slide rule. Although not a drawing instrument, the slide rule is essentially an engineer's tool, and proficiency in its use is a requirement of every modern drafting room. A good way for a beginner to learn to use a slide rule is in connection with a drawing course. Its use facilitates the rapid calculations of volumes and weights as an aid in reading drawings, or later as an essential part of drafting work. Of the several varieties of slide rules, those recommended for prospective engineers are a Polyphase Duplex[1] or a Log Log Duplex[1] in 10-inch size.

2·27 Additional instruments. The instruments and materials described in this chapter are all that are needed for ordinary practice and are, as a rule, with the exception of such supplies as paper, pencils, ink, erasers, etc., what a draftsman is expected to take with him into a drafting room.

There are many other special instruments and devices which are not necessary in ordinary work, but with which, nevertheless, the draftsman should be familiar, as they may be very convenient in some special cases and are often found as a part of the drafting-room equipment. Some are described in Chap. 30.

[1] Registered trade-marks.

Chapter 3

THE USE OF INSTRUMENTS

3·1 In beginning the use of drawing instruments, particular attention should be paid to the correct method of handling them. Read carefully the instructions given and observe strictly all the details of the technique.

Facility will come with continued practice, but from the outset *good form* must be insisted upon. One might learn to write fairly holding the pen peculiarly between the fingers or gripped in the closed hand, but it would be poor form. Bad form in drawing is distressingly common and may be traced in every instance to lack of care or knowledge at the beginning, and the consequent formation of bad habits. These habits, when once formed, are most difficult to overcome.

All mechanical drawings serve incidentally for practice in the use of instruments, but it is best for the beginner to make a few drawings solely to become familiar with the handling and "feel" of the instruments so that, later, in working a drawing problem, there may be no loss of time on account of faulty manipulation. With practice, the correct skillful use of the instruments will become a subconscious habit.

The requirements of good drawing ability are *accuracy* and *speed*, and in commercial work neither is worth much without the other. Accurate penciling is the first consideration. Inking should not be attempted until real proficiency in penciling has been attained. A good instructor knows that it is a mistaken kindness to the beginner to accept faulty or careless work. The standard held at the start will be carried through his professional life, and the beginner should learn that a *good* drawing can be made just as quickly as a *poor* one. Erasing is expensive and most of it can be avoided. The student allowed to continue in a careless way will grow to regard his erasers as the most important tools in his kit. The draftsman, of course, erases occasionally, and instructions in making corrections should be given, but the beginner should strive for sheets without blemish or inaccuracy.

3·2 Preparation for drawing. The drawing table should be set so that the light comes from the left, and adjusted to a convenient height, that is, from 36 to 40 inches, for use while sitting upon a standard drafting stool, or when standing. One may draw with more freedom standing than sitting, especially on large drawings. The board should be inclined at a slope of about 1 to 8. Wipe the table, board, and instruments with a dustcloth before starting to draw.

3·3 The pencil. The grade of pencil must be selected carefully, with reference to the surface of the paper used as well as the line quality desired.

For a pencil layout on detail paper of good texture, a pencil as hard as 5H or 6H may be used, while for finished pencil drawings on the same paper 2H, 3H, or 4H pencils give the blacker line needed. For finished pencil drawings or tracings on vellum, softer pencils, H to 3H, are employed to get printable lines. The F pencil is much used for technical sketching, and the H is popular for lettering. In every case the pencil chosen must be hard enough not to blur or smudge, but not so hard as to cut grooves in the paper under reasonable pressure.

To sharpen a pencil, cut away the wood from the unlettered end with a penknife to make a long conical point as shown in Fig. 3·1*A*, and then sharpen the lead as at *B* by twirling the pencil as the lead is rubbed with long even strokes against the sandpaper pad or file.

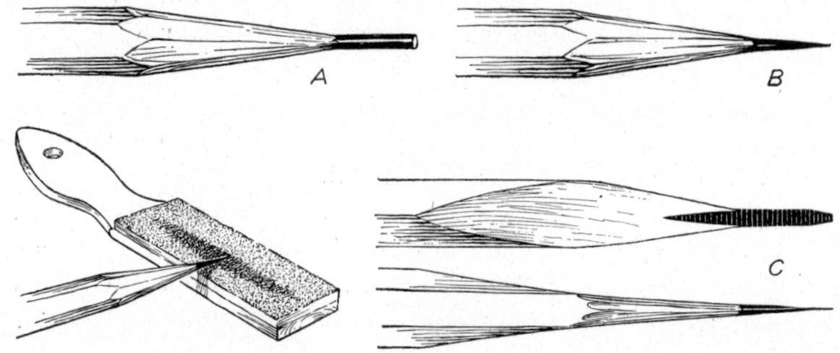

FIG. 3·1—Sharpening a pencil.

A flat or wedge point will not wear away in use so fast as a conical point and on that account is preferred by some draftsmen for straight-line work. The long wedge point illustrated at *C* is made by first sharpening as at *A*, then making the two long cuts on opposite sides, as shown, then flattening the lead on the sandpaper pad or file, and finishing by touching the corners to make the wedge point narrower than the diameter of the lead.

Have the sandpaper pad within easy reach and *keep the pencils sharp*. Some hang the pad or file on a cord attached to the drawing table. The professional draftsman sharpens his pencil every few minutes. After sharpening the lead, wipe off excess graphite dust before using the pencil. Form the habit of sharpening the lead as often as you might dip a writing pen into the inkwell. Most commercial and many college drafting rooms are equipped with Dexter or other pencil sharpeners to save the draftsman's time.

Not only must pencil lines be clean and sharp, but, for pencil drawings and tracings to be blueprinted, it is absolutely necessary that all the lines of each kind be uniform, firm, and opaque. This means a very careful choice of pencils and the proper use of them. The attempt to make a dark line with too hard a pencil results in cutting deep grooves in the paper. Hold the pencil firmly, yet with as much ease and freedom as possible.

Keep an even constant pressure on the pencil and, when using a conical point, rotate the pencil as the line is drawn so as to keep both the line and pencil sharp. Use a draftsman's brush or soft cloth occasionally to dust off excess graphite from the drawing.

Too much emphasis cannot be given to the importance of clean, careful, accurate penciling. Never entertain the thought that poor penciling can be corrected in tracing.

3·4 Placing the paper. Since the T-square blade is more rigid near the head than toward the outer end, the paper, if much smaller than the size of the board, should be placed close to the left edge of the board (within an inch or so) with its lower edge several inches from the bottom of the board. With the T square against the left edge of the board, square the top of the paper; hold in this position, slipping the T square down from the edge, and put a thumbtack in each upper corner, pushing it in up to the head so that the head aids in holding the paper. Now move the T square down over the paper to smooth out possible wrinkles, and put thumbtacks in the other two corners. Drafting tape may be used instead of thumbtacks.

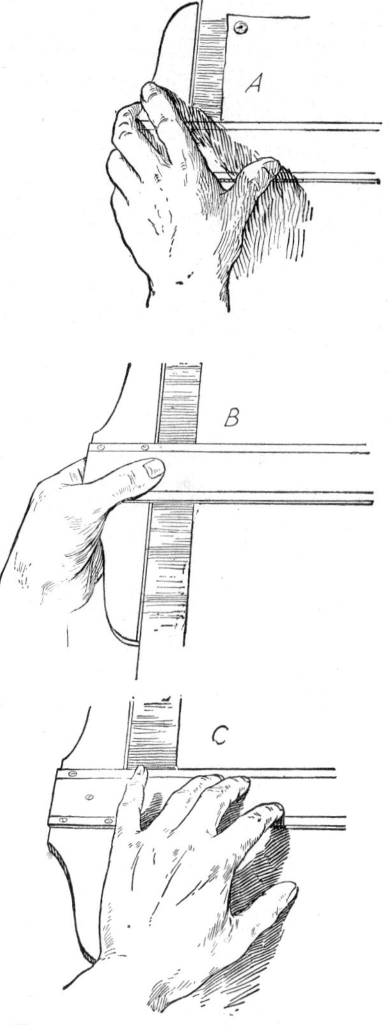

FIG. 3·2—Manipulating the T square.

3·5 Use of the T square. The T square is used with its head against the left edge of the drawing board. Manifestly, the T square is used for drawing horizontal lines, and is manipulated as follows: Holding the head of the tool as shown at *A*, Fig. 3·2, the draftsman slides it along the edge of the board to a spot very near the position desired. Then, for closer adjustment, he changes his hold either to that shown at *B*, in which the thumb remains on top of the T-square head and the other fingers press against the underside of the board, or, more often, to that shown at *C*, in which the fingers remain on the T square and the thumb is placed on the board.

Figure 3·3 shows the position of the hand and pencil for drawing horizontal lines. Note that the pencil is inclined in the direction the line is drawn, that is, toward the right, and also inclined slightly away from the body, so as to bring the pencil point as close as possible to the T-square blade.

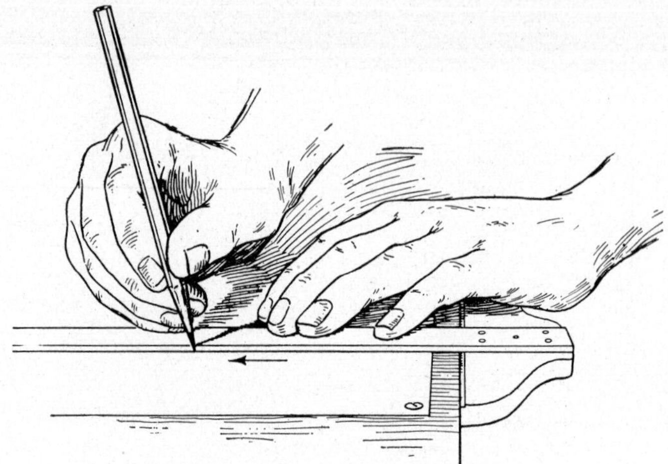

FIG. 3·3—Drawing a horizontal line.

In drawing lines, great care must be exercised to keep them accurately parallel to the guiding edge of the T square. The pencil should be held lightly, but close against the edge, and the angle should not vary during the progress of the line. These lines should always be drawn from left to right.

3·6 Use of the triangles. Vertical lines are drawn with the triangle set against the T square, with the perpendicular edge nearest the head of the square and thus toward the light, Fig. 3·4. These lines are always drawn upward, from bottom to top.

In drawing vertical lines, the T square is held in position against the left edge of the board by the thumb and little finger of the left hand while the other fingers of this hand adjust and hold the triangle. One may be sure that the T square is in contact with the board by hearing the little double click as the two come together, and slight pressure of the thumb and little finger toward the right will maintain the position. As the line is drawn, pressure against the board of all the fingers will hold the T square and triangle firmly in position.

As explained before for horizontal lines, care should be exercised to keep the line accurately parallel to the guiding edge. Note the position of the pencil in Fig. 3·4.

In both penciling and inking, the triangles should always be used in contact with a guiding straightedge. To ensure accuracy, never work to the extreme corner of a triangle; to avoid having to do so, keep the T square below the lower end of the line to be drawn.

With the T square against the edge of the board, lines at 45 degrees may be drawn with the standard 45-degree triangle, and lines at 30 and 60 degrees with the 30-60-degree triangle, as shown in Fig. 3·5. With vertical and horizontal lines included, lines at increments of 45 degrees may be drawn with the 45-degree triangle as at *B*, and lines at 30-degree increments

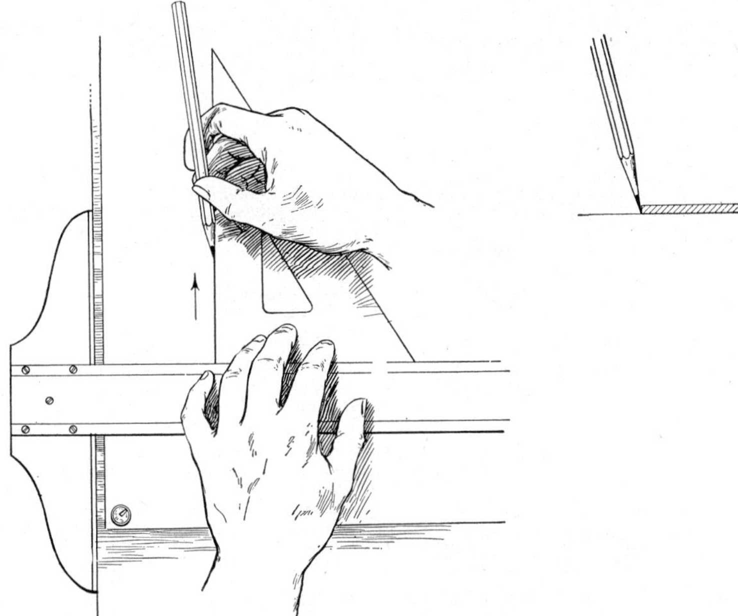

FIG. 3·4—Drawing a vertical line.

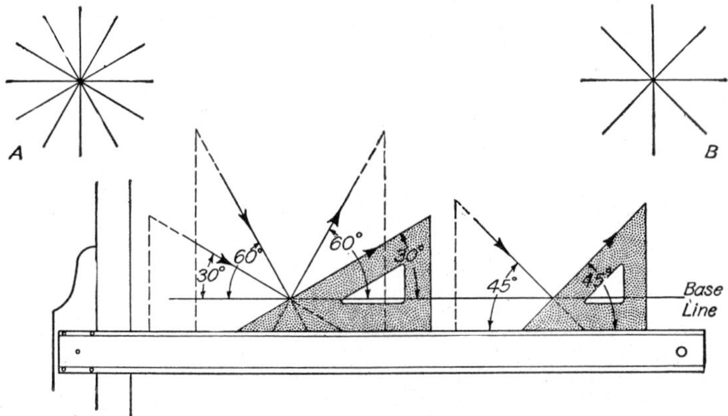

FIG. 3·5—To draw angles of 30°, 45°, and 60°.

with the 30-60-degree triangle as at *A*, Fig. 3·5. The two triangles are used in combination for angles of 15, 75, 105 degrees, etc., Fig. 3·6. Thus any multiple of 15 degrees can be drawn directly, and a circle can be divided with the 45-degree triangle into 8 parts, with the 30-60-degree triangle into 12 parts, and with both into 24 parts.

To draw one line parallel to another, Fig. 3·7, adjust to the given line a triangle held against a straightedge (T square or triangle), hold the guiding edge in position and slip the triangle on it to the required position.

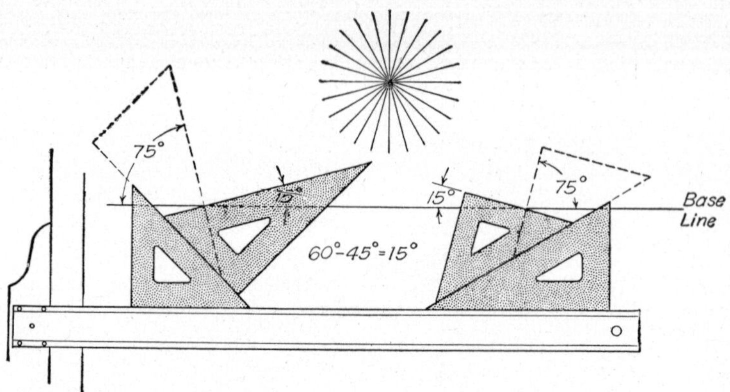

FIG. 3·6—To draw angles of 15° and 75°.

To draw a perpendicular to any line, Fig. 3·8*A*, place a triangle with one edge against the T square (or another triangle) and move the two until the hypotenuse of the triangle is coincident with the line; hold the T square in position and turn the triangle as shown until its other side is against the T square; the hypotenuse will then be perpendicular to the original line. Move the triangle to the required position. *Or* a quicker method is to set the triangle with its hypotenuse against the guiding edge, fit one side to the line, slide the triangle to the required point, and draw the perpendicular, as shown at *B*.

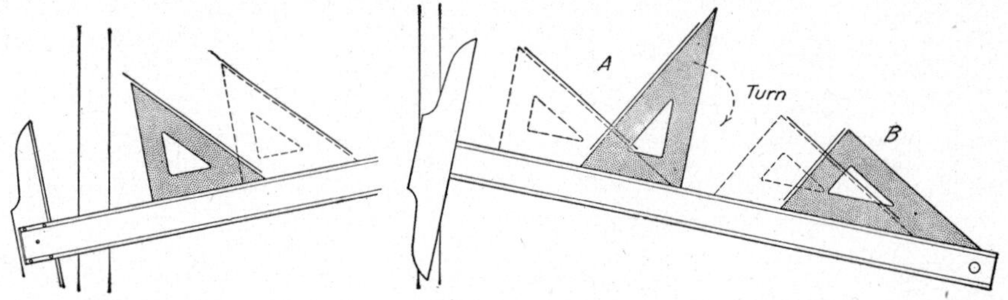

FIG. 3·7—To draw parallel lines.

FIG. 3·8—To draw perpendicular lines.

Never attempt to draw a perpendicular to a line with only one triangle by placing one leg of the triangle along the line.

3·7 The left-handed draftsman reverses the T square and triangles left-for-right as compared to the regular right-handed position. The head of the T square is used along the right edge of the board. Horizontal lines are drawn from right to left. The triangle is placed with its vertical edge to the right, and the line drawn from bottom to top. The drawing table should be placed with the light coming from the right.

3·8 Use of the scale. Scale technique is governed largely by the requirements of accuracy and speed. Beefore a line can be drawn its relative position must be found by scaling, and the speed with which the scale measurements can be made will greatly affect the total drawing time

Precise layouts, developments, etc., made for the workmen to scale, must be very accurately drawn, at the expense of speed; conversely, drawings having figured dimensions need not be quite so carefully scaled and better speed may be attained.

FIG. 3·9—Making a measurement.

To make a measurement, place the scale on the drawing where the distance is to be laid off, align the scale in the direction of the measurement, and make a light short dash with a sharp pencil at the proper graduation mark. Fig. 3·9. In layout work where extreme accuracy is required, a "pricker," or needle point set in a soft wood handle may be substituted for the pencil, and a *small* hole pricked into the paper in place of the pencil mark.

Measurements should not be made on a drawing by taking distances off the scale with dividers, as this method is time-consuming and no more accurate than the regular methods.

To avoid cumulative errors, successive measurements on the same line should, if possible, be made without shifting the scale.

3·9 Scale drawings. In representing objects that are larger than can be drawn to their natural or full size it is necessary to reduce the size of the drawing in some regular proportion, and for this purpose the mechanical engineer's (or architect's) scales are used. The first reduction is to what is commonly called "half size" or, correctly speaking, to the scale of 6″ = 1′-0″. This scale is used on working drawings even if the object is only slightly larger than could be drawn full size. If the draftsman hasn't a half-size scale, see Fig. 2·15, he should use the full-size scale, considering 6 inches on the scale to represent 1 foot. Thus the half-inch divisions become full inches, each of which is divided into eighths.

If this reduction is too large for the paper, the drawing is made to the scale of 3″ = 1′-0″, often called "quarter size"; that is, 3 inches measured on the drawing is equal to 1 foot on the object. This is the first reduction scale of the usual triangular scale; on it the distance of 3 inches is divided into 12 equal parts, and each of these is subdivided into eighths. This distance should be thought of not as 3 inches but as a foot divided into inches and eighths of an inch. Notice that the divisions start with the zero on the inside, the inches of the divided foot running to the left and the open divisions of feet to the right, so that dimensions given in feet and inches

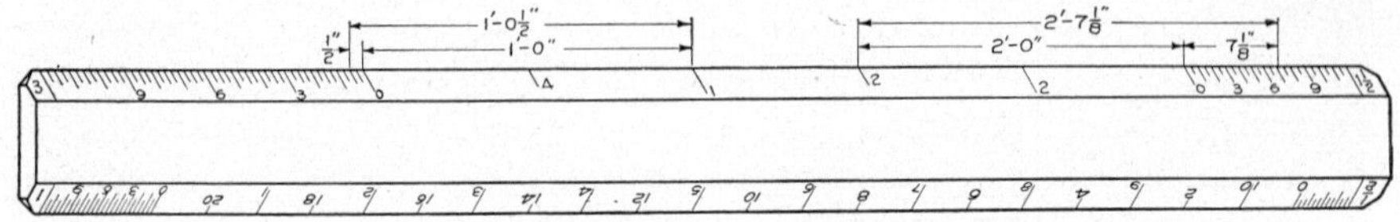

FIG. 3·10—Reading the scale.

may be read directly, as 1′-0½″, Fig. 3·10. On the other end will be found the scale of 1½″ = 1′-0″, or "eighth size," with the distance of 1½ inches divided on the right of the zero into 12 parts and subdivided into quarter inches, with the foot divisions to the left of the zero coinciding with the marks of the 3″ scale.

If the 1½″ scale is too large for the object, the next smaller size is the scale 1″ = 1′-0″, and so on down, as shown in the following table:

Scales

24″ = 1′-0″ (double size)	1″ = 1′-0″ (1/12 size)
12″ = 1′-0″ (full size)	¾″ = 1′-0″ (1/16 size)
6″ = 1′-0″ (½ size)	½″ = 1′-0″ (1/24 size)
4″ = 1′-0″ (⅓ size)	⅜″ = 1′-0″ (1/32 size)
[RARELY USED]	¼″ = 1′-0″ (1/48 size)
3″ = 1′-0″ (¼ size)	3/16″ = 1′-0″ (1/64 size)
2″ = 1′-0″ (⅙ size)	⅛″ = 1′-0″ (1/96 size)
[RARELY USED]	3/32″ = 1′-0″ (1/128 size)
1½″ = 1′-0″ (⅛ size)	

In stating the scale used on a drawing, the first figure should always refer to the drawing and the second to the object. Thus Scale 3″ = 1′-0″ means that 3 inches on the drawing is equal to 1 foot on the object.

Drawings to odd proportions such as 9″ = 1′-0″, 4″ = 1′-0″, etc., are used only in rare cases when it is desired to make it difficult or impossible for a workman to measure them with an ordinary rule.

The scale ¼″ = 1′-0″ is the usual one for ordinary house plans and is often called by architect's "quarter scale." This term should not be confused with the term "quarter size," as the former means ¼ inch to 1 foot and the latter ¼ inch to 1 inch.

The size of a circle is generally stated by giving its diameter, while to draw it the radius is necessary. In drawing to half size it is thus often convenient to lay off the amount of the diameter with a quarter-size scale and use this distance as the radius.

Small pieces are often made "double size," and very small mechanisms, such as drawings of watch parts, are drawn to greatly enlarged sizes: 10 to 1, 20 to 1, 40 to 1, and 50 to 1, using special enlarging scales.

For plotting and map drawing, the civil engineer's scale of decimal parts, with 10, 20, 30, 40, 50, 60, and 80 divisions to the inch, is used. This scale is not used for machine or structural work but is used in certain aircraft drawings.

The important thing in drawing to scale is to think of, and speak of, each dimension in its full size and not in the reduced (or enlarged) size it happens to be on the paper.

3·10 "Laying out" the sheet. The paper is usually cut somewhat larger than the desired size of the drawing and is trimmed to size after the work is finished. Suppose the finished size is to be 11″ × 17″ with a ½″ border inside. Lay the scale down on the paper close to the lower edge and measure 17″, marking the distance with the pencil; at the same time mark ½″ inside at each end for the border line. Use a short dash forming a continuation of the division line on the scale in laying off a dimension. Do not bore a hole with the pencil. Near the left edge mark 11″ and ½″ border-line points. Through these four marks on the left edge draw horizontal lines with the T square, and through the points on the lower edge draw vertical lines, using the triangle against the T square.

3·11 Use of the dividers. The dividers are used for transferring measurements and for dividing lines into any number of equal parts. Facility in the use of this instrument is most essential, and quick and absolute control of its manipulation must be gained. It should be opened with one hand by pinching the chamfer with the thumb and second finger. This will throw it into correct position with the thumb and forefinger outside of the legs and the second and third fingers inside, with the head resting just above the second joint of the forefinger, Fig. 3·11. It is thus under perfect control, with the thumb and forefinger to close it and the other two to open it. This motion should be practiced until an adjustment to the smallest fraction can be made. In coming down to small divisions, the second and third fingers must be gradually slipped out from between the legs while they are closed down upon them. Notice that the little finger is not used in manipulating the dividers.

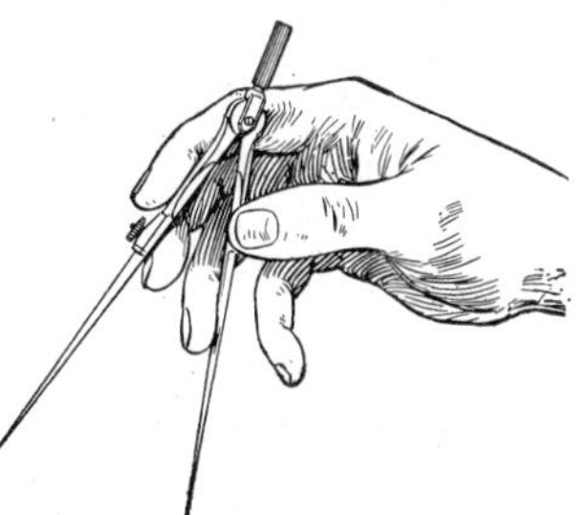

FIG. 3·11—Handling the dividers.

3·12 To divide a line by trial. In bisecting a line, the dividers are opened at a guess to roughly one-half the length. This distance is stepped off on the line, holding the instrument by the handle with the thumb and forefinger. If the division is short, the leg should be thrown out to one-half the remainder (estimated by the eye) without removing the other leg from the paper and the line spaced again with this new setting, Fig. 3·12. If the result should not come out exactly, the operation may be repeated. With a little experience a line may be divided very rapidly in this way. Similarly, a line, either straight or curved, may be divided into any number of equal parts, say five, by estimating the first division, stepping this lightly

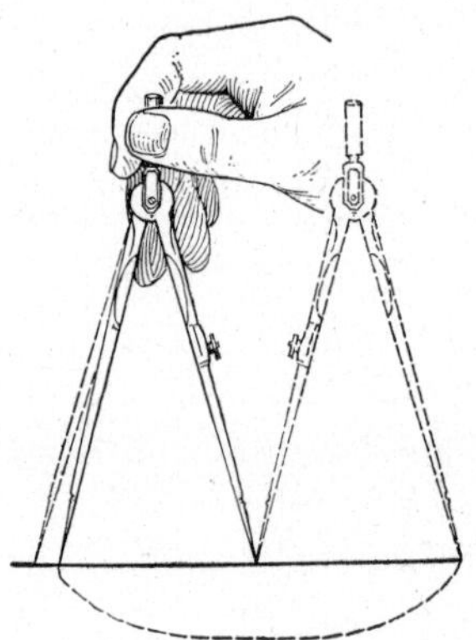

FIG. 3·12—Bisecting a line.

along the line, with the dividers held vertically by the handle, turning the instrument first in one direction and then in the other. If the last division falls short, one-fifth of the remainder should be added by opening the dividers, keeping the one point on the paper. If the last division is over, one-fifth of the excess should be taken off and the line respaced. If it is found difficult to make this small adjustment accurately with the fingers, the hairspring may be used. It will be found more convenient to use the bow spacers instead of the dividers for small or numerous divisions. Avoid pricking unsightly holes in the paper. The position of a small prick point may be preserved, if necessary, by drawing a small circle around it with the pencil. For most work, and until one is very proficient, it is best to divide a line into a number of parts with the scale as explained on page 62.

Proportional dividers, Fig. 30·2, are sometimes used to divide both straight lines and circles.

3·13 Use of the compasses. The compasses have the same general shape as the dividers and are manipulated in a similar way. First of all, the needle should be permanently adjusted. Insert the pen in place of the pencil leg, turn the needle with the shoulder point out and set it a trifle longer than the pen, Fig. 3·13, replace the pencil leg, sharpen the lead to a long bevel, as in Fig. 3·14, and adjust it to the needle point.

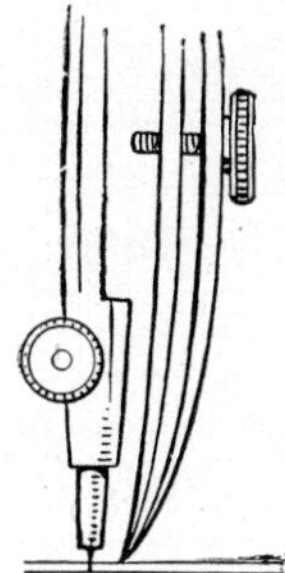
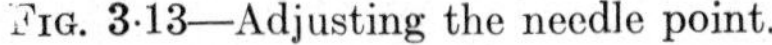

FIG. 3·13—Adjusting the needle point.

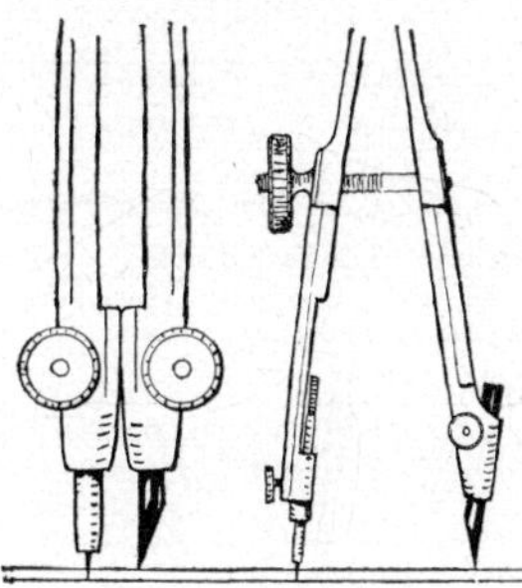

FIG. 3·14—Adjusting the pencil lead.

To draw a circle, set the compass on the scale and adjust it to the radius needed; then place the needle point at the center on the drawing, guiding it with the left hand, Fig. 3·15. Now raise the fingers to the handle and draw the circle in one sweep, rolling the handle with the thumb and forefinger, inclining the compass slightly in the direction of the line, Fig. 3·16.

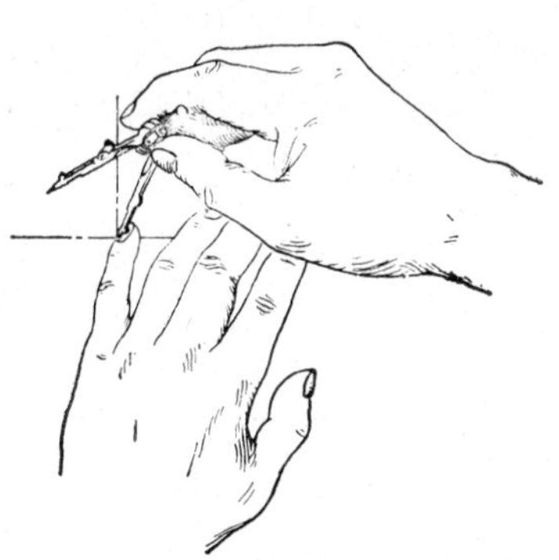

FIG. 3·15—Guiding the needle point.

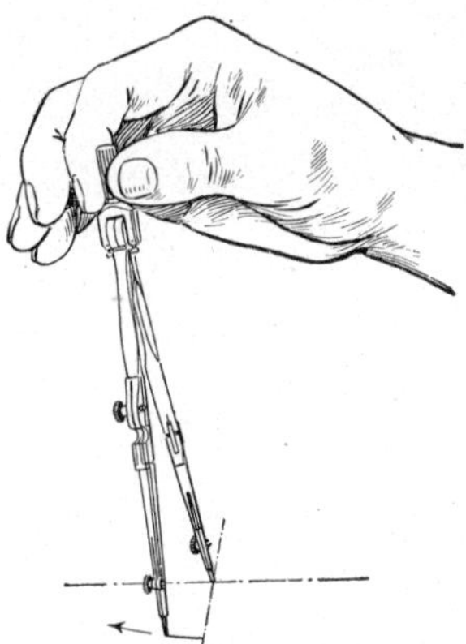

FIG. 3·16—Starting a circle.

The position of the fingers after the revolution is illustrated in Fig. 3·17. The pencil line may be brightened if necessary by making additional revolutions. Circles up to perhaps three inches in diameter may be drawn with the legs of the compasses straight but, for larger sizes, both the needle-point leg and the pencil or pen leg should be bent at the knuckle joints so as to be perpendicular to the paper, Fig. 3·18. The 6-inch compasses may be used in this way for circles up to perhaps 10 inches in diameter; larger circles are made by using the lengthening bar, as illustrated in Fig. 3·19, or by using the beam compasses, Fig. 2·8. In drawing concentric circles, the *smallest* should always be drawn *first,* before the center hole has become worn.

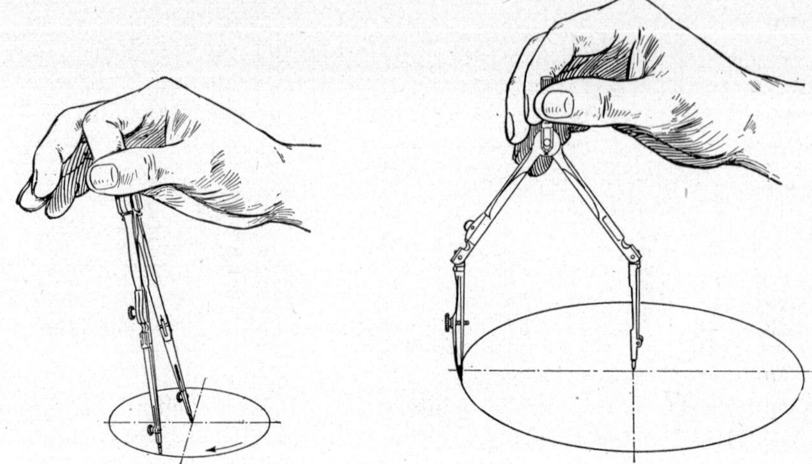

FIG. 3·17—Completing a circle. FIG. 3·18—Drawing a large circle.

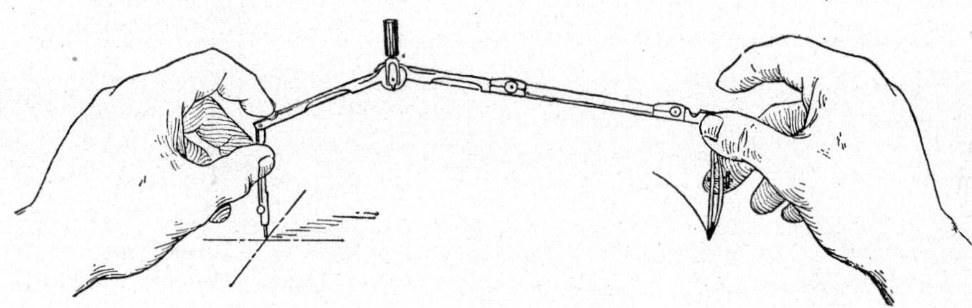

FIG. 3·19—Use of lengthening bar.

The bow instruments are used for small circles, particularly when a number are to be made of the same diameter. To avoid wear (on side-wheel instruments), the pressure of the spring against the nut may be relieved in changing the setting by holding the points in the left hand and spinning the nut in or out with the finger. Small adjustments should be made with one hand with the needle point in position on the paper, Fig. 3·20.

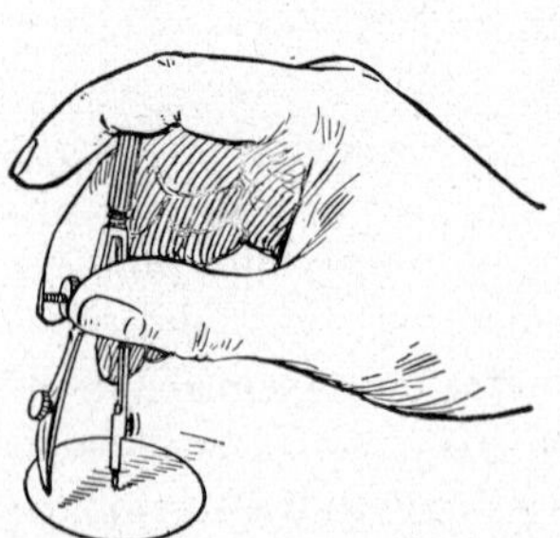

FIG. 3·20—Adjusting the bow pen.

When several concentric circles are to be drawn, a saving in time may be had by marking off the several radii on the paper from the scale, and then setting the compass to each mark as the circles are made.

Some draftsmen prefer to measure and mark the radius on the paper instead of setting the compass directly on the scale. This method must be used whenever the radius is greater than the length of the scale.

When extreme accuracy is required, the compass is set, a light circle is drawn on the paper, and the diameter checked with the scale; if the size is not satisfactory, the compass is adjusted and the operation repeated until the size needed is obtained.

3·14 The ruling pen. The ruling pen is for inking straight lines and noncircular curves. Several types are illustrated in Fig. 2·7. The impor-

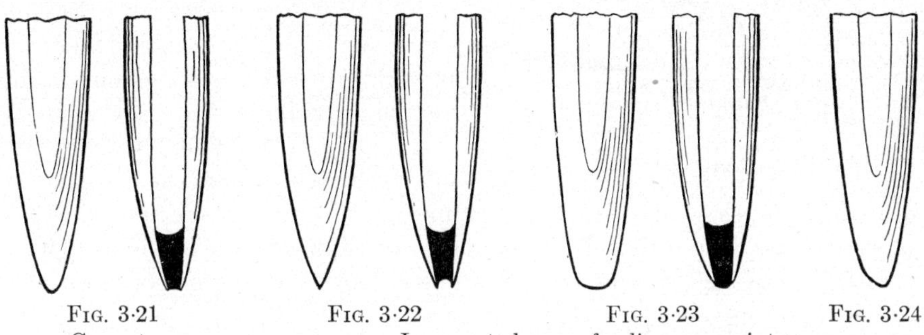

Fig. 3·21 Correct. Fig. 3·22 Fig. 3·23 Fig. 3·24 Incorrect shapes of ruling pen points.

tant feature is the shape of the blades; they should have a well-designed ink space between them, and their points should be rounded (actually elliptical in form) equally, as in Fig. 3·21. If pointed, as in Fig. 3·22, the ink will arch up as shown and will be provokingly hard to start. If rounded to a blunt point, as in Fig. 3·23, the ink will flow too freely, the result being bulbs and overruns at the ends of the lines. Pens in constant use become dull and worn, as illustrated in Fig. 3·24. It is easy to tell whether or not a pen is dull by looking for the reflection of light that travels from the side and over the end of the point when the pen is turned in the hand. If the reflection can be seen all the way the pen is too dull. A pen in poor condition is an abomination, but a well-sharpened one is a delight to use. Every draftsman should be able to keep his pens in fine condition.

High-grade pens usually come from the makers well sharpened. Cheaper ones often need sharpening before they can be used.

3·15 To sharpen a pen. The best stone for the purpose is a hard Arkansas knife piece. It is well to soak a new stone in oil for several days before using. The ordinary carpenter's oilstone is too coarse for drawing instruments.

The nibs must first be brought to the correct shape, as in Fig. 3·21. Screw the nibs together until they touch and, holding the pen as in drawing a line, draw it back and forth on the stone, starting the stroke with the handle at 30° or less with the stone, and swinging it up past the perpendicular as the line across the stone progresses. This will bring the nibs to exactly the same shape and length, leaving them very dull. Then open them slightly and sharpen each blade in turn, *on the outside only,* until the bright spot on the end has just disappeared. Now, as in Fig. 3·25, hold the pen at a small angle with the stone and rub it back and forth with a slight oscillating or rocking motion to conform to the shape of the blade. A stone three or four inches long held in the left hand with the thumb and fingers gives better control than one laid on the table. A pocket magnifying glass may be of aid in examining the points. The blades should not be sharp enough to cut the paper when tested by drawing a line across it without ink. If over-sharpened, the blades should again be brought to touch, and a line swung very lightly across the stone as in the first operation. When tested with ink, the pen should be capable of drawing clean sharp lines down to the finest hairline. If these finest lines are ragged or broken, the pen is not perfectly sharpened. It should not be necessary to touch the inside of the blades unless a burr has been formed, which might occur if the metal is very soft, the stone too coarse, or the pressure too heavy. To remove such a burr or wire edge, draw a strip of detail paper between the nibs, or open the pen wide and lay the entire inner surface of the blade flat on the stone and move it with a very light touch.

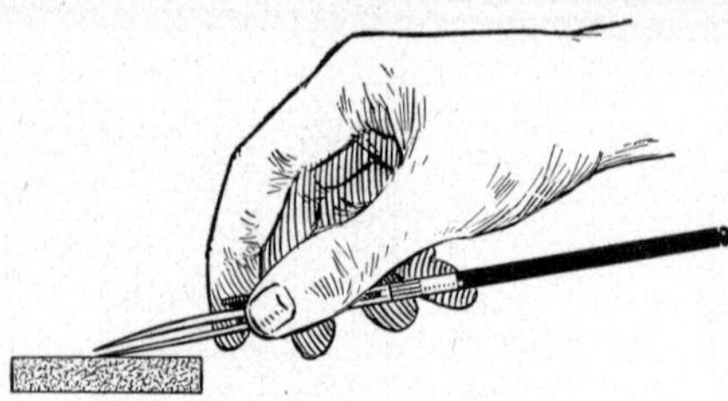

FIG. 3·25—Sharpening a pen.

3·16 Use of the ruling pen. The ruling pen is always used in connection with a guiding-edge, T square, triangle, straightedge, or curve. The T square and triangle should be held in the same positions as for penciling.

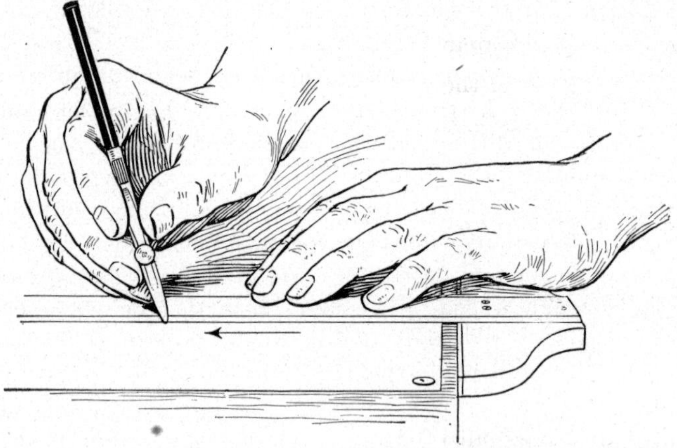

FIG. 3·26—Correct position of ruling pen.

To fill the pen, take it to the bottle and touch the quill filler between the nibs, being careful not to get any ink on the outside of the blades. Not more than $\frac{3}{16}$ to $\frac{1}{4}$ inch of ink should be put in, or the weight of the ink will cause it to drop out in a blot. The pen should be held in the finger tips, as illustrated in Fig. 3·26, with the thumb and second finger against the sides of the nibs and the handle resting on the forefinger. This hold should be observed carefully, as the tendency will be to bend the second finger to the position used when a pencil or writing pen is held. The position illustrated aids in keeping the pen at the proper angle and the nibs aligned with the ruling edge.

The pen should be held against the straightedge, with the blades parallel to it, the screw being on the outside and the handle inclined slightly to the right and always kept in a plane passing through the line and perpendicular to the paper. The pen is thus guided by the upper edge of the ruler, as illustrated in actual size in Fig. 3·27. If the pen point is thrown out from the perpendicular, it will run on one blade and a line ragged on one side will result. If turned in from the perpendicular, the ink is very apt to run under the edge of the ruler and cause a blot.

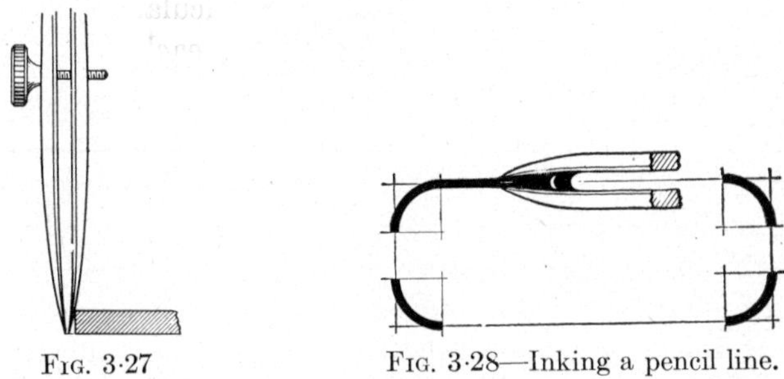

FIG. 3·27

FIG. 3·28—Inking a pencil line.

A line is drawn with a steady, even arm movement, the tips of the third and fourth fingers resting on, and sliding along, the straightedge, keeping the angle of inclination constant. Just before the end of the line is reached, the two guiding fingers on the straightedge should be stopped and, without stopping the motion of the pen, the line finished with a finger movement. Short lines are drawn with this finger movement alone. When the end of the line is reached, lift the pen quickly and move the straightedge away from the line. The pressure on the paper should be light, but sufficient to give a clean-cut line, and will vary with the kind of paper and the sharpness of the pen. The pressure against the T square, however, should be only enough to guide the direction.

If the ink refuses to flow, it may be because it has dried in the extreme point of the pen. If pinching the blades slightly or touching the pen on the finger does not start it, the pen should immediately be wiped out and fresh ink supplied. Pens must be wiped clean after using.

In inking on either paper or cloth, the full lines will be much wider than the pencil lines, and thus the beginner must be very careful to have the center of the ink line cover the pencil line, as shown in Fig. 3·28.

Instructions in regard to the ruling pen apply also to the compasses. The instrument should be slightly inclined in the direction of the line, and both nibs of the pen kept on the paper, bending the knuckle joints, if necessary, to effect this.

It is a universal rule in inking that *circles and circle arcs must be inked first.* It is much easier to connect a straight line to a curve than a curve to a straight line.

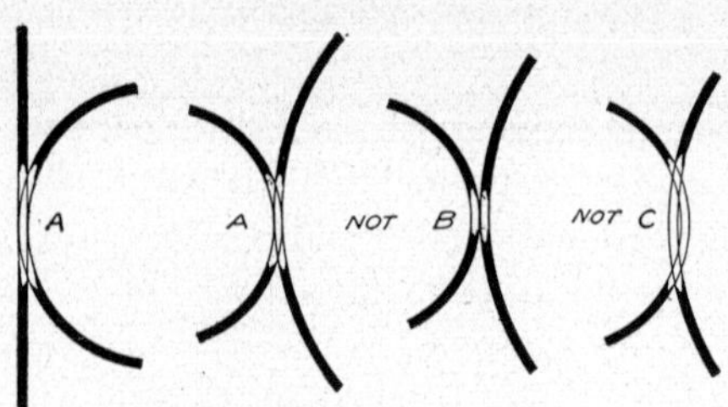

Fig. 3·29—Correct and incorrect tangents.

3·17 Tangents. It should be noted particularly that two lines are tangent to each other when the center lines of the lines are tangent and not simply when the lines touch each other; thus, at the point of tangency, the width will be equal to the width of a single line, Fig. 3·29. Before inking

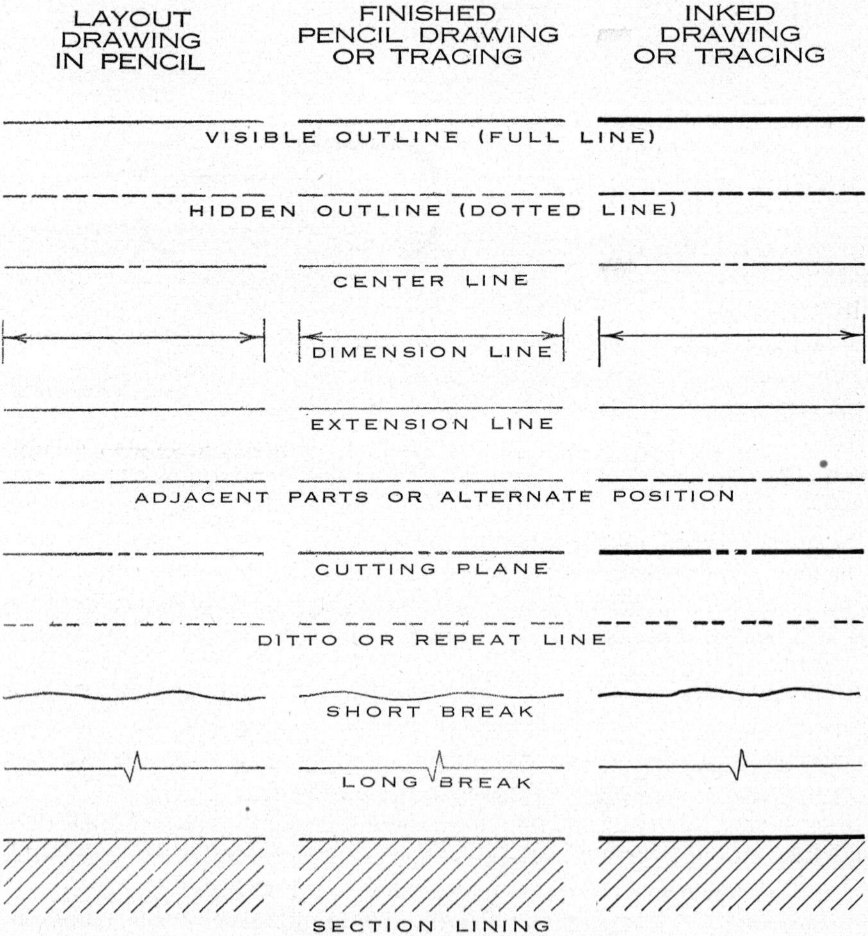

LAYOUT DRAWING IN PENCIL | FINISHED PENCIL DRAWING OR TRACING | INKED DRAWING OR TRACING

VISIBLE OUTLINE (FULL LINE)

HIDDEN OUTLINE (DOTTED LINE)

CENTER LINE

DIMENSION LINE

EXTENSION LINE

ADJACENT PARTS OR ALTERNATE POSITION

CUTTING PLANE

DITTO OR REPEAT LINE

SHORT BREAK

LONG BREAK

SECTION LINING

Fig. 3·30—The alphabet of lines.

tangent lines, the point of tangency should be marked in pencil. For an arc tangent to a straight line, this point will be on a line through the center of the arc and perpendicular to the straight line, and for two circle arcs will be on the line joining their centers as described in paragraphs 5·21 to 5·27.

3·18 The alphabet of lines. As the basis of drawing is the line, a set of conventional symbols covering all the lines needed for different purposes may properly be called an "alphabet of lines." Figure 3·30 shows the alphabet of lines adopted by the American Standards Association (ASA), as applied

1. To layout drawings in pencil on detail paper to be traced on tracing paper or cloth.
2. To drawings either made directly or traced in pencil on tracing paper or pencil cloth, from which blue-prints or other reproductions are to be made.
3. To tracing in ink on tracing cloth or tracing paper; and to inked drawings on white paper for display or photoreproductions.

The ASA recommends three weights of lines: heavy, medium, and light, for finished drawings, "both for legibility and appearance," but says that "for rapid practice this may be simplified to two weights: *medium* for outlines, hidden, cutting-plane, short-break, adjacent-part, and alternate-position lines, and *light* for section, center, extension, dimension, long-break, and ditto lines." The actual widths of the three weights of lines, on average drawings, should be about as given in Fig. 3·30. A convenient line gage designed by Dr. C. V. Mann is illustrated in Fig. 3·31. If applied to Fig. 3·30 this gage would show the heavy lines in ink to be between $\frac{1}{40}$ and $\frac{1}{50}$ of an inch, the medium lines $\frac{1}{80}$ of an inch, and the fine lines $\frac{1}{200}$ of an inch in width. Figure 3·32 shows the application of the alphabet of lines.

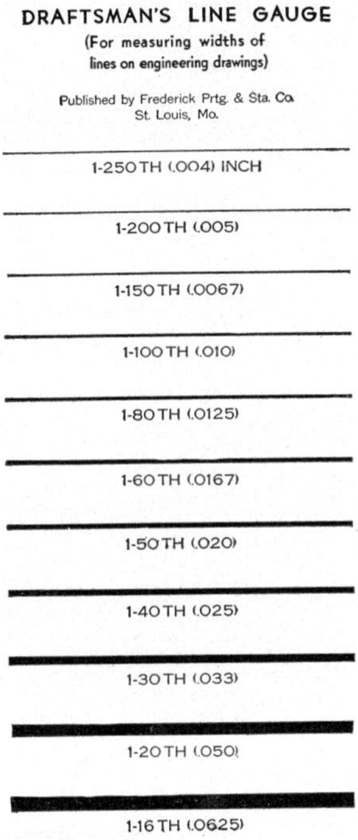

DRAFTSMAN'S LINE GAUGE
(For measuring widths of lines on engineering drawings)

Published by Frederick Prtg. & Sta. Co.
St. Louis, Mo.

1-250TH (.004) INCH

1-200TH (.005)

1-150TH (.0067)

1-100TH (.010)

1-80TH (.0125)

1-60TH (.0167)

1-50TH (.020)

1-40TH (.025)

1-30TH (.033)

1-20TH (.050)

1-16TH (.0625)

FIG. 3·31—Mann's line gage.

3·19 Line practice. After reading the preceding several paragraphs the beginner had best take a blank sheet of paper and practice making straight lines and circles in all the forms, full, dotted, etc., shown in Fig. 3·30. The practice should include starting and stopping lines, with special attention to tangents and corners.

In pencil, try to get all the lines uniform in width and color regardless of type. Circle arcs and straight lines should match exactly at tangent points.

In ink, proceed as for pencil practice and pay particular attention to the weight of lines and to the spacing of dashed-in dotted lines and center lines.

Extension line
Section lines (Cross hatching)
10"
Alternate position
Visible outline
Hidden outline
Cutting plane
Center line
3'-0"
Dimension line
Short break
Wood
Adjacent part
C. I. Base
Long break

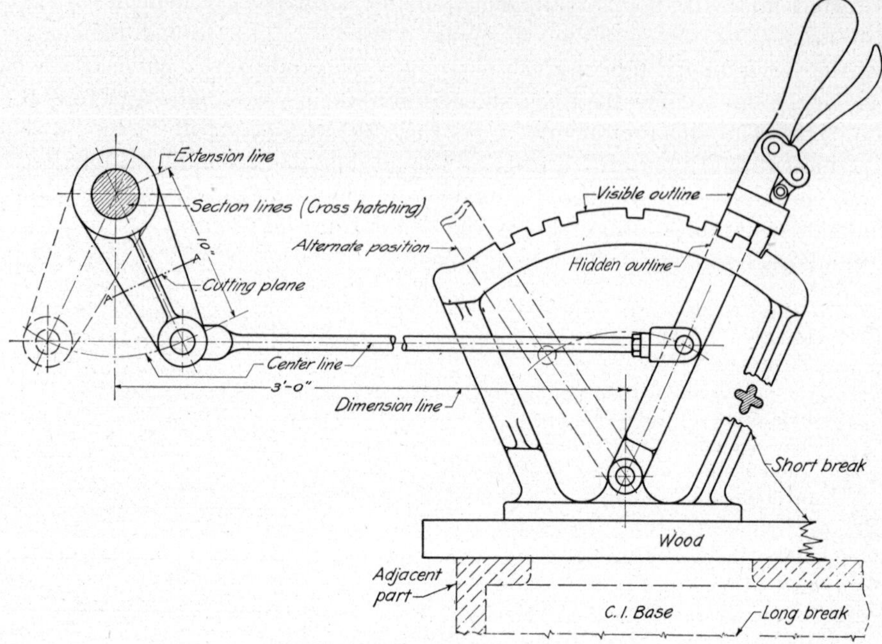

FIG. 3·32—The alphabet illustrated.

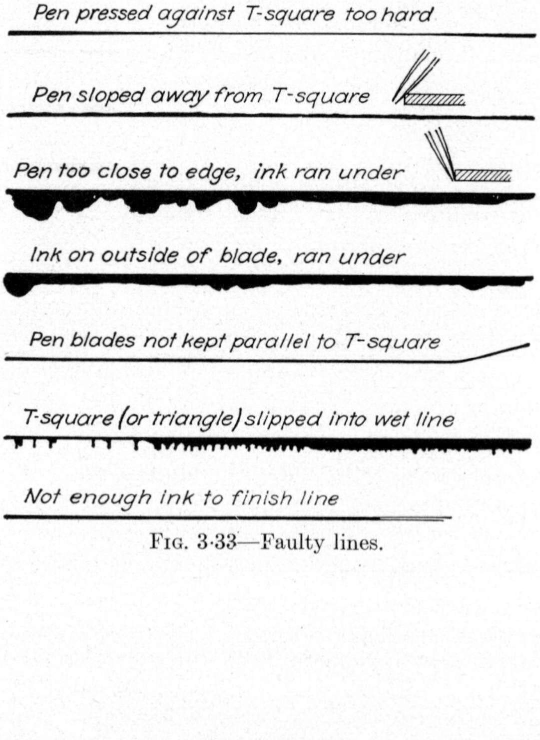

Pen pressed against T-square too hard
Pen sloped away from T-square
Pen too close to edge, ink ran under
Ink on outside of blade, ran under
Pen blades not kept parallel to T-square
T-square (or triangle) slipped into wet line
Not enough ink to finish line

FIG. 3·33—Faulty lines.

If inked lines appear imperfect in any way the reason should be ascertained immediately. It may be the fault of the pen, the ink, the paper, or the draftsman, but with the probabilities greatly in favor of the last.

Figure 3·33 illustrates the characteristic appearance of several kinds of faulty lines. The correction in each case will suggest itself.

3·20 Use of the french curve. The french curve, as has been stated on page 9, is a ruler for noncircular curves. When sufficient points have been determined, it is best to sketch in the line lightly in pencil, freehand, without losing the points, until it is clean, smooth, continuous, and satisfactory to

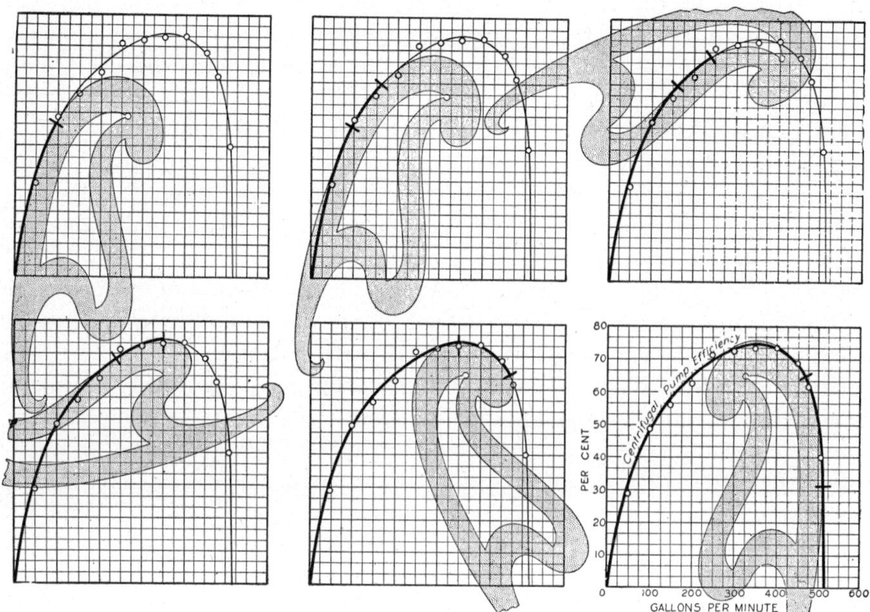

FIG. 3·34—Use of the french curve.

the eye. The curve should then be applied to it, selecting a part that will fit a portion of the line most nearly and seeing to it, particularly, that the curve is so placed that the direction in which its curvature increases is the direction in which the curvature of the line increases, Fig. 3·34. In drawing that part of the line matched by the curve, *always* stop a little short of the distance in which the ruler and the line seem to coincide. After drawing this portion, the curve is shifted to find another place that will coincide with the continuation of the line. In shifting the curve, care should be taken to preserve smoothness and continuity and to avoid breaks or cusps. This may be done if, in its successive positions, the curve is always adjusted so that it coincides for a short distance with the part of the line already drawn. Thus, at each juncture, the tangents will coincide.

If the curved line is symmetrical about an axis, marks locating this axis, after it has been matched accurately on one side, may be made in pencil on the curve and the curve then reversed. In such a case exceptional care must be taken to avoid a "hump" at the joint. It is often better to stop a line short of the axis on each side and close the gap afterward with another setting of the curve.

When using the curve in inking, the pen should be held perpendicular and the blades kept parallel to the edge. Inking curves will be found to be excellent practice.

Sometimes, particularly at sharp turns, a combination of circle arcs and curve may be used; in inking a long narrow ellipse, for example, the sharp curves may be inked by selecting a center on the major axis by trial, drawing as much of an arc as will practically coincide with the ends of the ellipse, and then finishing the ellipse with the curve. The experienced draftsman will sometimes ink a curve that cannot be matched accurately by varying the distance of the pen point from the ruling edge as the line progresses.

3·21 Erasing. The manner of erasing both pencil lines and ink lines is a necessary technique to learn. A designer, working freely but lightly, uses a soft pencil eraser when changing some detail so as not to damage the finish of the paper. Heavier lines are best removed with a Ruby pencil eraser. If the paper has been grooved by the line, it may be rubbed over with a burnisher, or even with the back of the thumbnail. In erasing an ink line, hold the paper down firmly and, with a Ruby pencil eraser, rub lightly and patiently, first along the line, then across it, until the ink is removed. A triangle slipped under the paper or cloth gives a good backing surface. When an erasure is to be made close to other lines, select an opening of the best shape on the erasing shield and rub through it, holding the shield down firmly, first seeing that both of its sides are clean. Wipe off the eraser crumbs from the paper with a dustcloth or brush. Never scratch out a line or a blot with a knife or razor blade, and use so-called ink erasers very sparingly, if at all. A skilled draftsman sometimes uses a sharp blade to trim a thickened spot or overrunning end on a line. For extensive erasing, an electric erasing machine is a great convenience. Several successful models are on the market.

3·22 Special instruments. Various instruments, such as drafting machines, parallel rules, pantographs, lettering machines, proportional dividers, etc., not in the usual draftsman's outfit, are used in commercial drafting work. A description of a number of these special instruments is given in Chap. 30.

3·23 Exercises in the use of instruments. The following may be used as progressive exercises for practice in using the instruments, doing them either as finished pencil drawings, or in pencil layout to be inked. Line work should conform to that given in the alphabet of lines, Fig. 3·30. Sheet layouts on American Standard sizes will be found in the Appendix.

The problems in Chap. 5 afford excellent additional practice in accurate penciling.

1. An exercise for the T square, triangle, and scale. Fig. 3·35. Through the center of the space draw a horizontal and a vertical line. Measuring on these lines as diameters lay off a 4″ square. Along the lower side and upper half of the left side measure ½″ spaces with the scale. Draw all horizontal lines with the T square and all vertical lines with the T square and triangle.

2. An interlacement. Fig. 3·36. For T square, triangle, and dividers. Draw a 4″ square. Divide left side and lower side into seven equal parts with dividers. Draw horizontal and vertical lines across the square through these points. Erase the parts not needed.

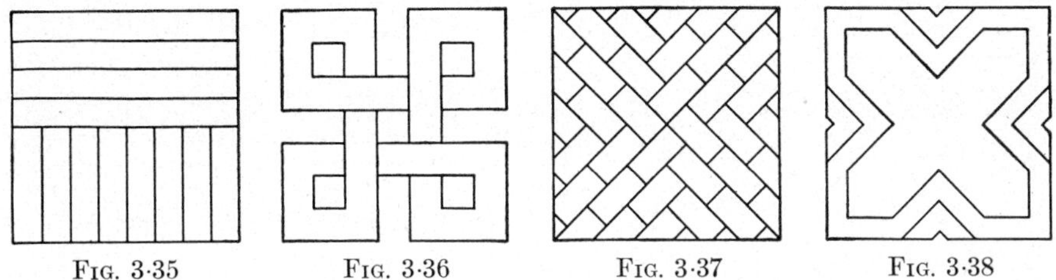

FIG. 3·35 FIG. 3·36 FIG. 3·37 FIG. 3·38

3. A street-paving intersection. Fig. 3·37. For 45° triangle and scale. An exercise in starting and stopping short lines. Draw a 4″ square. Draw its diagonals with 45° triangle. With the scale, lay off ½″ spaces along the diagonals from their intersection. With 45° triangle, complete figure, finishing one quarter at a time.

4. A square pattern. Fig. 3·38. For 45° triangle, dividers, and scale. Draw a 4″ square and divide its sides into three equal parts with dividers. With 45° triangle, draw diagonal lines connecting these points. Measure ⅜″ on each side of these lines and finish the pattern as shown.

5. Five cards. Fig. 3·39. Visible and hidden lines. Five cards 1¾″ × 3″ are arranged with the bottom card in the center, the other four overlapping each other and placed so that their outside edges form a 4″ square. Hidden lines indicate edges covered.

6. Concentric circles. Fig. 3·40. For compasses (legs straight) and scale. Draw a horizontal line through center of space. On it, mark off radii for eight concentric circles ¼″ apart. In drawing concentric circles, always draw the smallest first.

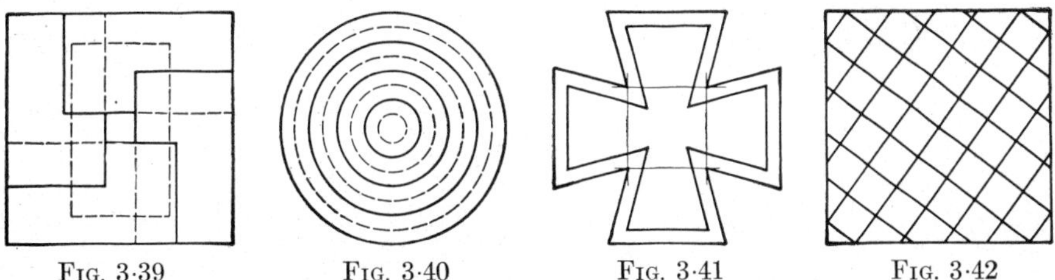

FIG. 3·39 FIG. 3·40 FIG. 3·41 FIG. 3·42

7. A maltese cross. Fig. 3·41. For T square, spacers, and both triangles. Draw a 4″ square and a 1⅜″ square. From the corners of inner square draw lines to outer square at 15° and 75°, with the two triangles in combination. Mark points with spacers ¼″ inside each line of this outside cross, and complete figure with triangles in combination.

8. A screen. Fig. 3·42. Two systems of parallel lines perpendicular to each other. Draw a 4″ square. Locate a point ½″ to the right of the lower left corner and another point ½″ to the left of the upper right corner. Connect these two points. Bisect this line with the dividers and draw a perpendicular bisector by the method of Fig. 3.8. On these two lines mark points ⅝″ apart and through these points, without moving the T square, draw the lines of the two systems.

9. A six-pointed star. Fig. 3·43. For compasses and 30°-60° triangle. Draw a 4″ construction circle and inscribe the six-pointed star with the T square and 30°-60° triangle. Accomplish this with four successive changes of position of the triangle.

10. A trefoil. Fig. 3·44. For compasses, 30°-60° triangle, and scale. Draw a 4″ circle. With 30°-60° triangle, draw three radii 120° apart. With mid-point of each radial line as center, draw a circle tangent to the 4″ circle. With same centers, draw smaller circles tangent to the other two 2″ circles. Connect centers to cut out middle of trefoil. Complete the figure, making all bands the same width.

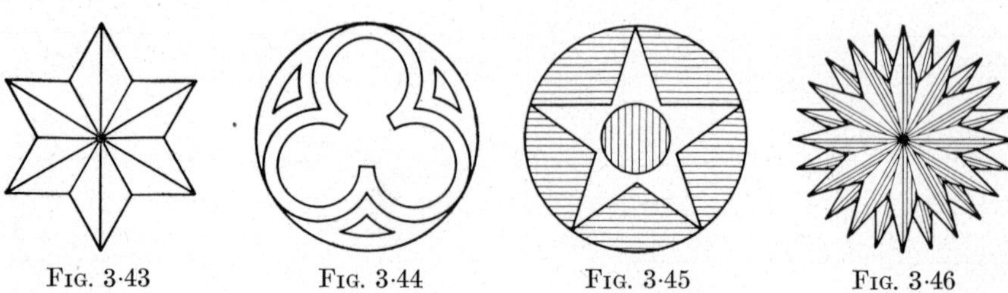

FIG. 3·43 FIG. 3·44 FIG. 3·45 FIG. 3·46

11. Aircraft insigne. Fig. 3·45. This device is a white star with red center on a blue background. Draw 4″ circle and a 1¼″ circle. Divide large circle into five equal parts with the dividers and construct star by connecting alternate points as shown. Red is indicated by vertical lines and blue by horizontal lines. Space these by eye approximately 1/16″ apart.

12. A 24-point star. Fig. 3·46. For T square and triangles in combination. In a 4″ circle draw 12 diameters 15° apart, using T square and triangles singly and in combination. With the same combinations, finish the figure as shown.

13. A quatrefoil knot. Fig. 3·47. For accuracy with compasses. On horizontal and vertical center lines draw a 2″ square. With the middle points of its sides as centers, draw semicircles 2″ and 1½″ in diameter. With the corners of the square as centers, draw quadrants to complete the figure.

14. A four-centered spiral. Fig. 3·48. For accurate tangents. Draw a ⅛″ square and extend its sides as shown. With the upper right corner as center, draw quadrants with ⅛″ and ¼″ radii. Continue with quadrants from each corner in order until four turns have been drawn.

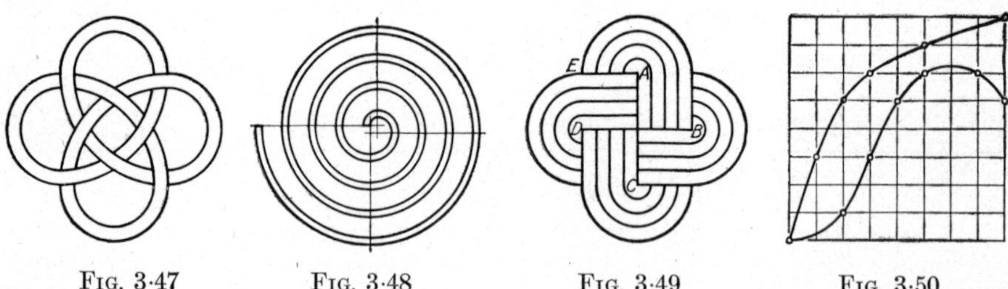

FIG. 3·47 FIG. 3·48 FIG. 3·49 FIG. 3·50

15. A loop ornament. Fig. 3·49. For bow compasses. Draw a 2″ square, about center of space. Divide AE into four ¼″ spaces with scale. With bow pencil and centers A, B, C, and D, draw four semicircles with ¼″ radius, and so on. Complete figure by drawing the horizontal and vertical tangents as shown.

16. A rectilinear chart. Fig. 3·50. For french curve. Draw a 4″ field with ½″ coordinate divisions. Plot points at the intersections shown, and through them sketch a smooth curve very lightly in pencil. Finish by marking each point with a 1/16″ circle and drawing a smooth bright line with the french curve.

17. Scale practice. Fig. 3·51. *a.* Measure lines *A* to *G* to the following scales: *A*, full size; *B*, half size; *C*, 3″ = 1′-0″; *D*, 1″ = 1′-0″; *E*, 3/4″ = 1′-0″; *F*, 1/4″ = 1′-0″; *G*, 3/16″ = 1′-0″.

b. Lay off distances on lines *H* to *N* as follows: *H*, 3 3/16″, full size; *I*, 7″, half size; *J*, 2′-6″, scale 1 1/2″ = 1′-0″; *K*, 7′-5 1/2″, scale 1/2″ = 1′-0″; *L*, 10′-11″, scale 3/8″ = 1′-0″; *M*, 28′-4″, scale 1/8″ = 1′-0″; *N*, 40′-10″, scale 3/32″ = 1′-0″.

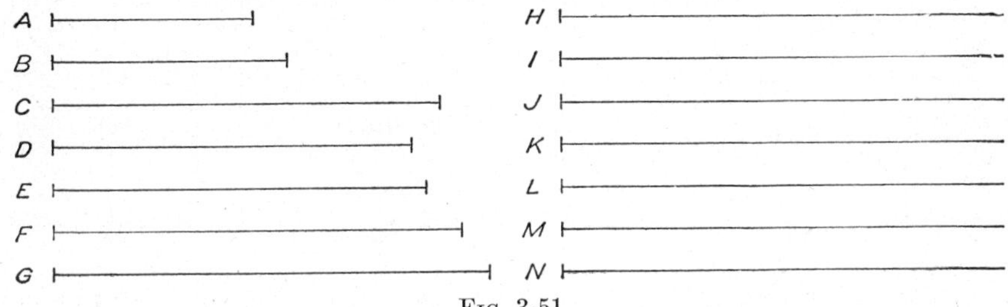

FIG. 3·51

c. For engineer's scale. Lay off distances on lines *H* to *N* as follows: *H*, 3.2″, full size; *I*, 27′-0″, scale 1″ = 10′-0″; *J*, 66′-0″, scale 1″ = 20′-0″; *K*, 105′-0″, scale 1″ = 30′-0″; *L*, 156′-0″, scale 1″ = 40′-0″; *M*, 183′-0″, scale 1″ = 50′-0″; *N*, 214′-0″, scale 1″ = 60′-0″.

18. A motor-lamination stamping. Fig. 3·52. Outside diameter, 5″; center to center of 1/4″ holes, 4″; inside diameter, 2 1/2″; center to center of slot, 3 11/16″; width of slot, 9/16″. Mark tangent points in pencil.

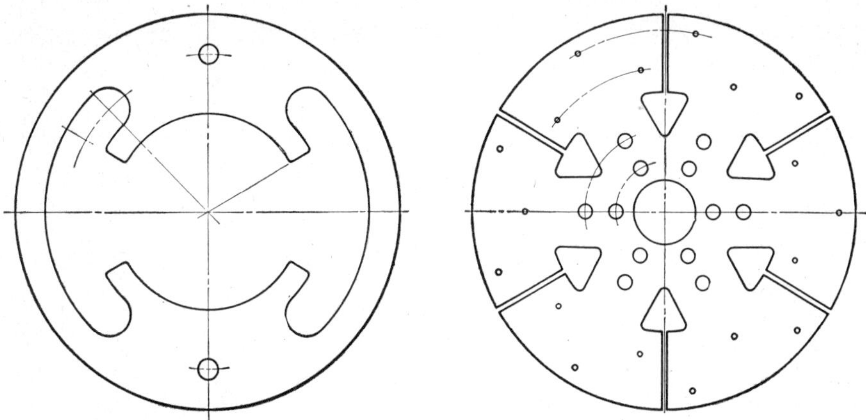

FIG. 3·52—A stamping.

FIG. 3·53—A clutch plate.

19. A clutch plate. Fig. 3·53. Outside diameter, 10 3/4″; bore, 1 3/4″; width of face, 2 1/8″. The arms (extended) are tangent to a 2″ circle at the center and are 1 1/2″ wide at intersection with inside diameter of face. Fillets have 1/4″ radius. Slots are 1/8″ wide. Diameter of outside rivet circle, 9 3/4″; inside rivet circle, 7 3/4″, for nine 1/8″ holes equally spaced. On a 4 3/8″ and a 2 3/4″ circle, space six 3/8″ holes each. Mark tangent points in pencil.

20. A telephone dial plate. Fig. 3·54. Draw double size from dimensions given.

21. A heraldic rose. Fig. 3·55. Draw full size.
22. A film-reel stamping. Fig. 3·56. Draw full size.
23. A film-reel stamping. Fig. 3·57. Draw to scale of 6″ = 1′ – 0″.

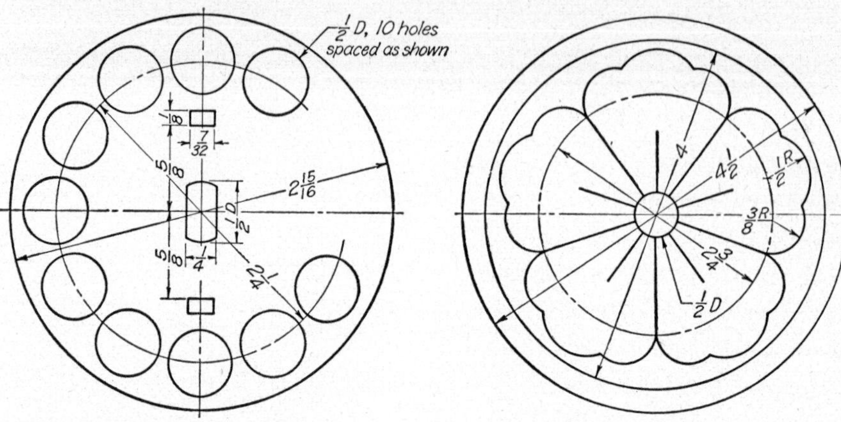

Fig. 3·54—A telephone dial plate.

Fig. 3·55—A heraldic rose.

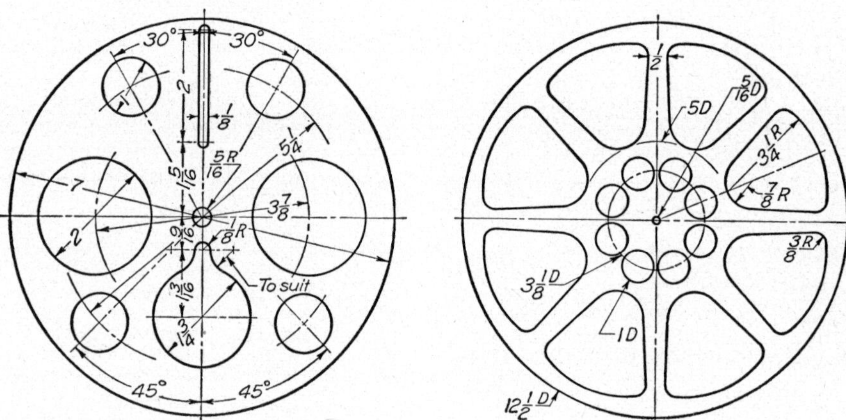

Fig. 3·56—A film-reel stamping.

Fig. 3·57—A film-reel stamping.

24. Box cover. Make one-view drawing for rectangular stamping 3″ × 4″, corners rounded with ½″ radius. Four holes, one in each corner, $\frac{3}{16}$″ diameter, 3″ and 2″ center to center, for fastenings. Rectangular hole in center, ⅜″ × 1″, with 1″ side parallel to 4″ side. Two slots ¼″ wide, 2″ long with semicircular ends, located midway between center and 4″ edges, with 2″ side parallel to 4″ side and centered between 3″ edges.

25. Spacer. Make one-view drawing for circular stamping 4″ OD, 2″ ID. Six ¼″ diameter holes equally spaced on 3″ diameter circle, with two holes on vertical center line. Two semicircular notches 180° apart made with ⅜″ radius centered at intersections of horizontal center line and 4″ OD circle.

26. Blank for wheel. Make one-view drawing for stamping 5″ OD; center hole ½″ diameter; eight spokes ⅜″ wide connecting 1½″ diameter center portion with ½″ rim. Eight ¼″ diameter holes with centers at intersection of center lines of spokes and 4½″ circle, ⅛″ fillets throughout, to break sharp corners.

A PAGE OF CAUTIONS

Never use the scale as a ruler.

Never draw horizontal lines with the lower edge of the T square.

Never use the lower edge of the T square as a horizontal base for the triangles.

Never cut paper with a knife and the edge of the T square as a guide.

Never use the T square as a hammer.

Never put either end of a pencil into the mouth.

Never work with a dull pencil.

Never sharpen a pencil over the drawing board.

Never jab the dividers into the drawing board.

Never oil the joints of compasses.

Never use the dividers as reamers or pincers or picks.

Never use a blotter on inked lines.

Never screw the pen adjustment past the contact point of the nibs.

Never leave the ink bottle uncorked.

Never hold the pen over the drawing while filling.

Never put into the drawing-ink bottle a writing pen which has been used in ordinary writing ink.

Never try to use the same thumbtack holes in either paper or board when putting paper down a second time.

Never scrub a drawing all over with an eraser after finishing. It takes the life out of the lines.

Never begin work without wiping off table and instruments.

Never put instruments away without cleaning. This applies with particular force to pens.

Never put bow instruments away without opening to relieve the spring.

Never work with the table cluttered with unneeded instruments or equipment.

Never fold a drawing or tracing.

Chapter 4

LETTERING

To give all the information necessary for the complete construction of a machine or structure there must be added to the "graphical language" of lines describing its shape, the figured dimensions, notes on material and finish, and a descriptive title, all of which must be lettered, freehand, in a style that is perfectly legible, uniform and capable of rapid execution. So far as its appearance is concerned there is no part of a drawing so important as the lettering. A good drawing may be ruined, not only in appearance but in usefulness, by lettering done ignorantly or carelessly, as illegible figures are very apt to cause mistakes in the work.

4·1 The paragraph above refers to the use of lettering on engineering drawings. In a broad sense, the subject of lettering is a distinct branch of design. There are two general classes of persons who are interested in its study: first, those who have to use letters and words to convey information on drawings; and second, those who use lettering in applied design, such as art students, artists, and craftsmen. The first group is concerned mainly with legibility and speed, the second with beauty of form and composition. Architects come under both classes, as they not only have to letter their working drawings but also have to design inscriptions and tablets to be executed in stone or bronze.

The engineering student takes up lettering as his first work in drawing and continues its practice throughout his course, becoming more and more skillful and proficient.

In the art of lettering there are various forms of alphabets used, each appropriate for some particular purpose. The parent of all these styles is the "Old Roman" of the classic Roman inscriptions. This beautiful letter is the basic standard for architects and artists, although they have occasional appropriate use for other forms, such as the gothic of the Middle Ages, one form of which is popularly known as **"Old English."** A variation known as Modern Roman is used by civil engineers in finished map and topographical drawing. For working drawings the simplified forms called commercial gothic are used almost exclusively.

There are two general divisions of lettering: *drawn*, or *built-up* letters, and *written* or *single-stroke* letters. Roman letters are usually drawn in outline and filled in; commercial gothic, except in the larger sizes, are generally made in single stroke.

Lettering is *not* mechanical drawing. Large, carefully drawn letters are often made with instruments, but the persistent use by some draftsmen of mechanical caricatures known as "geometrical letters," "block letters," etc., made up of straight lines ruled in with T square and triangle is to be condemned entirely.

4·2 General proportions. There is no one standard for the proportions of letters, but there are certain fundamental points in design and certain characteristics of individual letters that must be thoroughly learned by study and observation before composition into words and sentences may be attempted. Not only do the widths of letters in any alphabet vary, from *I* the narrowest, to *W*, the widest, but different alphabets vary as a whole. **Styles narrow in their proportion of width to height are called "COMPRESSED LETTERS" and are used when space is limited. Stylės wider than the normal are called "EXTENDED LETTERS."**

The proportion of the thickness of stem to the height varies widely, ranging all the way from one-third to one-twentieth. Letters with heavy stems are called **boldface** or **blackface,** those with thin stems LIGHTFACE.

4·3 The rule of stability. In the construction of letters, the well-known optical illusion in which a horizontal line drawn across the middle of a rectangle appears to be below the middle must be provided for. In order to give the appearance of stability, such letters as *BEKSXZ* and the figures *3* and *8* must be drawn smaller at the top than at the bottom. To see the effect of this illusion turn a printed page upside down and notice the letters mentioned.

4·4 Single-stroke lettering. By far the greatest amount of lettering on drawings is done in a rapid single-stroke letter, either vertical or inclined, and every engineer must have absolute command of these styles. The ability to letter well can be acquired only by continued and careful practice, but it can be acquired by anyone with normal muscular control of his fingers who will practice faithfully and intelligently and take the trouble to observe carefully the shapes of the letters, the sequence of strokes in making them, and the rules for their composition. It is not a matter of artistic talent, or even of dexterity, in handwriting. Many draftsmen who write very poorly letter well.

The terms "single-stroke" or "one-stroke" do not mean that the entire letter is made without lifting the pencil or pen, but that the width of the stroke of the pencil or pen is the width of the stem of the letter.

4·5 Guide lines. Light guide lines for both tops and bottoms of letters should always be drawn, using a sharp pencil. Figure 4·1 shows a method of laying off a number of equally spaced lines of letters. Draw the first base line, and above it mark the desired height of the letters; then set the bow spacers to the distance wanted between base lines and step off the required number of base lines. With the same setting, step down again from the upper point, thus obtaining points for the tops of each line of letters.

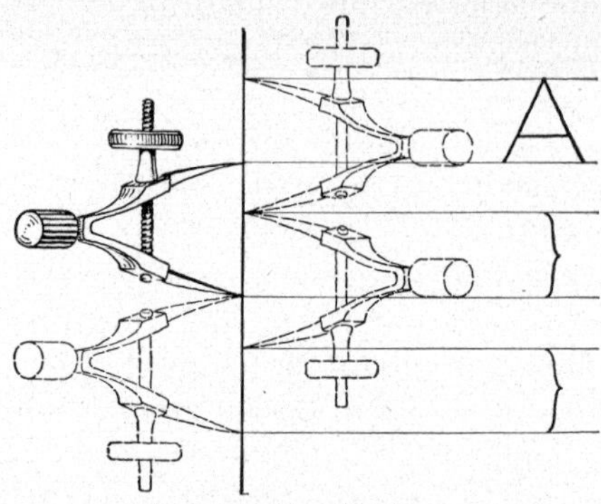

FIG. 4·1—Spacing lines.

The Braddock-Rowe triangle, Fig. 4·2, and the Ames lettering instrument, Fig. 4·3, are convenient devices for spacing lines of letters. A sharp pencil is inserted in the proper row of countersunk holes, and the instrument, guided by a T-square blade, is drawn back and forth by the pencil. The holes are grouped for capitals and lower case, the numbers indicating the height of capitals in thirty-seconds of an inch; thus No. 6 spacing means that the capitals will be $\frac{6}{32}''$ or $\frac{3}{16}''$ high.

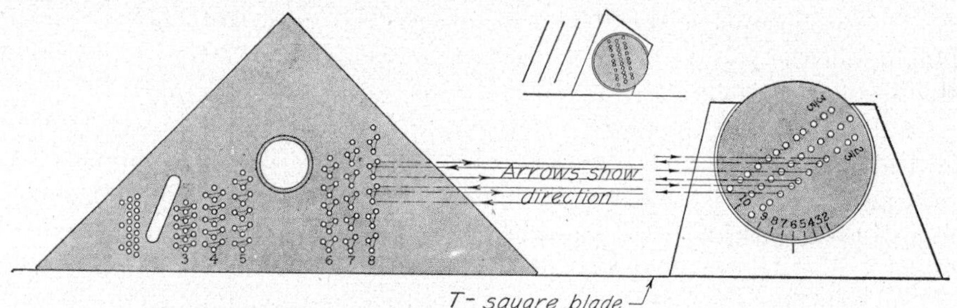

FIG. 4·2—Braddock-Rowe triangle. FIG. 4·3—Ames lettering instrument.

4·6 Lettering in pencil. In the previous chapter the necessity for fine pencil work in drawing was emphasized. This is equally true for lettering, since practically all lettering is done in pencil, either as finished work to be reproduced by one of the printing processes, or as part of a pencil drawing to be inked. In the first case the penciling will be clean, firm, and opaque, while in the second case it may be lighter. The lettering pencil should be selected carefully by trial on the paper. In one case the same grade as that used for the drawing may be chosen, in another case a grade or two softer may be preferred. Sharpen the pencil to a long conical point, then round the lead slightly on the end so that it is not so sharp as a point used for drawing.

The first requirement in lettering is the correct holding of the pencil or pen. Figure 4·4 shows the pencil held comfortably with the thumb, forefinger, and second finger on alternate flat sides, and the third and fourth fingers on the paper. Vertical, slanting, and curved strokes are drawn with a steady, even, finger movement; horizontal strokes are made similarly, but with some pivoting of the hand at the wrist, Fig. 4·5. Exert a firm uniform

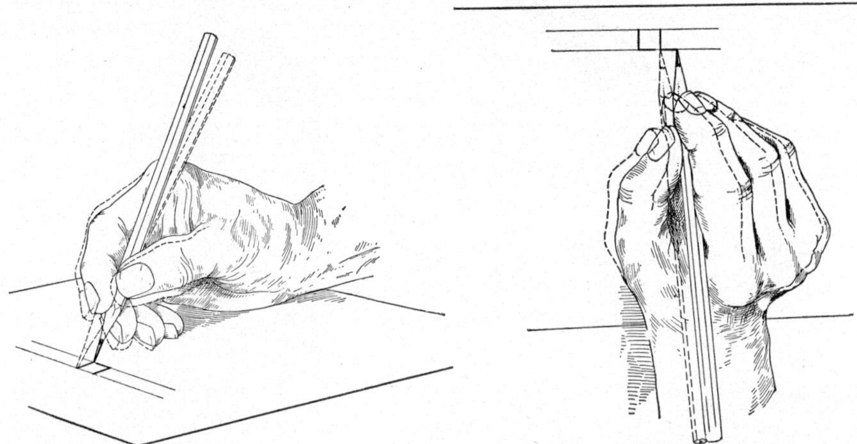

Fig. 4·4—Vertical strokes. Fig. 4·5—Horizontal strokes.

pressure, but not so heavy as to cut grooves in the paper. To keep the point symmetrical, the habit of rotating the pencil after every few strokes should be formed.

4·7 Lettering pens. There are many steel writing pens either adaptable to, or made especially for, lettering. The sizes of the strokes of a few popular

LEONARDT 516 F: 506 F

HUNT 512: ESTERBROOK 968

Esterbrook 1000 Spencerian No. 1

Gillott 404: Gillott 303 For very fine lines Gillott 170 and 290 or Esterbrook 356 and 355

Fig. 4·6—Pen strokes, full size.

ones are shown in full size in Fig. 4·6. Several special pens made in sets of graded sizes have been designed for single-stroke lettering, among which are those illustrated in Fig. 4·7. These are particularly useful for large work. The ink-holding reservoir of the Henry tank pen, Fig. 4·8, assists materially in maintaining uniform weight of line. A similar device may be made by bending a brass strip from a paper fastener, a piece of annealed watch spring or, perhaps best, a strip cut from a piece of shim brass into the shape shown in Fig. 4·9 and inserting it in the penholder so that the curved end just touches the nibs of the pen. The rate of feed can be increased by moving the end closer to the point of the pen.

Always wet a new pen and wipe it thoroughly before using to remove the oil film. Some draftsmen prepare a new pen by holding it in a match flame

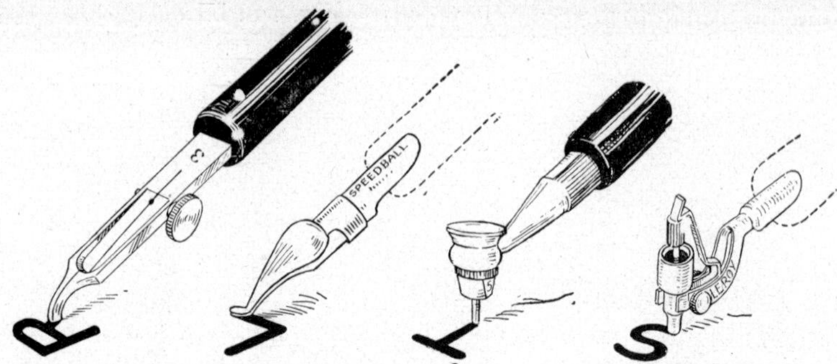

FIG. 4·7—Barch-Payzant, Speedball, Edco, and Leroy pens.

FIG. 4·8—Henry tank pen.

FIG. 4·9—Ink holder.

for 2 or 3 seconds. A lettering pen well broken in by use is worth much more than a new one. It should be kept with care and never lent. A pen that has been dipped into writing ink should never be put into drawing ink. When in use, a pen should be wiped clean frequently with a cloth penwiper. The use of a ruling pen for freehand lettering is not recommended.

4·8 Using the pen. A penholder with cork grip (the small size) should be chosen and the pen set in it firmly. Many prefer to ink the pen with the quill filler, touching the quill to the underside of the pen point, rather than

EHMNWTZ

FIG. 4·10—Too much ink.

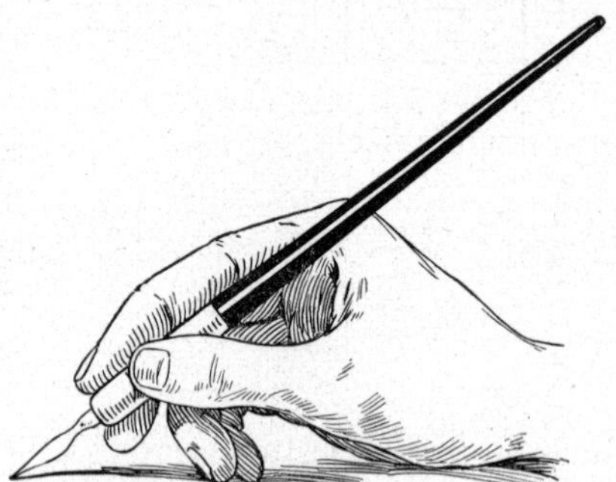

FIG. 4·11—Holding the pen.

to dip it into the ink bottle. If the pen is dipped, the surplus ink should be shaken back into the bottle or the pen touched against the neck of the bottle as it is withdrawn. Lettering with too much ink on the pen is responsible for results of the kind shown in Fig. 4·10.

With the penholder in the position shown in Fig. 4·11, it should be held in the fingers firmly but without pinching. The strokes of the letters should be made with a steady, even motion and a slight uniform pressure on the paper that will not spread the nibs of the pen.

4·9 Single-stroke vertical capitals. The vertical single-stroke commercial gothic letter is a standard for titles, reference letters, etc. As to the proportion of width to height, the general rule is that the smaller the letters the more extended should they be in width. A low extended letter is more legible than a high compressed one and, at the same time, makes a better appearance.

The basic requirement is to learn the form and peculiarity of each of the letters. Too many persons think that lettering is simply "printing" of the childish kind learned in the primary grades. There is an individuality in lettering often nearly as marked as in handwriting, but it must be based on a careful regard for the fundamental letter forms.

4·10 Order of strokes. In the following figures an alphabet of slightly extended vertical capitals has been arranged in family groups. The shape of each letter, with the order and direction of the strokes forming it, must be studied carefully and the letter repeatedly practiced until its form and construction are perfectly familiar. The first studies should be made in pencil to large size, perhaps 3/8″ high, afterward to smaller size, and finally directly in ink.

To aid in seeing the proportions of widths to heights and in learning the subtleties in the shapes of the letters, they are shown against a square background with its sides divided into sixths. It will be noted that several of the letters in this alphabet, such as *A*, *T*, etc., fill the square, that is, they are as wide as they are high; while some others, such as *H*, *D*, etc., are approximately five spaces wide, or five-sixths of their height. *These proportions must be learned visually* so well that letters of various heights can be drawn in correct proportion without hesitation.

The IHT group. Fig. 4·12. The letter *I* is the foundation stroke. It may be found difficult to keep the stems vertical. If so, direction lines may be drawn lightly an inch or so apart, to aid the eye. The *H* is nearly square (five-sixths) and, in accord with the rule of stability, the cross bar is just above the center. The top of the *T* is drawn first to the full width of the square and the stem started accurately at its middle point.

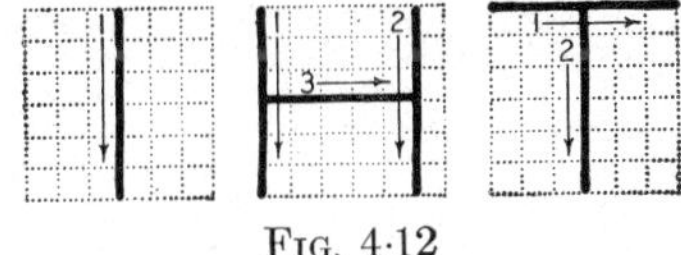

FIG. 4·12

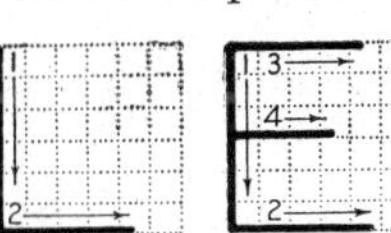

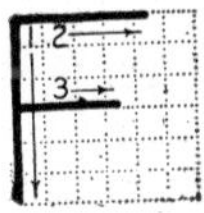

FIG. 4·13

The LEF group. Fig. 4·13. The *L* is made in two strokes. Note that the first two strokes of the *E* are the same as the *L*, that the third or upper stroke is slightly shorter than the lower, and that the last stroke is two-thirds as long and just above the middle. *F* has the same proportions as *E*.

The NZXY group. Fig. 4·14. The parallel sides of *N* are generally drawn first, but some prefer to make the strokes in consecutive order. *Z* and *X* are both started inside the width of the square on top and run to full width on the bottom. This throws the crossing point of the *X* slightly above the center. The junction of the *Y* strokes is at the center.

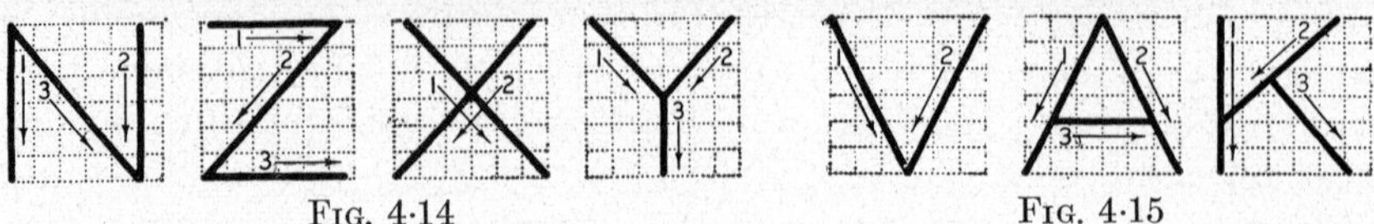

Fig. 4·14 Fig. 4·15

The VAK group. Fig. 4·15. *V* is the same width as *A*, the full breadth of the square. The *A* bridge is one-third up from the bottom. The second stroke of *K* strikes the stem one-third up from the bottom; the third stroke branches from it in a direction starting from the top of the stem.

The MW group. Fig. 4·16. These are the widest letters. *M* may be made either in consecutive strokes, or by drawing the two vertical strokes first, as with the *N*. *W* is formed of two narrow *V*'s, each two-thirds of the square in width. Note that with all the pointed letters the width at the point is the width of the stroke.

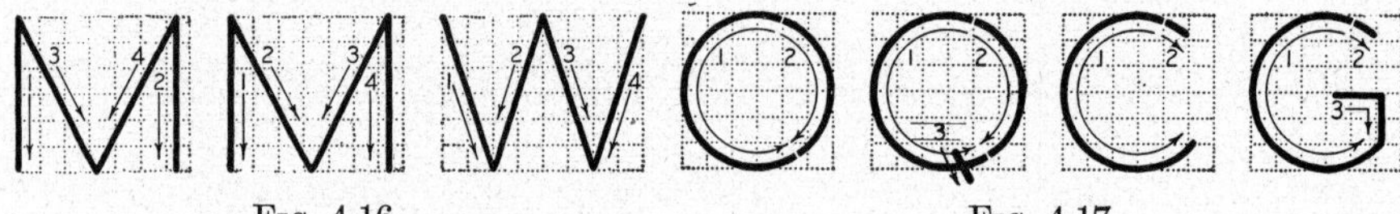

Fig. 4·16 Fig. 4·17

The OQCG group. Fig. 4·17. In this extended alphabet the letters of the *O* family are made as full circles. The *O* is made in two strokes, the left side a longer arc than the right, as the right side is harder to make. Make the kern of the *Q* straight. A large-size *C* and *G* can be made more accurately with an extra stroke at the top, while in smaller letters the curve is made in one stroke, Fig. 4·25. Note that the bar on the *G* is half-way up and does not extend past the vertical stroke.

The DUJ group. Fig. 4·18. The top and bottom strokes of *D* must be horizontal. Failure to observe this is a common fault with beginners. *U* in larger letters is formed of two parallel strokes to which the bottom stroke is added. For smaller letters it may be made in two strokes curved at the bottom to meet. *J* has the same construction as *U*, with stroke 1 omitted.

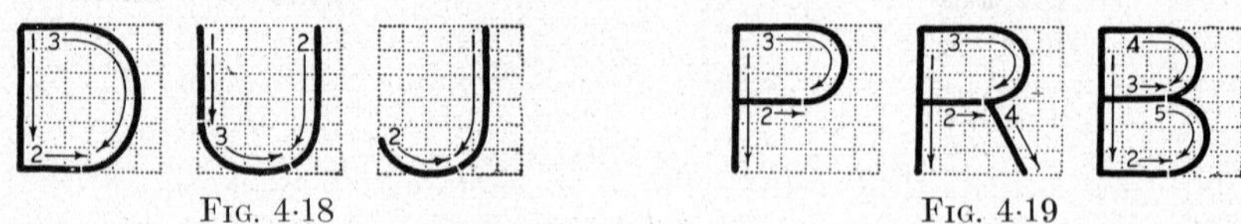

Fig. 4·18 Fig. 4·19

The PRB group. Fig. 4·19. With *P*, *R*, and *B*, the number of strokes used depends upon the size of the letter. For large letters the horizontal lines are started and the curves added, but for smaller letters only one stroke for each lobe is needed. The middle lines of *P* and *R* are on the center line, that of *B* observes the rule of stability.

The S83 group. Fig. 4·20. The *S*, *8*, and *3* are closely related in form, and the rule of stability must be observed carefully. For a large *S*, three strokes may be used, for a smaller one, two strokes, and, for a very small size, one stroke only is best. The *8* may be made on the *S* construction in three strokes, or in "head and body" in four strokes. A perfect *3* should be capable of being finished into an *8*. The *3* with flat top, sometimes seen, should not be used, on account of the danger of mistaking it for a *5*.

FIG. 4·20 FIG. 4·21

The 069 group. Fig. 4·21. The cipher is an ellipse, 5/6 the width of the letter *O*. The backbones of the *6* and *9* have the same curve as the cipher, and the lobes are two-thirds the height of the figure.

The 257& group. Fig. 4·22. The secret in making the *2* lies in getting the reverse curve to cross the center of the space. The bottom of *2* and the

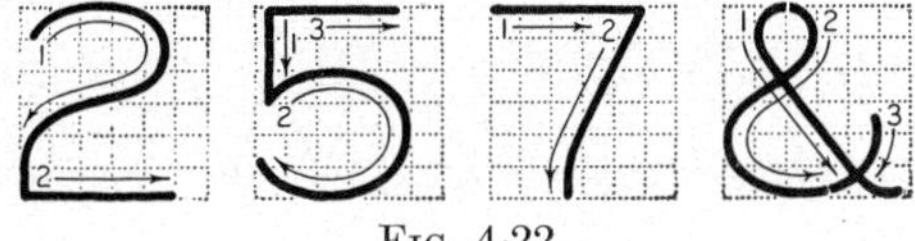

FIG. 4·22

tops of *5* and *7* should be horizontal straight lines. The second stroke of *7* terminates directly below the middle of the top stroke. Its stiffness is relieved by curving it slightly at the lower end. The ampersand (&) is made in three strokes for large letters and two for smaller ones, and must be carefully balanced.

The fraction group. Fig. 4·23. Fractions are always made with horizontal bar. Integers are the same height as capitals. The total fraction

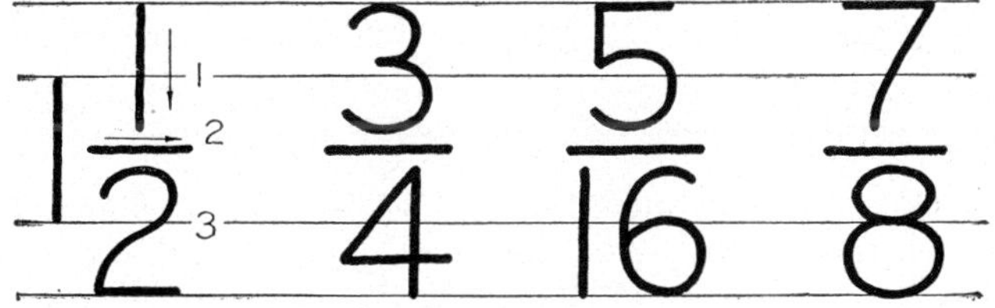

FIG. 4·23—Fractions.

height is best made twice the height of the integer. The numerator and denominator will be about three-fourths the height of the integer. Be careful to leave a clear space above and below the horizontal bar. Guide lines for fractions are easily obtained with lettering instruments by using the set of uniformly spaced holes, or by drawing the integer height above and below the center, the position of the horizontal bar.

4·11 Vertical lower case. The single-stroke, vertical lower-case letter is not commonly used on machine drawings but is used extensively in map drawing. It is the standard letter for hypsography in government topographical drawing. The bodies are made two-thirds the height of the capitals, with the ascenders extending to the cap line and the descenders dropping the same distance below. The basic form of the letter is the combination of a circle and a straight line, Fig. 4·24. The alphabet with some alternate shapes is shown in Fig. 4·25, which also gives the capitals in alphabetical order.

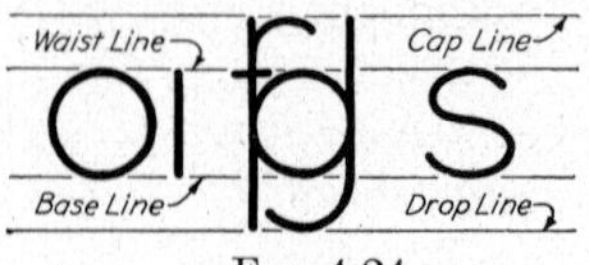

FIG. 4·24

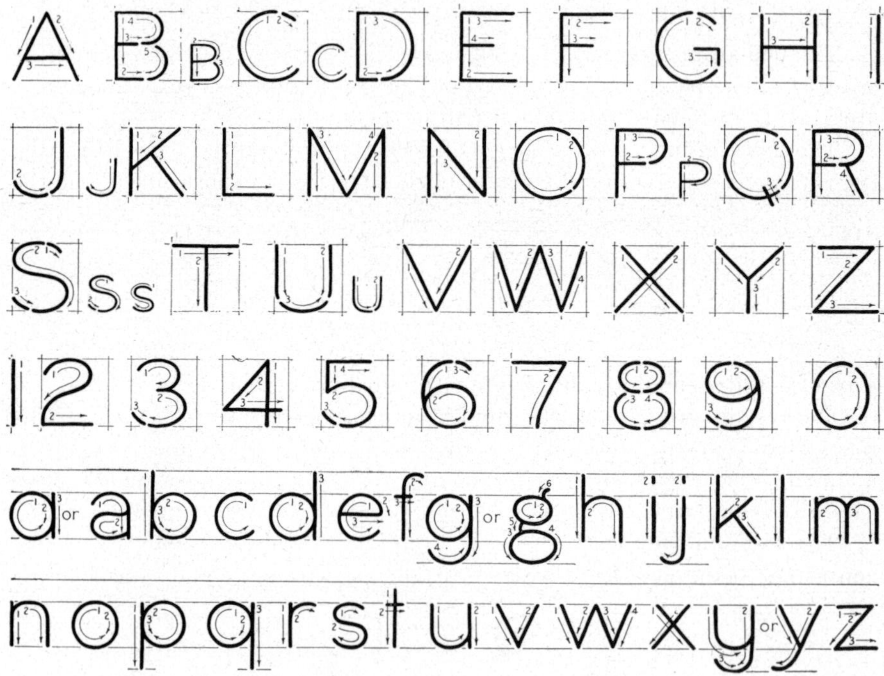

FIG. 4·25—Single-stroke vertical caps and lower case.

4·12 Single-stroke inclined caps. The inclined or slant letter is used in preference to the upright by many draftsmen. The order and direction of strokes are the same as in the vertical form.

After ruling the guide lines, slanting "direction lines" should be drawn across the sheet to aid the eye in keeping the slope uniform. These slope lines may be drawn with a special lettering triangle of about 67½°, or the slope of 2 to 5 may be fixed on the paper by marking two units on a horizontal line and five on a vertical line and using T square and triangle as shown in Fig. 4·26. The Braddock-Rowe triangle and the Ames instrument both provide for the drawing of slope lines, Figs. 4·2 and 4·3. The form taken by the rounded letters when inclined is illustrated in Fig. 4·27, which shows that curves are sharp in all upper right-hand and lower left-hand corners and flattened in the other two corners. Particular care must be observed with the letters having sloping sides, such as *A*, *V*, and *W*. The sloping sides of these letters must be drawn so that they appear to balance about a slope guide line passing through the intersection, as in Fig. 4·28. The alphabet is given in Fig. 4·29. Study the shape of each letter carefully.

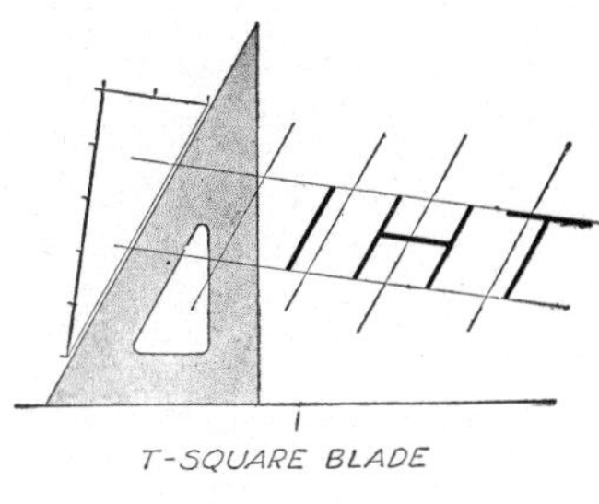

FIG. 4·26—Slope guide lines.

FIG. 4·27 FIG. 4·28

The snap and swing of professional work are due to three things: first, to keeping to a uniform slope; second, to having the letters full and well

FIG. 4·29—Single-stroke inclined caps and lower case.

shaped; and third, to keeping them close together. The beginner's invariable mistake is to cramp the individual letters and space them too far apart.

4·13 Single-stroke inclined lower case. The inclined lower-case letters, Fig. 4·29, have the bodies two-thirds the height of the capitals, with the ascenders extending to the cap line and the descenders dropping the same distance below the base line. This letter is generally known among older

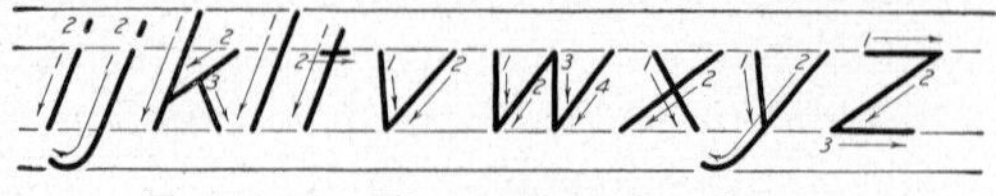

Fig. 4·30—The straight-line letters.

engineers, particularly among civil engineers, as the Reinhardt letter, in honor of Charles W. Reinhardt, who first systematized its construction. It is very legible and effective and, after its swing has been mastered, can be made very rapidly. The lower-case letter is suitable for notes and statements on drawings for the two reasons indicated: first, it is much more easily read than all caps, since we read words by the word shapes; and second, it can be done much faster.

Fig. 4·31—The loop letters.

All the letters of the Reinhardt alphabet are based on two elements: the straight line and the ellipse, and have no unnecessary hooks on appendages. They may be divided into four groups as shown in Figs. 4·30 to 4·33. The dots of *i* and *j* and the top of the *t* are on the "t line" halfway between the waistline and the cap line. The loop letters are made with an ellipse, whose long axis is inclined about 45°, in combination with a straight line. In lettering rapidly, this ellipse tends to assume a pumpkinseed form that should be guarded against.

Fig. 4·32—The ellipse letters.

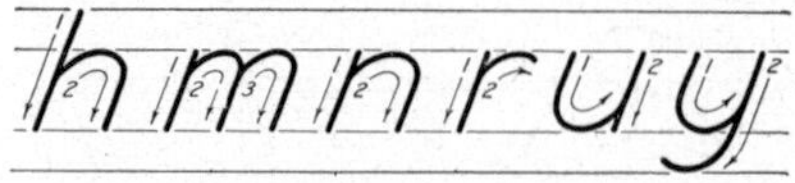

Fig. 4·33—The hook letters.

The *c*, *e*, and *o* are based on an ellipse of the shape of the capitals, but not inclined quite so much as the loop-letter ellipse. In rapid, small work the *o* is often made in one stroke, as are also *e*, *v*, and *w*. The *s* is similar to the capital but, except in letters more than 1/8 inch high, is made in one stroke. In the hook-letter group, note particularly the shape of the hook.

The single-stroke letter may, if necessary, be very much compressed and still be clear and legible, Fig. 4·34. It is also used sometimes in extended form.

COMPRESSED LETTERS ARE USED
when space is limited. Either vertical
or inclined styles may be compressed

EXTENDED LETTERS OF A
given height are more legible

FIG. 4·34—Compressed and extended letters.

4·14 For left-handers only. The order and direction of strokes in the preceding alphabets have been designed for right-handed persons. The principal reason that left-handers sometimes find lettering difficult is that, whereas the right-hander progresses away from the body, the left-hander progresses toward the body; consequently his pencil and hand partially hide the work he has done, making it harder to join strokes and to preserve uniformity. Also, in the case of inclined lettering, the slope direction, instead of running toward his eye, runs off into space to the left of his body, making this style so much harder for him that the left-hander is strongly advised to *use vertical letters exclusively*.

FIG. 4·35—Strokes for left-handers.

For the natural left-hander whose writing position is the same as a right-hander except reversed left for right, a change in the sequence of strokes of some of the letters will obviate part of the difficulty caused by interference with the line of sight. Figure 4·35 gives an analyzed alphabet with an alternate for some letters. In *E* the top bar is made before the bottom bar, and *M* is drawn from left to right, to avoid having strokes hidden by the pencil or pen. Horizontal curves are easier to make from right to left, hence the starting points for *O*, *Q*, *C*, *G*, and *U* differ from the standard right-hand stroking. *S* is the perfect letter for the left-hander and is best made in a single smooth stroke. 6 and 9 are difficult and require extra practice. In the lower-case letters, *a*, *d*, *g*, and *q*, it is better to draw the straight line before the curve even though it makes spacing a little harder.

The hook-wrist left-handed writer, who pushes his strokes from top to bottom, finds vertical lettering more difficult than does the natural left-hander. In Fig. 4·35, where alternate strokes are given for some of the letters, the hook-wrist writer will probably find the stroking of the second one easier for him than that of the first. Some prefer to reverse *all* the strokes, drawing vertical strokes from bottom to top and horizontal strokes from right to left.

By way of encouragement it may be said that many left-handed draftsmen letter beautifully.

4·15 Composition. Composition in lettering has to do with the selection, arrangement, and spacing of appropriate styles and sizes of letters. On engineering drawings, the selection of the style is practically limited to vertical or inclined single stroke, so that composition here means arrangement into pleasing and legible form. After the shapes and strokes of the individual letters have been learned, the entire practice should be on composition into words and sentences, since proper spacing of letters and words does more for the appearance of a block of lettering than the forms of the letters themselves. Letters in words are not spaced at a uniform distance from each other but are arranged so that the areas of white spaces (the irregular backgrounds between the letters) are approximately equal, thus making the spacing *appear* approximately uniform. Figure 4·36 illustrates these background shapes. Each letter is spaced with reference to its shape and the shape of the letter preceding it. Thus, adjacent letters with straight sides would be spaced farther apart than those with curved sides. Sometimes combinations such as *LT* or *AV* may even overlap. Definite rules for spacing are not successful; it is a matter of the draftsman's judgment and sense of design. Figure 4·37 illustrates word composition. The sizes of

Fig. 4·36—Background areas.

COMPOSITION IN LETTERING
REQUIRES CAREFUL SPACING, NOT ONLY
OF LETTERS BUT OF WORDS AND LINES

Fig. 4·37—Word composition.

letters to use in any particular case may be determined better by sketching them lightly than by judging from the guide lines alone. A finished line of letters always looks larger than the guide lines would indicate. Avoid the use of a coarse pen for small sizes, and one that makes thin wiry lines for large sizes. When caps and small caps are used, the height of the small caps should be about four-fifths that of the caps.

WORDSISPACEDIBYISKETCHINGIANIIIBETWEEN

WORDS SPACED BY SKETCHING AN I BETWEEN

FIG. 4·38—Word spacing.

In spacing words, a good method is to leave the space that would be taken by an assumed letter *I* connecting the two words into one, as in Fig. 4·38. The space would never be more than the height of the letters.

The clear distance between lines may vary from ½ to 1½ times the height of the letter but, for appearance sake, should not be exactly the same as the letter height. The instruments of Figs. 4·2 and 4·3 provide spacing two-thirds the letter height. Paragraphs should always be indented.

4·16 Titles. The most important problem in lettering composition that the engineering draftsman will meet is the design of titles. Every drawing has a descriptive title giving the necessary information concerning it, which is either all hand-lettered or filled in on a printed form. This information, of course, is not the same for all kinds of drawings (see working-drawing titles, page 314; architectural titles, page 555; structural titles, page 573; map titles, page 595).

  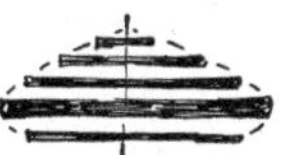  

FIG. 4·39—Shapes in symmetrical composition.

The usual form of lettered title is the *symmetrical title,* which is balanced or "justified" on a vertical center line and designed with an elliptical or oval outline. Sometimes the wording necessitates a pyramid or inverted pyramid ("bag") form. Figure 4·39 illustrates several shapes into which titles can be composed. The lower right-hand corner of the sheet is from long custom and on account of convenience in filing, the usual location for the title, and in laying out a drawing this corner is reserved for it. The space allowed is a matter of judgment and depends on the size and purpose of the drawing. On an 11″ × 17″ working drawing the title may be about three inches long.

4·17 To draw a title. When the wording has been determined, write out the arrangement on a separate piece of paper as in Fig. 4·40 (or, better, typewrite it). Count the letters, including the word spaces, and make a mark across the middle letter or space of each line. The lines must be displayed for prominence according to their relative importance as judged from the point of view of the persons who will use the drawing. Titles are usually made in all caps. Draw the base line for the most important line of the title and mark on it the approximate length desired. To get the letter height, divide this length by the number of letters in the line, and

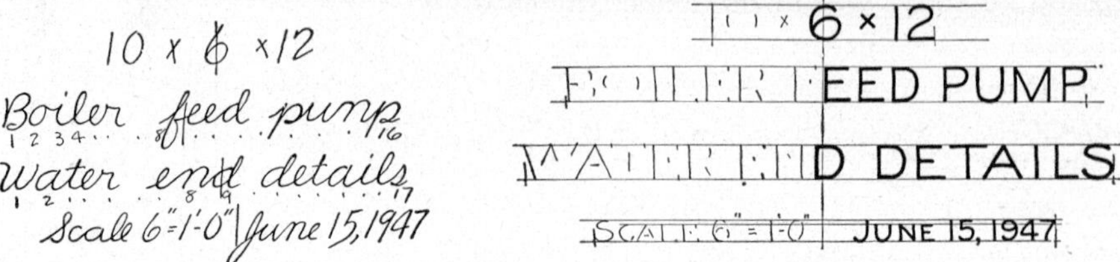

FIG. 4·40—Title composition.

draw the cap line. Start at the center line and sketch very lightly the last half of the line, drawing only enough of the letters to show the space each will occupy. Lay off the length of this right half on the other side and sketch that half, working either forward or backward. When this line is satisfactory in size and spacing, draw the remainder in the same way. Study the effect, shift letters or lines if necessary, and complete in pencil. Use punctuation marks only for abbreviations.

4·18 The scratch-paper methods. Sketch each line of the title separately on a piece of scratch paper, using guide lines of determined height. Find the middle point of each of these lines, fold the paper along the base line of the letters, fit the middle point to the center line on the drawing, and draw the final letters directly below the sketches. *Or* draw the letters along the edge of the scratch paper, using either the upper or the lower edge as one of the guide lines. *Or* letter the title on scratch paper, cut apart and adjust until satisfactory, and then trace it.

4·19 The proportional method. On account of the varying widths of roman letters, it is sometimes difficult to space a word or line to a given length by counting letters. Figure 4·41 illustrates the method of spacing by the principle of similar triangles. Suppose it is necessary to put the word "ROMAN" on the line to the length *ab*. A line *ac* is drawn from *a* at any angle (say 30°) and a second line *de* parallel to it, then the word is sketched in this space, starting at *a* and spacing each letter with reference to the one before it, allowing the word to end where it will. The end of the last letter, at *c*, is connected with *b*, and lines parallel to *cb* are drawn from each letter, thus dividing *ab* proportionately. The height *bf* is obtained from *ce* by the construction shown, after which the word can be sketched in its final position.

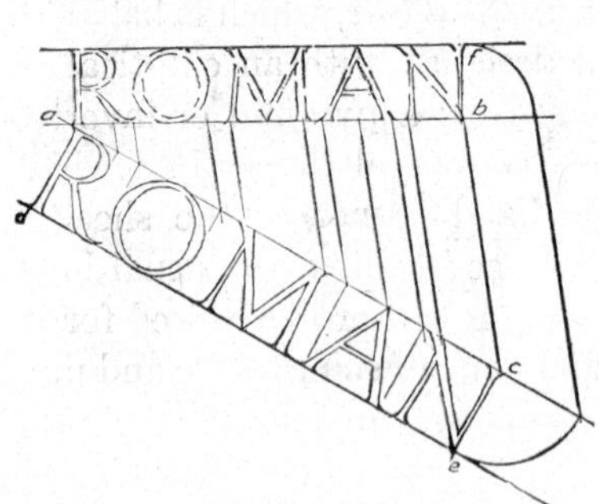

FIG. 4·41—Proportional method.

4·20 Outlined commercial gothic. Thus far the so-called "gothic" letter has been considered only as a single-stroke letter. For sizes larger than, say 5⁄16 inch, or for boldface letters, it is drawn in outline and filled in solid. For a given size, this letter is readable at a greater distance than any other style; hence it would be used in any place where legibility is the principal requirement. The stems may be from one-tenth to one-fifth of the height, and much care must be exercised in keeping them to uniform width at every point on the letter. In inking a penciled outline, keep the *outside* of the ink line on the pencil line, Fig. 4·42; otherwise the letter will be heavier than expected.

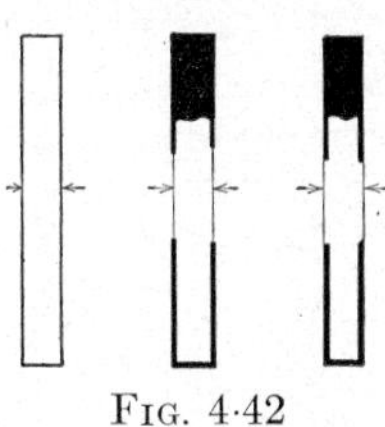

Fig. 4·42

Making two strokes in place of one, the general order and direction of penciling large commercial gothic letters is similar to the single-stroke analysis, as shown in the typical examples of Fig. 4·43. Free ends, such

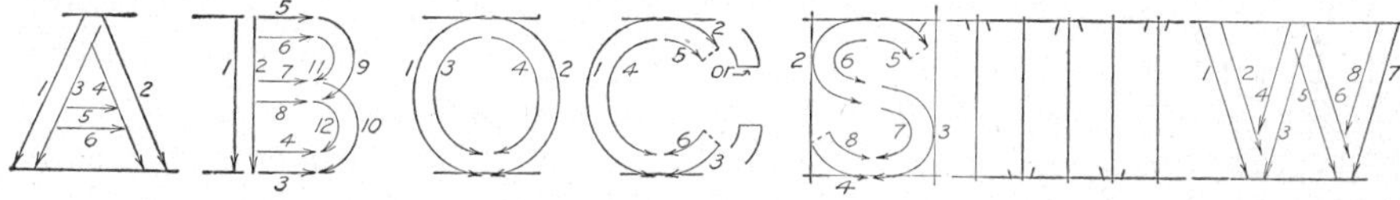

Fig. 4·43—Typical construction for large commercial gothic.

as on *C*, *G*, and *S*, are cut off perpendicular to the stem. The stiffness of plain letters is sometimes relieved by finishing the ends with a slight spur, as in Fig. 4·44. The complete alphabet in outline, with stems one-sixth

ABCDEFGHIJ
KLMNOPQRS
TUVWXYZ &

Fig. 4·44—Compressed commercial gothic.

of the height, is given in Fig. 4·45. The same scale of widths may be used for drawing lighter face letters. Figure 4·44 illustrates a commercial gothic alphabet compressed to two-thirds the normal width. In this figure the stems are drawn one-seventh of the height, but the scale is given in sixths, as in Fig. 4·45.

Fig. 4·45—Large commercial gothic construction.

Fig. 4·46—Old Roman capitals.

4·21 The roman letter. The roman letter has been mentioned as the parent of all the styles, however diversified, which are in use today. Although there are many variations of it there may be said to be three general forms: (1) the early or classic, (2) the Renaissance, (3) the Modern. The first two are very similar in effect and the general term "Old Roman" is used for both.

The roman letter is composed of two weights of lines, corresponding to the downstroke and the upstroke of the broad reed pen with which it was

FIG. 4·47—Old Roman lower case.

originally written. It is an inexcusable fault to shade a roman letter on the wrong stroke.

Rule for shading. All horizontal strokes are light. All vertical strokes are heavy except in *M*, *N*, and *U*. To determine the heavy stroke in letters containing slanting sides, trace the shape of the letter from left to right in one stroke and note which lines were made downward. Figure 4·46 is an Old Roman alphabet with the width of the body stroke one-tenth of the height of the letter and the light lines slightly over one-half this width. For inscriptions and titles, capitals are generally used, but sometimes the lower case, Fig. 4·47, is needed. This example is drawn with the waistline six-tenths high and the width of the stems one-twelfth of the cap height.

The Old Roman is the architect's one general-purpose letter. A single-stroke adaptation of it, Fig. 4·48, is generally used on architectural drawings.

4·22 Modern Roman. Civil engineers in particular must be familiar with the Modern Roman, as it is the standard letter for finished map titles

ABCDEFGHIJKLMN
OPQRSTUVWXYZ&
abcdefghijklmnopqrstuvwxyz
1234567890
SINGLE STROKE ROMAN *for*
ARCHITECTURAL DRAWINGS

ABCDEFGHIJKLMMNOPQRSTUV
WXYZ& 1234567890
COMPRESSED FORM *for* LIMITED SPACE

INCISED

ABCDEFGHIJKLMNOPQRS
TUVWXYZ&1234567890
aabcdefghijklmnopqrstuvwxyz

Notes on drawings are easier to read when they are done in lower-case letters than when lettered in all capital letters.

SINGLE STROKE ITALIC may be much compressed when restricted space makes it necessary. This example is drawn at an angle of 75 degrees.

FIG. 4·48—Single-stroke roman and italic.

and the names of civil divisions, such as countries and cities. It is a difficult letter to draw and can be mastered only by careful attention to details. The heavy or "body" strokes are from one-sixth to one-eighth the height

FIG. 4·49—Modern Roman capitals.

FIG. 4·50—Modern Roman lower case.

of the letter. Those in Fig. 4·49 are one-seventh. A paper scale made by dividing the height into seven parts will aid in penciling. Modern lower case, Fig. 4·50, is used on maps for names of towns and villages. Notice the difference in the serifs of Figs. 4·50 and 4·47.

The order and direction of strokes used in drawing Modern Roman letters are illustrated in the typical letters of Fig. 4·51. The serifs on the ends of the strokes extend one space on each side and are joined to the stroke by small stroke fillets altogether. It will be noticed that the curved letters are flattened slightly on their diagonals. A title in roman letters is illustrated in Fig. 4·52.

RIGHT
WRONG
RIGHT
WRONG
NOT
NOT
NOT
NOT

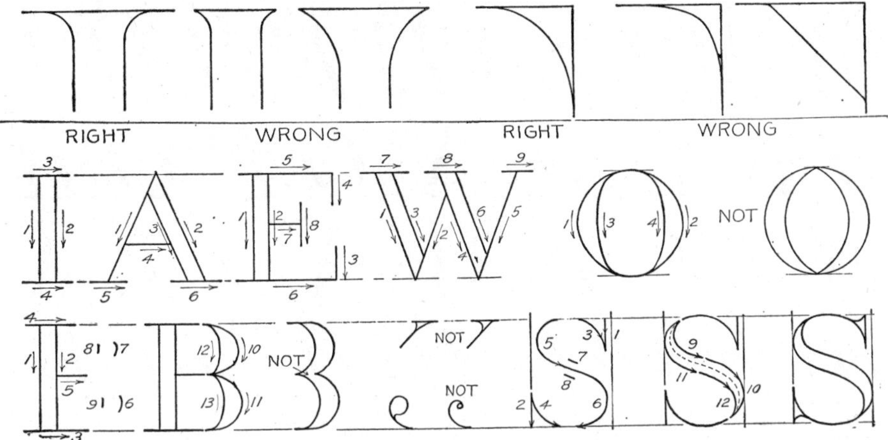

FIG. 4·51—Modern Roman construction.

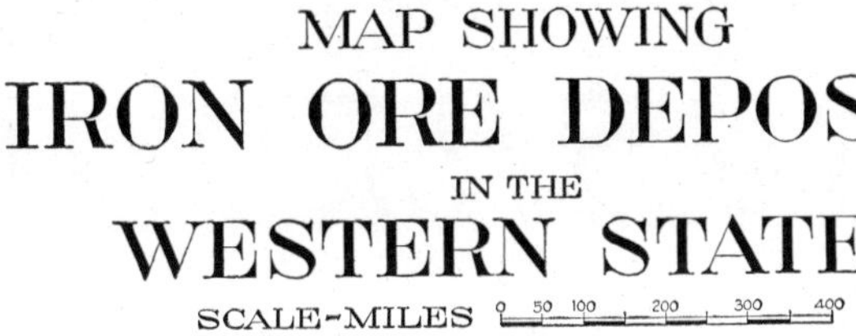

MAP SHOWING
IRON ORE DEPOSITS
IN THE
WESTERN STATES
SCALE-MILES
0 50 100 200 300 400

FIG. 4·52—A roman letter title.

The roman letter may be extended or compressed, as shown in Fig. 4·53. For these, a scale for widths may be made longer or shorter than the normal scale. For example, the compressed letters of Fig. 4·53 are made with a scale three-fourths of the height divided into sevenths.

EXTENDED ROMAN
BCGHJKLPQSUVW

COMPRESSED ROMAN-BHKTWG

FIG. 4·53—Modern Roman, extended and compressed.

4·23 Inclined roman. Inclined letters are used for water features on maps. An alphabet of inclined roman made to the same proportions as the vertical of Fig. 4·49 is shown in Fig. 4·54. The slope may be from 65° to 75°. Those shown are inclined 2 to 5. The lower-case letters in this figure are known as stump letters. For small sizes their lines are made with one stroke of a fine flexible pen, while larger sizes are drawn and filled in.

A B C D E F G H I
J K L M N O P Q R
S T U V W X Y Z &
a b c d e f g h i j k l m n o
p q r s t u v or v w or w x y or y z
1 2 3 4 5 6 7 8 9 0

FIG. 4·54—Inclined roman and stump letters.

EXERCISES

The following exercises are designed for a 5″ × 7″ working space. Lettering practice should be done in short intensive periods.

Series I. Single-stroke vertical capitals

1. Large letters in pencil, for careful study of the shapes of the individual letters. Starting 9/16″ from top border draw guide lines for five lines of 3/8″ letters. Draw each

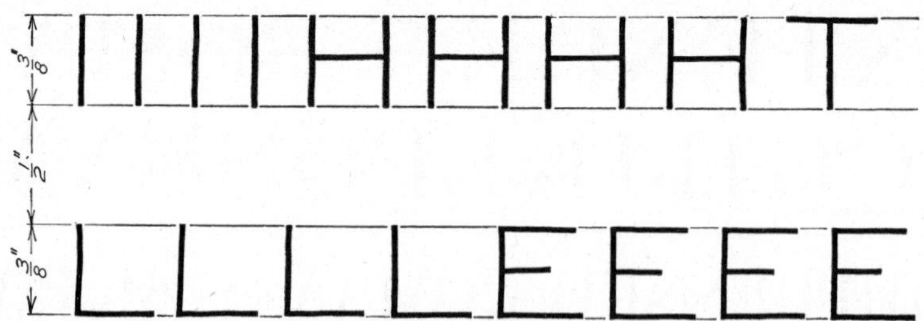

FIG. 4·55

of the straight-line letters *I H T L E F N Z Y V A M W X* four times in pencil only, studying carefully Figs. 4·12 to 4·16. Figure 4·55 is a full-sized reproduction of a corner of this exercise.

2. Same as Exercise 1 for the curved line letters *OQCGDUJBPRS*. Study Figs. 4·17 to 4·20.

3. Same as Exercise 1 for figures 3, 8, 6, 9, 2, 5, ½, ¾, ⅝, 7/16, 9/32. Study Figs. 4·21 to 4·23.

4. Composition. Same layout as for Exercise 1. Read paragraph on composition, then letter the following five lines in pencil (1) WORD COMPOSITION, (2) TOPOGRAPHIC SURVEY, (3) TOOLS AND EQUIPMENT, (4) BRONZE BUSHING, (5) JACK-RAFTER DETAIL.

5. Quarter-inch vertical letters in pencil and ink. Starting ¼″ from top, draw guide lines for nine lines of ¼″ letters. In the group order given, draw each letter first four times in pencil, then four times directly in ink, as in Fig. 4·56.

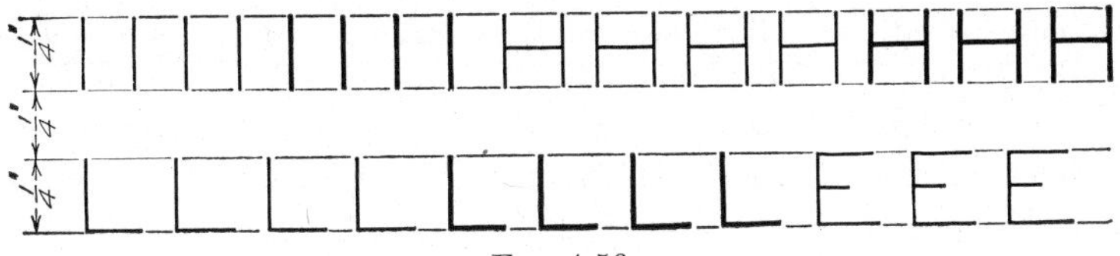

Fig. 4·56

6. Composition. Make a three-line design of the quotation from Benjamin Lamme on the Lamme Medals: "THE ENGINEER VIEWS HOPEFULLY THE HITHERTO UNATTAINABLE."

7. Eighth-inch vertical letters. Starting ¼″ from top, draw guide lines for 18 lines of ⅛″ letters. Make each letter and numeral eight times directly in ink. Fill the remaining lines with a portion of paragraph 4·15 on composition.

8. Composition. Letter the following definition: "Engineering is the art and science of directing and controlling the forces and utilizing the materials of nature for the benefit of man. All engineering involves the organization of human effort to attain these ends. It also involves an appraisal of the social and economic benefits of these activities."

Series II. Single-stroke inclined capitals

9 to 16. Same spacing and specifications as for Series I, Exercises 1 to 8, but for inclined letters. Study paragraph 4·12 and Figs. 4·26 to 4·29.

Series III. Single-stroke inclined lower case

17. Large letters in pencil for use with ⅜″ caps. The bodies are ¼″, the ascenders ⅛″ above, and the descenders ⅛″ below. Starting ⅜″ from top, draw guide lines for seven lines of letters. This can be done quickly by spacing ⅛″ uniformly down the sheet and bracketing cap and base lines. Make each letter of the alphabet four times in pencil only. Study Figs. 4·29 to 4·33.

18. Lower case for 3/16″ caps. Starting ½″ from top, draw cap, waist, and base lines for 13 lines of letters (Braddock or Ames No. 6 spacing). Make each letter six times in pencil, then six times in ink.

19. Composition. Same spacing as Exercise 18. Letter opening paragraph of this chapter.

20. Letter the first ten lines of paragraph 4·4.

Series IV. Titles

21. Design a title for the assembly drawing of a rear axle, drawn to the scale of 6″ = 1 ft., as made by the Chevrolet Motor Co., Detroit. The number of the drawing is C82746. Space allowed, 3″ × 5″.

22. Design a title for the front elevation of a powerhouse, drawn to quarter-inch scale by Burton Grant, Architect, for the Citizens Power and Light Company of Punxsutawney, Pennsylvania.

Chapter 5
APPLIED GEOMETRY

5·1 With the aid of a straightedge and compasses, all pure geometry problems may be solved. The principles of geometry are constantly used in mechanical drawing, but as the geometrical solution of problems and construction of figures differ in many cases from the draftsman's method, equipped as he is with instruments for gaining time and accuracy, all constructions are not included here. However, the application of these geometrical methods is occasionally necessary in work where the usual drafting instruments could not be used, as in laying out full-size sheet-metal patterns on the floor, or in aircraft lofting work. It is assumed that students using this book are familiar with the elements of plane geometry and will be able to apply their knowledge. If the solution of a particular problem is not remembered, it may readily be referred to in any of the standard handbooks. There are some constructions, however, with which the draftsman should be familiar, as they will occur more or less frequently in his work. The constructions in the chapter are given on this account and for the excellent practice they afford in the accurate use of instruments as well.

As an aid in recalling the names of various geometrical figures see Fig. 5·69 at the end of this chapter.

5·2 To divide a line—geometrical method. Fig. 5·1. To divide a line AB into, say, five equal parts, draw any line BC of indefinite length; on it

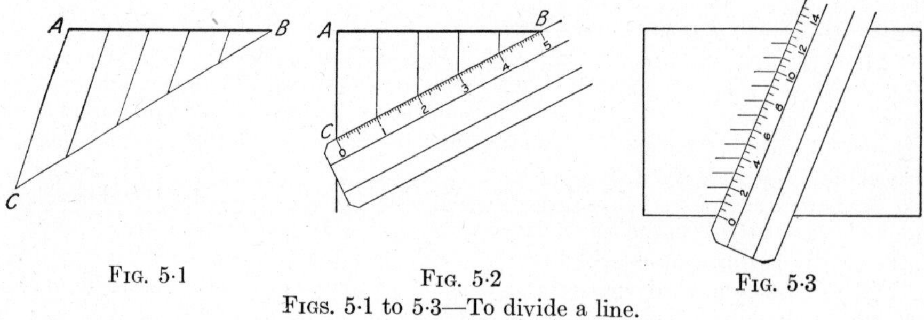

FIG. 5·1 FIG. 5·2 FIG. 5·3

FIGS. 5·1 to 5·3—To divide a line.

measure, or step off, five divisions of convenient length; connect the last point with A and, using triangles and straightedge as shown in Fig. 3·7, draw lines through the points parallel to CA intersecting AB.

Scale method. In the application of the foregoing principle the draftsman generally prefers the scale method. First draw a perpendicular AC from A, then place a scale so that five convenient equal divisions are included between B and the perpendicular, as in Fig. 5·2. With triangle and T square draw perpendiculars through the points marked, thus dividing the line AB as required. Figure 5·3 illustrates an application in laying off stair risers. This method may be used for dividing a line into any series of proportional parts.

5·3 To draw a straight line through a point parallel to another straight line. (When the method of Fig. 3·7 is not used.) Fig. 5·4. With P as center and a radius of sufficient length, draw an arc CE intersecting the line AB at C. With C as center and the same radius, draw the arc PD. With center C and radius DP, draw an arc intersecting CE at E. Then EP is the required line.

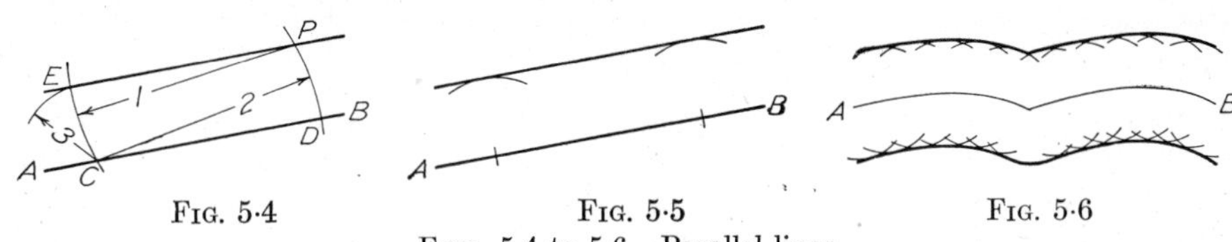

FIG. 5·4 FIG. 5·5 FIG. 5·6
FIGS. 5·4 to 5·6—Parallel lines.

5·4 To draw a line parallel to another at a given distance from it (1) *For straight lines.* Fig. 5·5. With the given distance as a radius and two points on the given line as centers (as far apart as convenient), draw two arcs. A line tangent to these arcs will be the required line.

(2) *For curved lines.* Fig. 5·6. Draw a series of arcs with centers along the line. Draw tangents to these arcs with french curve, see Fig. 3·34.

5·5 To erect a perpendicular from a point to a given straight line. Fig. 5·7. With point P as center, and any convenient radius R, draw a circle arc intersecting the given line at A and B. With any convenient radius R_2 and with centers at A and B, draw intersecting arcs locating Q. The required perpendicular is PQ, with S the intersection of the perpendicular and given line.

5·6 To erect a perpendicular from a point on a given straight line. Fig. 5·8. With point P on the line as center and any convenient radius R_1,

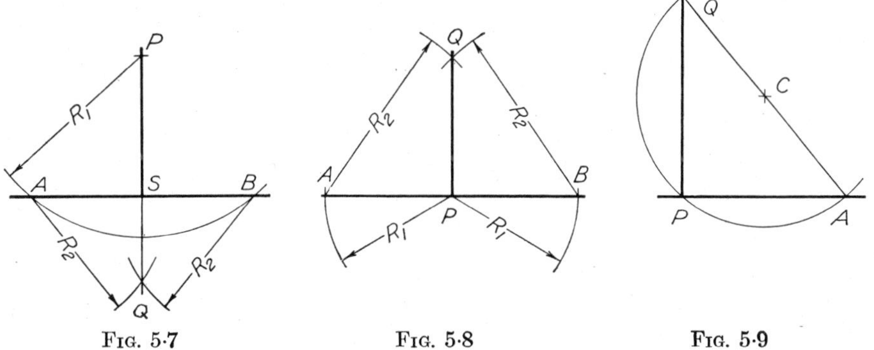

FIG. 5·7 FIG. 5·8 FIG. 5·9
FIGS. 5·7 to 5·9—Perpendicular lines.

draw circle arcs to locate points A and B equidistant from P. With any convenient radius R_2 longer than R_1, and with centers at A and B, draw intersecting arcs locating Q. PQ is the required perpendicular.

5·7 To erect a perpendicular from a point on a given straight line—second method. Fig. 5·9. With any convenient center C and radius CP, draw somewhat more than a semicircle from the intersection of the circle arc with the given line at A. Draw AC extended to meet the circle arc at Q. PQ is the required perpendicular.

5·8 To lay out a given angle—tangent method. Fig. 5·10. The trigonometrical tangent of an angle is the ratio of the side opposite divided by the side adjacent. Thus, $Y/X = \tan A$, or $X \tan A = Y$. To lay out a given angle, obtain the value of the tangent from a table of natural tangents, assume any convenient distance X, and multiply X by the tangent to get distance Y. Note that the angle between the sides X and Y must be a right angle.

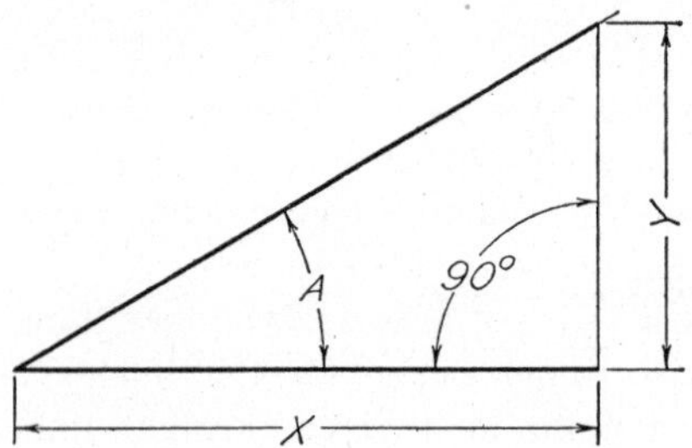

FIG. 5·10—Angle by tangent.

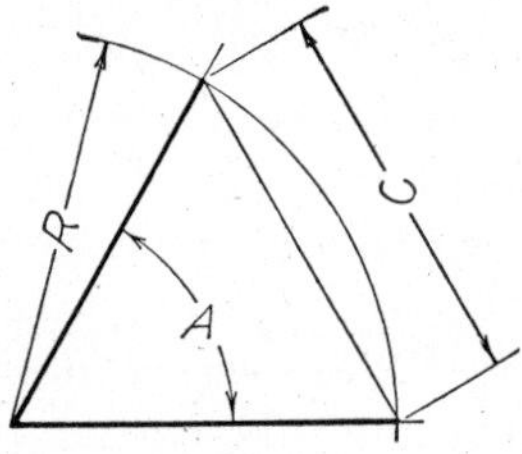

FIG. 5·11—Angle by chord.

5·9 To lay out a given angle—chordal method. Fig. 5·11. If the length of the chord is known for an arc of given radius and included angle, the angle may be accurately laid out. Given an angle in degrees, to lay out the angle: Obtain chord length for a 1-inch circle arc from the table on page 631, Appendix. Select any convenient arc length R and multiply the chord length for a 1-inch arc by this distance, thus obtaining the chord length C for the radius distance selected. Lay out chord length on the arc with compasses or dividers, and complete the sides of the angle.

The chord length for an angle may be had from a sine table by taking the sine of half the given angle and multiplying by two.

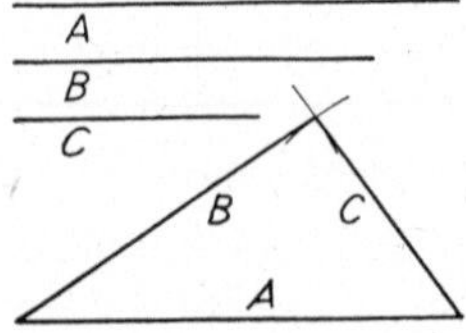

FIG. 5·12—To construct a triangle.

5·10 To construct a triangle having given the three sides. Fig. 5·12. Given the lengths A, B, and C. Draw one side A in the desired position. With its ends as centers and radii B and C, draw two intersecting arcs as shown. This construction is used extensively in developments by triangulation.

5·11 To transfer a polygon to a new base. *By triangulation.* Fig. 5·13. Given polygon $ABCDEF$ and new position of base $A'B'$. Consider each point as the vertex of a triangle whose base is AB. With centers A' and B' and radii AC and BC, describe intersecting arcs, locating the point C'. Similarly with radii AD and BD locate point D'. Connect $B'C'$ and $C'D'$ and continue the operation, always using A and B as centers.

Box or offset method. Fig. 5·14. Enclose the polygon in a rectangular "box." Draw the box on the new base (method of Fig. 3·8), locate the points $ABCEF$ on this box; then set point D by rectangular coordinates as shown.

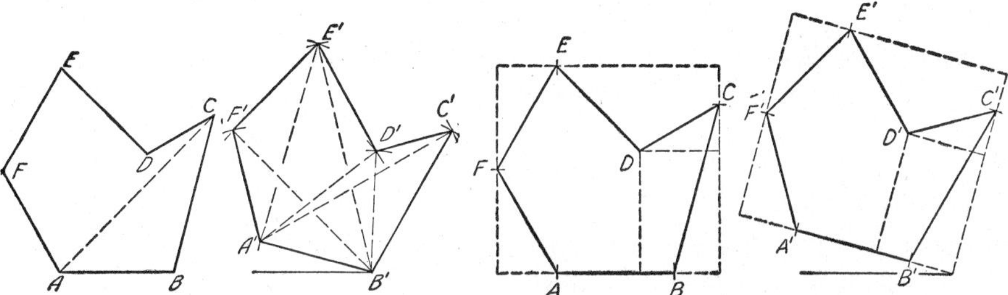

FIG. 5·13—To transfer a polygon—by triangulation.

FIG. 5·14—To transfer a polygon—box or offset method.

5·12 Uses of the diagonal. The diagonal may be used in many ways to simplify construction and save drafting time. Figure 5·15 illustrates the diagonal used at A for locating the center of a rectangle, at B for enlarging

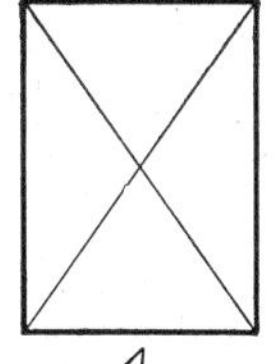

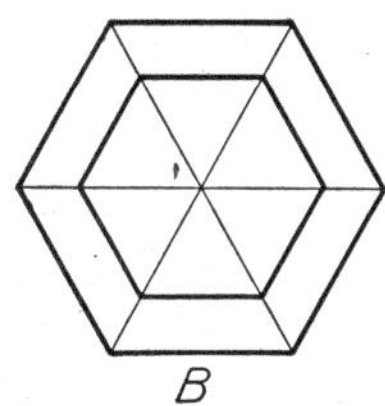

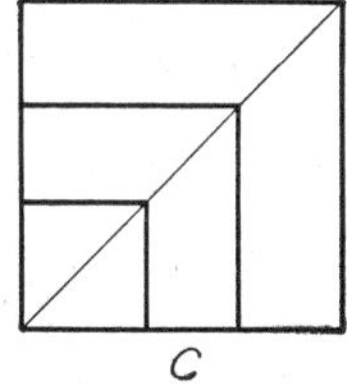

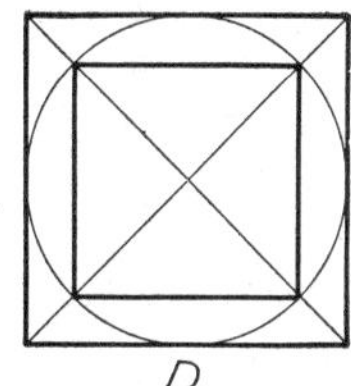

FIG. 5·15—Uses of the diagonal.

or reducing a geometrical shape, at C for producing similar figures having the same base, and at D for drawing inscribed or circumscribed figures.

5·13 To construct a regular hexagon. *Given the distance across corners AB. First method.* Fig. 5·16. Draw a circle on AB as a diameter. With the same radius and A and B as centers, draw arcs intersecting the circle and connect the points.

Second method (without compasses). Draw lines with the 30°-60° triangle in the order shown in Fig. 5·17.

Given the distance across flats. The distance across flats is the diameter of the inscribed circle. Draw this circle, and with the 30°-60° triangle draw tangents to it as in Fig. 5·18.

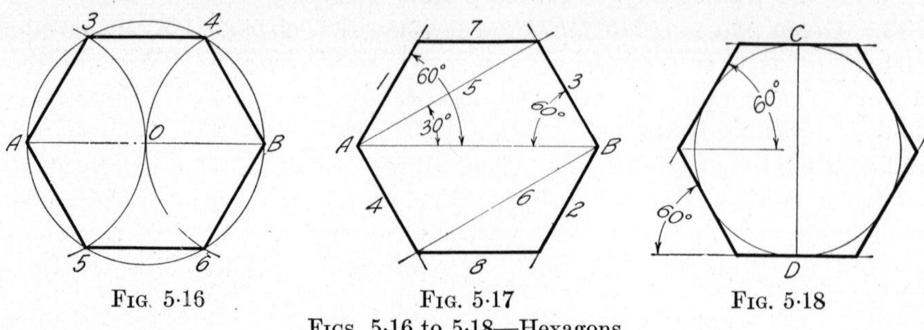

FIG. 5·16 FIG. 5·17 FIG. 5·18
FIGS. 5·16 to 5·18—Hexagons.

5·14 To inscribe a regular pentagon in a circle. Fig. 5·19. Draw a diameter *AB* and a radius *OC* perpendicular to it. Bisect *OB*. With this point *D* as center and a radius *DC*, draw arc *CE*. With center *C* and radius *CE*, draw arc *EF*. *CF* is the side of the pentagon. Step off this distance around the circle with the dividers. Instead of using this geometrical method, most draftsmen prefer to guess at *CF* and divide the circle by trial as described in paragraph 3·12.

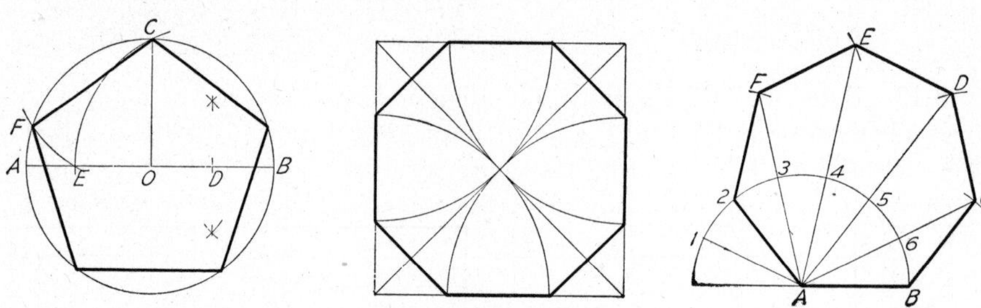

FIG. 5·19—Pentagon. FIG. 5·20—Octagon. FIG. 5·21—Polygon.

5·15 To draw a regular octagon in a square. Fig. 5·20. Draw the diagonals of the square. With the corners of the square as centers and a radius of half the diagonal, draw arcs intersecting the sides of the square and connect these points.

5·16 To construct a regular polygon. *Given one side.* Fig. 5·21. Let the polygon have seven sides. With the side *AB* as a radius and *A* as center, draw a semicircle and divide into seven equal parts with dividers. Through the second division from the left draw radial line *A*-2. Through points 3, 4, 5, and 6 extend radial lines as shown. With *AB* as radius and *B* as center, cut line *A*-6 at *C*. With *C* as center and same radius cut *A*-5 at *D*, and so on at *E* and *F*. Connect the points *or*, after *A*-2 is found, draw the circumscribing circle.

5·17 To locate the center of a circle. Fig. 5·22. Draw any chord *AB*; then draw *AC* and *BD* perpendicular to *AB*. Then *AD* and *BC* are diameters of the circle and cross at center *O*.

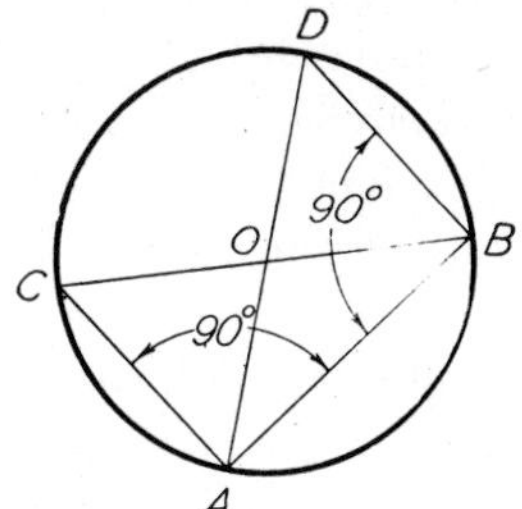

FIG. 5·22—Circle center.

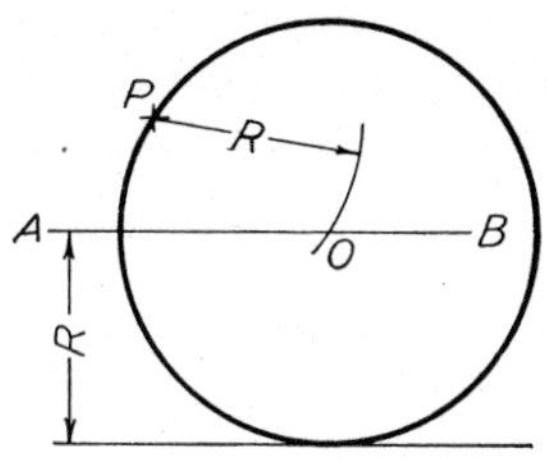

FIG. 5·23—Tangent circle.

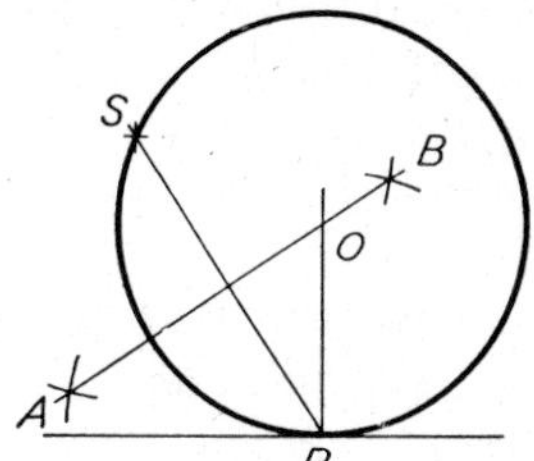

FIG. 5·24—Tangent circle.

5·18 Tangents. One of the most frequent geometrical operations in drafting is the drawing of tangents to circle arcs and the drawing of circle arcs tangent to straight lines or other circles. These should be constructed accurately, and on pencil drawings that are to be inked or traced the points of tangency should be located by short cross marks to show the stopping points for the ink lines. The method of finding these points is indicated in the following constructions.

5·19 To draw a circle of given size tangent to a line and passing through a point. Fig. 5·23. Draw a line *AB*, the given radius distance *R* away from and parallel to the given line; cut line *AB* at *O* with the given radius, using the given point *P* as center; *O* is the center of the circle. Note that there are two possible positions for the circle.

5·20 To draw a circle tangent to a line at a point and passing through a second point. Fig. 5·24. Connect the two points *P* and *S* and draw the perpendicular bisector *AB*; where *AB* crosses a perpendicular to the given line at *P* is the center *O* of the required circle.

5·21 To draw a circle arc through three given points. Fig. 5·25. Given the points *A*, *B*, and *C*. The intersection of the perpendicular bisectors of lines *AB* and *BC* will be the center of the required circle.

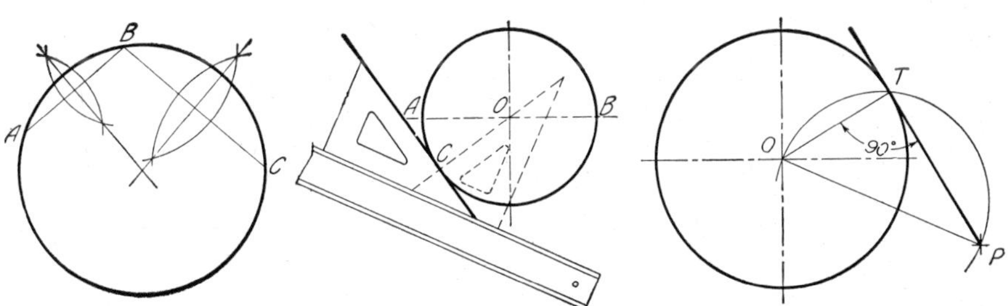

FIG. 5·25—Circle through three points. FIG. 5·26—Drawing a tangent. FIG. 5·27—Tangent from point outside.

5·22 To draw a tangent to a circle at a point on the circle. Fig. 5·26. Given the arc ACB, draw a tangent at the point C. Arrange a triangle in combination with the T square (or another triangle) so that its hypotenuse passes through center O and point C. Holding the T square firmly in place, turn the triangle about its square corner and move it until the hypotenuse passes through C; the required tangent then lies along the hypotenuse. (For small constructions, or with a large triangle, this may be done a little quicker by setting the hypotenuse of the triangle on the T square, as in Fig. 3·8 at B.)

5·23 To draw a tangent to a circle from a point outside. Fig. 5·27. Connect the point with the center of the circle. On this line OP as a diameter draw a semicircle. Its intersection with the given circle is the point of tangency.

5·24 To draw a tangent to two circles. *First case.* Fig. 5·28 (open belt). At center O draw a circle with a radius $R_1 - R_2$. From P draw a tangent to this circle by the method of Fig. 5·27. Extend OT to T_1 and draw PT_2 parallel to OT_1. Join T_1 and T_2.

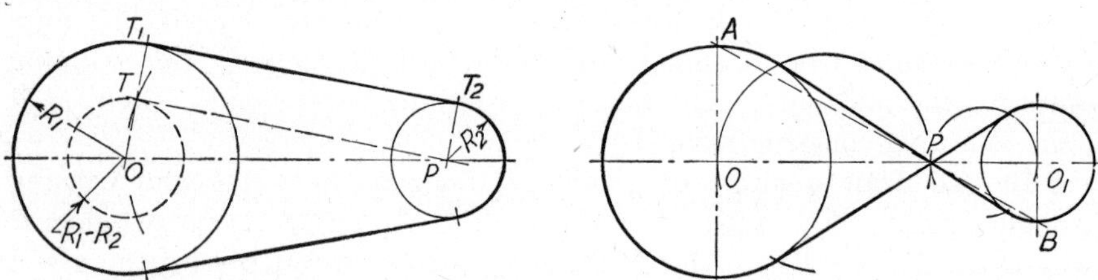

FIG. 5·28—Open belt.

FIG. 5·29—Crossed belt.

Second case. Fig. 5·29 (crossed belt). Draw OA and O_1B perpendicular to OO_1. From P, where AB crosses OO_1, draw tangents as in Fig. 5·27.

5·25 To draw a circle tangent to two straight lines. Fig. 5·30. Given the lines AB and CD and radius R. A line parallel to AB, at the distance R from it, is the locus of the centers of all circles of radius R tangent to AB. Its intersection with a straight-line locus parallel to, and at distance R from, CD will be the center of the required arc. Find the points of tangency by drawing perpendiculars from O to AB and CD. Figure 5·31 is the same

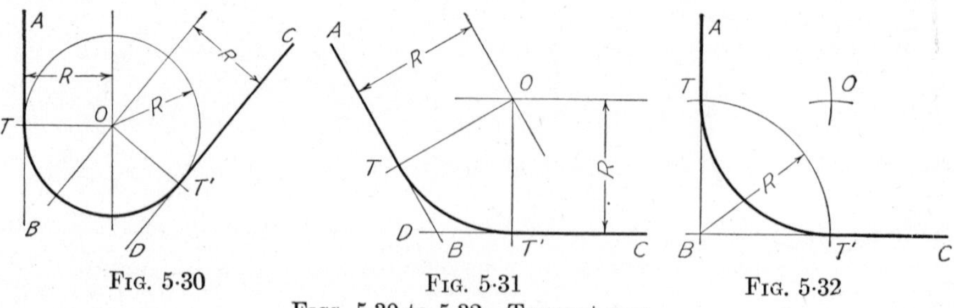

FIG. 5·30 FIG. 5·31 FIG. 5·32

FIGS. 5·30 to 5·32—Tangent arcs.

construction with an obtuse angle. For a right angle, Fig. 5·32, a quicker construction is to draw an arc of radius R with B as center, cutting AB and BC at T and T'. With T and T' as centers and same radius, draw arcs intersecting at O, the center for the required arc.

5·26 To draw a circle of radius R tangent to a given circle and a straight line. Fig. 5·33. Let AB be the given line, and R_1 the radius of the given circle. Draw a line CD parallel to AB at a distance R from it. With O as a center and radius $R + R_1$, swing an arc intersecting CD at X, the desired center. The tangent point for AB will be on a perpendicular to AB from X; the tangent point for the two circles will be on a line joining their centers X and O. Note that when two circles are tangent to each other the point of tangency *must* be on a line through their centers.

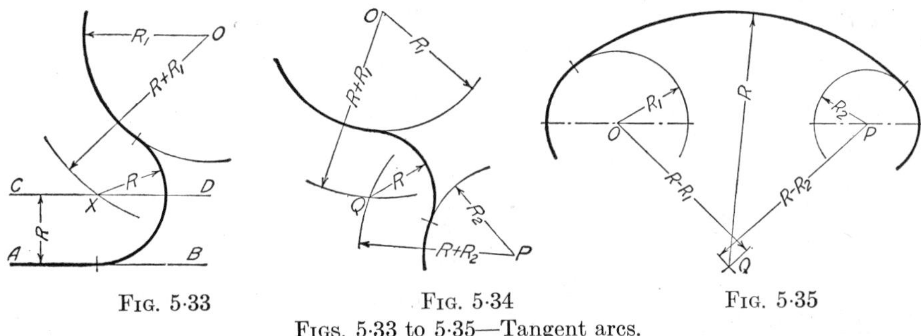

FIG. 5·33 FIG. 5·34 FIG. 5·35

FIGS. 5·33 to 5·35—Tangent arcs.

5·27 To draw a circle of radius R tangent to two given circles. *First case.* Fig. 5·34. For this case the centers of the given circles are outside the required circle. Let R_1 and R_2 be the radii of the given circles having centers O and P, respectively. With O as a center and a radius $R + R_1$, describe an arc. With P as a center and a radius $R + R_2$, swing another arc intersecting the first arc at Q, which is the center sought. Mark the tangent points in line with OQ and QP.

Second case. Fig. 5·35. For this case the centers of the given circles are inside the required circle. With O and P as centers and radii $R - R_1$ and $R - R_2$, describe arcs intersecting at the required center Q.

5·28 To draw a reverse or ogee curve. Fig. 5·36. Given two parallel lines AB and CD. Join B and C by a straight line. Erect perpendiculars at B and C. Any arcs tangent to lines AB and CD at B and C must have their centers on these perpendiculars. On the line BC assume point E, the point through which it is desired that the curve shall pass. Bisect BE and EC by perpendiculars. Any arc to pass through B and E must have its center somewhere on the perpendicular from the middle point. The intersection, therefore, of these perpendicular bisectors with the first two perpendiculars will be the centers for arcs BE and EC. This line might be the center line for a curved road or pipe. The construction may be checked by drawing the line of centers, which *must* pass through E. Figure 5·37 illustrates the principle of reverse-curve construction in various combinations.

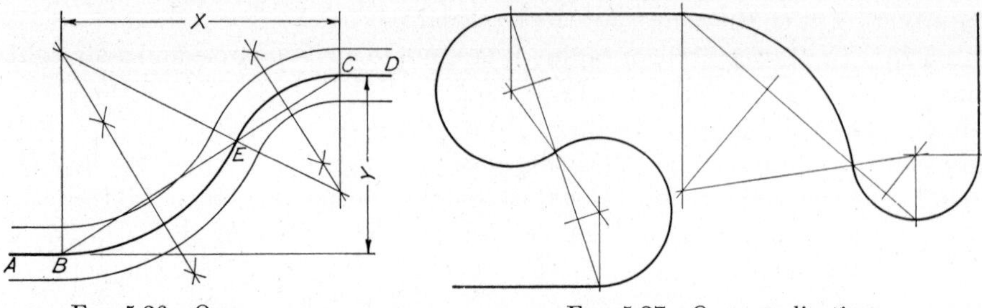

Fig. 5·36—Ogee curve. Fig. 5·37—Ogee applications.

5·29 To draw a reverse curve tangent to two lines and to a third secant line at a given point. Fig. 5·38. A, B, and C. Given two lines AB and CD

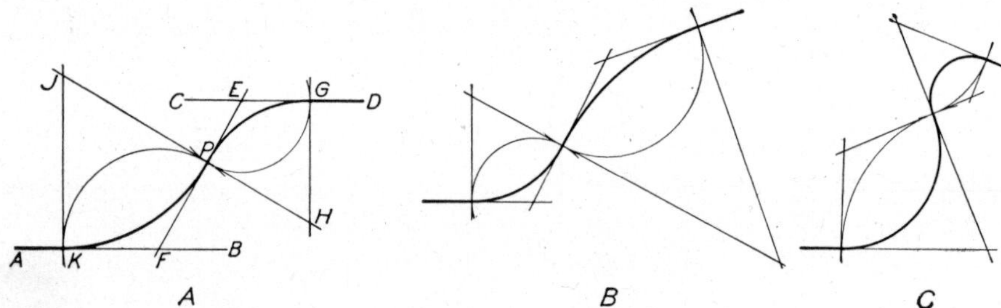

Fig. 5·38—Reverse curve tangent to three lines.

cut by the line EF at points E and F. Through a given point P on EF draw a perpendicular JH to EF. With E as a center and radius EP, intersect CD at G. Draw a perpendicular from G intersecting JH at H. With F as center and radius FP, intersect AB at K. Draw a perpendicular to AB from K intersecting JH at J. H and J will be centers for arcs tangent to the three lines.

5·30 To lay off on a straight line the approximate length of a circle arc. Fig. 5·39. Given the arc AB. At A draw the tangent AD and the chord produced, BA. Lay off AC equal to half the chord AB. With center C and radius CB, draw an arc intersecting AD at D; then AD will be equal in length to the arc AB (very nearly).[1] If the given arc is between 45° and 90°, a closer approximation will result by making AC equal to the chord of half the arc instead of half the chord of the arc.

The usual way of rectifying an arc is to set the dividers to a space small enough to be practically equal in length to the corresponding arc. Starting

[1] In this (Professor Rankine's) solution, the error varies as the fourth power of the subtended angle. For 60° the line will be $\frac{1}{900}$ part short, while at 30° it will be only $\frac{1}{14400}$ part short.

at B, step along the arc to the point nearest A and, without lifting the dividers, step off the same number of spaces on the tangent, as shown in Fig. 5·40.

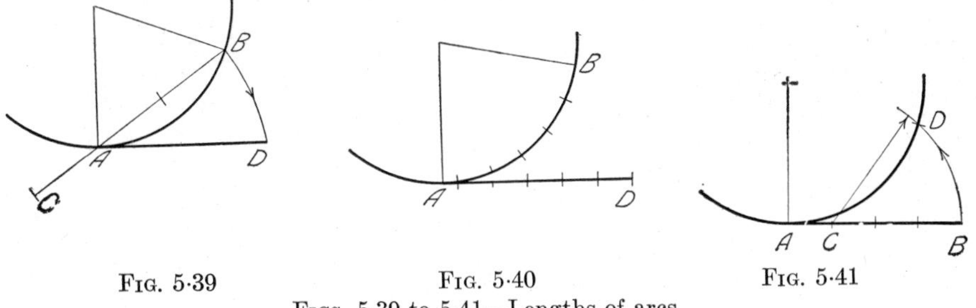

FIG. 5·39 FIG. 5·40 FIG. 5·41
FIGS. 5·39 to 5·41—Lengths of arcs.

5·31 To lay off on a given circle the approximate length of a straight line. Fig. 5·41. Given the line AB tangent to the circle at A. Lay off AC equal to one-fourth AB. With C as a center and radius CB, draw an arc intersecting the circle at D. The arc AD is equal in length to AB (very nearly).[1] If arc AD is greater than 60°, solve for one-half AB.

5·32 Conic sections. In cutting a right circular cone (a cone of revolution) by planes at different angles, four curves called *conic sections* are obtained, Fig. 5·42. These are the *circle*, cut by a plane perpendicular to

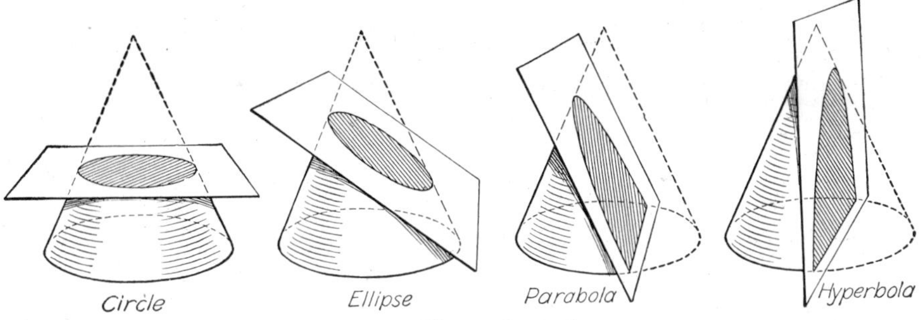

FIG. 5·42—The conic sections.

the axis; the *ellipse*, cut by a plane making a greater angle with the axis than do the elements; the *parabola*, cut by a plane making the same angle with the axis as do the elements; the *hyperbola*, cut by a plane making a smaller angle than do the elements. These curves are studied mathematically in analytic geometry but may be drawn without a knowledge of their equations by knowing something of their characteristics.

5·33 The ellipse. Fig. 5·43. An ellipse is the plane curve generated by a point moving so that the sum of its distances from two fixed points (F_1 and F_2), called the "focuses," is a constant equal to the long diameter, or major axis AB.

The minor axis, or short diameter, DE is the line through the center per-

[1] *Ibid.*

pendicular to the major axis. The focuses may be determined by cutting the major axis with an arc having its center at an end of the minor axis and radius equal to one-half the major axis.

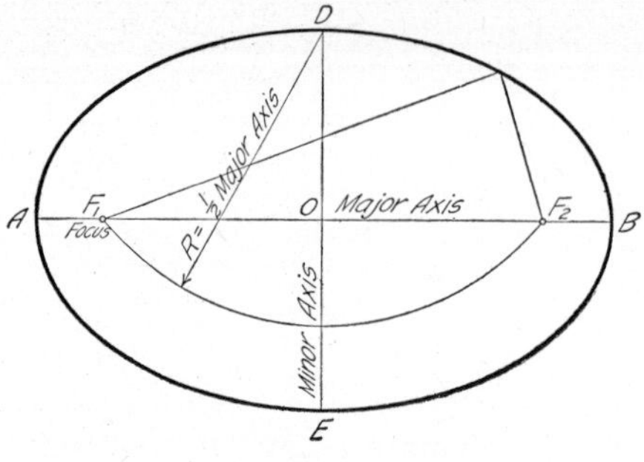

FIG. 5·43—The ellipse.

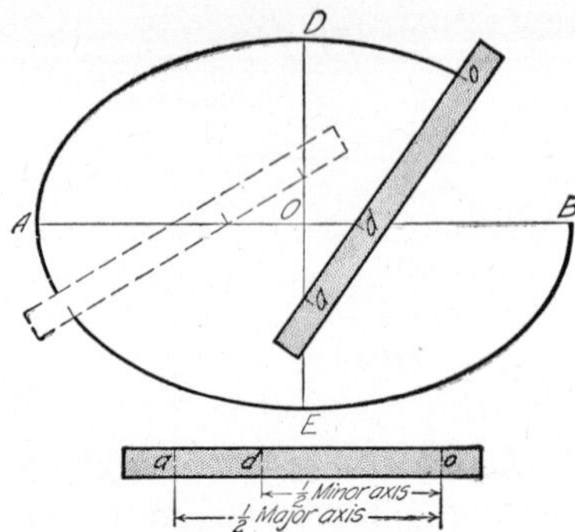

FIG. 5·44—Trammel method.

Aside from the circle, the ellipse is met with in practice much more often than any of the other conics, and draftsmen should be able to construct it readily; hence several methods are given for its construction, both as a true ellipse and as an approximate curve made by circle arcs. In the great majority of cases when this curve is required, its long and short diameters, that is, its major and minor axes, are known.

5·34 Ellipse—pin-and-string method. This well-known method, sometimes called the "gardener's ellipse," is often used for large work and is based on the definition of the ellipse. Drive pins at the points D, F_1, and F_2, Fig. 5·43, and tie an inelastic thread or cord tightly around the three pins. If the pin D is removed and a marking point moved in the loop, keeping the cord taut, it will describe a true ellipse.

5·35 Ellipse—trammel method. Fig. 5·44. On the straight edge of a strip of paper, thin cardboard, or sheet of celluloid mark the distance ao equal to one-half the major axis and do equal to one-half the minor axis. If the strip is moved, keeping a on the minor axis and d on the major axis, o will give points on the ellipse. This method will be found very convenient, as no construction is required, but, for accurate results, great care must be taken to keep the points a and d exactly on the axes. The ellipsograph, Fig. 30·6, is constructed on the principle of this method.

5·36 Conjugate diameters. Any line through the center of an ellipse may serve as one of a pair of conjugate diameters. A property of conjugate diameters, or conjugate axes, is that each is parallel to the tangents to the curve at the extremities of the other. Either one of a pair of conjugate diameters bisects all the chords parallel to the other.

To determine the major and minor axes of a given ellipse, a pair of conjugate axes being given. First method. Fig. 5·45. Given the conjugate axes CN and JG. With center O and radius OJ, draw a semicircle intersecting the ellipse at P. The major and minor axes will be parallel to the chords GP and JP, respectively.

Second method when the curve is not given. Fig. 5·46. Given the conjugate axes CN and JG. With center O and radius OJ, describe a circle

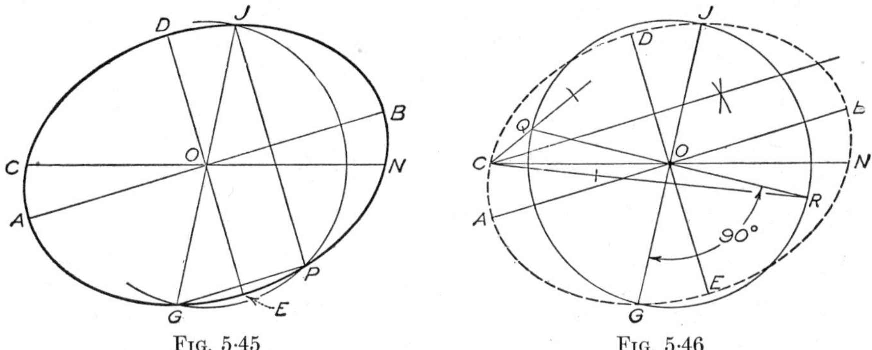

FIG. 5·45 FIG. 5·46

FIGS. 5·45 and 5·46—Conjugate axes.

and draw the diameter QR at right angles to JG. Bisect the angle QCR. The major axis will be parallel to this bisector and equal in length to $CR + CQ$. The length of the minor axis will be $CR - CQ$.

5·37 Ellipse—parallelogram method. Figs. 5·47 and 5·48. This method may be used either with the major and minor axes or with any pair of conjugate diameters. On the diameters construct a parallelogram.

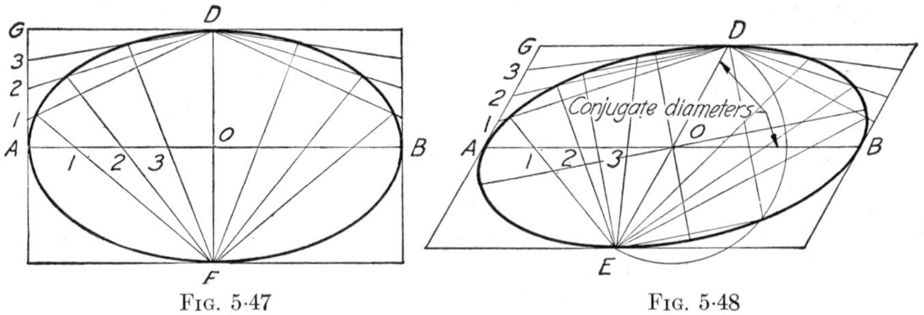

FIG. 5·47 FIG. 5·48

FIGS. 5·47 and 5·48—Parallelogram methods.

Divide AO into any number of equal parts and AG into the same number of equal parts, numbering points from A. Through these points draw lines from D and E, as shown. Their intersections will be points on the curve.

5·38 Ellipse—concentric-circle method. Fig. 5·49. This is perhaps the most accurate method for determining points on the curve. On the two principal diameters, which intersect at O, describe circles. From a number of points on the outer circle, as P and Q, draw radii OP, OQ, etc., intersecting the inner circle at P', Q', etc. From P and Q draw lines parallel to OD, and P' and Q' lines parallel to OB. The intersection of the lines through P and P' gives one point on the ellipse, the intersection of the lines through Q

and Q' another point, and so on. For accuracy, the points should be taken closer together toward the major axis. The process may be repeated in each of the four quadrants and the curve sketched in lightly freehand; or one quadrant only may be constructed and the remaining three repeated by marking the french curve.

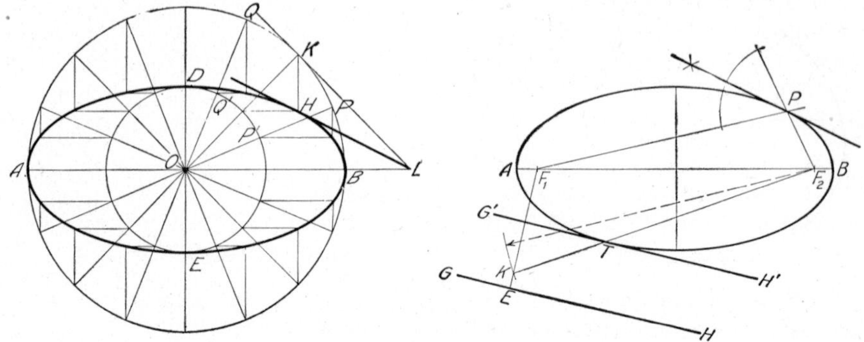

FIG. 5·49—Concentric-circle method.

FIG. 5·50—Tangents.

5·39 To draw a tangent to an ellipse. (1) *At a point P on the curve.* Fig. 5·50. Draw lines from the point to the focuses. The line bisecting the exterior angle of these focal radii is the required tangent.

When the ellipse has been drawn by the concentric-circle method, Fig. 5·49, a tangent at any point H may be drawn by drawing a line perpendicular to AB from the point to the outer circle at K and drawing the auxiliary tangent KL to the outer circle, cutting the major axis at L. From L draw the required tangent LH.

(2) *From a point outside.* Fig. 5·51. Find the focuses F_1 and F_2. With given point P and a radius PF_2, draw the arc RF_2Q. With F_1 as center and a radius AB, strike an arc cutting this arc at Q and R. Connect QF_1 and RF_1. The intersections of these lines with the ellipse at T_1 and T_2 will be the tangent points of tangents to the ellipse from P.

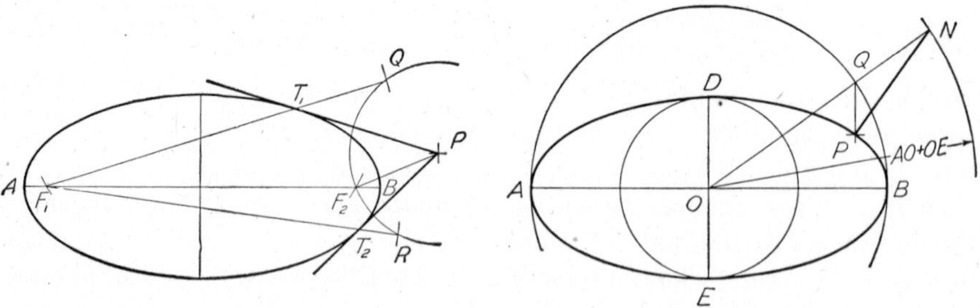

FIG. 5·51—Tangent from point outside.

FIG. 5·52—Normal to an ellipse.

(3) *Parallel to a given line GH.* Fig. 5·50. Draw F_1E perpendicular to GH. With F_2 as center and radius AB, draw an arc cutting F_1E at K. The

line F_2K cuts the ellipse at the required point of tangency T, and the required tangent passes through T parallel to GH.

5·40 To draw a normal to an ellipse. Fig. 5·52. From point P on the curve, project a parallel to the minor axis to intersect the major axis circle at Q. Draw OQ extended to intersect (at N) an arc with center at O and radius $AO + OE$. NP is the required normal.

Or, normals may be drawn perpendicular to the tangents of Figs. 5·49 and 5·50.

5·41 Approximate four-centered ellipse. Fig. 5·53. Join A and D. Lay off DF equal to $AO - DO$. Bisect AF by a perpendicular crossing AO at G and intersecting DE produced (if necessary) at H. Make OG' equal to OG, and OH' equal to OH. Then G, G', H, and H' will be centers for four tangent circle arcs forming a curve approximating the shape of an ellipse.

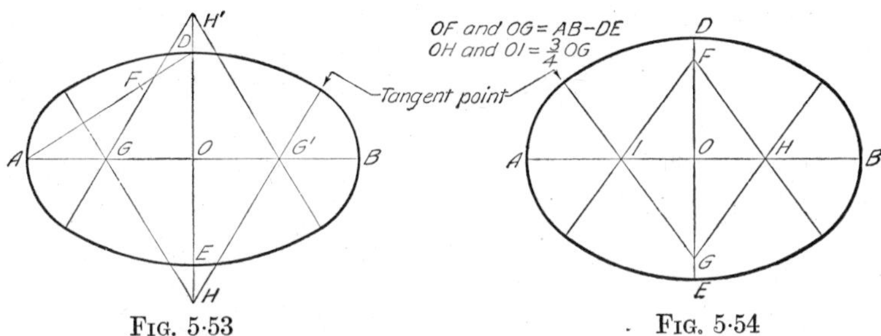

FIG. 5·53 FIG. 5·54

FIGS. 5·53 and 5·54—Approximate ellipses.

Another method is shown in Fig. 5·54. This should be used only when the minor axis is at least two-thirds the length of the major axis.

5·42 Approximate eight-centered ellipse. Fig. 5·55. When a closer approximation is desired, the eight-centered ellipse, the upper half of which is known in masonry as the "five-centered arch," may be constructed. Draw the rectangle $AFDO$. Draw the diagonal AD and the line from F perpendicular to it, intersecting the extension of the minor axis at H. Lay off OK equal to OD and, on AK as a diameter, draw a semicircle intersecting the extension of the minor axis at L. Make OM equal to LD. With center H and radius HM, draw the arc MN. From A, along AB, lay off AQ equal to OL. With P as center and radius PQ, draw an arc intersecting the arc MN at N; then P, N, and H are centers for one quarter of the eight-centered approximate ellipse. This method is based on the principle that the radius of curvature at the end of the minor axis is the third proportional to the semiminor and semimajor axes, and, inversely, at the end of the major axis is the third proportional to the semimajor and semiminor axes. The intermediate radius found is the mean proportional between these two radii.

It should be noted that an ellipse is changing its radius of curvature at every successive point and that these approximations are therefore not ellipses, but simply curves of the same general shape and, incidentally, not nearly so pleasing in appearance.

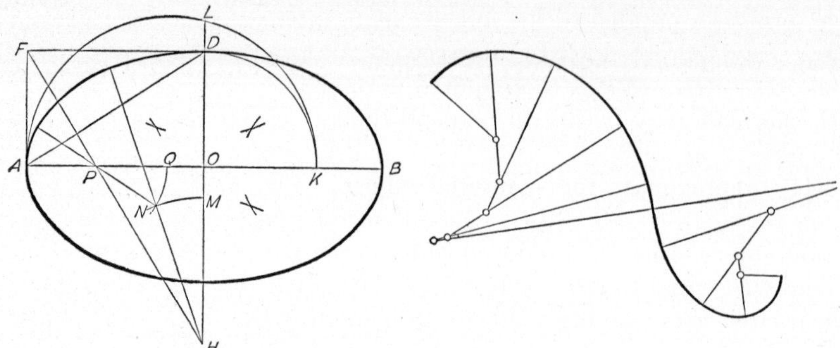

FIG. 5·55—Approximate ellipse. FIG. 5·56—Curve made with circle arcs.

5·43 Any noncircular curve may be approximated by tangent circle arcs, as follows: select a center by trial, draw as much of an arc as will practically coincide with the curve, and then, changing the center and radius, draw the next portion, remembering always that, *if arcs are to be tangent, their centers must lie on the common normal at the point of tangency.* Draftsmen sometimes prefer to ink curves in this way rather than to use irregular curves. Figure 5·56 illustrates the construction.

5·44 The parabola. The parabola is a plane curve generated by a point so moving that its distance from a fixed point, called the *focus*, is

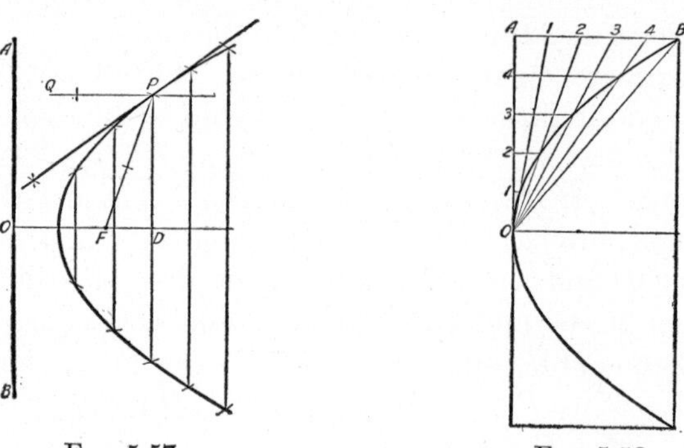

FIG. 5·57 FIG. 5·58
FIGS. 5·57 and 5·58—Methods of drawing the parabola.

always equal to its distance from a straight line, called the *directrix*. Among its practical applications are included searchlights, parabolic reflectors, some loud-speakers, road sections, certain bridge arches, etc.

When the focus F and the directrix AB are given, Fig. 5·57, draw the axis through F perpendicular to AB. Through any point D on the axis draw a line parallel to AB. With the distance DO as radius and F as a center, draw an arc intersecting the line, thus locating a point P on the curve. Repeat the operation as many times as needed.

To draw a tangent at any point P. Draw PQ parallel to the axis; and bisect the angle FPQ.

5·45 Parabola—parallelogram method. Usually when a parabola is required, the dimensions of the enclosing rectangle, that is, the width and depth of the parabola (or span and rise), are given, as in Fig. 5·58. Divide OA and AB into the same number of equal parts. From the divisions on AB draw lines converging at O. The intersections of these with the lines from the corresponding divisions on OA that are drawn parallel to the axis will be points on the curve.

5·46 Parabola—offset method. Given the enclosing rectangle, the parabola, Fig. 5·59, may be plotted by computing the offsets from the line

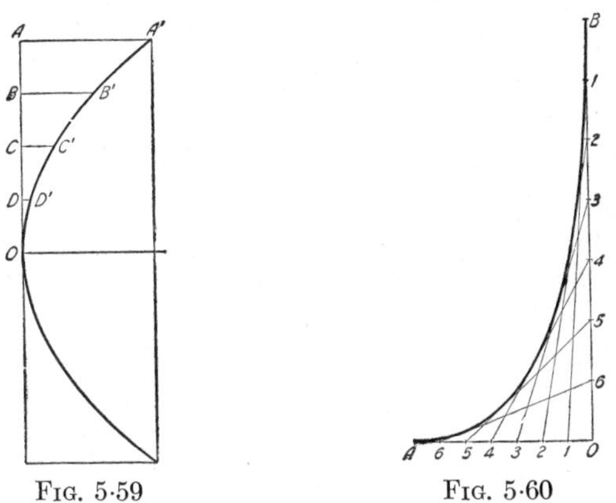

FIG. 5·59 FIG. 5·60

FIGS. 5·59 and 5·60—Methods of drawing the parabola.

OA. These offsets vary in length as the square of their distances from O. Thus, if OA is divided into four parts, DD' will be one-sixteenth of AA'; CC', since it is twice as far from O as DD' is, will be four-sixteenths of AA', and BB' nine-sixteenths. If OA had been divided into five parts, the relations would be $\frac{1}{25}$, $\frac{4}{25}$, $\frac{9}{25}$, and $\frac{16}{25}$, the denominator in each case being the square of the number of divisions. This method is the one generally used by civil engineers in drawing parabolic arches.

5·47 Parabolic envelope. Fig. 5·60. This method of drawing a pleasing curve is often used in machine design. Divide OA and OB into the same number of equal parts. Number the divisions from O and B and connect corresponding numbers. The tangent curve will be a portion of a parabola, but a parabola whose axis is not parallel to either ordinate.

5·48 The hyperbola. The hyperbola is a plane curve generated by a point moving so that the difference of its distances from two fixed points, called the "focuses," is a constant. (Compare this definition with that of the ellipse.)

Draw a hyperbola when the focuses F_1F_2 and the transverse axis AB (constant difference) are given, Fig. 5·61. With F_1 and F_2 as centers and any radius greater than F_1B, as F_1P, draw arcs. With the same centers, and radius $F_1P - AB$, strike arcs intersecting these arcs, giving points on the curve.

To draw a tangent at any point P, bisect the angle F_1PF_2.

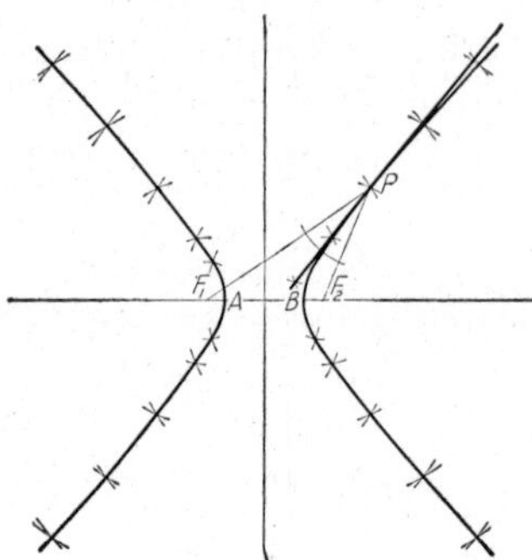

FIG. 5·61—Hyperbola.

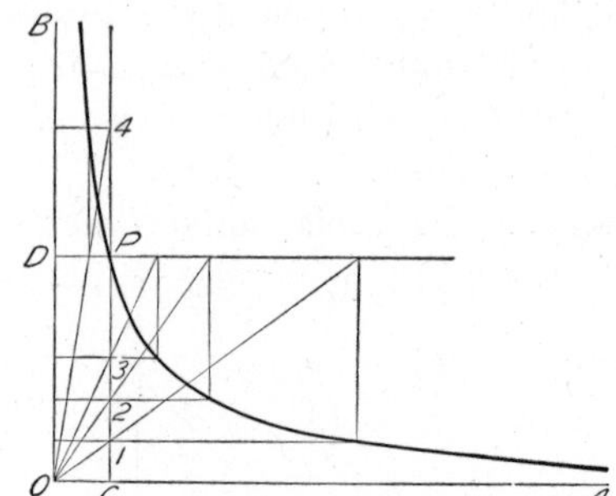

FIG. 5·62—Equilateral hyperbola.

5·49 Equilateral hyperbola. The case of the hyperbola of commonest practical interest to the engineer is the equilateral, or rectangular, hyperbola referred to its asymptotes. With it the law $pv = c$, connecting the varying pressure and volume of a portion of steam or gas, can be graphically represented.

To draw the equilateral hyperbola. Fig. 5·62. Let OA and OB be the asymptotes of the curve, and P any point on it (this might be the point of cutoff on an indicator diagram). Draw PC and PD. Mark any points 1,2,3, etc., on PC and through these points draw a system of lines parallel to OA, and a second system through the same points converging to O. From the intersections of these lines of the second system with PD extended, draw perpendiculars to OA. The intersections of these perpendiculars with the corresponding lines of the first system give points on the curve.

5·50 Cycloidal curves. A cycloid is the curve generated by the motion of a point on the circumference of a circle rolled in a plane along a straight line. If the circle is rolled on the outside of another circle, the curve generated is called an "epicycloid"; if rolled on the inside it is called a "hypocycloid." These curves are used in drawing the cycloid system of gear teeth.

To draw a cycloid. Fig. 5·63. Divide the rolling circle into a convenient number of parts (say, eight) and, using these divisions, lay off on the tangent AB the rectified length of the circumference. Draw through C the line of centers CD, and project the division points up to this line by perpendiculars to AB. About these points as centers, draw circles representing different positions of the rolling circle, and project in order the division points of the original circle across to these circles. The intersections thus determined will be points on the curve. The epicycloid and hypocycloid may be drawn similarly, as illustrated in Fig. 5·64.

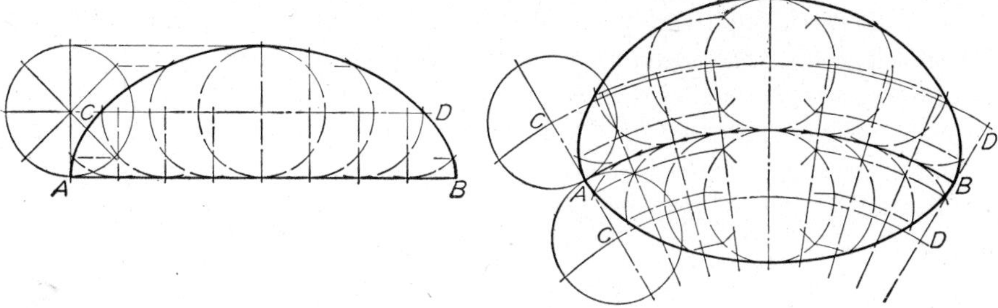

Fig. 5·63—Cycloid. Fig. 5·64—Epicycloid and hypocycloid.

5·51 The involute. An involute is the spiral curve traced by a point on a taut cord unwinding from around a polygon or circle. Thus the involute of any polygon may be drawn by extending its sides, as in Fig. 5·65, and, with the corners of the polygon as successive centers, drawing arcs terminating on the extended sides.

In drawing a spiral in design, as, for example, of bent ironwork, the easiest way is to draw it as the involute of a square, as in Fig. 3·48.

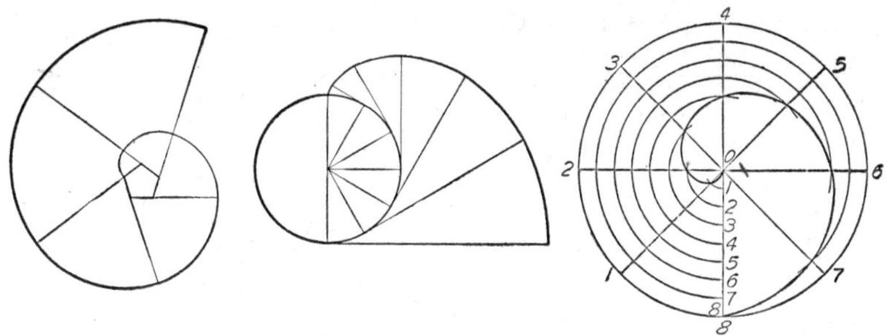

Fig. 5·65—Involute of a pentagon. Fig. 5·66—Involute of a circle. Fig. 5·67—Spiral of Archimedes.

A circle may be conceived as a polygon of an indefinite number of sides. Thus, to draw the involute of a circle, Fig. 5·66, divide it into a convenient number of parts, draw tangents at these points, lay off on these tangents the rectified lengths of the arcs from point of tangency to the starting point, and connect the points by a smooth curve. The involute of the circle is the basis for the involute system of gearing.

5·52 The spiral of Archimedes. The spiral of Archimedes is the plane curve generated by a point moving uniformly along a straight line while the line revolves about a fixed point with uniform angular velocity.

To draw a spiral of Archimedes that makes one turn in a given circle,

Fig. 5·67, divide the circle into a number of equal parts, drawing the radii and numbering them. Divide the radius O-8 into the same number of equal parts, numbering from the center. With O as a center, draw concentric arcs intersecting the radii of corresponding numbers, and draw a smooth curve through these intersections. The Archimedean spiral is the curve of the heart cam used for converting uniform rotary motion into uniform reciprocal motion.

5·53 The helix. The helix is a space curve generated by a point moving uniformly along a straight line while the line revolves uniformly about another line as an axis. If the moving line is parallel to the axis, it will generate a cylinder. The word "helix" alone always means a cylin-

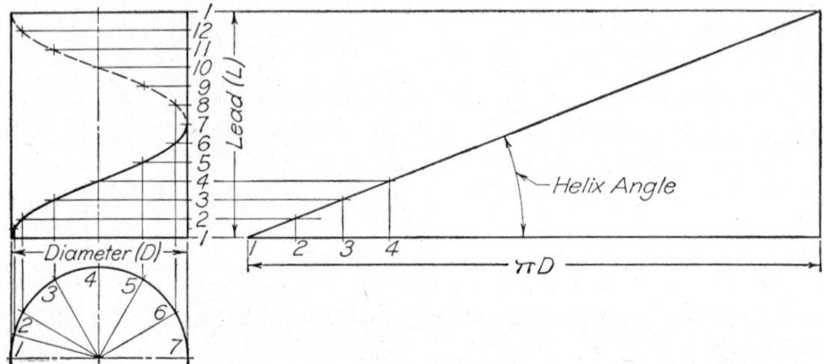

FIG. 5·68—The helix and its development.

drical helix. If the moving line intersects the axis at an angle less than 90°, it will generate a cone, and the curve made by the point moving on it will be a "conical helix." The distance parallel to the axis through which the point advances in one revolution is called the "lead." When the angle becomes 90°, the helix degenerates into the Archimedean spiral.

To draw a helix. Fig. 5·68. Draw the two views of the cylinder and measure the lead along one of the contour elements. Divide this lead into a number of equal parts (say, 12), and the circle of the front view into the same number. Number the divisions on the top view starting at point 1, and the divisions on the front view starting at the front view of point 1. When the generating point has moved one-twelfth of the distance around the cylinder, it has also advanced one-twelfth of the lead; when halfway around the cylinder, it will have advanced one-half the lead. Thus points on the top view of the helix may be found by projecting the front views of the elements, which are points on the circular front view of the helix, to intersect lines drawn across from the corresponding divisions of the lead. The conical helix is drawn similarly, the lead being measured along the axis. If the cylinder is developed, the helix will appear on the development as a straight line inclined to the base at an angle, called the "helix angle," whose tangent is L/D, where L is the lead and D the diameter.

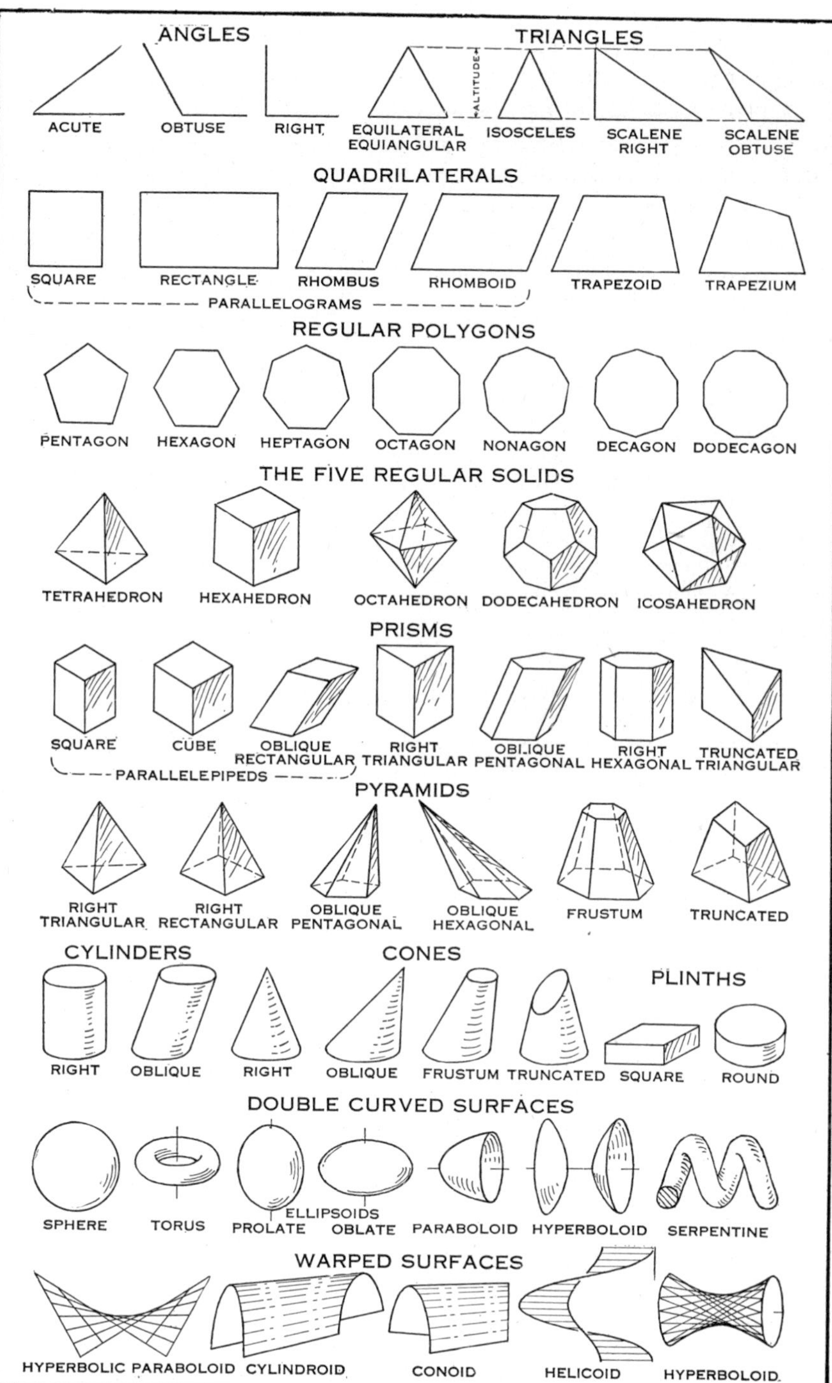

FIG. 5·69—Geometric shapes.

PROBLEMS

5·54 To be of value both as drawing exercises and as solutions, geometrical problems should be worked very accurately. The pencil must be kept very sharp, and comparatively light lines must be used. A point should be located by two intersecting lines, and the length of a line should be indicated by short dashes across the line. The following problems are dimensioned to fit in a space of not over 5″ × 7″, except as noted. Thus either one or two may be drawn on a standard 8½″ × 11″ sheet, and either two or four on an 11″ × 17″ sheet.

1. Near the center of the space, draw a horizontal line 4½″ long. Divide it into seven equal parts by the method of Fig. 5·2.

2. Draw a vertical line 1″ from left edge of space and 3⅞″ long. Divide it into parts proportional to **1, 3, 5,** and **7.**

3. Construct a polygon as shown in Fig. 5·70, drawing the horizontal line AK, of indefinite length, ⅝″ above bottom of space. From A draw and measure AB. Proceed in the same way for the remaining sides. The angles may all be obtained by proper combinations of the two triangles, see Figs. 3·5 and 3·6.

4. Draw line AK making an angle of 15° with the horizontal. With this line as a base, transfer the polygon of Fig. 5·70.

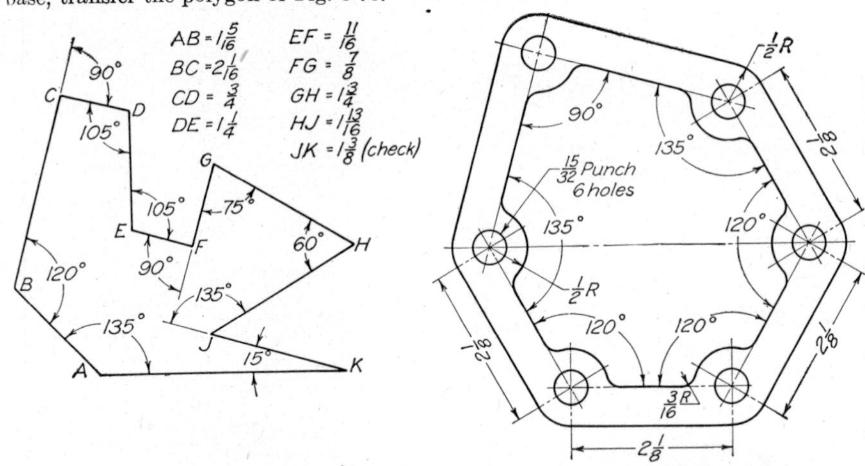

Fig. 5·70—Irregular polygon. Fig. 5·71—Gasket.

5. Draw gasket, Fig. 5·71, in position shown.

6. Draw gasket, Fig. 5·71, turning it so that its two parallel sides are horizontal.

7. Draw a regular hexagon having a distance across corners of 4″.

8. Draw a regular hexagon, short diameter 3⅜″.

9. Draw a regular dodecagon, short diameter 3⅜″.

TANGENT PROBLEMS

These problems are given for practice in the accurate joining of tangent lines. Read carefully paragraphs 5·18 to 5·28 before beginning. Locate centers for all circle arcs geometrically. If inked, ink outlines and center lines only.

10. Draw two lines AB and AC making an included angle of 30°. Locate point P, 4″ from A and ½″ from line AB. Draw a circle arc through point P and tangent to lines AB and CD. Two solutions.

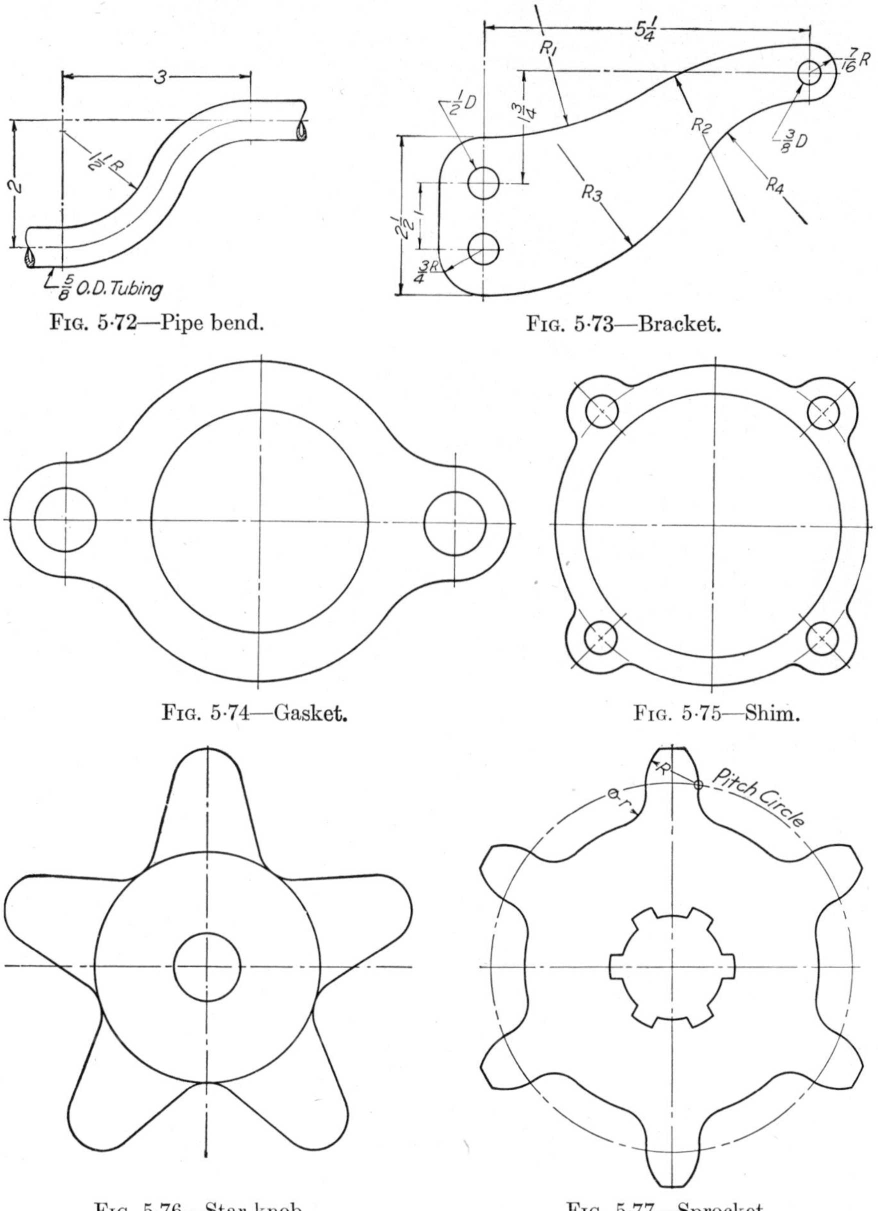

FIG. 5·72—Pipe bend.

FIG. 5·73—Bracket.

FIG. 5·74—Gasket.

FIG. 5·75—Shim.

FIG. 5·76—Star knob.

FIG. 5·77—Sprocket.

11. Construct an ogee curve joining two parallel lines AB and AC as in Fig. 5·36, making $X = 4''$, $Y = 2\frac{1}{2}''$, and $BE = 3''$. Consider this as the center line for a rod 1¼″ diameter and draw the rod.

12. Make a drawing of an ogee pipe bend from data in Fig. 5·72.

13. Make the contour view of the bracket shown in Fig. 5·73. In the upper ogee curve the radii R_1 and R_2 are equal. In the lower one, R_3 is twice R_4.

14. Draw an arc of a circle having a radius of 3¹³⁄₁₆″, with its center ½″ from top of space and 1¼″ from left edge. Find the length of an arc of 60° by construction; compute the length arithmetically and check the result.

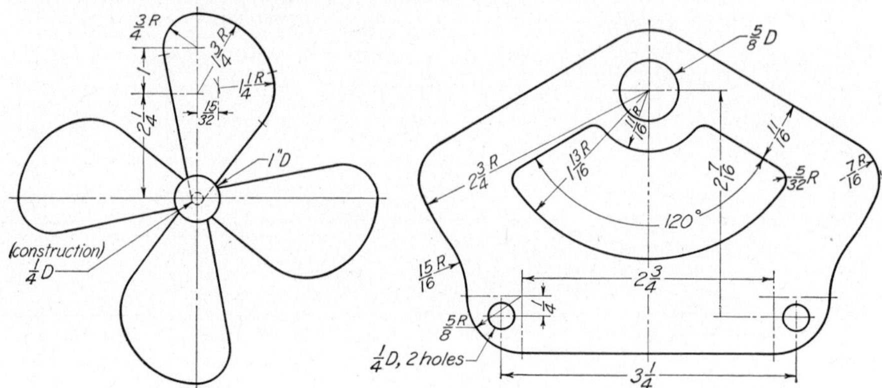

FIG. 5·78—Fan. FIG. 5·79—Level plate.

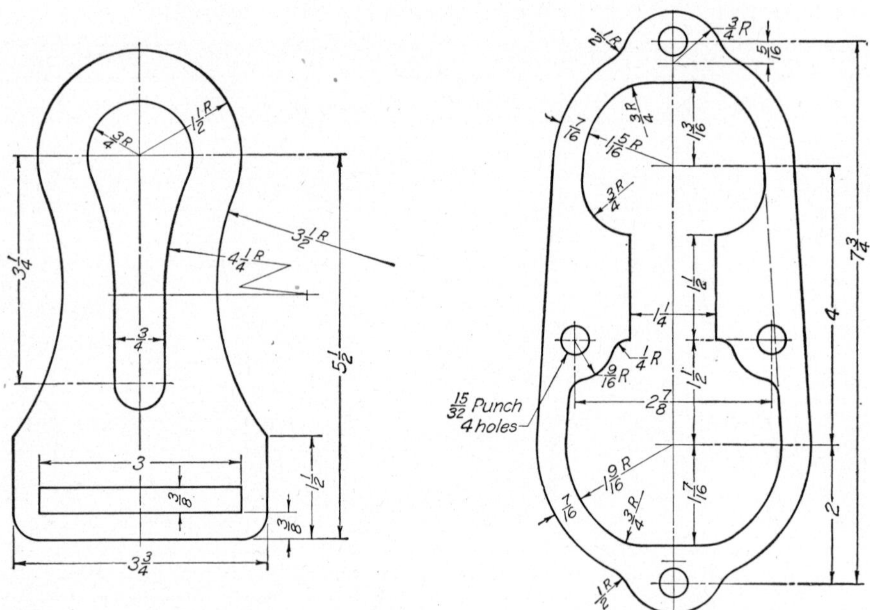

FIG. 5·80—Eyelet. FIG. 5·81—Stamping.

15. A *gasket*, Fig. 5·74. Outside diameter 4″. Inside diameter 2¾″. Two ¾″ holes, 5″ center to center. Ears ¾″ radius, 1″ fillets. Mark tangent points in pencil, as in Fig. 5·34.

16. A *shim*, Fig. 5·75. Outside diameter 4″. Inside diameter 3⁵⁄₃₂″. Holes 1³⁄₃₂″. Ears ⁷⁄₁₆″ radius, ³⁄₁₆″ fillets. Draw center lines and on them measure and mark radii for given diameters. Mark all tangent points in pencil, as in Fig. 5·34.

17. Front view of a *star knob*, Fig. 5·76. Radius of circumscribing circle $2\frac{3}{8}''$. Diameter of hub $2\frac{1}{2}''$. Diameter of hole $\frac{3}{4}''$. Radius at points $\frac{3}{8}''$. Radius of fillets $\frac{3}{8}''$. Mark tangent points in pencil.

18. Front view of a *sprocket*, Fig. 5·77. Outside diameter $4\frac{3}{4}''$, pitch diameter $4''$, root diameter $3\frac{1}{4}''$, bore $1\frac{1}{4}''$. Thickness of tooth at pitch line is $\frac{9}{16}''$. Splines $\frac{1}{4}''$ wide by $\frac{1}{8}''$ deep. Mark tangent points in pencil.

19. Front view of a *fan*, Fig. 5·78. Draw full size to dimensions given ($9'' \times 9''$ space).

20. Front view of a *level plate*, Fig. 5·79. Draw to full size.

21. Front view of an *eyelet*, Fig. 5·80. Draw to dimensions given ($5'' \times 8''$ space).

22. Front view of a *stamping*, Fig. 5·81. Draw to dimensions given ($5'' \times 9''$ space).

23. Front view of a *cam*, Fig. 5·82.

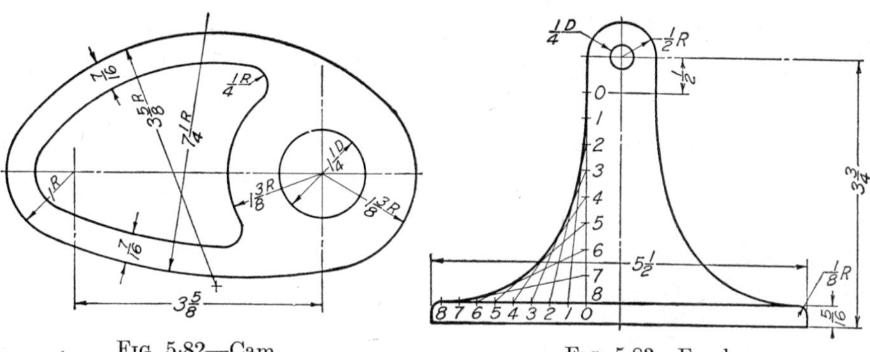

FIG. 5·82—Cam.

FIG. 5·83—Fan base.

24. Front view of a drawn-metal *fan base*, Fig. 5·83. The curve profile is a parabolic envelope. Refer to Fig. 5·60.

25. Front view of *spline lock*, Fig. 5·84.

26. Front view of *gage cover plate*, Fig. 5·85.

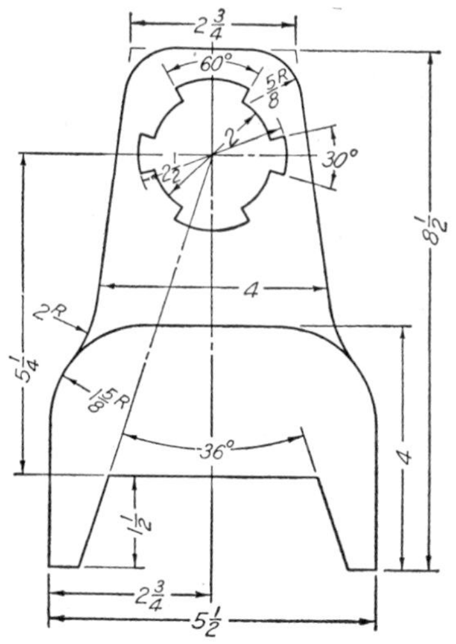

FIG. 5·84—Spline lock.

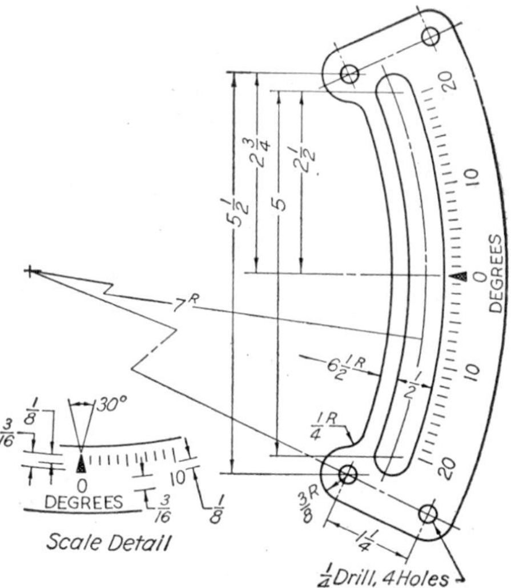

FIG. 5·85—Gage cover plate.

CURVE PROBLEMS

In locating a curve, the number of points to be determined will depend upon the size of the curve and the rate of change of curvature. More points should be found on the sharp turns. For most of the following problems, points may average about 1/4 inch apart.

27. Draw an ellipse having a major axis of 4½″ and minor axis of 3″, using the trammel method as explained in paragraph 5·35.

28. Draw an ellipse having a major axis of 4⅝″ and minor axis of 1½″, using the concentric-circle method as explained in paragraph 5·38.

29. Draw an ellipse on a major axis of 4″. One point on the ellipse is 1½″ to the left of the minor axis and ⅞″ above the major axis.

30. Draw an ellipse whose minor axis is 2 3/16″ and distance between focuses is 3¼″. Draw a tangent at a point 1⅜″ to the right of the minor axis.

31. Draw an ellipse, major axis 4″. A tangent to the ellipse intersects the minor axis 1¾″ from the center, at an angle of 60°.

32. Draw a five-centered arch with a span of 5″ and a rise of 2″. Refer to paragraph 5·42.

33. Draw an ellipse having conjugate axes of 4¾″ and 2¾″ making an angle of 75° with each other. Determine the major and minor axes.

34. Draw the major and minor axes for an ellipse having a pair of conjugate diameters 60° apart, one horizontal and 6¼″ long, the other 3¼″ long.

35. Draw a parabola, axis vertical, in a rectangle 4″ × 2″.

36. Draw a parabolic arch, with 6″ span and 2½″ rise, by the offset method, dividing the half span into eight equal parts.

37. Draw an equilateral hyperbola passing through a point P, ½″ from OB and 2½″ from OA. (Reference letters correspond to Fig. 5·62.)

38. Draw two turns of the involute of a pentagon whose circumscribed circle is ½″ in diameter.

39. Draw one-half turn of the involute of a circle 3¼″ in diameter whose center is 1″ from the left edge of space. Compute the length of the last tangent and compare with the measured length.

40. Draw a spiral of Archimedes making one turn in a circle 4″ in diameter.

41. Draw the cycloid formed by a rolling circle 2″ in diameter. Use 12 divisions.

42. Draw the epicycloid formed by a 2″-diameter circle rolling on a 15″-diameter directing circle. Use 12 divisions.

43. Draw the hypocycloid formed by a 2″-diameter circle rolling inside a 15″-diameter directing circle. Use 12 divisions.

Chapter 6

THE THEORY OF PROJECTION DRAWING

6·1 The previous chapters have been preparatory to the real subject of engineering drawing as a language. In Chap. 1 attention was directed to the difference between the representation of an object by the artist, in which he seeks to convey certain impressions or emotions, and the representation by the engineer, where the main intent is to convey information. The full information required from the engineer includes the description

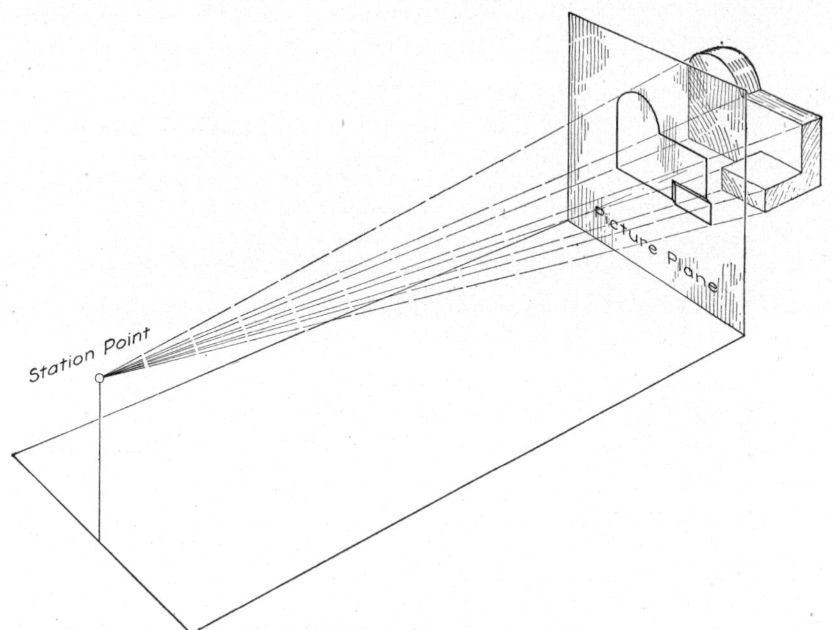

FIG. 6·1—Perspective projection.

of the *shape* of the object and the specification of the *size* of every detail in it. In this chapter we are concerned with the different methods of describing the *shape*.

When an object is looked at from a particular station point, one may usually get a good idea of its shape because (1) generally more than one side is seen, (2) the light and shadow on it tell something of its configuration, and (3), since it is looked at with both eyes, there is a stereoscopic effect which aids in judging shapes and dimensions. In technical drawing the third point is never considered, but the object is represented as if seen with one eye; and only in special cases is the effect of light and shadow rendered. In general we have to do with outline alone.

On the supposition that a transparent plane may be set up between an object and the station point of an observer's eye, Fig. 6·1, the intersection of this plane with the rays formed by lines of sight from the eye to all points

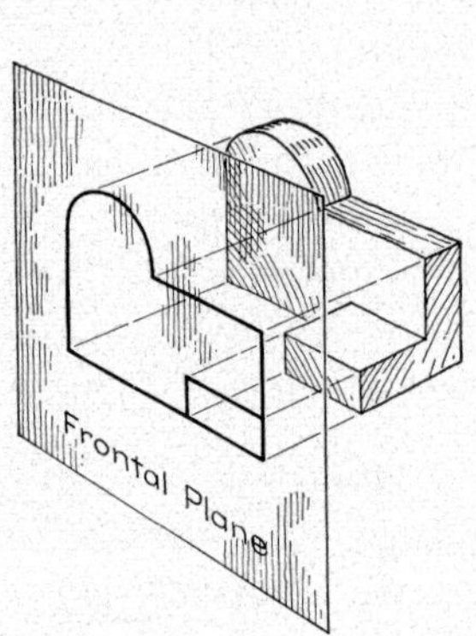

Fig. 6·2—Orthographic projection.

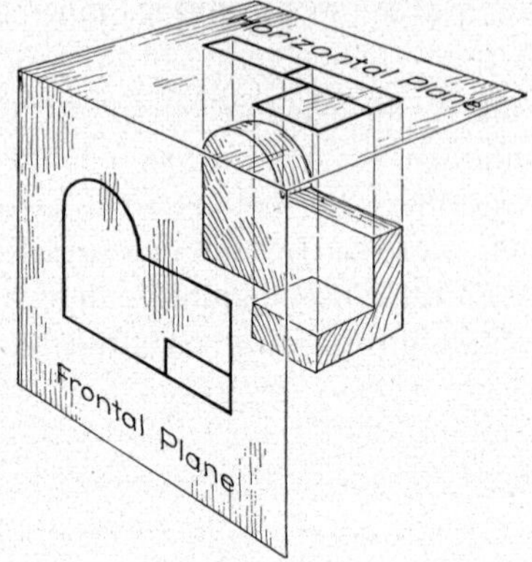

Fig. 6·3—Frontal and horizontal planes of projection.

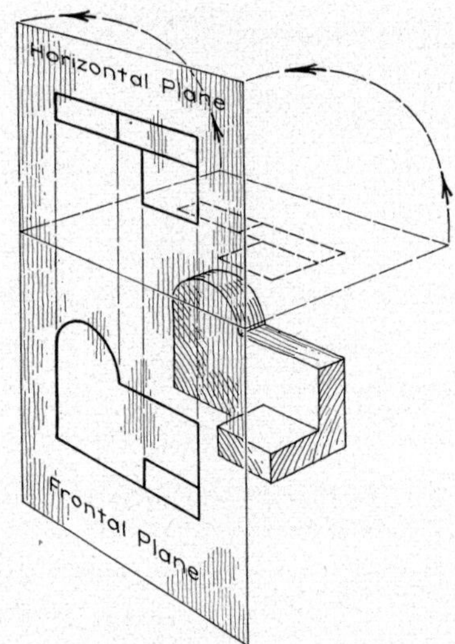

Fig. 6·4—The horizontal plane revolved.

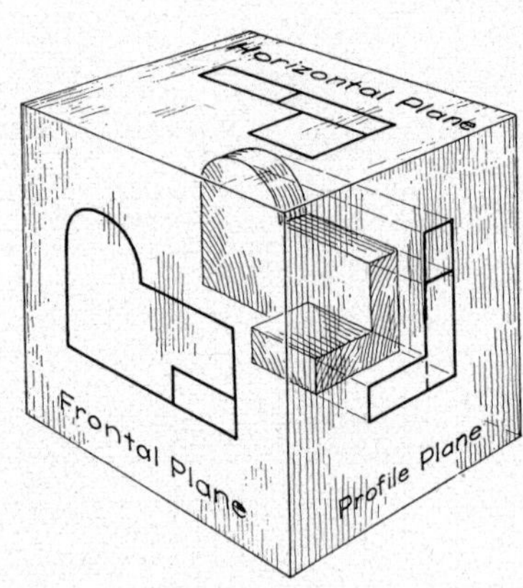

Fig. 6·5—The three planes of projection.

of the object will give a picture that will be practically the same as the image formed in the eye of the observer. Drawing made on this principle is known as "perspective drawing" and is the basis of all artists' work. In a technical way, it is used chiefly for illustrative work wherein the pictorial appearance is of greater importance than actual constructional features of the object.

6·2 If the observer will imagine himself as walking backward from the station point until he reaches a theoretically infinite distance, the rays formed by the lines of sight from his eye to the object will grow longer and finally become infinite in length, parallel to each other and perpendicular to the picture plane. The picture so formed on the picture plane is what is known as orthographic projection. If now all the rays from the picture plane to infinity are discarded, the picture can be thought of as being found by extending perpendiculars to the plane from all points of the object, Fig. 6·2. This picture, or projection on a frontal plane, will show the shape of the object when viewed from the front, but it will not tell the shape or distance from front to back, hence more than one projection will be required to describe the object.

In addition to the frontal plane, another transparent plane is then imagined as placed horizontally above the object, as in Fig. 6·3. The projection on this plane, found by extending perpendiculars to it from the object, will give the appearance of the object as if viewed from directly above, and will show the distance front to rear. If this horizontal plane is now revolved into coincidence with the vertical plane, as in Fig. 6·4, the two views of the object will then be in the same plane, as if on a sheet of paper. A third plane, called a profile plane, may be imagined, perpendicular to the first two, Fig. 6·5, and on it a third view may be projected. The third view will show the shape of the object when viewed from the side, and the distance bottom to top and front to rear. The horizontal and profile planes are shown revolved into the same plane as the frontal plane (again thought of as the plane of the drawing paper) in Fig. 6·6; moreover, thus related in the same plane, they will correctly give the three-dimensional shape of the object. The practical drawing procedures using this theory are described in the next chapter.

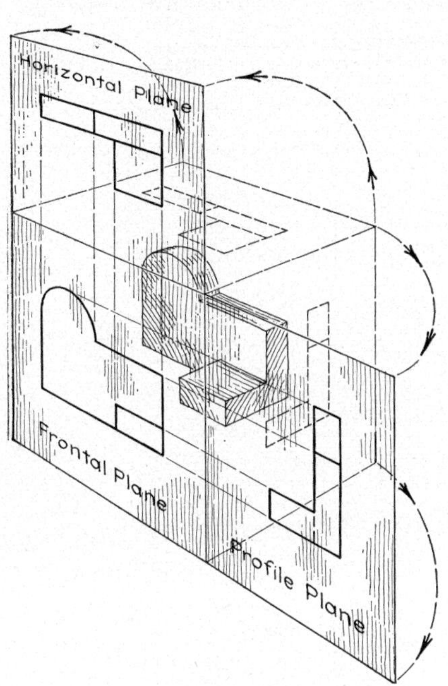

FIG. 6·6—The horizontal and profile planes revolved.

In orthographic projection, the picture planes are called *planes of projection* and the perpendiculars *projecting lines* or *projectors*.

In looking at these theoretical projections, or views, the observer should not think of the views as being flat surfaces on the transparent planes, but should imagine himself as looking *through* the transparent planes at the object itself.

6·3 Definition. Theoretically, in a broad way, orthographic[1] projection could be defined as any single projection made by dropping perpendiculars to a plane. However, it has been accepted through long usage and common consent to mean the combination of two or more of such views, hence the following definition: *Orthographic projection is the method of representing the exact shape of an object in two or more views on planes generally at right angles to each other, by extending perpendiculars from the object to the planes.* (The term "orthogonal[2] projection" is sometimes used for this system of drawing.)

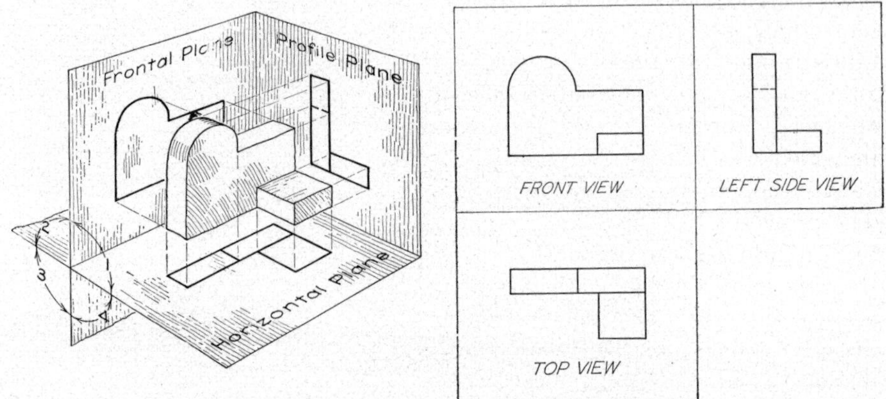

FIG. 6·7—First-angle projection.

6·4 First-angle projection. The system of orthographic projection explained in this chapter is known as "third-angle projection." It is the official American Standard, universally adopted in the United States and Canada.

If the horizontal and vertical planes of projection should be extended beyond their intersection, four dihedral angles would be formed, which are called, in order, "first," "second," "third," and "fourth angles," numbered as illustrated in Fig. 6·7. Theoretically, the object might be placed in any one of the four angles or quadrants, projected to the planes, and the planes folded about their intersection. Practically, the second and fourth angles would be eliminated, leaving the first and third as possibilities. If the object is placed in the *first angle*, projected to the planes and the planes opened up into one plane, the top view would evidently fall below the front view and, if a profile plane were added, the view of the left side of the figure would be to the right of the front view. The system of first-angle projection was formerly in universal use, but was generally abandoned in this country some sixty years ago. The student should understand and recognize it, however, as it may be encountered occasionally in old drawings and illustrations, as well as in drawings from some foreign countries. Argument and confusion

[1] Right-writing.
[2] Right-angled.

have arisen, and sometimes expensive mistakes have occurred, through the misreading of first-angle drawings as made by foreign-trained engineers.

6·5 One-plane methods. If, instead of being placed in its natural position parallel to the frontal plane of projection, the object is turned at an angle, then tilted forward, so that three of its faces can be seen, a special kind of "orthographic" projection, known as *axonometric projection,* will result. It has three subdivisions; isometric, dimetric, and trimetric, all explained in Chap. 21.

Another division in the classification of methods of projection is that of oblique projection, in which the projectors, a system of parallel projecting lines, make an angle other than 90° with the plane.

Axonometric and oblique projection are classified, along with perspective, as one-plane pictorial methods; thus they are distinguished from the usual orthographic projection, in which at least two planes are required to show the three dimensions of the object.

The different systems of projection are classified in tabular form below.

Map projection, covering the numerous methods of representing the curved surfaces of the earth on a plane, is not included in this table.

CLASSIFICATION OF PROJECTIONS

Projection	Subdivision	Methods
Orthographic Projection Projectors perpendicular to planes of projection	**Multiplanar** (Two or more planes)	**Two-view drawings** **Three-view drawings** **Drawings with auxiliary views.** *Page* 138.
	Axonometric (One plane)	**Isometric projection** Three axes making equal angles with plane. *Page* 460. **Isometric drawing.** *Page* 460. **Dimetric projection** Two of the three axes making equal angles with plane. *Page* 466. **Trimetric projection** Three axes making unequal angles with plane. *Page* 467.
Oblique Projection Projectors oblique to planes of projection	(One plane)	**Cavalier projection** Two axes parallel to plane, projectors making an angle of 45° with it, in any direction. *Page* 467. **Cabinet projection** Two axes parallel to plane, projectors making an angle 63°25′, approximately, with it. *Page* 471. **Various oblique positions.** *Page* 468. **Clinographic projection** (obsolete) Object turned at an angle whose tangent is ⅓. Projectors at an angle whose tangent is ⅙. (Formerly used in crystallography.)
Perspective Projection Projectors converging to a fixed point	(One plane)	**Parallel perspective** Object with one face parallel to plane. *Page* 489. **Angular perspective** Two faces of object inclined to plane. *Page* 483. **Oblique perspective** Three faces of object inclined. (*Rarely used.*)

Chapter 7

ORTHOGRAPHIC PROJECTION

7·1 Orthographic projection, as explained in the previous chapter, provides a means of describing the exact shape of any material object. Practically, the drawing is made up of a set of separate views of the object taken by the observer from different positions and arranged relative to each other in a definite way. Each of these views will show the shape of the object for a particular view direction, and a combination of two or more views will completely describe the object. Illustrating with the block

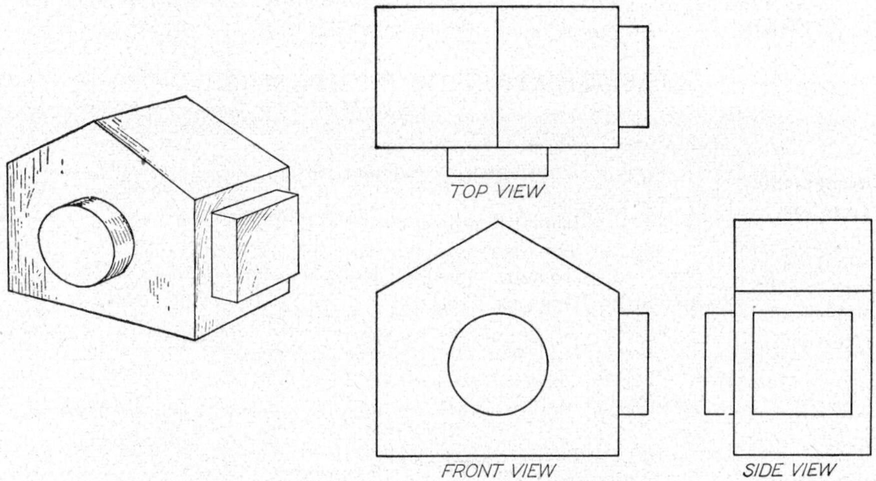

Fig. 7·1—A block and its three views.

shown in Fig. 7·1, if the observer will imagine himself in a position directly in front of the object (theoretically at an infinite distance, practically at a reasonable seeing distance but still assuming the rays from the object to his eye as parallel), the separate views, front, top, and side, would appear as marked. The *front view* tells the shape of the object when viewed from the front and gives the space occupied by the block from left to right and bottom to top, but tells nothing of the shape or distance front to rear. Similarly, the *top view* shows the shape when the object is viewed from the top, and gives the space distance left to right and front to rear, but not the shape or distance bottom to top. The *side view* shows the shape when viewed from the side and gives the distance front to rear and bottom to top, but not the distance, or shape left to right. Thus each of the views will show the shape of the object for a particular view direction and will give two of the three space dimensions.

7·2 The three space dimensions. As all material objects from single pieces to complicated structures are definitive and measurable by three space dimensions,[1] it is desirable for drawing purposes to define these dimensions and to fix their direction.

Height is the difference in elevation between any two points, measured as the perpendicular distance between a pair of horizontal planes that contain the points, Fig. 7·2. Edges of the object may or may not correspond

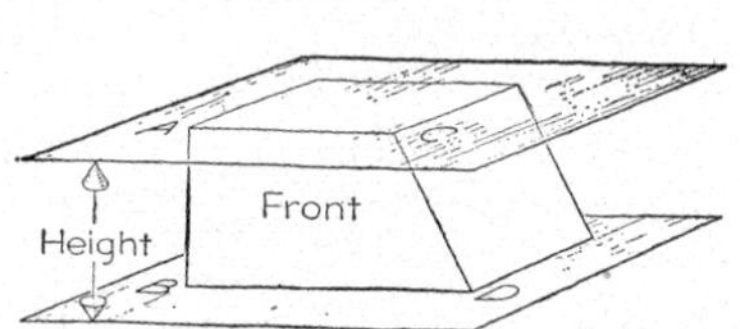

FIG. 7 2—Measurement of height.

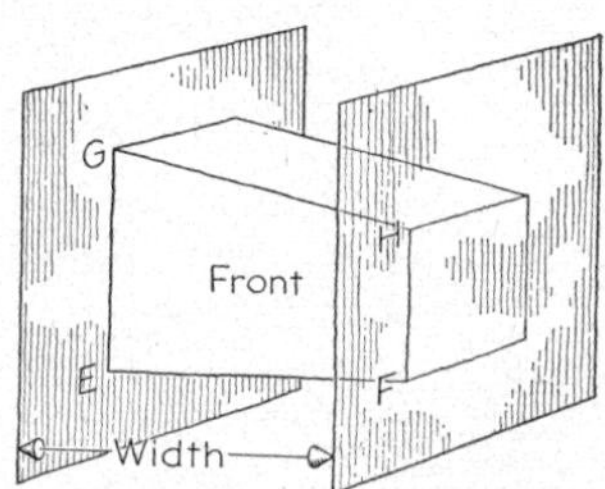

FIG. 7·3—Measurement of width.

with the height dimensions. Edge AB corresponds with the height dimension while edge CD does not, but the *space height* of A and C are the same, as are B and D. Height is always measured in a vertical direction and has no relationship whatever to the shape of the object.

Width is the positional distance of left to right, between any two points measured as the perpendicular distance between a pair of profile planes containing the points. The relative width between points E and G on the left, and H and F on the right of an object is shown by the dimension marked *width*, Fig. 7·3. The object edge EF is parallel to the width direction and corresponds with the width dimension, but edge GH slopes downward from G to H, thus making the actual object edge longer than the width separating points G and H.

Depth[2] is the positional distance front to rear, between any two points measured as the perpendicular distance between two frontal planes containing the points. Figure 7·4 shows two frontal planes, one at the front of the object containing points J and L, the other at the rear containing points K and M. The relative depth separating the front and rear of the object is the perpendicular distance between the planes as shown.

[1] *Space dimensions* and *dimensions of the object* should not be confused. The function of orthographic projection is to show the *shape*. Size is not established until the figured dimensions and/or the scale is placed on the drawing. Space dimensions are *only* the measure of three dimensional space.

[2] The term "depth" is used in the civil engineering sense, as the depth of a lot.

Any point may be located in space by giving its height, width, and depth relative to some other known point. Figure 7·5 shows a cube with four identified corners, *A*, *B*, *C*, and *D*. Assuming that the plane containing points *A* and *B* is the front of the object, height, width, and depth would be as marked. Assuming also that point *A* is fixed in space, point *B* may be located from point *A* by giving the width dimension, including the statement that height and depth measurements are zero. *C* may be located

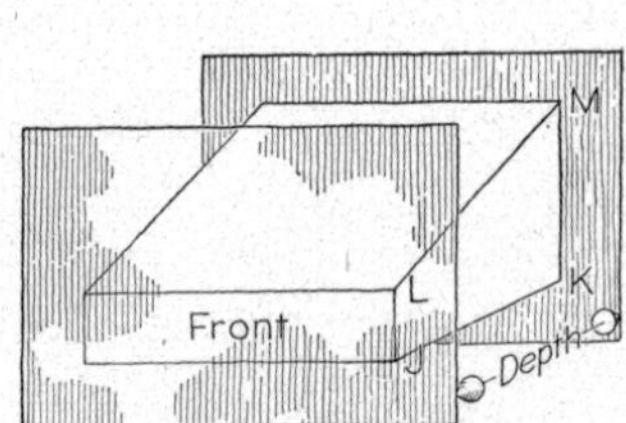

FIG. 7·4—Measurement of depth.

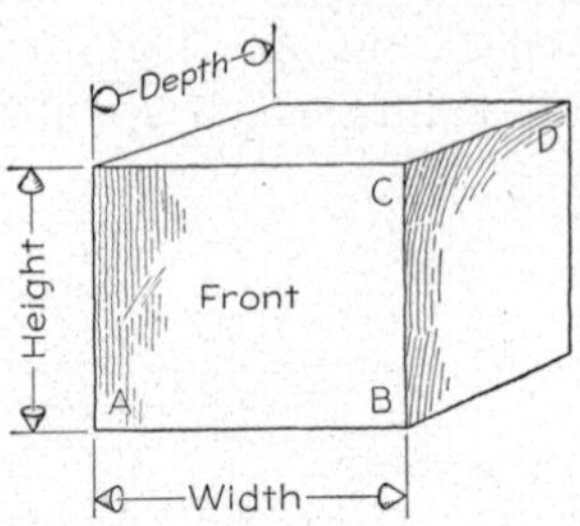

FIG. 7·5—Location of points in space.

from *A* by giving width, height, and zero depth. *D* may be located from *A* by giving width, height, and depth measurements.

7·3 The planes of projection. Under the theory explained in Chap. 6, the object to be drawn may be thought of as surrounded by transparent planes upon which the actual views are projected. The three space dimensions, height, width, and depth, and the planes of projection are unchangeably oriented and connected with each other and with the view directions, Fig. 7·6. Each of the planes of projection is perpendicular, respectively, to its own view direction. Thus the frontal plane is perpendicular to the front-view direction, the horizontal plane is perpendicular to the top-view direction, and the profile plane is perpendicular to the side-view direction.

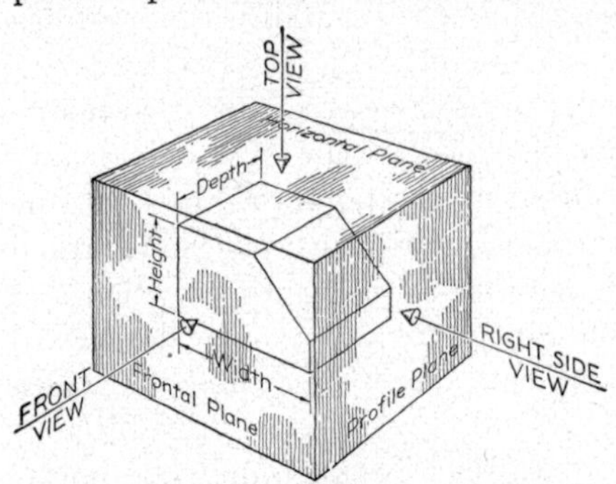

FIG. 7·6—The relationship of space directions and the planes of projection.

The two space measurements for a view are parallel to the plane of that view and perpendicular to the view direction. Therefore, height and width are parallel to the frontal plane and perpendicular to the front-view direction; width and depth are parallel to the horizontal plane and perpendicular to the top-view direction; height and depth are parallel to the profile plane and perpendicular to the side-view direction. Note that the three planes of projection are *mutually* perpendicular as are the three space measurements and also the three view directions.

7·4 Object orientation. An object may be drawn in any of several possible positions. The simplest position should be used, with the object oriented so that the principal faces are perpendicular to the sight directions for the views, and parallel to the planes of projection, Fig. 7·7.

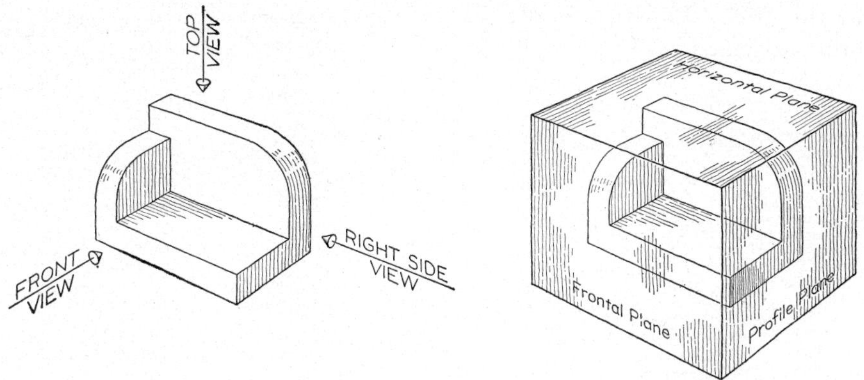

FIG. 7·7—Object orientation.

7·5 Projection. Orthographic views are theoretically produced on the planes of projection by extending perpendiculars to the planes from the object, Fig. 7·8. The projections on these planes are what would be seen

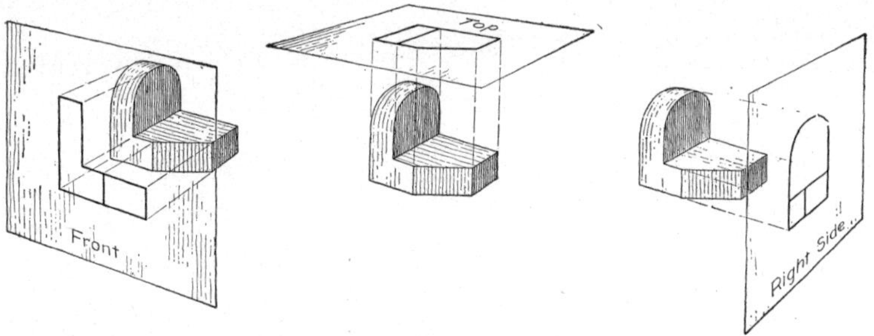

FIG. 7·8—Orthographic views.

by looking straight at the object from positions directly in front, above, and from both sides, as well as from the bottom and rear. When all of the views then obtained are considered, the planes of projection would form a transparent box completely surrounding the object, Fig. 7·9. The six sides, or planes, of the box are then thought of as being opened up, as illustrated in Fig. 7·10, into one plane, the plane of the paper. The front is considered to be originally in the plane of the paper, and the other sides hinged and rotated into position as shown. The projection on the front plane is known as the *front view*, *vertical projection*, or *front elevation;* that on the horizontal plane the *top view*, *horizontal projection*, or *plan;* that on the side or "profile" plane the *side view*, *profile projection*, *side elevation*, or sometimes *end view* or *end elevation*. By reversing the direction of sight, a *bottom view* will be obtained instead of a top view, or a *rear view* instead of a front view. In comparatively rare cases either a bottom view or a rear view or both may be required to show some detail of shape or construction. Figure 7·11 shows the relative positions of the six views as set by the ASA. In actual work there is rarely ever an occasion where all six principal views would be needed on one drawing but, no matter how many

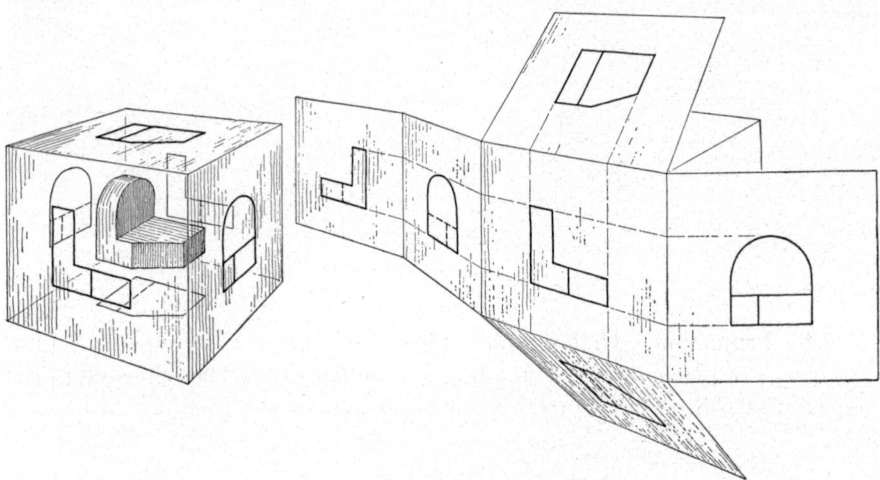

FIG. 7·9—The transparent box. FIG. 7·10—The box as it opens.

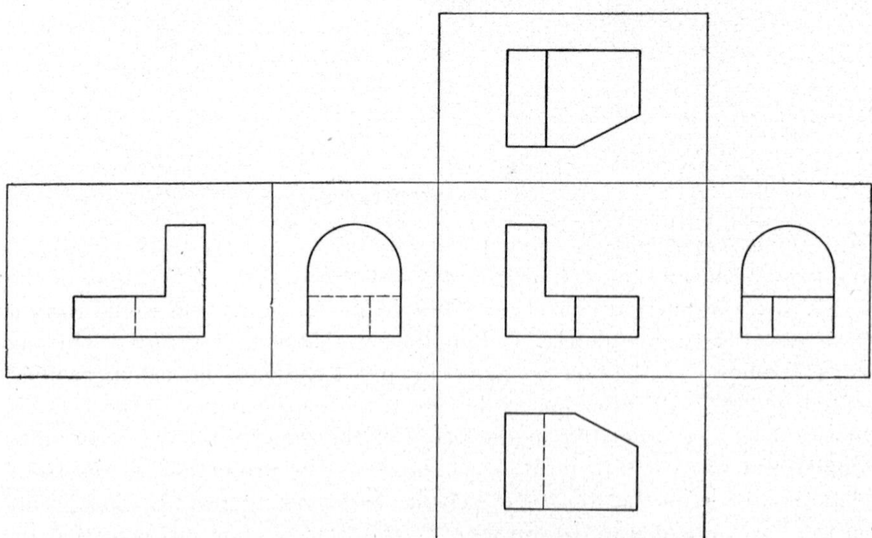

FIG. 7·11—Relative position of the six views.

are required, their positions relative to each other would be as given in Fig. 7·11. All of these views are principal views. Each view shows two of the three dimensions of height, width, and depth.

7·6 Combinations of views. The most usual combination selected from the six possible views consists of the *top*, *front*, and *right-side* views, as shown in Fig. 7·12, which, in this case, best describes the shape of the given block. Sometimes the left-side view will help describe an object more clearly than the right-side would. Figure 7·13 shows the arrangement of *top, front,* and *left-side* views (in this case the right-side view would

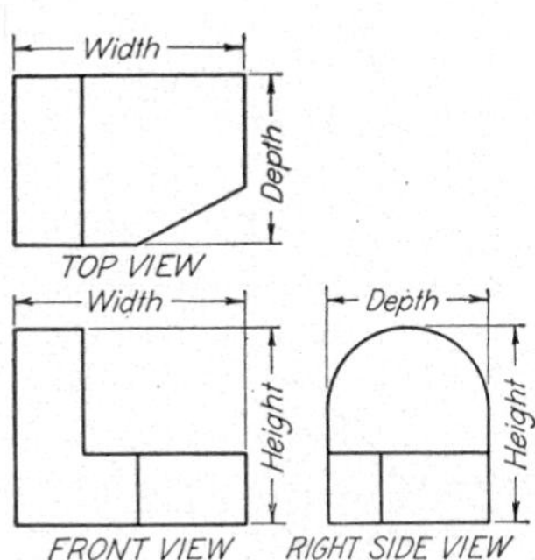

FIG. 7·12—Three projections.

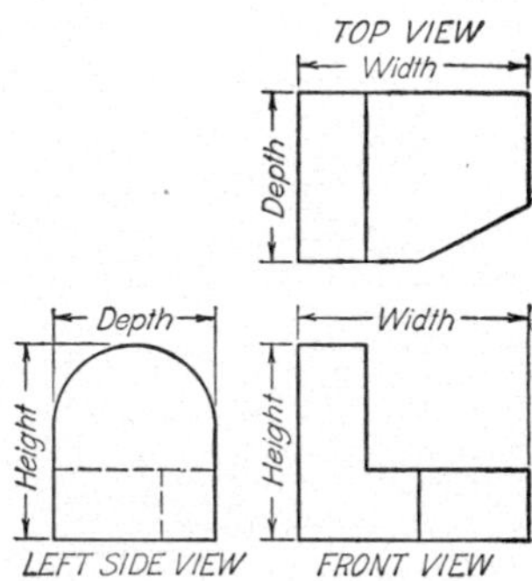

FIG. 7·13—Three projections.

be preferred as it has no hidden lines). Note that the *side view of the front face of the object is adjacent to the front view*, and that the side view of any point will be the same distance from the front surface as is its distance from the front surface on the top view. The combination of *front, right-side,* and *bottom views* is shown in Fig. 7·14 and that of *front, top, left-side,* and *rear* views in Fig. 7·15.

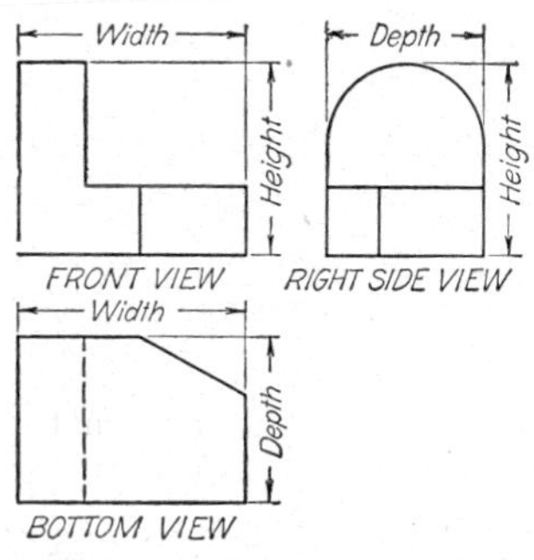

FIG. 7·14—Three projections.

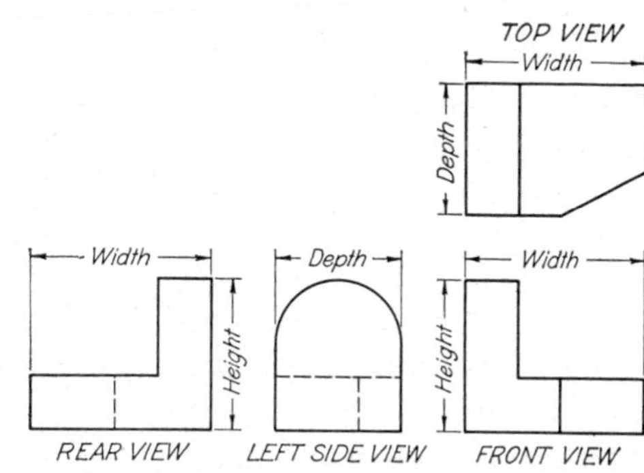

FIG. 7·15—The position of the rear view.

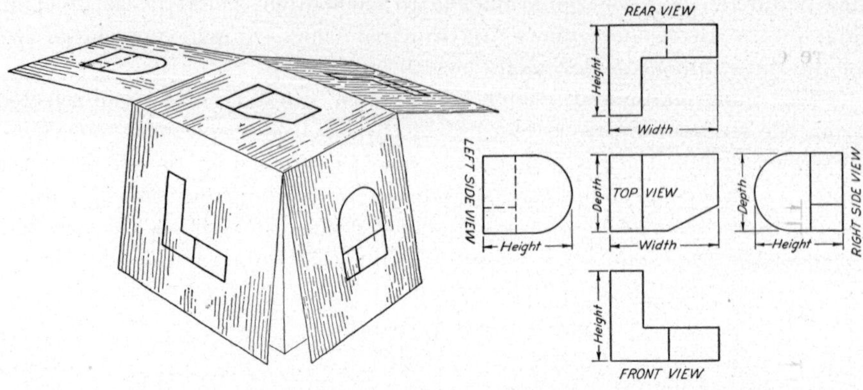

FIG. 7·16—The box opening for alternate position.

FIG. 7·17—Alternate position views.

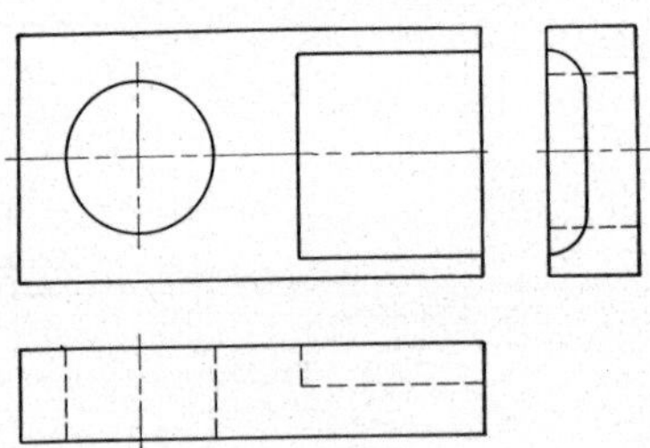

FIG. 7·18—Side view in alternate position.

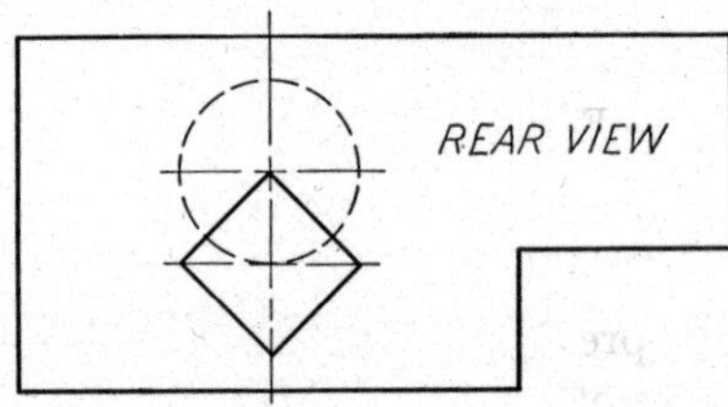

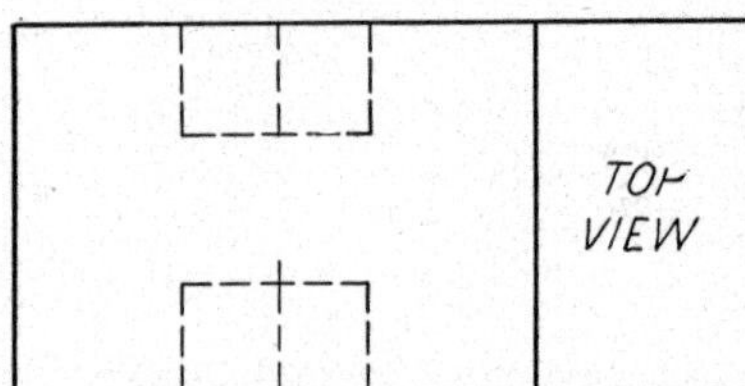

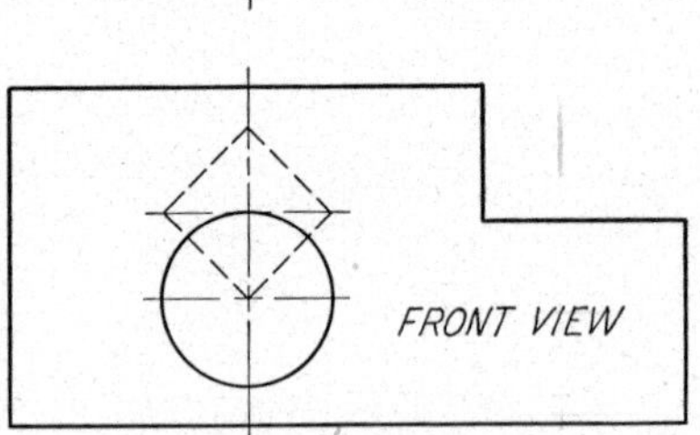

FIG. 7·19—Rear view in alternate position.

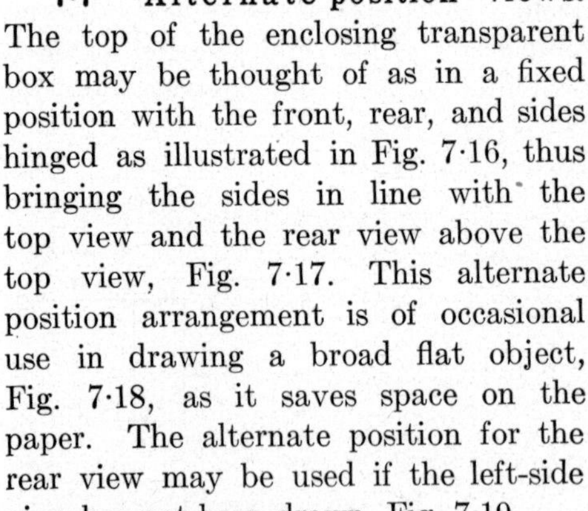

7·7 "Alternate position" views. The top of the enclosing transparent box may be thought of as in a fixed position with the front, rear, and sides hinged as illustrated in Fig. 7·16, thus bringing the sides in line with the top view and the rear view above the top view, Fig. 7·17. This alternate position arrangement is of occasional use in drawing a broad flat object, Fig. 7·18, as it saves space on the paper. The alternate position for the rear view may be used if the left-side view has not been drawn, Fig. 7·19.

7·8 Numbering corners. In comparing projections with the object or its picture, it will be of much help to the beginner to letter (or number) the corners of the object and, with these identifying marks, to letter similarly the corresponding points on each of the views, as in Fig. 7·20. Hidden points directly behind visible points are lettered to the right of the letter of the visible point and in this figure they have been further differentiated

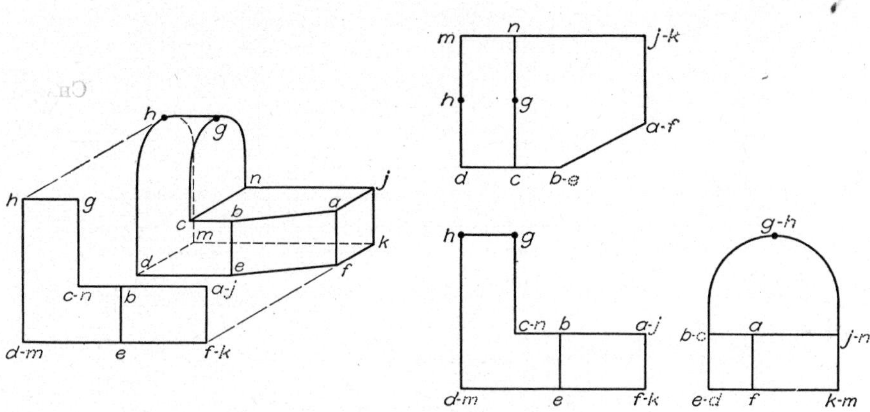

FIG. 7·20—Identified corners.

by the use of dotted or "phantom" letters. Study Fig. 7·21 by numbering the corners of the three views to correspond to those of the pictorial view.

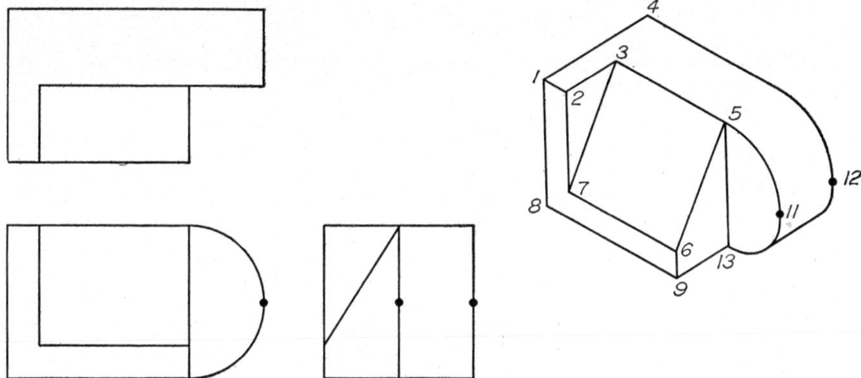

FIG. 7·21—Projection study.

7·9 Projections of edges and surfaces. An object, depending upon its shape and space position, may or may not have edges and surfaces parallel or perpendicular to the planes of projection. A line in, or parallel to, a plane of projection receives its name from the plane. Thus a *horizontal line* is a line in a horizontal plane, a *frontal line* is a line in a frontal plane, and a *profile line* is a line in a profile plane. When a line is parallel to two planes the line takes the name of both planes, as *horizontal-frontal*, *horizontal-profile*, or *frontal-profile.* A line not parallel to any plane of projection is called an *oblique line.* Figure 7·22 illustrates various positions of lines.

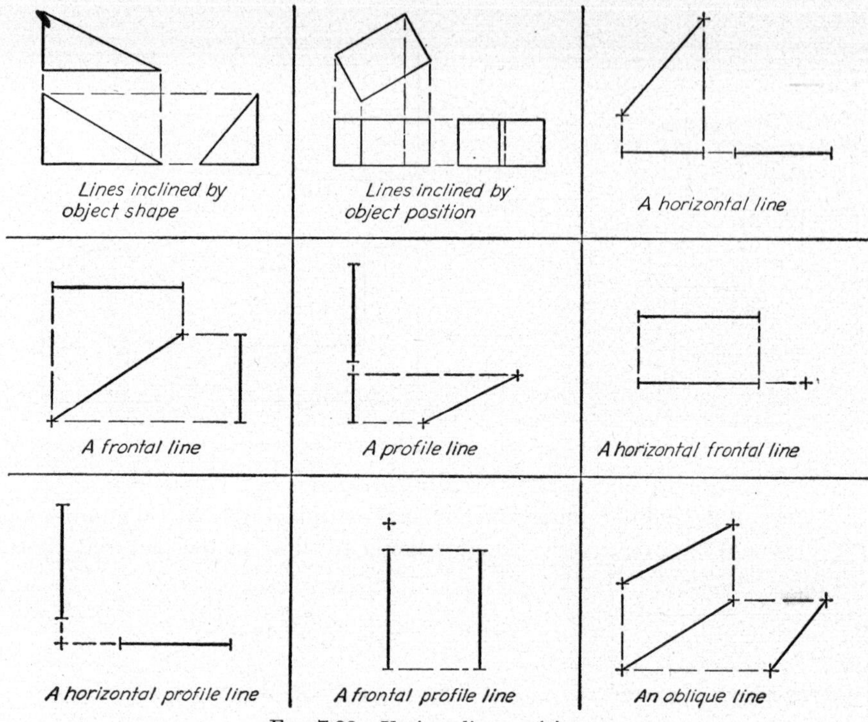

FIG. 7·22—Various line positions.

Surfaces are classified according to their space relationship with the planes of projection. *Horizontal*, *frontal*, and *profile* surfaces are illustrated at *A*, Fig. 7·23. When a surface is inclined to two of the planes of projection

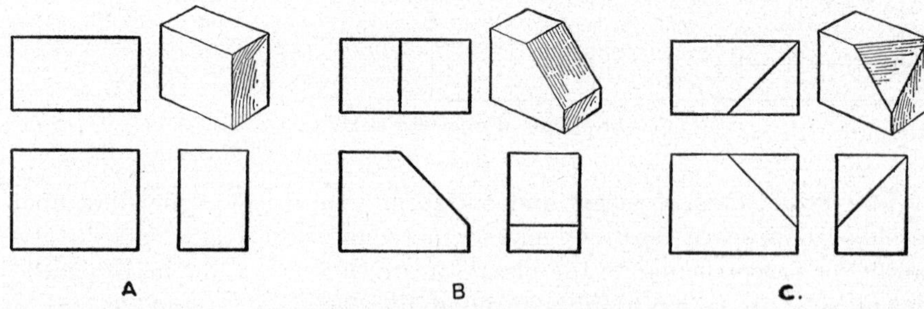

FIG. 7·23—Surface positions.

(but perpendicular to the third), as at *B*, the surface is said to be *auxiliary.* If the surface is at an angle to all three planes, as at *C*, the term *oblique* is used.

An edge relative to a plane of projection appears in true length when parallel, as a point when perpendicular, and shorter than true length when inclined. Similarly, a surface relative to a plane of projection appears in its true shape when parallel, as a line when perpendicular, and foreshortened when inclined. As an example, Fig. 7·23 shows at *A* an object with its faces parallel to the planes of projection; top, front, and right side surfaces are shown in true shape, and the object edges appear either in true length or as points. The inclined surface of the object at *B* does not show in true shape in any of the views but appears as an edge in the front view.

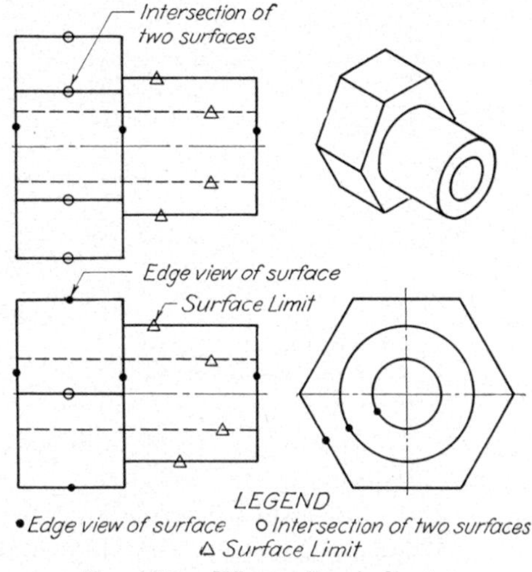

FIG. 7·24—What a line indicates.

The front and rear edges of the inclined surface are in true length in the front view and foreshortened in the top and side views. The top and bottom edges of the inclined surface appear in true length in top and side views and as points in the front view. The oblique surface of the object at *C* does not show in true shape in any of the views, but each of the bounding edges shows in true length in one view and is foreshortened in the other two views.

7·10 Representation of lines. Although uniform in appearance, the lines on a drawing may indicate three different types of directional change on the object. An *edge view* is a line showing the edge of a receding surface (a surface perpendicular to the plane of projection). An *intersection* is the line formed by the meeting of two surfaces. A *surface limit* is the reversal element line of a curved surface (or the series of points of reversal on a warped surface). Figure 7·24 illustrates the different line meanings.

7·11 Hidden lines. To describe an object completely, a drawing should contain lines representing all the edges, intersections, and surface limits of the object. *In any view there will be some parts of the object that cannot be seen from the position of the observer, as they will be covered by por-*

tions of the object closer to the observer's eye. The edges, intersections, and surface limits of these hidden parts are indicated by a line made up of short dashes, sometimes called "dotted lines" by draftsmen. In Fig. 7·25, the drilled hole[1] that is visible in the right-side view is hidden in the top and front views, and therefore it is indicated by a dotted line showing the hole

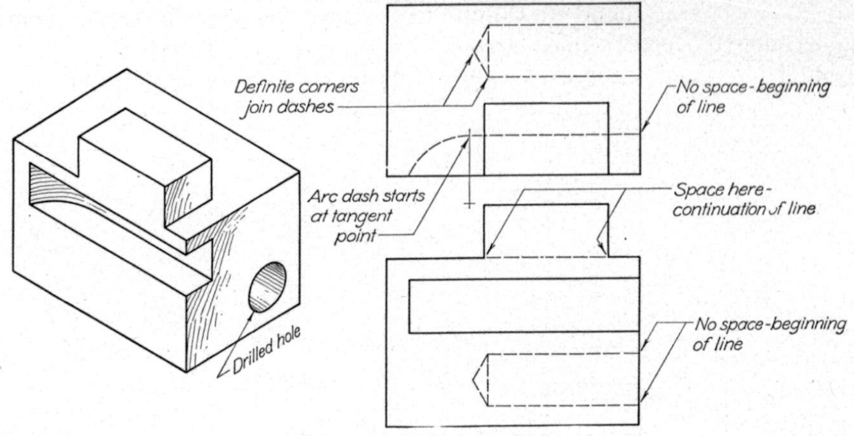

FIG. 7·25—Hidden features.

and the shape as left by the drill point. The milled slot[1] is visible in the front and side views but is hidden in the top view.

The beginner must pay particular attention to the execution of these hidden lines. If carelessly drawn, they will not only ruin the appearance of a drawing but will make it much harder to read. The line is drawn lighter than the full lines, of short dashes uniform in length, with the space between

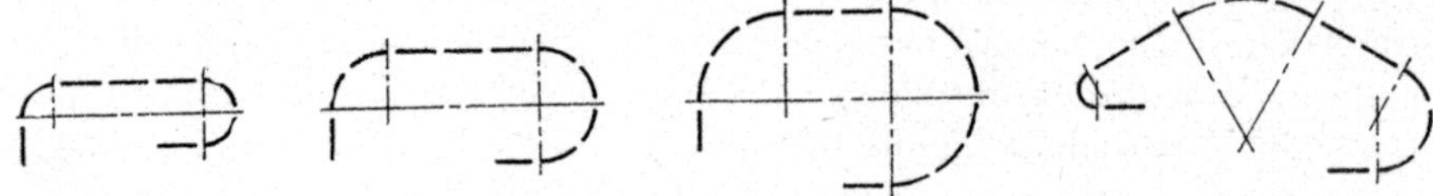

FIG. 7·26—Dotted arcs (actual size).

them very short, about one-fourth the length of the dash. It is important that they start and stop correctly. A dotted line always starts with a dash except when it would form a continuation of a full line, in which case a space is left, as shown in Fig. 7·25. Dashes always meet at corners. An arc must start with a dash at the tangent point except when it would form a continuation of a full line, straight or curved. The number of dashes used in a tangent arc should be carefully judged to maintain a uniform appearance, Fig. 7·26. Study carefully all dotted lines in Figs. 7·25 and 7·27.

[1] See Glossary.

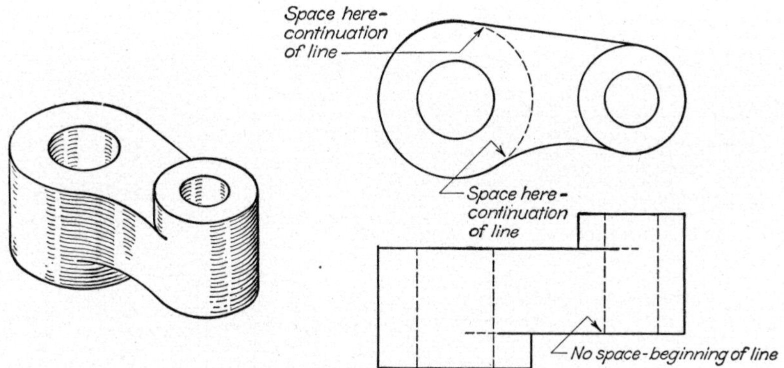

FIG. 7·27—Dotted lines and arcs.

7·12 Center lines. In general, the first lines to be drawn in the layout of an engineering drawing are the center lines, thereby forming the axes of symmetry for all symmetrical views or portions of views: (1) Every part with an axis, as a cylinder or a cone, will have the axis drawn as a center line before the part is drawn. (2) Every circle will have its center at the intersection of two center lines. Note that center lines intersect on the long dashes.

The standard symbol for center lines on finished drawings is a fine line made up of alternate long and short dashes, as shown in the alphabet of lines, Fig. 3·30. They are always extended slightly beyond the outline of the view, or portion of view, to which the center line applies. Center lines form the skeleton construction of the drawing, from and to which the important measurements are made and dimensions given. Study the center lines in Figs. 7·116 and 7·117.

7·13 Precedence of lines. In any view there is likely to be a coincidence of lines. Hidden portions of the object may project identically with visible portions. Center lines may likewise occur where there is the visible or invisible outline of some part of the object.

As the physical features of the object *must* be represented, full and dotted lines take precedence over all other lines. As the visible outline is more prominent by space position, full lines take precedence over dotted lines. A visible line could cover up a hidden line, but a hidden line could not cover a visible line. It is evident, also, that a hidden line could not occur as one of the boundary lines of a view.

When a center line and cutting-plane line coincide, the one that is more important for the readability of the drawing should take precedence over the other.

Break lines should be placed so that they do not spoil the readability of the over-all view.

Dimension and extension lines must always be placed so as not to coincide with other lines of the drawing.

The following list gives the order of precedence of lines:

1. Full line.
2. Dotted line.
3. Center line or cutting plane.
4. Break lines.
5. Dimension and extension lines.
6. Crosshatch lines.

Note the coincident lines in Fig. 7·28.

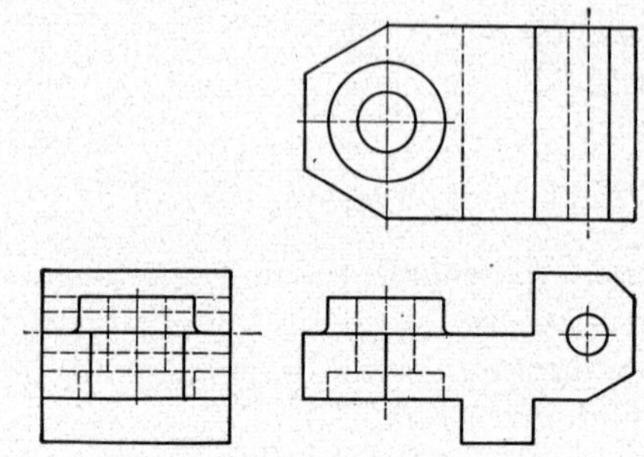

FIG. 7·28—Coincident-line study.

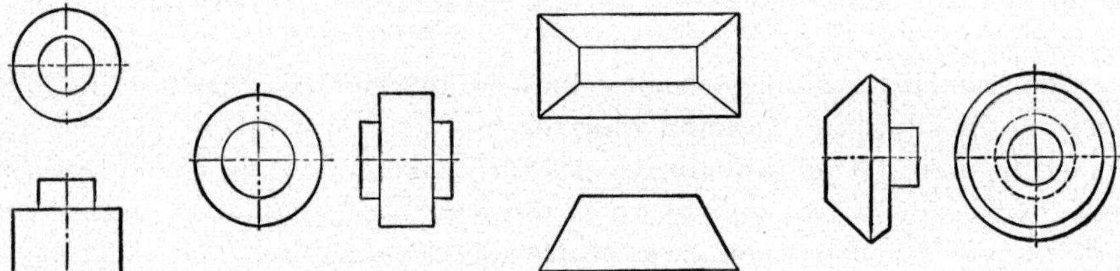

FIG. 7·29—Two-view drawings.

7·14 Selection of views. In practical work it is very important to choose the combination of views that will describe the shape of an object in the best and most economical way. Often only two views are necessary as, for example, a cylindrical shape which, if on a vertical axis, would require only a front and top view and, if on a horizontal axis, only a front and side view. Conical and pyramidal shapes also may be described in two views. Figure 7·29 illustrates two-view drawings. On the other hand, some shapes will need more than the three regular views for adequate description.

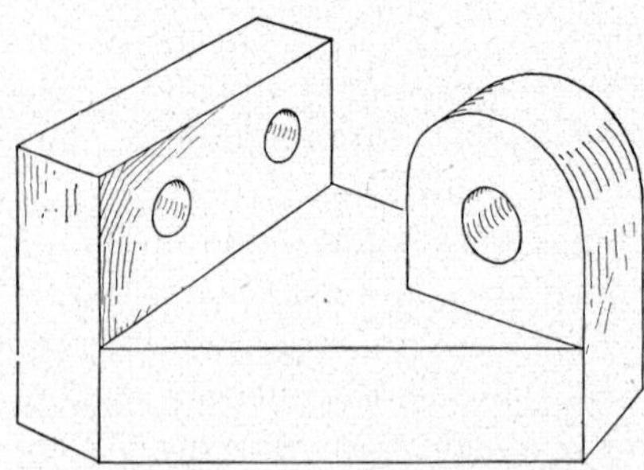

FIG. 7·30—Geometric shapes combined.

Objects may be thought of as being made up of combinations of simple geometrical solids, principally cylinders and rectangular prisms, and the views necessary to describe any object would be determined by the directions from which it would have to be viewed to see the characteristic contour shapes of these parts. Figure 7·30, for example, is made up of several prisms and cylinders. If each of these simple shapes is described and their relation to each other is shown, the object will be fully represented. In the majority of cases, the three regular views, top, front, and side, are sufficient to do this.

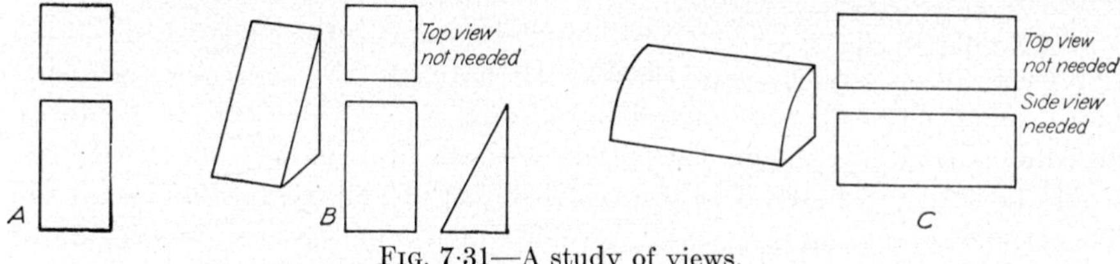

FIG. 7·31—A study of views.

Sometimes two views are proposed as sufficient for some object, on the assumption that the contour in the third direction would be of the shape that would naturally be expected. For instance *A*, in Fig. 7·31, would be assumed to have a uniform cross section and be a square prism. But the two views *might* be the top and front views of a wedge, as shown in three views at *B*. Two views of an object, as drawn at *C*, do not describe the piece at all. It might be assumed to be square in section, but it could as easily be round, triangular, quarter round, or other shape, which should have been indicated by a required side view. Sketch several different front views for each top view (*A*, *B*, and *C*), Fig. 7·32.

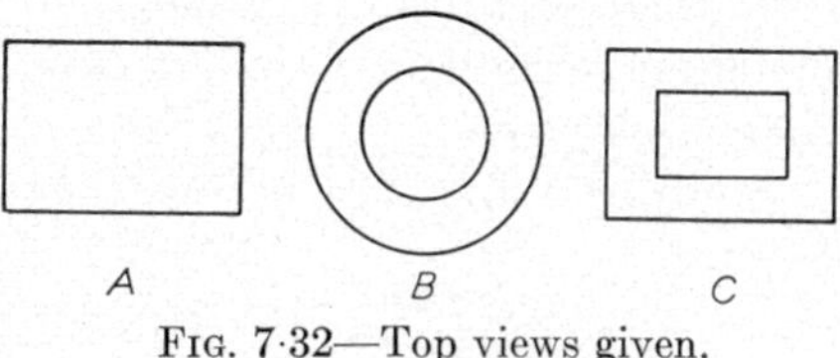

FIG. 7·32—Top views given.

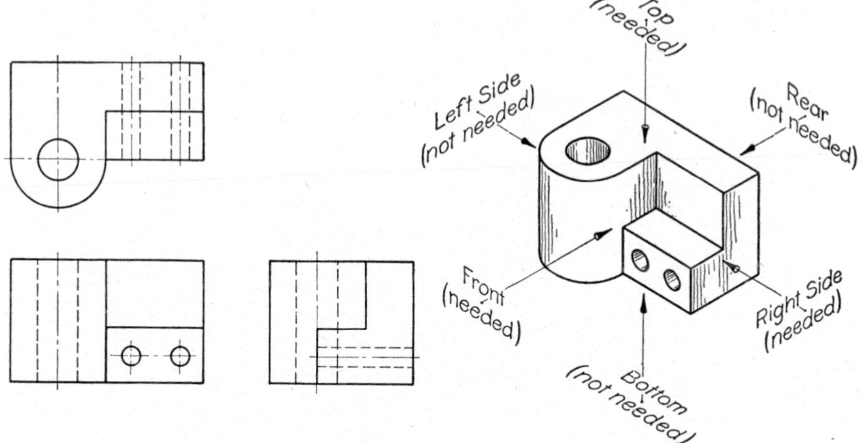

FIG. 7·33—Selection of views.

With the object preferably in its functioning position, and with its principal surfaces parallel to the planes of projection, visualize the object, mentally picturing the orthographic views one at a time to decide on the best combination. In Fig. 7·33 the arrows show the direction of observation for the six principal views of an object and indicate the mental process of the draftsman. He notes that the front view should show the two horizontal holes, as well as the width and height of the piece; that a top view is needed to show the contour of the vertical cylinder; and that the cut-out corner will require a side view to show its shape. He notes, further, that the right-side view would show this cut in full lines, while on the left side it would be invisible. He notes, incidentally, that neither a bottom view nor a rear view would be of any value in describing this object. Thus he has arrived at the correct choice of front, top, and right-side views for the best description of the piece. As a rule, the side view containing the fewer hidden lines should be preferred. If there is no choice, the right-side view is preferred in standard practice.

In inventive and design work, any simple object should be visualized mentally, and the view selected without a picture sketch. In complicated work, a pictorial or orthographic sketch may be used to advantage, but it should not be necessary, in any case, to sketch all possible views in order to make a selection.

Study the drawings in Fig. 7·34 and determine why the views are so chosen.

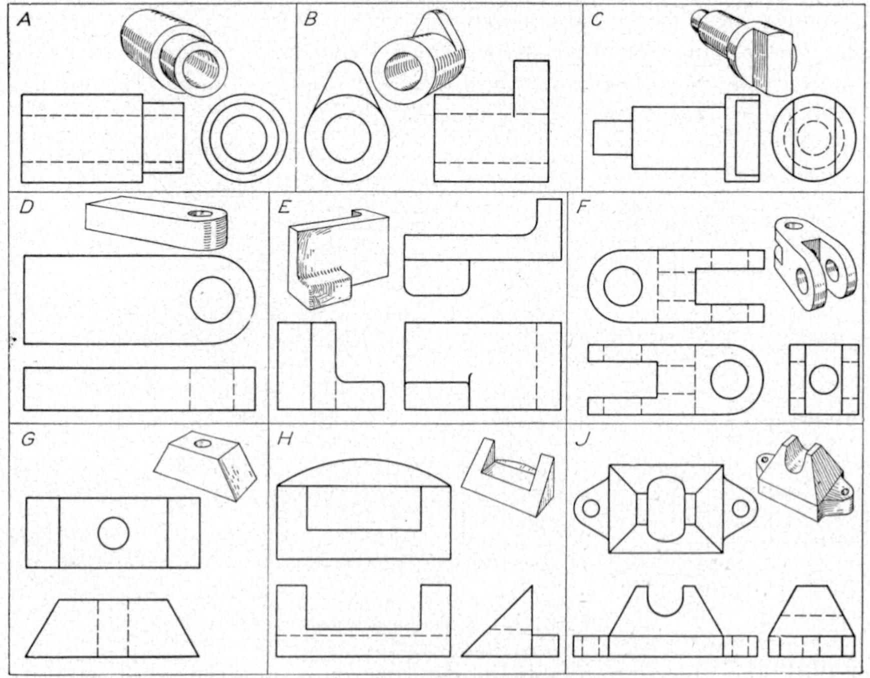

FIG. 7·34—Choice of views.

7·15 Drawing freehand in orthographic projection. In beginning the study of projections, it is best to draw freehand the three views of a number of simple pieces, developing the ability to "write" the language and exercising the constructive imagination in seeing the object itself by looking at the three projections. Figures 7·36 to 7·50 contain a number of pictorial sketches of pieces of various shapes. These are to be translated into three-view orthographic freehand drawings. Make them of fairly large size, the front view say 1½ to 2 inches in length, and estimate the proportions of the different parts by eye or from the proportionate marks shown, but without measuring. Observe the following order of working:

1. Study the pictorial sketch and decide what combination of views will best describe the shape of the piece.
2. Block in the views, as at *A*, Fig. 7·35, using a very light stroke of a soft pencil (F or No. 2), spacing the views so as to give a well-balanced appearance to the drawing.

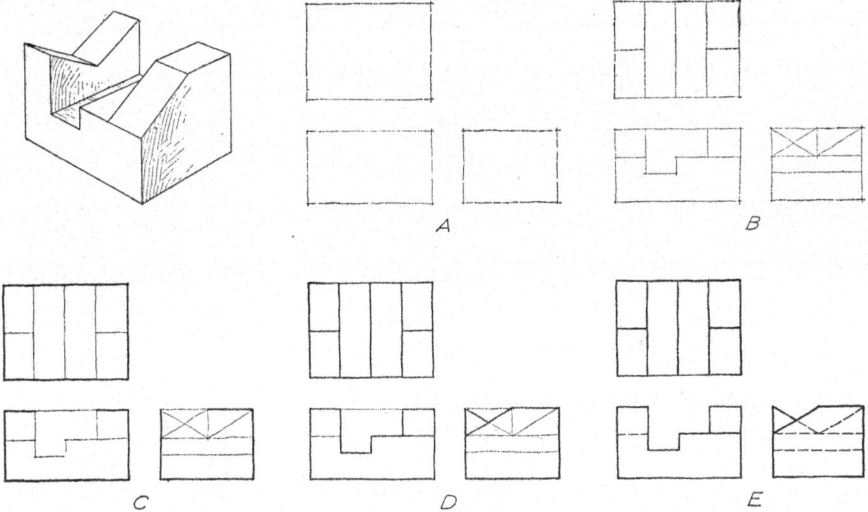

FIG. 7·35—Stages in making an orthographic freehand drawing.

3. Build up the detail in each view, carrying the three views along together, as at *B*.
4. Brighten the outline of each view with bold strokes as at *C*.
5. Brighten the detail with bold strokes, thus completing the full lines of the sketch, as at *D*.
6. Sketch in all dotted lines, using a stroke of medium weight, lighter than the full lines, as at *E*, thus completing the shape description of the block.
7. Check the drawing carefully, then cover the pictorial sketch and visualize the object from the three views.

In making three-view sketches from measured models or dimensioned pictorial drawings, as Figs. 7·66 to 7·101, faintly ruled cross-section paper is sometimes used to advantage.

It will be of interest to read Chap. 19 on technical sketching before working the problems of Figs. 7·36 to 7·50.

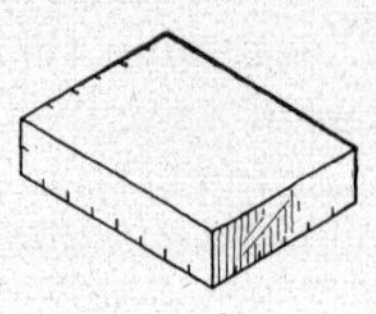

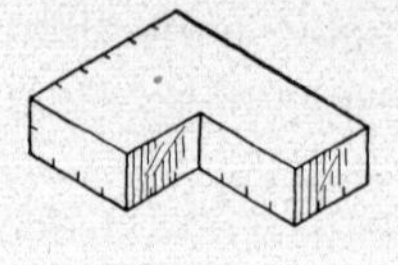

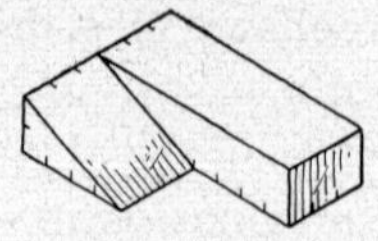

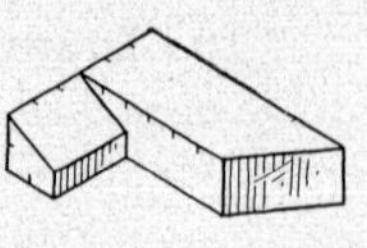
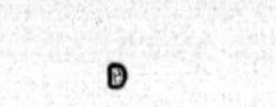

Fig. 7·36

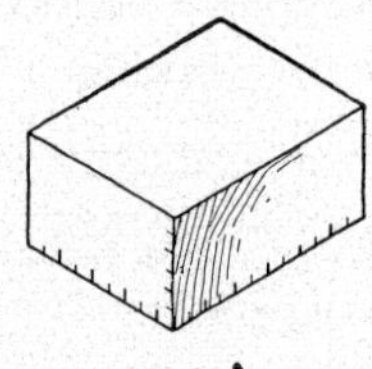

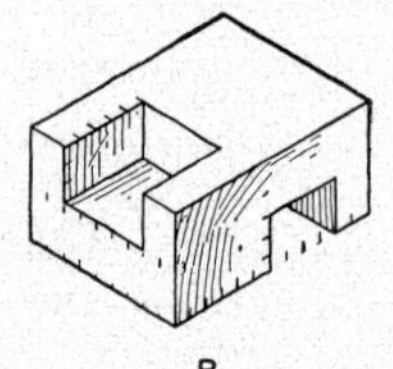

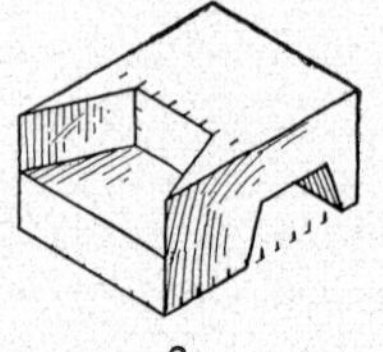

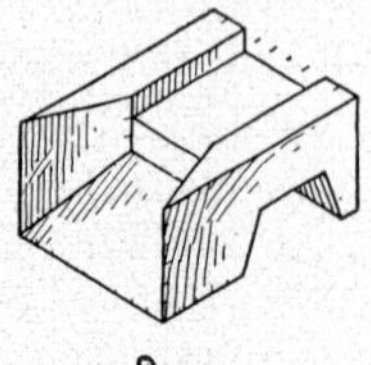

Fig. 7·37

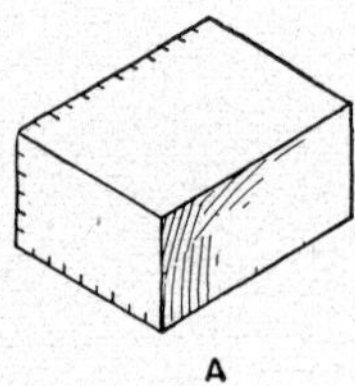

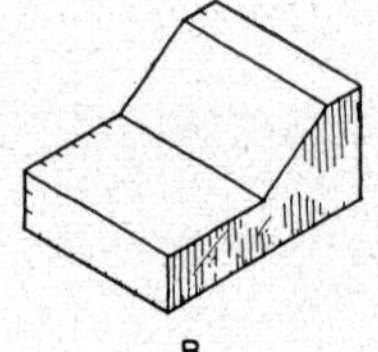

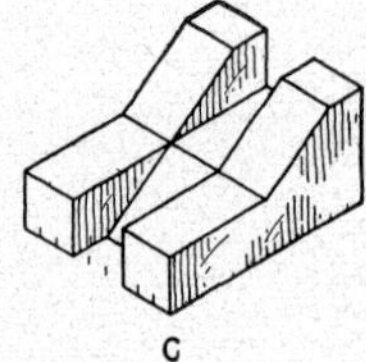

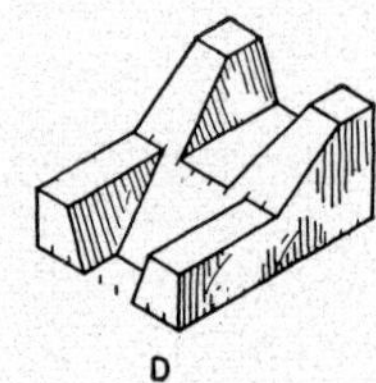

Fig. 7·38

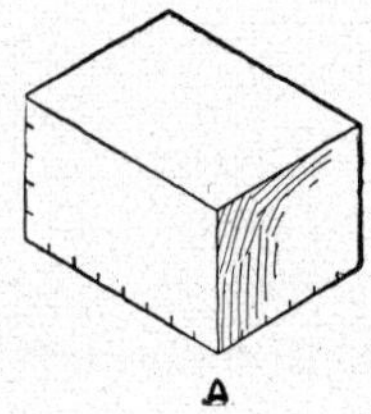

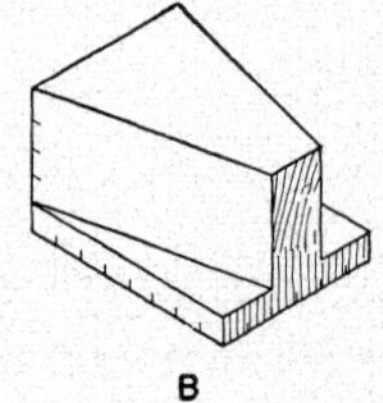

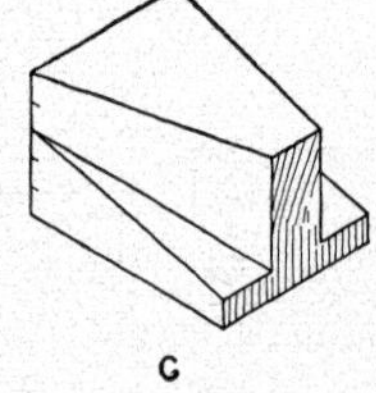

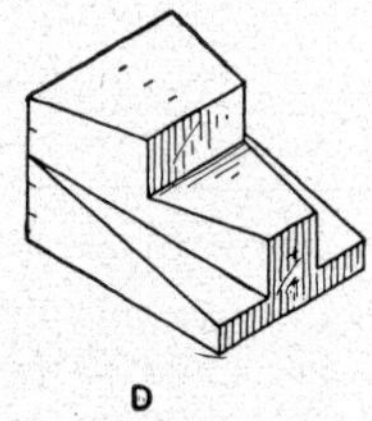

Fig. 7·39

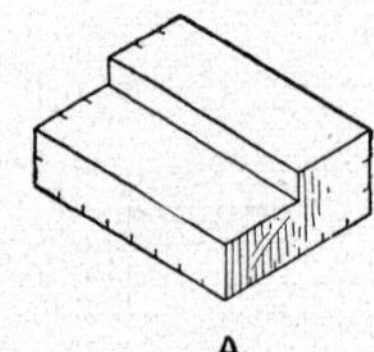

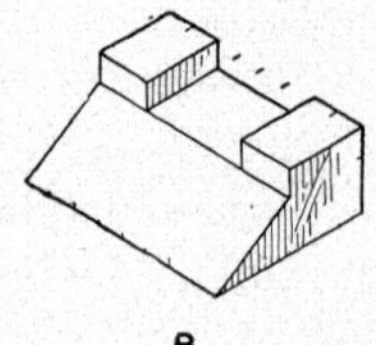

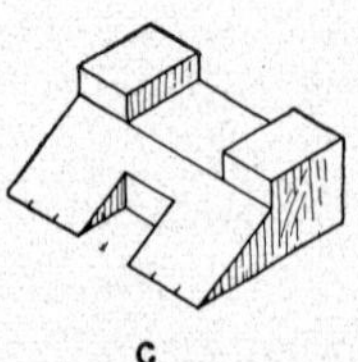

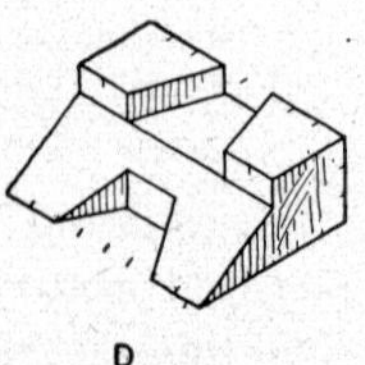

Fig. 7·40

Figs. 7·36 to 7·40—Pieces to be drawn freehand in orthographic projection.

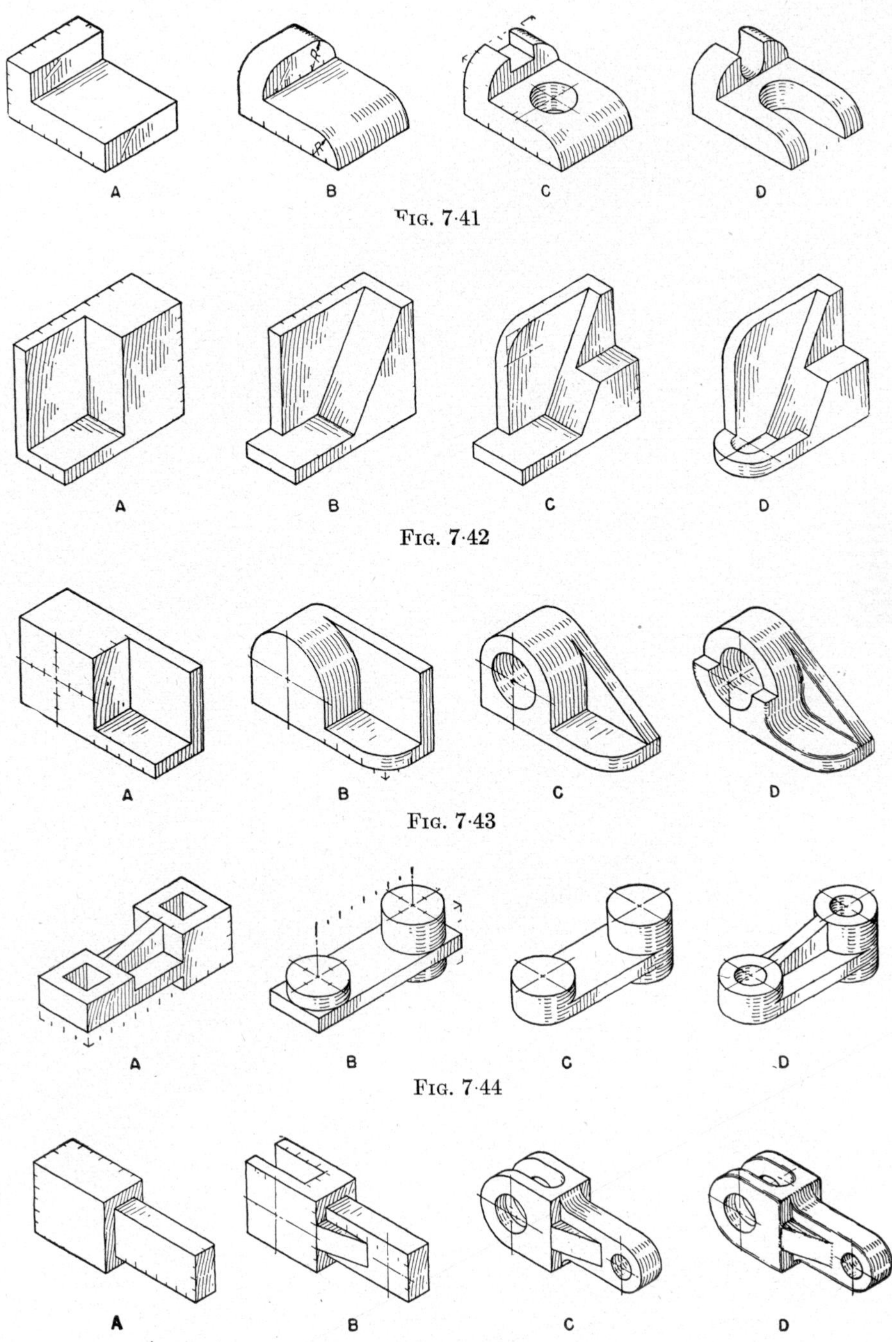

FIG. 7·41

FIG. 7·42

FIG. 7·43

FIG. 7·44

FIG. 7·45

FIGS. 7·41 to 7·45—Pieces to be drawn freehand in orthographic projection.

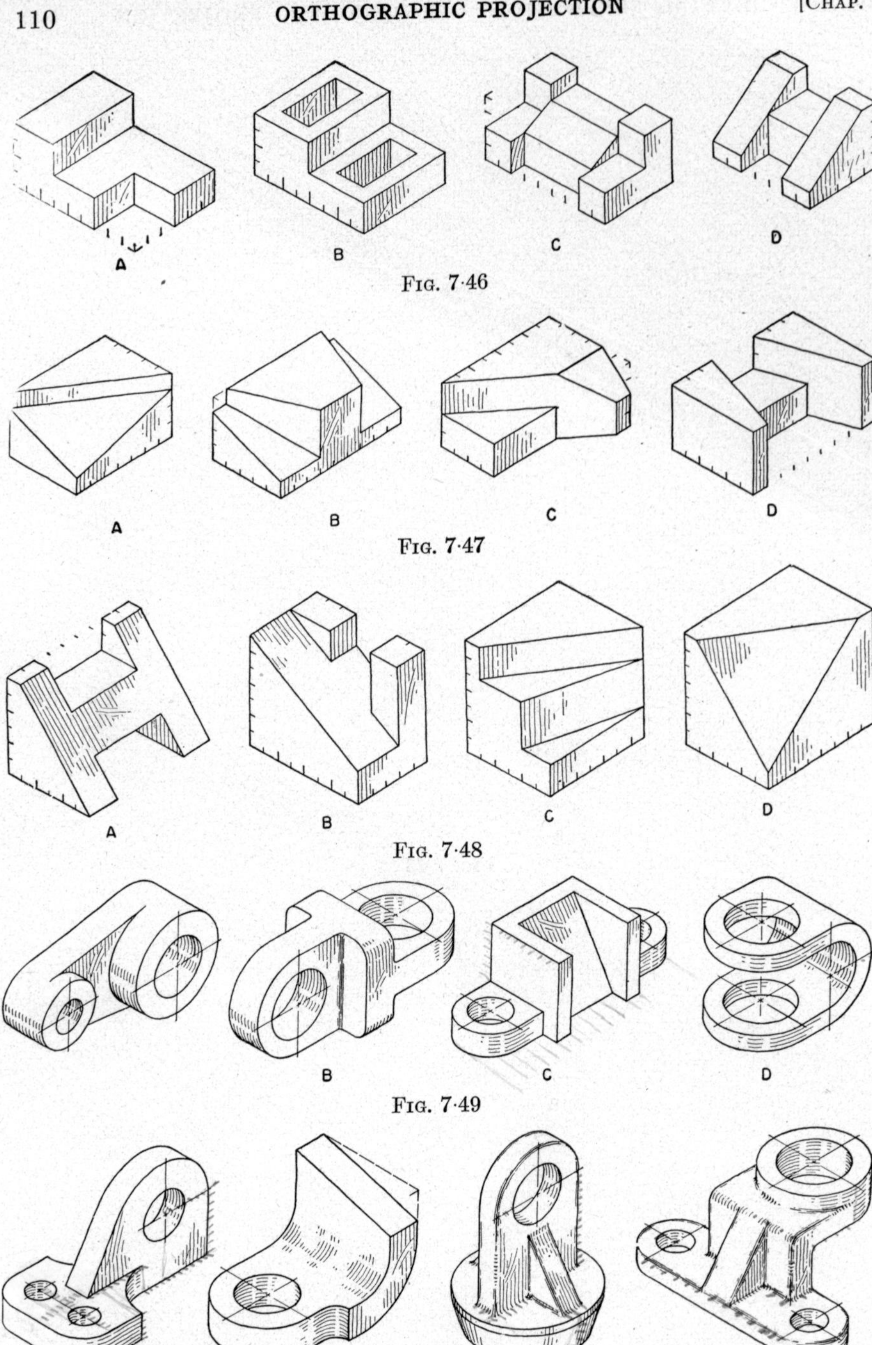

FIG. 7·46

FIG. 7·47

FIG. 7·48

FIG. 7·49

FIG. 7·50

FIGS. 7·46 to 7·50—Pieces to be drawn freehand in orthographic projection.

7·16 Drawing in orthographic projection. In addition to an understanding of the methods of projection, *instrument drawing* demands, for technique, a knowledge of applied geometry with skill and facility in the use of instruments. An instrument drawing is far more precise in its projections and line technique than is a freehand drawing, and therefore requires careful attention to accuracy and neatness. Chapter 3, The Use of Instruments, and Chap. 5, Applied Geometry, should be studied before an instrument drawing is attempted.

Standard sheets, based on multiples of 8½″ × 11″ are specified by the ASA for drawings. Trimmed sizes of drawing paper and cloth, with recommended border and title dimensions, are given on page 323.

View spacing is necessary in order that the drawing may be balanced within the space provided. The draftsman therefore must do a little pre-

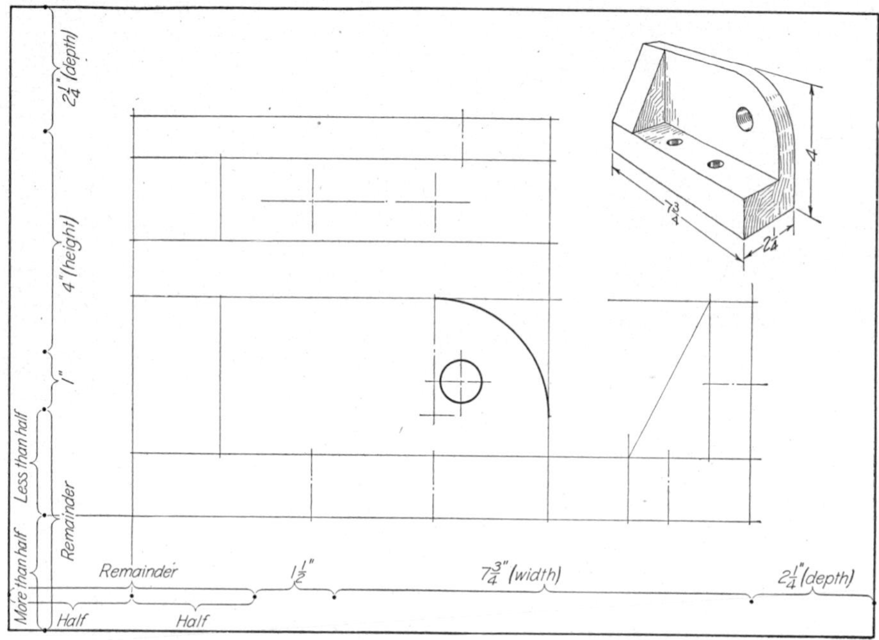

FIG. 7·51—Spacing views.

liminary measuring to locate the views. The following example will describe the procedure. Suppose the piece illustrated in Fig. 7·51 is to be drawn full size on an 11″ × 17″ sheet. With an end-title strip the working space inside the border will be 10½″ × 15″. The front view will require 7¾″ and the side view 2¼″. This leaves 5″ to be distributed between the views and at the ends.

The draftsman locates the views graphically and very quickly by measuring with his scale along the bottom border line. Starting at the lower *right* corner, lay off first 2¼″, then 7¾″. The distance between views may now be decided upon. It is chosen arbitrarily to separate the views without crowding, yet sufficiently close to have the drawing read easily (in this case 1½″) and the distance measured; half the remaining distance to the left corner is the starting point of the front view. For the vertical location, the front view is 4″ high and the top view 2¼″ deep. Starting at the upper left corner, lay off first 2¼″, then 4″; judge the distance between views (in this case 1″) and lay it off; then a point marked at less than half the remaining space will locate the front view, allowing more space at the bottom than at the top, for appearance sake. Now block out the views and locate center lines and base lines as shown.

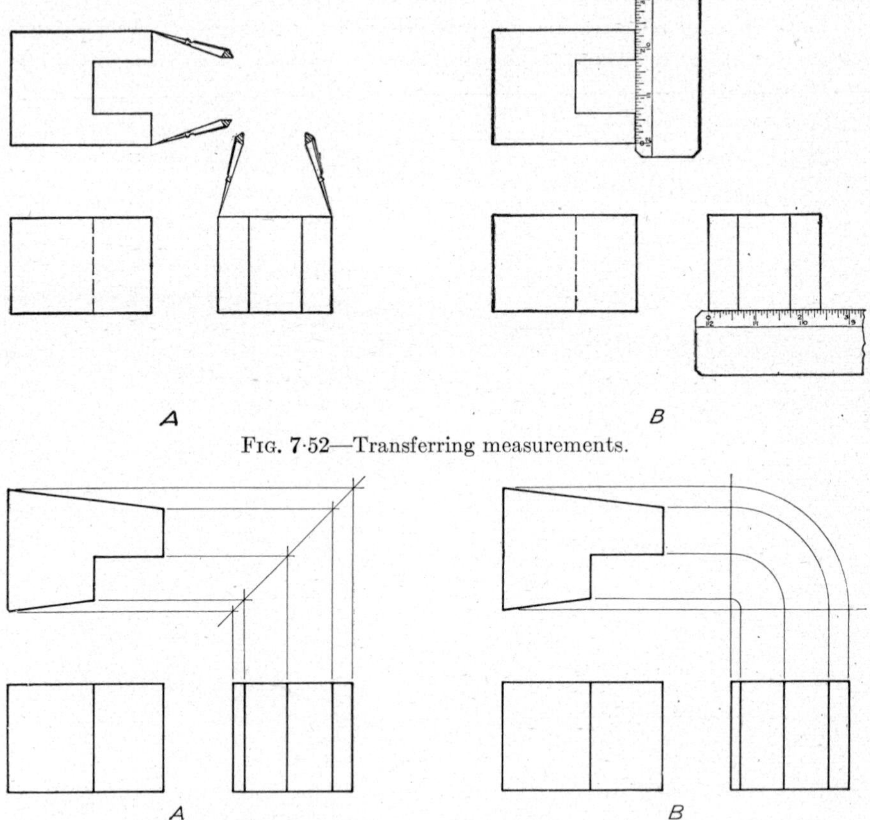

FIG. 7·52—Transferring measurements.

FIG. 7·53—Projecting depth measurements.

Projections are easily made from one to the other of the front and top views or the front and side views by employing the T square and triangle to draw vertical or horizontal lines as needed, but a depth measurement of the top and side views must be transferred, as the distance cannot be projected directly. In carrying the top and side views along together, the draftsman usually transfers the depth measurement from one to the other either with his dividers, as at *A*, Fig. 7·52, or with his scale, as at *B*. Sometimes, however, as in the case of an irregular figure, he prefers to "miter" the points around, using a 45-degree line drawn through the point of intersection of the top and side views of the front face, extended as shown in Fig. 7·53*A*; or, going back to the method of the glass box, to swing them around with the compasses, as at *B*. The methods of Fig. 7·53, however, require more time and care to maintain accuracy than do the methods of Fig. 7·52.

7·17 Order of drawing. The order of working is important, as speed and accuracy depend largely upon the methods employed in laying down lines. Duplications of the same measurement should be avoided, and changing from one instrument to another should be kept at a minimum. Naturally, *all* measurements cannot be made with the scale at one time, or *all* circles and arcs drawn before laying down the compasses, but as much work as possible should be done before shifting to another instrument. An orderly placement of the working tools on the drafting table will save much time when changing from the use of one instrument to another. The usual order of working is

1. Decide what combination of views will best describe the object. A freehand sketch will aid in choosing the views and in planning the general arrangement of the sheet.
2. Decide what scale is to be used and, by calculation or measurement, find a suitable standard sheet size, *or* pick one of the standard drawing sizes, and find a suitable scale.
3. Space the views on the sheet, as described in paragraph 7·16.
4. Lay off the principal dimensions and then "block in" the views with light, sharp, accurate outlines and center lines. Center lines are drawn for the axes of all symmetrical views or parts of views. Thus every cylindrical part should have a

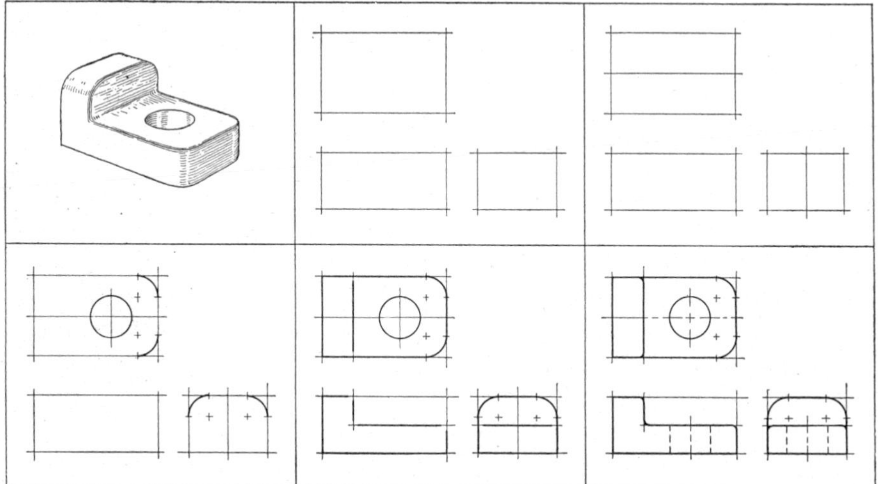

FIG. 7·54—Stages in penciling.

center line—the projection of the axis of the piece. Every circle should have two center lines intersecting at its center.

5. Draw in the details of the part, beginning with the dominant characteristic shape and progressing to the minor details such as fillets, rounds, etc. The different views should be carried along together, projecting a characteristic shape as shown on one view to the other views, not finishing one view before starting another. Use a minimum of construction and draw the lines to finished weight, if possible, as the views are carried along. *Do not make the drawing lightly and then "heavy" the lines later.*
6. Lay out and letter the title.
7. Check the drawing carefully.

Figure 7·54 illustrates the stages of penciling.

7·18 Order of tracing. If the drawing is to be traced[1] in ink as an exercise in the use of instruments, or for a finished orthographic drawing without dimensions, the order of working is

1. Place the pencil drawing to be traced on the drawing board, carefully align it with the T square, and put thumbtacks in the two upper corners. Then place the tracing paper or cloth (dull side up) over the drawing. Holding the cloth in position, lift the tacks one at a time and replace them to hold both sheets. Then put tacks in the two lower corners.
2. To remove any oily film, prepare the surface of the cloth or paper by dusting it lightly with prepared pounce or soft white chalk. Then wipe the surface perfectly clean with a soft cloth.
3. Carefully set the compasses to the correct line width and ink all full-line circles and circle arcs, beginning with the smallest. Correct line weights are given on page 28.
4. Ink dotted circles and arcs in the same order as full-line circles.
5. Carefully set the ruling pen to draw exactly the same width line as the full-line circles. The best way to match the straight lines to the circles is to draw with the compasses and ruling pen outside of the trim line of the sheet or on another sheet of the same kind, and adjust the ruling pen until the lines match.
6. Ink irregular curved lines.
7. Ink straight full lines in this order: horizontal (top to bottom), vertical (left to right), and inclined (uppermost first).
8. Ink straight dotted lines in the same order. Be careful to match these straight lines with the dotted circles.
9. Ink center lines.
10. Crosshatch all areas representing cut surfaces.
11. Draw pencil guide lines and letter the title.
12. Ink the border.
13. Check the tracing for errors and omissions.

7·19 Reading a drawing. As already stated, the engineer must be able to *read* and *write* the language of drawing. The necessity of learning to *read* is absolute, as everyone connected with technical industry must be able to read a drawing without hesitation. Not to have that ability would be an admission of technical illiteracy.

Reading a drawing is essentially a reversal of the mental processes used

[1] A discussion of tracing and reproduction methods will be found in Chap. 15.

in writing the graphic language. When making a drawing, progress is from visual knowledge of the shape of the object to the complete representation of that shape; when reading a drawing, progress is from no knowledge whatever of the shape of the object to an understanding of every detail of the shape.

A drawing is read by visualizing units or details one at a time from the orthographic representation, orienting and connecting these details together to finally interpret the whole object. *One cannot expect to read a whole drawing at once any more than he would expect to read a whole page of print at a glance. Both must be read a line at a time.* With a little practice, all the features of a fairly complicated object can be retained in the mind and called to visual clarity when needed.

In reading a drawing, one should first gain a general idea of the shape of the object by a rapid survey of all the views given, then select for more careful study the view that best shows the characteristic shape of some portion and, by referring back and forth to the adjacent view, see what each line represents.

When looking at any view, one should always imagine that it is the object itself, not a flat projection of it, that is seen; and, in glancing from one view to another, the reader should imagine himself as moving around the actual object and looking at it from the direction the view was taken.

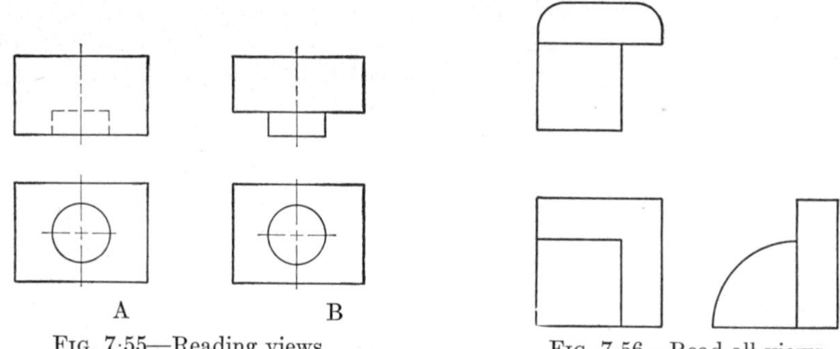

FIG. 7·55—Reading views.

FIG. 7·56—Read all views.

As explained in paragraph 7·10, a line on a drawing always indicates either (1) *the edge view of a surface*, (2) *an intersection*, or (3) *a surface limit.* Each line on a view means a change in the direction of a surface, but the corresponding part of another view must be consulted to tell what the change is. For example, a circle on a front view, may mean either a hole, Fig. 7·55*A*, or a projecting boss, as at *B*. A glance at the top view will tell at once which it is. One cannot read a drawing by looking at a single view. Two views will not always describe the shape of an object, and when three views are given, all three must be consulted to be sure the shape has been read correctly. For example, the front and top views of Fig. 7·56 show what appears to be a rectangular projection on the front of the object, but the side view shows this projection to be quarter round. The front and side views apparently indicate the rear portion of the object to be a rectangular prism, but the top view shows that the two vertical rear edges are rounded. Never assume a shape from some of the views—read all views carefully. The steps in reading a drawing are

1. Orient yourself with the views given.
2. Note the general over-all shape of the object. Study the dominant features and their relationship to each other.
3. Start reading individual features beginning with the most dominant and progressing to the subordinate details.
4. As the reading proceeds, note the relationship between the various features of the object.
5. Reread any detail or relationship not understood at the first reading.

7·20 Learning to read by sketching. A drawing cannot be read aloud but is interpreted by mentally understanding the shape of the object represented. Proof that the drawing has been read and understood may be shown by making the piece in wood or metal, by modeling it in clay, or by making a pictorial sketch of it, the latter being the usual method. Since facility in freehand sketching is so important to every engineer, its practice should be started early. Before attempting to make a pictorial sketch, a preliminary study of the method of procedure will be required.

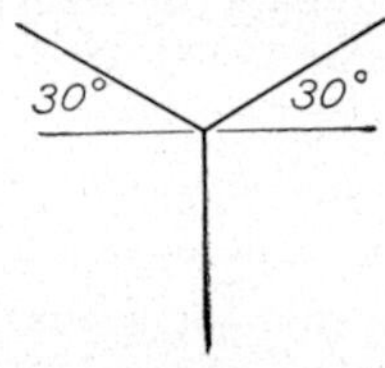

FIG. 7·57—Pictorial axes.

Pictorial sketching may be based on a skeleton of three axes, one vertical, the other two at 30 degrees,[1] representing three mutually perpendicular lines, Fig. 7·57. On these axes are marked the proportionate width, depth,

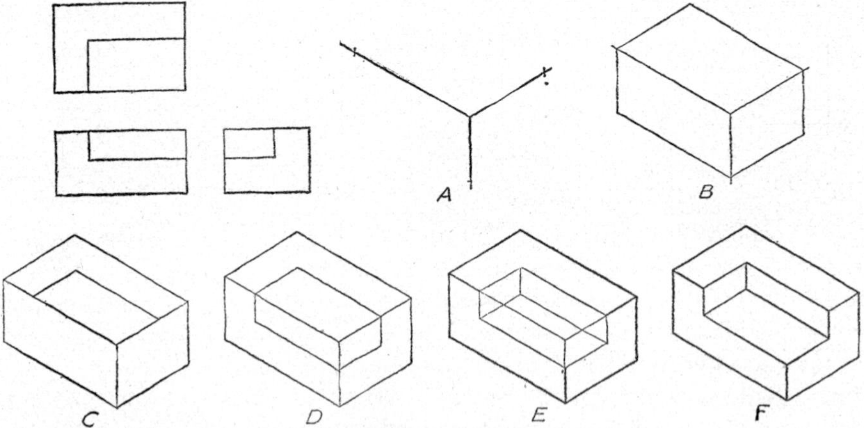

FIG. 7·58—Stages in making a pictorial sketch.

and height of any rectangular figure. Circles are drawn in their circumscribing square.

[1] Isometric position. Oblique or other pictorial methods may also be used.

In Fig. 7·58 look at the views given, as described in paragraph 7·19. Then with a soft pencil (F) and notebook paper make a *very light* pictorial construction sketch, estimating the height, width, and depth of the object and laying the distances off on the axes as at *A*; then sketch the rectangular box that would enclose the piece, or the block from which it could be cut, Fig. 7·58*B*. On the top face of this box sketch very lightly the lines that occur on the top view of the orthographic drawing, Fig. 7·58*C*. Note that, as will be found later, some of the lines on top views may not be in the top plane. Next sketch lightly the lines of the front view on the front face of the box or block, and, if a side view is given, outline it similarly, Fig. 7·58*D*. Now begin to cut the figure from the block, strengthening the visible edges and adding the lines of intersection where faces of the object meet, as in Fig. 7·58*E*. Edges that do not appear as visible lines are omitted unless necessary to describe the piece. Finish the sketch, checking back to the three-view drawing. The construction lines need not be erased unless they confuse the sketch.

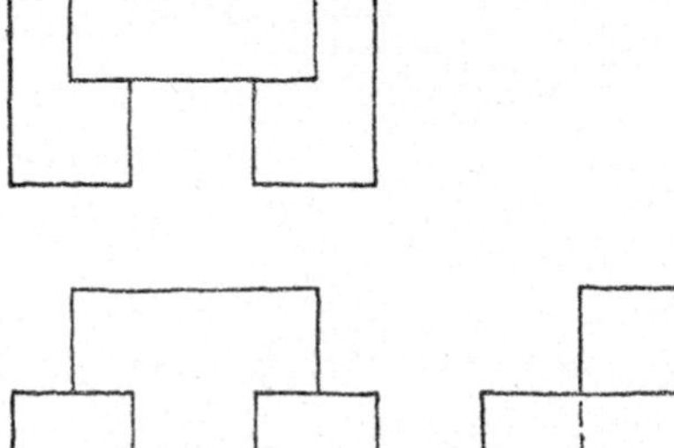

FIG. 7·59—A drawing to be read.

7·21 Learning to read by modeling. An interesting and effective learning method is to model the object in clay or modeling wax, working in much the same way as when reading by pictorial sketching. Some shapes may be modeled by cutting out from the enclosing block, others may be modeled more easily by first analyzing and dividing the object into its basic geometric shapes and then combining these shapes.

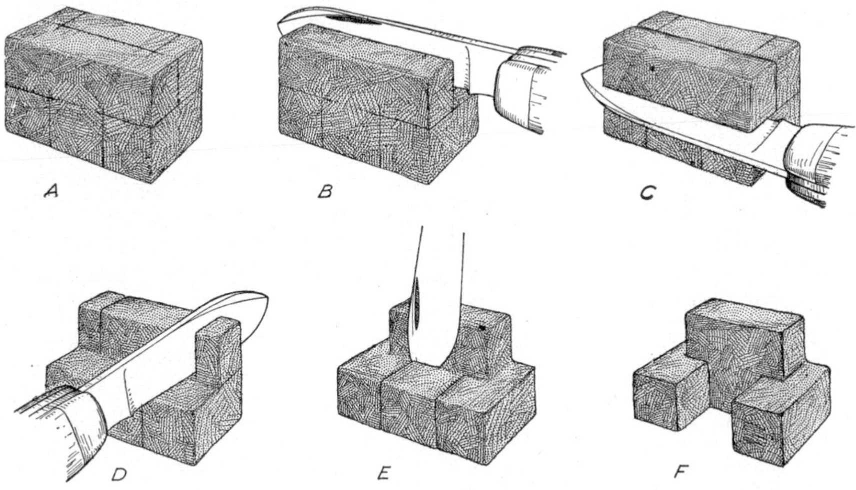

FIG. 7·60—Stages in modeling.

Starting with a rectangular block of clay, perhaps one inch square and two inches long, read Fig. 7·59 by cutting the figure from the solid. Scribe very lightly, with the point of the knife or a scriber, the lines of the three views on the three corresponding faces of the block, Fig. 7·60. Evidently the first cut could be as shown at *B*, and the second as at *C*. Successive cuts are indicated at *D* and *E* and the finished model at *F*.

Figure 7·61 illustrates the type of model that can be made by building up the shapes of which the object is composed.

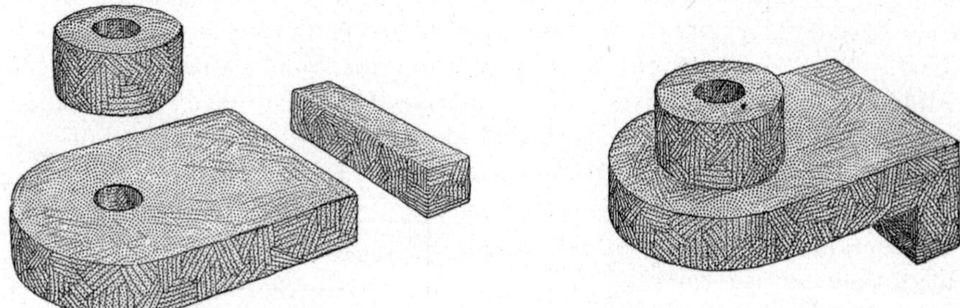

FIG. 7·61—A built-up model.

7·22 Exercises in reading. Figures 7·62 and 7·63 contain a number of three-view drawings of block shapes made for exercises in reading orthographic projection and translating into pictorial sketches or models. Proceed as described in the previous paragraphs, making sketches not less than four inches over all. Check each sketch to be sure that all intersections are shown, and that the original three-view drawing could be made from the sketch.

In each three-view drawing of Fig. 7·64 some lines have been intentionally omitted. Read the drawings and supply the missing lines.

7·23 Calculation of volume as an aid in reading. In calculating the volume of an object, one is forced to break the part down into its simple geometrical elements, and then carefully to analyze the shape of each element *before computation is possible.* Thus the calculation of volume is primarily an exercise in reading a drawing. Usually, before the computations are completed, the object has been visualized, but the mathematical record of the volume of each portion and the correct total volume and weight are proof that the drawing has been read and understood.

The procedure closely follows the usual steps in reading a drawing. Figure 7·65 will illustrate the method.

1. Study the orthographic drawing and pick out the principal masses (*A*, *B*, and *C*, shown on the breakdown and in the pictorial drawing). Pay no attention in the beginning to holes, rounds, etc., but study each principal over-all shape and its relation to the other masses of the object. Record the dimensions of each of these principal portions and indicate plus volume by placing a check mark in the plus-volume column.

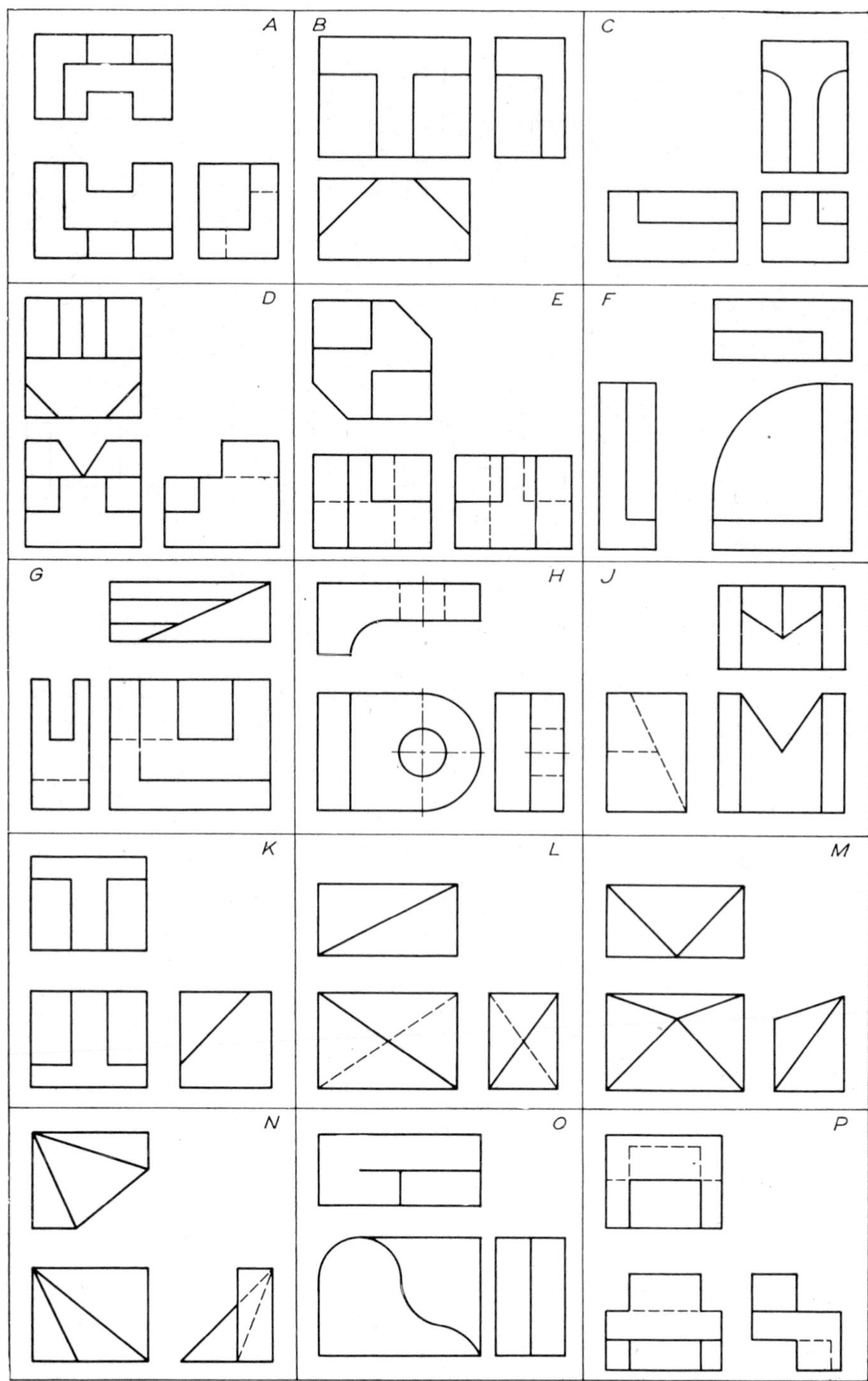

FIG. 7·62—Reading exercises.

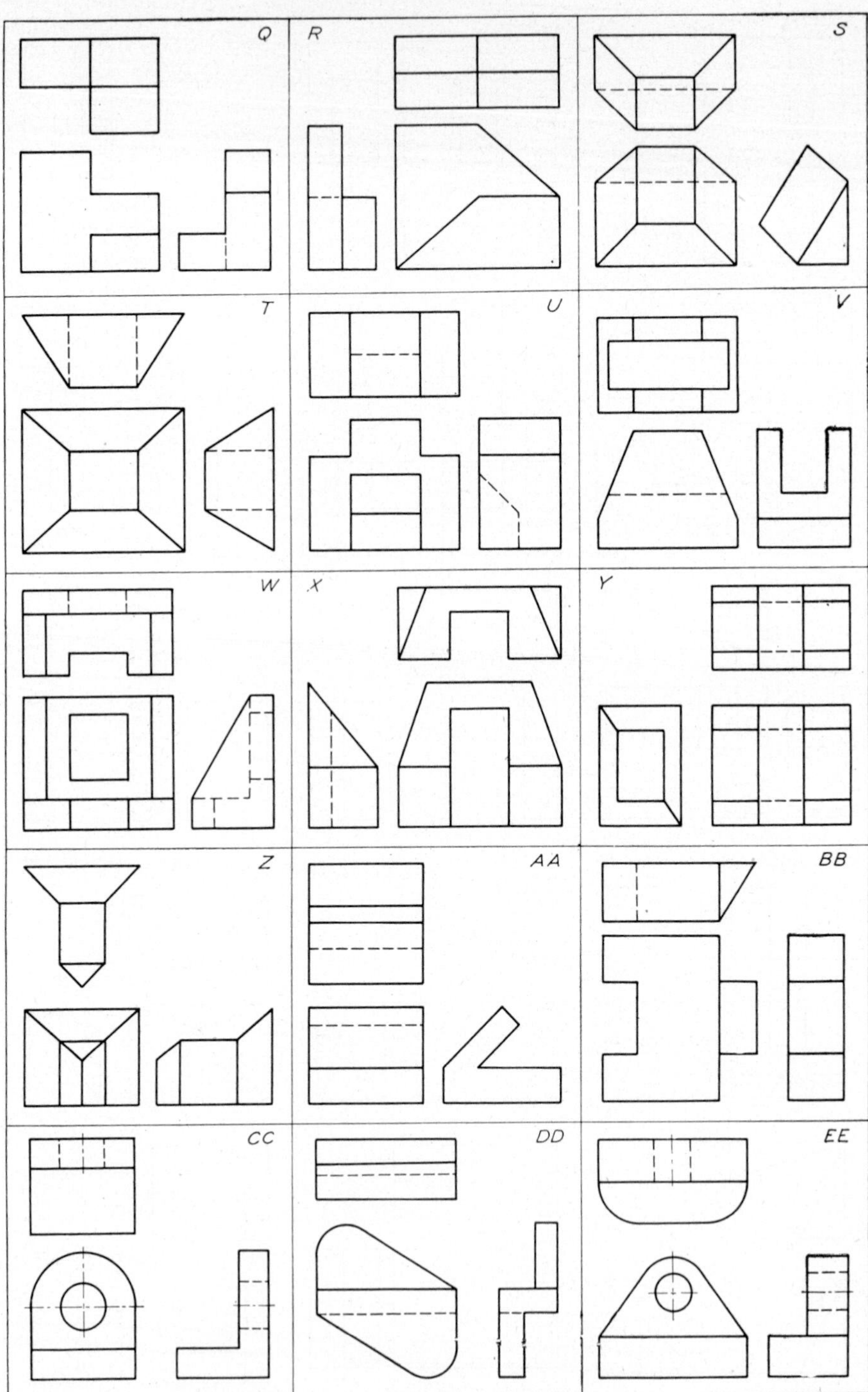

FIG. 7·63—Reading exercises.

FIG. 7·64—Missing-line exercises.

2. Examine each principal mass and find the secondary masses (D and E) that must be either added to or subtracted from the principal portions. Bosses, lugs, etc., must be added; cut-out portions, holes, etc., subtracted. Record the dimensions of these secondary masses, being careful to indicate plus or minus volume.
3. Further limit the object to its actual shape by locating smaller details such as holes, fillets, rounds, etc. (parts E, F, G, and H). Record the dimensions of these parts.
4. Compute the volume of each portion. This may be done by longhand multiplication or, more conveniently, with a slide rule. Record each volume in the proper column, plus or minus. When all unit volumes are completed, find the net volume by subtracting total minus volume from total plus volume.
5. Multiply net volume by the weight per cubic inch of metal to compute the total weight.

The calculations are simplified if all fractional dimensions are converted to the decimal form. When a slide rule is employed, fractions *must* be converted to decimals. A partial conversion table is given in Fig. 7·65, and a more complete table on page 632.

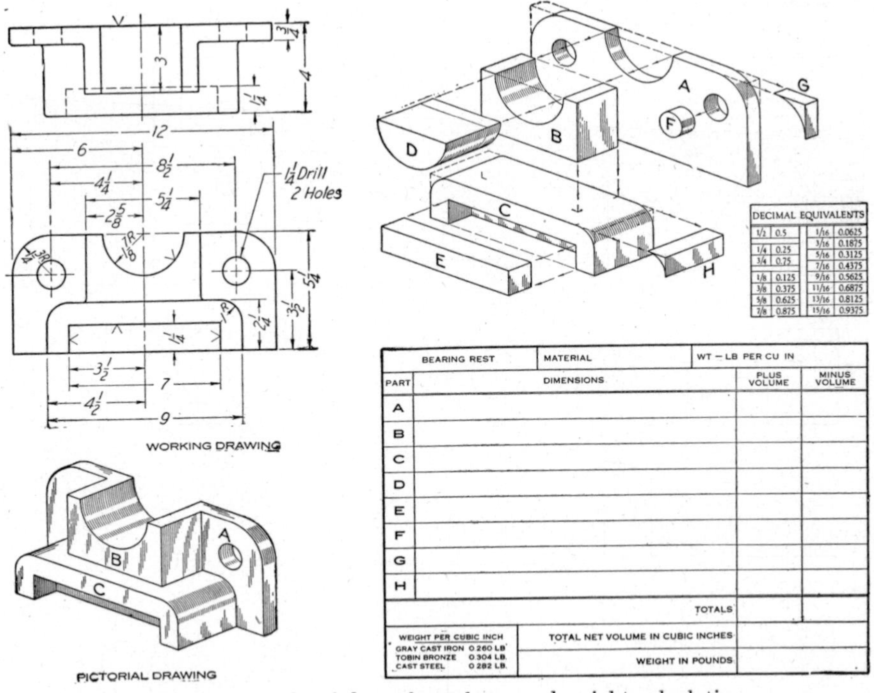

DECIMAL EQUIVALENTS			
1/2	0.5	1/16	0.0625
		3/16	0.1875
1/4	0.25	5/16	0.3125
3/4	0.75	7/16	0.4375
1/8	0.125	9/16	0.5625
3/8	0.375	11/16	0.6875
5/8	0.625	13/16	0.8125
7/8	0.875	15/16	0.9375

BEARING REST	MATERIAL	WT – LB PER CU IN	
PART	DIMENSIONS	PLUS VOLUME	MINUS VOLUME
A			
B			
C			
D			
E			
F			
G			
H			
	TOTALS		
WEIGHT PER CUBIC INCH GRAY CAST IRON 0.260 LB TOBIN BRONZE 0.304 LB. CAST STEEL 0.282 LB.	TOTAL NET VOLUME IN CUBIC INCHES		
	WEIGHT IN POUNDS		

FIG. 7·65—Shape breakdown for volume and weight calculations.

The complete volume and weight calculation not only gives training in recognition of the fundamental geometrical portions of an object, but serves also to teach neat and concise working methods in the recording of engineering data.

PROBLEMS

7·24 Selections from several groups of problems following are to be made for practice in projection drawing. Most of them are intended to be drawn with instruments but will give valuable training done freehand on either plain or coordinate paper.

The groups are as follows:

I. Projections from pictorial views.
II. Views to be supplied.
III. Views to be changed.
IV. Reading exercises.
V. Drawing from memory.
VI. Volume and weight calculations, with slide rule.

Group I. Projections from pictorial views *Problems 1 to 36*

1. Fig. 7·66. Draw the front, top, and right-side views of the step block.
2. Fig. 7·67. Draw the front, top, and right-side views of the notched tenon.
3. Fig. 7·68. Draw three views of the slotted wedge.
4. Fig. 7·69. Draw three views of the inclined support.
5. Fig. 7·70. Draw three views of the vee rest.
6. Fig. 7·71. Draw three views of the corner stop.

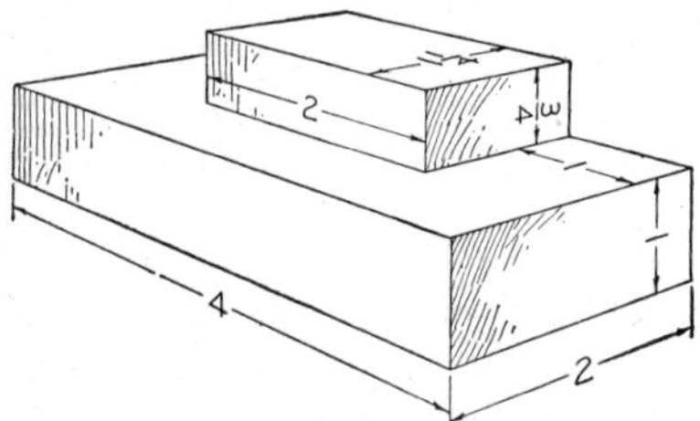

Fig. 7·66—Step block.

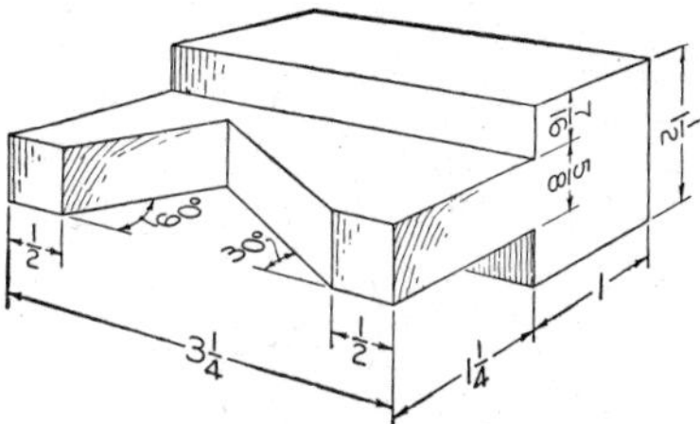

Fig. 7·67—Notched tenon.

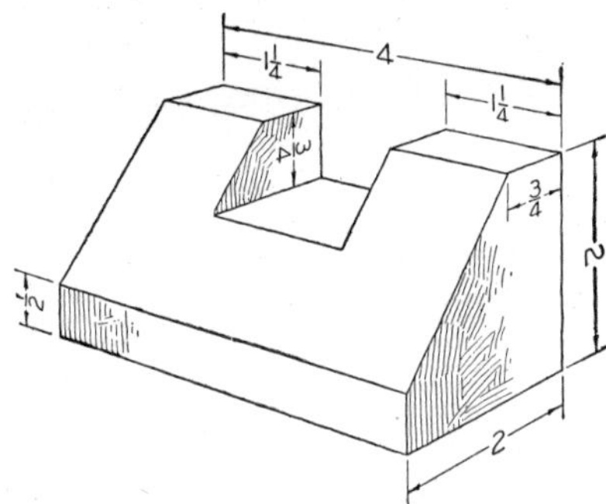

Fig. 7·68—Slotted wedge.

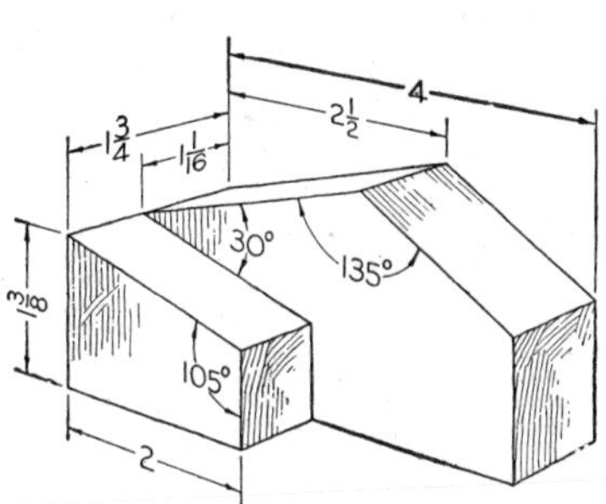

Fig. 7·69—Inclined support.

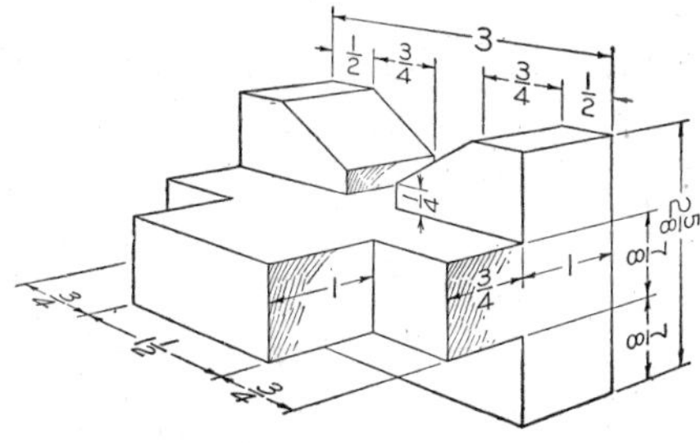

Fig. 7·70—Vee rest.

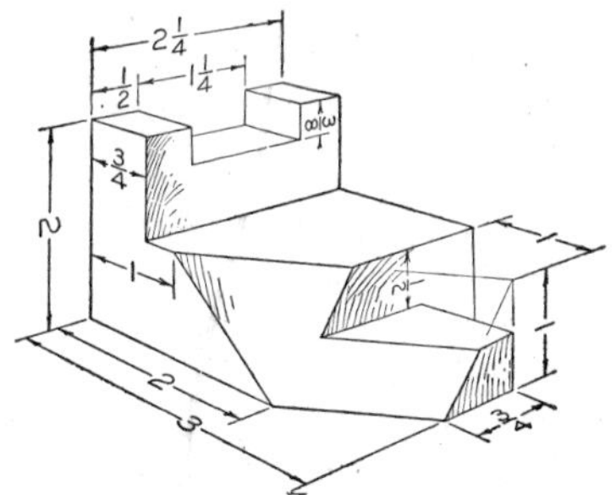

Fig. 7·71—Corner stop.

7. Fig. 7·72. Draw three views of the saddle bracket.
8. Fig. 7·73. Draw three views of the wedge block.
9. Fig. 7·74. Draw three views of the switch base.
10. Fig. 7·75. Draw three views of the adjusting bracket.
11. Fig. 7·76. Draw three views of the bearing rest.
12. Fig. 7·77. Draw three views of the guide base.

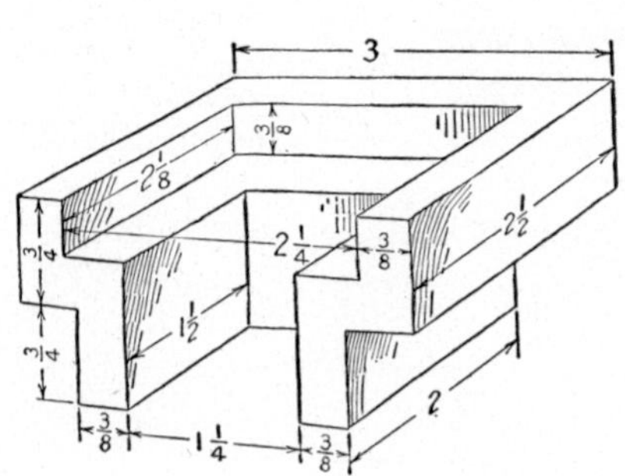

Fig. 7·72—Saddle bracket.

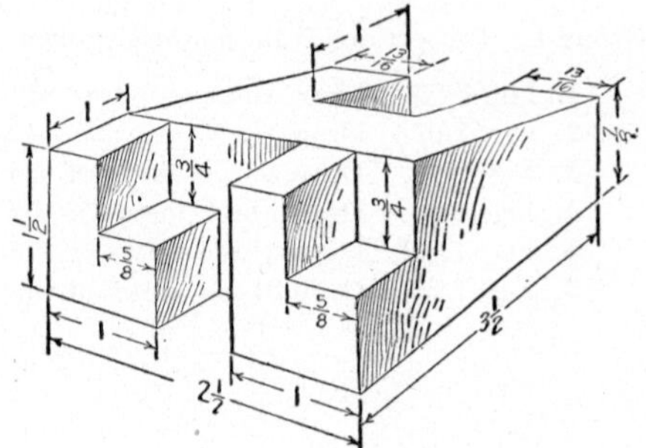

Fig. 7·73—Wedge block.

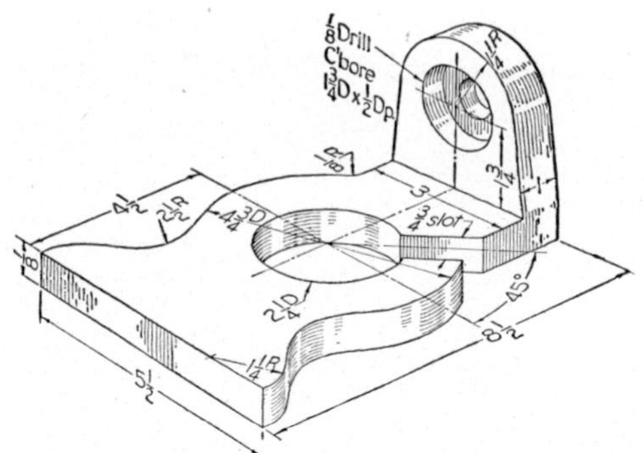

Fig. 7·74—Switch base.

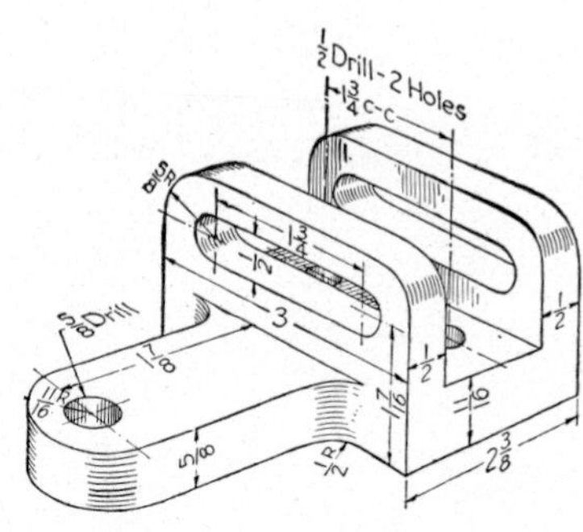

Fig. 7·75—Adjusting bracket.

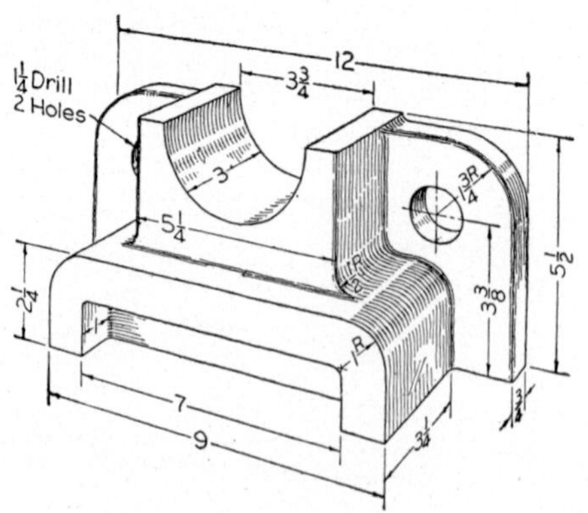

Fig. 7·76—Bearing rest.

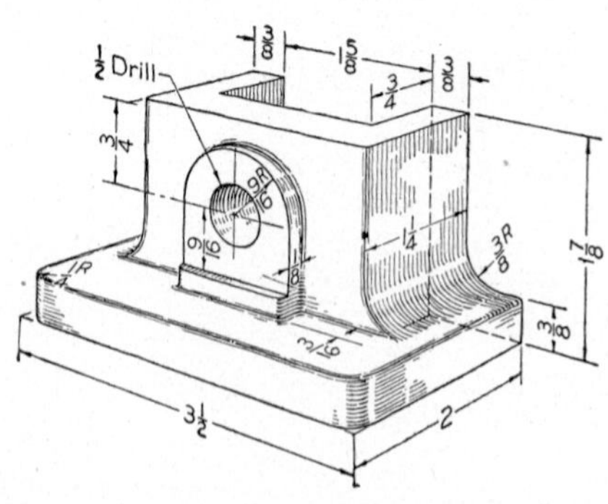

Fig. 7·77—Guide base.

13. Fig. 7·78. Draw three views of the clamp frame.
14. Fig. 7·79. Draw three views of the truss bearing.
15. Fig. 7·80. Draw two views of the eccentric.
16. Fig. 7·81. Draw two views of the elliptical cam.
17. Fig. 7·82. Draw two views of the flanged collar.
18. Fig. 7·83. Draw two views of the eccentric.

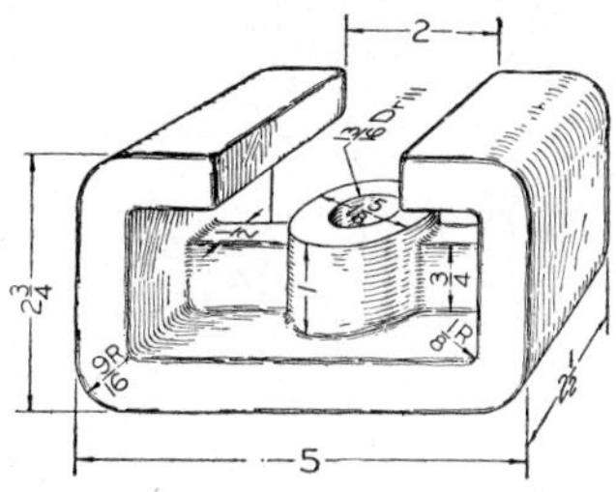
FIG. 7·78—Clamp frame.

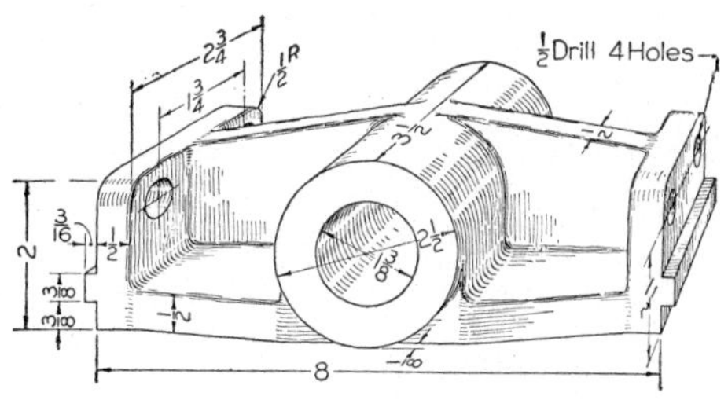

FIG. 7·79—Truss bearing.

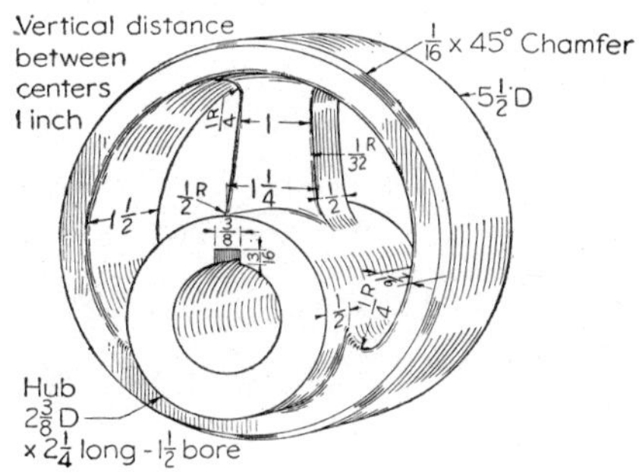

FIG. 7·80—Eccentric.

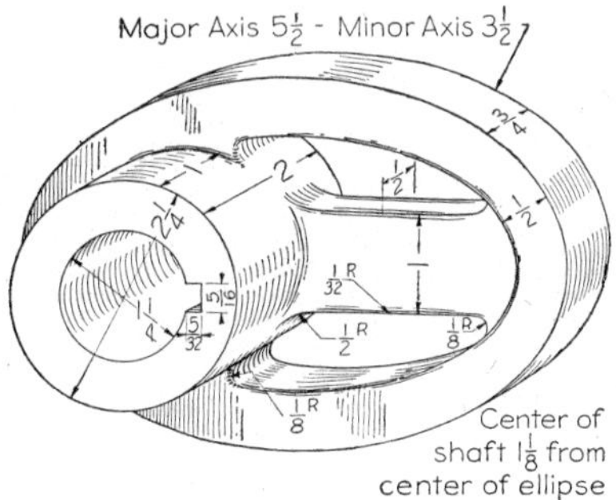

FIG. 7·81—Elliptical cam.

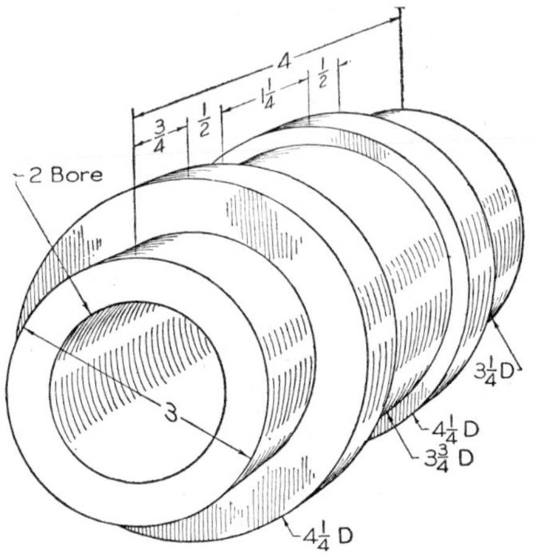

FIG. 7·82—Flanged collar.

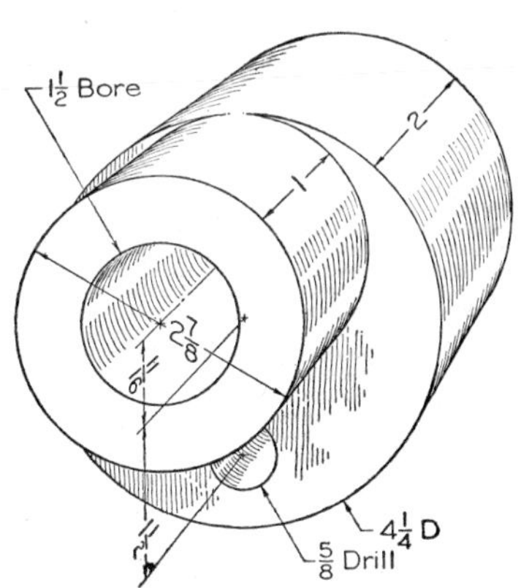

FIG. 7·83—Eccentric.

19. Fig. 7·84. Draw two views of the shifter fork.
20. Fig. 7·85. Draw three views of the mounting bracket.
21. Fig. 7·86. Draw three views of the tube hanger.
22. Fig. 7·87. Draw three views of the gage holder.
23. Fig. 7·88. Draw three views of the shaft guide.
24. Fig. 7·89. Draw three views of the clamp block.

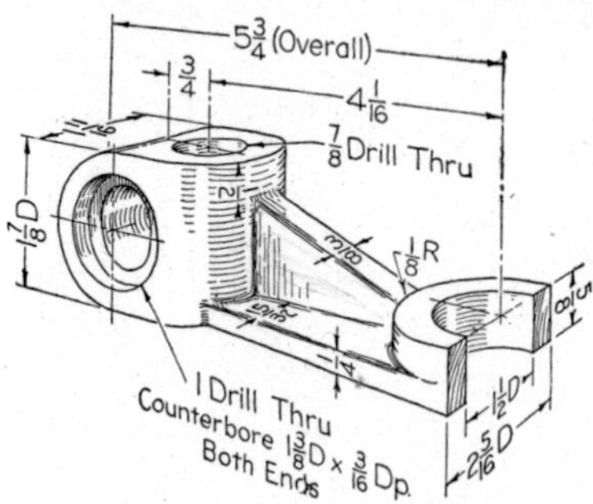

FIG. 7·84—Shifter fork.

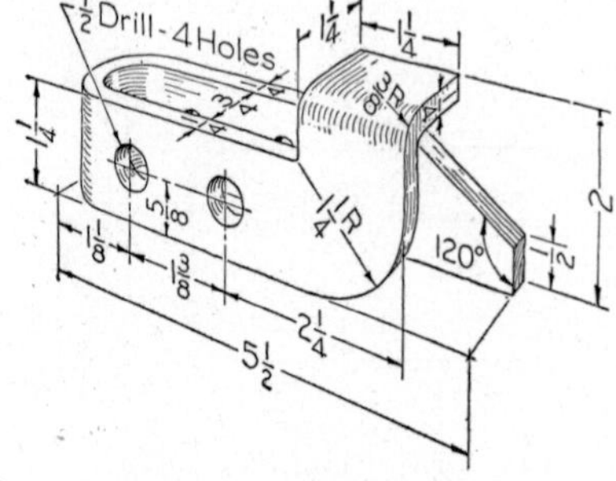

FIG. 7·85—Mounting bracket.

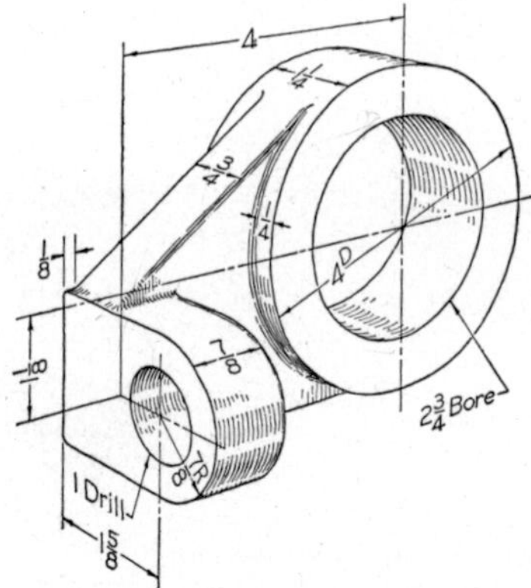

FIG. 7·86—Tube hanger.

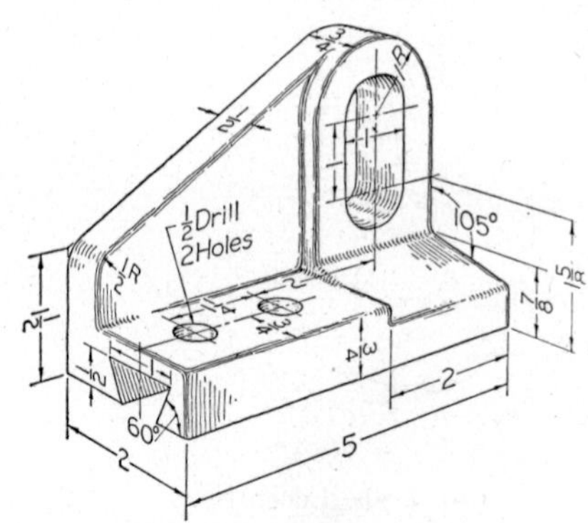

FIG. 7·87—Gage holder.

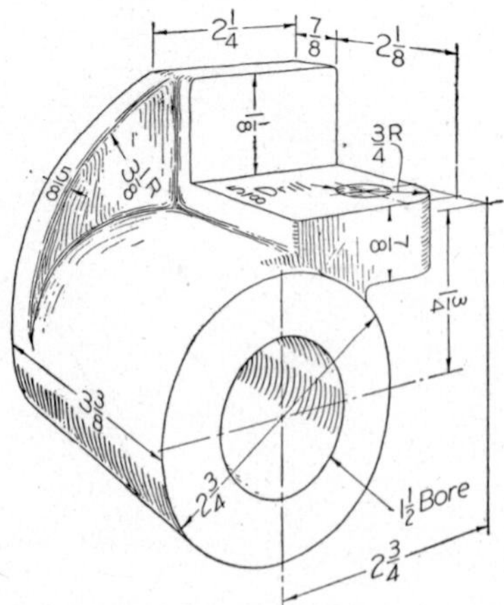

FIG. 7·88—Shaft guide.

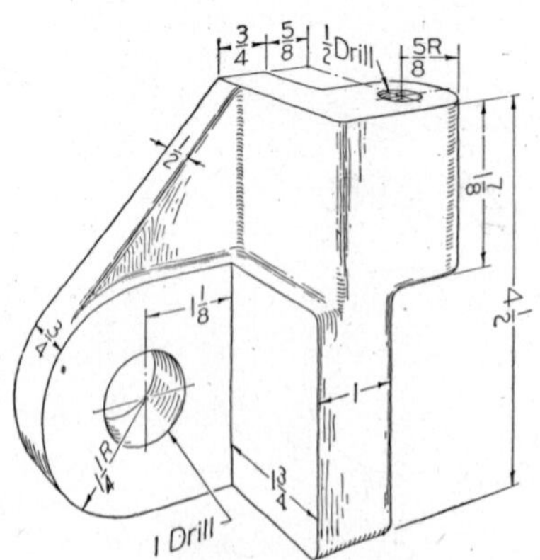

FIG. 7·89—Clamp block.

25. Fig. 7·90. Draw three views of the bedplate stop.
26. Fig. 7·91. Draw top, front, and a partial side view of the spanner bracket.
27. Fig. 7·92. Draw three views of the angle connector.
28. Fig. 7·93. Draw three views of the slotted crank (side view in alternate position).
29. Fig. 7·94. Draw three views of the angle bracket.
30. Fig. 7·95. Draw three views of the stop base.

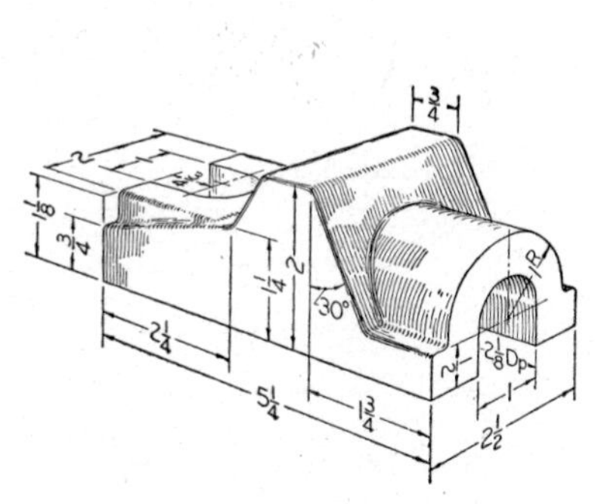

Fig. 7·90—Bedplate stop.

Fig. 7·91—Spanner bracket.

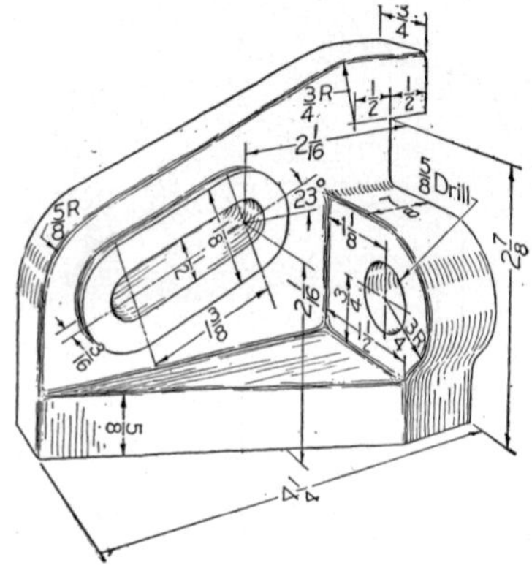

Fig. 7·92—Angle connector.

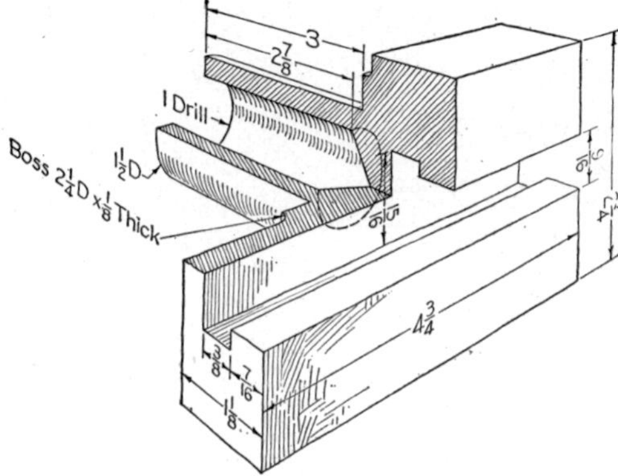

Fig. 7·93—Slotted crank.

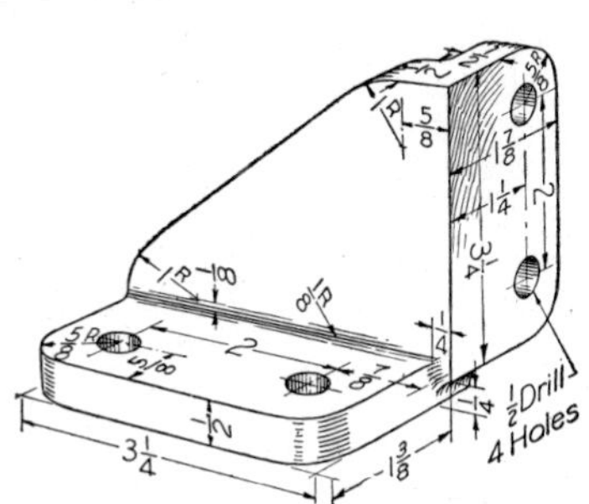

Fig. 7·94—Angle bracket.

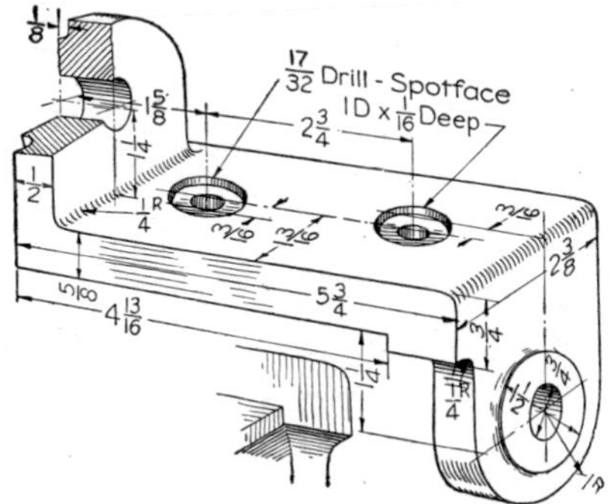

Fig. 7·95—Stop base.

31. Fig. 7·96. Draw three views of the hinged bearing.
32. Fig. 7·97. Draw two views of the clamp lever.
33. Fig. 7·98. Draw three views of the sliding hook.
34. Fig. 7·99. Draw two views of the clamp.
35. Fig. 7·100. Draw three views of the plastic switch base.
36. Fig. 7·101. Draw two views of the pawl hook.

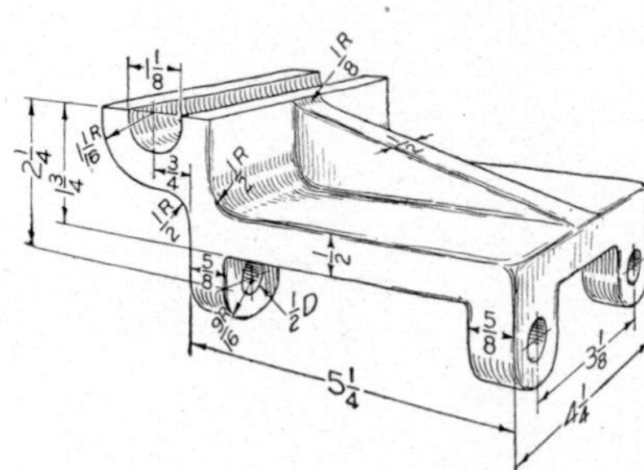

FIG. 7·96—Hinged bearing.

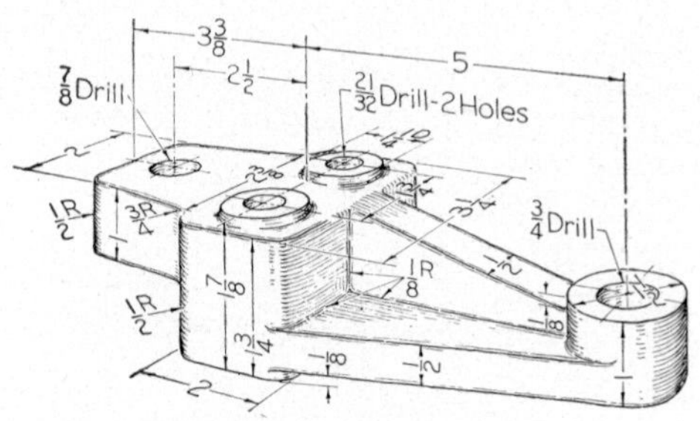

FIG. 7·97—Clamp lever.

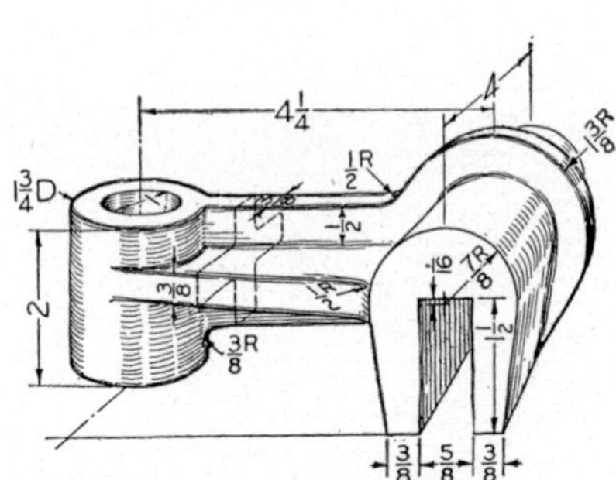

FIG. 7·98—Sliding hook.

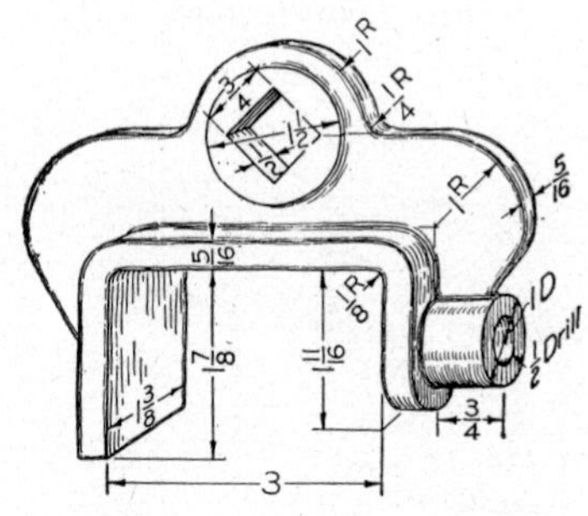

FIG. 7·99—Clamp.

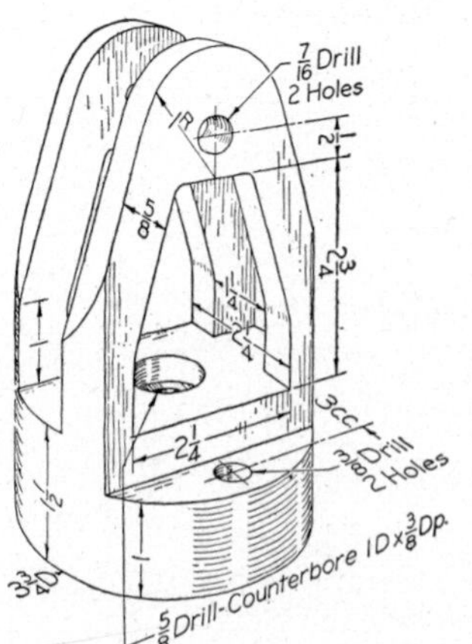

FIG. 7·100—Plastic switch base.

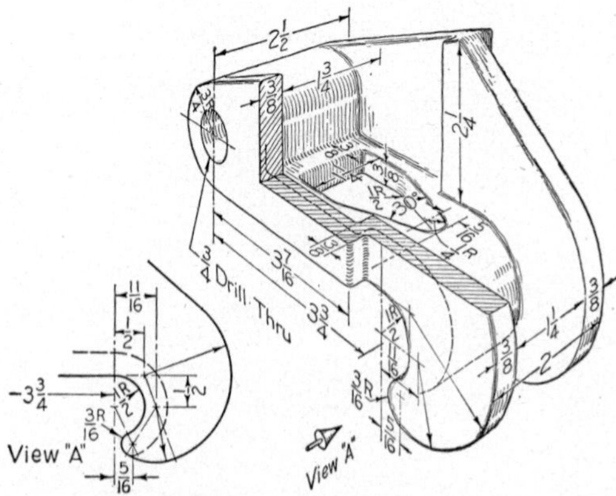

FIG. 7·101—Pawl hook.

Group II. Views to be supplied *Problems 37 to 54*

37. Fig. 7·102. Draw the views given, completing the top view from information given on the front and side views. Carry the views along together.

38. Fig. 7·103. Given top and front views of block. Required, top, front, and side views. See that dotted lines start and stop correctly.

39. Fig. 7·104. Given front and right-side views. Add top view.

40. Fig. 7·105. Given front and right-side views. Add top view.

41. Fig. 7·106. Given front and top views. Add side view.

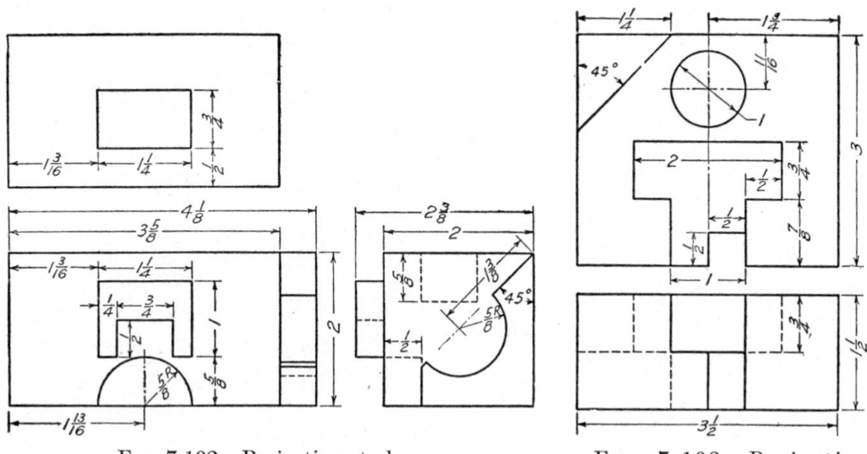

FIG. 7·102—Projection study.

FIG. 7·103—Projection study.

FIG. 7·104—Projection study.

FIG. 7·105—Bit-point-forming die.

FIG. 7·106—Projection study.

42. Fig. 7·107. Given top and front views. Add right-side view.
43. Fig. 7·108. Complete the three views given.
44. Fig. 7·109. Given front and side views. Add top view.
45. Fig. 7·110. Given front and side views. Add top view.
46. Fig. 7·111. Given front and top views. Add side view.
47. Fig. 7·111. Assume this part to be right-hand. Draw three views of left-hand part.

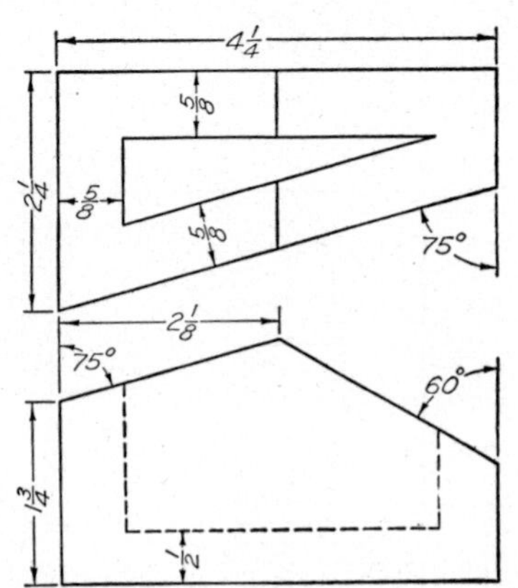

Fig. 7·107—Wedge block.

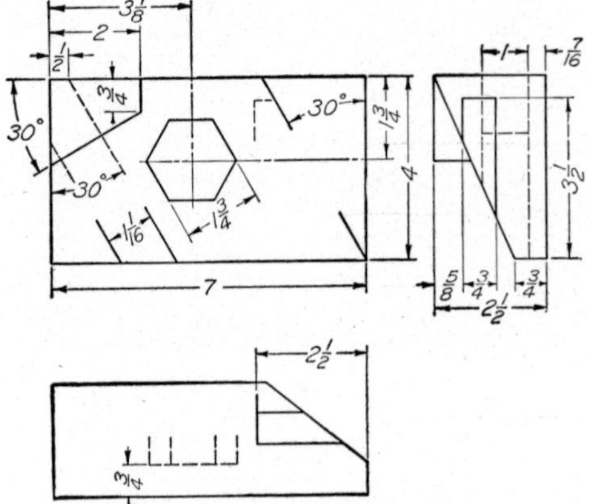

Fig. 7·108—Projection study.

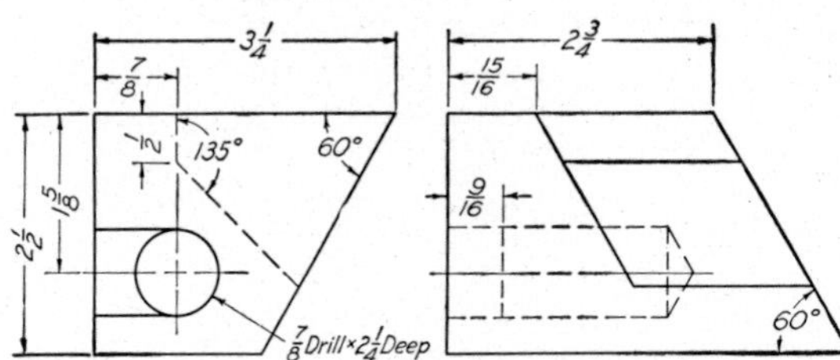

Fig. 7·109—Burner-support key.

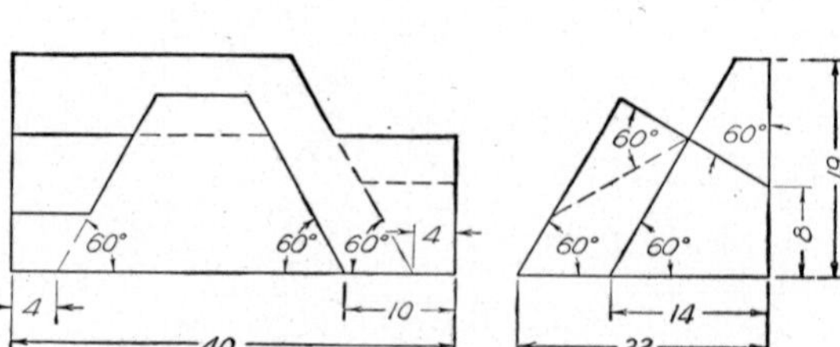

Fig. 7·110—Abutment block.

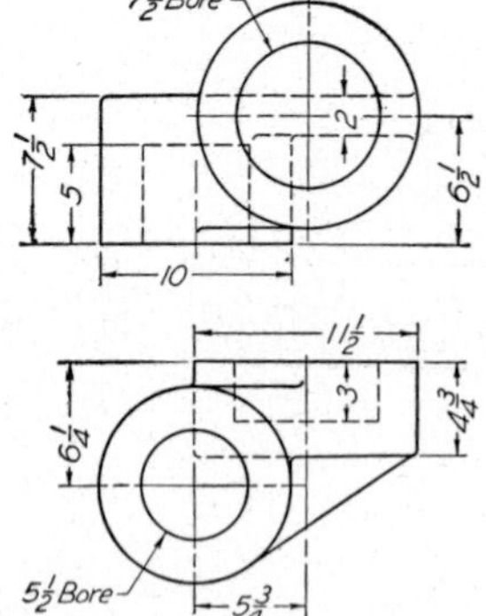

Fig. 7·111—Bumper support and post cap.

48. Fig. 7·112. Given front and top views. Add side view.
49. Fig. 7·113. Given front and top views. Add side view.
50. Fig. 7·114. Given front and top views. Add side view.
51. Fig. 7·115. Given front and side views. Add top view.

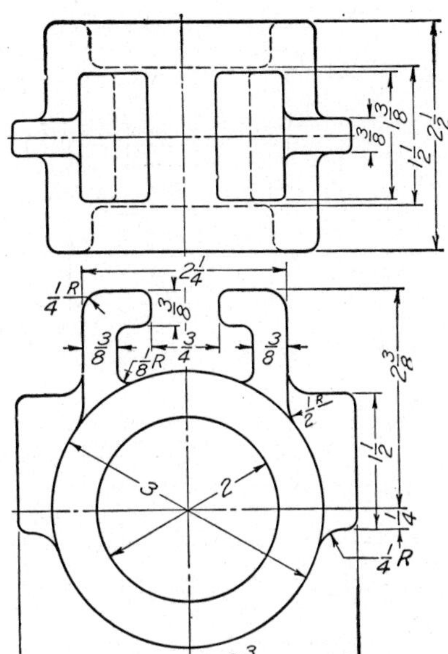

FIG. 7·112—Forging blank.

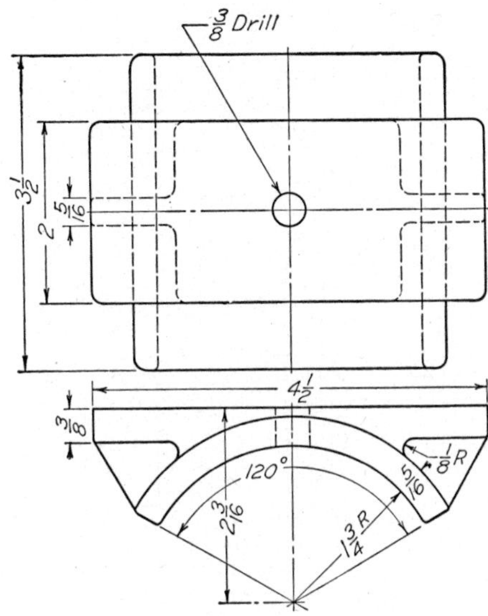

FIG. 7·113—Spring saddle.

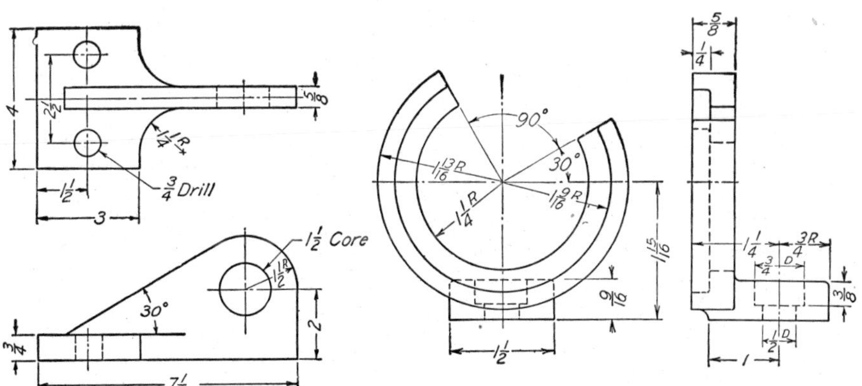

FIG. 7·114—Anchor bracket.

FIG. 7·115—Saddle collar.

52. Fig. 7·116. Given front and side views. Turn to a better position and draw three views.

53. Fig. 7·117. Given front and top views. Add both side views.

54. Fig. 7·118. Given front and top views. Add side view.

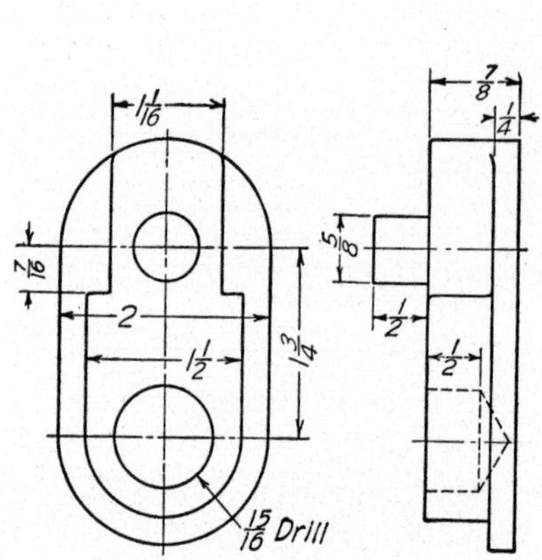

FIG. 7·116—Lock plate.

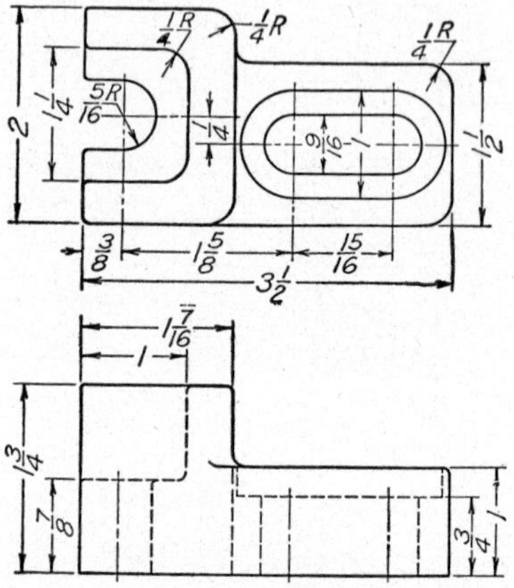

FIG. 7·117—Toolholder.

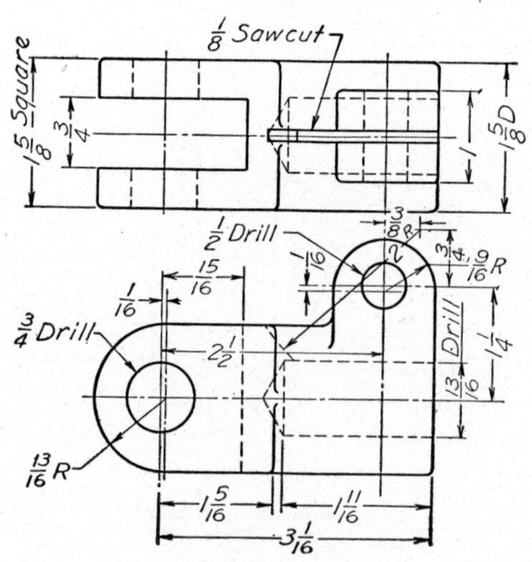

FIG. 7·118—Rod yoke.

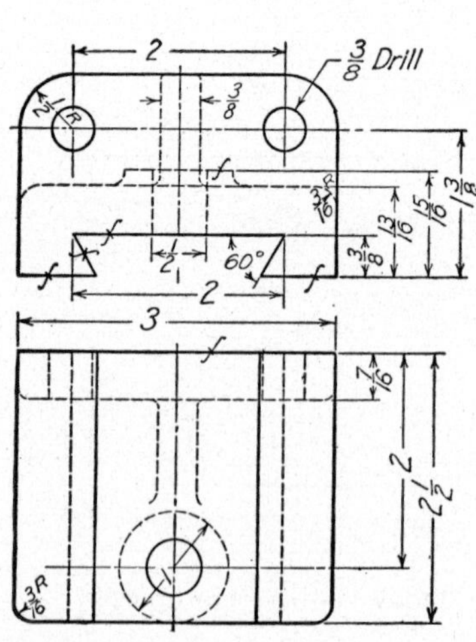

FIG. 7·119—Sliding block.

Group III. Views to be changed

Problems 55 to 62

This group furnishes a more difficult test of the reader's constructive imagination. These problems are given to develop the ability to visualize the actual piece in space and, from this mental picture, to draw the required views as they would appear if the object were looked at in the directions specified. Students will find it of much assistance to make a pictorial sketch, or perhaps a clay model, of the piece before starting the drawing.

55. Fig. 7·119. Given front and top views. Required new front, top, and side views, turning the block so that the back becomes the front and the top becomes the bottom. The rib contour is straight.

56. Fig. 7·120. Given front, left-side, and bottom views. Draw front, top, and right side.

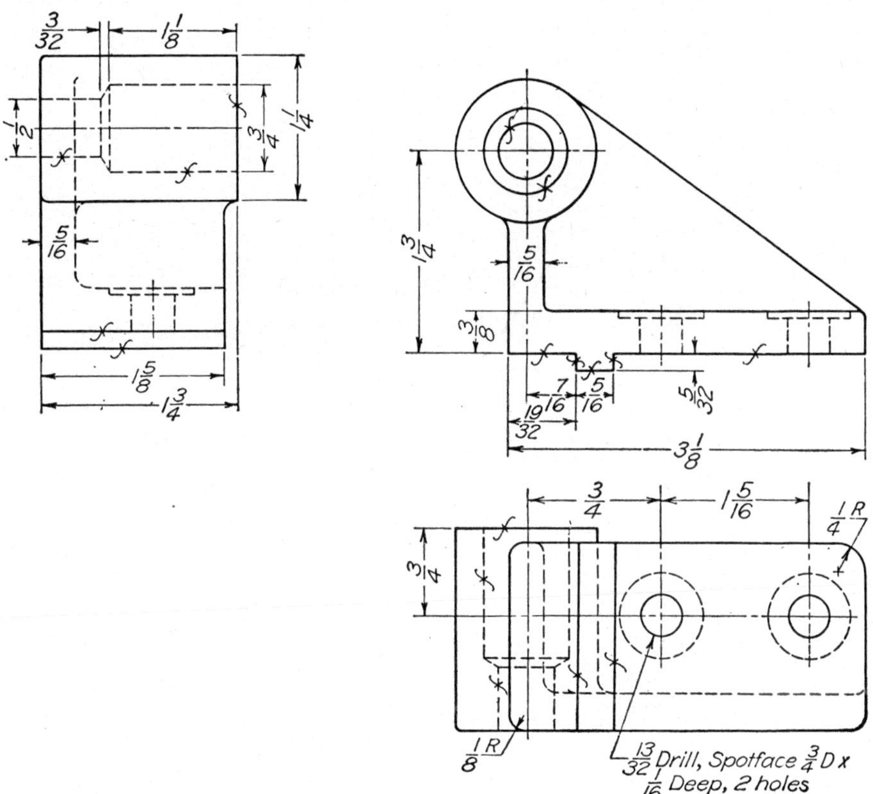

FIG. 7·120—Plunger bracket.

57. Fig. 7·121. Given front, right-side, and bottom views. Draw front, top, and left side.

58. Fig. 7·122. Given front, right-side, and bottom views. Draw new front, top, and right-side views, turning the support around so that the back becomes the front.

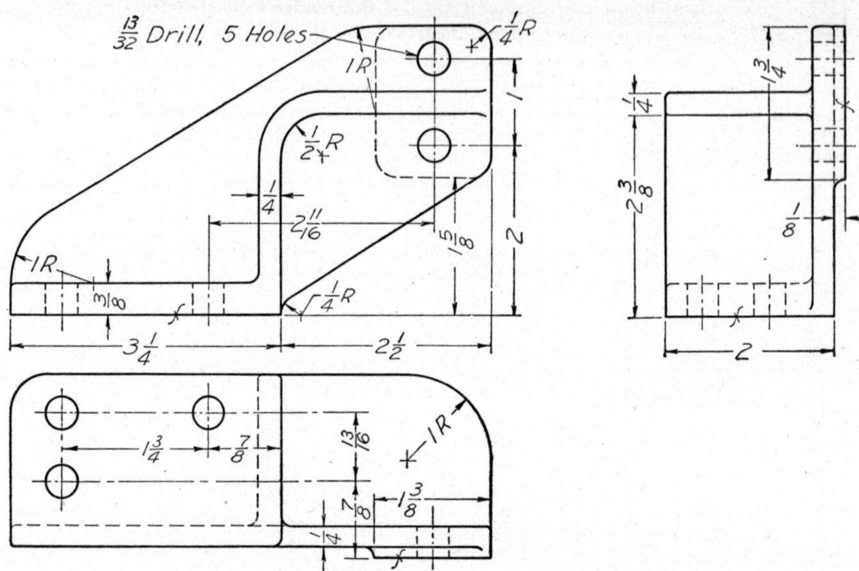

FIG. 7·121—Offset bracket.

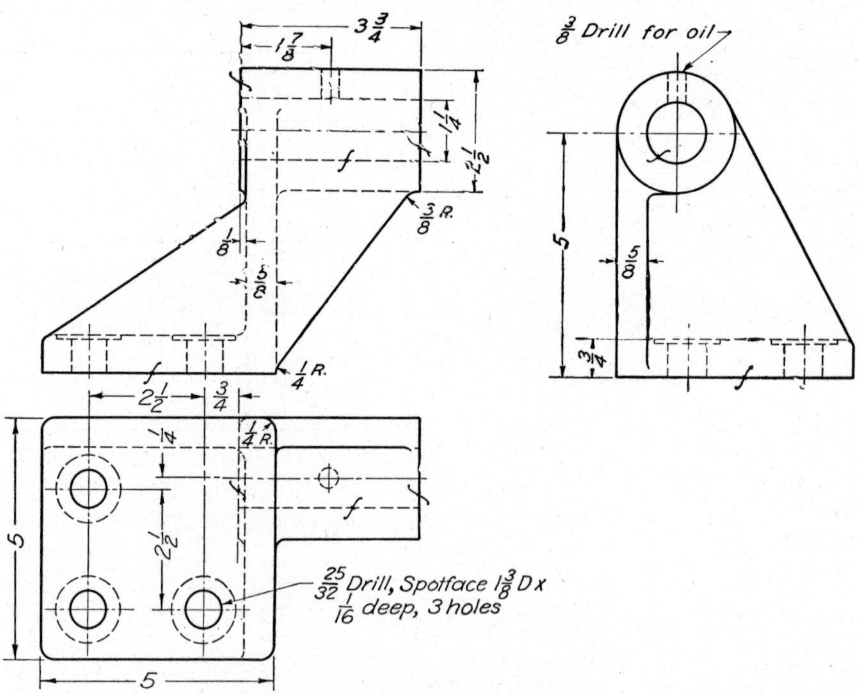

FIG. 7·122—Toggle-shaft support.

59. Fig. 7·123. Given front and left-side views. Draw front, top, and right-side.

60. Fig. 7·124. Given top, front, and right-side views. Change the position of the object so that the object is resting on its square base, with the two $1\frac{7}{32}''$ holes toward the front, and draw three views.

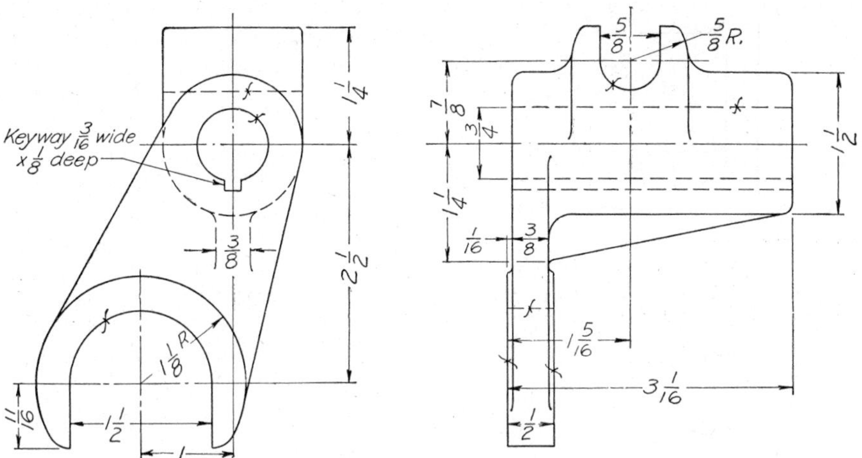

FIG. 7·123—Shifter fork.

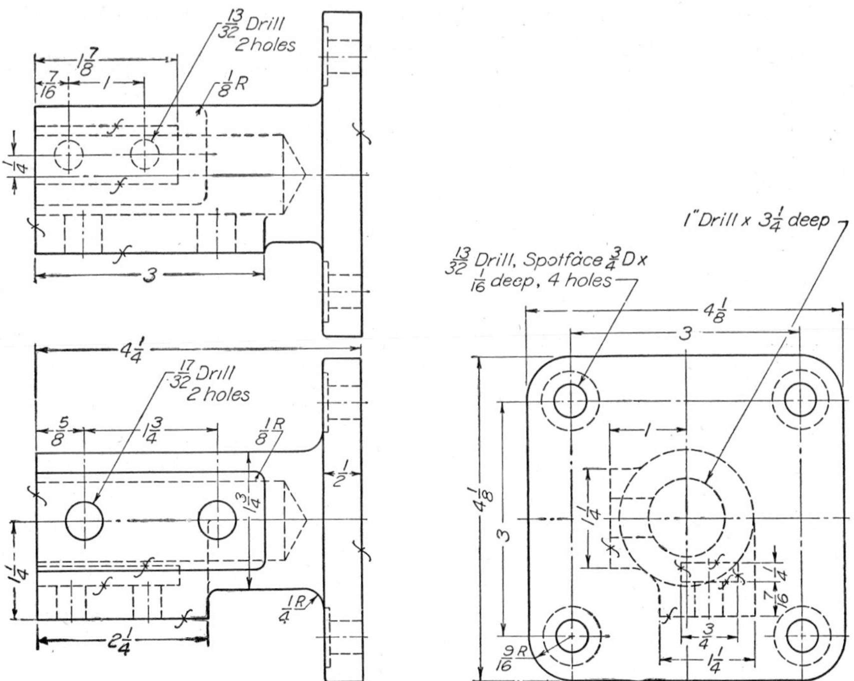

FIG. 7·124—Tool base.

61. Fig. 7·125. Given front and left-side views, with a detail of pad. Draw front, top, and right-side views.

62. Fig. 7·126. Given front, left-side, and bottom views. Draw front, top, and right-side views.

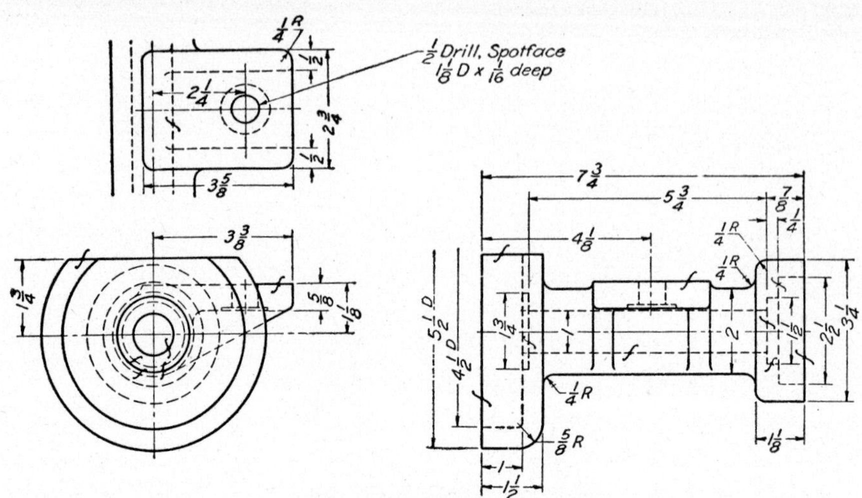

FIG. 7·125—Indicator bracket.

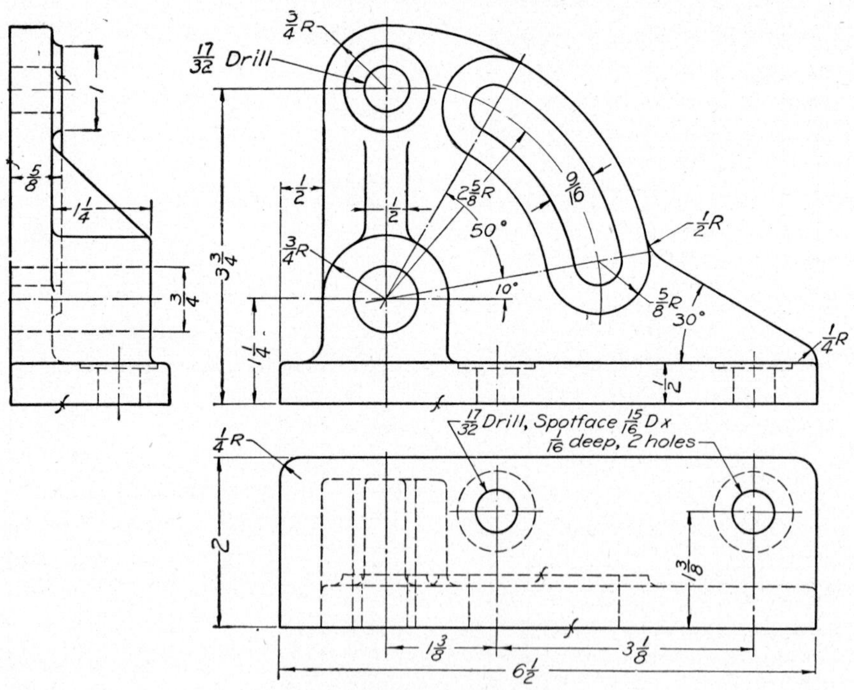

FIG. 7·126—Sector bracket.

Group IV. Reading exercises

Read any of the objects of Figs. 7·62, 7·63, 21·87, 21·88, and 21·89. Make freehand pictorial drawings or models as proof that the drawings have been read and understood.

Group V. Drawing from memory

One of the valuable assets of an engineer is a trained memory for form and proportion. The graphic memory may be developed to a surprising degree in accuracy and power by systematic exercises in drawing from memory. This training may be commenced as soon as a knowledge of orthographic projection has been acquired.

Select an object not previously used, such as one from Figs. 7·36 to 7·50, inclusive, or Figs. 7·66 to 7·101, inclusive; look at it with concentration for a certain time (from 5 seconds to ½ minute or more); close the book and make an accurate orthographic sketch. Check with the original, and correct any mistakes or omissions. Follow with several different figures. The next day allow a 2-second view of one of the objects and repeat the orthographic views of the previous day. As indicated in Chap. 19, paragraph 19·6, this practice may be varied in several ways after one has become proficient in sketching. If continued faithfully, it will strengthen wonderfully the power of observation.

Group VI. Volume and weight calculations, with slide rule

In calculating the weight of a piece from the drawings, the object should be divided or broken up into the geometric solids (prisms, cylinders, pyramids, cones) of which it is composed. The volume of each of these shapes should be calculated and these added, or sometimes subtracted, to find the total volume which, multiplied by the weight of the material per unit of volume, will give the weight of the object.

A table of weights of materials will be found in the Appendix.

63. Find the weight of the cast-iron jig block, Fig. 21·34.
64. Find the weight of the bearing brass, Fig. 21·36.
65. Find the weight of the wrought-iron guide block, Fig. 21·37.
66. Find the weight of the cast-steel dovetail stop, Fig. 21·38.
67. Find the weight of the malleable-iron bracket, Fig. 21·39.
68. Find the weight of the bronze swivel block, Fig. 21·40.
69. Find the weight of the aluminum hinged catch, Fig. 21·41.
70. Find the weight of the cast-aluminum base plate, Fig. 21·58.

TEXT-FILMS

The following McGraw-Hill Text-Film has been produced for specific correlation with Chaps. 6 and 7:

Orthographic Projection (20-min. sound motion picture).

Demonstrates the theory of orthographic projection; shows how objects, planes, and lines appear from different points of view; gives the methods of projection for separate views; explains concepts of height, width, and depth and their relationship in the projected views; demonstrates the making and reading of a drawing.

This film is accompanied by a coordinated silent filmstrip that reviews and further clarifies the principles of orthographic projection and may be used for oral discussion and examination.

Chapter 8

AUXILIARY VIEWS

8·1 A surface is shown in its true shape when projected on a plane parallel to that surface. As the majority of objects are rectangular, they may be placed with their three principal faces parallel to the three planes of projection and be fully described by the principal views. Sometimes, however, the object will have one or more inclined faces whose true shape

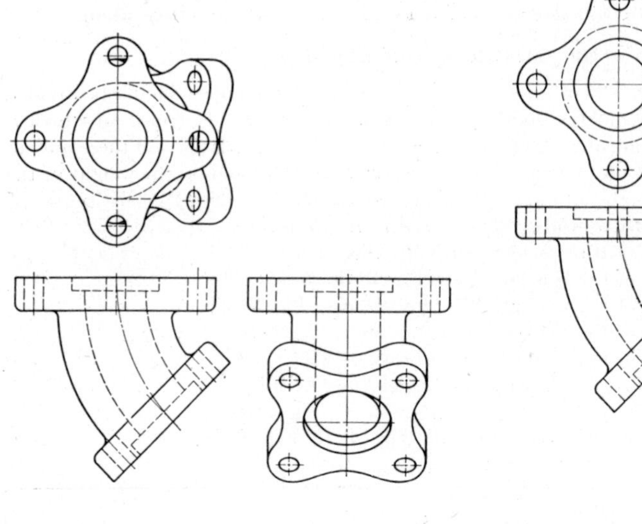

FIG. 8·1—Front, top, and right-side views.

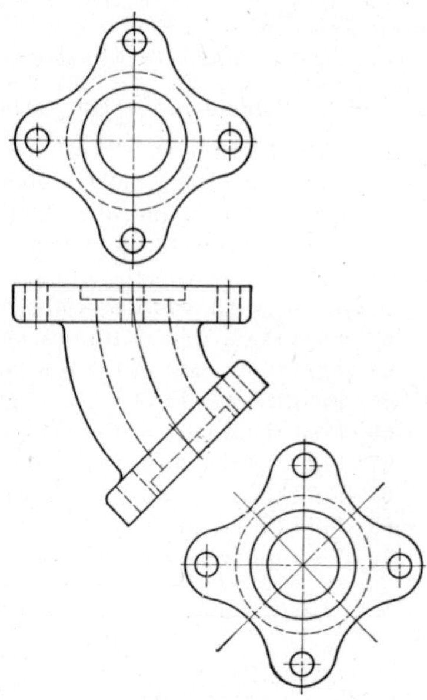

FIG. 8·2—Front, partial top, and auxiliary views.

it is desirable or necessary to show, especially if irregular in outline. An example is the flanged angle in Fig. 8·1, a casting having an irregular inclined face which not only cannot be shown in true shape in either of the principal views, but also is difficult to draw in foreshortened position. An easier and more practical selection of views for this piece is shown in Fig. 8·2, using what is known as an auxiliary view looking in a direction perpendicular to the inclined face, that is, imagining a projection on an extra or auxiliary plane parallel to the face and revolving it into the plane of the paper.

8·2 Definition: *An auxiliary view is an orthographic projection on a plane not one of the principal planes,* specifically:

1. *Single auxiliaries,* a projection on a plane perpendicular to one of the principal planes and inclined to the other two.

2. *Double auxiliaries,* a projection on a plane inclined to all three principal planes, requiring two auxiliary views; a *first auxiliary* giving the edge view of the inclined plane, and a *second auxiliary* projected from the first, giving the normal (true shape) view of the plane.

8·3 Single auxiliaries. Since the reason for using an auxiliary view is to obtain the true shape of a slanting surface, in practical drafting an auxiliary plane is always placed parallel to the slanting surface. The edge view of this plane, therefore, will be parallel to the edge view of the slanting surface, and the auxiliary plane would show as an edge view on the plane to which it is perpendicular. The auxiliary plane is revolved into the plane of the paper by considering it to be hinged to the plane to which it is perpendicular.

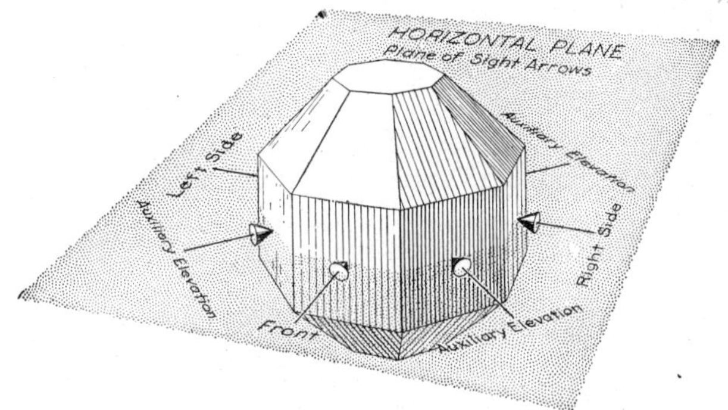

FIG. 8·3—Directions from which auxiliary elevations are taken.

In projecting an object on an auxiliary plane, the inclined surface will be shown in its true shape but the other faces of the object will evidently be foreshortened. In practical work these foreshortened parts are usually omitted, as in Fig. 8·2. Views thus drawn are called *partial views.* The exercise of drawing a complete view, however, may aid the student in understanding the subject.

There are three kinds of single-auxiliary views: *auxiliary elevations,* projected from the top view; *right and left auxiliaries,* projected from the front view; and *front and rear auxiliaries,* projected from either one of the side views.

8·4 Auxiliary elevations. Auxiliary elevations are the views that would be seen if one walked around the object, starting at the position from which the front view is taken and following a circle with all sight arrows in a horizontal plane as shown in Fig. 8·3. In this trip the observer would successively pass the points from which the right-side view, the rear view, the left-side view, and finally the front view again would be seen. A view from any other point in this plane, as indicated, would be an auxiliary elevation. An auxiliary elevation may thus be taken from the right-front, right-rear, left-rear, or left-front directions. On any drawing, the front view, or front elevation, shows the *height* of the object. For an auxiliary elevation the observer looks in a horizontal direction; hence the height of any point on the auxiliary elevation will be the same as in the front view. Thus all height measurements will be made from some fixed horizontal reference plane called a "datum plane."

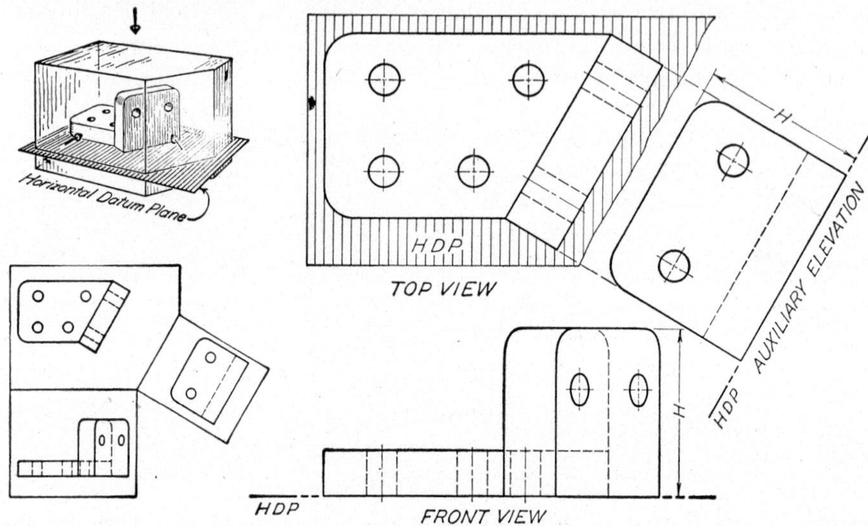

FIG. 8·4—Auxiliary elevation.

In Fig. 8·4 the right end of the piece is at an angle to the front and side planes and perpendicular to the horizontal plane; thus its edge would show in the top view, but its true shape would not appear in either the front or side views. An auxiliary elevation taken as if looking directly at the surface would show the true shape. Assume the horizontal plane of the base of the object to be the datum plane *HDP*; draw the edge of the datum plane for the auxiliary view parallel to the top view of the edge of the inclined surface, project the points of the inclined surface from the top view perpendicular to the datum plane, and transfer the necessary heights from the front view. The auxiliary view of the base is not completed, as it is fully described by the front and top views.

8·5 Right and left auxiliary views. The right and left auxiliary views are made on planes perpendicular to the frontal plane but inclined to the horizontal plane; thus they are the views that might be imagined if one were to travel around the object in a vertical circle with all sight arrows parallel to the frontal plane. Starting at the point from which the right-side view would be seen, move up counterclockwise until directly above the object, from which point the top would be seen, Fig. 8·5. A view taken anywhere between the two stops would be a right auxiliary view. Continuing, any view from the circle between the top and left-side views would be a left-auxiliary view. Similarly, right and left auxiliaries can be imagined from the lower half of the frontal circle, as indicated on the figure. The depth from front to back of all these auxiliary views is exactly the same as that of the top and side views. Thus all depth measurements on right and left auxiliary views would be made from a frontal datum plane *FDP*. Figure 8·6 gives the top and front views of a bent plate and the use of both right and left auxiliary part views to show the shape and drilling of the ends. The auxiliary views are projected from the front view and their depths taken from the top view, measuring, in this case, on each side of a frontal datum plane through the center of the top view.

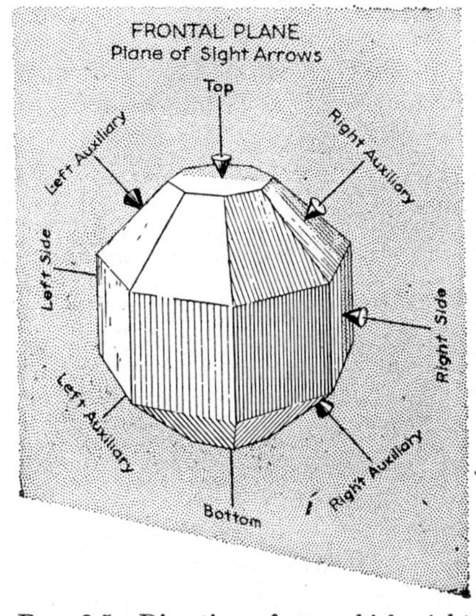

FIG. 8·5—Directions from which right and left auxiliaries are taken.

8·6 Front and rear auxiliary views. Front and rear auxiliary views are made on planes perpendicular to the side, or profile, plane. For such views, the location of the sighting points is in the profile plane that passes

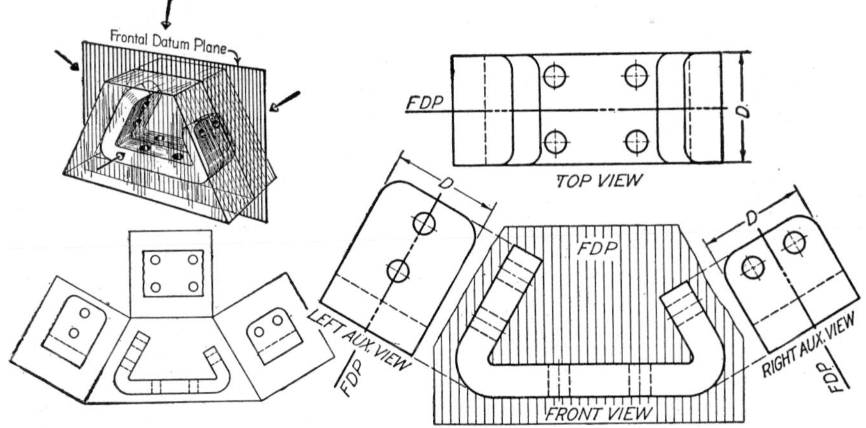

FIG. 8·6—Right and left auxiliaries.

through the sight arrows for the front, top, rear, and bottom views, as illustrated in Fig. 8·7. Figure 8·8 shows the use of a partial front auxiliary view projected from the side view, together with a top view and partial front view to describe the piece illustrated. The datum plane *PDP* will be a profile plane whose edge shows on the front and top views and, since the piece is symmetrical, it is taken through the center. Thus measurements are taken from the front view and transferred to each side of the datum plane on the auxiliary view.

8·7 Use of auxiliary views. An auxiliary view not only shows the shape of an inclined part to better advantage, but often saves making one or more of the principal views. A second and very important use of an auxiliary view is in the case where a principal view will have some part in a foreshortened position, which cannot be drawn without first constructing an auxiliary view in its true shape, from which the part can be projected back to the principal view. Figure 8·9 is an illustration of this application. In practical work, extensive use is made of auxiliary views. They are generally only partial views showing that part of the object which is parallel to the auxiliary plane, as in Figs. 8·4, 8·6, and 8·8, where nothing would be gained by projecting the whole piece. As a further example, a casting as pictured in Fig. 8·10 would be drawn as shown, making both the auxiliary views and top view as partial views. Figure 8·11 is an example of a dimensioned drawing with a right auxiliary view, making a top view and some hidden lines in the left-side view unnecessary. An auxiliary view may be placed at any convenient distance from the view from which it is projected.

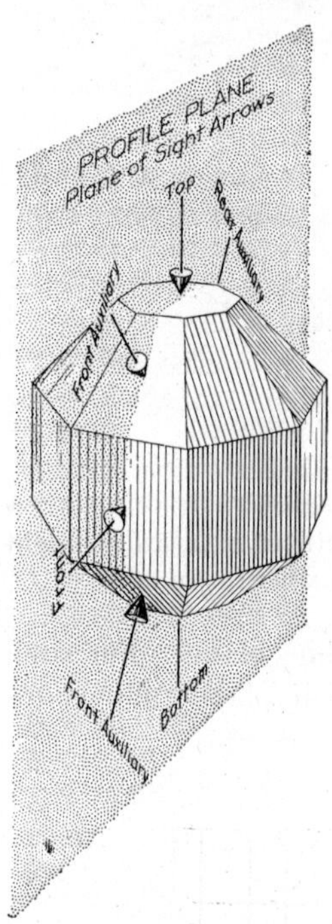

Fig. 8·7—Directions from which front and rear auxiliaries are taken.

8·8 To draw an auxiliary elevation. The key to drawing an auxiliary view easily and quickly is to locate and draw the edge view of the datum plane on the principal view, then locate and draw it for the auxiliary view. For an auxiliary elevation, *first* draw the edge of the horizontal datum plane from which to measure heights on the front view. This may be taken anywhere, above or below or through the view. For an object having a base, the bottom-plane face of the base is often taken as the datum plane, as *HDP* in Fig. 8·4. If the front view is symmetrical about a horizontal central line, as in Fig. 8·12, the datum plane is taken through the center. *Second*, draw the edge view of the datum plane for the auxiliary view parallel to, and at a convenient distance from, the top view of the face to be shown, Fig. 8·12*B*. *Third*, project points of the object from the top view perpendicular to the datum plane of the auxiliary view, as at *C*; measure their distances, H and H_1, from the datum plane on the front view, as at *D*, and transfer these measurements with dividers or scale to the auxiliary view, measuring from the auxiliary datum plane. Complete the drawing as illustrated at *E* and *F*.

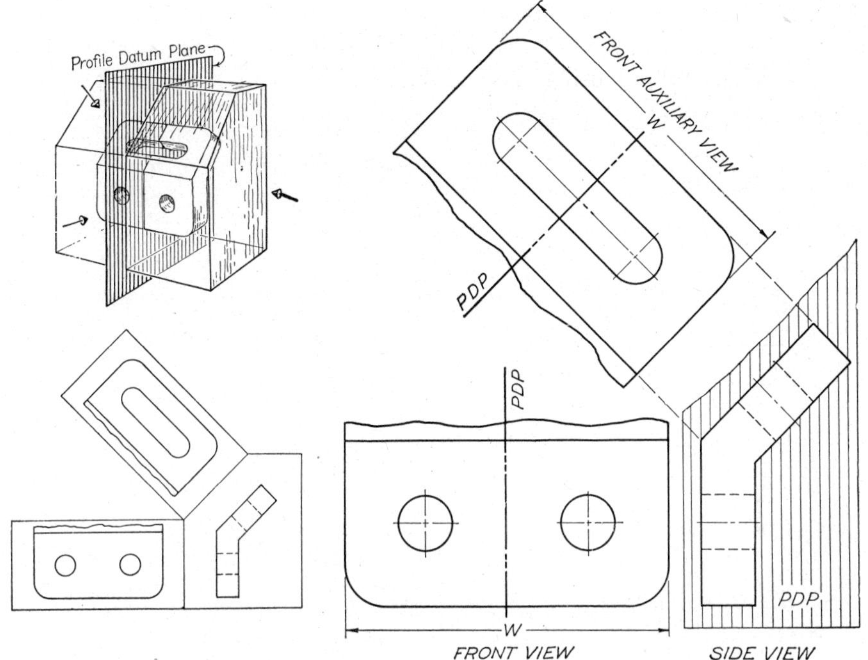

FIG. 8·8—Front auxiliary view.

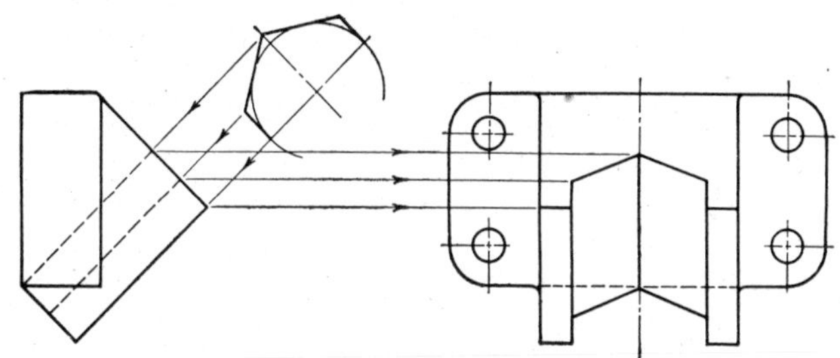

FIG. 8·9—Use of constructional auxiliary for completing front view.

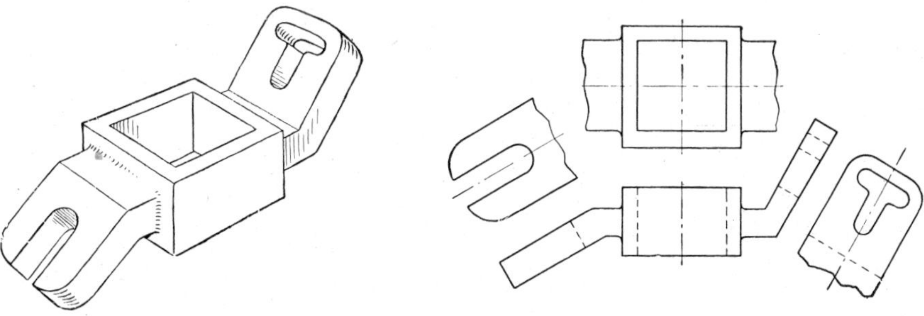

FIG. 8·10—Use of part views.

Note that any measurement made *toward* the top view is transferred *toward* the top view. Note also in Fig. 8·12 that the front view could not be completed without using the auxiliary view. To get the front view of

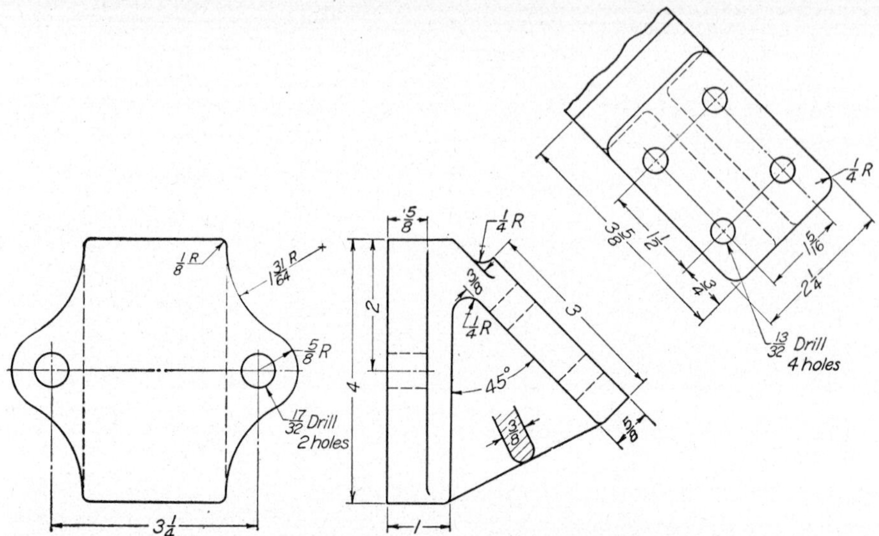

FIG. 8·11—Working drawing with auxiliary view (strut base).

the circle arcs, whose true shape shows on the auxiliary view, points are selected on the auxiliary view, projected back to the top view and thence down to the front view. On these projectors, the heights H_2 and H_3 are

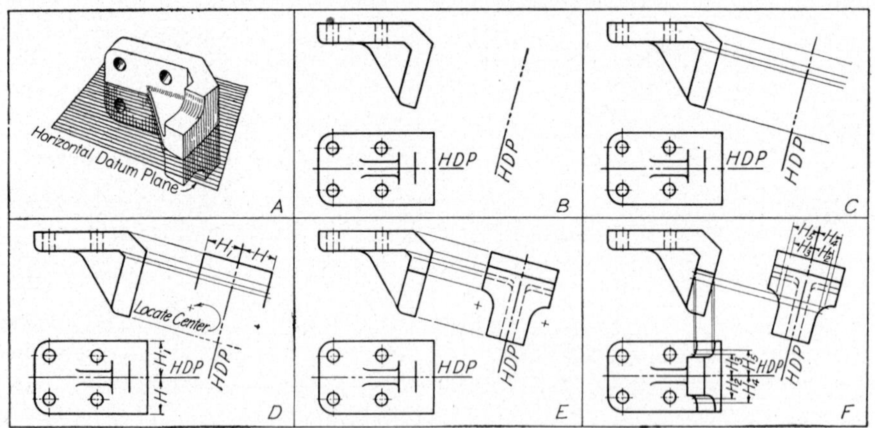

FIG. 8·12—Stages in drawing an auxiliary elevation.

transferred from the auxiliary view to find the corresponding points in the front view. H_4, H_5, and others complete the curve.

8·9 To draw a right auxiliary view. The datum plane for a right or left auxiliary view will be a frontal plane whose edge *FDP* shows in the top view. If the top view is symmetrical, it will be most convenient to pass the datum plane through the center of the piece. If the object is not symmetrical, the datum plane may be located on the back face of the object and the view carried on as illustrated progressively in Fig. 8·13. Draw the datum plane *FDP* for the auxiliary view parallel to the slanting face of the front view, Fig. 8·13*B*. Project each point of this face by drawing projecting lines from the front view perpendicular to the datum plane, as at *C*. The depth of the auxiliary view will be the same as the depth of the top view.

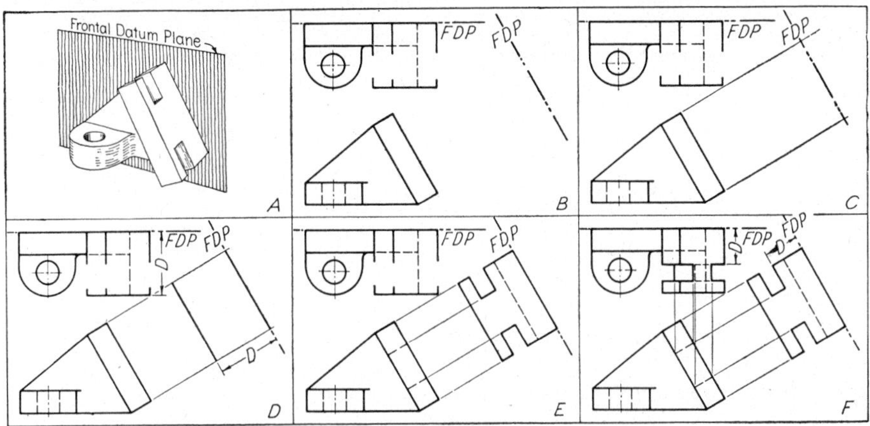

FIG. 8·13—Stages in drawing a right auxiliary.

Thus, for each point, measure its depth from the datum plane on the top view and lay off this distance from the datum plane on the auxiliary view, as at *D*. Notice that the points are in front of the datum plane on the top view and therefore are measured toward the front on the auxiliary view. Complete the auxiliary view as at *E*. Note again that the top view of the notch was not finished until after the auxiliary view was made, as shown at *F*. Obviously a *left auxiliary view* would require the same steps reversed left for right.

8·10 To draw a front or rear auxiliary view. As a front or rear auxiliary view is always projected from the side view, there must be a side view as well as a front view from which to work in drawing this type. There may, of course, be a top view also. The datum plane will be a profile plane whose edge will show on the front view (and also on the top view). If the front view is symmetrical about a vertical center line, draw the datum plane *PDP* through the center, otherwise at the right or left, as in Fig. 8·14*A*. Locate the datum plane for the auxiliary view parallel to the slanting face in the side view, project the points from the side view perpendicular to the datum plane, and transfer to the auxiliary view the width measurements of each point from the datum plane on the front view, noting that measurements made toward the side view are transferred toward the side view. Study the progressive steps in Fig. 8·14.

8·11 Double auxiliary or oblique views. To find the true shape of an oblique surface, that is, a surface not perpendicular to any one of the principal planes, Fig. 8·15, two operations are required: *first*, an auxiliary view of the object from such a position that the oblique surface is seen as an

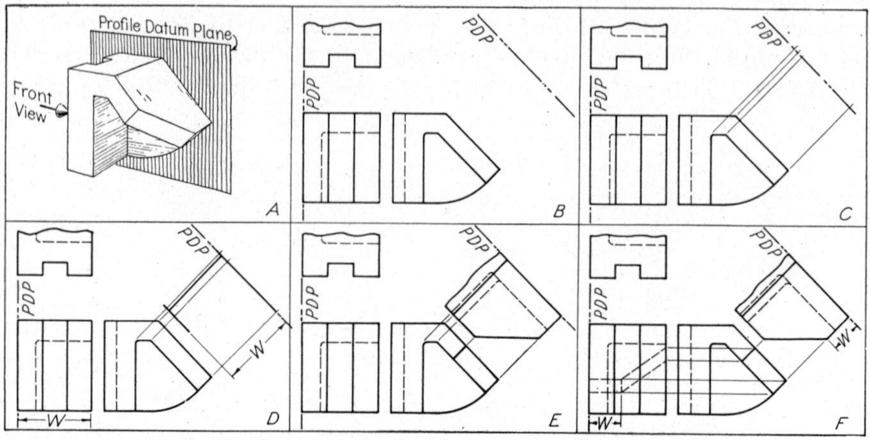

FIG. 8·14—Stages in drawing a rear auxiliary.

edge; *second*, an auxiliary view from the first auxiliary showing the true shape. To get this first (edge) view of the surface, the auxiliary view must be taken on a plane *perpendicular* to the surface and, at the same time, perpendicular to one of the principal planes.

If, in Fig. 8·16, the oblique surface of the skew guide is looked at in the direction of arrow 1, or, in other words, is projected on the vertical plane DP_B perpendicular to it, the surface would be seen as an edge, and the view when revolved up into the plane of the paper will be as at *B*. If, from this position, the oblique surface is looked at in the direction of arrow 2, or perpendicular to the oblique surface, its true size will be seen as at *C*.

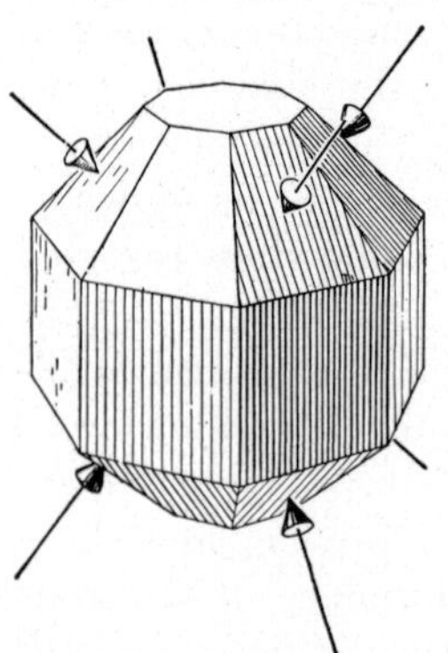

FIG. 8·15—Directions from which oblique views are taken.

Figure 8·17 illustrates the operations in progressive steps showing first at *B* an auxiliary elevation looking in a horizontal direction parallel to the line *AB* of the oblique surface, thus getting the line to project as a point and the oblique surface to project as a line. Then a second auxiliary at *C* is added looking directly toward the required surface and showing the true size. This second auxiliary is made by setting up the datum plane in the oblique view and drawing the view from given dimensions of the surface.

The datum plane *DP* should be visualized as a plane perpendicular to the horizontal orienting line AB of the oblique surface. The top and oblique views both show the line AB in true length; therefore these views show the edge view of the datum plane perpendicular to the line AB. Note that, in any view, *the datum plane is always perpendicular to the rays of projection for the view.*

As an aid in checking the location of the datum plane and the correct

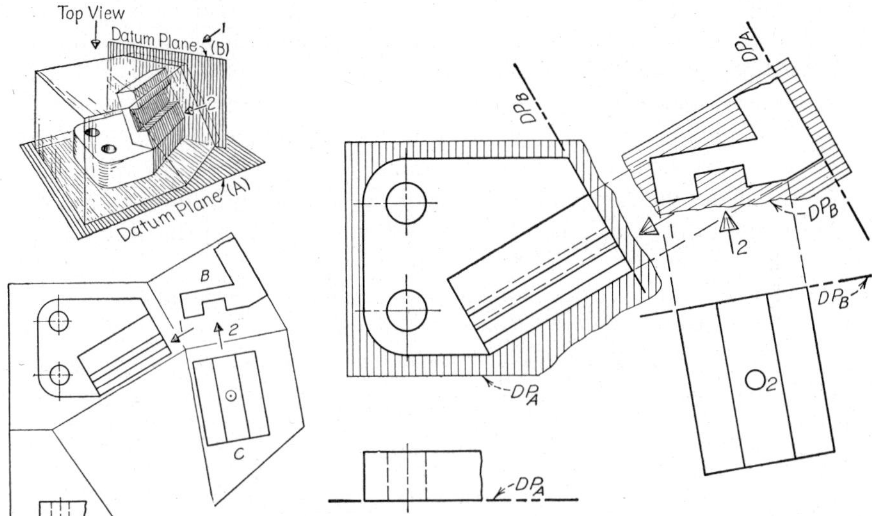

FIG. 8·16—Double auxiliary or oblique view.

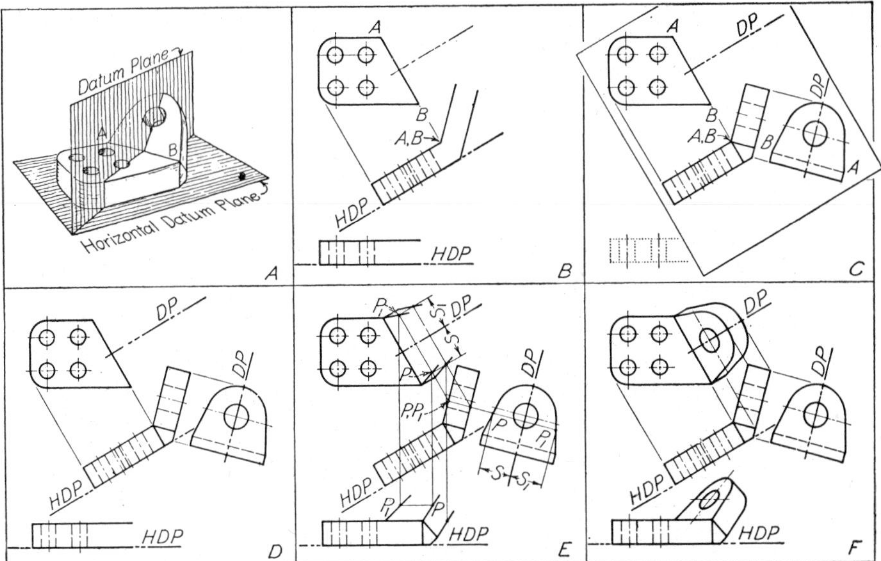

FIG. 8·17—Stages in drawing an oblique view.

projection of the oblique view, the original top view and the auxiliary view may be thought of as two regular views, top and front; the oblique view then becomes a simple auxiliary. In following this procedure, the draftsman must orient these two views in a different position on the paper, thinking of them as straightened up into the more familiar position of front and top views, or actually turning the paper as indicated at *C*. With the views in this position, it is very simple to make a right auxiliary showing the true size of the inclined face, as already explained in paragraphs 8·5 and 8·9. At *D* the orienting frame shown at *C* is removed, and the completed oblique view shown with the incomplete top and front views of the piece. *E* and *F* of the progressive series illustrate the method of finishing the top and front views, if required, by projecting back from the oblique view. Select any point, say *P*, on the oblique view and project it across to the auxiliary view. From this edge view extend a perpendicular projecting line to cross the datum plane in the top view. Measure the distance *S* on the oblique view and mark it on the top view. Project down from the top view, measure the height of the point from the horizontal *datum plane* on the auxiliary view, and mark the distance from the datum plane *HDP* on the front view. Carry on this procedure with as many points as necessary.

8·12 Revolution. The term "revolution," as used in projection drawing, means the rotation of an object into a specified position about an axis

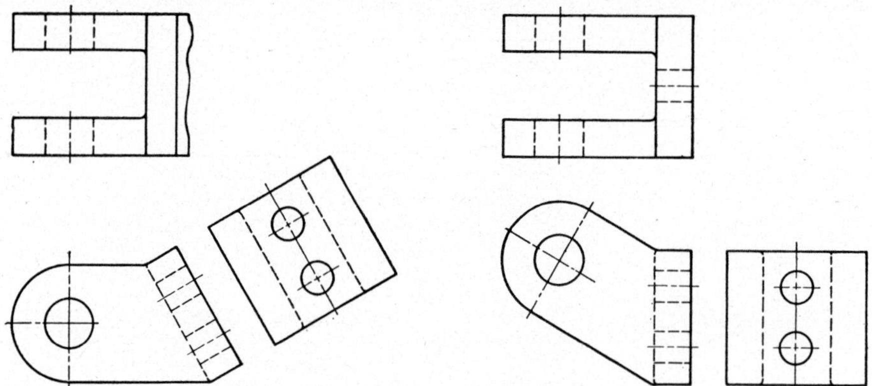

FIG. 8·18—Comparison of auxiliary and revolution.

(usually) perpendicular to one of the principal planes. The axis is generally assumed to pass through, or be tangent to, the object, and the *direction* of rotation is specified as clockwise or counterclockwise on the view in which the axis is projected as a point. The *amount* of revolution may be specified either in degrees or so that one of the faces or edges comes to a certain position.

The *purpose* of revolution is to make it possible to draw an object in an oblique position by first drawing it in a simpler position and then revolving it to the required position. Conversely, an object given in an oblique position may be brought into a simpler position by *counterrevolution.*

The difference between the method of revolution and the method of auxiliary projection is that in the former the object is moved, while in the latter the observer is moved. The result is the same, as illustrated in Fig. 8·18.

8·13 Rule of revolution. If an object is revolved about an axis perpendicular to a plane then (1) its projection *on that plane will change only in position, not in shape or size;* and (2) *the dimensions that are parallel to the axis on the other views will be unchanged.* Illustration: If the object in Fig. 8·19 is revolved through 30° from the position *A* about a vertical axis, the top view will not change in shape but will take a position as shown in *B*. The vertical heights of all the points of the object remain unchanged in the

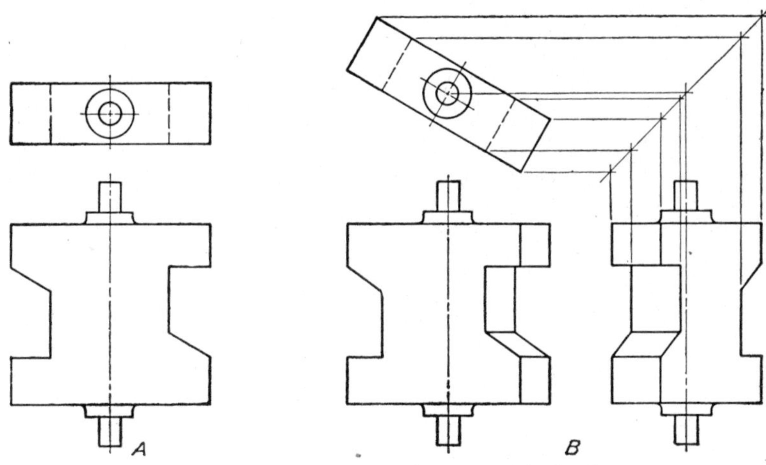

FIG. 8·19—Revolution about a vertical axis.

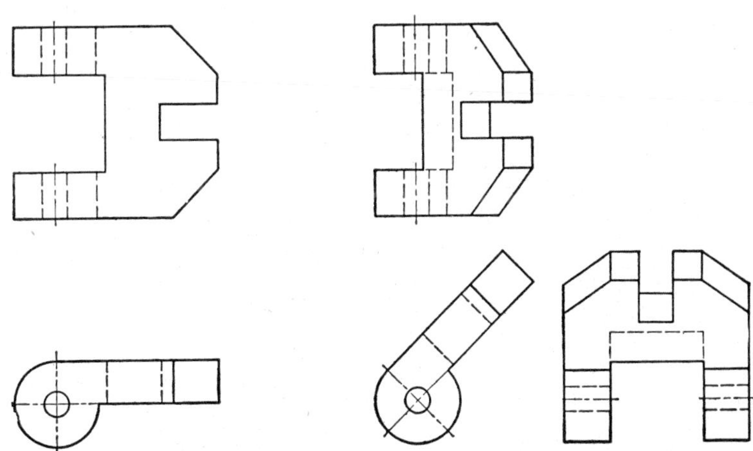
FIG. 8·20—Revolution about a horizontal axis.

revolution; thus the new front view can be found by projecting each point across from the original front view to meet a projecting line dropped from the corresponding point on the new top view. The side view is then drawn by the method of projection shown. To avoid confusion, it is a good practice to number or letter the corresponding points on each view.

If an object is revolved about a horizontal axis, perpendicular to the frontal plane, as in Fig. 8·20, the front view is unchanged in shape and is simply transferred by copying in the new position. The new top view can then be found by projecting across from the original top view and up from the new front view. The side view can be found as usual.

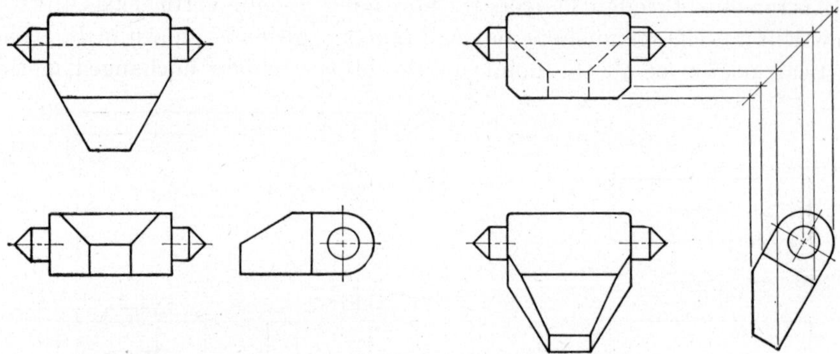

Fig. 8·21—Revolution about an axis perpendicular to the profile plane.

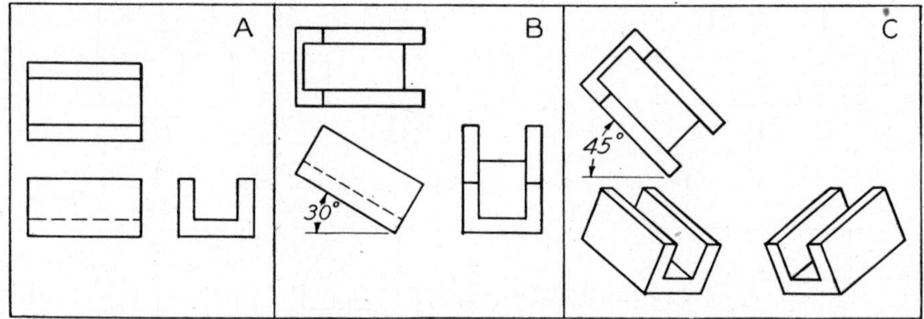

Fig. 8·22—Successive revolutions.

In a revolution forward or backward about an axis perpendicular to the profile plane, the side view is the unchanged view. Thus the new front view is found by projecting across from the revolved side view and obtaining the widths from the original front view, Fig. 8·21.

Successive revolutions may be made under the same rules. Figure 8·22 shows a piece revolved first about a horizontal axis (perpendicular to the frontal plane) through 30° and then from this position about a vertical axis through 45°.

Counterrevolution simply reverses the normal procedure of revolution. As an example, assume that the object of Fig. 8·22 is given in the position shown at C. To get the object into its simplest position it is first revolved until its front face is parallel to the frontal plane, giving position B; then it is revolved until the base is horizontal.

8•14 The true length of a line. A line oblique to the principal planes will not show in its true length in any of its principal views. If it is revolved into a position parallel to one of the principal planes, its true length will be shown in that view. This may be easily understood by assuming the line

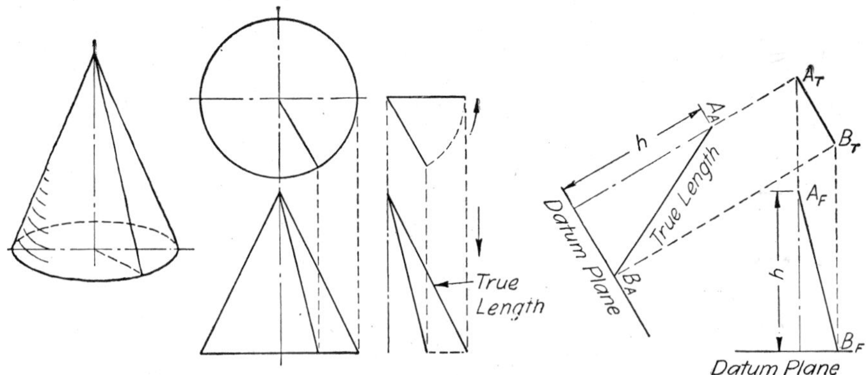

FIG. 8·23—True length of a line, revolution method.

FIG. 8·24—True length of a line, auxiliary view method.

to be an element of a cone, as in Fig. 8·23. The slant lines of the front view of the cone show the true lengths of its elements. If the cone is imagined as revolving about its axis, each element, in turn, will take a position parallel to the plane of projection. Thus if the line is assumed to be on a cone, as in the figure, its true length is found by revolving the top view until the line is parallel to the frontal plane, and by projecting the revolved end down to meet the horizontal line corresponding to the front view of the base of the cone.

The true length of a line may also be found by making an auxiliary view of it on a plane parallel to it and perpendicular to a plane of projection, as illustrated in Fig. 8·24.

PROBLEMS

Group I.	Single auxiliary views.
Group II.	Progressive series (single and double auxiliaries).
Group III.	Double auxiliaries.
Group IV.	Revolution and counterrevolution.
Group V.	True lengths of lines.
Group VI.	Drawing from description.

Group I. Single auxiliary views

Problems 1 to 19

1, 2, 3. Figs. 8·25 to 8·27. Draw views given and add auxiliary views on center lines or datum lines indicated.

4, 5. Figs. 8·28, 8·29. Draw views given and add auxiliary views indicated.

6. Fig. 8·30. Draw front view, partial top view, and partial left auxiliary view.

7. Fig. 8·31. Draw partial front view, right-side view, partial top view, and partial front auxiliary view.

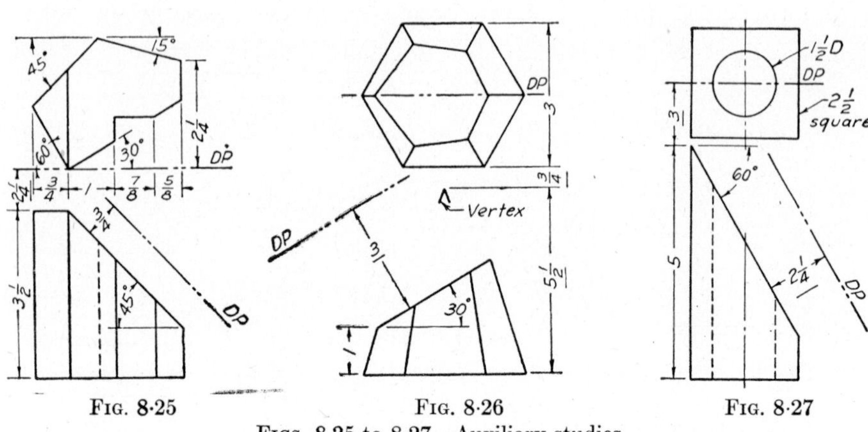

FIG. 8·25 FIG. 8·26 FIG. 8·27

FIGS. 8·25 to 8·27—Auxiliary studies.

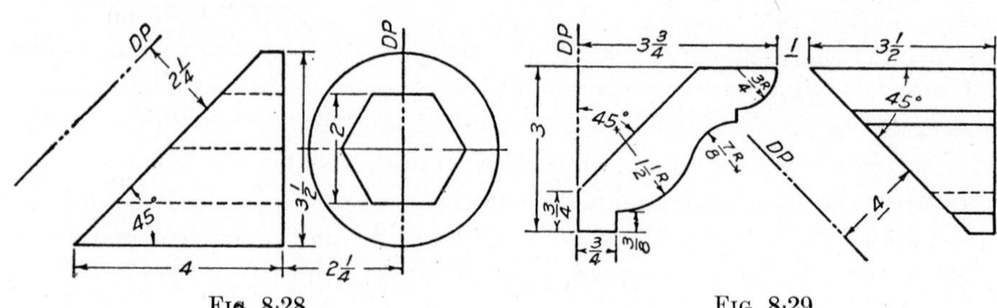

FIG. 8·28 FIG. 8·29

FIGS. 8·28 and 8·29—Auxiliary studies.

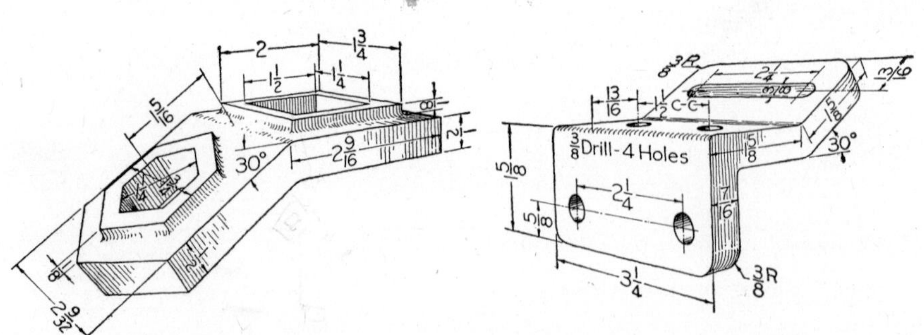

FIG. 8·30—Holder.

FIG. 8·31—Slotted anchor.

8. Fig. 8·32. Draw front view, partial top or bottom view, and partial right auxiliary view.

9. Fig. 8·33. Draw top view, partial front view, and two auxiliary elevations.

10. Fig. 8·34. Draw given front and left-side views and add right auxiliary view.

11. Fig. 8·35. Draw front view, partial right-side view, and partial right auxiliary view.

12, 13. Figs. 8·36 and 8·37. Determine what views and part views will best describe the piece. Submit sketch before starting the drawing.

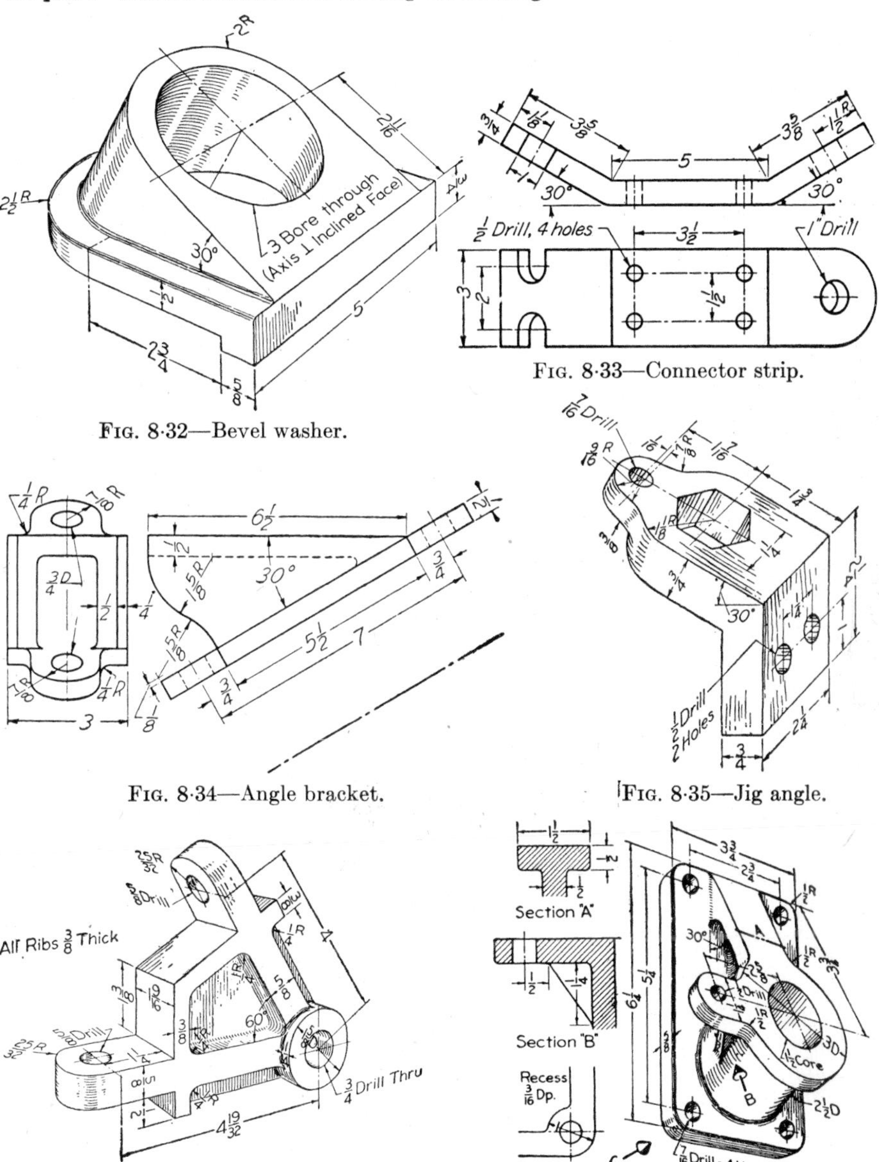

FIG. 8·32—Bevel washer.

FIG. 8·33—Connector strip.

FIG. 8·34—Angle bracket.

FIG. 8·35—Jig angle.

FIG. 8·36—Radial swing block.

FIG. 8·37—Angle-shaft base.

14, 15. Figs. 8·38 and 8·39. Determine what views and part views will best describe the piece. Submit sketch before starting the drawing.

16. Fig. 8·40. Draw front view, partial bottom view, partial left auxiliary view.

17. Fig. 8·41. Determine what views and part views will best describe the piece. Submit sketch before starting the drawing.

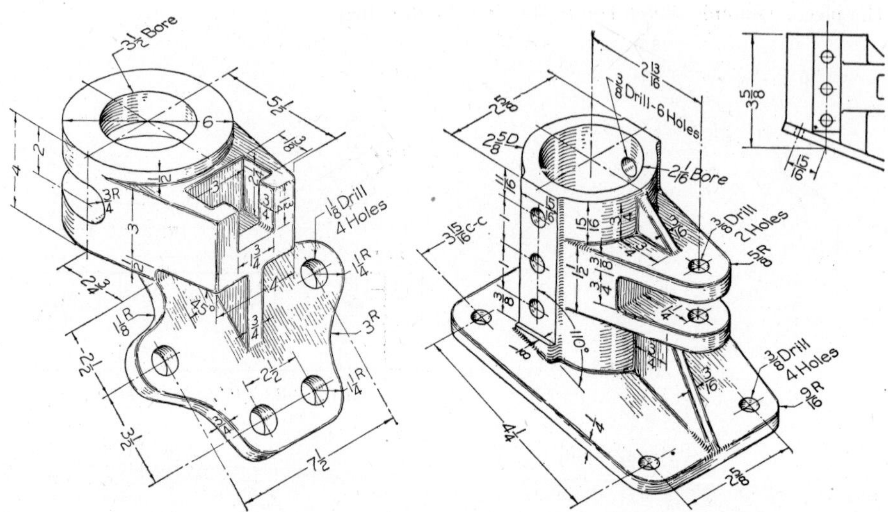

FIG. 8·38—Conveyor hanger.

FIG. 8·39—Strut base.

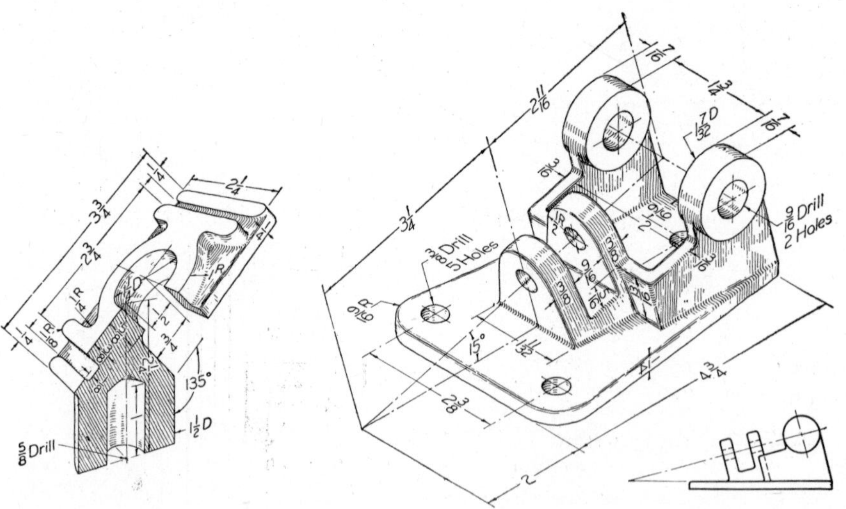

FIG. 8·40—Catenary clip.

FIG. 8·41—Brace plate.

18. Fig. 8·42. Draw given front view; add partial bottom view and partial auxiliary views.

19. Fig. 8·43. Draw given front view; add part views and auxiliaries to best describe the piece.

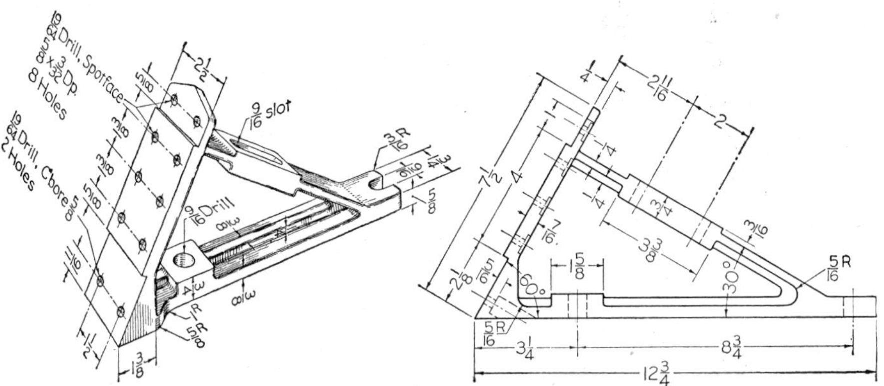

Fig. 8·42—Corner brace.

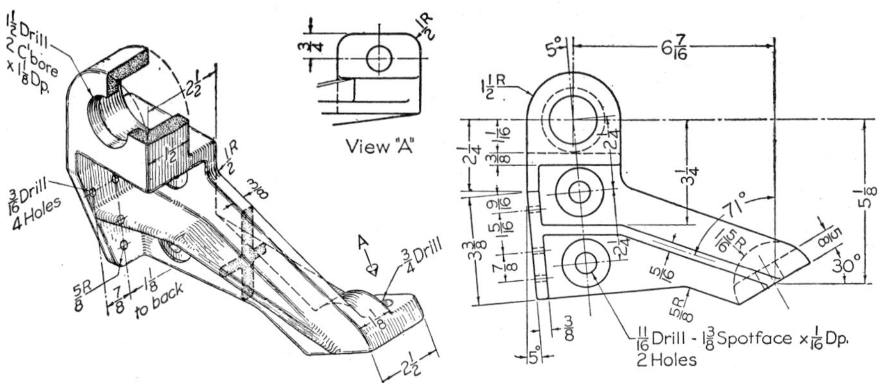

Fig. 8·43—Hinge bracket.

Group II. Progressive series

Problems 20 to 22

20, 21, 22. Figs. 8·44, 8·45, and 8·46. This set shows the upper lug in three different positions, requiring, Prob. 20, a principal view; Prob. 21, a single auxiliary; Prob. 22, a double auxiliary, or oblique, view. Layouts for 11 × 17 paper. Draw views and part views as indicated on layouts.

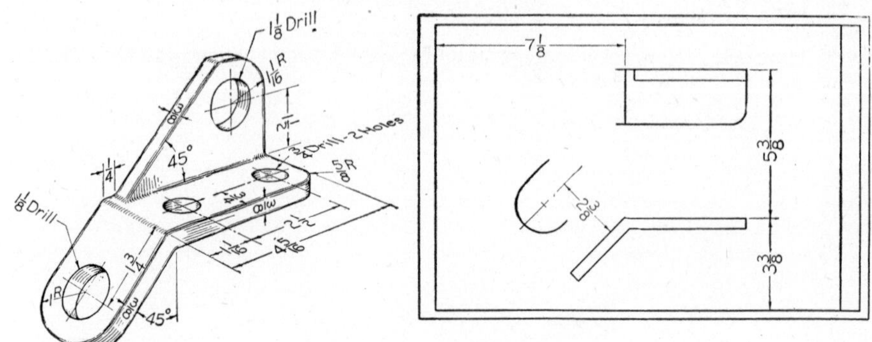

FIG. 8·44—Spar clip, 90°.

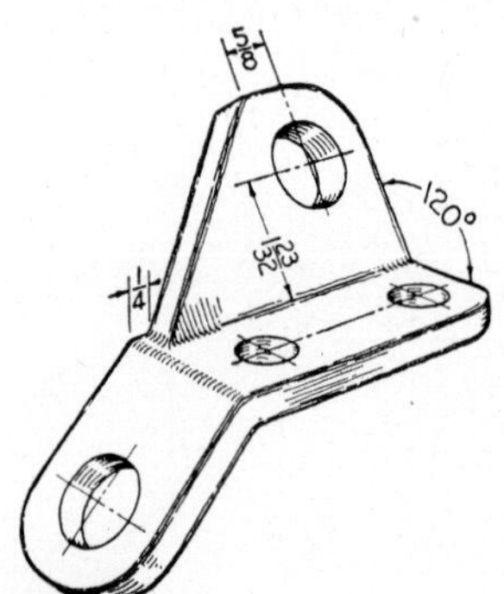

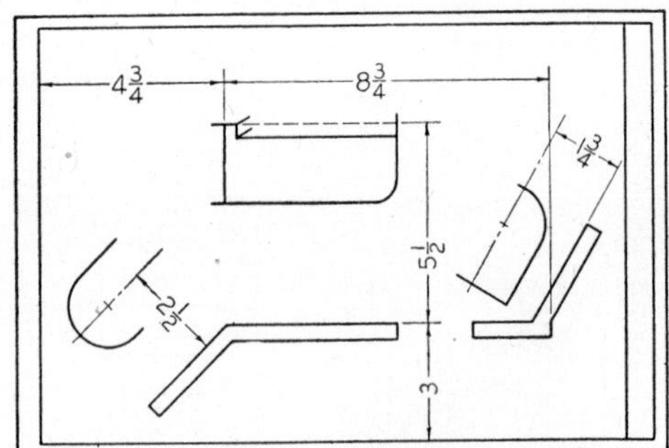

FIG. 8·45—Spar clip, 120°.

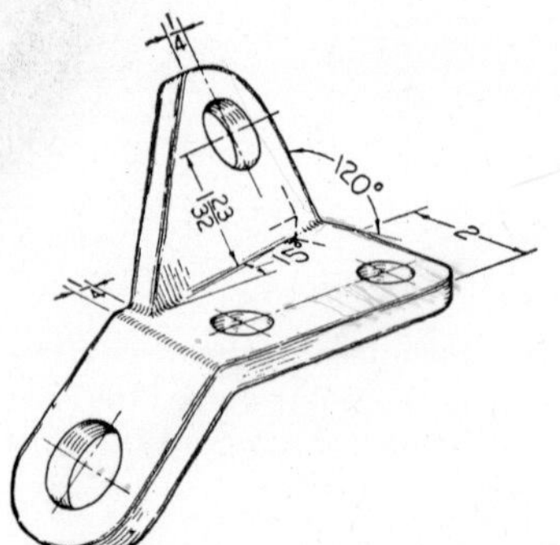

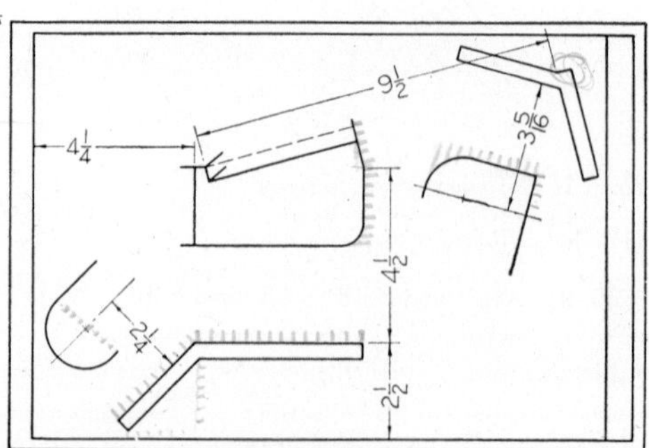

FIG. 8·46—Spar clip, oblique.

Group III. Double auxiliaries. *Problems 23 to 31*

23. Fig. 8·47. Given front and right-side views. Draw front view, partial left-side view, and first and second part-auxiliaries to describe the semicylindrical cut.

24. Fig. 8·48. Draw partial top, front, right auxiliary, and first (auxiliary elevation) and second auxiliaries.

25, 26. Figs. 8·49 and 8·50. Draw necessary views using double-auxiliary method.

27, 28. Figs. 8·51 and 8·52. Draw views given by using double-auxiliary method.

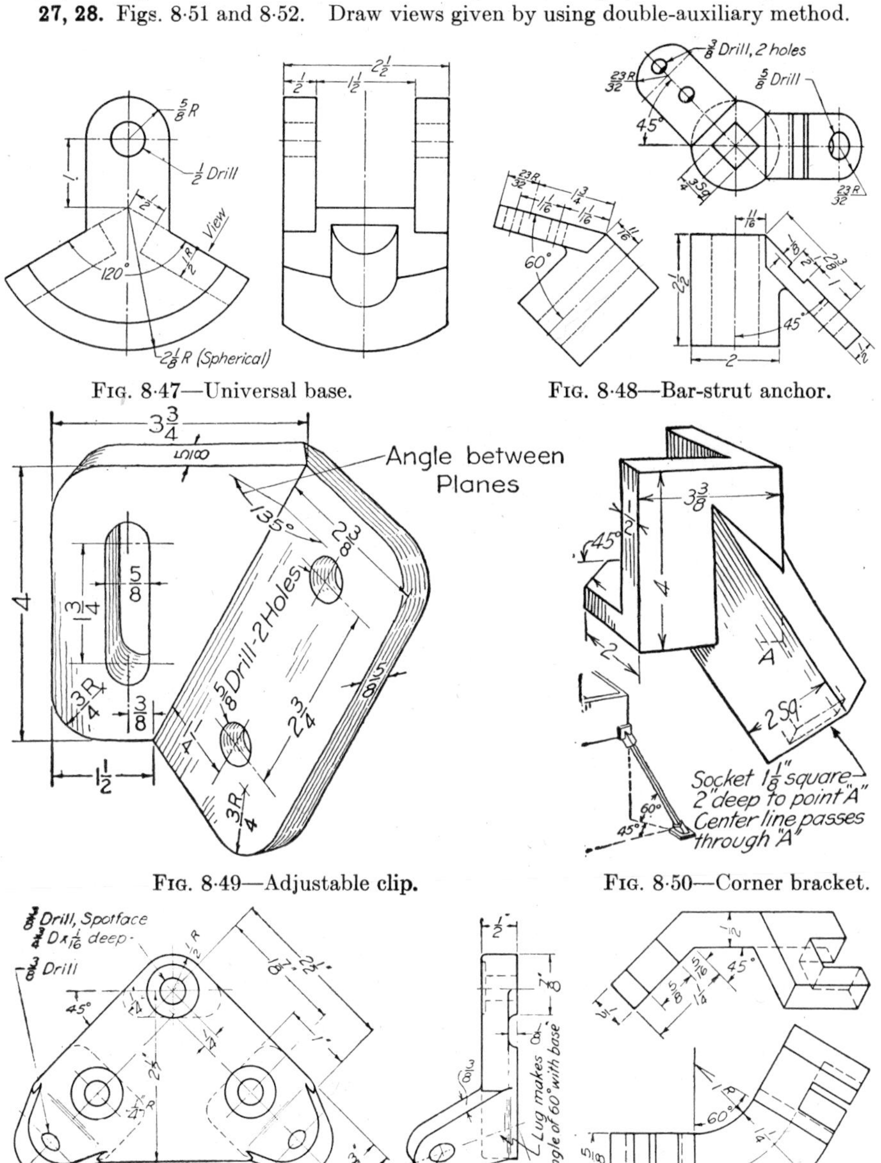

FIG. 8·47—Universal base.

FIG. 8·48—Bar-strut anchor.

FIG. 8·49—Adjustable clip.

FIG. 8·50—Corner bracket.

FIG. 8·51—Cable anchor.

FIG. 8·52—Segment clip.

29. Fig. 8·53. Draw top, front, left-side (alternate position), auxiliary elevation (part), and second auxiliary views.

30. Fig. 8·54. Draw top, front, auxiliary elevation (part), and second auxiliary views. The piece is symmetrical about main axis.

31. Fig. 8·55. Draw the layout of the views given and such additional auxiliary views as are necessary for the description of the piece.

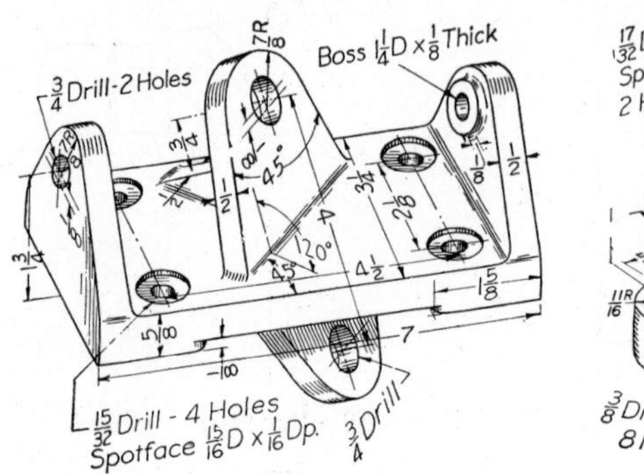

FIG. 8·53—Transverse connection.

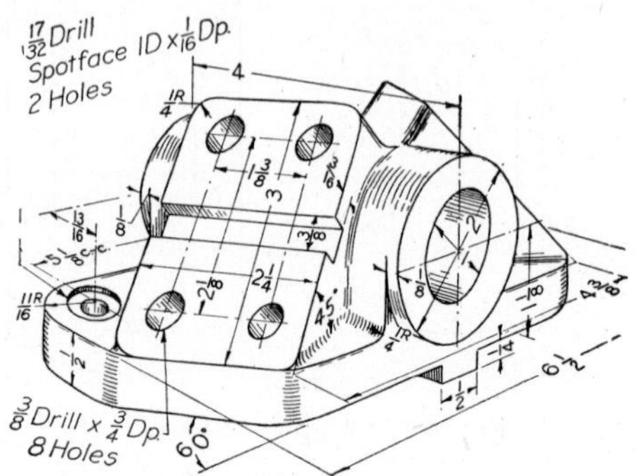

FIG. 8·54—Chamfer tool base.

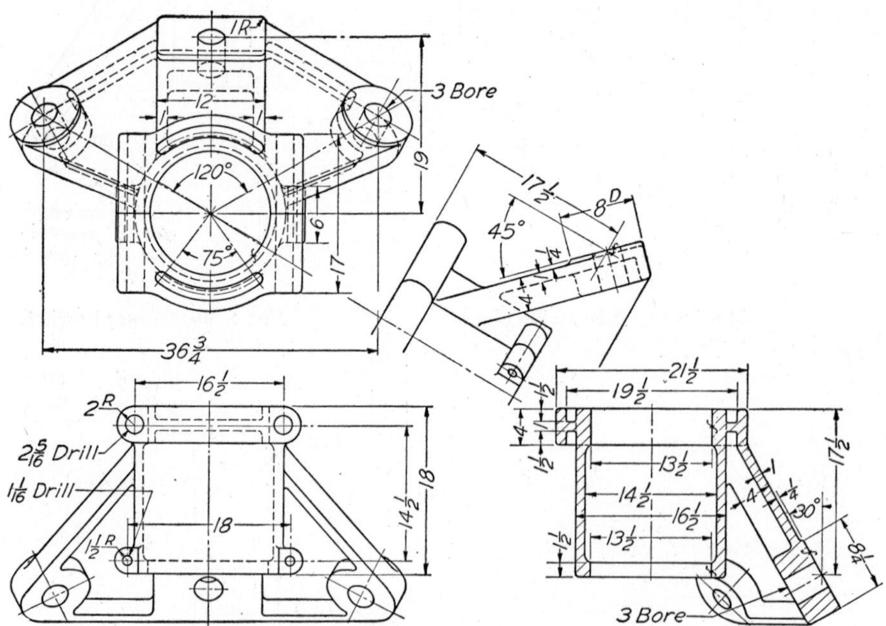

FIG. 8·55—Crane masthead collar and cap.

Group IV. Revolution and counterrevolution

Problems 32 to 34

32. Fig. 8·56. (1) Draw three views of one of the blocks A to K in the position shown. (2) Revolve from position (1) about an axis $\perp H$ through 15°. (3) Revolve from position (2) about an axis $\perp F$ through 45°. (4) Revolve from position (1) about an axis $\perp P$ forward through 30°. (5) Revolve from position (2) about an axis $\perp P$ forward through 30°. (6) Revolve from position (3) about an axis $\perp P$ forward through 30°. (4), (5), and (6) may be placed to advantage under (1), (2), and (3) so that the widths of front and top views may be projected down directly.

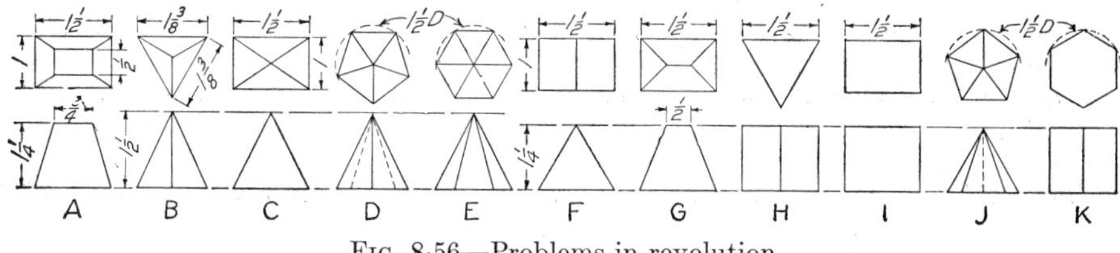

FIG. 8·56—Problems in revolution.

33. Fig. 8·57. The triangle ABC is the base of a triangular pyramid, altitude $2\frac{1}{2}''$, whose apex is equidistant from A, B, and C. Counterrevolve until the base is horizontal and complete the figure.

34. Fig. 8·57. The triangle ABC is the base of a triangular pyramid, altitude $1\frac{1}{4}''$, whose faces make equal angles with the base. Counterrevolve in two operations until the base is horizontal and complete the figure.

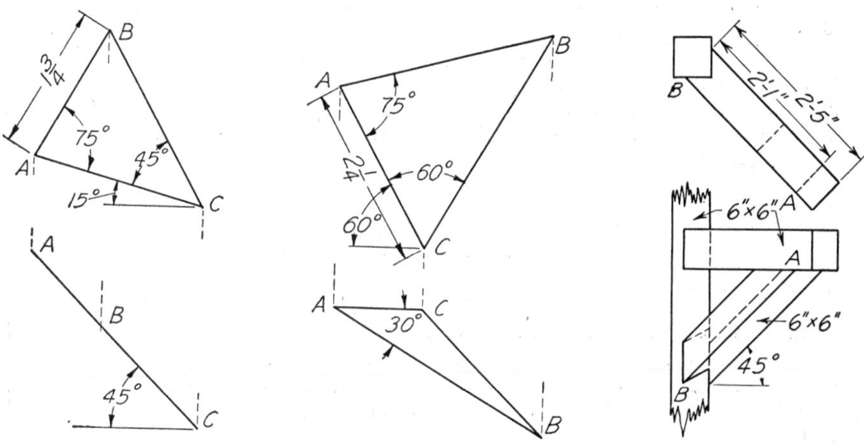

FIG. 8·57—Counterrevolution.

FIG. 8·58—Timber brace.

Group V. True lengths of lines

Problems 35 to 39

35. Find the true length of the body diagonal of a $2\frac{1}{2}''$ cube.

36. Find the true length of an edge of one of the pyramids of Fig. 8·56.

37. Fig. 8·58. Find the true length of the line AB. Make a detail drawing of the brace.

38. Fig. 8·58. With the timbers in position shown, draw the brace with the true length of AB, 3′-0″.

39. Make a detail drawing of the brace of Prob. 38.

Group VI. Drawing from description. *Problems 40 to 49*

40. Draw three views of a triangular card each edge of which is 2¾″ long. One edge is perpendicular to *P*, and the card makes an angle of 30° with *H*.

41. Draw three views of a circular card of 2½″ diameter, inclined 30° to *H*, and perpendicular to *F*. (Find eight points on the curve.)

42. Draw three views of a cylinder of 1½″ diameter, 2″ long, with hexagonal hole, 1″ long diameter, through it. Axis of cylinder parallel to *H* and inclined 30° to *F*.

43. Draw top and front views of a hexagonal plinth whose faces are 1″ square and two of which are parallel to *H*, pierced by a square prism 3″ long, base ⅞″ square, two faces of which are parallel to *H*. The axes coincide, are parallel to *H*, and make an angle of 30° with *F*. The middle point of the axis of the prism is at the center of the plinth.

44. Draw the two projections of a line 3″ long making an angle of 30° with *F*, and whose *F* projection makes 45° with a horizontal line, the line sloping downward and backward to the left.

45. Draw three views of a square pyramid whose faces are isosceles triangles 1¾″ base and 2¼″ altitude, lying with one face horizontal, and the *H* projection of its axis at an angle of 30° with the vertical.

46. Draw the top and front views of a right rectangular pyramid, base 1⅛″ × 2″, altitude 1⅞″, long edges of base parallel to *F*. By two revolutions, place the pyramid so that the short edges are parallel to *H* and make an angle of 60° with *F* while the apex is in the same horizontal plane as one of the short edges of the base.

47. Draw three views of a triangular pyramid formed of four equilateral triangles whose sides are 2¼″. The base makes an angle of 45° with *H*, and one of the edges of the base is perpendicular to *F*.

48. Draw top and front views of a rectangular prism, base 1″ × 1¾″, whose body diagonal is 2½″ long. Find projection of prism on an auxiliary plane perpendicular to the body diagonal.

49. Draw the top and front views of a cube whose body diagonal, 2½″ long, is parallel to *F*. Make an auxiliary projection of the cube on a plane perpendicular to the body diagonal.

TEXT-FILMS

The following Text-Films have been designed for direct correlation with Chap. 8:

Auxiliary Views: Single Auxiliaries (20-min. sound motion picture).
Explains and defines auxiliary projection; demonstrates the theory and methods of constructing different types of single auxiliaries; shows that the auxiliary view is sometimes needed for completion of one of the principal views.

The coordinated silent filmstrip may be used to reemphasize the principles of auxiliary projection and for purposes of class review and discussion.

Auxiliary Views: Double Auxiliaries (15-min. sound motion picture).

Reviews orthographic projection on three principal planes and on auxiliary planes; shows why a single auxiliary view does not give an accurate picture of an oblique face; describes in detail the theory of the double-auxiliary or oblique view; demonstrates method of drawing an object with an oblique face.

The coordinated silent filmstrip may be used further to illustrate the theory of oblique views and to provide class reviews and discussion.

Chapter 9

SECTIONS AND CONVENTIONS

9·1 Sectional views. The two previous chapters have dealt with the method of describing the shape of an object by orthographic views, using dotted lines to indicate the hidden parts. If the object is very simple in its interior construction, these hidden lines are not hard to read and understand. Often, however, when the interior is complicated or when several different pieces are assembled in place, an attempt to show the construction on an exterior view would result in a confusing mass of dotted lines, annoying to draw and difficult, if not impossible, to read clearly. In such cases one (or more) of the views is made "in section."

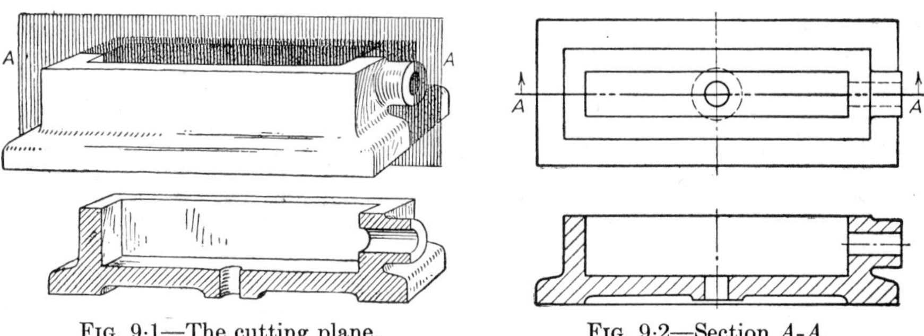

FIG. 9·1—The cutting plane.

FIG. 9·2—Section *A-A*.

Definition: A *sectional view*, or *section*, is a conventional representation in which a part of an object or machine is imagined to be cut or broken away and removed so as to expose the interior. It must be understood clearly that, in thus removing the nearer portion of the object in order to make the sectional view, this portion, assumed to be removed, is *not* omitted in making the other views.

When an object has **more** than one view drawn in section, each sectional view should be considered separately without any reference to what has been imagined as cut away in other views.

9·2 Figure 9·1 shows the picture of a casting intersected by a cutting plane, giving the appearance that the casting had actually been sawed through by the plane and the front part removed, exposing the interior. Figure 9·2 shows the drawing of the casting with the front view in section. The edge of the cutting plane is indicated on the top view by a line symbol (line 7 in the alphabet of lines, Fig. 3·30), with reference letters and arrows, the latter showing the direction in which the view is taken.

Wherever material has been cut by the section plane, the cut surface is indicated by section lining, sometimes called "crosshatching," done with fine lines, generally at 45 degrees, spaced uniformly to give an even tint.

9·3 Five principles in sectioning.

1. The cutting plane need not be a continuous single plane but may be offset or changed in direction so as to show the construction to the best advantage, Fig. 9·3.

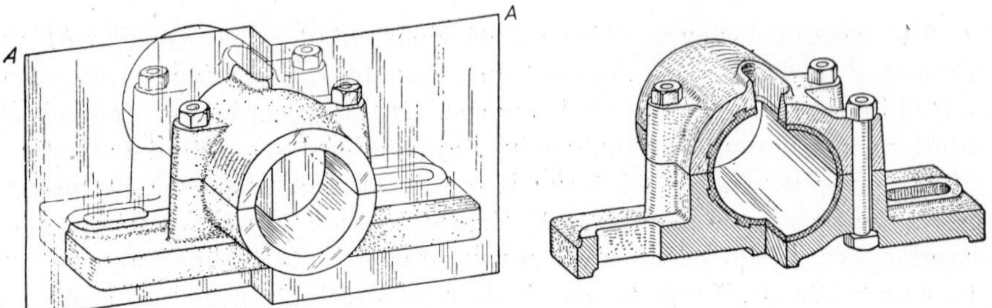

FIG. 9·3—Picture of an offset cutting plane.

2. Shafts, bolts, nuts, rods, rivets, keys, and the like, whose axes occur in the plane of the section, have no internal parts to be shown and therefore are left in full and not sectioned, Fig. 9·4.

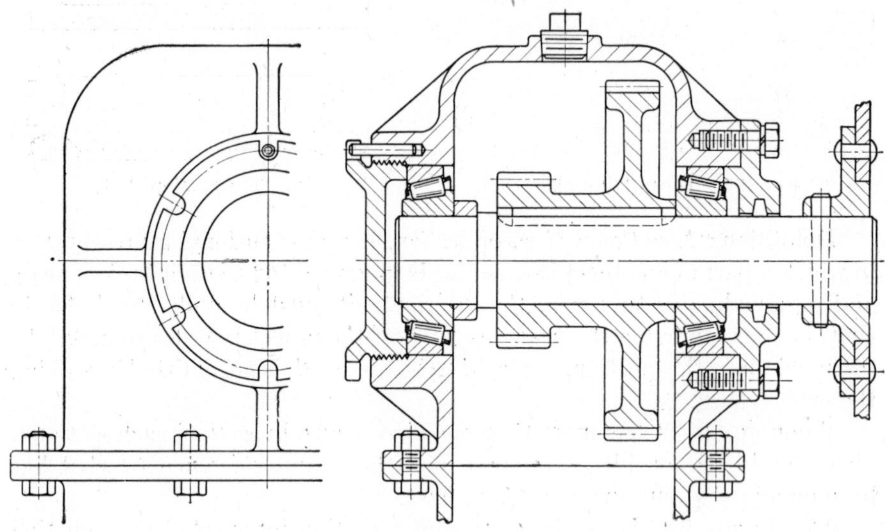

FIG. 9·4—Section study.

3. Hidden lines should not be drawn unless necessary for the description of the piece, Figs. 9·5 and 9·6.
4. Adjacent pieces are section-lined in opposite directions and are often brought out more clearly by varying the pitch of the section lines for each piece, using closer spacing for the smaller pieces, Fig. 9·16.
5. Section lining, either (1) for the same piece in different views or (2) for the same piece in different parts of the same view, should be identical in spacing and direction.

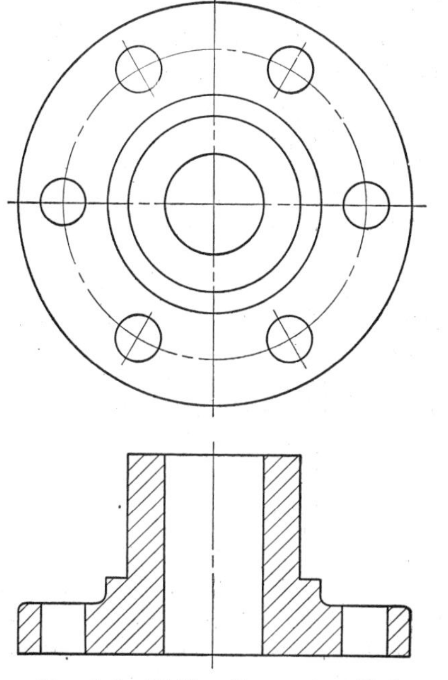

FIG. 9·5—Hidden lines not needed.

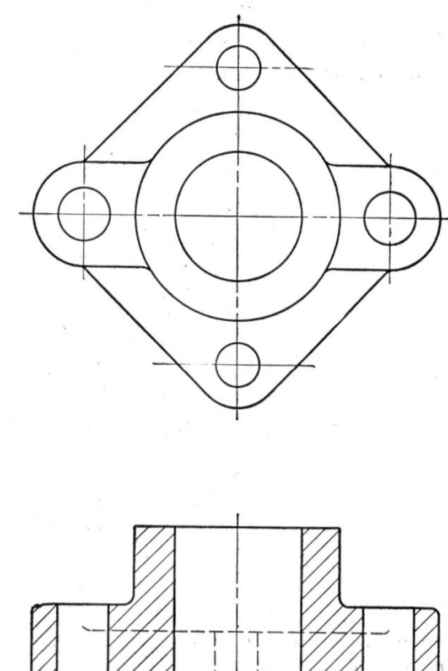

FIG. 9·6—Hidden lines needed.

9·4 A full section is a sectional view in which the cutting plane cuts entirely across the object, showing the whole view in section. The cutting plane is usually taken straight through on the main axis or center line, as in Fig. 9·2, but may be offset or changed in direction to go through some detail not on the axis, as in Fig. 9·3. Where the position of the section is evident, the cutting plane may be omitted. Examples of full sections are shown in Figs. 15·60 and 15·79.

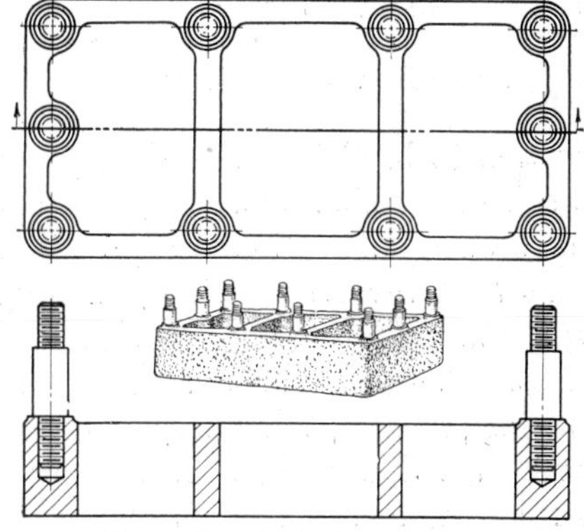

FIG. 9·7—Omission of detail.

In general, the rules of projection are followed in making sectional views, but confusion in reading a complicated piece may occur if all the detail behind the cutting plane is drawn. To ensure clearness, such detail as is not required in explaining the construction should be omitted, as in Fig. 9·7.

9·5 A half section is a view sometimes used with symmetrical objects, in which one half is drawn in section and the other half as a regular exterior view, Fig. 9·8. The cutting plane is imagined to extend halfway across, stopping at the axis or center line. A half section has the advantage of showing both the exterior and the interior on one view but has the disadvantage that inside diameters cannot be dimensioned well. Hidden lines are not drawn on either side except for clarity or assistance in dimensioning.

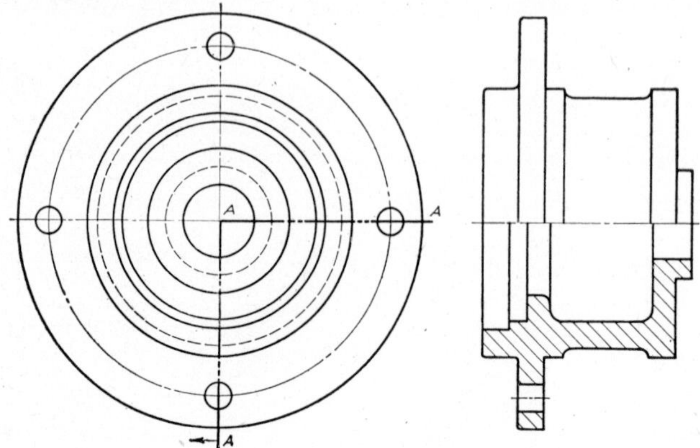

FIG. 9·8—A half section.

Examples of half sections are given in Figs. 15·49 and 15·56. Note that a center line divides the sectioned and unsectioned portions of the view, since the object is only imagined to be cut in this manner, and there is no edge or surface on the object at this position.

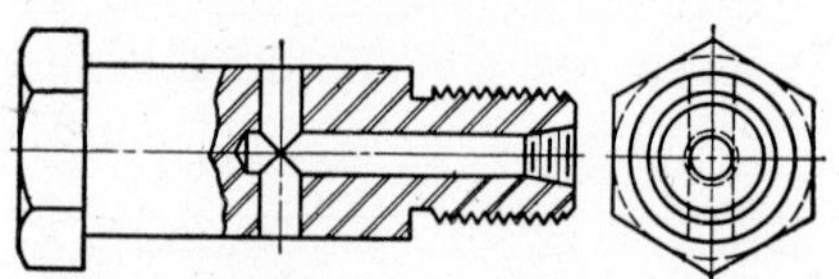

FIG. 9·9—A broken-out section.

9·6 A broken-out section is a partial section used on an exterior view to show some interior detail without drawing a complete full or half section. The object is imagined to be sawed by a cutting plane through the portion to be shown, and the part in front broken out, leaving an irregular break line, which, along with part of the contour of the object, will bound the broken-out section. Figure 9·9 is an example.

9·7 A revolved section, made directly on an exterior view, provides a very convenient and useful method of showing the shape of the cross section of some detail of construction, such as a rib or the arm of a wheel. The cutting plane is passed perpendicular to the center line or axis of the part to be sectioned, and the resulting section revolved or turned up in place, Fig. 9·10. These are used primarily for shape description rather than size description. When lines of the outline interfere with the section, as is sometimes the case, the view may be broken away to make a clear space for the sectional view. Figures 9·29, *B*, *C*, *E*, and *F*, and Fig. 9·30 show some examples of revolved sections or, as they are sometimes called, "interpolated sections."

9·8 Detailed sections, or removed sections, are used for the same purpose as revolved sections but, instead of being drawn on the view, they are set off, or shifted, to some adjacent place on the paper, Fig. 9·11. The cutting plane, with reference letters, should always be indicated unless the place from which the section has been taken is obvious. Removed sections are used whenever restricted space for the section, or the dimensioning of it, prevents the use of an ordinary revolved section. When the shape of a

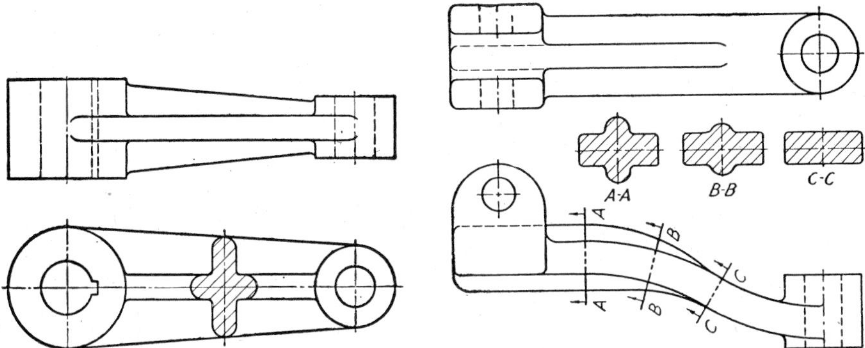

FIG. 9·10—A revolved section. FIG. 9·11—Removed sections.

piece changes gradually, or is not uniform, several sections may be required, Fig. 9·12. It is often an advantage to draw them to larger scale than that of the main drawing, in order to show dimensions more clearly. Sometimes sections are removed to a separate drawing sheet. When this practice is employed, the section must be carefully shown on the main drawing with

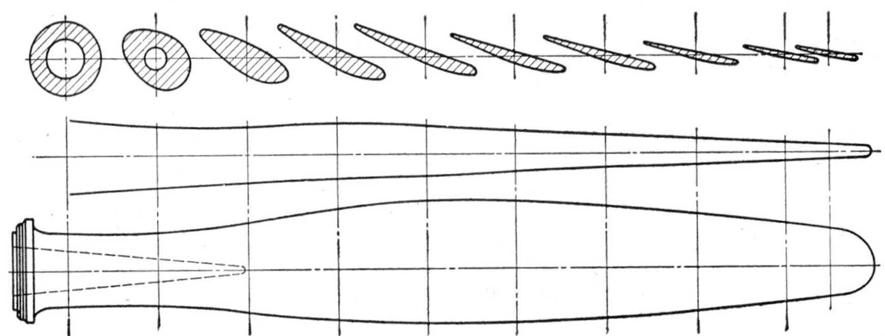

FIG. 9·12—Removed sections.

cutting plane and identifying letters. Often these identifying letters are made as a fraction in a circle, with the numerator a letter identifying the section and the denominator a number identifying the sheet. The sectional view is then marked with the same letters and numbers. Detail sections are sometimes called "separate sections," "shifted sections," or "sliced sections."

9·9 An auxiliary section is a sectional view made on an auxiliary plane, and conforms to all the principles of auxiliary views as explained in the previous chapter; thus there may be an auxiliary sectional elevation, a right or left auxiliary section, a front or rear auxiliary section, or an oblique section. Similarly, half sections, broken-out sections, revolved sections, and removed sections may be used on auxiliary views. Figure 9·13 is an example of an auxiliary in section. Figure 9·14 shows the use of right auxiliary partial sections.

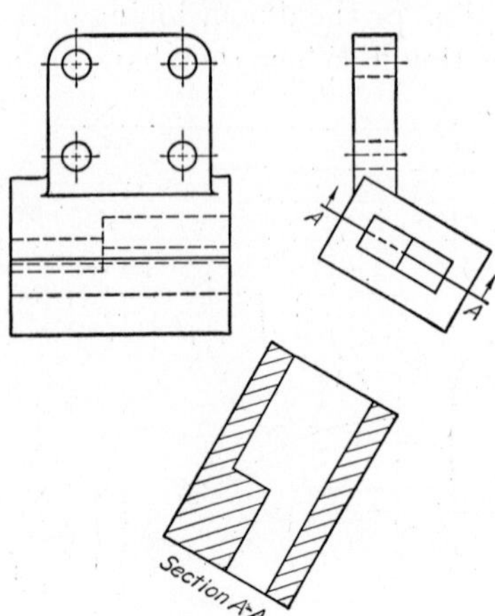

FIG. 9·13—An auxiliary section.

9·10 A phantom section is an exterior view with the interior construction brought out by dotted crosshatching, Fig. 9·15. It is rarely used, its only advantage being that it enables a detail to be preserved in those cases where a broken-out section would cut away this detail on the outside. The term "phantom" is also used to indicate an absent part, dotted in to show the relative position of a piece, as in Figs. 15·60 and 15·61.

9·11 Section lining, or **crosshatching,** is used to produce a "tint" on the cut surface, and is done with fine sharp lines, spaced entirely by eye, except when some form of mechanical section liner is used. The pitch, or distance between lines, is governed by the size of the surface. For ordinary working

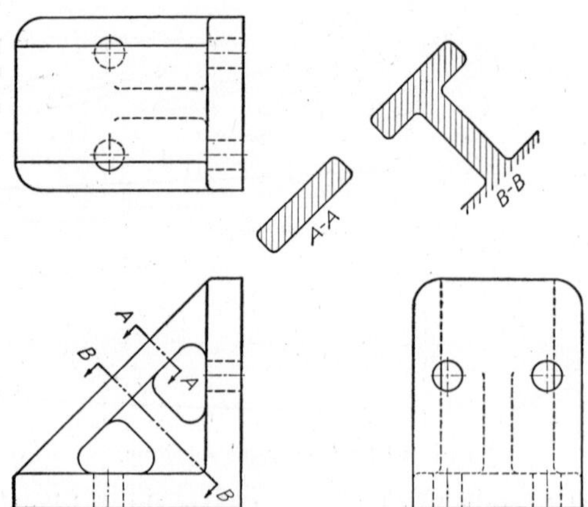

FIG. 9·14—Auxiliary sections (partial).

drawings it will not be much less than 1/16 inch and rarely more than 1/8 inch. Very small pieces will have closer spacing. Care should be exercised in setting the pitch by the first two or three lines and one should glance back at the first lines often in order that the pitch may not gradually increase or decrease. Nothing mars the appearance of a drawing more than poor section lining. The "Alphabet of lines," page 28, gives the weight of crosshatch lines.

Two adjacent pieces in an assembly section are crosshatched in opposite directions. If three pieces adjoin, one of them may be sectioned at other than 45 degrees (usually 30° or 60°), Fig. 9·16. If a part is so shaped that

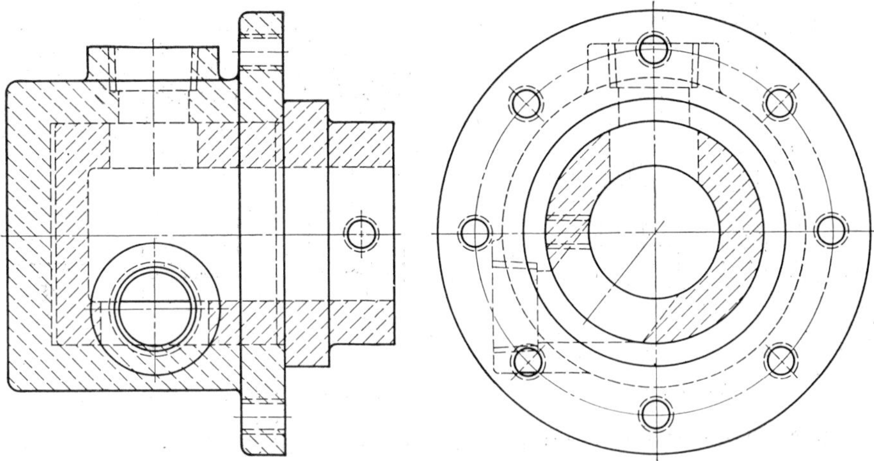

FIG. 9·15—A phantom section.

45-degree sectioning runs parallel, or nearly so, to its principal outlines, another direction should be chosen, Fig. 9·17.

Large surfaces are sometimes sectioned only around the edge, as illustrated by Fig. 9·18.

Very thin sections, as of gaskets, sheet metal, or structural steel shapes to small scale, may be shown in solid black, with white spaces between the parts where thin pieces are adjacent, Fig. 9·19.

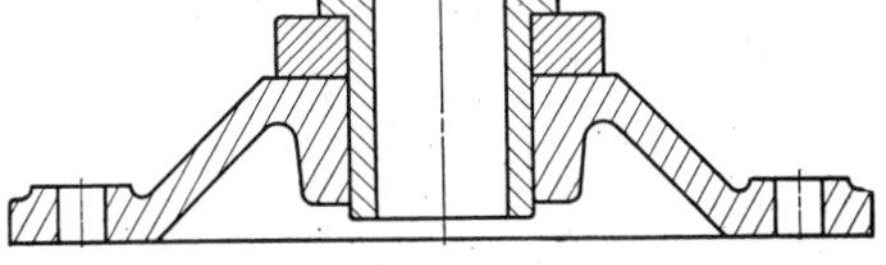

FIG. 9·16—Adjacent parts.

9·12 Code for materials in section. Symbolical section lining is not commonly used on ordinary working drawings, but sometimes in an assembly section it is desired to show a distinction between materials, and a

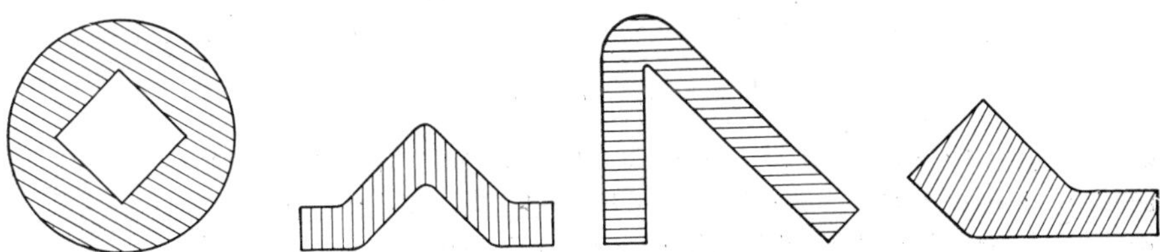

FIG. 9·17—Section-line directions for unusual shapes.

recognized standard code is of obvious advantage. The American Standards Association's symbols for indicating different materials will be found in the Appendix, page 669. Code section lining is used only as an aid in reading the drawing and is not to be taken as the official specification of the materials. Exact specifications of the material for each piece are always given on the detail drawing.

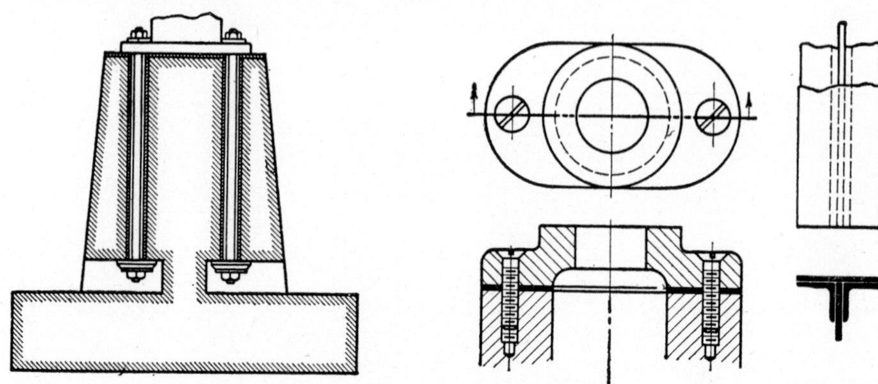

FIG. 9·18—Outline sectioning. FIG. 9·19—Thin material in section.

9·13 Conventional sections. Sometimes added clearness may be gained by violating the strict rules of projection. This is often done in making sectional views, as in a section of a pulley. Compare Figs. 15·63 and 15·60, one of a three-arm pulley, the other of a pulley with solid web. The true projection of a section of the handwheel, Fig. 9·20, is unsymmetrical

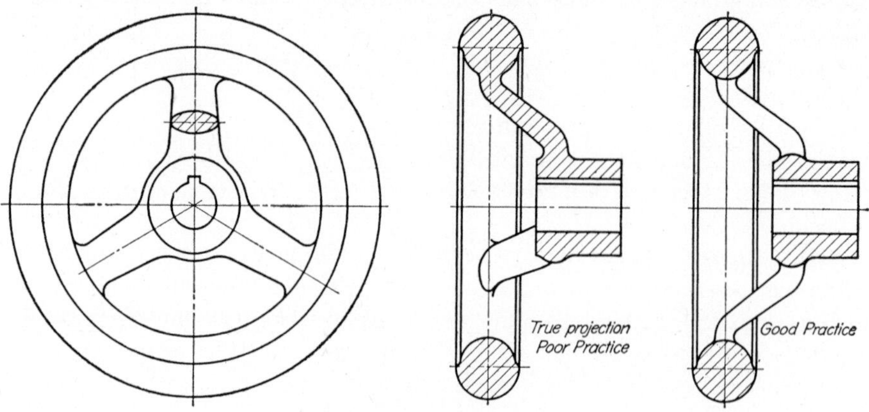

FIG. 9·20—Aligned section.

and misleading, therefore not good practical drawing. The preferred form is shown in the second view, where the foreshortened arm is drawn as if revolved, or aligned, and neither arm section-lined.

9·14 Ribs in section. When the cutting plane passes longitudinally through the center of a rib or web, a true sectional view with the rib cross-hatched gives a heavy and misleading effect. The standard conventional method of drawing such a view is to omit the section lines from the rib, as if the cutting plane were just in front of it, Fig. 9·21. At *B* an *aligned section* is shown. The cutting plane goes through the rib on the left side and through one of the holes in the base on the right side. The parts are aligned or revolved to the cutting plane, then projected to the front view to make a symmetrical section. The prominent fillets in the sectional view show that the ribs run to the bottom of the piece and are not small spokes at

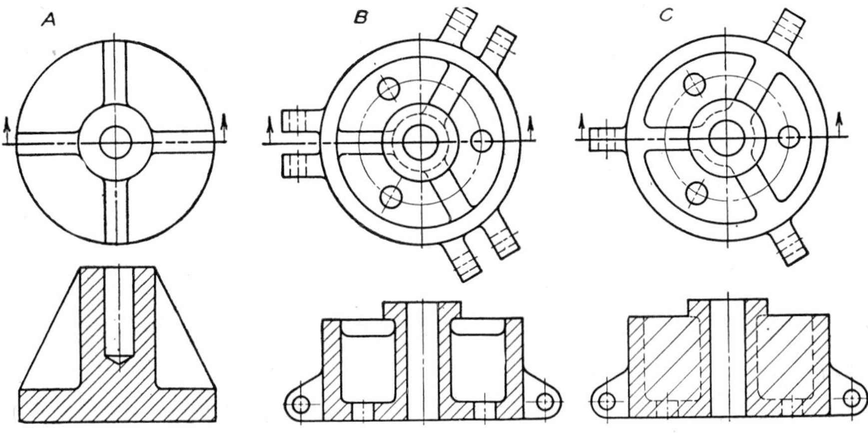

FIG. 9·21—Ribs in section.

the top. The lugs are, of course, not sectioned because the cutting plane does not cut through them. The object at *C* is similar to *B* except that the ribs extend to the top of the piece. Here alternate crosshatching is used to identify the ribs in the sectional view. Half the crosshatch lines are carried through the rib, and the line of intersection between the solid body and the rib is dotted. Section lines are omitted on the lugs for the same reason as given for *A*. Alternate crosshatching is rarely necessary and should be used only when the conventional method is inadequate or ambiguous.

9·15 Drilled flanges in section should show the holes at their true distances from the center, whether or not their axes come in the plane of the section. In Fig. 9·22 the true projection of the holes is misleading. It is better practice to show them at their true radial distance, as if they were swung around into the plane of the section. This applies also to flanges in full views. Pipe fitters use the terms "one up" and "two up" to indicate whether a flange on a horizontal run has one or two holes at the top.

9·16 Conventional practices. There are violations of the rules of true projection in full views, as well as in sectional views, that are recognized as good practice because they add to the clearness of the drawing. For example, if a front view shows a hexagonal bolthead "across corners," the theoretical projection of the side view would be "across flats"; but in a working drawing, when boltheads occur, they should be drawn across corners in both views, to show better the shape and the space needed.

Some typical examples, in which true lines of intersection are of no value as aids in reading the drawing and are therefore ignored, are shown in Fig. 9·23.

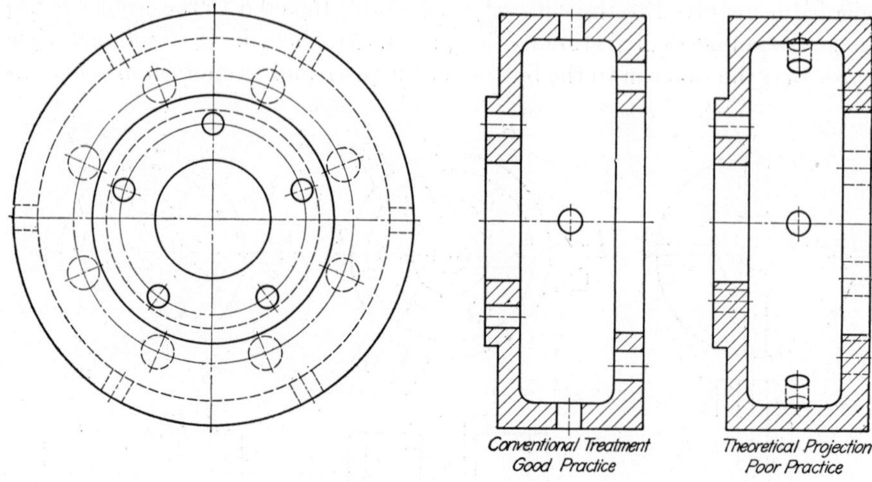

FIG. 9·22—Conventional representation of drilling.

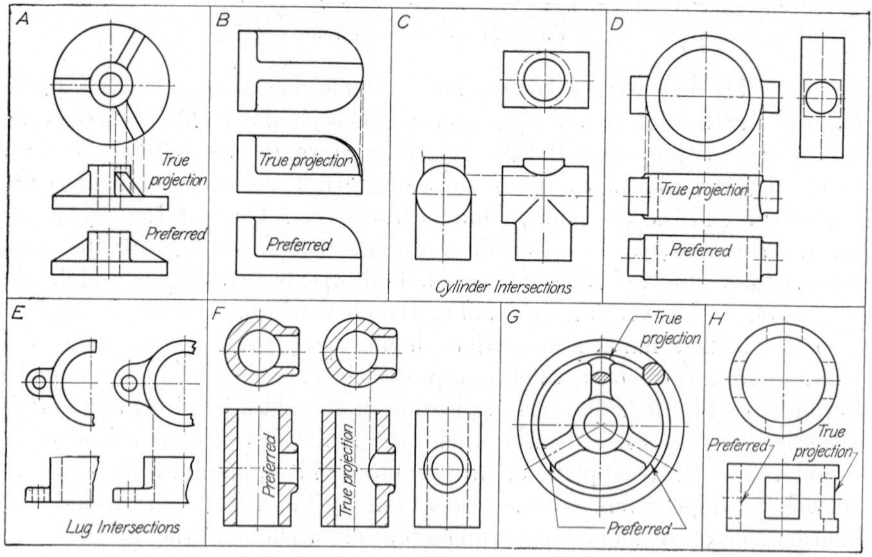

FIG. 9·23—Conventional intersections.

Pieces that have parts at an angle with each other, as the lever of Fig. 9·24, may be shown straightened out, or aligned, in one view. Similarly, bent pieces of the type of Fig. 9·25 should have one view made as a developed view of the *blank* to be punched and formed. Extra metal must be allowed for bends, see paragraph 25·23.

Lugs or parts cast on for holding purposes and to be machined off are shown in phantom in dashed lines. If in section, the section lines are dotted. Dashed lines are also used for indicating the limiting positions of moving parts and for showing adjacent parts that aid in locating the position or use of the piece.

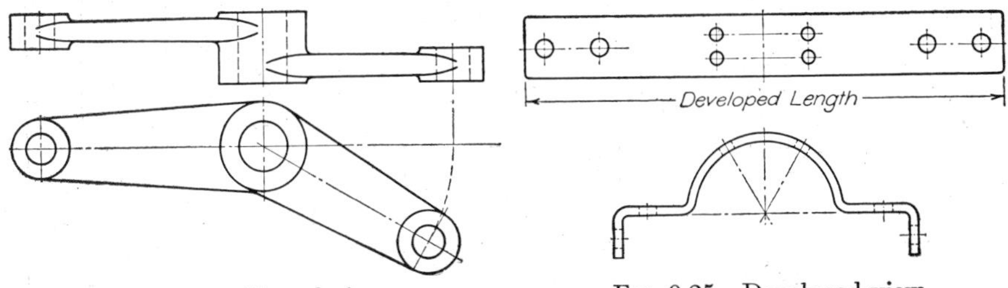

FIG. 9·24—Aligned view.

FIG. 9·25—Developed view.

9·17 Half views. When space is very limited, it is allowable practice to make the top or the side view of a symmetrical piece as a half view. If the front is an exterior view, the *front* half of the top or the side view would be used, as in Fig. 9·26, but if the front view is a sectional view, the *rear* half would be used, as in Fig. 9·27. Figure 9·28 shows another space-saving combination of a half view with a half section. Examples of half views occur in Figs. 15·56, 15·61, and 15·69.

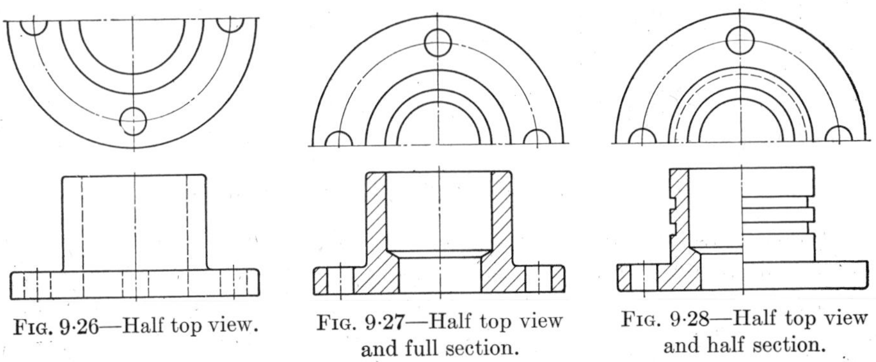

FIG. 9·26—Half top view.

FIG. 9·27—Half top view and full section.

FIG. 9·28—Half top view and half section.

9·18 Fillets and rounds. In designing a casting, sharp internal angles must never be left because of the liability to fracture at those points. The radius of the fillet depends on the thickness of the metal and other design conditions. When not dimensioned, it is left to the patternmaker. External angles may be rounded for appearance or comfort, with radii ranging from enough merely to remove the sharp edges, to an amount nearly equal to the thickness of the piece. An edge made by the intersection of two unfinished surfaces of a casting should always be "broken" by a very small round. A sharp corner on a drawing thus indicates that one or both of the intersecting surfaces are machined. Small fillets, rounds, and "runouts" are best put in freehand both in pencil and ink.

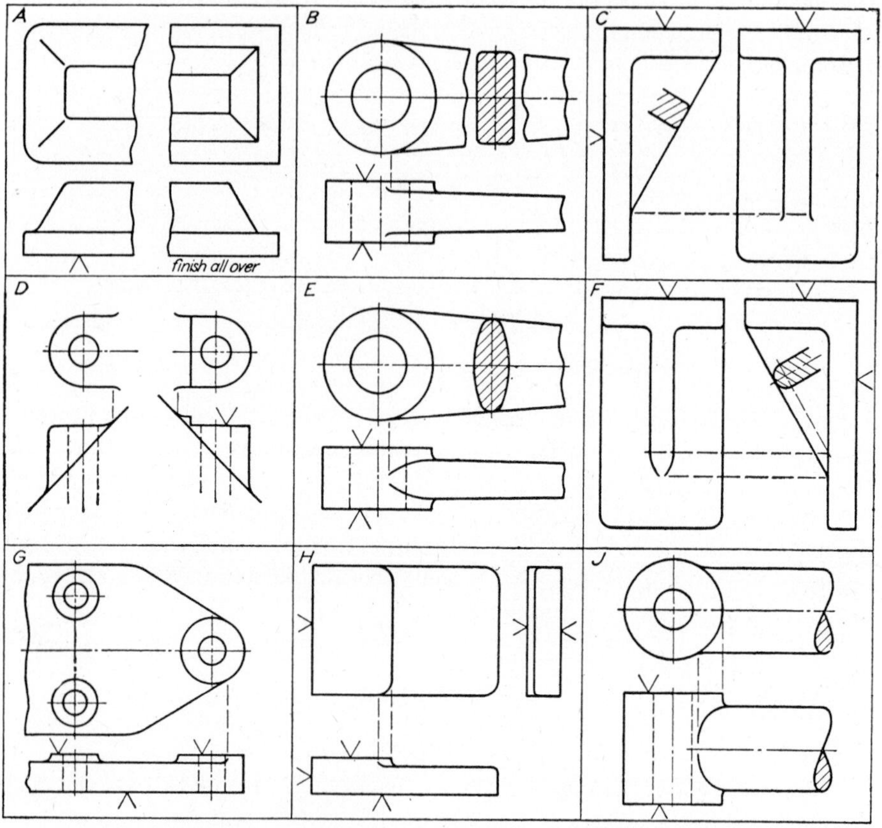

FIG. 9·29—Conventional fillets, rounds, and runouts.

Runouts, or *die-outs*, as they are sometimes called, are conventional indications of filleted intersections where theoretically there would be no line because there is no abrupt change in direction. Figure 9·29 shows some conventional representations of fillets and rounds, with runouts of arms and brackets intersecting other surfaces.

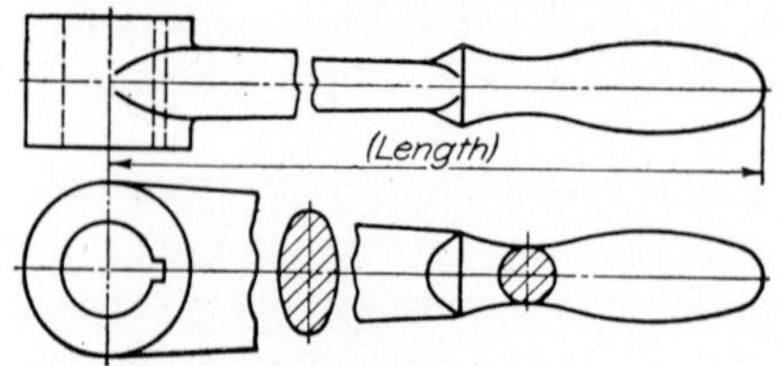

FIG. 9·30—Broken view with revolved sections.

9·19 Conventional breaks. In making a detail of a long bar or piece with uniform shape of cross section, there is evidently no necessity for drawing its whole length. It may be shown to a larger, and thus better, scale by breaking out a piece, moving the ends together, and giving the true length by a dimension, as in Fig. 9·30. The shape of the cross section is indicated either by a revolved section or, more often, by a semipictorial break line, as in Fig. 9·31. This figure also shows some other conventional symbols.

9·20 Conventional symbols. Draftsmen use conventional representation for indicating many details, such as screw threads, springs, pipe fittings, electrical apparatus, etc. These have been standardized by the ASA, whose code for materials in section has already been referred to in paragraph 9·12.

The symbols of two crossed diagonals is used for two distinct purposes: first, to indicate on a shaft the position of finish for a bearing; and second, to indicate that a certain surface (usually parallel to the picture plane) is flat. These two uses are not apt to be confused, Fig. 9·31.

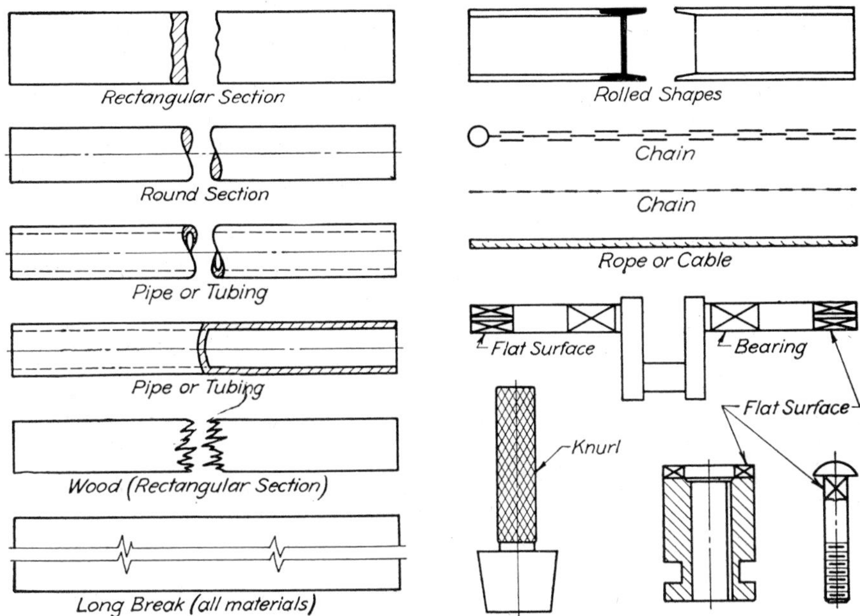

FIG. 9·31—Conventional breaks and other symbols.

Because of constant recurrence, the representation of screw threads is one of the most important items under conventional symbols. Up to the time of their official standardization by the ASA, there were a dozen different thread symbols in use. Now one regular symbol and one simplified one are adopted for American drawings, and both are understood internationally. The symbols for indicating threads on bolts, screws, and tapped holes are given in Chap. 13. This chapter also shows the conventional representation of helical springs. The conventional methods of representing pipe and fittings are given in Chap. 14. Welding symbols are shown in Chap. 16.

The conventional symbols mentioned in the last paragraph are used principally on machine drawings. Architectural drawing, because of the small scales employed, uses many conventional symbols, and topographic drawing is made up entirely of symbols.

PROBLEMS

9·21 Selections from the following problems may be used only for shape description, or as working drawings by adding dimensions.

1, 2, 3. Figs. 9·32 to 9·34. Given side view. Draw full front and side view in section. Scale to suit.

4. Fig. 9·35. Draw top view and change front and side views to sectional views as indicated.

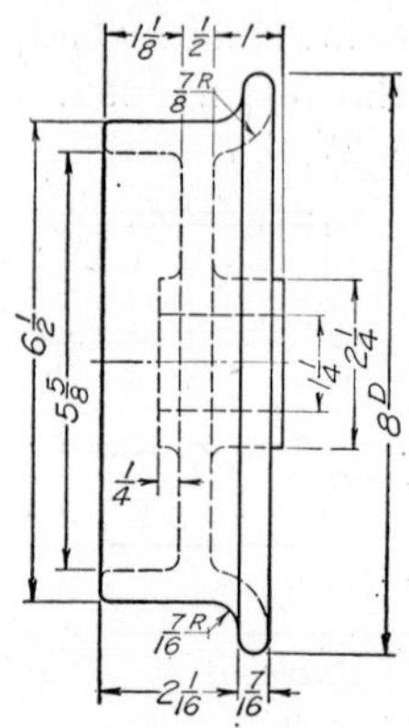

Fig. 9·32—Flanged wheel.

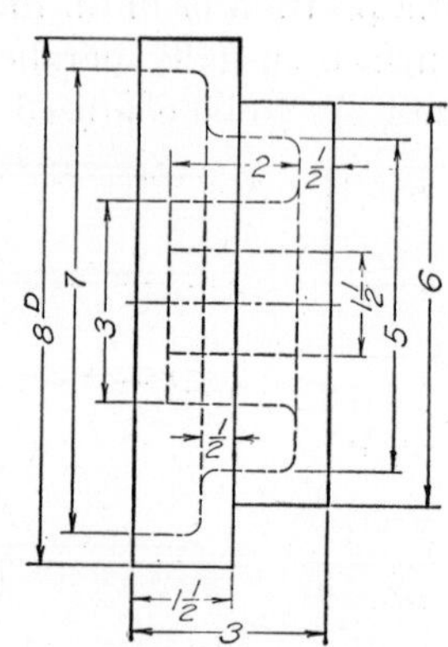

Fig. 9·33—Step pulley.

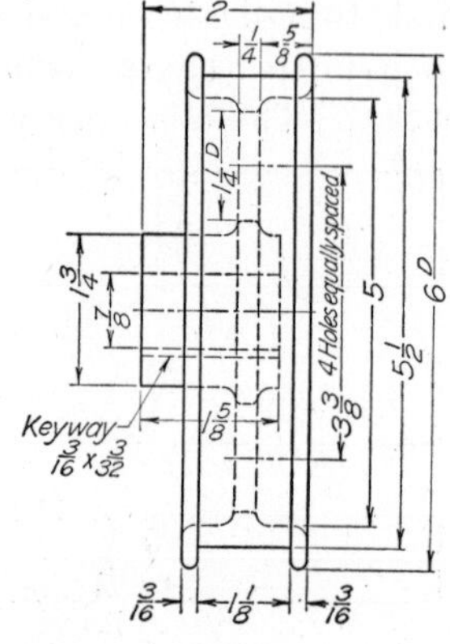

Fig. 9·34—Flanged pulley.

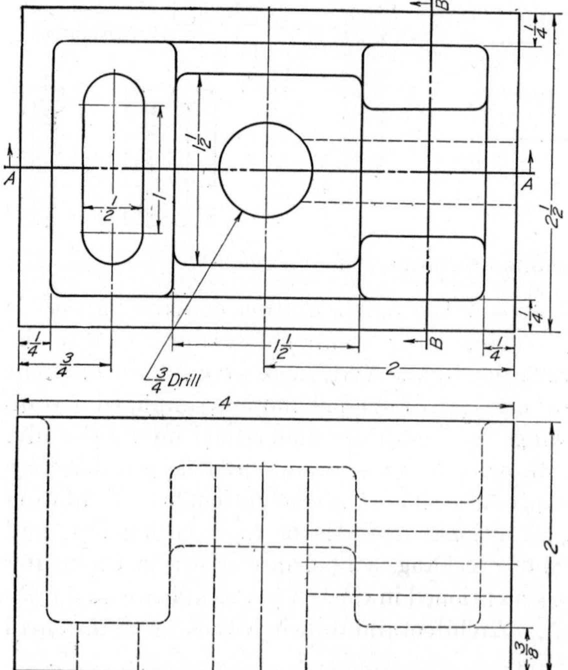

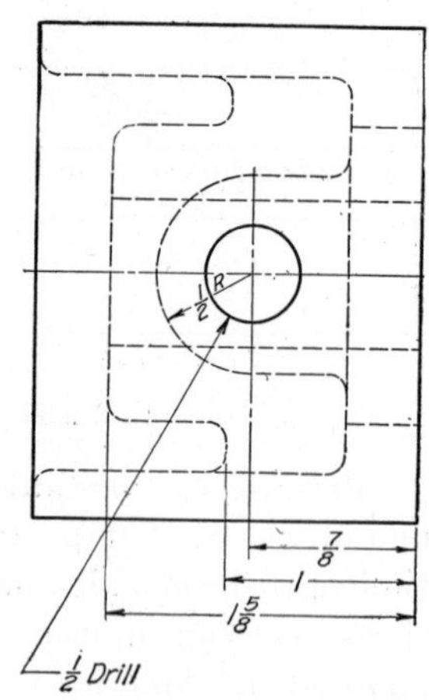

Fig. 9·35—Section study.

5. Fig. 9·36. Draw top view and make front and two side views in section on cutting planes indicated. Scale to suit.

6, 7. Figs. 9·37 and 9·38. Change right-side view to a full section.

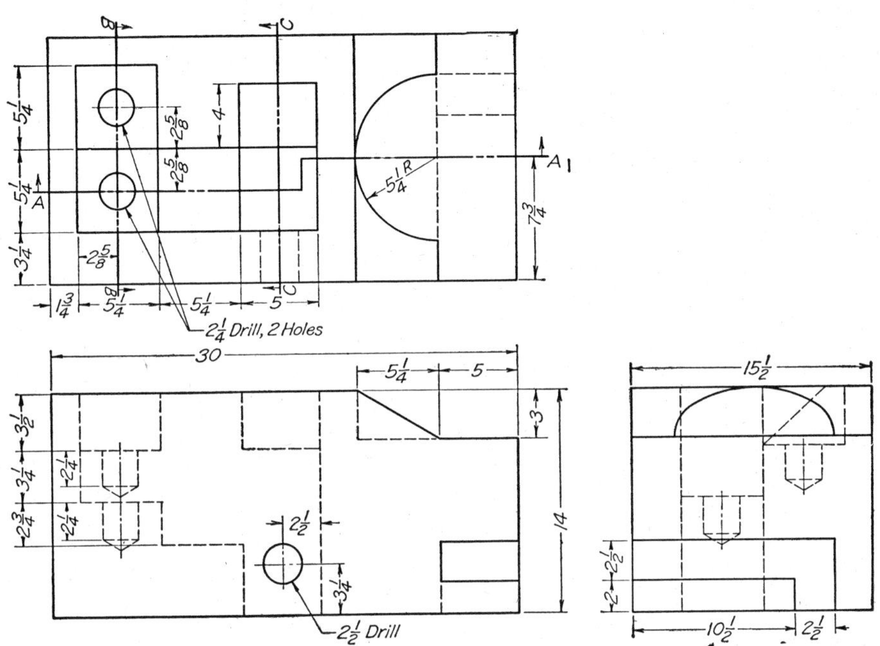

FIG. 9·36—Section study.

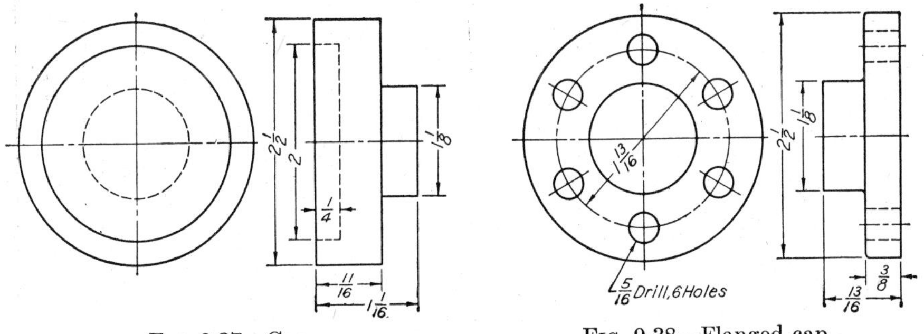

FIG. 9·37—Cap.

FIG. 9·38—Flanged cap.

8, 9. Figs. 9·39 and 9·40. Change right-side view to a full section.
10, 11. Figs. 9·41 and 9·42. Change right-side view to a full section.
12. Fig. 9·43. Change front view to a full section.
13. Fig. 9·44. Change right-side view to sectional view as indicated.

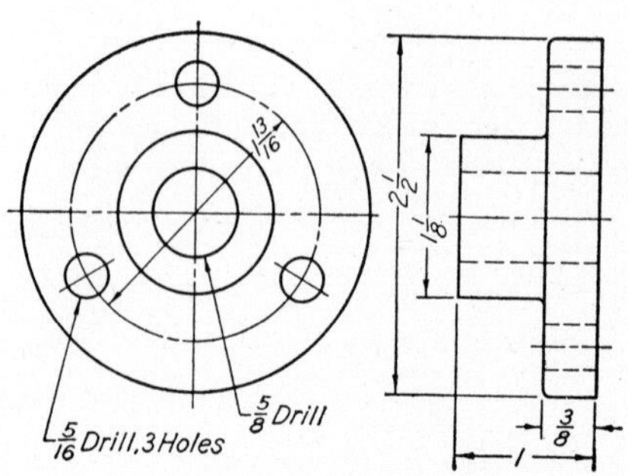

FIG. 9·39—Pump-rod guide.

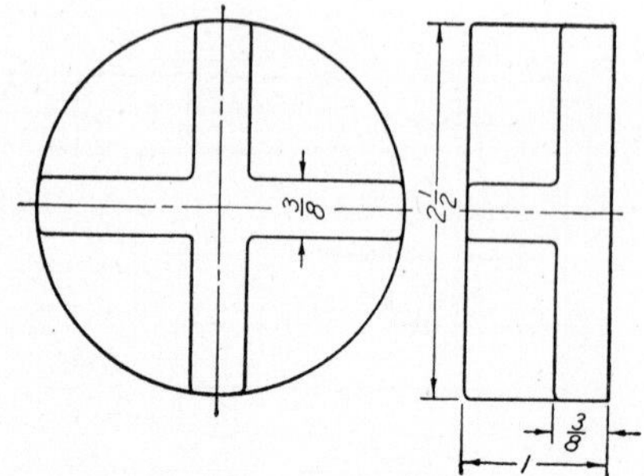

FIG. 9·40—Ribbed plate.

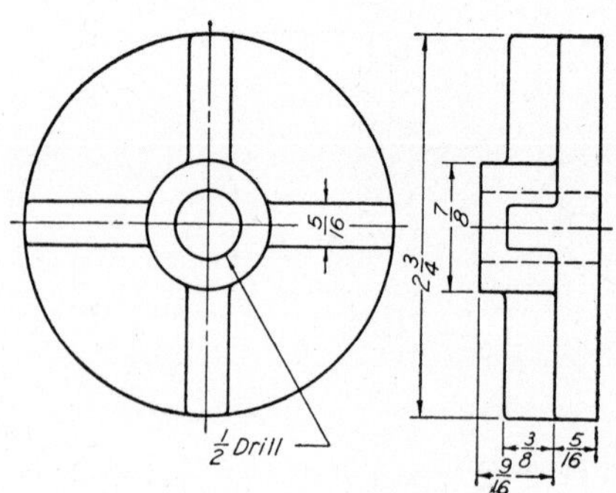

FIG. 9·41—Faceplate.

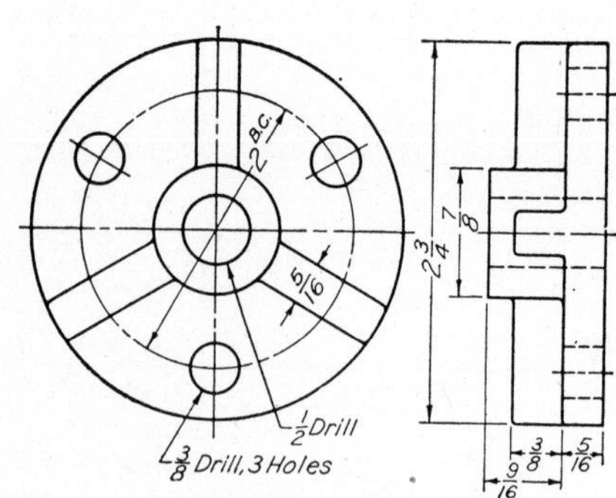

FIG. 9·42—Ribbed support.

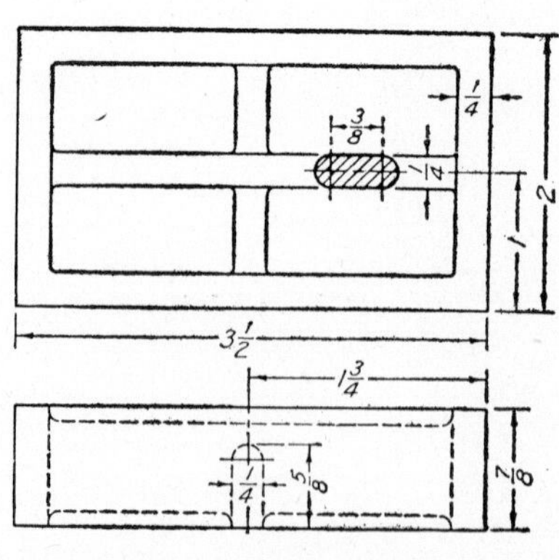

FIG. 9·43—Filler block.

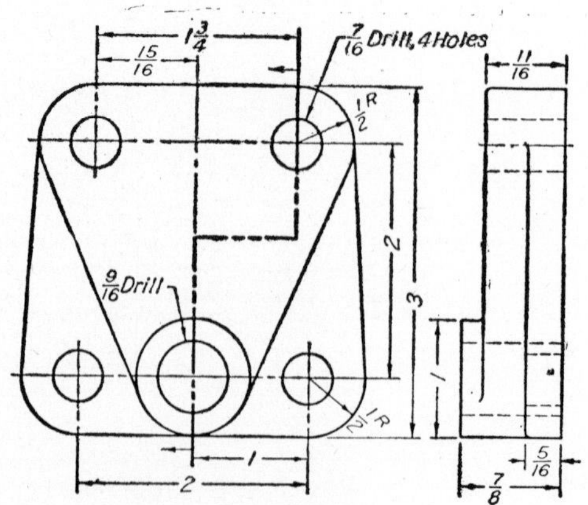

FIG. 9·44—Housing cover.

14. Fig. 9·45. Draw top view as shown and front view as a full section.

15. Fig. 9·46. Draw top view as shown and front view in half section on *A-A*.

16. Fig. 9·47. Draw top view as shown and change front and side views to sections as indicated.

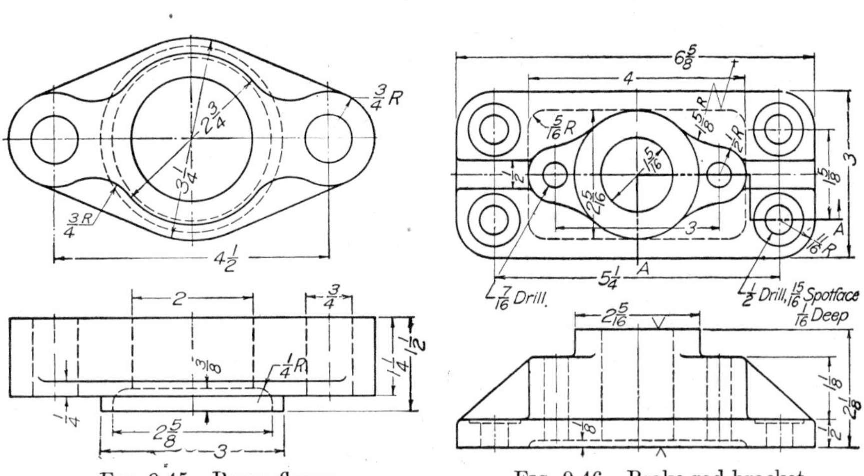

Fig. 9·45—Pump flange.

Fig. 9·46—Brake-rod bracket.

Fig. 9·47—Bolted anchor block.

17. Fig. 9·48. Draw top view and necessary sectional view or views to best describe the object.

18. Fig. 9·49. Draw three views making side view as a section on *A-A*.

19. Fig. 9·49. Draw three views making top view as a section on *B-B*.

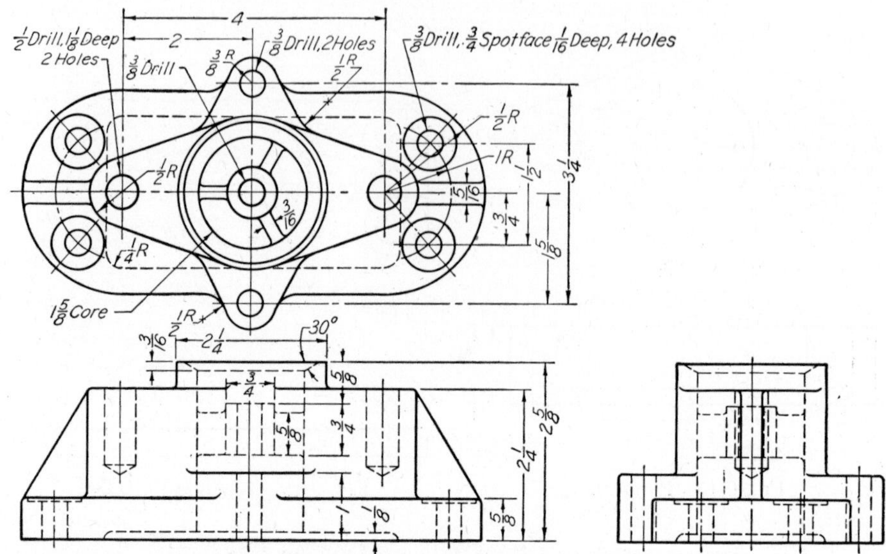

Fig. 9·48—Cover and valve body.

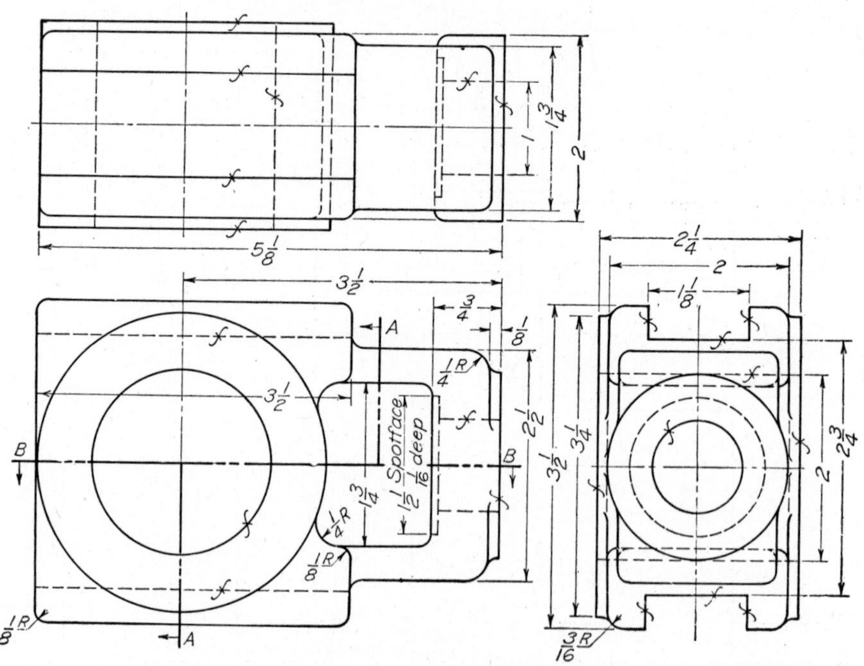

Fig. 9·49—Crosshead.

20. Fig. 9·50. Draw given front view as new top view; then make new front view as section *B-B*, and auxiliary elevation section *A-A*.

21. Fig. 9·51. Draw front view and longitudinal section. The assembly comprises a cast-iron base, a bronze bushing, a bronze disk, and two steel dowel pins.

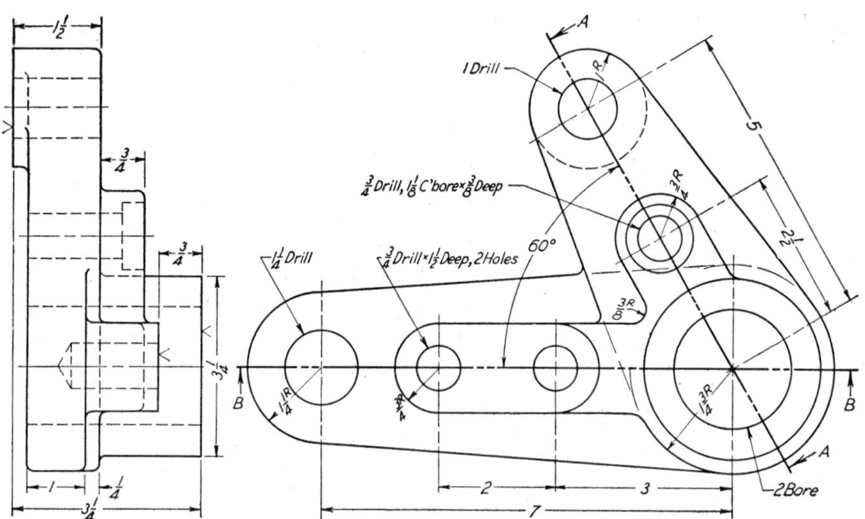

FIG. 9·50—Compound bell crank.

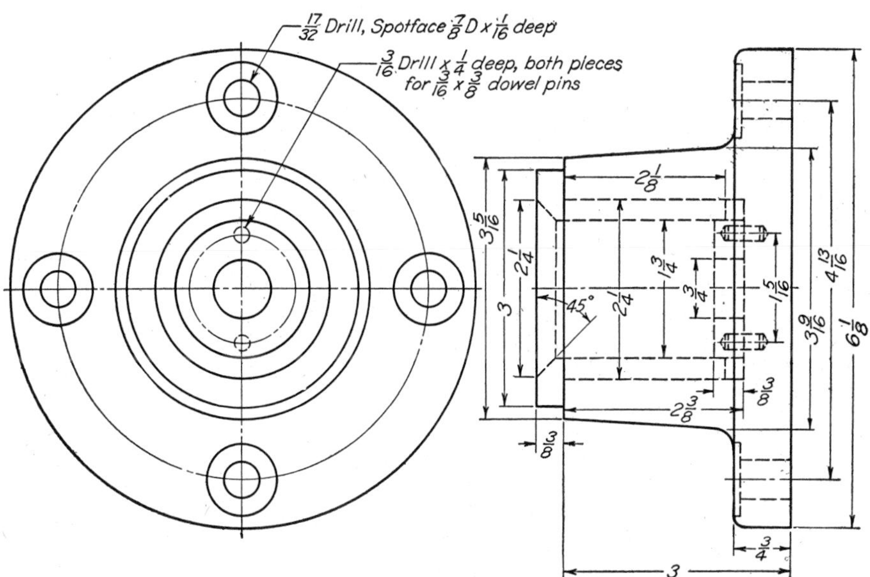

FIG. 9·51—Step bearing.

22. Fig. 9·52. Draw two-half-end views and longitudinal section. The assembly consists of cast-iron body, two bronze bushings, steel shaft, cast-iron pulley, and steel taper pin.

23. Fig. 9·53. Draw top view as shown and new front view in section. Show cross section of link with revolved or removed section. The assembly comprises a cast-steel link, two bronze bushings, steel toggle pin, steel collar, steel taper pin, and part of the cast-steel supporting lug.

24. Fig. 9·54. Select views that will best describe the piece.

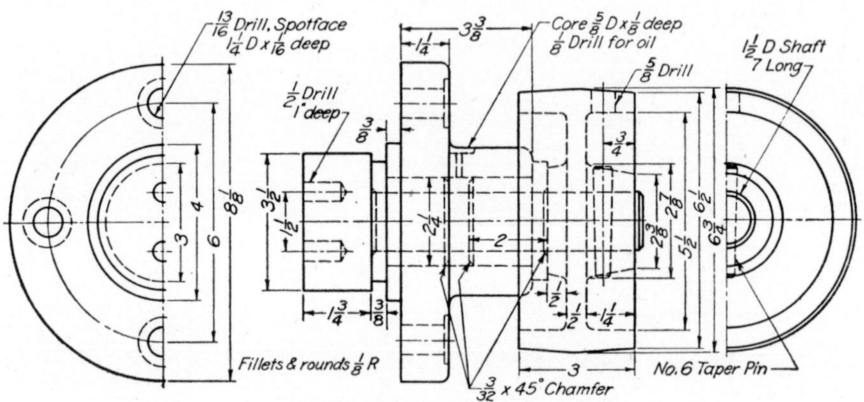

Fig. 9·52—Pulley bracket assembly.

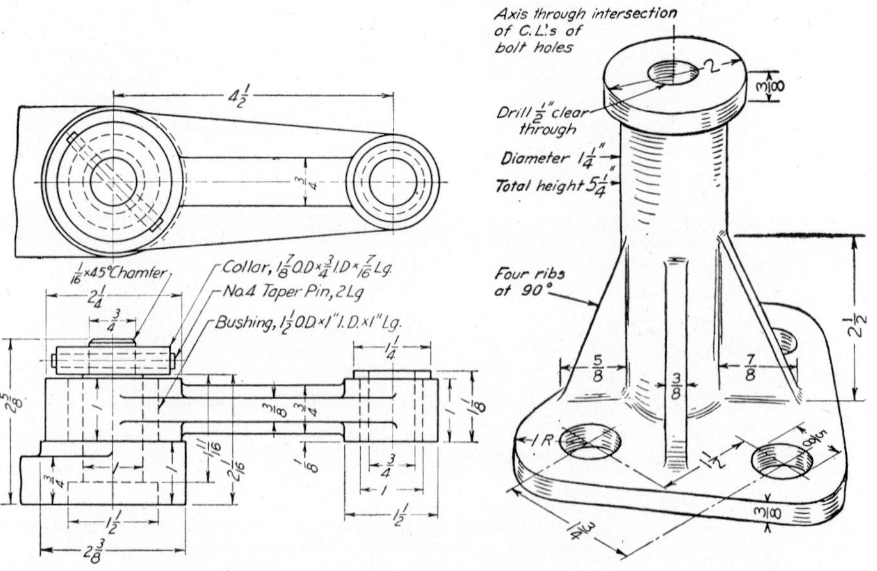

Fig. 9·53—Link assembly.

Fig. 9·54—Stem support.

25. Fig. 9·55. Draw front view, and side view in section.

26. Fig. 9·56. Draw top view and sectional view, or views, to best describe the object.

27. Fig. 9·57. Select views that will best describe the piece.

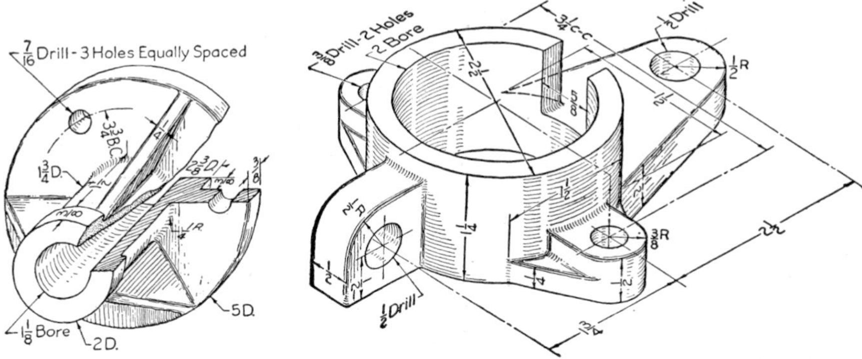

Fig. 9·55—Support.

Fig. 9·56—Column collar.

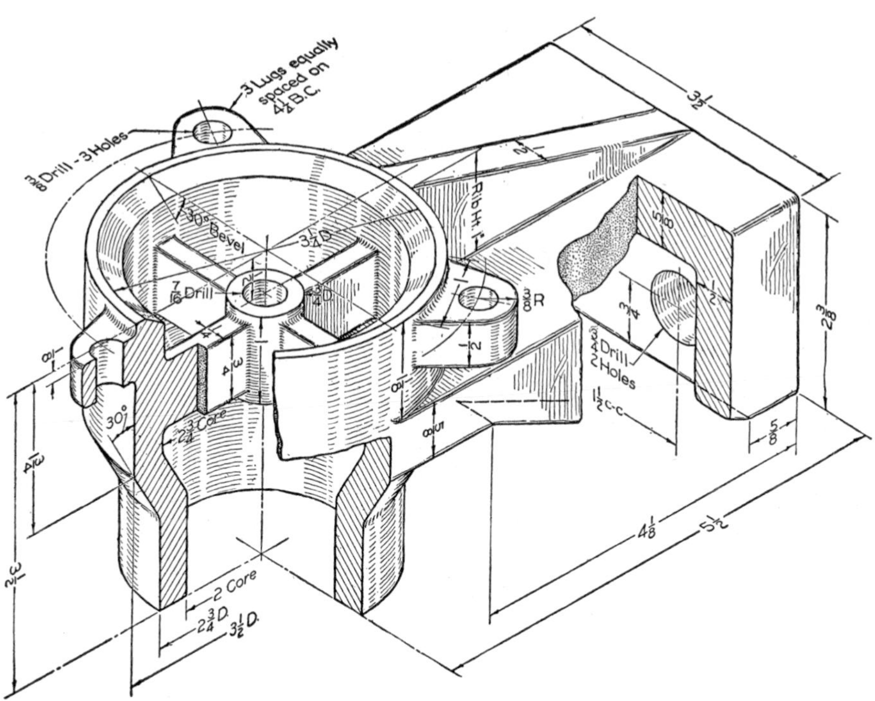

Fig. 9·57—Relief-valve body.

TEXT-FILMS

The following McGraw-Hill Text-Film was produced for specific use with Chap. 9:

Sections and Conventions (15-min. sound motion picture).

This Text-Film describes the theory and use of sectional views, their various types, and the principles and practices followed in their construction; explains the meaning of symbols used in sectioning; shows other types of conventional practices.

A coordinated silent filmstrip designed as a follow-up to this film summarizes the important facts about sectioning and reemphasizes the key points in the film.

Chapter 10

THE DRAWINGS AND THE SHOP

10·1 The test of any working drawing for legibility, completeness, and accuracy is the production of the object or assembly by the shop without further information than that given on the drawing. The draftsman's knowledge of shop methods will, to a great extent, govern the effectiveness and completeness of the dimensioning and notes; the proper specification of machining operations, heat-treatment and finish; the accuracy to be

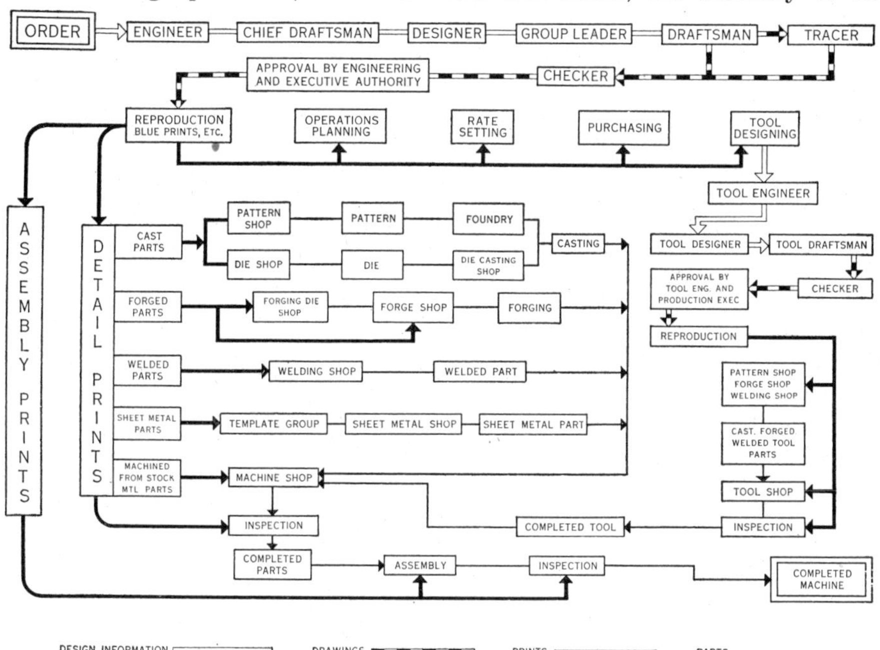

FIG. 10·1—Development and distribution of drawings.

maintained on mating parts; and, in some cases, the order of machining. The young draftsman, whenever opportunity permits, should follow operations through the shops, get acquainted with shop men, and enlarge his knowledge by reading and discussion. The glossary of shop terms, page 673, should be studied, in connection with the dimensioning and notes on the various working drawings in this book, to gain an acquaintance with the terms and the form of designation in the notes. This chapter is thus given as an introduction to those following on dimensioning and working drawings.

The relation of drawings, and the prints made from them, to the operations of production is illustrated in the graphical chart, Fig. 10·1. This chart shows in diagrammatic form the different steps in the development of the drawings and their distribution and use in connection with the shop operations from the time the order is received until the finished machine is delivered to the shipping room.

10·2 Effect of the manufacturing method on the drawing. In the drawing of any machine part, a first consideration is the manufacturing process to be used, as on this depends the representation of the detailed

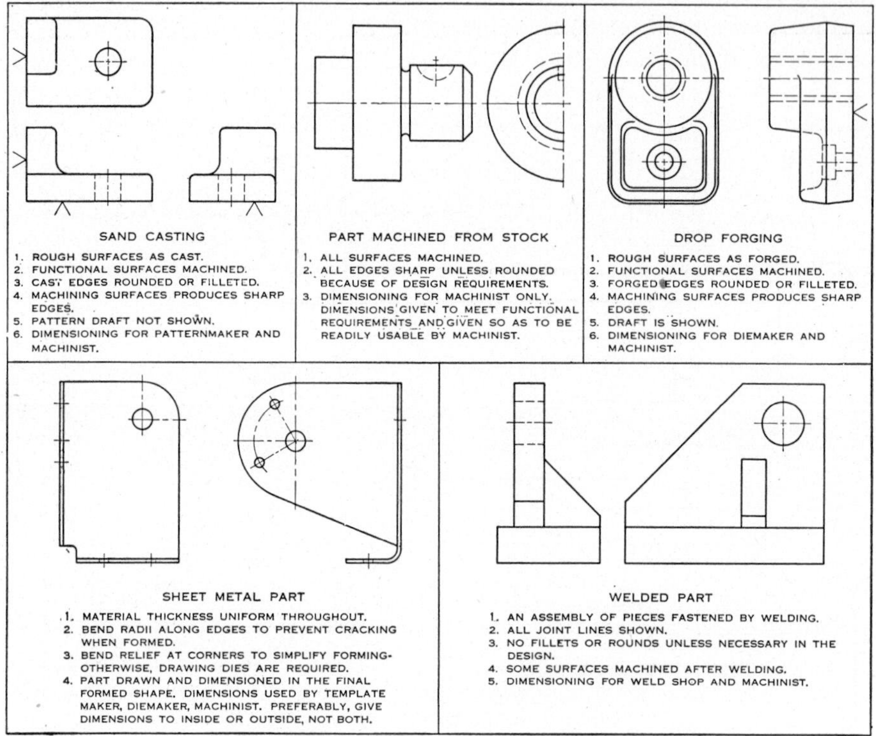

FIG. 10·2—Drawing requirements for different manufacturing methods.

features of the part and, to some extent, the choice of dimensions. Special or unusual methods may occasionally be used, but most machine parts are produced by (1) casting, (2) forging, (3) machining from standard stock, (4) welding, or (5) forming from sheet stock.

Each of the different methods will produce a characteristic detailed shape and appearance of the parts, and these features must be shown on the drawing. Figure 10·2 shows and lists typical features of each method and indicates the differences in drawing practice.

10·3 The drawings. For the production of any part, a detail working drawing is necessary, complete with shape and size description, and giving, where needed, the operations that are to be performed by the shop. Machined surfaces must be clearly indicated, with dimensions chosen and placed so as to be useful to the various shops without the necessity of adding or subtracting dimensions or scaling the drawing.

Two general practices may be followed: (1) the "single-drawing" system, in which only one drawing, showing the finished part, is made to be used by all of the shops involved in producing the part; and (2) the "multiple-drawing" system, in which different drawings are prepared, one for each shop, giving only the information required by the shop for which the drawing is made.

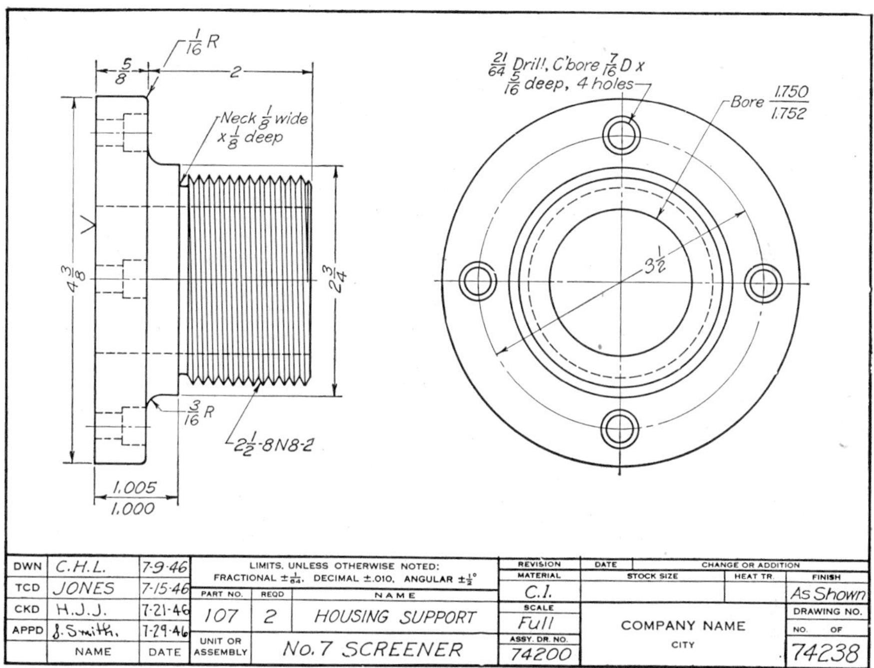

FIG. 10·3—A working drawing.

The second practice is recommended, as the drawings are much easier to dimension without ambiguity, are somewhat simpler and more direct, and are therefore easier for the shop to use. Figure 10·3 is a "single drawing," to be used by both the pattern shop and the machine shop. Figures 12·3 and 12·4 are "multiple" drawings, Fig. 12·3 for the patternmaker, and Fig. 12·4 for the machine shop.

10·4 Sand castings. The drawing, Fig. 10·3, shows (in the title strip) that the material to be used is cast iron (CI), indicating that the part will be formed by pouring molten iron into a mold, in this case a "sand mold," resulting in a sand casting. Before the part can be cast, however, the shape of the part must be produced in the sand mold.

10·5 The pattern shop. The drawing is first used by the patternmaker who will make a pattern, or "model," of the part in wood. From this, if a large quantity of castings is required, a metal pattern, often of aluminum, is made. The patternmaker provides for the shrinkage of the casting by making the pattern oversize, using a "shrink rule" for his measurements. He also provides additional metal (machining allowance) for the machined surfaces, indicated on the drawing either (1) by finish marks, (2) by dimensions indicating a degree of precision attainable only by machining, or (3) by notes giving machining operations. The patternmaker also provides the "draft" or slight taper, not shown on the drawing, so that the pattern can be withdrawn easily from the sand. A "core box," for the making of sand cores for the hollow parts of the casting, is also made in the pattern shop. A knowledge of patternmaking is of great aid in dimensioning, as almost all the dimensions are used by the patternmaker, while only the dimensions for finished features will be used by the machine shop.

10·6 Drawings of castings. Casting drawings are usually made as a single drawing of the machined casting, having dimensions for both the patternmaker and machinist, Fig. 10·3. If the "multiple" drawing system is followed, a drawing of the unmachined casting, with allowances for machining accounted for and having no finish marks or finish dimensions, will be made for the patternmaker; then a second drawing for the machinist shows the finished shape and gives machining dimensions.

For complicated or difficult castings, a special "pattern drawing" may be made, Fig. 10·4, showing every detail of the pattern, including the amount of draft, the parting line, "core prints" for supporting the cores in the mold, and the pattern material. Similar detail drawings may also be made for the core boxes.

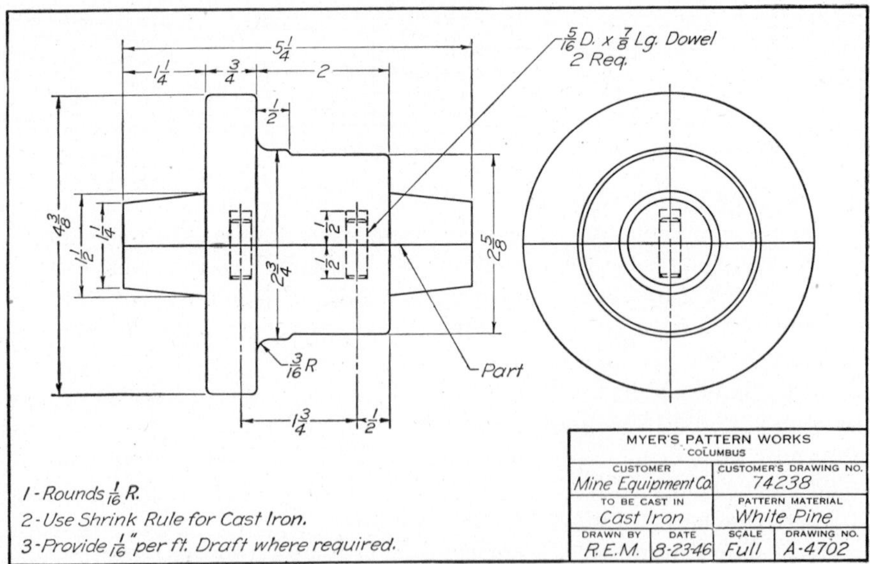

FIG. 10·4—A pattern drawing.

10·7 The foundry. The pattern and core box, or boxes, are sent to the foundry, and sand molds made so that molten metal may be poured into the molds and allowed to cool, forming the completed rough casting Figure 10·5 shows a cross section of a two-part mold, showing the space left by the pattern, and the core in place. Only in occasional instances does the foundryman call for assistance from the drawing, as his job is simply to reproduce the pattern in metal.

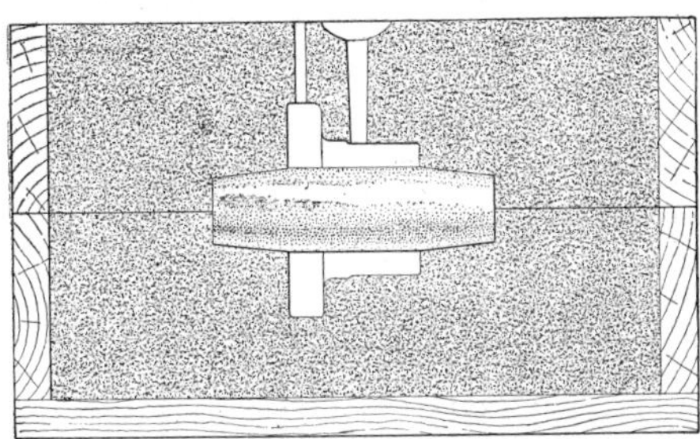

FIG. 10·5—Cross section of a two-part mold.

Permanent molds, made of cast iron coated on the molding surfaces with a refractory material, are sometimes an advantage in that the mold may be used over and over again, thus saving the time to make an individual sand mold for each casting. This method is usually limited to small castings.

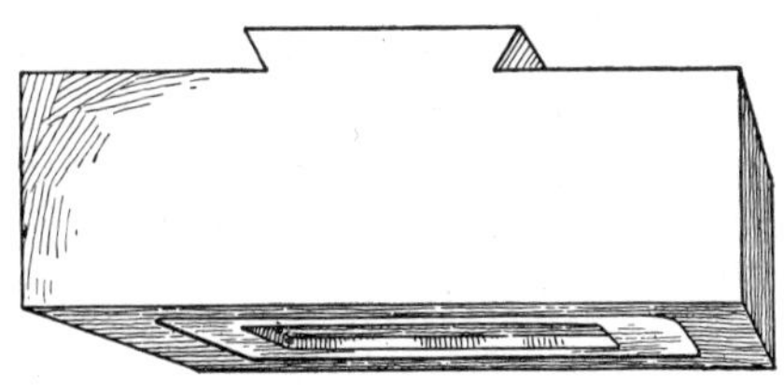

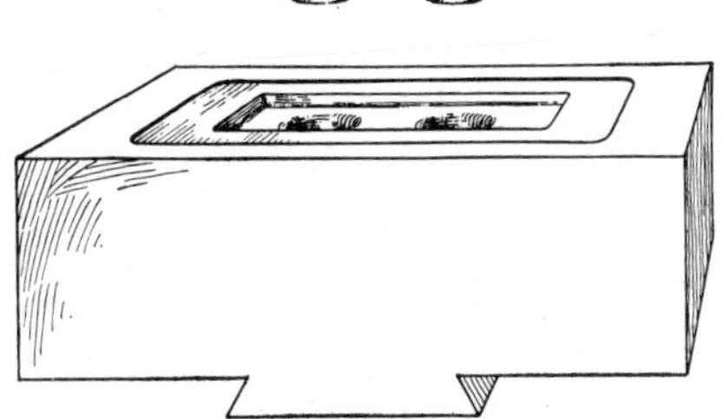

FIG. 10·6—Drop-forging dies and the forged part.

Die castings are made by forcing molten metal under pressure into a steel die mounted in a special die-casting machine. Alloys with a low melting point are used in order to avoid damaging the die. Because of the accuracy possible in making the die, a fine finish and accurate dimensions of the part may be obtained; thus machining is rarely necessary.

10·8 Forgings. Forgings are made by heating metal to make it plastic and then forming the metal to shape on a power hammer with or without the aid of special steel dies. Large parts are often hammered with dies of generalized all-purpose shape. Smaller parts in quantity may warrant the expense of making special dies. Some small forgings are made with the metal cold.

Drop forgings are the most common and are made in dies of the kind shown in Fig. 10·6. The lower die is held on the bed of the drop hammer and the upper die is raised by the hammer mechanism. The hot metal is placed between the dies and the upper die dropped several times, causing the metal to flow into the cavity of the dies. The slight excess of material will form a "flashing" surrounding the forging at the parting plane of the dies, Fig. 10·6. This flashing is then cut off with a pair of shearing dies made for the purpose. Considerable draft must be provided for release of the forging from the dies.

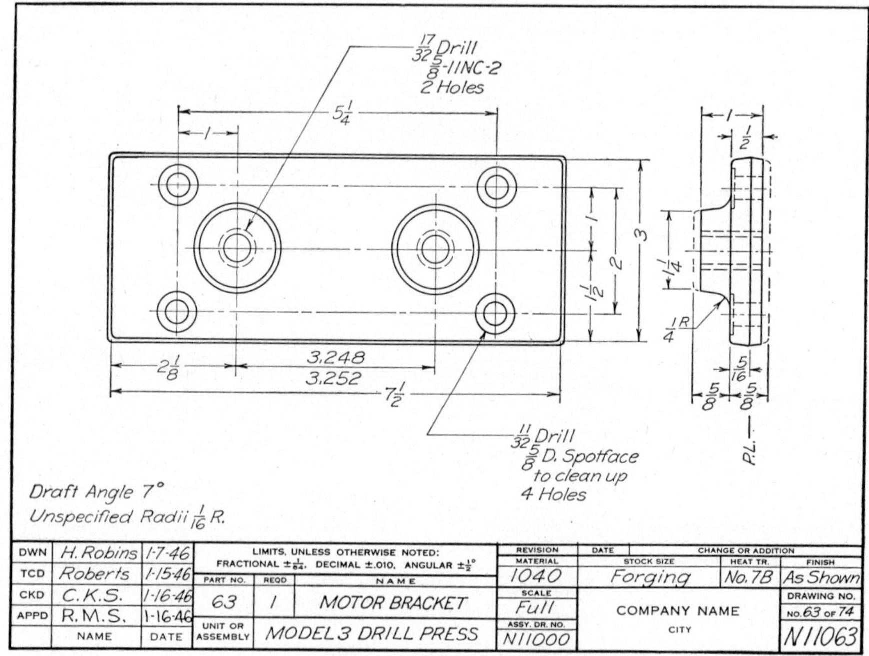

FIG. 10·7—A working drawing.

10·9 Drawings of forgings. Forging drawings are either prepared according to the multiple system, one drawing for the diemaker and one for the machinist, or are made as a single drawing for both, Fig. 10·7. In either case, the parting line and draft should be shown, and the amount of draft specified. On the single drawing, the shape of the finished forging is shown in full outline and the machining allowance is indicated by "alternate position" lines, thus completing the shape of the rough forging. This single drawing therefore combines two drawings into one, with complete dimensions for both diemaker and machinist.

10·10 The machine shop. The machine shop produces parts machined from stock material, and finishes castings, forgings, etc., requiring finished surfaces. Cylindrical and conical surfaces are machined on a lathe. Flat or plane surfaces are machined on a planer, shaper, milling machine, broaching machine, or, in some cases (facing), on a lathe. Holes are drilled, reamed, counterbored, and countersunk on a drill press or lathe; holes are bored on a boring mill or lathe. For exact work, grinding machines with wheels of abrasive material are used. Grinders are also coming into greatly increased use for operations formerly made with cutting tools. In quantity production, many special machine tools and automatic machines are in use. The special tools, jigs, and fixtures made for the machine parts are held in the toolroom ready for the machine shop.

10·11 Fundamentals of machining. All machining operations remove metal, either to make a smoother and more accurate surface, as by planing of turning, or to produce a surface not previously existing, as by drilling, punching, etc. The metal is removed by a hardened steel or diamond cutting tool (machining) or an abrasive wheel (grinding); the product, or "work piece," as well as the tool or wheel, being held and guided by the machine. When ordinary cutting tools are used, the product must remain relatively soft until after all machining has been performed upon it, but if carbide or diamond-tipped tools are used, or if grinding wheels are employed, the product may be hardened or heat-treated before finishing.

All machining methods may be classified according to the operating principle of the machine performing the work.

1. The surface may be *generated* by moving the work with respect to a cutting tool, or the tool with respect to the work, following the geometric laws for producing the surface.
2. The surface may be *formed* with a specially shaped cutting tool, moving either work or tool while the other is stationary.

The forming method is, in general, less accurate than the generating method, as any irregularities in the cutter are reproduced on the work. In some cases a combination of the two methods is used.

10·12 The lathe. Called the "king of machine tools," the lathe is said to be capable of producing all other machine tools. Its primary func-

FIG. 10·8—Facing.

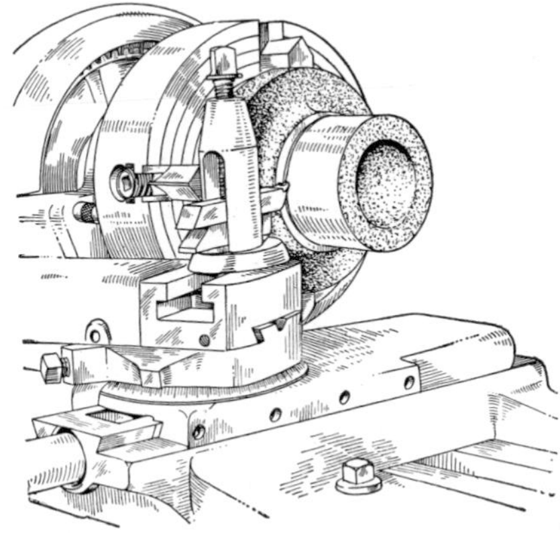

FIG. 10·9—Turning.

tion is for machining cylindrical, conical, and other surfaces of revolution, but with special attachments a great variety of operations can be performed. Figure 10·8 shows the casting made from the drawing of Fig. 10·3 held in the lathe chuck. As the work revolves, the cutting tool is moved across perpendicular to the axis of revolution, removing metal from the base and producing a plane surface by generation. This operation is called *facing*. After being faced, the casting is turned around and the finished base is aligned against the face of the chuck, bringing the cylindrical surface into position for *turning* to the diameter indicated in the thread note on the drawing. The neck shown at the intersection of the base with the body is turned first, running the tool into the casting to a depth slightly greater

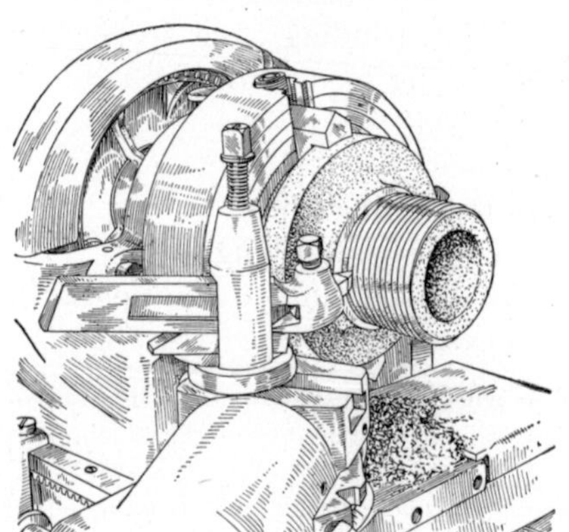

Fig. 10·10—Threading.

Fig. 10·11—Boring.

than the depth of the thread. The cylindrical surface is then turned (generated) by moving the tool parallel to the axis of revolution, Fig. 10·9. Figure 10·10 shows the thread being cut on the finished cylinder. The tool is ground to the profile of the thread space, carefully lined up to the work, and moved parallel to the axis of revolution by the lead screw of the lathe. This operation is a combination of the fundamental processes, the thread profile being formed while the helix is generated.

The hole through the center of the casting, originally cored, is now finished by *boring*, as the cutting of an interior surface is called, Fig. 10·11. The tool is held in a boring bar and moved parallel to the axis of revolution, thus generating an internal cylinder.

Note that in these operations the dimensions used by the machinist have been (1) the finish mark on the base and thickness of the base, (2) the thread note and outside diameter of the thread, (3) the dimensions of the neck, (4) the distance from the base to the shoulder, and (5) the diameter of the bored hole.

Long cylindrical pieces to be turned in the lathe are supported by conical centers, one at each end. Figure 10·19 illustrates the principle.

10·13 The drill press. The partially finished piece is now taken to the drill press for drilling and counterboring the holes in the base according to the dimensions on the drawing. These dimensions give the diameter of the drill, the diameter and depth of the counterbore, and the location of

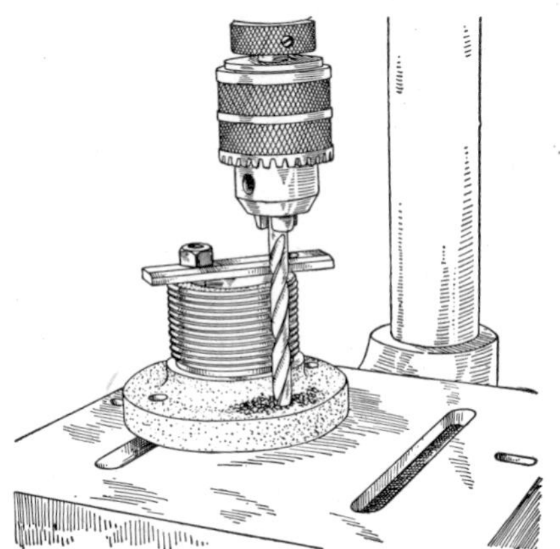

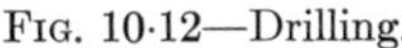

FIG. 10·12—Drilling.

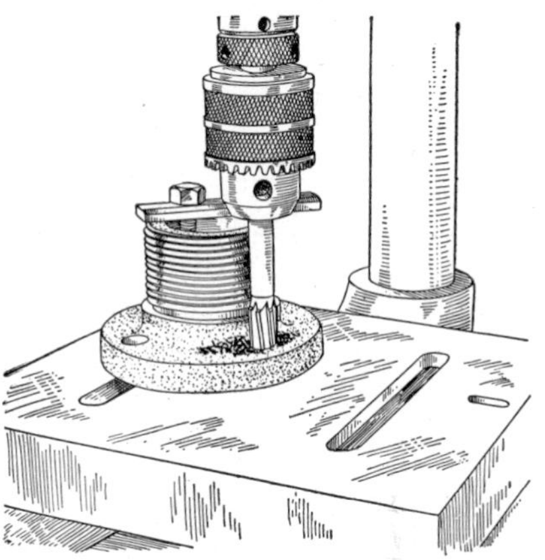

FIG. 10·13—Counterboring.

the holes. The casting is clamped to the drill-press table, Fig. 10·12, and the rotating drill brought into the work by a lever operating a rack and pinion in the head of the machine. The cutting is done by two ground lips on the end of the drill, Fig. 10·21*A*. Drilling can be done in a lathe, the work revolving while the drill is held in, and moved by, the tailstock. In Fig. 10·13 the drill has been replaced by a counterboring tool, Fig. 10·21*C*, whose diameter is the size specified on the drawing, which has a pilot on the end to fit into the drilled hole, thus ensuring concentricity. This tool is fed in to the depth shown on the drawing.

FIG. 10·14—Shaping.

Study the drawing of Fig. 10·3 with the illustrations of the operations, and check, first, the dimensions that would be used by the patternmaker, and, second, those required by the machinist.

10·14 The shaper and the planer. The drop forging of Fig. 10·7 requires machining on the base and boss surfaces.

Flat surfaces of this type may be machined on a shaper or a planer. In this case the shaper is used because of the relatively small size of the part, Fig. 10·14. The tool is held in a ram which moves back and forth across the work, taking a cut at each pass forward. Between the cuts the table moves laterally, so that closely spaced parallel cuts are made until the surface is completely machined.

The planer differs from the shaper in that its bed, carrying the work, moves back and forth under a stationary tool. It is generally used for a larger and heavier type of work than that done on a shaper.

10·15 Parts machined from standard stock. The shape of a part will often lend itself to machining directly from standard stock, such as bars, rods, tubing, plates, and blocks; or from extrusions and rolled shapes, such

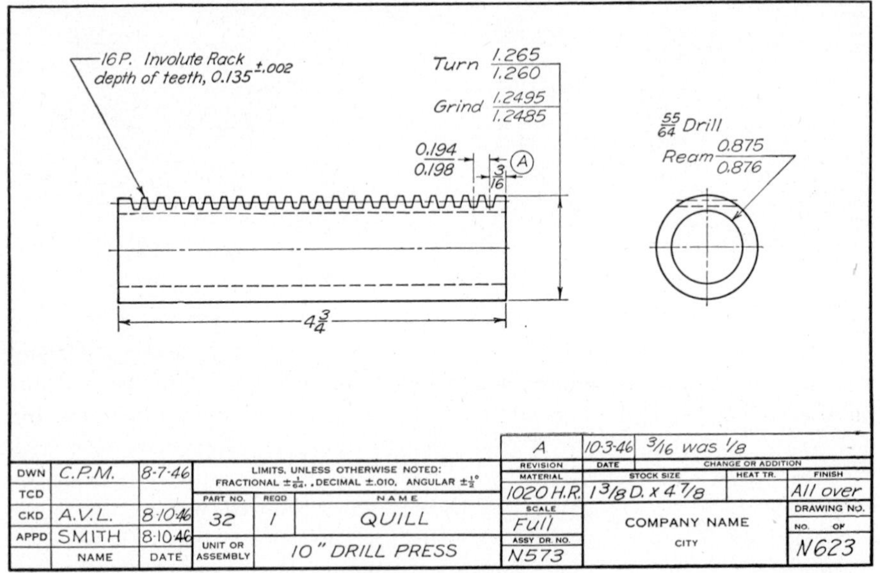

FIG. 10·15—A working drawing.

as angles, channels, etc. Hot-rolled (HR) and cold-rolled (CR) steel are common materials.

Parts produced from stock are usually finished on all surfaces and a general note "Finish All Over" on the drawing eliminates the use of finish marks. Figure 10·15 is the drawing of a part to be made from bar stock. Note the specification of material, stock size, etc., in the title.

10·16 The turret lathe. The *quill* of Fig. 10·15, produced in quantity, may be made in a turret lathe, except for the rack teeth and the outside diameter grinding. The stock is held in the collet chuck of the lathe. First the end surface is faced and then the cylindrical surface (OD) is turned. The work piece is then ready for drilling and reaming. The turret holds the various tools and swings them around into position as needed. A center drill starts a small hole to align the larger drill and then the drill and reamer are brought successively into position. The drill provides a hole slightly undersize, and then the reamer, cutting with its fluted sides, cleans out the hole and gives a smooth surface finished to a size within the dimensional limits on the drawing. Figure 10·16 shows the turret indexed so that the drill is out of the way and the reamer is in position. At the right is seen the cut-off tool ready to cut the piece to the length shown on the drawing.

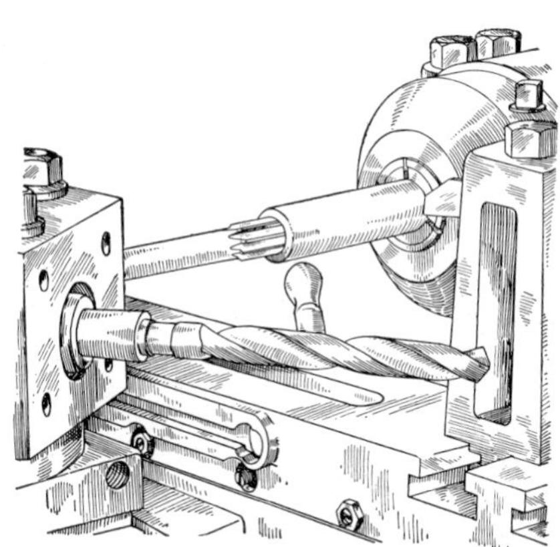

Fig. 10·16—Reaming.

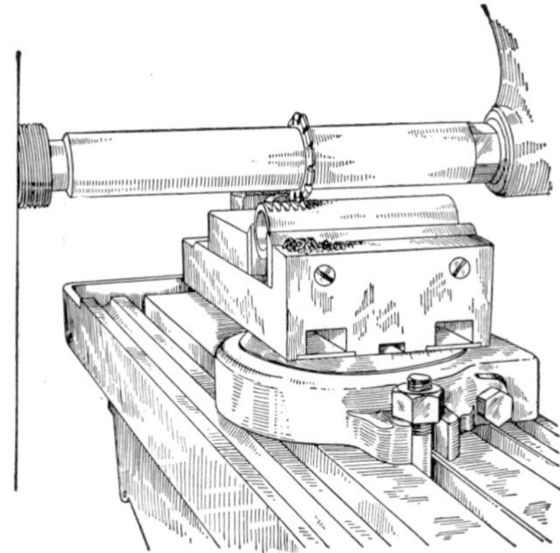

Fig. 10·17—Milling.

10·17 The milling machine. The dimensions of the rack teeth, Fig. 10·15, give the depth and spacing of the cuts, and also the specifications for the cutter to be used. This type of work is usually done on a milling machine. The work piece is held in a vise and moved horizontally into the rotating milling cutter, which, in profile, is the shape of the space between the teeth, Fig. 10·17. The cuts are spaced by moving the table of the machine to correspond with the distance shown on the drawing. Note that this operation is a forming process, as the shape depends upon the contour of the cutter. With several cutters mounted together (gang milling), a number of teeth can be cut at the same time.

There are many types of milling cutters made to cut on their periphery, their sides, or their ends, for forming flat, curved, or special surfaces. Three milling cutters are shown in Fig. 10·18.

10·18 The grinder. The general purpose of grinding is to make a smoother and more accurate surface than can be obtained by turning, planing, milling, etc. In many cases, pieces hardened by heat-treatment will warp slightly, and as ordinary machining methods are impractical with hardened materials, such parts are finish-ground after hardening.

The limit dimensions for the outside diameter of the quill, Fig. 10·15, indicate a grinding operation on a cylindrical grinder, Fig. 10·19. The abrasive wheel rotates at high speed, while the work piece, mounted on a mandrel between conical centers, rotates slowly in the opposite direction. The wheel usually moves laterally to cover the surface of the work piece. The work piece is gaged carefully during the operation to bring the size within the limits shown on the drawing and to check for a cylindrical surface without taper. The machine for flat surfaces, called a "surface grinder," holds the work piece on a flat table moving back and forth under the abrasive wheel. The table "indexes" laterally after each pass under the work.

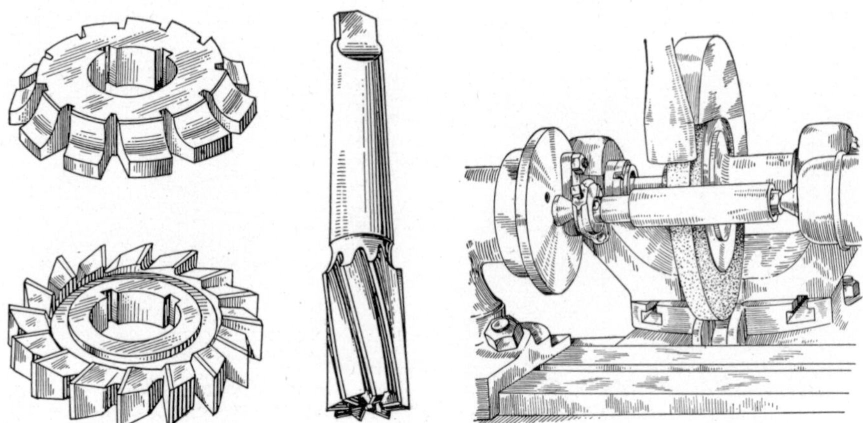

FIG. 10·18—Milling cutters. FIG. 10·19—Grinding.

Lapping, honing, and superfinishing are methods of producing smooth, accurate, mirror-like surfaces after grinding. All three methods use very fine abrasives, either powdered and carried in oil on a piece of formed soft metal (lapping) or fine-grained compact stones (honing and superfinishing) to rub against the surface to be finished and reduce scratches and waviness.

10·19 The broaching machine. A broach is a long tapered bar having a series of cutting edges (teeth), each successively removing a small amount of material until the last edge forms the shape desired. For flat or irregular external surfaces, the broach and work piece are held by the broaching machine and the broach passed across the surface of the work piece. For internal surfaces, the broach is either pulled or pushed through a hole to give the finished size or to change the shape.

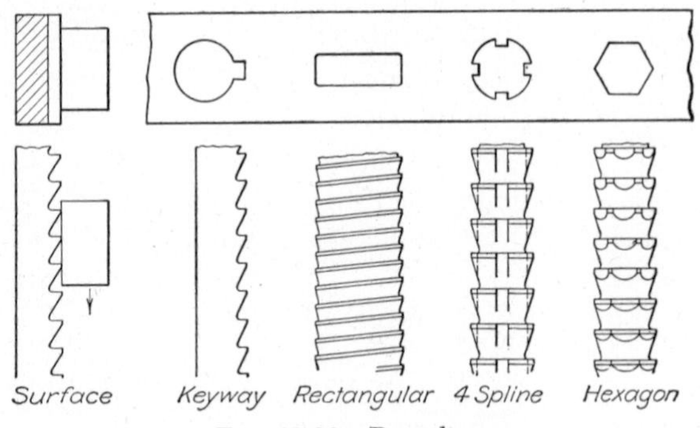

FIG. 10·20—Broaches.

Many machined shapes can be more easily produced by broaching than by any other method. Figure 10·20 shows several forms of broaches and the shapes they produce.

10·20 Small tools. The shop uses a variety of small tools, both in powered machines and as hand tools. Figure 10·21 shows, at *A*, a *twist drill*, available in a variety of sizes (numbered, lettered, fractional, and metric) for producing holes in almost any material; at *B*, a *reamer* used to enlarge and smooth a previously existing hole and to give greater accuracy than is possible by drilling alone; at *C*, a *counterbore*, and at *D*, a *countersink*,

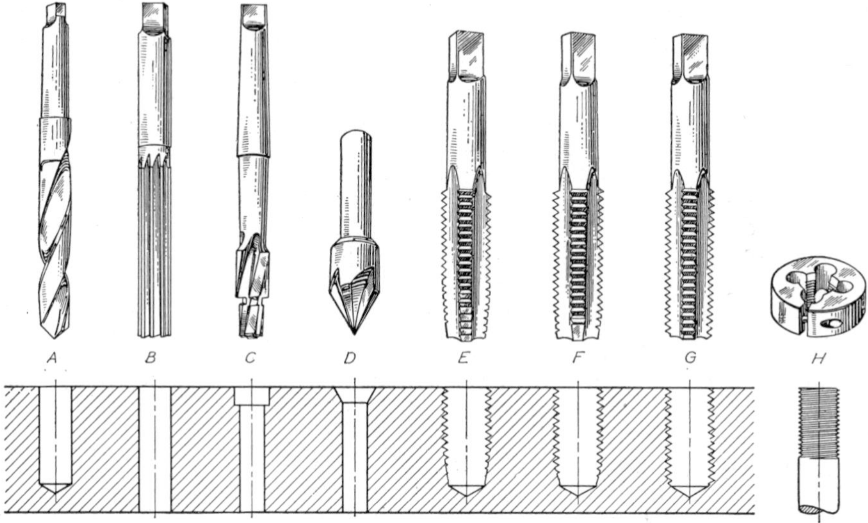

FIG. 10·21—Various tools.

both used to enlarge and alter the end of a hole (usually for screw heads). A *spot-facing tool* is similar to a counterbore. *Taper*, *plug*, and *bottoming* taps for cutting the thread of a tapped hole are shown at *E*, *F*, and *G*. A die for threading a rod or shaft is shown at *H*.

10·21 Welded parts. Simple shapes cut from standard rod, bar, or plate stock may be combined by welding to form a finished part. Some machining after welding is frequently necessary. Chapter 16 discusses welding drawings.

10·22 Parts from standard sheet. A relatively thin sheet or strip of standard thickness may first be cut to size "in the flat," then bent, formed, punched, etc., to form the final required part. The drawing should be made so as to give information for the "template maker," and also information required for bending and forming the sheet. Sometimes separate developments (Chap. 20) are made. The thickness of sheet stock is specified by (1) giving the gage (see table, page 663) and the equivalent thickness in decimals of an inch, or (2) only the decimal thickness (the practice followed in specifying aluminum sheet). Figure 12·7 is a working drawing of a sheet-metal part.

10·23 Plastics. Plastics are available either in standard bar, rod, tubing, sheet, etc., from which parts can be made by machining, or in granular form to be used in "molding," a process similar to die-casting in which the material is heated to a plastic state and compressed by a die (compression molding) or injected under pressure into a die (injection molding). Metal inserts for threads, wear bushings, etc., are sometimes cast into the part, as in the plastic fan base, Fig. 15·90. Consideration should be given the diemaker when dimensioning the drawing.

10·24 Heat-treatment is a general term applied to the processing of metals by heat and chemicals to change the physical properties of the material.

The glossary of shop terms, page 673, gives definitions of such heat-treatment processes as *annealing*, *carburizing*, *case-hardening*, *hardening*, and *tempering*.

The specification of heat-treatment may be given on the drawing in several ways: (1) by a general note listing the steps, temperatures, and baths to be used; (2) by a standard heat-treatment number (SAE, or company standard) in the space provided in the title block; (3) by giving the Brinell or Rockwell hardness number to be attained; or (4) by giving the tensile strength, psi, to be attained through heat-treatment.

Figures 10·7, 12·1, 12·2, and 12·6 illustrate these methods.

10·25 Tools for mass production. Many special machine tools, either semi- or fully automatic, are used in modern factories. These machines are basically the same as ordinary lathes, grinders, etc., but contain mechanisms to control the movements of cutting tools and produce identical parts with little attention from the operator, once the machine is "tooled up." Automatic screw machines and centerless grinders are examples.

10·26 Jigs and fixtures. *Jigs* for holding the work and guiding the tool, or *fixtures* for holding the work, greatly extend the production rate for general-purpose machine tools. Chapter 18 describes their use.

10·27 Inspection. Careful inspection is an important feature of modern production. Good practice requires inspection after each operation. For production in quantity, special gages are usually employed, but in small quantity production the usual measuring instruments, calipers and scale, micrometers, dial gages, etc., are used. For extreme accuracy in gaging, either air or optical gages are employed.

10·28 Assembly. The finished separate pieces come to the assembly department to be put together according to the assembly drawings. Sometimes it is desirable or necessary to perform some small machining operation during assembly, often drilling, reaming, or hand finishing. In such cases the assembly drawing should carry a prominent note explaining the required operation, and give dimensions for the alignment or location of the pieces. If some parts are to be combined before final assembly, either a subassembly drawing or the detail drawings of each piece will give the required information. "1/8 drill in assembly with piece No. 107" is a typical note form for an assembly machining operation.

TEXT-FILMS

The following McGraw-Hill Text-Film has been designed for direct correlation with Chapter 10:

The Drawings and the Shop (15-min. sound motion picture).

Portrays the relationship between the drawing and the various production operations in shop and factory; demonstrates the working of basic machines and the organization of modern production methods; shows the importance of the drawing in giving the basic information for production processes.

The accompanying coordinated silent filmstrip reviews the material in the film and presents questions for discussion and examination.

Chapter 11

DIMENSIONS AND NOTES

11·1 After the shape of an object has been described by orthographic (or pictorial) views, the value of the drawing for the construction of the object depends upon the dimensions and notes to give the description of *size*. The description of shape and size together give complete information for producing the object represented.

The dimensions put on the drawing are *not necessarily* those used in making the drawing but are those needed for the proper functioning of the parts after assembly, given so as to be easily usable by the workers who are to make the piece. The draftsman must thus first study the machine and understand its functional requirements and then put himself in the place of the patternmaker, diemaker, machinist, etc., and mentally construct the object to discover what dimensions would give the information in the best way.

11·2 Method. Three basic steps are involved in the study of dimensioning practice:

(1) *Fundamentals and technique.* One must first have a thorough knowledge of the lines and symbols used for dimensions and notes, and the weight and spacing of the lines on the drawing. These lines, symbols, and techniques are the "tools" for clear, concise representation of size.

(2) *Selection of distances to be given.* The most important consideration from the standpoint of ultimate operation of a machine and the proper working of the individual parts, is the selection of distances to be given. From the functional requirements, the "breakdown" of the part into its geometrical elements, and the requirements of the shop for production, this selection is made.

(3) *Placement.* After the distances to be given have been decided upon, the next step is the actual placement of the dimensions showing these distances on the drawing. In general, the dimensions should be placed in an arrangement clear and easy to read and readily usable by the shop.

11·3 Dimension forms. Two basic methods are used to give a distance on the drawing, a *dimension,* Fig. 11·1, or a *note,* Fig. 11·2. A dimension is used to give the distance between two points, lines, or planes, or some combination of points, lines, and planes. The numerical size gives the actual distance, the dimension line indicates the direction in which the distance applies, and the arrowheads give the extent of the dimension line. Extension lines refer the distance to the view when the dimension is placed outside of the view. A note provides the means of giving explanatory information with a size or distance. The leader and arrowhead refer the word statement (of the note) to the proper place on the drawing. Notes applying to the drawing as a whole are given without a leader in some convenient place on the drawing.

Complete dimensions are made up of dimension lines, arrowheads, extension lines, leaders, figures, notes, and finish marks.

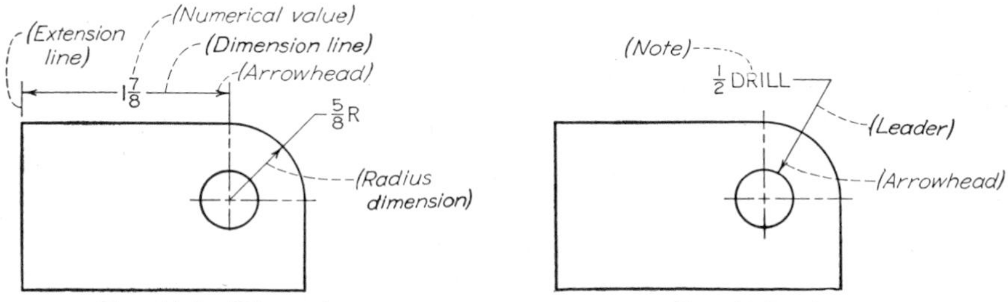

FIG. 11·1—Dimensions.

FIG. 11·2—A note.

11·4 Line weights. Dimension lines, extension lines, and leaders are made with fine full lines the same weight as the center lines, so as to contrast with the heavier outlines of the views. Note the line weights given in the alphabet of lines, page 28.

11·5 Arrowheads are carefully drawn freehand, making the sides either in one stroke, or in two strokes from the point, as shown in enlarged form in Fig. 11·3. The general preference, particularly on large drawings, is for

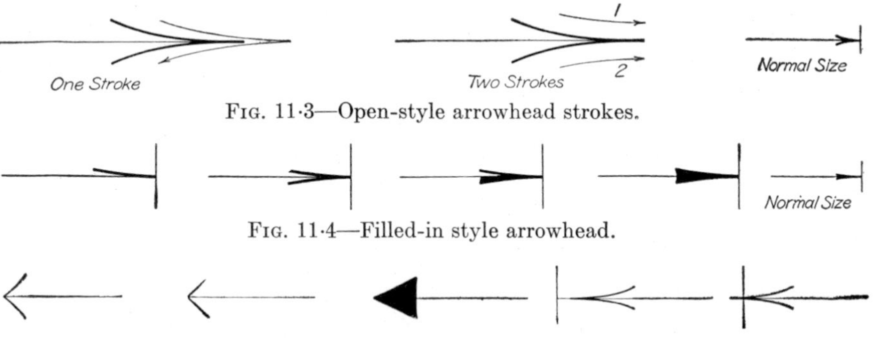

FIG. 11·3—Open-style arrowhead strokes.

FIG. 11·4—Filled-in style arrowhead.

FIG. 11·5—Incorrect arrowheads.

the filled-in head, Fig. 11·4. The filled-in head is usually made thinner and longer than the open head and has less curvature on the sides. It is made either in one or two strokes and then filled in without lifting the pen or pencil. The base of the arrowhead should not be made wider than one-third the length. All arrowheads on the same drawing should be the same type, either open or filled in, and the same size, except in restricted spaces. Arrowhead lengths will vary somewhat depending upon the drawing size. One-eighth inch is a good general length for small drawings and $\frac{3}{16}''$ for larger drawings.

Poor arrowheads ruin the appearance of an otherwise carefully made drawing. Avoid the incorrect shapes and placements shown in Fig. 11·5.

11·6 Extension lines are fine lines extending outside the view to show the distance measured. They should not touch the outline but should start about 1/16″ from it and extend about 1/8″ beyond the last dimension line, Fig. 11·6*A*. This example is printed approximately one-half size.

Dimensions are preferably kept outside the views but occasionally may be placed to better advantage inside. Thus dimensions may terminate at *center lines* or visible *outlines of the view*, *B* and *C*, Fig. 11·6. Where a

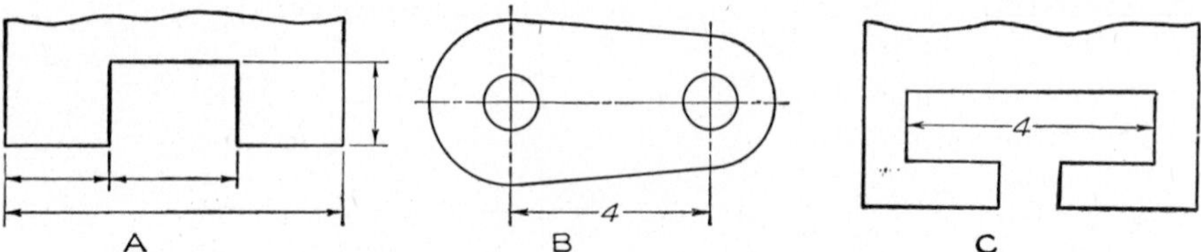

FIG. 11·6—Dimension terminals.

measurement between centers is to be shown as at *B*, the center lines are continued to serve as extension lines, extending about 1/8″ beyond the last dimension line. The outline of the view becomes the terminal for arrowheads when a dimension must be placed inside the view. This might occur because of limited space, when extension lines in crossing parts of the view would cause confusion, or when very long extension lines would make the dimension difficult to read.

11·7 Leaders are *straight* lines leading from a dimension value or an explanatory note to the feature on the drawing to which the note applies, Fig. 11·7. An arrowhead is used on the pointing end of the leader, but never on the note end. The note end of the leader should terminate with a short horizontal bar at the mid-height of the lettering, and should run either to the beginning or the end of the note, never to the middle.

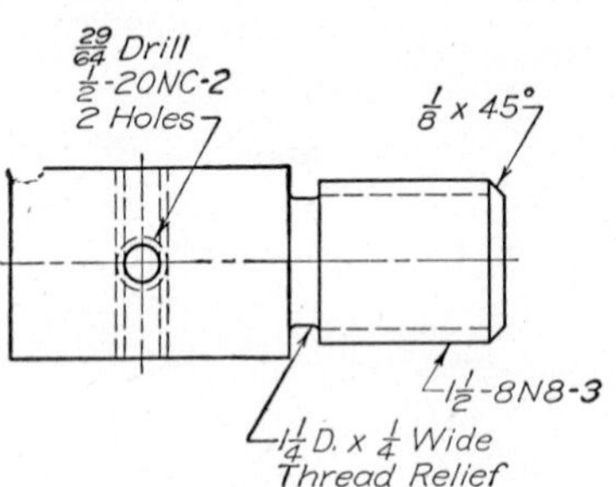

FIG. 11·7—Leaders for notes.

Leaders should be drawn at an angle to contrast with the principal lines of the drawing. As the lines of the drawing are mainly horizontal and vertical, leaders are drawn at 30°, 45°, or preferably 60° to the horizontal. When several leaders are used, the appearance of the drawing is improved if the leaders can be kept parallel.

11·8 Figures must be carefully lettered in either vertical or inclined style. In an effort for neatness the beginner often gets them too small. One-eighth inch for small drawings and 5/32″ for larger drawings are good general heights.

In machine-drawing practice, a space is left in the dimension line for the figured dimension, Fig. 11·8. It is universal in structural practice and is very common in architectural practice to place the figures above a continuous dimension line, Fig. 11·8.

FIG. 11·8—Placing figures.

11·9 Common fractions must be made with the fraction bar parallel to the guide lines of the figure, and with the numerator and denominator each somewhat smaller than the height of the whole number, so that the total fraction height is twice that of the whole number, Fig. 11·9. Avoid the incorrect forms shown. The figures should not touch the fraction bar.

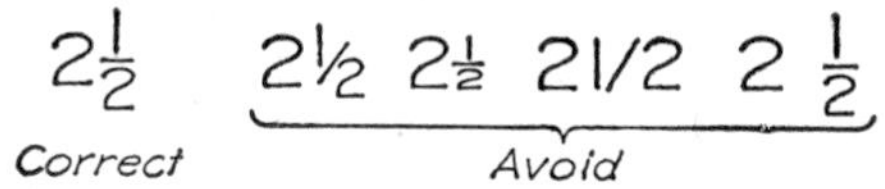

FIG. 11·9—Common fractions.

11·10 Feet and inches are indicated thus: 9′-6″. When there are no inches it should be so indicated, as 9′-0″, 9′-0½″. When dimensions are all in inches, the inch mark is preferably omitted from all the dimensions and notes, unless there is some possibility of misunderstanding; thus "1 bore" is clearer as, and should be, "1″ bore."

In some machine industries all dimensions are given in inches. In others, where feet and inches are used, the ASA recommends that dimensions up to and including 72 inches be given in inches, and greater lengths in feet and inches.

In structural drawing, length dimensions should be given in feet and inches. Plate widths, beam sizes, etc., are given in inches. Inch marks are omitted, even though the dimension is in feet and inches, Fig. 11·8.

11·11 The reading direction of figures is arranged according to either the aligned system or the unidirectional system.

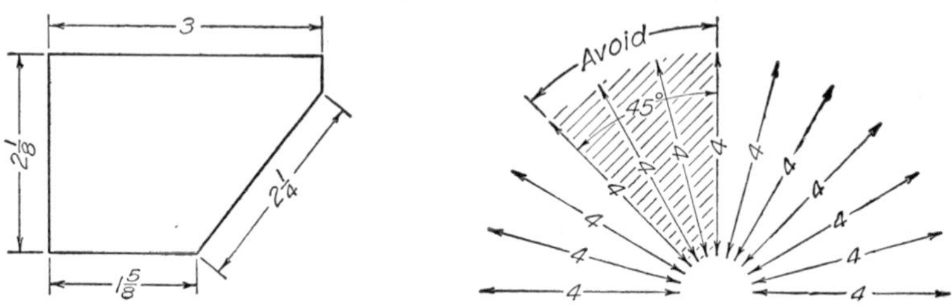

FIG. 11·10—Reading direction, aligned system.

The aligned system is the older of the two methods. The figures are oriented to be readable from a position perpendicular to the dimension line; thus the guide lines for the figures will be parallel to the dimension line, and the fraction bar in line with the dimension line, Fig. 11·10. The figures should be oriented so as to be readable from the bottom or right side of the drawing. Avoid running dimensions in the directions included in the shaded area; if this is unavoidable, they should read downward with the line.

The unidirectional system originated in the automotive and aircraft industries. Sometimes called the "horizontal system," all figures are oriented to read from the bottom of the drawing. Thus the guide lines and fraction

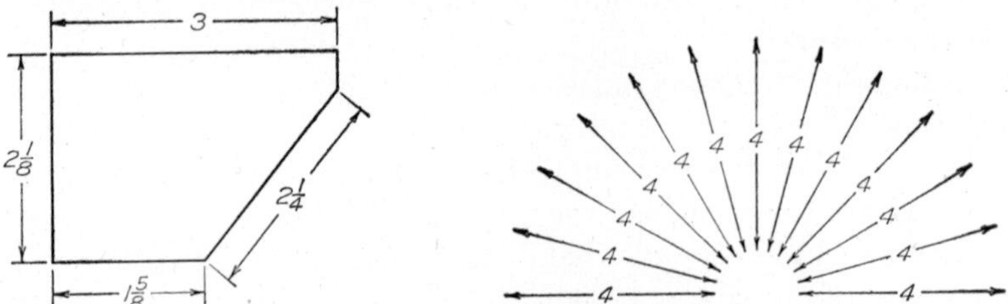

FIG. 11·11—Reading direction, unidirectional system.

bars are horizontal regardless of the direction of the dimension, Fig. 11·11. The "avoid" zone of Fig. 11·10, has no significance with this system.

Notes must be lettered horizontally and read from the bottom of the drawing in either system.

11·12 Finish marks are used to indicate that certain surfaces of metal parts are to be machined, and that allowance must therefore be made on a casting or forging for finish. Finish marks need not be used for parts made by machining from rolled stock, as the surfaces are necessarily machined. Neither are they necessary on drilled, reamed, or counterbored holes nor on similar machined features when the machining operation is specified by note.

FIG. 11·12—ASA finish mark.

The standard mark recommended by the ASA is a 60° V with its point touching the line representing the edge view of the surface to be machined. The V is placed on the "air side" of the surface. Figure 11·12 shows the normal size of the V and its position for lines in various directions as applied on a drawing.

The symbol which has been in use for many years is an italic *f* with its cross mark intersecting the line representing the surface to be finished, Fig. 11·13.

Finish marks should be placed on all views in which the surface to be machined appears as a line, including dotted lines. If the part is to be machined on all surfaces, the note "finish all over," or "FAO" is used, and the marks on the views omitted.

In addition to the finish mark indicating a machined surface, it may be necessary in some cases to indicate the degree of smoothness of the surface. The ASA proposes a set of symbols to indicate various conditions of *surface quality*. These symbols are explained and illustrated in the following chapter, paragraph 12·30.

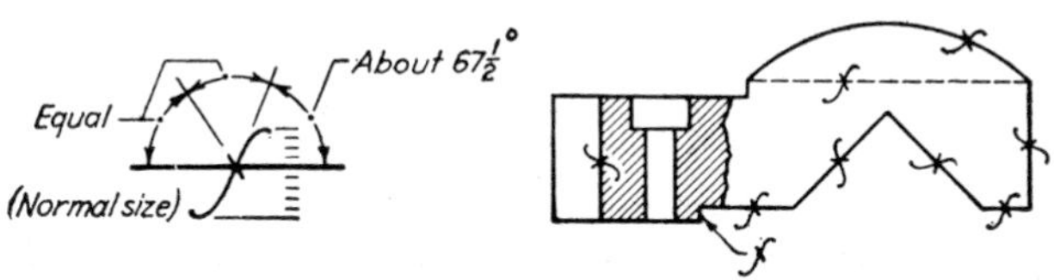

FIG. 11·13—Finish mark, *f*.

11·13 Systems of writing dimension values. Dimension values may be given either as common fractions, ¼, ⅜, etc., or as decimal fractions, 0.25, 0.375, etc., and from these, three systems are evolved.

The common-fraction system, used in architectural and structural work, and for the less accurate class of machine drawings, has all dimensions written as units and common fractions as, 3½, 1¼, ⅜, 1/16, 3/32, 1/64. Dimensions thus written can be laid out with a steel tape or with a machinist's scale graduated in sixty-fourths of an inch.

The common-fraction, decimal-fraction system, is used principally in mechanical work whenever it becomes necessary, for reasons of accuracy, to use fractions of the inch smaller than those on the ordinary steel scale. To continue the use of common fractions below 1/64, such as 1/128 or 1/256, is considered impractical. The method followed is to give dimensions (1) in units and common fractions for distances not requiring accuracy closer than 1/64″; and (2) in units and decimal fractions, as 2.375, 1.250, 0.1875, etc., for distances requiring greater accuracy. The decimal fractions are given to as many decimal places as the accuracy requires.

FIG. 11·14—Decimal scale.

The complete decimal system, introduced originally by the Ford Motor Company in 1932, uses decimal fractions exclusively for all dimensions. This system has the advantages of the metric system, but uses the inch as its basis, thus making it possible to use present measuring equipment.

The ASA complete decimal system[1] uses a two-place decimal for all dimensions where common fractions would ordinarily be used.

The figures after the decimal point are written in even fiftieths, .02, .10, .36, etc., so that when halved for center distances, two-place decimals will result. Exceptions may have to be made but they should be kept at a minimum. Two-place decimals allow the use of scales divided in fiftieths,

[1] Z14.1, 1946.

Fig. 11·14. These special scales are much easier to use than are scales divided in hundredths.

Dimensions requiring greater accuracy than that expressed by the two-place decimal are written to three, four, or more decimal places as the accuracy may require.

Figure 11·15 is a detail drawing dimensioned according to the ASA decimal system. The advantage of this system in calculating, adding, and checking, and in doing away with all conversion tables, as well as in lessening chances for error, is apparent.

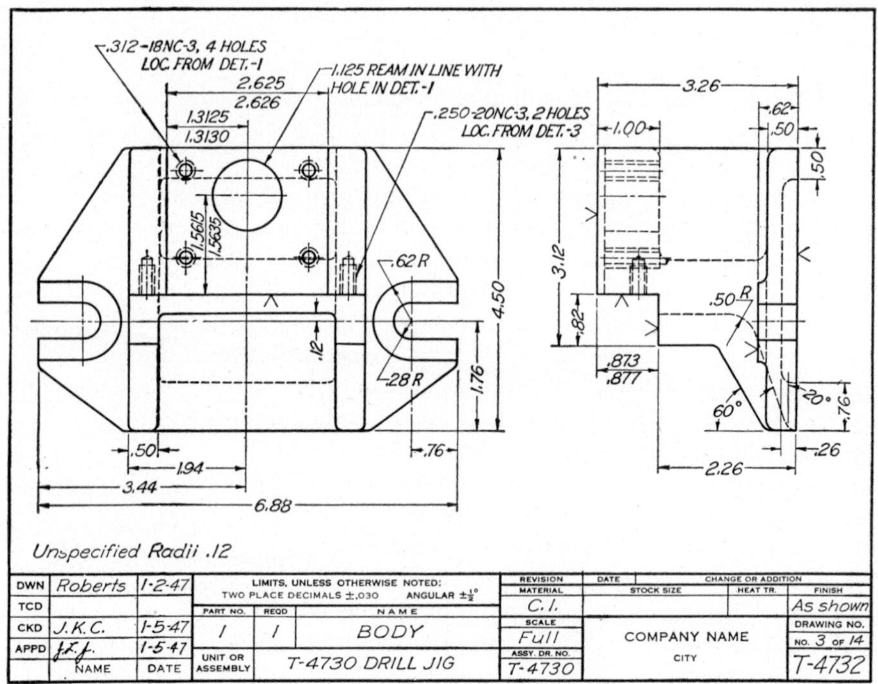

FIG. 11·15—A drawing dimensioned in the ASA complete decimal system.

Designers and draftsmen working in the complete decimal system will find it necessary to think in terms of tenths and hundredths of inches instead of thinking in common fractions. New designs must be made in decimal sizes without reference to common fractional sizes. However, until standard-stock materials, tools, and commercial parts are available in decimal sizes, some dimensions will have to be given as the decimal equivalent of a common fraction. Thus, for example, a standard ⅜-16 NC-2 thread would be given as 0.375-16 NC-2.

Decimal equivalents of some common fractions come out to a greater number of decimal places (significant digits) than is necessary or desirable for use as a dimension value and, in such cases, the decimal should be adjusted or "rounded off" to a lesser number of decimal places. The following procedure from the American Standards[1] is recommended:

When the figure beyond the last figure to be retained is less than 5, the last figure retained should not be changed. *Example:* 3.46325, if cut off to three places, should be 3.463.

When the figures beyond the last place to be retained amount to more than 5, the last figure retained should be increased by 1. *Example:* 8.37652, if cut off to three places, should be 8.377.

When the figure beyond the last place to be retained is exactly 5 with only zeros following, the preceding number, if even, should be unchanged; if odd, it should be increased by 1. *Example:* 4.365 becomes 4.36 when cut off to two places Also 4.355 becomes 4.36 when cut off to two places.

11·14 Theory of dimensioning. Any object can be "broken down" into a combination of basic geometrical shapes, principally prisms and cylinders. Occasionally, however, there will be parts of pyramids and cones, now and then a double-curved surface, and very rarely, except for surfaces of screw threads, a warped surface. Any of the basic shapes may be either positive or negative, taken in the sense that a hole is a negative cylinder. Figure 7·65 illustrates a machine part broken down into its fundamental shapes.

If the *size* of each of these elemental shapes is dimensioned and the relative location of each is given, measuring from center to center, from base lines, or from the surfaces of each other, the dimensioning of any piece can be done systematically. Dimensions may thus be classified as *size dimensions* and *location dimensions.*

11·15 Size dimensions. As every solid has three dimensions, each of the geometrical shapes making up the object must have its height, width, and depth indicated in the dimensioning.

The prism, often in plinth or flat form, is the most common shape and requires three dimensions for square, rectangular, or triangular, Fig. 11·16*A*. For regular hexagonal or octagonal types, usually only two dimensions are given, either the distance "across corners" and the length, or "across flats" and the length.

The cylinder, found on nearly all mechanical pieces as a shaft or a boss or a hole, is the second most common shape. A cylinder obviously requires only two dimensions, diameter and length, Fig. 11·16*B*. Partial cylinders, such as fillets and rounds, are dimensioned by radius instead of diameter. A good general rule is to dimension complete circles with a diameter, and circle arcs (partial circles) with a radius.

Right cones may be dimensioned with the altitude and the diameter of the base. They usually occur as frustums, however, and require the diameters of the ends and the length, Fig. 11·16*C*. Often it is desirable to dimension cone frustums as tapers, as described in paragraph 11·29.

[1] Z25.1, 1940.

Right pyramids are dimensioned by giving the dimensions of the base and the altitude. These also are often frustums, requiring dimensions of both bases, Fig. 11·16*D*.

Oblique cones and pyramids are dimensioned in the same way as right cones and pyramids, but with an additional dimension parallel to the base to give the offset of the vertex.

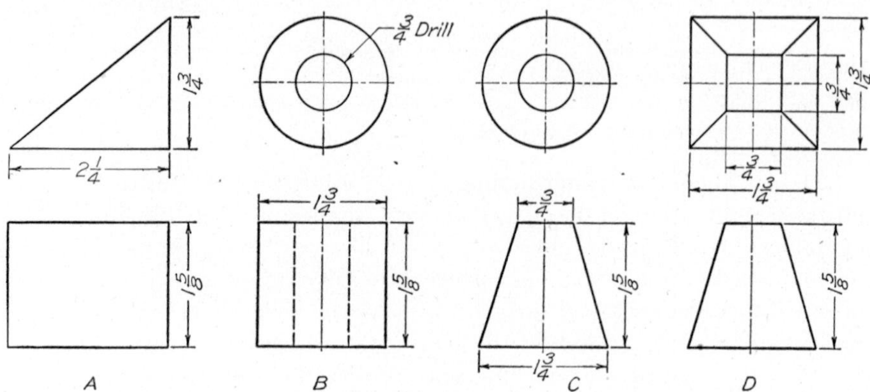

FIG. 11·16—Size dimensions—prism, cylinders, cone, and pyramid.

Spheres are dimensioned by giving the diameter; other surfaces of revolution by dimensioning the generating curve.

Warped surfaces are dimensioned according to their method of generation and, as their representation requires numerous sections, each of these must be fully dimensioned.

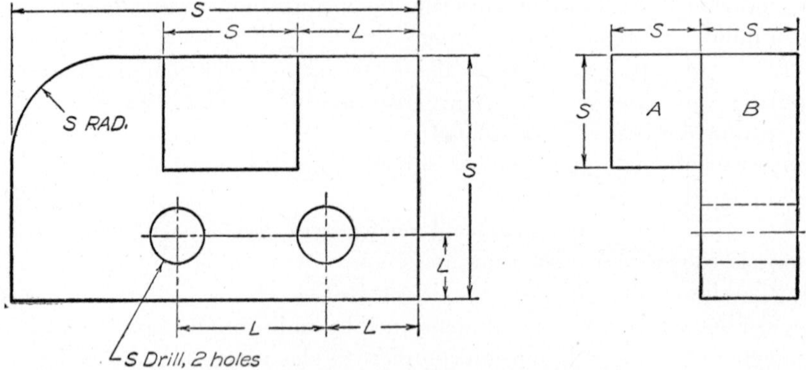

FIG. 11·17—Size and location dimensions.

11·16 Location dimensions. After the basic geometric shapes have been dimensioned for size, the location of each relative to the others must be given. *Location must be established in height, width, and depth directions.* Rectangular shapes are located with reference to their faces; cylindrical and conical shapes to their center lines and their ends.

A basic shape will often coincide or align with another on one or more of its faces. In such cases, the alignment serves partially to locate the parts and eliminates the need of a location dimension in a direction perpendicular to the line of coincidence. Thus in Fig. 11·17, prism *A* requires only one dimension for complete location with respect to prism *B*, as two surfaces are in alignment and two in contact.

Coincident center lines often eliminate the use of location dimensions. In the cylinder, Fig. 11·16*B*, the center line of the hole and cylinder coincide and no location dimensions are needed. The two holes of Fig. 11·17 are on the same center line and the dimension perpendicular to the coincident center line locates both holes in that direction.

11·17 The selection of dimensions. The dimensions arrived at by reducing the part to its basic geometry will, in general, fulfill the requirements of practical dimensioning. These dimensions, however, sometimes require alteration to ensure satisfactory functioning of the part and also to

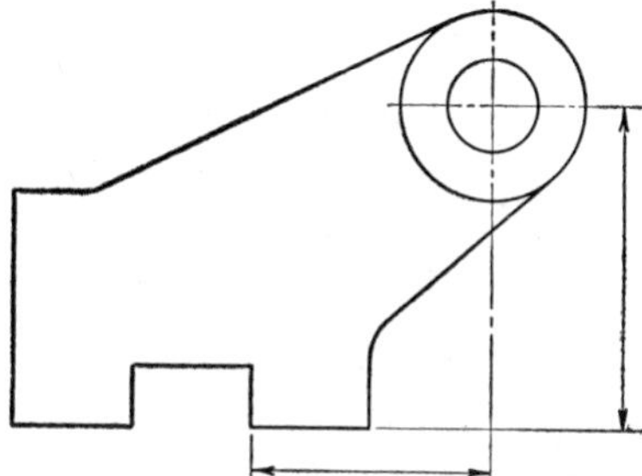

FIG. 11·18—Location by offsets.

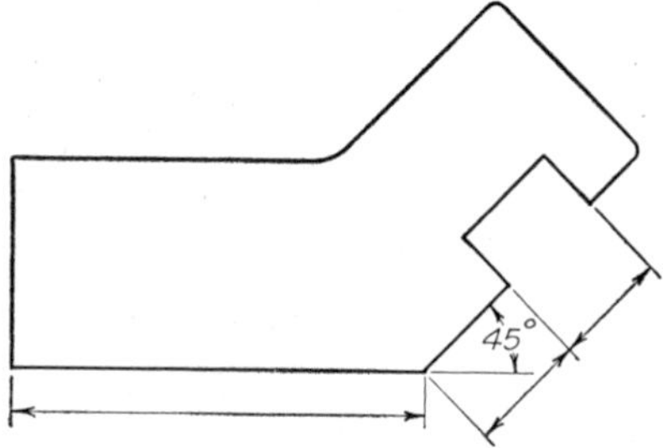

FIG. 11·19—Location by angle.

give the information in the best way from the standpoint of production. The draftsman must therefore correlate the dimensions on drawings of mating parts to ensure satisfactory functioning and, at the same time, select dimensions convenient for the workmen to use.

Here our study of drawing as a language must be supplemented by a knowledge of shop methods. To be successful, the machine draftsman must have an intimate knowledge of patternmaking, foundry practice, forging, and machine-shop practice; as well as, in some cases, sheet-metal working, metal and plastic die casting, welding, and structural-steel fabrication.

The beginning student without this knowledge should not depend upon his instructor alone but, as recommended in the previous chapter, should set about to inform himself by observing work going through the shops and reading books and periodicals on methods used in modern production work.

The selection of size dimensions arrived at by "shape breakdown" will usually meet the requirements of the shop since the basic shapes result from the fundamental shop operations. However, size dimensions are preferred in note form instead of a regular dimension whenever a shop process is involved, such as drilling, reaming, counterboring, punching, etc.

The selection of location dimensions requires more consideration than for size dimensions because there are, usually, several ways in which a location might be given. In general, location dimensions will be given between finished surfaces, center lines, or a combination thereof, Fig. 11·20. Remember that rough castings or forgings will vary in size, and do not locate machined surfaces from unfinished surfaces. The only exception is when an initial or *starting dimension* is given to locate the first surface to be machined from which, in turn, the other machined surfaces are located. *Coinciding center lines of unfinished and finished surfaces often take the place of a starting dimension.*

The location of a point or center by offset dimensions from two center lines or surfaces, Fig. 11·18, is preferred over angular dimensions, Fig. 11·19,

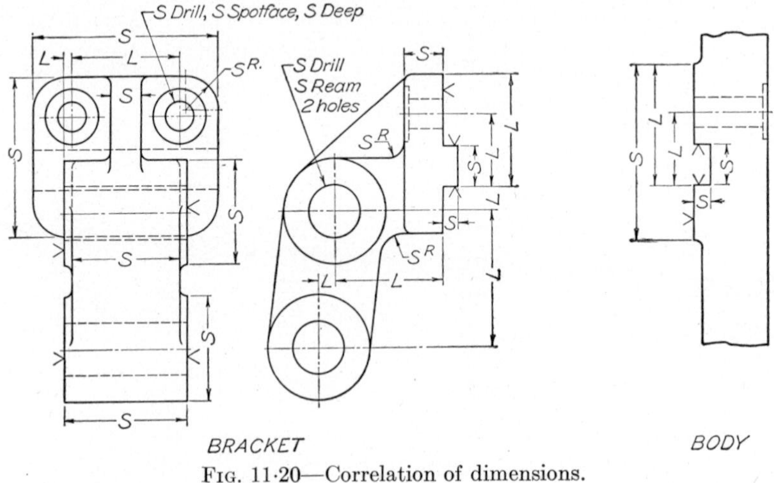

FIG. 11·20—Correlation of dimensions.

unless the angular dimension is more practical from the standpoint of construction.

11·18 The correlation of dimensions. Mating parts must have their dimensions given so that the two parts will fit and function as intended. Figure 11·20 will illustrate this principle. Note that the tongue of the bracket is to fit the groove in the body and also note that the drilled holes in both pieces must align. Then study the dimensioning of both pieces and note that the location dimensions are given so that the intended alignment and fitting of the parts will be accomplished.

Dimensions must not only be correlated with the dimensions of the mating part, but the accuracy of these dimensions must meet certain standards or the parts may not fit and function properly. Distances between the surfaces or center lines of finished features of an object must usually be more accurately made than unfinished features. In Fig. 11·21, note that the location dimensions between center lines or surfaces of finished features are given as three-place decimals, as dimension *A*. Location dimensions for unfinished features are given as common fractions, as dimension *B*. The decimal dimensions indicate greater accuracy in manufacture than do the common fractions. Dimension *B* is in this case used by the patternmaker to locate cylinder *C* from the right end of the piece. The machinist will first locate the finished hole in this cylinder, making it concentric with the cylinder; then all other machined surfaces are located from this hole, as, for example, the spline location by dimension *A*. The four spot-faced holes

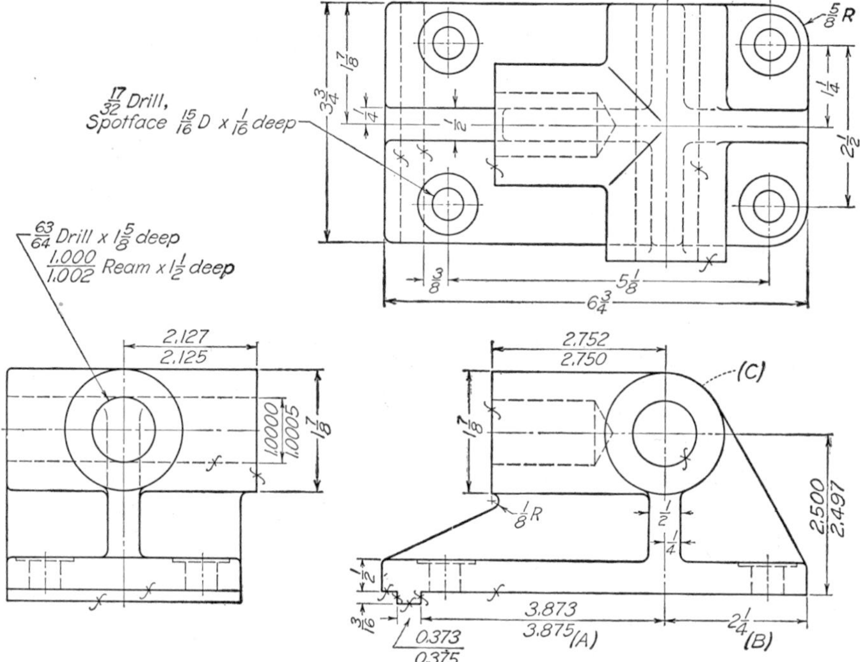

FIG. 11·21—An example of dimensioning.

are located with reference to each other with fractional dimensions (since the holes are oversize for the fastenings used), allowing enough shifting of the fastenings in the holes so that great accuracy in location is not necessary. The mating part, with its holes to receive the screws, would be similarly dimensioned.

Study Fig. 11·21 and note the classification, size, or location of each dimension.

11·19 Superfluous dimensions. *Duplicate* or *unnecessary* dimensions are to be avoided because of the confusion and delay they may cause. An unnecessary dimension is any dimension, not a duplicate, that is not essential in making the piece. Actually, because of variations in manufacture, it should not be possible to establish a distance in any given direction from more than one surface. Unnecessary dimensions will always occur when all the individual dimensions are given in addition to the over-all dimension, Fig. 11·22. One dimension of the series must be omitted if the over-all is used; thus allowing only one possible location from each dimension, Fig. 11·23. Occasionally it is desirable, for reference or checking purposes, to give all dimensions in a series and also give the over-all dimension. In such

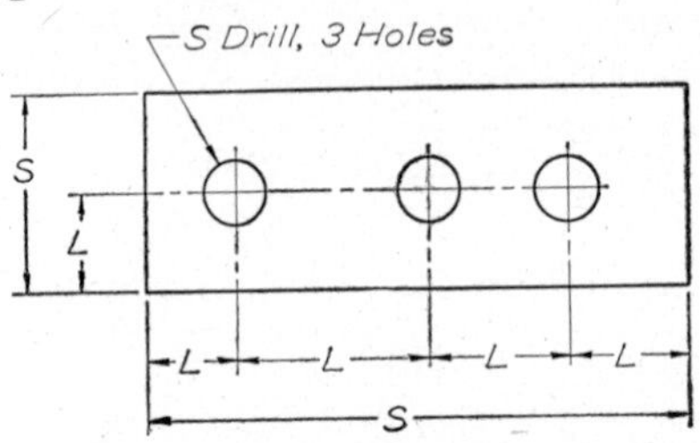

FIG. 11·22—One dimension unnecessary.

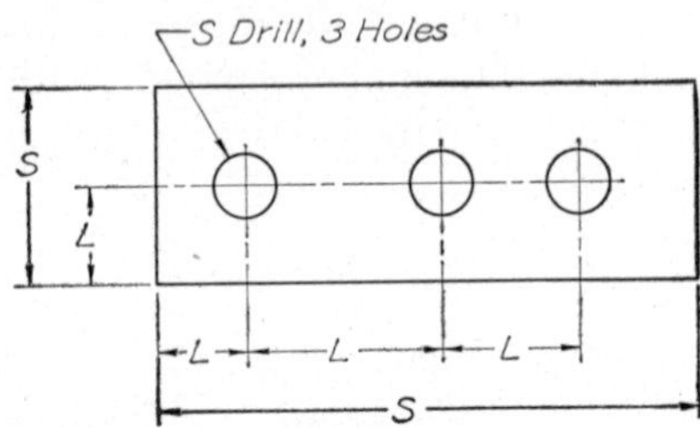

FIG. 11·23—Unnecessary dimension omitted.

cases, one dimension not to be "worked to" in manufacturing, is marked with the abbreviation "Ref.," as indicated in Fig. 11·24.

In architectural and structural work, because of the relatively large variations allowed in construction, unnecessary dimensions cause no difficulty and all dimensions are given as in Fig. 11·22.

Although, as pointed out, it is important not to "overdimension" a part, it is equally important that sufficient dimensions be given to locate every point, line, or surface of the object. The workman should never be required to scale a dimension from the drawing. All necessary distances must be given.

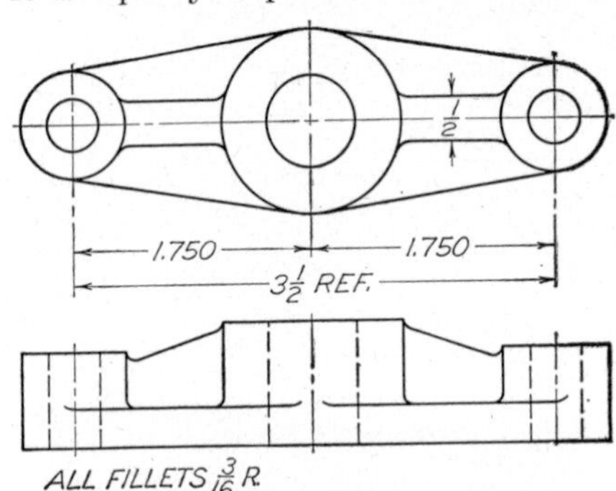

FIG. 11·24—One reference dimension.

However, dimensions for similar features, such as the thickness of several ribs obviously of the same shape, need not be repeated, Fig. 11·24. Also such details as the size of fillets and rounds can be provided for with a general note.

If the draftsman will mentally go through the manufacture of the part, checking each dimension as he needs it, he will easily discover any superfluous or omitted dimensions.

11·20 The placement of dimensions. After the distances have been selected as outlined in paragraph 11·2, it is then possible to decide (1) the *view* on which the distance will be indicated, (2) the particular *place* on that view, and (3) the *form* of the dimension itself. Numerous principles, some with the force of a rule, can be given, but in any case the important consideration is *clarity*.

11·21 Views—the contour principle. One of the views of an object will usually describe the shape of some detailed feature better than will the other view or views, and the feature is then said to be "characteristic" in that particular view. In reading a drawing, it is natural to look for the dimensions of a given feature wherever that feature appears most characteristic, and it certainly follows that an advantage in clarity and in ease of reading will be had by following this principle in dimensioning the drawing. In Fig. 11·25, the rounded corner, the drilled hole, and the lower notched corner are all characteristic in, and dimensioned on, the front view. The projecting shape on the front of the object is more characteristic in the top view and is dimensioned there.

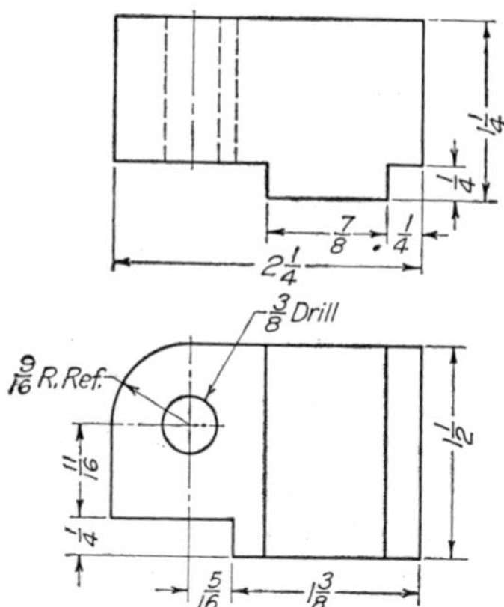

Fig. 11·25—The contour principle applied.

Dimensions for prisms should be placed so that two of the three dimensions are on the view showing the contour shape and the third on one of the other views, Figs. 11·16 and 11·25.

Dimensions for cylinders, the diameter and length, are usually best placed on the noncircular view, Fig. 11·26*A*. This practice keeps the dimensions on one view, a convenience for the workman. Occasionally a cylindrical hole may be dimensioned with the diameter at an angle on the circular view, as indicated at *B*. This practice should never be used unless there is a clear space for the dimension value. In some cases, however, the

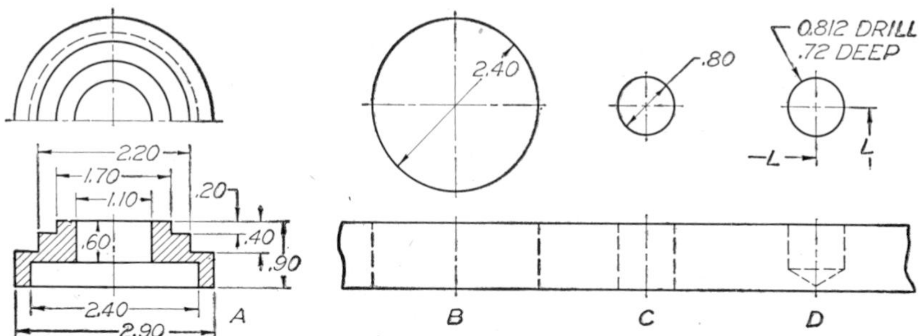

Fig. 11·26—Dimensions for cylinders.

value can be carried outside the view as in *C*. When a hole is specified by a note, as at *D*, the leader should point to the circular view if possible. The note has an advantage in that the diameter, operation, and depth may all be given together. Giving the diameter on the circular view as at *B*, *C*, or *D* may make for ease of reading, as the location dimensions will likely be given there also, as indicated at *D*. When it is not obvious from the drawing, a dimension may be indicated as a diameter by following the value with the letter *D*, as shown in Fig. 11·27.

PRINCIPLES FOR THE PLACEMENT OF DIMENSIONS

1. Dimensioning outside the view is preferred, unless added clearness, simplicity, and ease of reading will result from placing some of them inside. For appearance' sake they should be kept off the cut surfaces of sections. When it is necessary that they be placed there, the section lining is omitted around the numbers, Fig. 11·27.

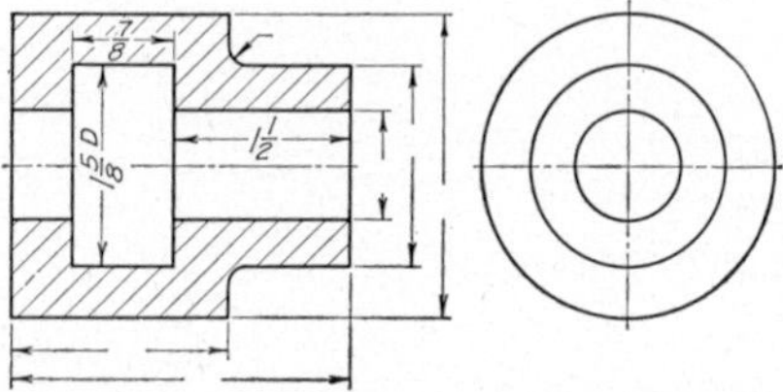

FIG. 11·27—Dimensions inside the view.

2. Dimensions between the views are preferred unless there is some reason for placing them elsewhere, as there was in Fig. 11 25, where the dimension for the lower notched corner and the location of the hole must come at the bottom of the front view.

3. Dimensions should be applied to one view only, that is, with dimensions between views, the extension lines should be drawn from one view, not from both views, Fig. 11·28.

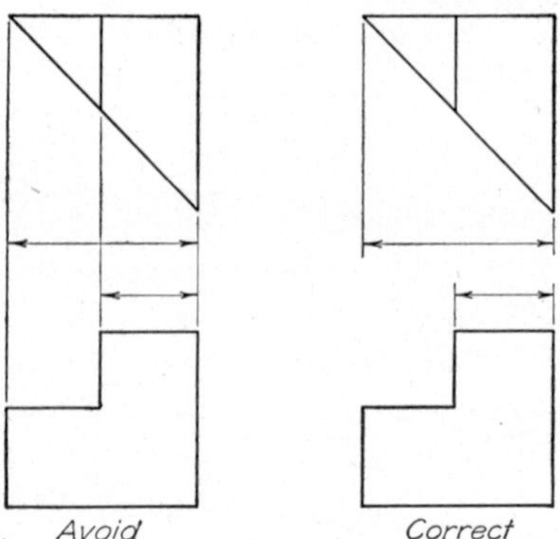

FIG. 11·28—Dimensions applied to one view only.

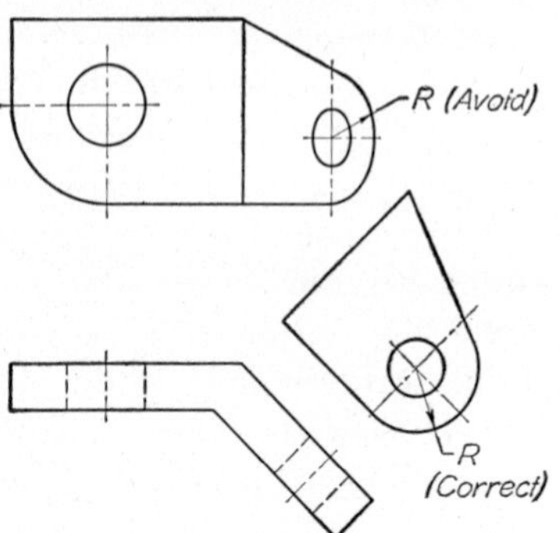

FIG. 11·29—Dimension distance normal.

4. Dimensions should be placed on the view that shows the distance in its true length (not foreshortened), Fig. 11·29.

5. Dimension lines should be spaced, in general, ½ inch away from the outlines of the view. This applies to a single dimension or the first dimension of several in a series.

6. Parallel dimension lines should be spaced uniformly with at least ⅜ of an inch between lines.

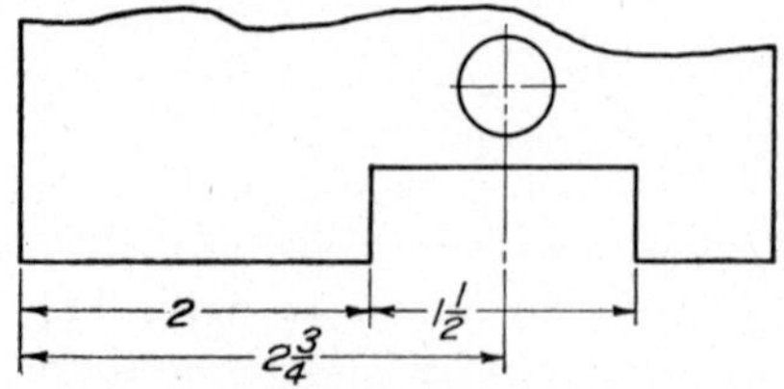

FIG. 11·30—Figures midway between arrowheads.

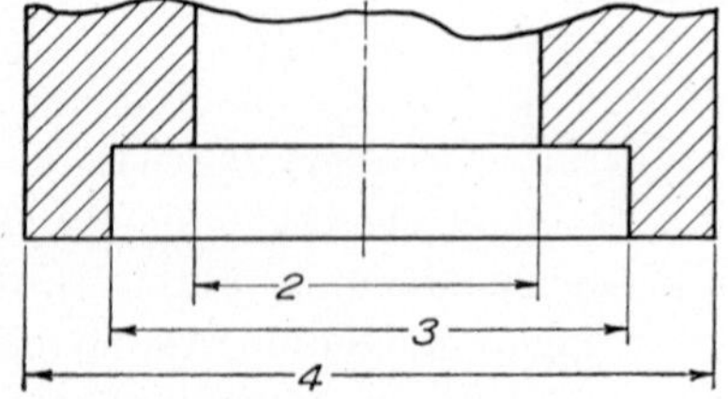

FIG. 11·31—Staggered figures.

7. **Figures** should be midway between the arrowheads, except when a center line interferes, Fig. 11·30, or when the figures of several *parallel dimensions* are staggered, Fig. 11·31.

8. **Continuous or staggered dimension lines** may be used depending upon convenience and readability. Continuous dimension lines are preferred where possible, Figs. 11·32 and 11·33.

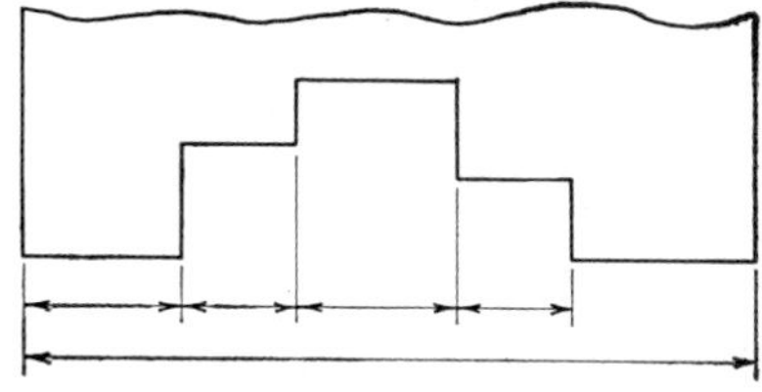

FIG. 11·32—Continuous dimensions.

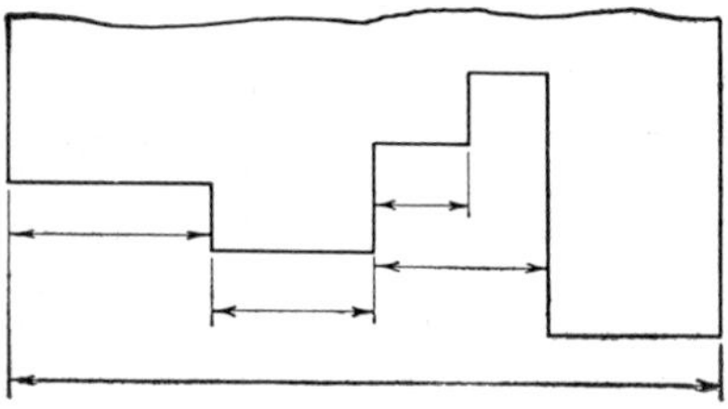

FIG. 11·33—Staggered dimensions.

9. **Always place the longer dimension outside** the shorter ones to avoid crossing dimension lines with the extension lines of other dimensions. Thus an over-all dimension (maximum size of piece in a given direction) will be outside of all other dimensions.

10. **Dimensions should never be crowded.** If the space is small, follow one of the methods of paragraph 11·22, Dimensioning in Limited Space.

11. **Center lines** are used to indicate the symmetry of shapes and as such frequently eliminate the need of a location dimension. They should be considered as part of the dimensioning and drawn in finished form at the time of dimensioning. They should extend about ⅛″ beyond the shape for which they indicate symmetry unless they are carried farther to serve as extension lines. Center lines should not be continued between views.

12. **All notes** should read horizontally (from the bottom of the sheet) if possible.

Practices to Avoid

1. **Never** use a center line, a line of the drawing, or an extension line as a dimension line.

2. **Never** place a dimension line on a center line or place a dimension line where a center line should properly be.

3. **Never** allow a line of any kind to pass through a dimension figure.

4. **Avoid** the crossing of two dimension lines or the crossing of an extension line and a dimension line.

5. **Avoid** dimensioning to hidden lines if possible.

11·22 Dimensioning in limited space. Dimensions should never be crowded into a space too small to contain them. One of the methods of Fig. 11·34 may be used to avoid the difficulty. Sometimes a note may be appropriate. If the space is very small and crowded, an enlarged removed section or part view may be used, Fig. 11·35.

11·23 Arcs and curves. Arcs should be dimensioned by giving the radius on the view that shows the true shape of the curve. The dimension line for a radius should always be drawn as a radial line at an angle, Fig. 11·36, never horizontal or vertical, and only one arrowhead is used. There is no arrowhead at the arc's center. The figured size should be followed by the letter *R*. Depending upon the size of the radius and the available space for the figured size, the dimension line and figure are either both inside; or the line inside and the figure outside; or, for small arcs, both outside as shown.

When the center of an arc lies outside the limits of the drawing, the center is moved closer along a center line of the arc and the dimension line is jogged to meet the new center, Fig. 11·37. The portion of the dimension line adjacent to the arc is a radial line of the true center.

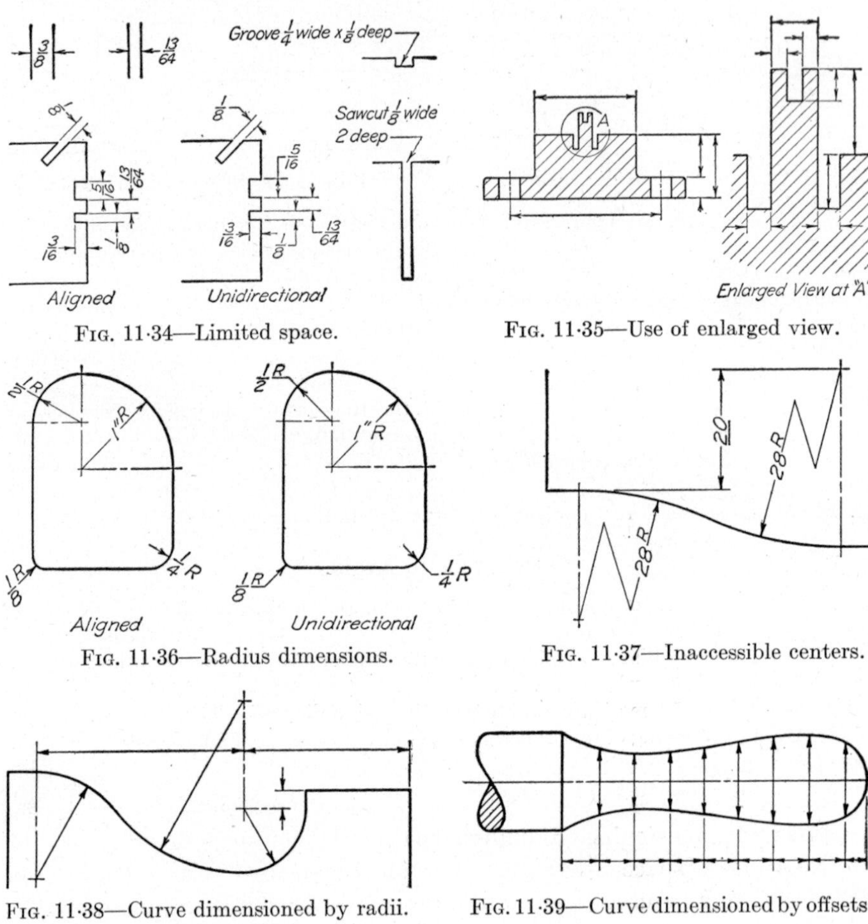

FIG. 11·34—Limited space.

FIG. 11·35—Use of enlarged view.

FIG. 11·36—Radius dimensions.

FIG. 11·37—Inaccessible centers.

FIG. 11·38—Curve dimensioned by radii.

FIG. 11·39—Curve dimensioned by offsets.

A curved line made up of circle arcs is dimensioned by radii with the centers located, as in Fig. 11·38. Irregular curves are usually dimensioned by offsets, as in Fig. 11·39.

11·24 Angles. The dimension line for an angle is a circle arc with its center at the intersection of the sides of the angle, Fig. 11·40. The figures are placed to read horizontally with the exception that, in the aligned system, large arcs only have the figures aligned with the dimension arc.

Angular values should be written in the form 35°7′ with no dash between the degrees and minutes.

11·25 Notes. Notes are word statements giving information that cannot be given by the views and dimensions. They may be classified as either *general* or *specific*. A general note applies to the entire part, and a specific note applies to an individual feature. Occasionally a note will save making an additional view, or even, for example, with a note used to indicate right- and left-hand parts, save making an entire drawing.

Do not be afraid to put notes on drawings. Supplement the graphic language by the English language whenever added information can be conveyed, but be careful to word it so clearly that the meaning cannot possibly be misunderstood.

General notes do not require the use of a leader and should be grouped together in the lower left-hand corner of the working space of the drawing.

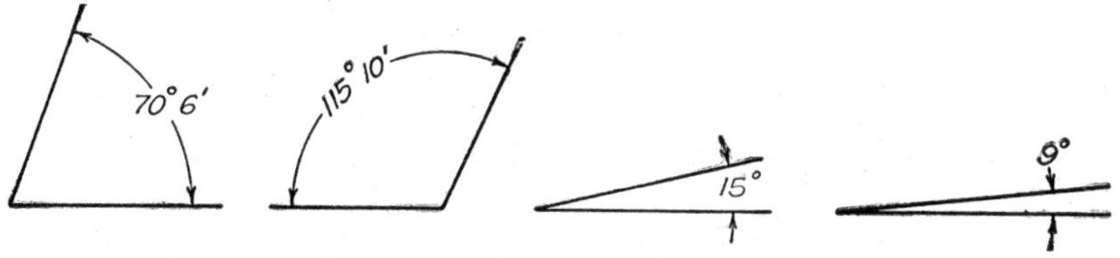

FIG. 11·40—Dimensions for angles.

Examples are, "Finish all over," "Fillets ¼ R, rounds ⅛ R, unless otherwise specified," "All draft angles 7°," "Remove burs," etc.

Much of the information provided in the title strip of a machine drawing is a grouping of general notes. Stock size, material, heat-treatment, etc., are general notes in the title of the drawing of Fig. 12·1.

Specific notes almost always require a leader and therefore should be placed fairly close to the feature to which they apply. Most common are notes giving an operation with a size, as "½″ Drill, 4 Holes."

Notes should be lettered horizontally to read from the bottom of the drawing. Recommended forms for the wording of notes occurring more or less frequently are given in Fig. 11·41.

11·26 Dimensions and specifications for holes. Drilled, reamed, bored, punched, or cored holes are preferably specified by note giving the diameter, operation, and, if there is more than one, the number of holes. If there is more than one hole of the same kind, the leader needs point to but one hole, Fig. 11·42. All necessary operations may be given in one note. Figures 11·42 to 11·45 show typical dimensioning practice for drilled and reamed, counterbored, countersunk, and spot-faced holes.

The ASA specifies that standard drill sizes be given as decimal fractions, such as 0.250, 0.375, 0.750, 1.500. If the size is given as a common fraction, the decimal equivalent should be added.

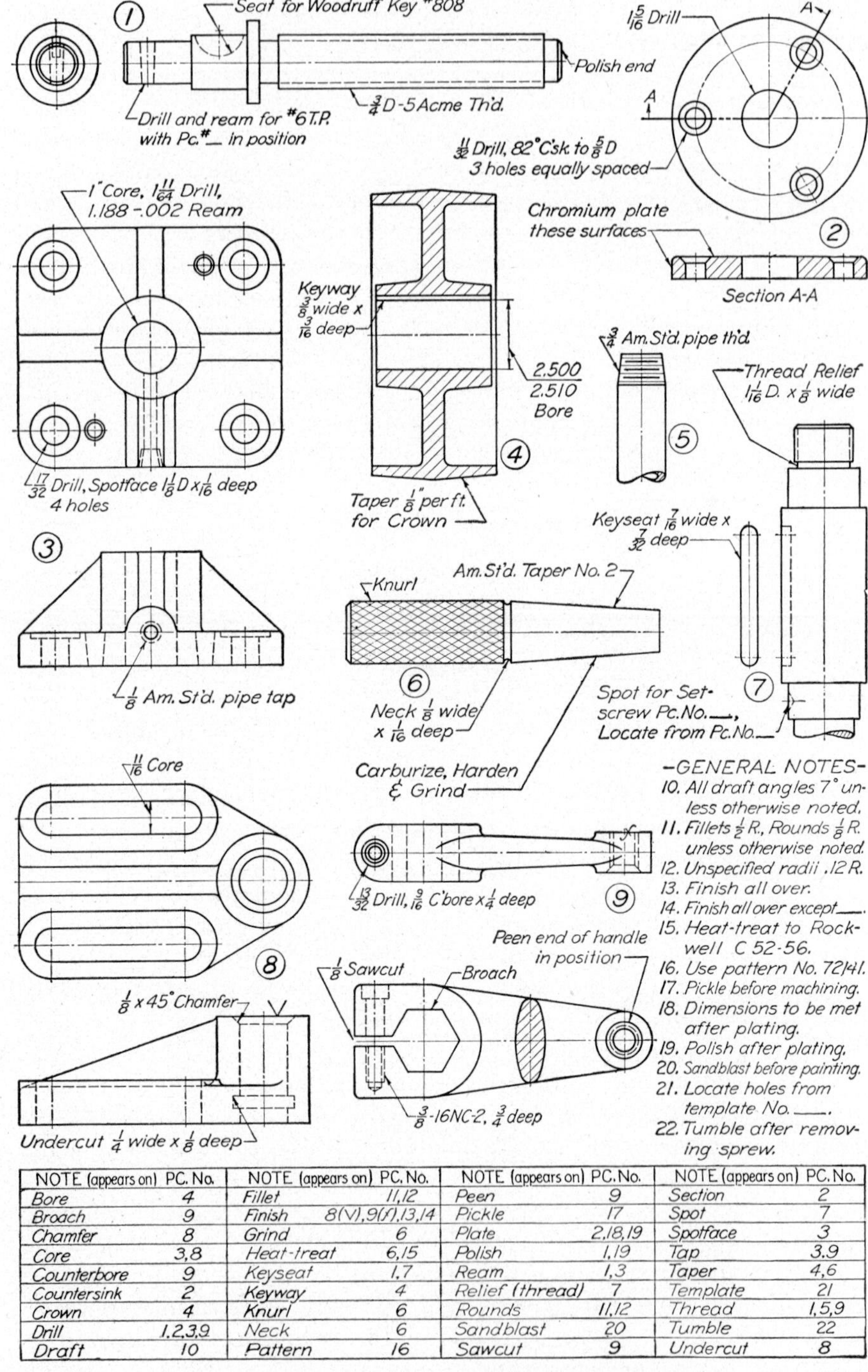

NOTE (appears on)	PC. No.	NOTE (appears on)	PC. No.	NOTE (appears on)	PC. No.	NOTE (appears on)	PC. No.
Bore	4	Fillet	11,12	Peen	9	Section	2
Broach	9	Finish	8(V),9(f),13,14	Pickle	17	Spot	7
Chamfer	8	Grind	6	Plate	2,18,19	Spotface	3
Core	3,8	Heat-treat	6,15	Polish	1,19	Tap	3,9
Counterbore	9	Keyseat	1,7	Ream	1,3	Taper	4,6
Countersink	2	Keyway	4	Relief (thread)	7	Template	21
Crown	4	Knurl	6	Rounds	11,12	Thread	1,5,9
Drill	1,2,3,9	Neck	6	Sandblast	20	Tumble	22
Draft	10	Pattern	16	Sawcut	9	Undercut	8

FIG. 11·41—Approved wording for notes on drawings.

The leader to a hole should point to the circular view if possible. In general, the arrowhead should touch the inner circle (usually the first

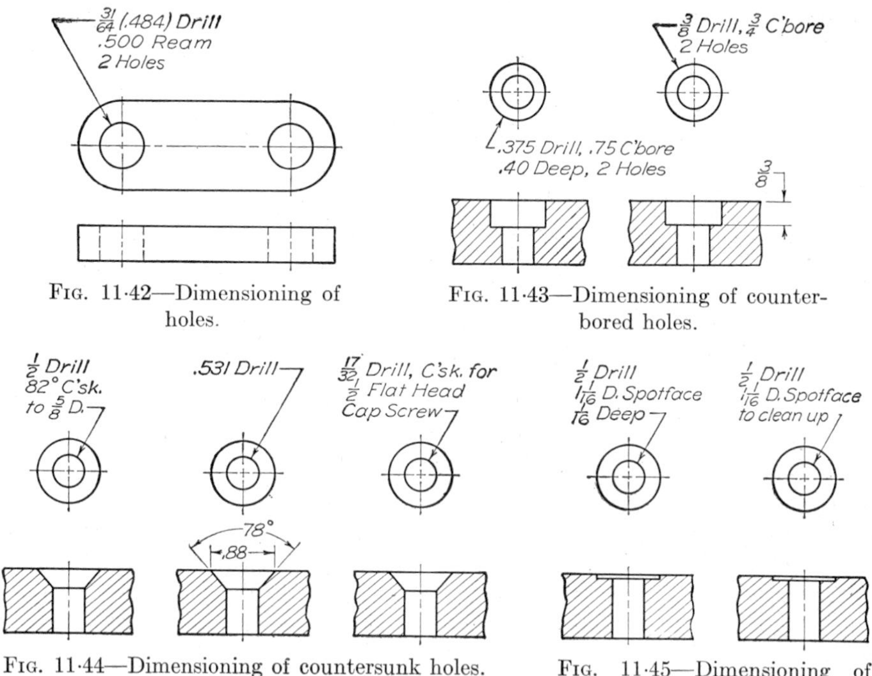

FIG. 11·42—Dimensioning of holes.

FIG. 11·43—Dimensioning of counterbored holes.

FIG. 11·44—Dimensioning of countersunk holes.

FIG. 11·45—Dimensioning of spot-faced holes.

operation) unless an outer circle would pass through the arrowhead. In such a case the arrow should be drawn to touch the outer circle.

Holes made up of several diameters and involving several stages of manufacture may be dimensioned as shown in Fig. 11·46. This method of dimensioning combines notes with the regular dimensions.

Tapped holes are dimensioned and specified as described in Chap. 13.

11·27 Location of holes. Mating parts held together by bolts, screws, rivets, etc., must have their holes for fastenings located from common datum surfaces or lines, in order to assure matching of the holes. When two or more holes are on an established center line, the holes will require location in one direction only, Fig. 11·47. If the holes are not on a common center line, they will require location in two directions, as in Fig. 11·48. The method at *B*, where the locations are referred to a common base line, is preferred for precision work.

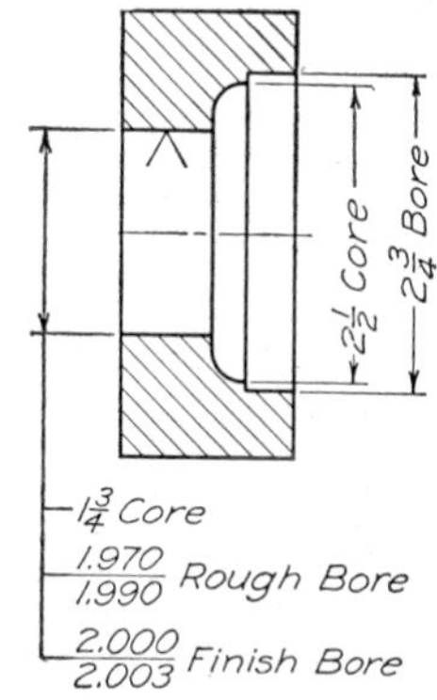

FIG. 11·46—Specifying several operations on large holes.

Hole circles are circular center lines often called "bolt circles" on which the centers of a number of holes are located.

One practice is to give the diameter of the hole circle and a note specifying the size of the holes, the number required, and the spacing, as in Fig. 11·49*A*. If one or more holes are not in the regular equally spaced position, their location may be given by an offset dimension as shown at *B*. An angular dimension is sometimes used for this purpose but should be avoided if accuracy is essential.

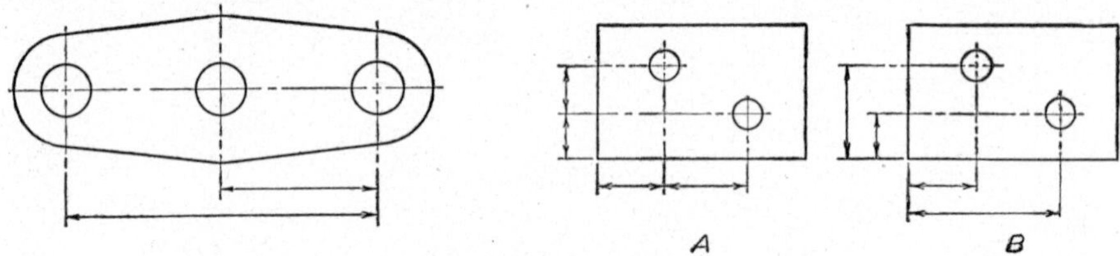

FIG. 11·47 FIG. 11·48
FIGS. 11·47 and 11·48—Location of holes.

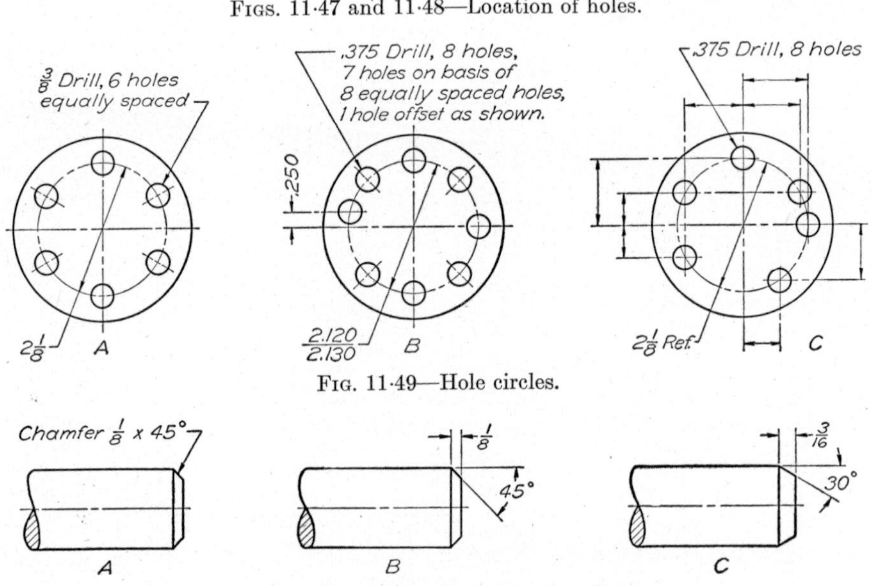

FIG. 11·49—Hole circles.

FIG. 11·50—Dimensioning of chamfers.

The coordinate method for locating holes, Fig. 11·49*C*, is preferred in precision work. The hole circle is often drawn and its diameter given for reference purposes, as indicated on the figure.

11·28 Chamfers. Chamfers may be dimensioned by note, as in Fig. 11·50*A*, if the angle is 45 degrees. The linear size is understood to be the short side of the chamfer triangle in conformity with the dimensioning without a note as shown at *B*. If the chamfer angle is other than 45 degrees, it should be dimensioned as at *C*.

11·29 Tapers. The term "taper" as used in machine work usually means the surface of a cone frustum. The dimensioning will depend on the method of manufacture and the accuracy required. If a standardized taper (see Appendix, page 656) is used, the specification should be accompanied by one diameter and the length, Fig. 11·51*A*. At *B* is illustrated the general method of giving the diameters of both ends and the taper per foot. An alternate method is to give one diameter, the length, and the taper per foot. *Taper per foot* is defined as the difference in diameter in inches for 1 foot of length. *C* illustrates the method of dimensioning for precision work where a close fit between the parts, as well as a control of entry distance, is required. Because of the inaccuracy resulting from measuring at one of the ends, a gage line is established where the diameter is to be measured. The entry distance is controlled through the allowable variation in the location of the gage line, and the fit of the taper is controlled by the accurate specification of the angle.

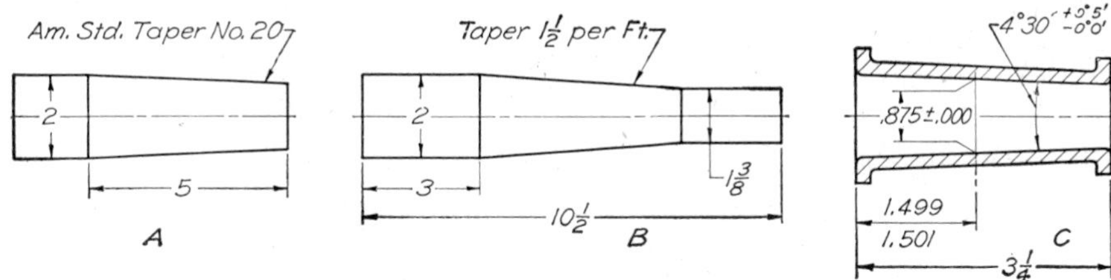

FIG. 11·51—Dimensioning of tapers.

11·30 Batters, slopes, grades. Batter is a deviation from the vertical such as is found on the sides of retaining walls, piers, etc., and slope is a deviation from the horizontal. Both are expressed as a ratio with one factor equal to unity, as illustrated in Fig. 11·52. Grade is identical to slope but is expressed in percentage, the inclination in feet per hundred feet. In structural work, angular measurements are shown by giving the ratio of run to rise with the larger side 12″, Fig. 27·2.

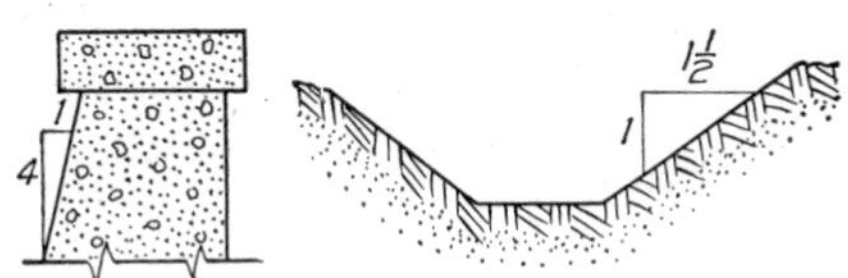

FIG. 11·52—Dimensioning of batters and slopes.

11·31 Shapes with rounded ends should be dimensioned according to their method of manufacture. Figure 11·53 shows several similar contours and the typical dimensioning for each. The link *A*, to be cut from thin material, has the radius of the ends and the center distance given as it would be laid out. At *B* is shown a cast pad dimensioned similar to *A*, with dimensions most usable for the patternmaker. The drawing at *C* shows a slot machined from solid stock with an end-milling cutter. The dimensions give the diameter of the cutter and the travel of the milling-machine table. The slot at *D* is similar to *C* but is dimensioned for quantity production

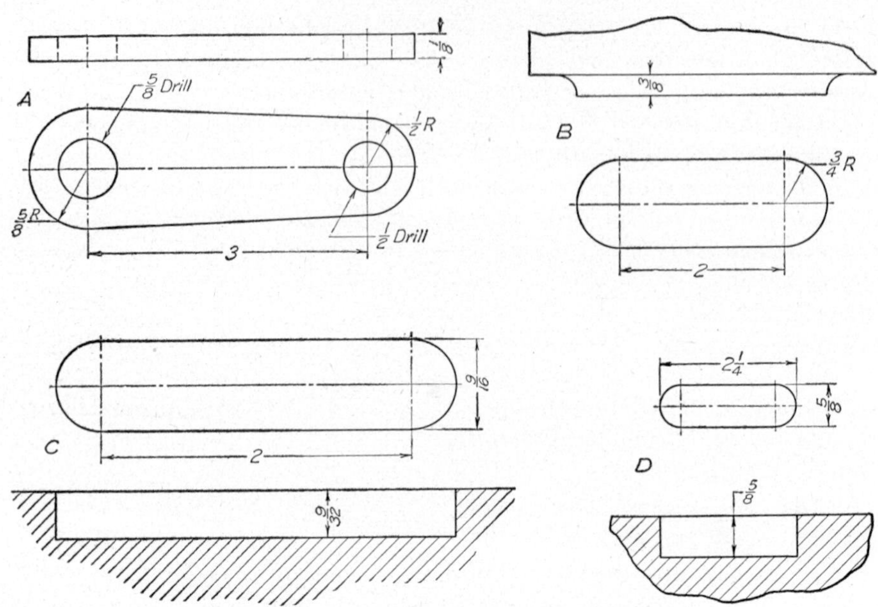

FIG. 11·53—Dimensioning of round-end shapes.

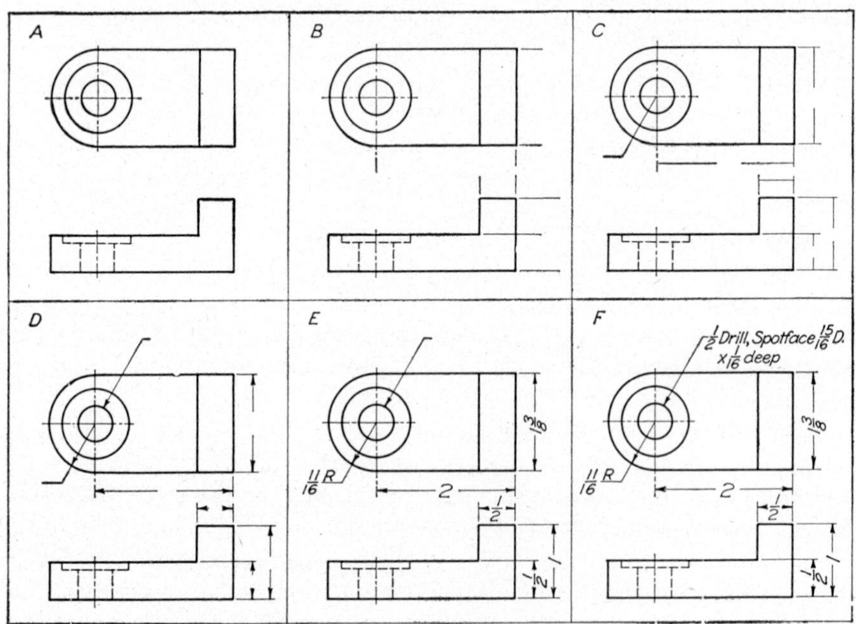

FIG. 11·54—Order of dimensioning.

where, instead of the table travel, the over-all length is wanted for gaging purposes. Pratt and Whitney keys and key seats are dimensioned by this method.

11·32 The order of dimensioning. A systematic order of working is a great help in placing dimensions. Figure 11·54 will illustrate the procedure. At *A* the shape description is complete. *B* shows the extension lines placed and center lines extended where necessary, thus planning for the positions of both size and location dimensions. Here the placement of each dimension can be studied and alterations made if desirable or necessary. At *C* the dimension lines have been added. Next, arrowheads and leaders for notes are drawn as at *D*. Figures are then added and notes lettered as at *E* and *F*.

It is desirable to add the notes *after* the dimensions have been placed. If the notes are placed first, they may occupy a space desired for a dimension. Because of the freedom allowed in the use of leaders, notes may be given in almost any available space.

11·33 Revision of dimensions. As a project is being developed, changes in design, engineering methods, etc., may make it necessary to

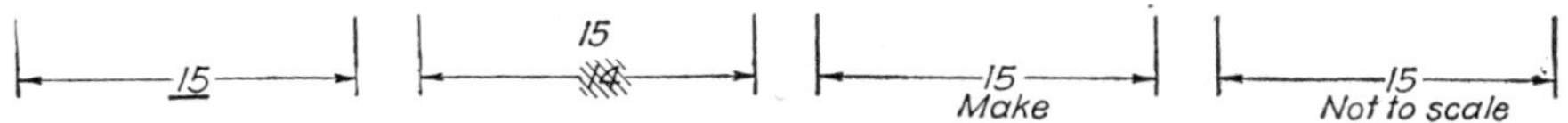

FIG. 11·55—Out-of-scale dimensions.

change some drawings either before or after they have been released to the shop. If the change is a major one, the drawing may have to be remade, but if the change is minor, in many cases the dimension values may be altered and the shape description left unchanged. In this case the out-of-scale dimensions should be indicated by one of the methods of Fig. 11·55. Drawing changes should be listed in tabular form above the title, with reference letters and the date, as explained in paragraph 15·22.

11·34 Half sections. In general, the half section is difficult to dimension clearly without some possibility of giving misleading, ambiguous, or crowded information. Generous use of notes and careful placement of the dimension lines, leaders, and figures will in most cases make the dimensioning clear; but, if a half section cannot be clearly dimensioned, an extra view or part view should be added to describe the size.

Inside diameters should be followed by the letter *D*, and the dimension line carried over the center line, as in Fig. 11·56, to prevent the possibility of reading the dimension as a radius. Sometimes the view and the dimensioning may both be clarified by showing the dotted lines on the unsectioned side. Dimensions of internal parts, if placed inside the view, will prevent the confusion between extension lines and the outline of external portions.

11·35 Pictorial drawings. When isometric or other pictorial forms are used as working drawings, the size description is often more difficult than the shape description. With the principles in this chapter as a basis, the general rule to follow is to have all the extension lines and dimension lines parallel to the axes, and to have the figures so made that they appear to lie in the plane of the face containing the feature dimensioned. To do this, the figures should be pictorial drawings of *vertical* figures. Leaders and dimen-

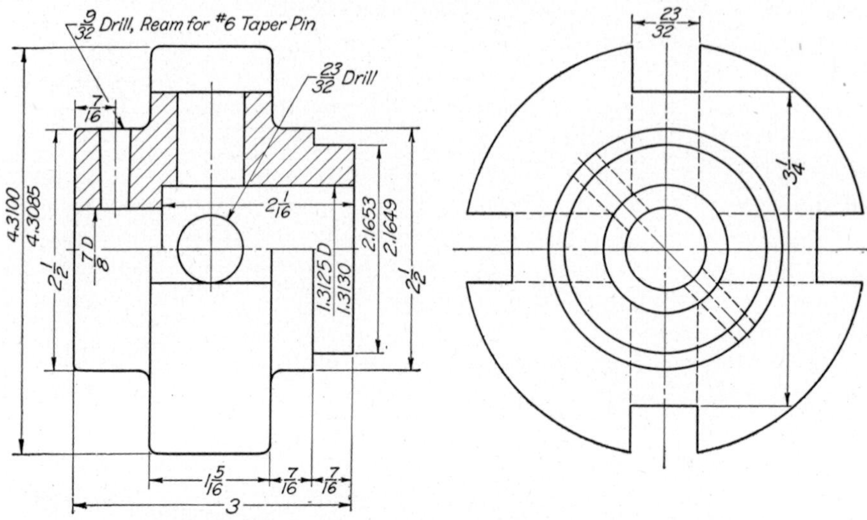

FIG. 11·56—Dimensioning of a half section (pintle block).

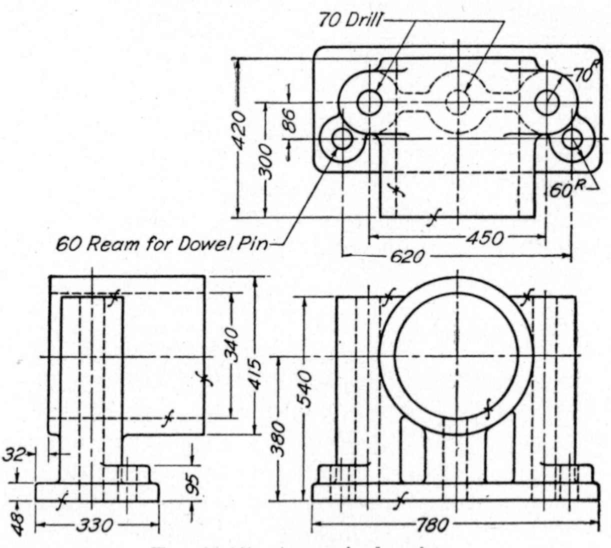

FIG. 11·57—A metric drawing.

sions in note form will be necessary more often on pictorial drawings than on orthographic drawings. Figures 7·77, 8·39, and 15·35 illustrate this method.

11·36 The metric system. Knowledge of the metric system will be an advantage, as it will be found on all drawings from countries where this system is standard and with increasing frequency on drawings made in the United States. The first instance of international standardization of a mechanical device is that of ball bearings, which have been standardized in the metric system.

Scale drawings in the metric system are not made to English or American scales but are based on divisions of ten as, full size, then 1 to 2, 1 to 2½, 1 to 5, 1 to 10, 1 to 20, 1 to 50, and 1 to 100. The unit of measurement is the millimeter (mm), and the figures are all understood to be millimeters, without any indicating marks. Figure 11·57 is an example of metric dimensioning. A table of metric equivalents is given in the Appendix.

11·37 Standard sizes, parts, and tools. In the dimensioning of any machine part, there is often the necessity of specifying some standard thickness or diameter, or the size produced by some standard tool. The American Standard, prevailing company standard, or manufacturer's standard should be consulted in order to assure giving correct information.

Wire and sheet-metal gages are given by number and are followed by the equivalent thickness or diameter in decimal form.

Bolts and screws are supplied in fractional and numbered sizes. Keys are available in manufacturer's numbered sizes or, for square and flat keys, in fractional sizes. Rivets, depending upon the variety, are to be had in fractional or numbered sizes.

Drills are available in numbered, lettered, fractional, and metric sizes. Reamers, milling cutters, and other standard tools are available in a variety of standard sizes.

The Appendix gives tables of standard wire and metal gages, bolt and screw sizes, key sizes, etc. ASA or manufacturers' standards will give further information as required.

11·38 Dimensioning practice by industry. As already indicated to some extent, special dimensioning practices may prevail in the several branches of engineering and in architecture. These practices are discussed in the chapters on architectural drawing, structural drawing, aircraft drawing, jigs and fixtures, welding drawings, etc., and also in the chapter on working drawings.

PROBLEMS

11·39 The problems following are given as studies in dimensioning on which to apply the principles of this chapter. Attention should be given to the methods of manufacture as described in Chap. 10. A function for the part should be assumed in order to fix the location of finished surfaces and to limit the possibilities in the selection of dimensions.

Group I. Pieces to be drawn and dimensioned

The illustrations are printed to scale, as indicated in each problem. Transfer distances with dividers or by scaling, and draw the objects to a convenient scale on a paper size to suit. For proper placement of dimensions, more space should be provided between views than is shown in the illustrations.

Use the aligned or horizontal dimensioning systems as desired. It is suggested that some problems be dimensioned in the complete decimal system.

1. Fig. 11·58. Stud shaft, shown half size. Machined from steel bar stock.

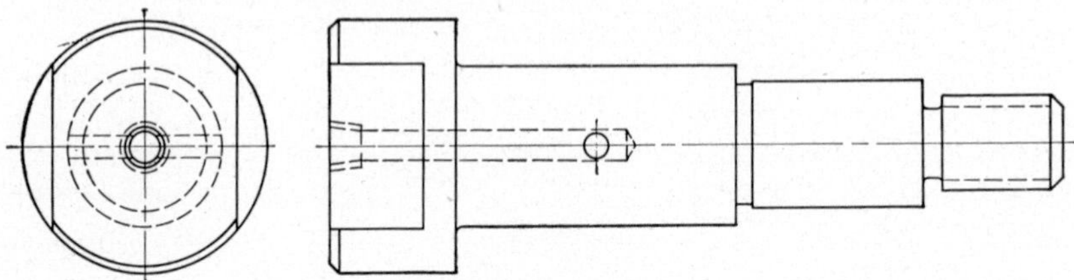

FIG. 11·58—Stud shaft.

2. Fig. 11·59. Shaft bracket, shown half size. Malleable iron. Hole in base is drilled and counterbored for a socket-head cap screw. Base slot and front surface of hub are finished. Hole in hub is bored and reamed. The function of this part is to support a shaft at a fixed distance from a machine bed, as indicated by the small pictorial view.

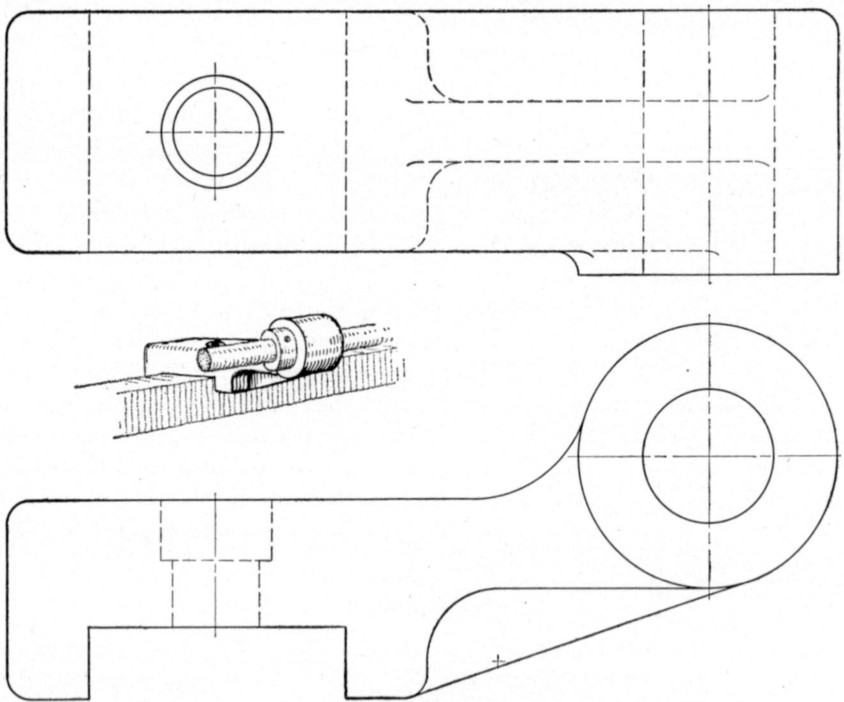

FIG. 11·59—Shaft support.

3. Fig. 11·60. Idler bracket, shown half size. Cast iron. Hole is bored and reamed. Slot is milled.

4. Fig. 11·60. See Prob. 3. Draw and dimension the right-hand part.

5. Fig. 11·61. Filter flange, shown half size. Cast aluminum. The small holes are drilled. Add spot faces.

6. Fig. 11·62. Boom-pin rest. Steel drop forging. Shown half size, draw half size or full size. Add top view if desired. Show machining allowance with alternate position

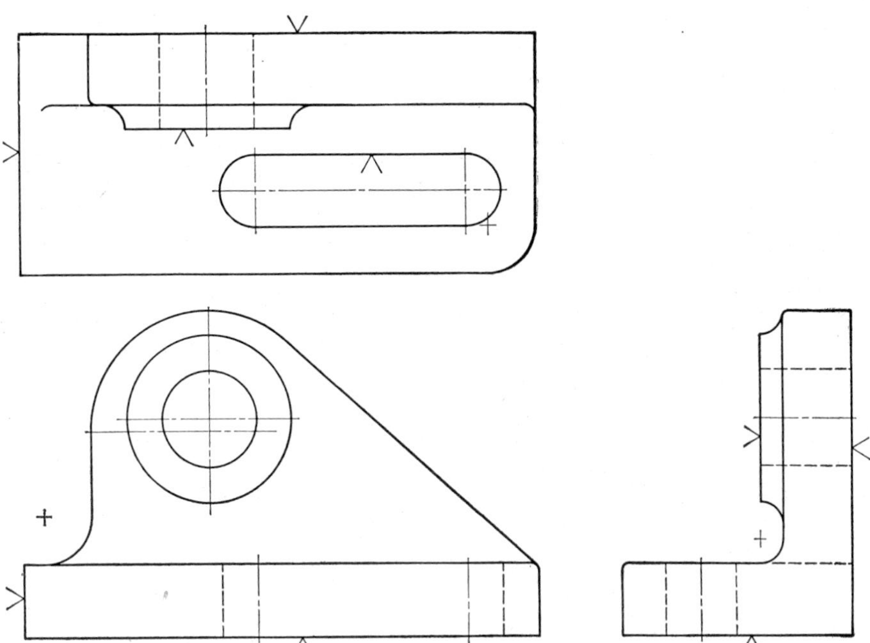

FIG. 11·60—Idler bracket, left hand.

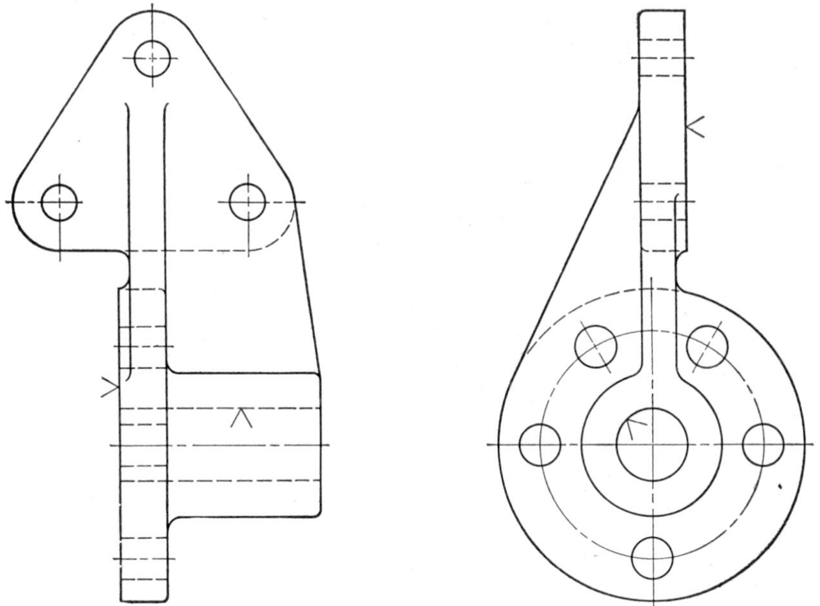

FIG. 11·61—Filter flange.

lines and dimension as in Fig. 10·7. All draft angles 7°. Holes are drilled, corner notches milled.

7. Fig. 11·62. Same as Prob. 6, but make two drawings: (1) the unmachined forging dimensioned for the diemaker, and (2) the machined forging dimensioned for the machinist. Reference, Fig. 12·6.

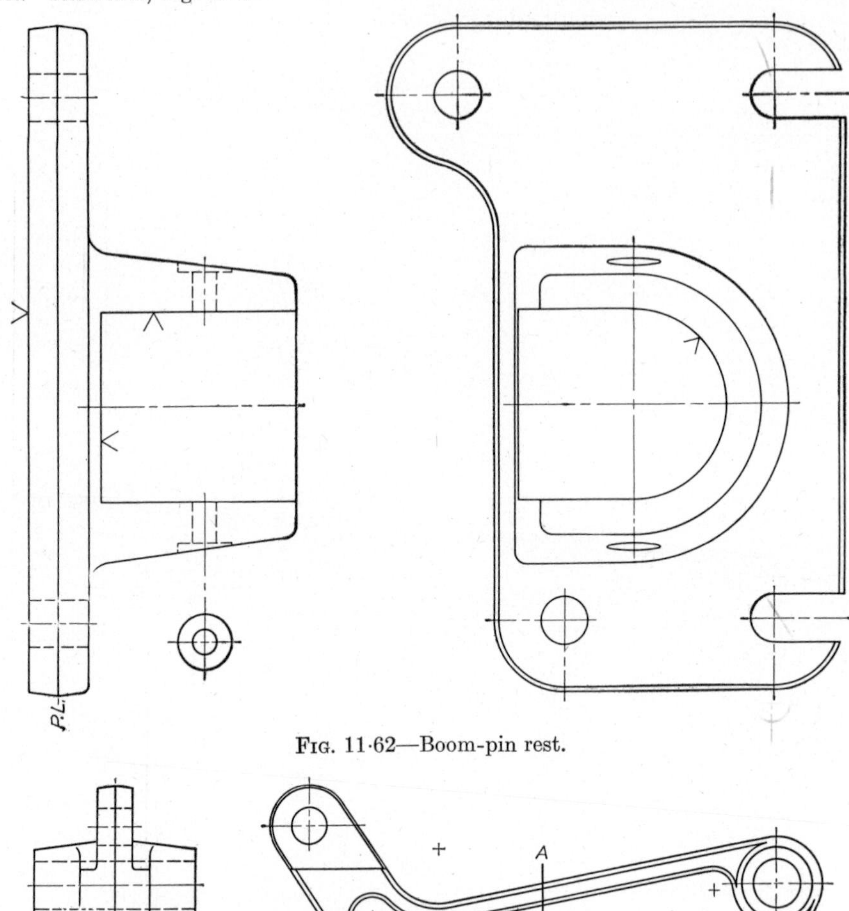

FIG. 11·62—Boom-pin rest.

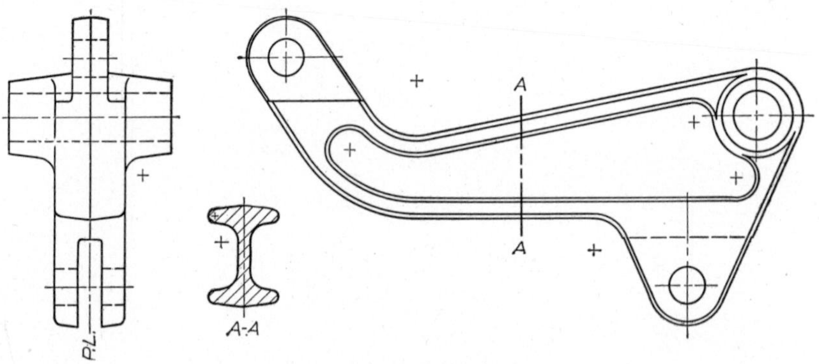

FIG. 11·63—Clutch lever.

8. Fig. 11·63. Clutch lever. Aluminum drop forging. Shown half size, draw full size or twice size. Add top view if desired. Holes are drilled and reamed; ends of hub are finished; left-end lug is straddle milled; slot in lower lug is milled. Show machining allowance with alternate position lines and dimension as in Fig. 10·7. All draft angles 7°.

9. Fig. 11·63. Same as Prob. 8, but make two drawings: (1) the unmachined forging dimensioned for the diemaker, and (2) the machined forging dimensioned for the machinist. Reference, Fig. 12·6.

10. Fig. 11·64. Radiator mounting clip, LH, No. 16 (0.0625) steel sheet. Shown half size. Holes and slot are punched.

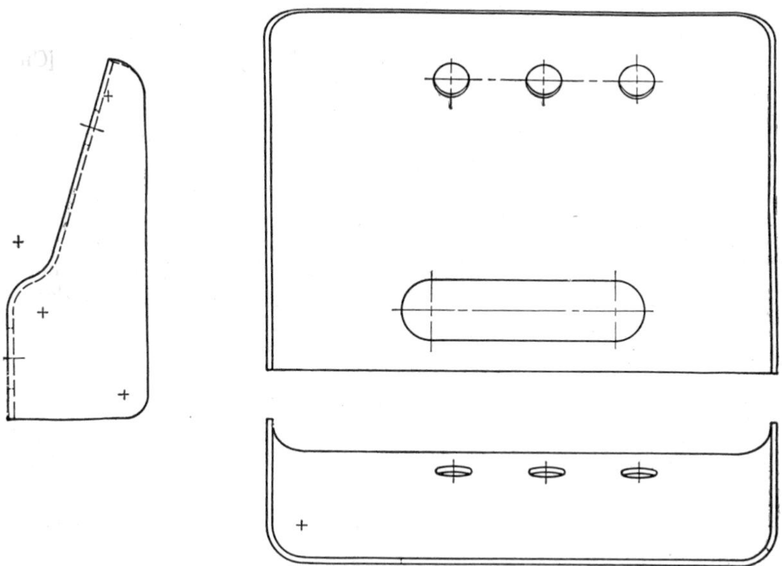

FIG. 11·64—Radiator mounting clip, left hand.

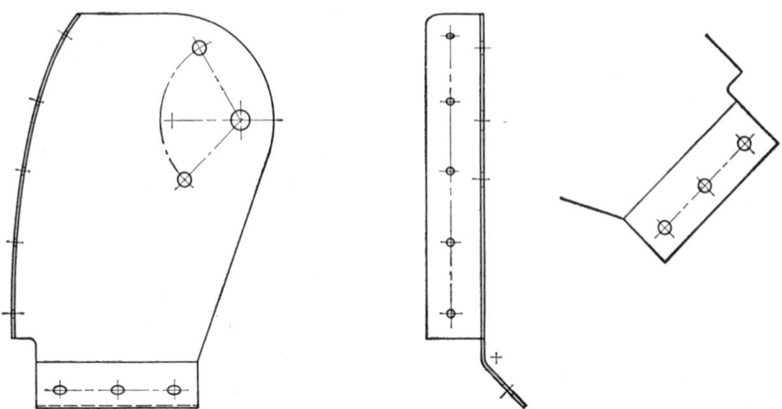

FIG. 11·65—Pulley bracket.

11. Fig. 11·65. Pulley bracket. Shown half size. Aluminum sheet, 24ST, 0.032 thick.

Group II. Dimensioned drawings from models

An excellent exercise in dimensioning is to make a detail drawing from a pattern, casting, or forging, or from a model made for the purpose. Old or obsolete patterns can often be obtained from companies manufacturing a variety of small parts, and "throw-out" castings or forgings are occasionally available. Familiarity with the methods of measuring is essential, as explained in Chap. 19. In taking measurements from a pattern, a shrink rule should always be used, and allowance must be made for finished surfaces.

Group III. Dimensioned drawings from pictorial views

The problems presented in pictorial form in Chaps. 7 to 9 may be used as dimensioning problems, either dimensioning one already drawn as an exercise in shape description or, for variety, one not previously made. A selection of 12 problems, graded in order of difficulty, is given below.

12. Fig. 7·66. Step block. No finished surfaces.
13. Fig. 7·68. Slotted wedge. Slot and base finished.
14. Fig. 7·71. Corner stop. Slot at top, cut corner, and base finished.
15. Fig. 7·77. Guide base. Vertical slot, boss on front, and base finished.
16. Fig. 7·83. Eccentric. Finished all over.
17. Fig. 7·84. Shifter fork. All contact surfaces finished.
18. Fig. 7·88. Shaft guide. L-shaped pad and end of hub finished.
19. Fig. 8·35. Jig angle. Finished all over.
20. Fig. 8·37. Angle shaft base. Base and slanting surface finished.
21. Fig. 8·36. Radial swing block. All contact surfaces finished.
22. Fig. 8·53. Transverse connection. Base pads finished.

TEXT-FILMS

The following McGraw-Hill Text-Films have been correlated directly with Chaps. 11 and 12:

Dimensioning Techniques (silent filmstrip).

Stresses techniques, choice, and placement in standard dimensioning practice; illustrates and explains the various dimensioning symbols; demonstrates proper techniques of applying these symbols to various drawings.

Selection of Dimensions (20-min. sound motion picture).

Introduces the principles that govern the choice of dimensions; shows that these principles are based on (*a*) the functional characteristics of the object and (*b*) the manufacturing methods used in making the object.

Chapter 12

THE DIMENSIONING OF MACHINE DRAWINGS

12·1 Modern production methods are based on the principle that the engineering department is responsible for the correctness and completeness of the drawings and that manufacturing then proceeds in the various shops to produce exactly what is called for by the drawings. This procedure clearly defines the responsibility of the designing and manufacturing groups, minimizes confusion in the drafting room and in the shop, ensures the interchangeability of parts, and guarantees, in so far as is possible, proper functioning of a completed machine. Thus working drawings must be clearly and completely dimensioned from the standpoint of the functioning of the part, the method of production, and the manufacturing process to be used so that nothing is left to the discretion of the shop.

12·2 Precision and tolerance. In the manufacture of any machine or structure, the degree of "fineness" or "quality" is a first consideration. The "workmanship," or degree of manufacturing care put into the product, determines the relative quality together with the accompanying relative cost and selling price.

Precision is the degree of accuracy necessary to ensure functioning as intended. As an example, a cast part will usually have on it two types of surfaces: (1) mating surfaces and (2) nonmating surfaces. The mating surfaces will be machined to the proper smoothness and at the correct distance from some other surface. The nonmating surfaces, exposed to the air and having no important relationship to other parts or surfaces, will be left in the original rough cast form. Thus the mating surfaces require much greater manufacturing precision than do the nonmating surfaces. The dimensions on the drawing must indicate which surfaces are to be finished and the precision required in finishing. However, because of the impossibility of producing any distance to an absolute size, some variation must be allowed in manufacture.

Tolerance is the allowable variation for any given size and provides a means of controlling the precision required. The tolerance on any given dimension varies according to the degree of precision necessary for that particular dimension. For nonmating surfaces, the tolerance may vary from 0.01 inch for small parts to as much as 1 inch on very large parts. For mating surfaces, tolerances as small as a few millionths of an inch are sometimes necessary (for extremely close-fitting surfaces) but usually surfaces are finished to an accuracy of from 0.001 to 0.010, depending upon the function of the part. Figure 12·1 shows variously toleranced dimensions on a machine drawing.

In some cases, particularly in structural and architectural work, tolerances are not stated on the drawing but are given in a set of specifications or are understood to be of the order stated in standards for the industry.

12·3 Production methods and dimensioning practice. Production methods may be classified as (1) *unit production,* the term applied when one or only a few devices or structures are to be built, and (2) *quantity* or *mass production,* indicating that a large number of identical machines or devices are to be made with the parts interchangeable from one machine to another.

Unit production methods almost always apply to large machines and structures, especially if custom made. The large size often eliminates the need

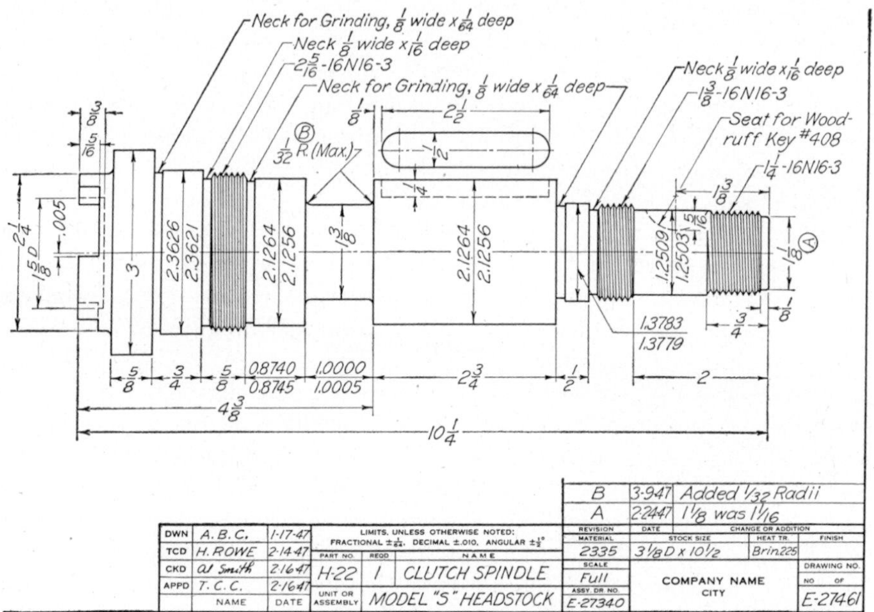

FIG. 12·1—Toleranced dimensions.

for great accuracy, and common fractional dimensions are used. Tolerances are not given except as general directions in the specifications, and each individual part is produced to fit, or is fitted to the adjacent parts, frequently on the job, by experienced workmen in accordance with the dimensions and directions given on the drawings.

Similar methods are employed for unit production of smaller machines and mechanical devices. The drawings may have common fractional dimensions exclusively on the assumption that the parts will be individually fitted in the shop. Thus, in this case, the manufacturing group accepts the responsibility for the proper functioning of the machine and, in some cases, even the design of some of the parts. Skilled workmen are employed for this work. Usually each machine is completed before another is started, and the parts will not be interchangeable.

Quantity production methods will usually be employed whenever a great number of identical machines are to be made. After a part has been detailed, the operations-planning group of the engineering department will plan the shop operations step by step. Then special tools are designed by the tool-design group so that, in production, semiskilled workmen may perform operations that would otherwise require skilled workmen. These tools, built by the highly skilled toolmaker, simplify production and greatly increase the rate.

One workman performs a single operation on the part, then it is passed on to a second workman who performs another operation, and so on until the completed part results. The specially designed tools and equipment make it possible to produce parts of high quality at low cost; moreover, it is relatively simple to produce parts with dimensional accuracy consistent with the requirements for interchangeability. The assembly may also be made by semiskilled workers by using special assembly fixtures and tools.

Nothing can be left to the judgment of the workman. In preparing drawings intended for quantity production, it is necessary for the engineering department to assume full responsibility for the success of the resulting machine by making the drawings so exact and complete that, if followed to the letter, the resulting parts cannot fail to be satisfactory. The engineering department alone is in a position to correlate corresponding dimensions of mating parts, establish dimensional tolerances, and give directions for the complete manufacturing job.

12·4 Principles for the selection of dimensions. Systematic selection of dimensions demands attention to the *use* or *function* of the part and the *manufacturing process* to be used in producing the part.

The functional principle recognizes that it is essential to give dimensions between those points or surfaces that either have a specific relationship to each other or control the location of other component or mating parts. This is accomplished by correlating the dimensions on a drawing of one part with the mating dimensions on the drawing of a mating part and arranging the tolerances of these dimensions to ensure interchangeability and proper functioning.

The process principle or "workman's rule," as it is sometimes called, recognizes that manufacture is simplified and made more direct by giving the dimensions the shop will "work to" in producing the part. Here again a knowledge of manufacturing processes and procedure is necessary, as explained in Chaps. 10 and 11.

In some cases there may be a conflict between these two principles and whenever this occurs the functional principle must take precedence; any attempt to satisfy both principles in this case would result in overdimensioning, as described in paragraph 12·23, causing confusion for the workman and possible malfunctioning of the part. With few exceptions, however, dimensions can be chosen to satisfy both principles.

12·5 Procedure for the selection of dimensions. A systematic procedure is, of course, desirable. The following steps will illustrate and serve as a guide:

1. The part should be carefully studied along with the mating part or parts. Pay particular attention to the mating and controlling surfaces. Dimensions meeting functional requirements are planned before any dimensions are placed on the drawing so that the correlation with dimensions of mating parts may be made.
2. Study the part to determine whether or not the manufacturing process may be simplified by some alteration of any of the functional dimensions. Changes should not be made if the functioning of the part would be impaired in any way.
3. Select the nonfunctional dimensions, being guided by the process principle, so that the dimensions are readily usable by the workmen. Avoid overdimensioning and duplication.

In general, dimensions for mating surfaces are governed by the functional and process principles, and the dimensions for nonmating surfaces are governed by the process principle only.

Occasionally the manufacturing process will not be known at the time of dimensioning. This may happen either when there are optional methods of manufacture, all equally good, or when the details of the manufacturing equipment of a contracting firm are unknown. In such cases, the dimensions should be selected and toleranced in the most logical manner so that the part cannot fail to be satisfactory. The size and location dimensions arrived at by the shape-breakdown system described in Chap. 10 will apply here to a great extent, since these dimensions will fulfill most production requirements. Contracting firms will often redraw incoming part drawings, dimensioning them to make for the most economical production with their own shop equipment.

12·6 Methods of part production. In following the process principle, the basic method, casting, forging, etc., as described in Chap. 10, must be known; then, following logically, the methods used in the shops and by the workmen must be known. The only workman to be considered in dimensioning a part cut from solid stock is the machinist. For parts produced by casting, the workmen to be considered are the patternmaker (for sand castings) or the diemaker (for die castings) and, for finishing, the machinist. Forged parts subject to quantity production will be dimensioned for the diemaker and machinist. For parts produced from sheet stock, the template maker, the diemaker, and the machinist must be considered; information for making the template and for forming the blank is obtained from a detail drawing showing the part as it should be when completed. In any case, *one drawing, appropriately dimensioned, must show the finished part.*

The several paragraphs following give examples of the dimensioning of machine parts for quantity production.

12·7 Dimensioning a part machined from stock. Figure 12·2 is a detail drawing of the stud from the rail-transport hanger, Fig. 15·75. This assembly drawing should be studied to determine the function of the stud. The stud is produced by machining on a lathe. Cold-rolled steel stock, 1¼″ in diameter is used. The stock diameter is the same as the large end of the stud, thus eliminating one machining operation.

Shape breakdown of the part results in a series of cylinders each requiring two dimensions, diameter and length. The important functional dimensions have been marked (on Fig. 12·2) with the letters *A*, *B*, *C*, and *D*. Dimension *A* is given as a four-place decimal limit to provide an accurate fit with the bore of the bearings. Dimension *B* is a three-place decimal limit to

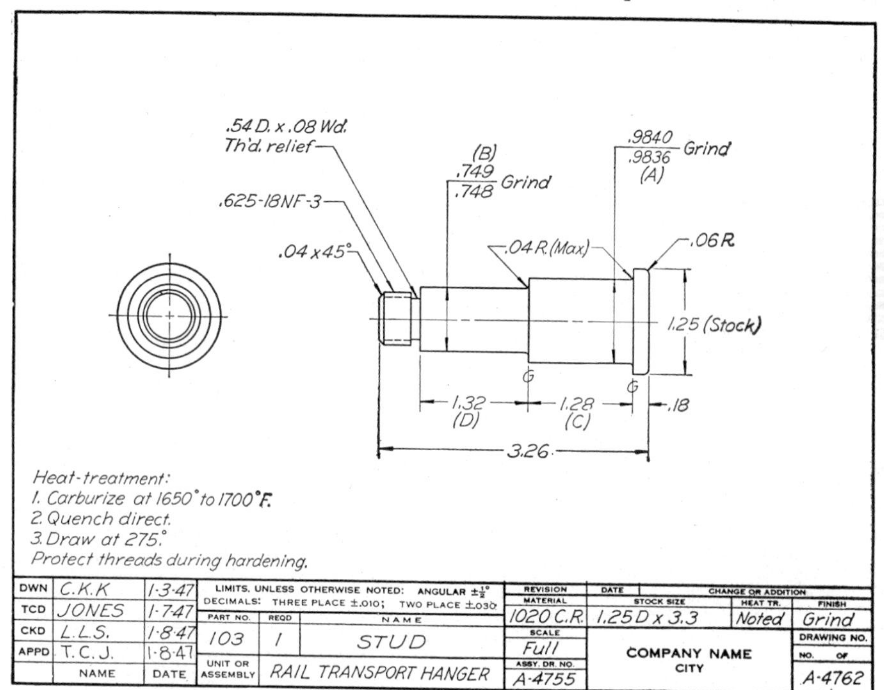

FIG. 12·2—Dimensioning for a part machined from stock.

correlate with a similar dimension for the hole in the hanger. Dimension *C* is made 0.03″ larger than the combined width of the two bearings in order to allow the inner races of the bearings to "creep." Dimension *C*, a two-place decimal, can vary by ±0.010″, but clearance for the bearings is assured under all conditions. Dimension *D* is made approximately 0.05″ less than the length of the hanger hub to ensure that the nut will clamp against the hanger before coming to the shoulder of the stud.

Functional dimensions need not always be extremely accurate dimensions. Note that dimensions *C* and *D*, with the relatively broad tolerances of two-place decimals, will allow the part to function as intended.

The thread specification may be considered as a functional dimension wherein the tolerance is provided by the class of fit.

The remainder of the dimensions have been selected to best suit shop requirements. Note that the thread length and over-all dimension cannot both be given or the part would be overdimensioned.

12·8 Dimensioning a casting. The dimensions required for sand castings may be separated into those used by the patternmaker and those used by the machinist. Since a cast part has two distinct phases in its manufacture, the drawings, in this case, have been made according to the multiple system explained in Chap. 10, one for the patternmaker, Fig. 12·3, and one

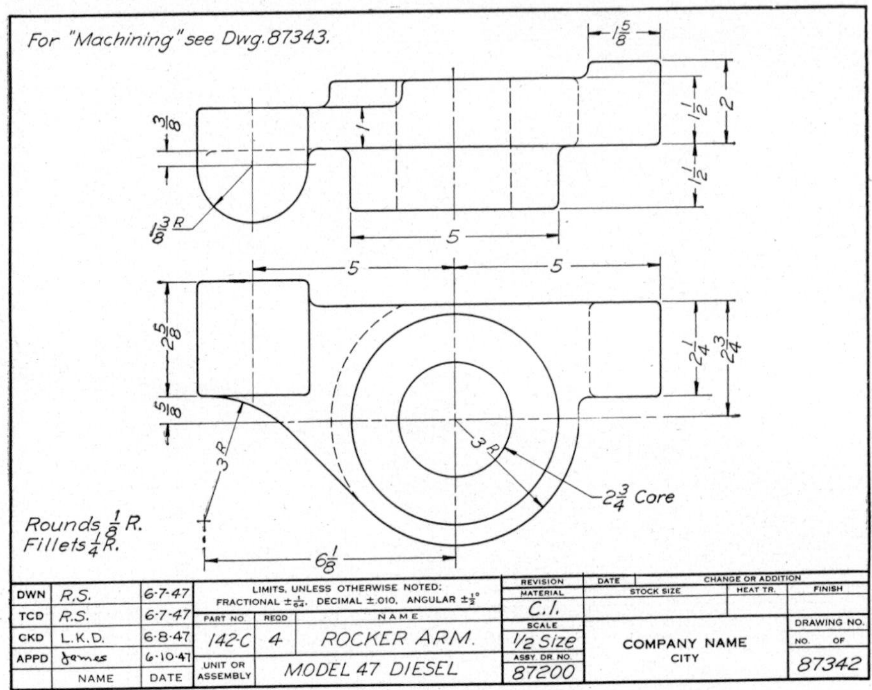

FIG. 12·3—Dimensions for a rough casting.

for the machinist, Fig. 12·4. This method allows a separation of patternmaker's and machinist's dimensions for study purposes.

The casting drawing gives the shape of the rough casting and has dimensions only for the patternmaker. Shape breakdown will show that each geometric shape has been dimensioned for size and then located, resulting in dimensions easily usable by the workman. Some of the dimensions might be altered, depending upon how the pattern is made; the most logical and easily usable combination should always be used. Note that the main central shape is dimensioned as it would be laid out on a board. Note also that several of the dimensions have been selected to agree with required functional dimensions of the machined part.

The machining drawing shows only the dimensions required by the machinist. These are almost all functional dimensions and have been

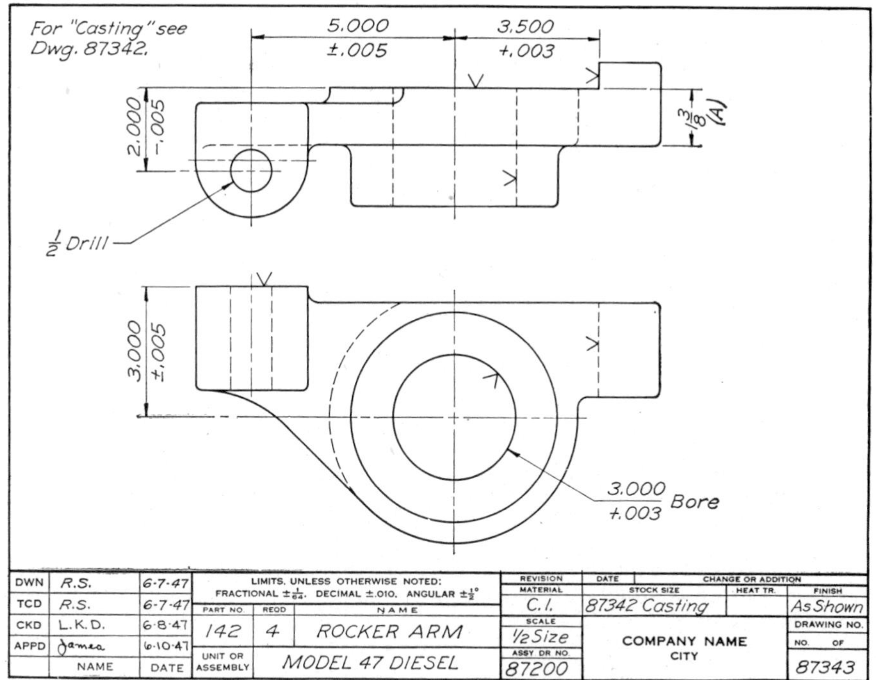

FIG. 12·4—Dimensions for machining a casting.

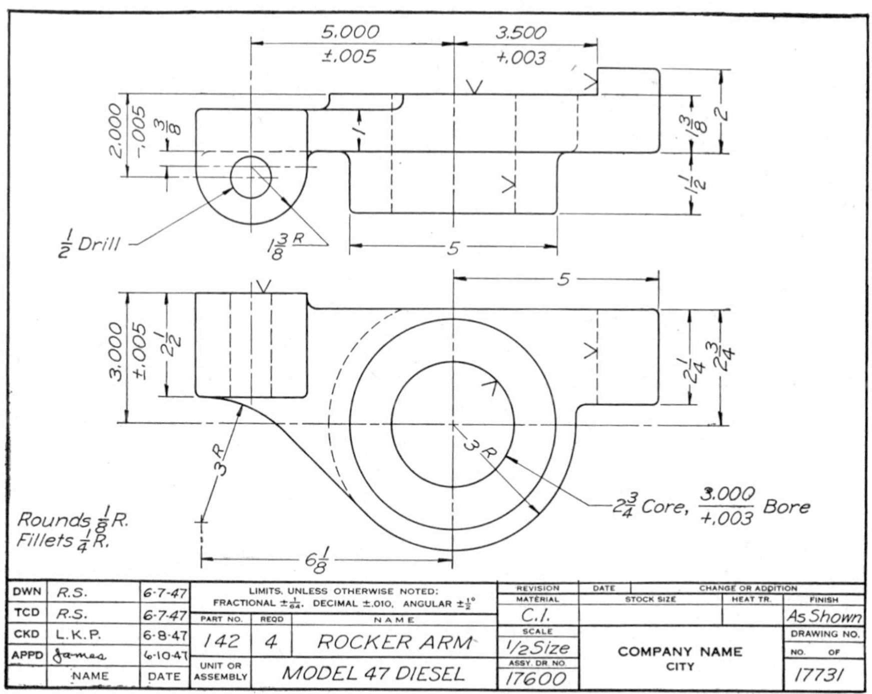

FIG. 12·5—All dimensions for a casting.

selected to correlate with mating parts. It is important to note that a starting point must be established in each of the three principal directions for machining the casting. In this case, a starting point is provided by (1) the coincidence of the center lines of the large hole and cylinder (location in two directions) and (2) dimension *A* to locate the machined surface on the back, from which is located the drilled hole. Dimension *A* is fractional, carrying the broad tolerance of $\pm 1/64''$, as there is no functional reason for working to greater accuracy.

Figure 12·5 is a drawing of the same part used in Figs. 12·3 and 12·4, but with the casting drawing dispensed with and the patternmaker's dimensions incorporated in the drawing of the finished part. In combining the two drawings, some dimensions are eliminated, as the inclusion of all the dimensions of both drawings would result in overdimensioning. In working from the drawing of Fig. 12·5, the patternmaker makes allowance for machining stock, being guided by the finish marks. If the drawing of Fig. 12·3 is used, the engineering department allows for the finishing stock by showing the rough casting oversize where necessary for machining. No finish marks are used.

12·9 Dimensioning a drop forging. Figure 12·6 is a drawing of a drop forging showing, at the left, the rough forging and, at the right, the machined forging. The drawing of the rough forging has only the dimensions needed by the diemaker for producing the forging dies. As the draft on drop forgings is considerable, it is shown on the drawing and dimensioned, usually, by a note. If the draft varies for different portions of the part, the angles may be given on the views. The dimensions parallel to the horizontal surfaces of the die are usually given so as to specify the size at the bottom of the die cavity. Thus, in dimensioning, one may visualize the draft as stripped off; then its apparent complication will no longer be a difficulty.

The machining drawing shows the dimensions for finishing. These dimensions are all functional, selected from the required function of the part. Study the illustration carefully.

12·10 Dimensioning a sheet-metal part. Parts to be made of thin material are usually drawn showing the part in its finished form, as in Fig. 12·7. The template maker first uses this drawing to lay out a flat pattern of the part. If only a few parts are to be made, this template will serve as a pattern for cutting the blanks. Then the part is formed and completed by hand. If a large number of parts are to be made, the diemaker will use the template and drawing in making up the necessary dies for blanking, punching, and forming. The work of both template maker and diemaker is greatly simplified by giving the dimensions to the same side of the material (either inside or outside, whichever is more important from the functional standpoint), as shown in Fig. 12·7. Dimensions to rounded edges (bends) are given to the theoretical sharp edges, which are called *mold lines.* The thickness of the material is given in the stock block of the title strip.

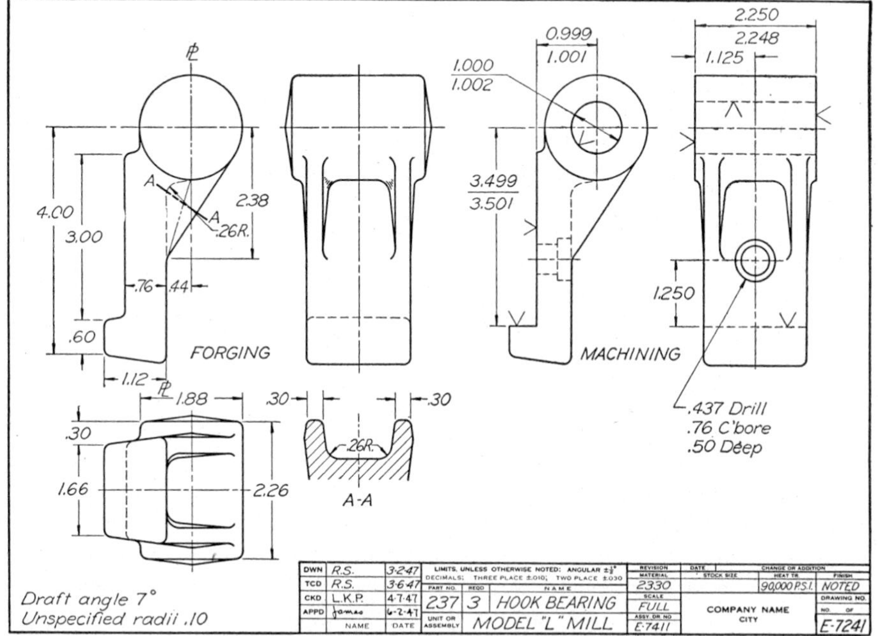

FIG. 12·6—Dimensioning for a drop forging.

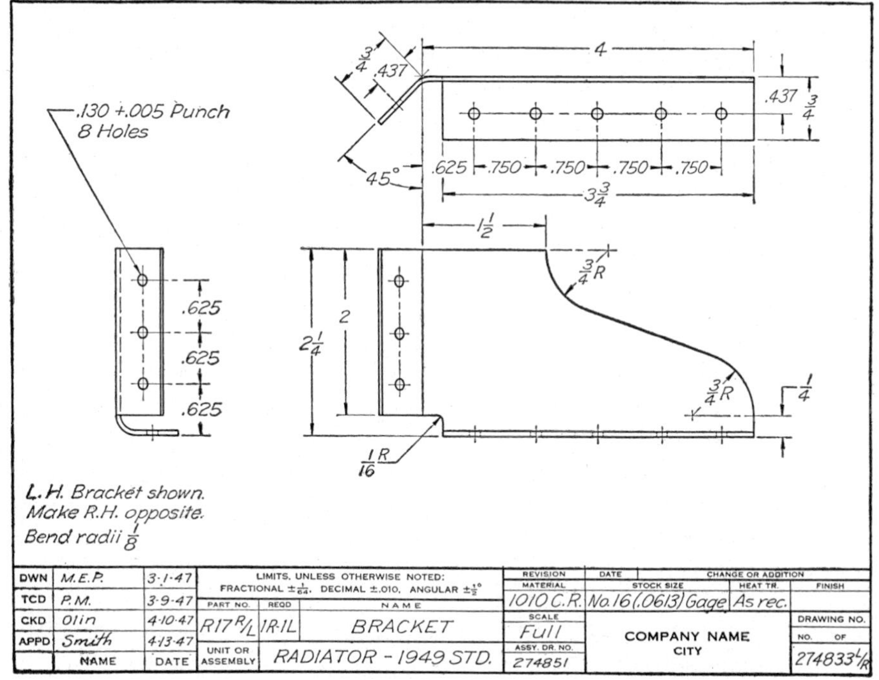

FIG. 12·7—Dimensioning for a sheet-metal part.

Note that in the figure the holes are located in groups (because of functional requirements) and that important functional dimensions are three-place decimals.

12·11 Fits of mating parts. The working parts of any machine will have some definite relationship to their mating parts in order to achieve a particular function, as free rotation, free longitudinal movement, clamping action, permanent fixed position, etc. In accomplishing these, the old practice was to mark the drawings of both parts with the same fractional dimension and add a note such as "running fit," "drive fit," etc., leaving the amount of allowance to the experience and judgment of the machinist.

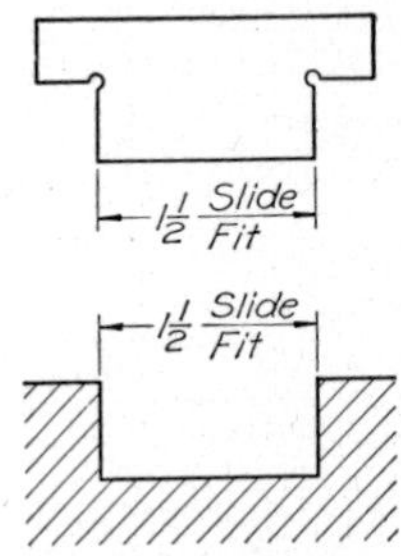

FIG. 12·8—Dimensioning a fit, old practice.

The tongue of Fig. 12·8 is to slide longitudinally in the slot. Thus, if the slot is machined first and measures 1.499″, the machinist, from his experience, assumes an allowance of approximately 0.004″, carefully machines the tongue to 1.495, and the parts will fit and function as desired. In making up a second machine, if the slot measures, say 1.504 after machining, the tongue is made 1.500, and an identical fit obtained; but the tongue of the first machine would be much too loose in the slot of the second machine, and the tongue of the second would not enter the slot of the first. The parts are, therefore, not interchangeable.

Since it is not possible to work to absolute sizes, it is necessary in the modern system of quantity production, where interchangeable assembly is required, to give the dimensions of mating parts with "limits," that is, the maximum and minimum sizes within which the actual measurements must fall in order for the part to be accepted. The dimensions for each piece are given in three- or four-place decimals, the engineering department taking all of the responsibility for the correctness of the kind of fit required.

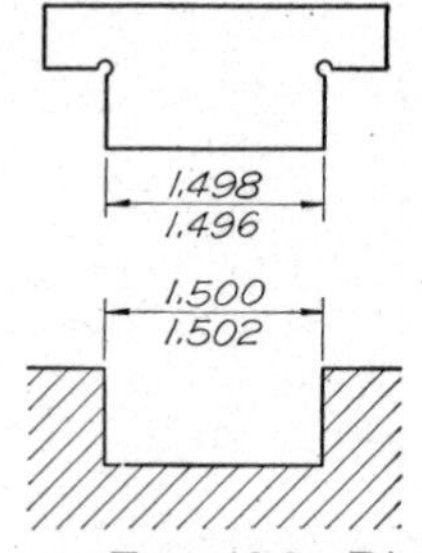

FIG. 12·9—Dimensioning a fit with limits.

Figure 12·9 shows the same tongue and slot of Fig. 12·8, but dimensioned for interchangeable parts in quantity production. In this case, for satisfactory functioning, it is decided that the tongue must be at least 0.002″ smaller than the slot but not more than 0.006″ smaller. This would provide an average fit similar to that used in the previous example. The maximum and minimum sizes acceptable for each part can then be figured.

The value 1.500″ has been assigned as the size of the minimum acceptable slot. This value minus the minimum clearance 0.002″ gives a size for the maximum tongue of 1.498. The maximum allowable clearance 0.006 minus the minimum allowable clearance 0.002 gives the amount 0.004 available as the total manufacturing tolerance for both parts. This has been evenly divided and applied as 0.002 to the slot and 0.002 to the tongue. Thus the size of the maximum slot will be the size of the minimum slot, *plus* the slot tolerance, or, 1.500 + 0.002 = 1.502. The size of the minimum tongue will be the size of the maximum tongue *minus* the tongue tolerance, or, 1.498 − 0.002 = 1.496.

Thus a study of Fig. 12·9 will show that, made in quantity, the two parts will allow interchangeable assembly and that any pair will fit approximately the same as any other pair, as planned.

12·12 Nomenclature. The terms used in limit dimensioning are so interconnected that their meaning should be clearly understood before a detailed study of the method is attempted.

The ASA gives the following definitions:

Nominal size. A designation given to the subdivision of the unit of length having no specified limits of accuracy but indicating a close approximation to a standard size.

Basic size. The exact theoretical size from which all limiting variations are made.

Allowance (neutral zone). An intentional difference in the dimensions of mating parts; that is, the minimum clearance space (or maximum interference) which is intended between mating parts. It represents the condition of the tightest permissible fit, or the largest internal member mated with the smallest external member. It is to provide for different classes of fit.

Tolerance. The amount of variation permitted in the size of a part.

Limits. The extreme permissible dimensions of a part.

In illustration of these terms, a pair of mating parts are dimensioned in Fig. 12·10. In this example the *nominal size* is 1½ inches. The *basic size* is 1.500. The *allowance* is 0.004. The *tolerance* on the tongue is 0.002, and on the slot it is 0.001. The *limits* are, for the tongue, 1.496 (max) and 1.494 (min), for the slot, 1.501 (max) and 1.500 (min).

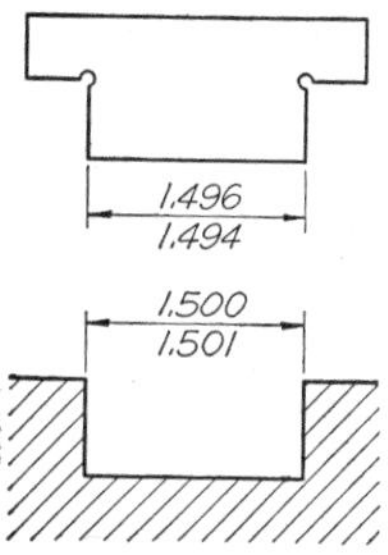

FIG. 12·10—An example of limit dimensioning.

Sometimes a somewhat broader definition is used for *basic size,* in which both shaft and hole are considered to be basic in their most desirable size. Following this conception, the basic tongue of Fig. 12·10 would be 1.496 and the basic slot would be 1.500.

The allowance may either be positive or negative. For clearance fits the allowance is positive, for interference fits it is negative.

12·13 General fit classes. The fits established on machine parts will, in general, be termed either a *clearance fit,* or an *interference fit,* depending upon the allowance, positive or negative, and the tolerance.

A *clearance fit* is the condition when the internal part is smaller than the external part, as illustrated by the dimensioning of Fig. 12·11. In this case, the largest shaft is 1.495″ and the smallest hole 1.500″, leaving a clearance of 0.005 for the tightest possible fit.

An *interference fit* is the opposite of a clearance fit, having a definite interference of metal for all possible conditions. The parts must be assembled by pressure or by heat expansion of the external member. Figure 12·12 is an illustration where the shaft is 0.001″ larger than the hole for the loosest possible fit. The allowance in this case is −0.003″.

A *transition fit* is the condition when either a clearance fit or an interference fit may be had; a minimum shaft in a maximum hole will give clearance, and a maximum shaft in a minimum hole will give interference. Figure 12·13 illustrates a transition fit where the smallest shaft in the largest hole gives 0.0003″ clearance, and the largest shaft in the smallest hole gives 0.0007″ interference.

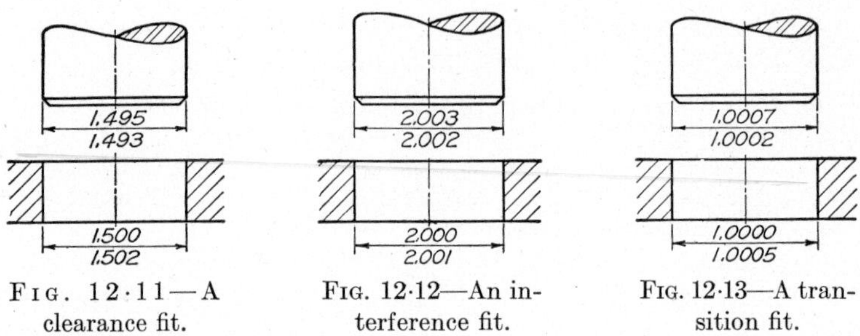

FIG. 12·11—A clearance fit. FIG. 12·12—An interference fit. FIG. 12·13—A transition fit.

12·14 Selective assembly. Sometimes the fit desired may be so close and the tolerances so small that the cost of producing interchangeable parts is prohibitive. Transition and interference fits often require a selection of parts in order to get the amount of clearance or interference desired; in this case, tolerances as small as practical are established, then the parts are gaged and graded as, say, *small, medium,* and *large.* A small shaft in a small hole, medium in medium, or large in large, will produce approximately the same fit allowance. Antifriction bearings are often assembled selectively.

12·15 Basic-hole and basic-shaft systems. Production economy depends to some extent upon which mating part is taken as a standard. In the basic-hole system, the hole can often be made with a standard tool, and the minimum size of the hole is taken as a base from which all variations are made.

Where a number of different fits of the same nominal size are required on one shaft, as for example when bearings are fitted to line shafting, the basic-shaft system is employed in which the maximum shaft size is taken as the basic size.

12·16 Methods of expressing tolerances. Tolerances may be either *specific,* given with the dimension value, or they may be *general,* as a note in the title block. The general tolerances apply to all dimensions not carrying a specific tolerance. The general tolerance should be allowed to apply whenever possible, using a specific tolerance only when necessary. If no tolerances are specified, the value usually assumed for fractional dimension is $\pm\frac{1}{64}''$, for angular dimensions $\pm\frac{1}{2}°$, and for decimal dimensions ± the nearest significant figure as, for example, ±0.01″ for a two-place decimal and ±0.001″ for a three-place decimal.

There are several methods for expressing tolerances. The method preferred in production work, where gages are extensively employed, is to write the two limits representing the maximum and minimum acceptable sizes, as in Fig. 12·14.

The internal dimension has the *minimum* size above the line, and the external dimension has the *maximum* size above the line. This is for convenience in machining.

Another method is to give the basic size followed by the tolerance, plus and minus (with the plus above the minus), Fig. 12·15*A*. If only one tolerance value is given, as at *B*, the other value is assumed to be zero.

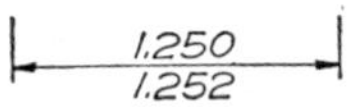

1.250
1.252

FIG. 12·14—A tolerance as limits.

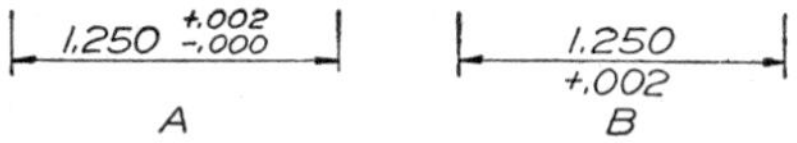

1.250 +.002 −.000
A

1.250
+.002
B

FIG. 12·15—Tolerances, plus and minus.

12·17 Unilateral and bilateral tolerances. A unilateral tolerance is one in which the total allowable variation is in *one* direction, either plus or minus (not both) from the basic value. A bilateral tolerance is one in which the tolerance is divided, with part plus and the remainder minus from the basic value.

Unilateral tolerances may be expressed by giving the two limits, as in Fig. 12·14, or by giving one limiting size and the tolerance, as 2.750 +0.005 or $2.750\ {}^{+0.005}_{-0.000}$; for fractional dimensions $\frac{1}{2} - \frac{1}{32}$ or $\frac{1}{2}\ {}^{+0}_{-\frac{1}{32}}$; for angular dimensions 64°15′30″ + 0°45′0″ or $64°15'30''\ {}^{+0°45'0''}_{-0°0'0''}$.

Bilateral tolerances are expressed by giving the basic value followed by the divided tolerance, both plus and minus (usually equal in amount), as $1.500\ {}^{+0.002}_{-0.002}$ or 1.500 ±0.002; for fractional dimensions $1\frac{1}{2}\ {}^{+\frac{1}{64}}_{-\frac{1}{64}}$ or $1\frac{1}{2}$ $\pm\frac{1}{64}$; for angular dimensions $30°0'\ {}^{+0°10'}_{-0°10'}$ or 30°0′ ±0°10′.

12·18 Decimal places of a dimension value should be carried to the same number of places as the tolerance. For example, with a tolerance of 0.0005 on a nominal dimension of $1\frac{1}{2}$″, the basic value should be written 1.5000. Tolerances for common fractional values should be given as common fractions, as $\frac{7}{8} \pm \frac{1}{64}$. Tolerances for decimal values should be given as decimal fractions, as 0.750 ±0.010.

12·19 Selecting tolerances. Experience in manufacturing is needed as well as a study of the particular mechanism involved before the engineer is able to know just the accuracy necessary and can specify proper fits and tolerances. The following quotation from the ASA Standard is pertinent:

In choosing the class of fit for manufacture, the engineer should keep in mind that cost usually increases proportionately to the accuracy required, and no finer class of fit should be chosen than the functional requirements actually demand. It is axiomatic that the closer the fit the smaller the manufacturing tolerance, and usually the greater the cost. The length of engagement of the fit also plays an important part in the selection of the class of fit for a piece of work. It is obvious that a long engagement will tolerate more looseness than a short one, and due regard should be paid to this feature.

A table of fits such as the ASA table of cylindrical fits explained in paragraph 12·22 may be taken as a guide for all ordinary work.

In many cases practical experience is required in determining the fit conditions to guarantee proper performance; often it is difficult to determine the definite size at which performance fails, and critical tolerances are sometimes obtained through exhaustive testing of experimental models.

It is essential to know the accuracy that can be attained with various machine tools and machining methods. As an example, a hole to be produced by drilling must not have a smaller tolerance specified than can be attained by drilling. Attainable accuracies are discussed in paragraph 12·21. A knowledge of the kind and type of equipment is needed to assure that the tolerances specified can be attained.

12·20 Application of tolerances. The following procedure is an ideal method for applying tolerances:

The two basic sizes, one for each mating part, differing from each other by the allowance representing the ideal fit condition, are first selected. The tolerances are then applied to each basic size *in the least dangerous direction.* This will result in unilateral tolerances. If the variation in size is equally dangerous in either direction, the tolerances should be made bilateral.

In general, mating surfaces should be toleranced unilaterally and non-mating surfaces toleranced bilaterally. One important exception is in the location of holes that *mate* with other holes or pins, as shown in Fig. 12·29. In this case, the basic size is the same for both parts, and the tolerances are bilateral as the variation is equally dangerous in both directions. The sizes of pins and holes, however, are dimensioned with unilateral tolerances.

12·21 Attainable accuracies. The different manufacturing processes all have inherent minimum possible accuracies, depending upon the size of the work, the condition of the equipment, and, to some extent, the skill of the workmen. The following *minimum* tolerances are given as a guide and are based on the assumption that the work is to be done on a production basis with equipment in good condition. Greater accuracies may be attained by highly skilled workmen on a unit production basis.

In general, the following are recommended as tolerances for dimensions *having no effect on the function of the part:* for sizes of 0 to 6 inches, $\pm 1/64$; 6 to 18 inches, $\pm 1/32$; 18 inches and larger $\pm 1/16$ (or more).

Sand castings. For the unmachined surfaces, a tolerance of $\pm 1/32$ is recommended for small castings and a tolerance of $\pm 1/16$ for medium-size castings. On larger castings, the tolerance should be increased to suit the size. Small and medium-size castings will rarely be below the nominal size, since the pattern is "rapped" for easy removal from the sand, thus tending to increase the size.

Die castings and plastic moldings. A tolerance of $\pm 1/64$ or less can easily be held with small and medium-size parts; for large parts the tolerance should be increased slightly. Hole center distances can be maintained within 0.005 to 0.010 depending on the distance of separation. Certain alloys may be die-cast to tolerances of 0.001 or less.

Forgings. The rough surfaces of drop forgings weighing 1 lb or less can be held to $\pm 1/32$; for weights up to 10 lb, $\pm 1/16$; for weights up to 60 lb, $\pm 1/8$. Due to die wear, drop forgings tend to increase in size as production from the die increases.

Drilling. For drills from No. 60 to No. 30, +0.002 − 0.000; No. 29 to No. 1, +0.004 − 0.000; from ¼ to ½ inches, +0.005 − 0.000; from ½ to ¾ inches, +0.008 − 0.000; from ¾ to 1 inch, +0.010 − 0.000; from 1 to 2 inches, +0.015 − 0.000.

Reaming. In general, a tolerance of +0.0005 − 0.000 can be held with diameters up to ½″. For diameters from ½ to 1 inch, +0.001 − 0.000, and from 1 inch and larger, +0.0015 − 0.000.

Lathe turning. Rough work: For diameters of ¼ to ½ inch, a total tolerance of 0.005; for diameters of ½ to 1 inch, 0.007; for diameters of 1 to 2 inches, 0.010; for diameters of 2 inches and larger, 0.015.

Finish turning. For diameters of ¼ to ½ inch, a total tolerance of 0.002; for diameters of ½ to 1 inch, 0.003; for diameters of 1 to 2 inches, 0.005; for diameters of 2 inches and larger, 0.007.

Milling. When single surfaces are to be milled, tolerances of 0.002 to 0.003 can be maintained. With two or more surfaces to be milled, the most important may be toleranced to 0.002 and the remainder as 0.005. In general, 0.005 is a good value to use with most milling work.

Planing and shaping. These operations are not commonly used with small parts in quantity production work. For larger parts, tolerances of 0.005 to 0.010 may be maintained.

Broaching. Diameters up to 1 inch may be held within 0.001; diameters from 1 to 2 inches, 0.002; diameters of 2 to 4 inches, 0.003. Surfaces up to 1 inch apart may be held within 0.002; 1 to 4 inches apart, 0.003; 4 inches apart and over, 0.004.

Threads. Tolerances for ASA threads are provided on the pitch diameter through the fit classification number given with the specification. For a given class of fit, the tolerance increases as the size of the thread increases. These tolerances may be found in ASA B1.1 1935.

Grinding. For both cylindrical and surface grinding, a tolerance of 0.0005 can be maintained.

12·22 ASA cylindrical fits. The ASA has made a classification of eight kinds of fits and has compiled tables of limits for external and internal members for different sizes in each class. These limits are tabulated in the Appendix.

ASA CLASSIFICATION OF FITS

Loose fit (class 1)—large allowance. This fit provides for considerable freedom and embraces certain fits where accuracy is not essential.

Examples: Machined fits of agricultural and mining machinery; controlling apparatus for marine work; textile, rubber, candy, and bread machinery; general machinery of a similar grade; some ordnance material.

Free fit (class 2)—liberal allowance. For running fits with speeds of 600 rpm or over and journal pressures of 600 lb per sq in. or over.

Examples: Dynamos, engines, many machine-tool parts, and some automotive parts.

Medium fit (class 3)—medium allowance. For running fits under 600 rpm and with journal pressures less than 600 lb per sq in.; also for sliding fits and the more accurate machine-tool and automotive parts.

Snug fit (class 4)—zero allowance. This is the closest fit that can be assembled by hand and necessitates work of considerable precision. It should be used where no perceptible shake is permissible and where moving parts are not intended to move freely under a load.

Wringing fit (class 5)—zero to negative allowance. This is also known as a "tunking fit" and it is practically metal-to-metal. Assembly is usually selective and not interchangeable.

Tight fit (class 6)—slight negative allowance. Light pressure is required to assemble these fits, and the parts are more or less permanently assembled, such as the fixed ends of studs for gears, pulleys, rocker arms, etc. These fits are used for drive fits in thin sections or extremely long fits in other sections and also for shrink fits on very light sections. Used in automotive, ordnance, and general machine manufacturing.

Medium force fit (class 7)—negative allowance. Considerable pressure is required to assemble these fits, and the parts are considered permanently assembled. These fits are used in fastening locomotive wheels, car wheels, armatures of dynamos and motors, and crank disks to their axles or shafts. They are also used for shrink fits on medium sections or long fits. These fits are the tightest which are recommended for cast-iron holes or external members as they stress cast iron to its elastic limit.

Heavy force and shrink fit (class 8)—considerable negative allowance. These fits are used for steel holes where the metal can be highly stressed without exceeding its elastic limit. These fits cause excessive stress for cast-iron holes. Shrink fits are used where heavy force fits are impractical, as on locomotive wheel tires, heavy crank disks of large engines, etc.

Example of limit dimensioning and use of the ASA tables. Suppose a 1″ shaft is designed to run with a class 1 fit, basic-hole system. The *nominal size* is then 1″ and the *basic size* is 1.000″. The ASA table, page 652, shows that the hole may vary from 0.000 to +0.003 which is the *tolerance on the hole.* The tolerance applied to the basic size of 1.000 would give 1.000 as the minimum size of the hole and 1.003 as the maximum, Fig. 12·16.

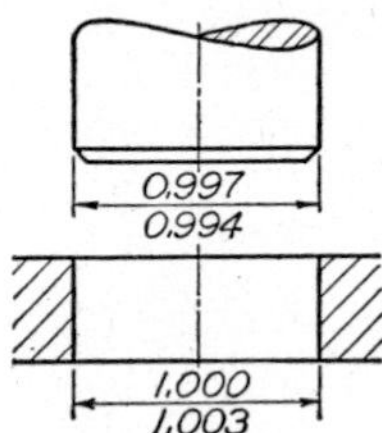

FIG. 12·16—An ASA clearance fit.

The table shows that the shaft may vary from −0.003 to −0.006. The actual *tolerance on the shaft* is the difference between these two minus values, or 0.003″. The two minus values applied to the basic size of 1.000 would give 0.997 as the maximum size of the shaft and 0.994 as the minimum. From the definition of allowance, the difference between maximum shaft (0.997) and minimum hole (1.000) would be +0.003.

The foregoing example is a clearance fit since the allowance is positive. The first four classes of the ASA fits will all give positive or zero allowances and will result in clearance fits and interchangeable parts. The last four classes will give zero or negative allowances requiring selective assembly in most cases for satisfactory results.

In the following example, the shaft is to be permanently assembled in a hole (hub) with an interference fit, Fig. 12·17.

Nominal size 2″. Class 8 fit. Basic size 2.000. From the ASA table, page 652.

Hole or External Member	Shaft or Internal Member
+0.0008 and 0.0000	+0.0028 and +0.0020

These values applied to the basic size give the limit dimensioning, Fig. 12·17.

Tolerance on hole: 2.0008 − 2.0000 = 0.0008
Tolerance on shaft: 2.0028 − 2.0020 = 0.0008
Allowance: 2.0000 − 2.0028 = −0.0028

12·23 Base-line dimensioning. Dimensions may be given either (1) in *successive* form, having each dimension from the one immediately preceding, Fig. 12·18; or (2) in *coordinate* or "base-line" form, having all dimensions referred to a common datum or reference, Fig. 12·19. To save space, base-line dimensions are sometimes arranged along a single line in *progressive* fashion, as indicated by the horizontal dimensions of Fig. 12·20. This method should be used only in limited space and when many dimensions are needed. The position of a point dimensioned by the base-line system is not dependent upon the cumulative tolerances of preceding dimensions.

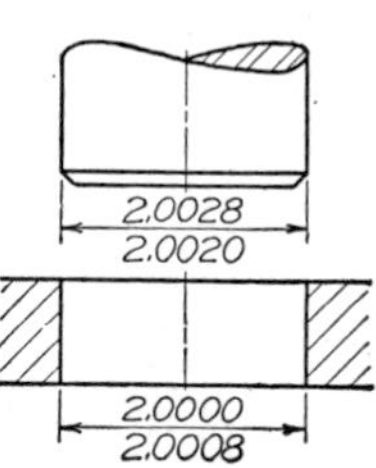

FIG. 12·17—An ASA interference fit.

12·24 Cumulative tolerances. Tolerances are said to be cumulative when a position in a given direction is controlled by more than one tolerance. Thus in Fig. 12·21, the position of surface Y with respect to surface W is controlled by the additive tolerances on dimensions A and B. If it is important, functionally, to hold surface Y with respect to surface X, the dimensioning used is good. If, however, it is more important to hold surface Y with respect to surface W, the harmful effect of cumulative tolerances can be avoided by dimensioning as in Fig. 12·22. Cumulative tolerance, however, is always present; thus in Fig. 12·22, the position of surface Y with respect to surface X is now subject to the cumulative tolerances of dimensions A and C.

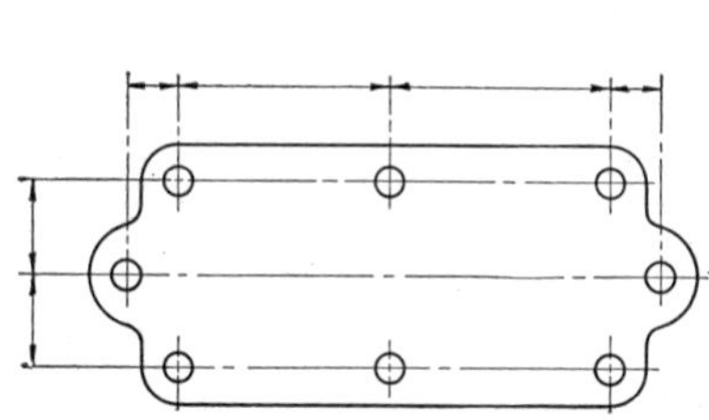

FIG. 12·18—Successive dimensioning.

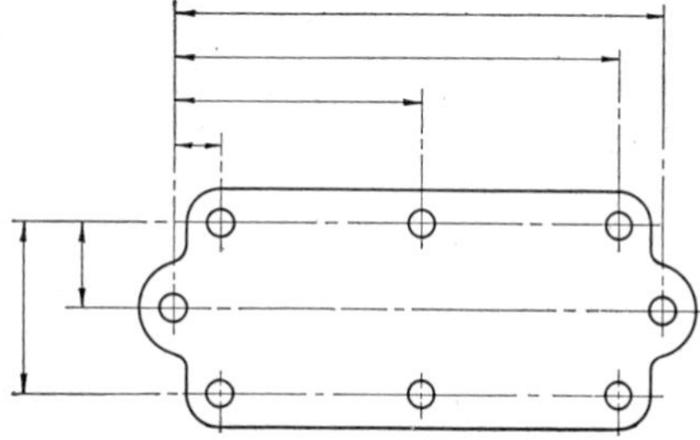

FIG. 12·19—Base-line dimensioning.

In machine drawing, confusion in the shop may result from cumulative tolerances when the drawing is over dimensioned. This is illustrated in

Fig. 12·23 where one of the surfaces will be positioned by two dimensions, both of which are subject to a tolerance. Thus surface Z may be positioned with respect to surface W by means of dimensions A, B, and D and be within $\pm 0.003''$ of the basic position; this variation is inconsistent with the tolerance on dimension E. The situation may be clarified by assigning smaller tolerances to dimensions A, B, and D so that, cumulatively, they

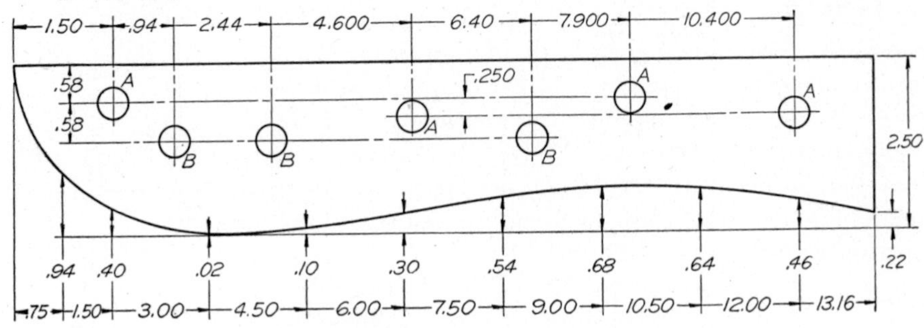

FIG. 12·20—Progressive dimensioning.

will be equal to ± 0.001 or less. This is poor practice, however, since it will probably increase the production cost. Another solution is to increase the tolerance on dimension E to ± 0.003 if the function of the part will permit. The best solution, however, is to eliminate one of the four dimensions, since one dimension is superfluous. If all four dimensions are given, *one* should be marked "ref," and its tolerance eliminated.

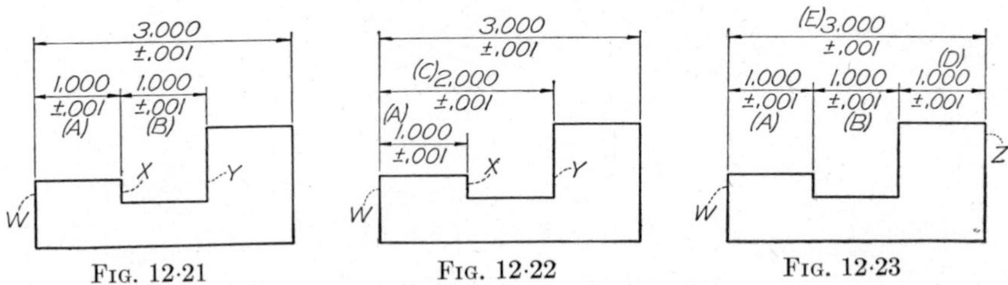

FIG. 12·21 FIG. 12·22 FIG. 12·23

12·25 Tolerance for symmetry. Older practice in dimensioning symmetrical pieces frequently took advantage of the symmetry to avoid giving certain location dimensions. Following this practice, the part illustrated in Fig. 12·24, which is symmetrical about the vertical center line, has no horizontal dimension to locate the hole. The assumption is that the shop will center the hole in the part.

The above practice is to be avoided on drawings intended for quantity production, however, since with no locating dimension there is no tolerance to indicate how much the hole can be out of symmetry with the rest of the part and still function satisfactorily. Modern practice is to give a center-line locating dimension with a value of one-half the total size; this dimension provides a tolerance on the symmetry of the piece, Fig. 12·25.

12·26 Coinciding center lines and dimensions. In many cases there will be a coincidence of the center lines for two different features of a part. Often one center line is for an unfinished feature and the other (and coincident) center line for a finished feature. Figure 12·26 shows at *A* the draw-

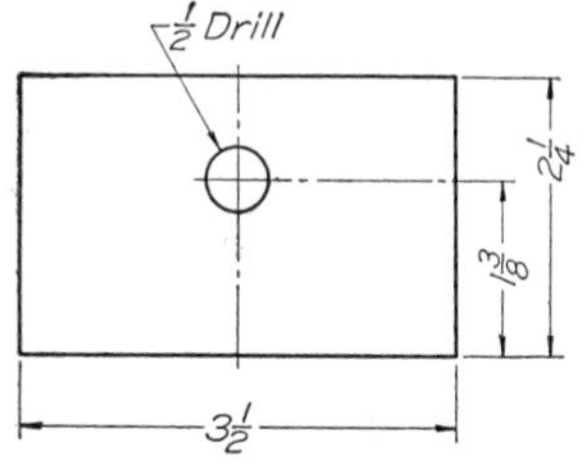

FIG. 12·24—Symmetry assumed.

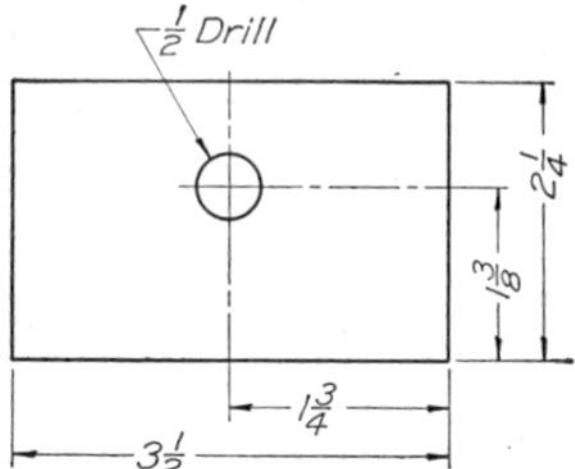

FIG. 12·25—Symmetry controlled.

ing of a link dimensioned for the patternmaker. If holes are to be machined in this link, the drawing would be as at *B*; the patternmaker would not use the dimension between centers, as shown, but would assume the nominal dimension of 1½″ with the usual pattern tolerance of ±1⁄32″. The clearest dimensioning in this case would be as at *C*.

In any case where there is a coincidence of centers, it may be difficult to indicate the limits within which the coincidence must be maintained. In example *C* of Fig. 12·26, there are actually two horizontal center lines, one for the cast link and another for hole centers. One method of con-

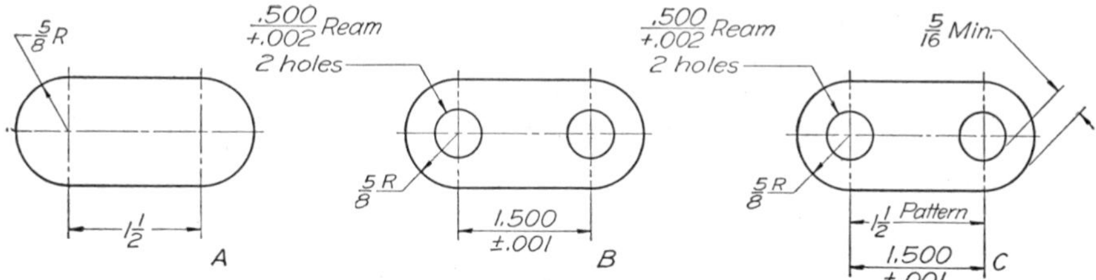

FIG. 12·26—Coinciding center lines and dimensions.

trolling the deviation from coincidence is to give the wall thickness as a minimum, which is understood to apply in all radial directions.

In cases where the coincident center lines are both for finished features with differing tolerances, there may be a serious ambiguity on the drawing unless the dimensioning is specially arranged. Figure 12·27 shows at *A* a milled slot with nominal dimensions and, on the coincident center lines, two accurate holes with a closely toleranced center distance. Unless the dimensioning is cleared by two separate dimensions as shown, the machinist would not know the difference in tolerance. A somewhat more difficult case is shown at *B* where pairing holes are diagonally opposite. Unless all the holes are to be toleranced the same on their center distance, the dimensioning must be made clear with notes as shown.

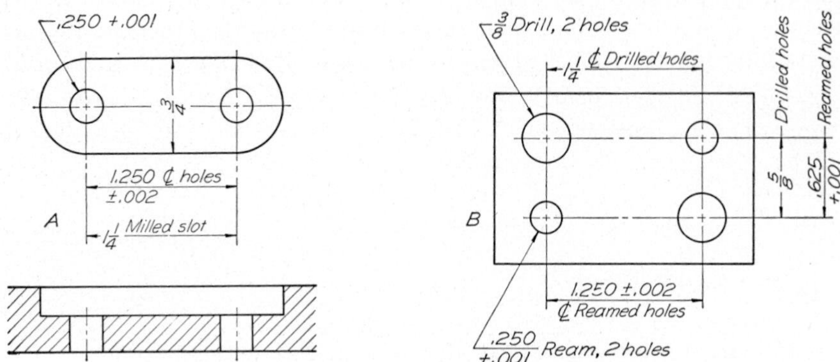

FIG. 12·27—Coinciding center lines and dimensions.

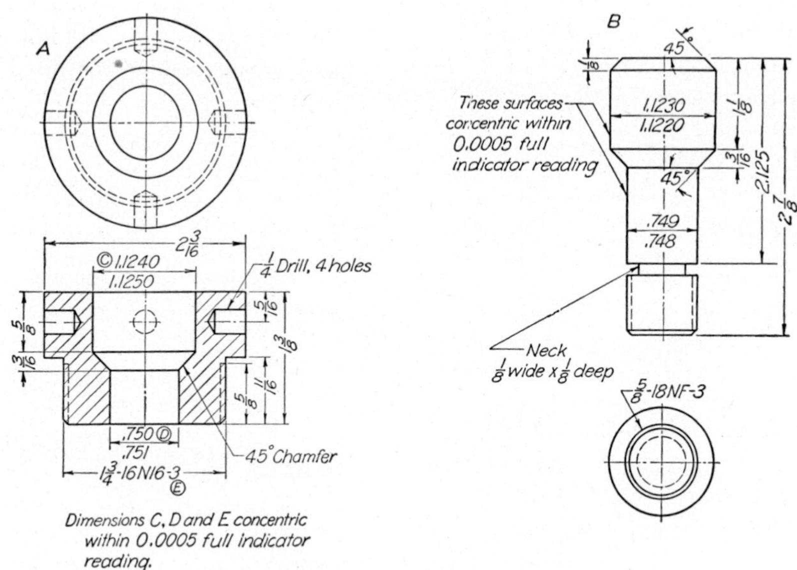

FIG. 12·28—Tolerance of concentricity.

The Army Ordnance method of dimensioning and tolerancing described in paragraph 12·31, provides a simple and direct means of handling the above and other problems.

12·27 Tolerance of concentricity. Tolerance of concentricity is a special case of tolerance on symmetry in which there is a coincidence of centers. In most cases, concentric cylinders, cones, etc., generated on common centers in manufacture, will be concentric to a degree of precision more than adequate for functional requirements and nothing needs to be said on the drawing concerning the allowable variation. However, mating pairs of two (or more) precise, close-fitting, machined cylindrical surfaces must have the axes of adjoined cylinders nearly concentric in order to permit assembly of the parts; thus a method of giving the permissible deviation from concentricity is sometimes necessary. Since the center lines of adjoining cylinders coincide on the drawing, the tolerance cannot be given as a dimension. One method is to mark the diameters with reference letters and give the tolerance in note form as at *A*, Fig. 12·28. The reference letters may be dispensed with if the note is applied directly to the surfaces as at *B*.

12·28 Tolerance on centers. In any case where centers are arranged for interchangeable assembly, the tolerance on shaft, pins, etc., and also the tolerance on bearings or holes in the mating piece will affect the possible tolerance on centers. In Fig. 12·29, note that smaller tolerances on the pins and holes would necessitate a smaller tolerance on the center distances. A smaller allowance for the fit of the pins would make a tighter fit and reduce the possible tolerances for the center-to-center dimensions. Study carefully the dimensions of both pieces.

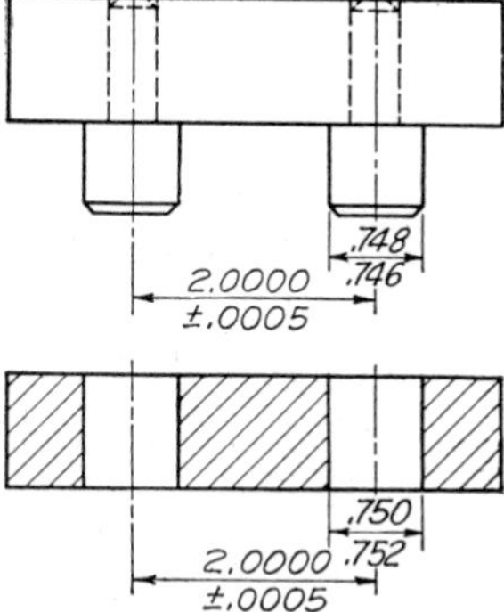

FIG. 12·29—Tolerance on centers.

12·29 Tolerance for angular dimensions. When it is necessary to give the accuracy required in an angular dimension, the tolerance is generally bilateral, as 32° ±½°. When the tolerance is given in minutes, it is written ±0°10′, and when given in seconds is written ±0′30″. Where the location of a hole or other features is dependent upon an angular dimension, the length along the leg of the angle governs the angular tolerance permitted. A tolerance of ±1° gives a variation of 0.035 inch for a length of 1 inch and may be used as a basis for computing the tolerance in any given problem.

As an example, assume an allowable variation of 0.007 inch; then $(0.007/0.035) \times 1° = 1/5°$ is the angular tolerance at 1 inch. If the length is assumed as 2″, then the tolerance would be ½ the tolerance computed for 1 inch, or $1/5° \times 1/2 = 1/10°$, or 0°6′.

12·30 Surface quality. The proper functioning and wear life of a part frequently depends upon the smoothness quality of its surfaces. An American Standard (B46) has been developed that defines the factors of surface quality and describes the meaning and use of symbols for use on drawings. Any surface, despite its apparent smoothness, will be found to have minute peaks and valleys, the height of which is termed *surface roughness* and which may or may not be superimposed on a more general *waviness.* The most prominent direction of tool marks and minute scratches is called *lay.*

The degree of surface roughness may be either the maximum peak-to-valley height, average peak-to-valley height, or average deviation from the mean (root-mean-square value). The latter is usually preferred and may be measured with instruments such as the Profilometer.[1] Master gages

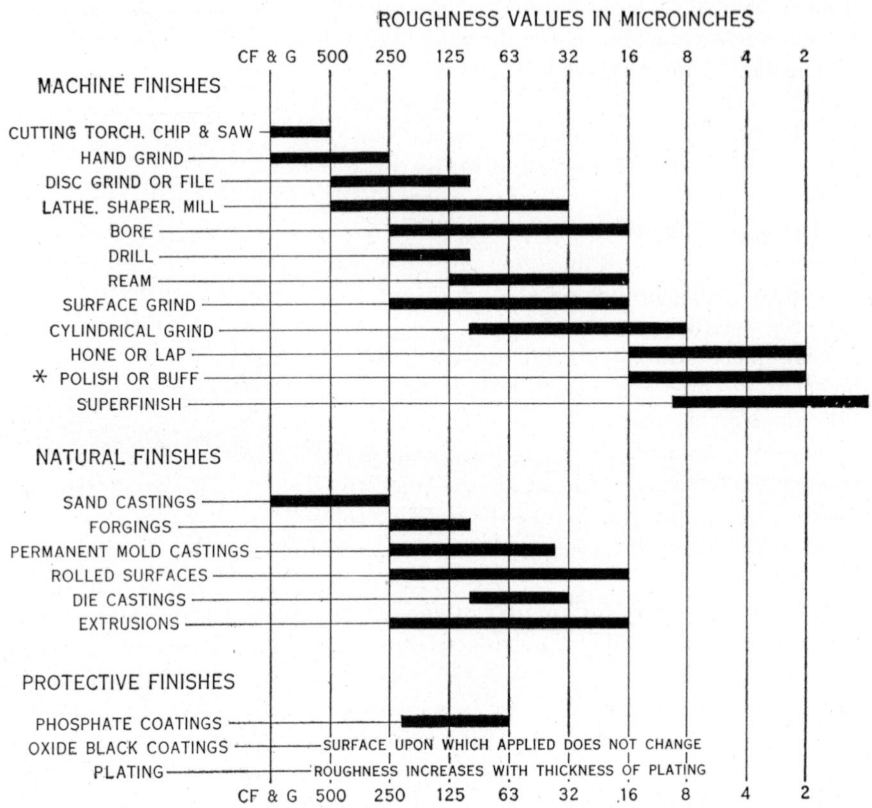

FIG. 12·30—Surface-roughness values.

may be made up, measured, and marked with the roughness value, and comparison made with these gages visually, either with or without optical apparatus, and by the sense of touch. This ability to make accurate measurements of roughness permits precise specification of the surface required. Figure 12·30 is a chart adapted from the U.S. Army Ordnance Standard (URAX6) which gives the roughness in microinches for various surfaces.

[1] Physicists Research Co., Ann Arbor, Mich.

The following explanations pertaining to symbols for the control of surface quality are adapted from the ASA standard:

A surface whose quality is to be specified should be marked with a symbol having the general form of a check mark (√) so the point of the symbol is (1) on the line indicating the surface or (2) on a leader pointing to the surface.

Where it is desired to specify only the surface-roughness height, and the width of roughness or direction of tool marks is not important, the simplest form of the symbol should be used, Fig. 12·31*A*. The numerical value may be any one of the three roughness values mentioned above in connection with surface roughness, placed in the √ as shown.

Where it is desired to specify waviness height in addition to roughness height, a straight horizontal line should be added to the top of the simple symbol, Fig. 12·31*B*, and the numerical value of waviness height is shown above this line.

If the nature of the preferred lay is to be shown, it is indicated by the addition of a combination of lines as shown in Fig. 12·31*C* and *E*.

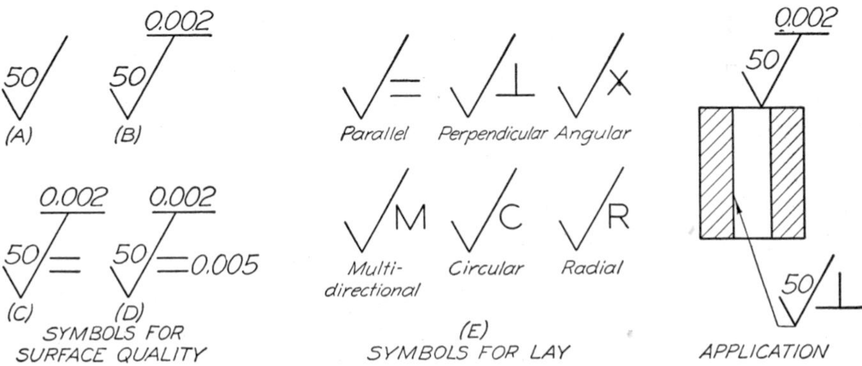

FIG. 12·31—ASA surface-quality symbols.

The parallel and perpendicular part of the symbol indicates that the dominant lines on the surface are parallel or perpendicular to the boundary line of the surface in contact with the symbol. The complete symbol, including the roughness width placed to the right of the lay symbol, is shown in Fig. 12·31*D*.

The use of only one number to specify the height or width of roughness or waviness indicates the maximum value. Any lesser degree of roughness will be satisfactory. When two numbers separated by a dash are used, they indicate the maximum and minimum permissible values.

The surface-quality symbol should not be thought of as a finish mark in the same sense as the old symbol *f* and the newer V. These marks indicate the removal of material, whereas the surface-roughness symbol may be used to indicate the quality of a surface from which no material is to be removed as, for example, a die-cast or even a sand-cast surface. On the other hand, should a metal-removal process be required in order to obtain the surface quality specified, the surface-roughness symbol is used in place of the finish mark.

12·31 Positional and locational tolerances.[1] The language of engineering drawing has developed along with the improvement of manufacturing methods. As quantity production systems have been developed and accuracies improved, demands have been made for the drawings to depict the parts with greater exactness, particularly in the dimensioning. Examples of the trend in dimensioning are found in the methods of specifying tolerances, surface quality, and similar modern practices. Finished holes are now often specified by limit dimensions with, in addition, the surface-roughness specification, instead of the older practice of giving the size and operation, such as drilling, reaming, etc.

With improved manufacturing methods and better part accuracies has come a demand for a method of indicating the parallelism, perpendicularity, concentricity, and symmetry of surfaces. The Ordnance Department of the

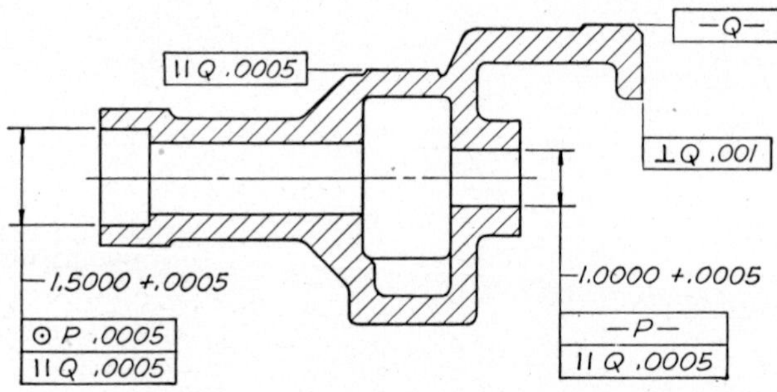

FIG. 12·32—Army Ordnance positional-tolerance symbols.

U.S. Army has developed a set of symbols for indicating positional tolerances. Figure 12·32 illustrates the procedure.

The letter *P*, preceded and followed by dashes (—*P*—), connected to the diameter dimension of the small hole at the right, indicates that this hole is serving as a datum or reference surface with which one or more other surfaces will be checked for parallelism, perpendicularity, concentricity, or symmetry. Thus the concentricity symbol ⊙, the datum letter *P*, and the tolerance value 0.0005, connected to the diameter dimension of the hole at the left indicate that this surface is to be concentric with the datum surface —*P*— within 0.0005″ full indicator reading or, that the total permissible eccentricity (runout) is 0.0005″.

The datum symbol —*Q*— will be found assigned to the horizontal surface at the upper right while the adjoining vertical surface carries the perpendicularity symbol ⊥, the datum letter *Q*, and the tolerance 0.001; therefore this surface must be perpendicular to the datum surface —*Q*— within 0.001″ over its entire surface.

[1] Adapted from the Ordnance Department's "Manual on Dimensioning and Tolerancing" prepared by the inspection gage suboffice, Office of the Chief of Ordnance, A.S.F., U.S. Army.

The method for specifying permissible errors in parallelism is similar to that used for concentricity and perpendicularity. Accordingly, the three surfaces in Fig. 12·32 carrying the parallelism symbol || must each be parallel to the indicated datum surface —*Q*— within 0.0005″ over their entire surface.

The U.S. Army Ordnance Department has also developed a system for expressing *locational* tolerances.[1] The new system simplifies the design calculations for the size and locational tolerances on mating parts, simplifies the appearance and readability of the drawing, and allows a maximum manufacturing variation without affecting the function of the parts.

Figure 12·33 illustrates the usual method for dimensioning a part, and Fig. 12·34 shows the Ordnance method. In the Ordnance system, dimen-

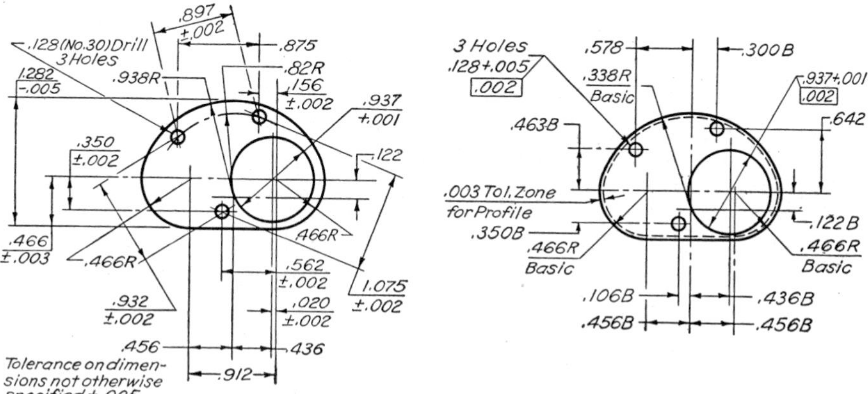

FIG. 12·33—Locational tolerances, usual method.

FIG. 12·34—Locational tolerances, Army Ordnance method.

sions for locating the centers of cylindrical shapes are given as basic values followed by the letter *B*. Beneath the size dimension for the cylinder an additional positional tolerance value enclosed in a rectangle is given which represents the permissible variation for the location of the cylinder and indicates that its center must lie within an imaginary circle of a diameter equal to the positional tolerance. The center of this positional tolerance circle must, of course, be at the center located by the basic dimensions. In Fig. 12·35, the symbol *P*0.010 indicates that the centers of the small holes must be located by the dimensions given, within a positional tolerance circle of 0.010″ (diameter) with reference to the datum —*P*— (the large hole, whose position is basic).

An important advantage of the Ordnance system, compared to the conventional method, is that an increase in manufacturing variation is permitted without affecting the functioning of the parts. In the conventional

[1] This system is based on ideas first proposed by Mr. G. A. Gladman of the National Physical Laboratory, Great Britain.

method, having direct tolerances given on location dimensions, the positional variation area is an inscribed square of the Ordnance positional tolerance circle. Also, the effective area for gaging acceptable parts is usually restricted to the inscribed circle of the square. Thus parts rejected by inspection according to the conventional system may prove to be acceptable by the Ordnance method.

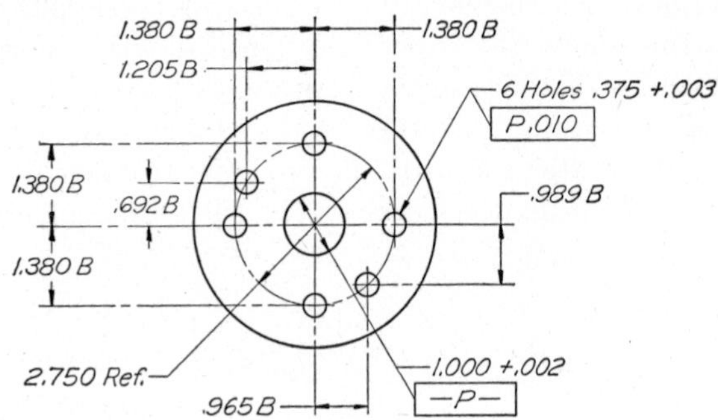

FIG. 12·35—Locational tolerances, Army Ordnance method.

The Ordnance tolerancing system may also be applied to the location of rectangular shapes. The only difference is that the tolerance circle used with cylindrical shapes will be replaced by a tolerance rectangle within which the center of the form may vary.

PROBLEMS

The assembly drawings of Chap. 15 are well suited for exercises in dimensioning detail working drawings. The assembly shows the position of each part, and the function may be understood by a study of the motion, relationship, etc., of the different parts. Note particularly the mating and controlling surfaces and the logical reference surfaces for dimensions of location. The following are suggested:

1. Fig. 15·60. Detail drawing of shaft.
2. Fig. 15·60. Detail drawing of bushing.
3. Fig. 15·60. Detail drawing of bracket.
4. Fig. 15·64. Detail drawing of body.
5. Fig. 15·75. Detail drawing of hanger.
6. Fig. 15·70. Detail drawing of rack.
7. Fig. 15·70. Detail drawing of rack housing.
8. Fig. 15·70. Detail drawing of cover.
9. Fig. 15·54. Detail drawing of base.
10. Fig. 15·91. Detail drawing of base.
11. Fig. 15·91. Detail drawing of jaw.
12. Fig. 15·91. Detail drawing of screw.
13. Fig. 15·91. Detail drawing of screw bushing.
14. Fig. 15·92. Detail drawing of frame (drop forging).
15. Fig. 15·93. Detail drawing of base.
16. Fig. 15·93. Detail drawing of frame.
17. Fig. 15·94. Detail drawing of frame.
18. Fig. 15·94. Detail drawing of ram.

19. Fig. 15·94. Detail drawing of pinion shaft.
20. Fig. 15·62. Detail drawing of base.
21. Fig. 15·62. Detail drawing of cover.
22. Fig. 15·62. Detail drawing of sleeve ball.
23. Fig. 15·62. Detail drawing of stud ball.
24. Fig. 15·89. Detail drawing of body.
25. Fig. 15·89. Detail drawing, with development, of spring.

TEXT-FILMS

The following McGraw-Hill Text-Films have been correlated directly with Chaps. 11 and 12:

Dimensioning Techniques (silent filmstrip).

Stresses techniques, choice, and placement in standard dimensioning practice; illustrates and explains the various dimensioning symbols; demonstrates proper techniques of applying these symbols to various drawings.

Selection of Dimensions (20-min. sound motion picture).

Introduces the principles that govern the choice of dimensions; shows that these principles are based on (*a*) the functional characteristics of the object and (*b*) the manufacturing methods used in making the object.

Chapter 13

BOLTS, SCREWS, KEYS, RIVETS, AND SPRINGS

13·1 In the practical application of the graphic language in making working drawings, there occurs the necessity of representing the methods of fastening parts together, either with permanent fastenings, as rivets and welding, or with removable ones, as bolts, screws, and keys. The engineer must know the fundamental forms of fastenings, how they are specified, and be thoroughly familiar with the methods of their representation.

13·2 The earliest records of the screw are found in the writings of Archimedes (278–212 B.C.). Although specimens of ancient Greek and Roman screws are so rare as to indicate that they were seldom used, in the later Middle Ages many are found, and it is known that both lathes and dies were used to cut threads. Most early screws, however, were made by hand, forging the head, cutting the slot with a saw, and fashioning the screw with a file. In colonial times, wood screws were blunt on the end, the gimlet point not appearing until 1846. Iron screws were made for each tapped hole. There was no interchanging of parts, and nuts had to be tied to their own bolts. Sir Joseph Whitworth made the first attempt at a uniform standard in 1841. This was generally adopted in England but not in the United States.

13·3 The initial attempt to standardize screw threads in the United States came in 1864 with the adoption of a report prepared by a committee appointed by the Franklin Institute. This system, designed by William Sellers, came into general use and was known as the "Franklin Institute thread," the "Sellers' thread," or the "United States thread." It fulfilled the need of that period but with the coming of the automobile, the airplane, and other modern equipment it was not adequate. Through the efforts of the various engineering societies, the Bureau of Standards and others, the National Screw Thread Commission was authorized by Act of Congress in 1918 and inaugurated the present standards. This work has been carried on by the American Standards Association, 29 West 39th Street, New York City, from whom complete copies of the Standards may be obtained. The essential items appear in this chapter and in the Appendix.

13·4 Screw-thread terminology

Form. The profile shape (cross section) of the thread. Various forms are shown in Fig. 13·3.

External thread. A thread on the outside of a member, Fig. 13·1.

Internal thread. A thread on the inside of a member, Fig. 13·1.

Axis. The longitudinal central line through the threaded part, Fig. 13·1.

Major diameter. The largest diameter of a screw thread, Fig. 13·1.

Minor diameter. The smallest diameter of a screw thread, Fig. 13·1.

Pitch diameter. The mean diameter between the major and minor diameters of the screw thread.

Pitch. The distance between corresponding points of consecutive threads measured parallel to the axis, Fig. 13·1.

Lead. The distance, parallel to the axis, that a screw advances in one complete revolution. See "multiple threads" and Fig. 13·2.

Crest. The top edge or surface joining the two sides of a thread, Fig. 13·1.

Root. The bottom edge or surface joining the sides of two adjacent threads, Fig. 13·1.

Depth of thread. The distance between crest and root measured normal to the axis, Fig. 13·1.

Thread angle. The dihedral angle between the sides of the thread, Fig. 13·1.

Right-hand thread. A thread that advances into engagement when turned clockwise. Threads are always right-hand unless otherwise specified.

Left-hand thread. A thread that advances into engagement when turned counterclockwise.

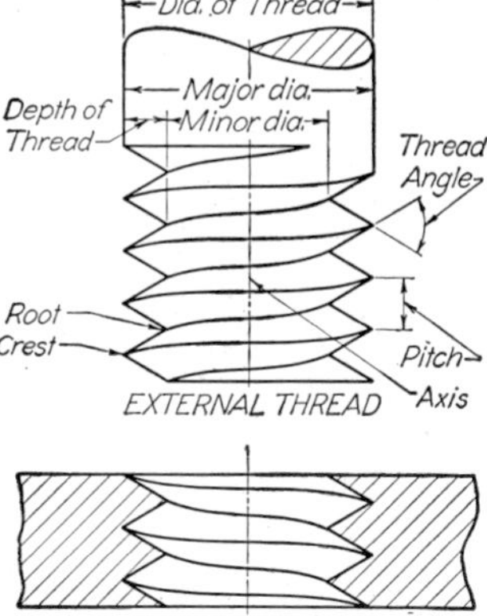

FIG. 13·1—Screw-thread terminology.

Single thread. A thread having any thread form cut on one helix of the cylinder, Fig. 13·2. Threads are always single unless otherwise specified. On a single thread the pitch and lead are equal.

Multiple threads. A thread combination having the same form cut on two or more helices of the cylinder, Fig. 13·2. A more rapid advance is obtained without a coarser thread. On a *double thread* the lead is twice the pitch, and on a *triple thread* it is three

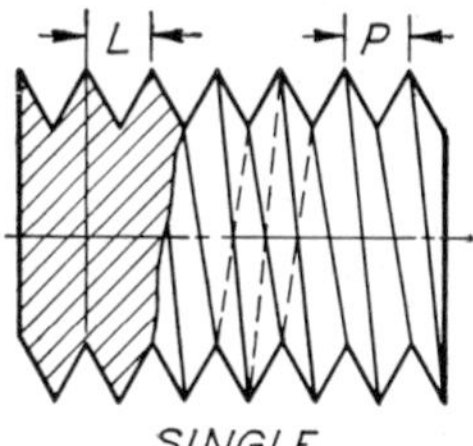

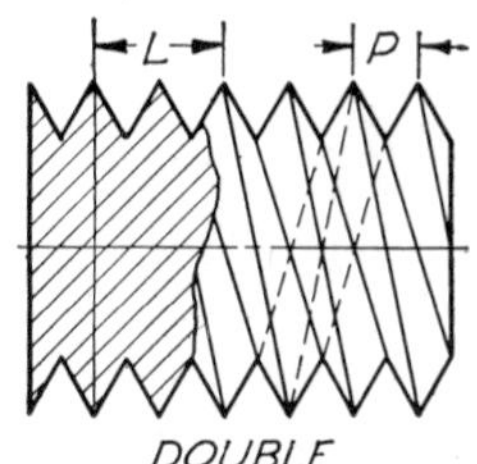

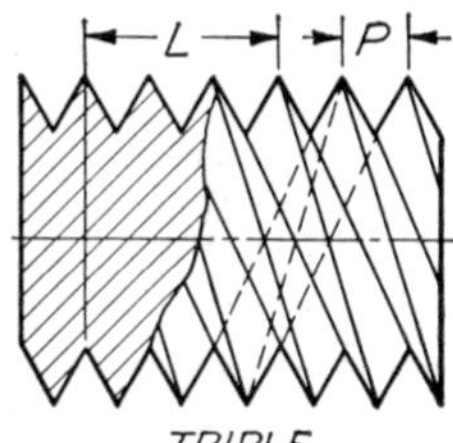

FIG. 13·2—Single, double, and triple threads.

times the pitch. Note that the helices of a double thread start 180° apart; those of a triple thread 120° apart. Fountain-pen caps often have quadruple threads, so that with a minimum of turning the cap is securely fastened to the barrel.

13·5 Forms of screw threads. Screws are used for fastenings, for adjustments, and for transmitting power and motion. For these different purposes several different forms of threads are in use, Fig. 13·3. For fastenings, the *American Standard V thread,* with its crest and root flattened, is used in this country. The American Standard is discussed in detail in a following paragraph. The sharp *V* at 60° is still used to some extent, although it has little to recommend it except the increased holding power for setscrews and perhaps a better liquid-tight joint, such as on stay bolts for boilers. It is often used on brass fittings and brass pipe as well as in modified form on self-tapping screws. The British Standard is the *Whitworth* thread, cut at 55°, with tops and bottoms rounded one-sixth of the depth of the triangle, as shown in the figure. *The British Association Standard* at 47½° is used on very small threads. *The French and the International Standards* have the same form as the American Standard but are dimensioned in the metric system. The *Dardelet self-locking* thread, designed by Commandant Dardelet, a French military officer, is a special thread requiring no auxiliary locking devices to hold the nut under vibration. A more complete description is found in paragraph 13·36.

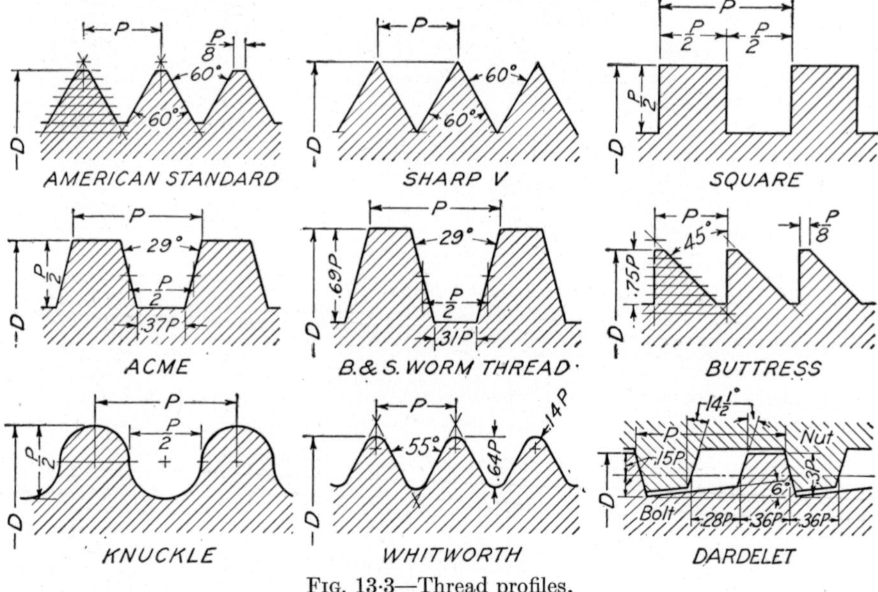

FIG. 13·3—Thread profiles.

For transmitting power the V shapes are not desirable, since part of the thrust tends to burst the nut. The square thread avoids this, as it transmits all the forces nearly parallel to the axis of the screw. It can have, evidently, only half the number of threads in the same axial space as a V thread of the same pitch, and thus in shear is only half as strong. A modification used very generally is the *Acme*, or 29° thread. It is stronger, much more easily cut, and permits the use of a disengaging or split nut that cannot be used on a square thread. The *Brown and Sharpe* worm thread used on the worm of the worm-and-wheel mechanism resembles the Acme thread but is deeper for the same pitch. The *buttress* thread for transmitting power in only one direction has the efficiency of the square thread and the strength of the V thread. It is sometimes called the breechblock thread, as it is used to take the recoil in guns. The *knuckle* thread is used for rough work and can be cast in a mold. It may be seen in shallower forms in sheet-metal rolled threads, as on an ordinary incandescent lamp.

Screw threads are formed by cutting or rolling. Laboratory tests show as much as 14 per cent greater strength in rolled threads over cut threads of the same diameter. By crimping the fibers in the metal, rolling adds toughness and strength to the threaded portion. A rolled thread fastening requires a collar under the head to bring the shaft diameter up to the thread diameter.

13·6 To draw a screw thread we must know the form of the thread, the diameter of the shaft on which it is cut, the number of threads per inch, whether it is single or multiple, and whether it is right hand or left hand.

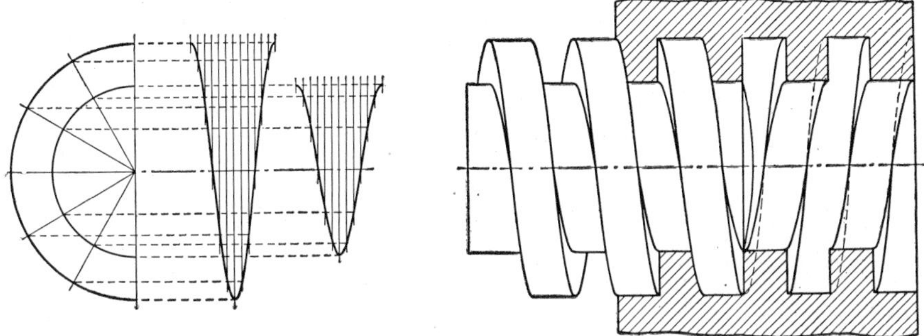

FIG. 13·4—Square thread, internal and external.

For true representation, the thread shapes can be drawn with the lines of their crests and roots shown as the projections of helices (see Helix, paragraph 5·52) having the same pitch but different diameters, as illustrated in Fig. 13·4. If many threads are to be drawn in this way, a template may be made by laying out the projection of the helices on cardboard, celluloid, or thin wood, and cutting out with a sharp knife.

13·7 Semiconventional threads—square and Acme. Drawing the actual helix curves of a screw is a laborious proceeding and is rarely done, and

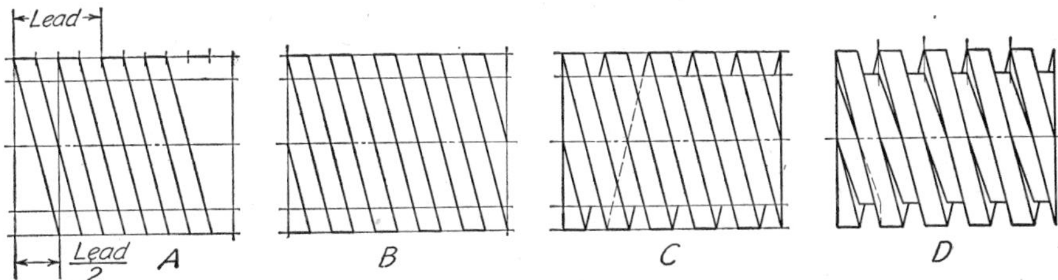

FIG. 13·5—Stages in drawing a square thread.

then only on screws of large diameters. In ordinary practice the labor is altogether unnecessary, so the projection of the helix is conventionalized into a straight line.

A double square-thread screw would thus be drawn as shown in the stages in Fig. 13·5. This, although not so realistic or pleasing as Fig. 13·4, requires much less time. It is not necessary to draw the threads on the whole length of a long screw. They may be started at each end, as in Fig. 13·6.

In the Acme thread the 29° angle may, for convenience, be drawn at 30°. The stages in drawing an Acme thread are shown in Fig. 13·7.

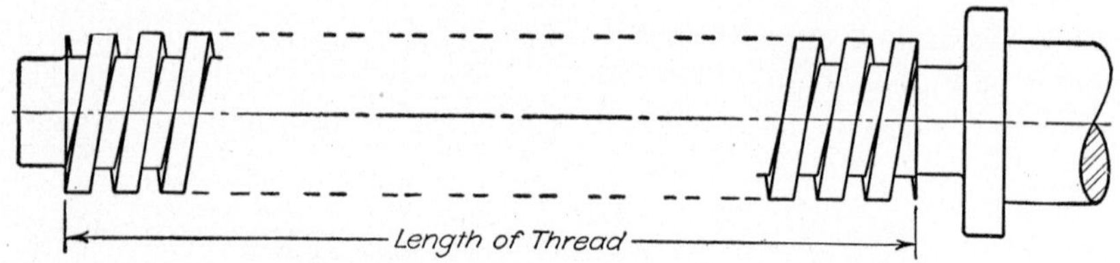

FIG. 13·6—Thread representation on a long screw.

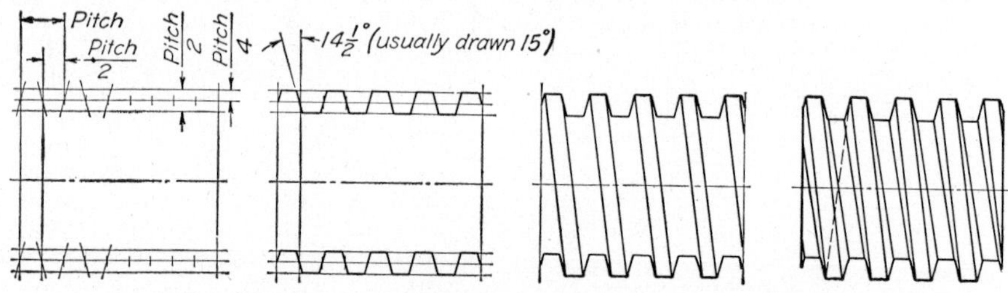

FIG. 13·7—Stages in drawing an Acme thread.

13·8 Semiconventional threads—American Standard form. It is suggested that threads of 1 inch and over in actual measurement, on both detail and assembly drawings, should show the thread form as in Figs. 13·8 and 13·9. In general, true pitch should be shown, though a small increase or

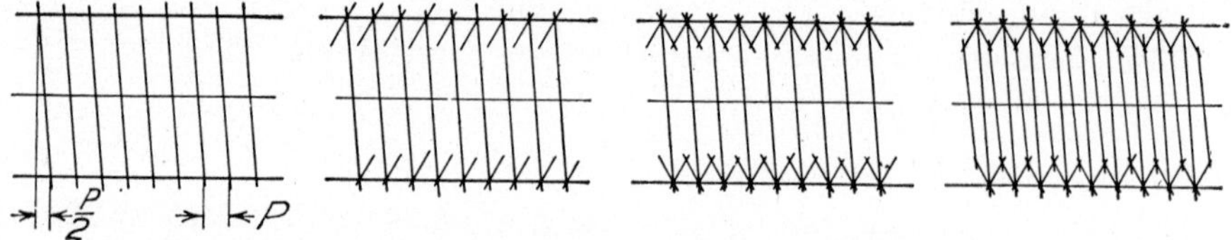

FIG. 13·8—Stages in drawing a V thread.

decrease in pitch is permissible so as to have even units of measure in making the drawing. For example, seven threads per inch may be increased to eight threads per inch, or four and one-half threads per inch may be decreased to four threads per inch. The student must keep in mind that this is to simplify the drawing, and that actual pitch must be specified in the dimensioning.

Thread form on diameters less than an inch is also shown in some sectioned views, Fig. 13·18. The pitch per inch must usually be decreased for ease of drawing and readability.

A V thread is drawn in the stages shown in Fig. 13·8, spacing the pitch on the lower line only. It should be inked in the same order. The flats of crests and roots are not drawn.

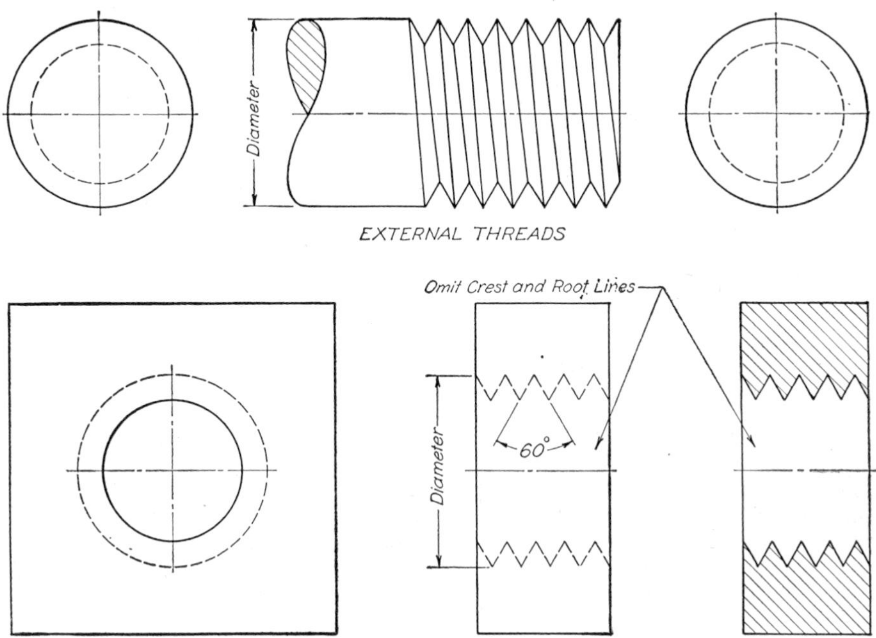

FIG. 13·9—Thread representation. (Suggested for threads drawn 1″ or over on both assembly and detail drawings.)

13·9 Conventional thread symbols. The ASA provides two forms of thread symbols, "regular" and "simplified." It is recommended that these symbols be used for indicating threaded parts less than one inch in diameter (drawing size), and also that the regular symbols be used on assembly drawings and the simplified symbols on detail drawings.

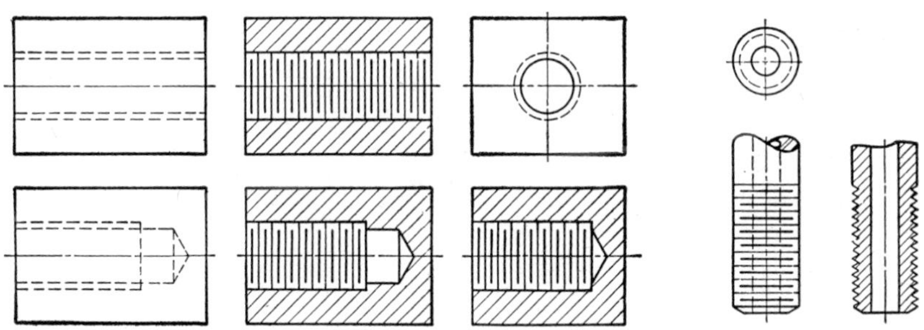

FIG. 13·10—ASA regular thread symbols.

13·10 The ASA regular thread symbols, Fig. 13·10, omit the V profile and indicate the crests and roots by lines perpendicular to the axis.

13·11 The ASA simplified symbols, Fig. 13·11, omit both profile and crest lines and indicate the threaded portion by dotted lines parallel to the axis at the approximate depth of thread. The simplified method does not have the descriptive effect of the regular symbol but, as it saves much time, it is preferred on detail drawings.

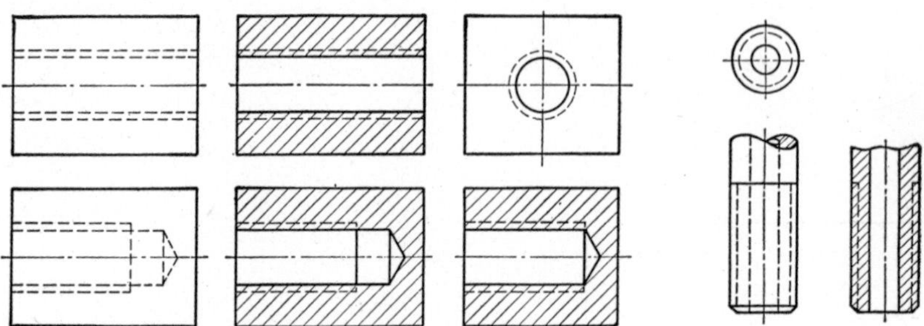

FIG. 13·11—ASA simplified thread symbols.

13·12 To draw the ASA symbols. The two sets of symbols should be carefully studied and compared. Note that the regular and simplified symbols are identical for hidden threads. Also note that the end view of an external thread differs from the end view of an internal thread, but that *regular and simplified end-view symbols are identical.*

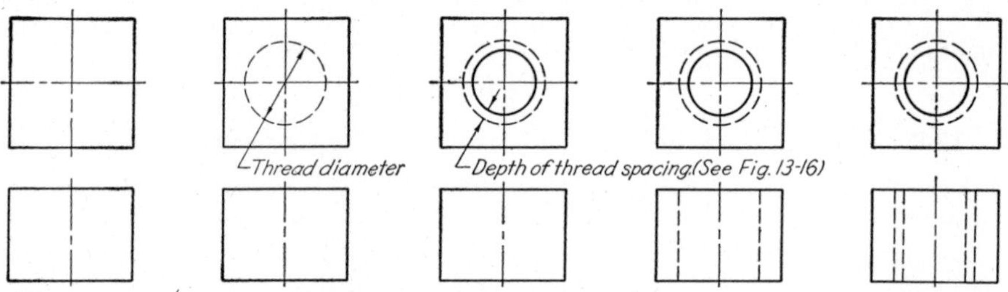

FIG. 13·12—Stages in drawing internal regular and simplified symbols (plan and elevation).

No attempt needs be made to show either the actual pitch of the threads or their depth by the spacing of lines in the symbol. Identical symbols may be used for several different threads. It is possible only in the larger sizes to show the actual pitch and the true depth of thread without a confusion of lines that would defeat the purpose of the symbol. The symbols should therefore be made so as to read clearly and look well on the drawing, without other considerations.

To draw a symbol for any given thread, the diameter and length of thread must be known, and for a blind tapped hole the depth of the tap drill is also needed.

A regular or simplified symbol for a tapped hole is drawn in the stages shown by Fig. 13·12. As already stated, the lines representing depth of thread are not drawn to actual scale, but are spaced so as to look well on the drawing and to avoid crowding of the lines.

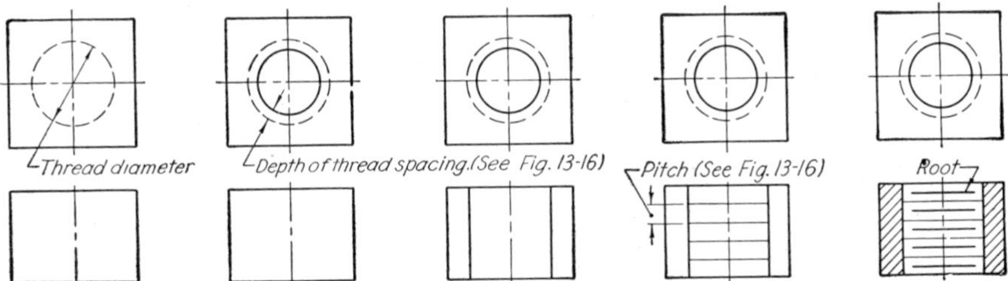

FIG. 13·13—Stages in drawing regular thread symbols in section.

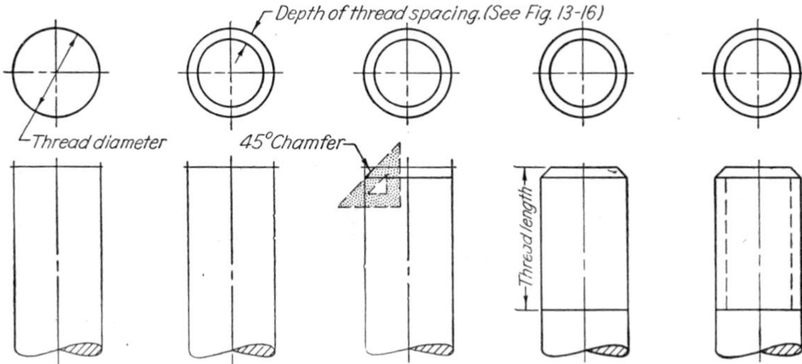

FIG. 13·14—Stages in drawing simplified external-thread symbols.

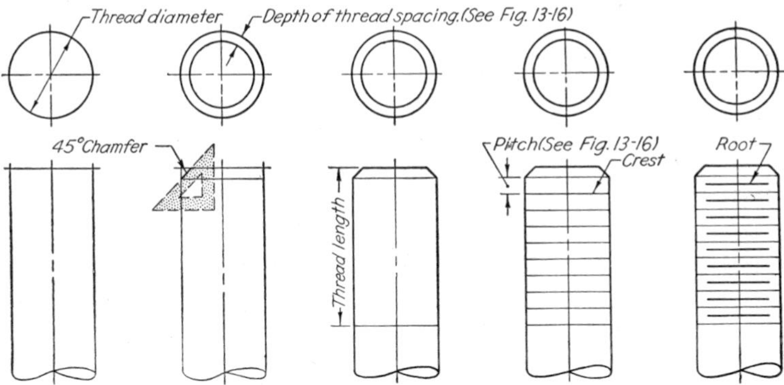

FIG. 13·15—Stages in drawing regular external-thread symbols.

A regular symbol for a tapped hole in section is drawn in the stages shown by Fig. 13·13. The lines representing the crests are spaced by eye or scale to look well, and need not conform to the actual thread pitch. The lines representing the roots of the thread are equally spaced by eye between the crest lines and are usually drawn heavier. Their length need not indicate actual depth of thread, but should be kept uniform by using light guide lines.

A simplified symbol for an external thread is drawn in the stages shown by Fig. 13·14. The 45° chamfer extends to the root line of the thread. Note that in the end view the chamfer line is shown.

A regular symbol for external threads is drawn in the stages shown by Fig. 13·15. The chamfer is 45° and to the depth of thread. Crest lines are spaced by eye or scale. Root lines are spaced by eye, are usually drawn heavier, and need not conform to actual thread depth.

Line spacings. The table, Fig. 13·16, gives suggested values for "depth of thread" for screw diameters of 1/8″ to 1″. Figure 13·17 shows both regular and simplified symbols, full size, drawn according to the values given in Fig. 13·16. No distinction is made in the symbol between coarse and fine threads.

Diameter of thread, D	Pitch, P	Depth of thread, $P/2$
1/8 and 3/16	1/16 scant	1/32 scant
1/4 and 3/8	1/16	1/32
1/2 and 5/8	1/8	1/16
3/4 and 7/8	3/16	3/32

FIG. 13·16—Suggested values for drawing thread symbols.

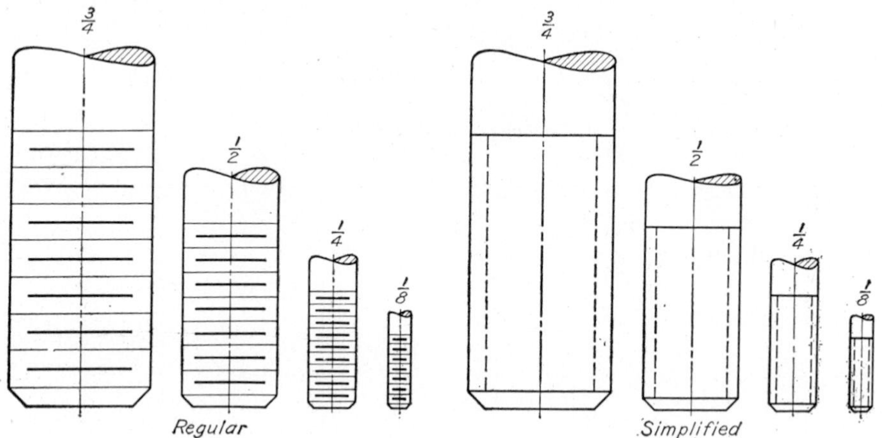

FIG. 13·17—Thread symbols, drawing size.

13·13 Threads in section. Figure 13·4 shows the true form of an internal square thread in section. Observe that the far side of the thread is visible, causing the root and crest line to slope in the opposite direction from those on the external thread. Figure 13·9 shows the semiconventional treatment for V threads over 1″ in diameter. Note that the crest and root lines are omitted. The regular and simplified symbols for threads in section are shown in Figs. 13·10 and 13·11. When two pieces screwed together are shown in section, the thread form should be drawn to aid in reading, Fig. 13·18. In the small diameters it is desirable to decrease the number of threads per inch, thus eliminating monotonous detail and greatly improving the readability of the drawing.

13·14 American (National) screw threads. The form of the American Standard is a 60° V shape with the crest flattened to a width equal to one-eighth of the pitch and with the root filled in a like amount. This form was previously known as the "United States Standard" or "Sellers' Profile."

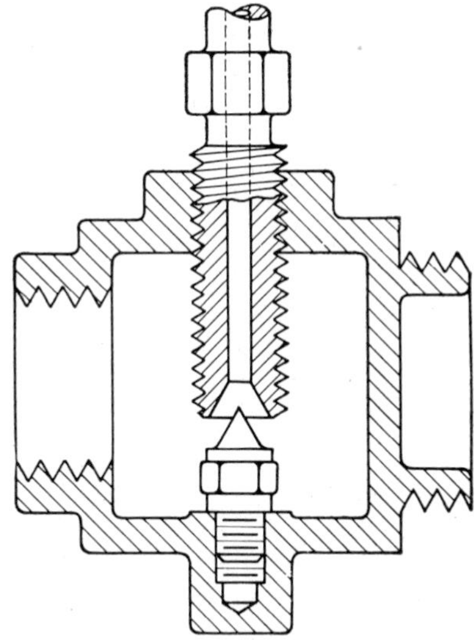

Fig. 13·18—Threads in section, drawing size.

The American Standard covers five series of screw threads, all of the same thread form but differing in the relation of pitch to diameter. These are the coarse thread series, the fine thread series, and three special series—the 8-pitch, the 12-pitch, and the 16-pitch thread series.

The coarse thread series is the former United States Standard supplemented by 12 numbered sizes below ¼ inch from the ASME Standards. It is the series recommended for general use. See table, page 634, Appendix.

The fine thread series is the former regular series of the Society of Automotive Engineers supplemented by 13 numbered sizes below ¼ inch from the ASME Standards. It is used where special conditions require a fine thread. See table, page 634.

The 8-pitch thread series. Eight threads per inch. Sizes 1″ to 6″.

Bolts for high-pressure pipe flanges, cylinder-head studs, and similar fastenings against pressure, require that an initial tension be set up in the fastening by elastic deformation of the fastening, and require that the component be held together so that the joint will not open when the steam or other pressure is applied. To secure a proper initial tension, it is not practicable that the pitch should increase with the diameter of the thread, as the torque required to assemble the fastening would be excessive. Accordingly, for such purposes, the 8-pitch thread has come into general use for all classes of engineering work. See table, page 635.

The 12-pitch thread series. Twelve threads per inch. Sizes ½″ to 6″.

Sizes of 12-pitch threads from ½ to 1¾ inches in diameter are used in boiler practice, which requires that worn stud holes be retapped with the next larger size. Twelve-pitch threads are also widely used in machine construction for thin nuts on shafts and sleeves. See table, page 635.

The 16-pitch thread series. Sixteen threads per inch. Sizes ¾″ to 4″.

This is a uniform-pitch series used primarily on threaded adjusting collars and bearing retaining nuts. See table, page 635.

The SAE extra-fine thread series. In addition to the five series provided by the ASA, The SAE (Society of Automotive Engineers) uses another series called the "extra-fine series."

The form and identification symbols follow those used by the American Standards. The only difference is the number of threads per inch. The SAE extra-fine series has more threads per inch than any series in the American Standards.

13·15 Classification of fits. One of the important features of the work of the Committee on Standardization and Unification of Screw Threads (ASA B1a 1934) is the standardizing of classes of fits between bolts and nuts. Four classes are provided, with detailed tables of dimensions and tolerances for manufacture to meet these classifications. These are:

Class 1 fit. This is "recommended only for screw-thread work where clearance between mating parts is essential for rapid assembly and where shake or play is not objectionable."

Class 2 fit. This "represents a high quality of commercial screw-thread product and is recommended for the great bulk of interchangeable screw-thread work."

Class 3 fit. This "represents an exceptionally high quality of commercially threaded product and is recommended only in cases where the high cost of precision tools and continual checking is warranted."

Class 4 fit. This requires "selective assembly," there being an actual interference between a maximum screw and a minimum hole. It is wrench-tight in certain cases and is little used for fasteners.

13·16 Thread specification. For specifying American (National) Standard threads on drawings, in correspondence, specifications, stock lists, etc., the diameter (or screw number) and number of threads per inch are given first, then the initial letters of the series, NC (National Coarse),

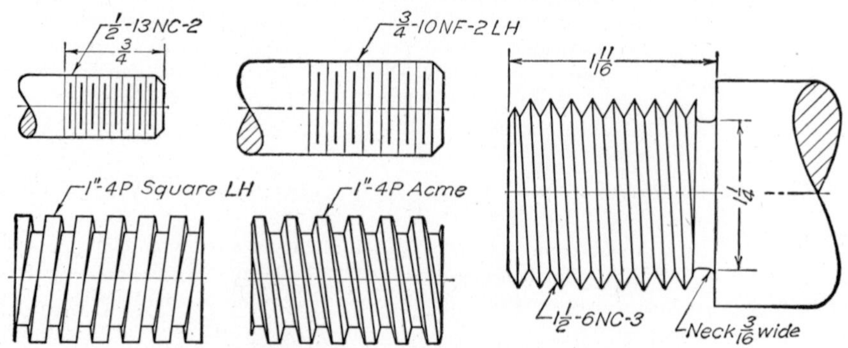

FIG. 13·19—External-thread specifications.

NF (National Fine), or N (National Form but special pitch), followed by the class of fit. If the thread is left-hand, the letters LH follow the fit number, Fig. 13·19.

Examples:

1″-8 NC-2	2″-12 N12-3
1″-14NF-3 LH	2″-16 N16-3
2″-8 N8-2	$3\frac{3}{4}$″-10 N-2

13·17 Tapped-hole specifications. Always specify by note, giving the tap-drill diameter and depth of hole, followed by the thread specification and length of thread, Fig. 13·20. For tap-drill sizes, see Appendix. It is

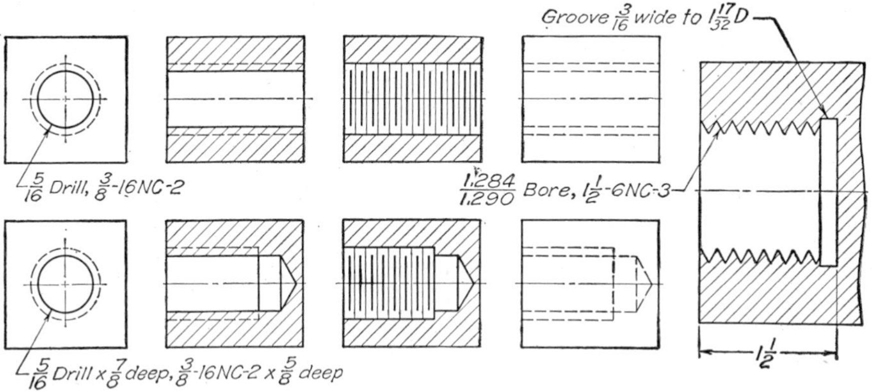

FIG. 13·20—Internal-thread specifications.

general commercial practice to use 75 per cent of the theoretical depth of thread for tapped holes. This gives about 95 per cent of the strength of a full thread and is much easier to cut. A bolt inserted in an experimental nut made with only one-half a full depth of thread will break before the thread will strip.

13·18 Depth of tapped holes and entrance length for threaded rods, tap bolts, studs, cap screws, machine screws, and similar fastenings may be found by using an empirical formula based on the diameter of the fastening and the material tapped, see Fig. 13·21 and accompanying table.

Material	Entrance length for studs, etc., A	Thread clearance at bottom of hole, B	Thread length, C	Unthreaded portion at bottom of hole, E	Depth of drilled hole, F
Aluminum.....	$2D$	$4/n$	$2D + 4/n$	$4/n$	$C + E$
Cast iron......	$1\frac{1}{2}D$	$4/n$	$1\frac{1}{2}D + 4/n$	$4/n$	$C + E$
Brass.........	$1\frac{1}{2}D$	$4/n$	$1\frac{1}{2}D + 4/n$	$4/n$	$C + E$
Bronze........	$1\frac{1}{2}D$	$4/n$	$1\frac{1}{2}D + 4/n$	$4/n$	$C + E$
Steel....	D	$4/n$	$D + 4/n$	$4/n$	$C + E$

D = diameter of fastening.
A = entrance length for fastening.
B = thread clearance at bottom of hole.
C = total thread length.
E = unthreaded portion at bottom of hole.
n = threads per inch.
F = depth of tap-drill hole.

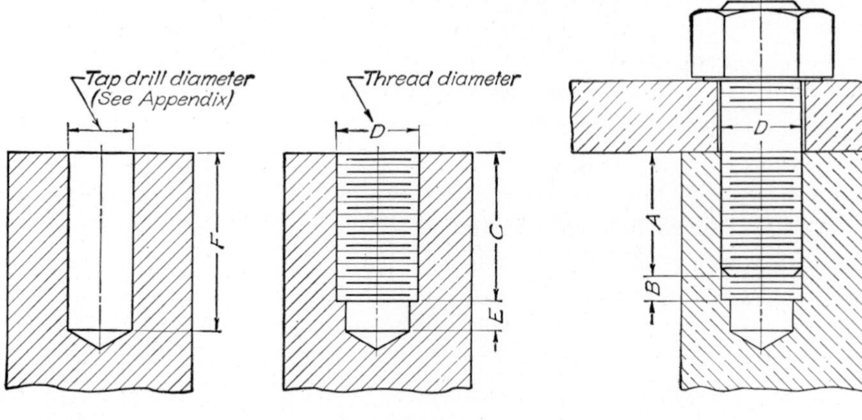

FIG. 13·21—Proportions for tapped holes.

13·19 Threaded fastenings. Threaded fastenings, in almost unlimited variety, are in common use. Most fastenings have descriptive names, as the "setscrew" which holds a part in a set or fixed position. The bolt derives its name from an early English use where it was a temporary fastening or pin for bolting a door. Five types, the bolt, stud, cap screw, machine screw, and setscrew represent the bulk of threaded fastenings.

A bolt, Fig. 13·22*A*, having an integral head on one end and a thread on the other end, is passed through clear holes in two parts and draws them together by means of a nut screwed on the threaded end.

A stud, Fig. 13·22*B*, is a rod threaded on each end. As used normally, the part passes through a clear hole in one piece and screws permanently into a tapped hole in the other. A nut then draws the parts together.

A cap screw, Fig. 13·22*C*, passes through a clear hole in one piece, and screws into a tapped hole in the other. The head, an integral part of the screw, draws the parts together as the screw enters the tapped hole.

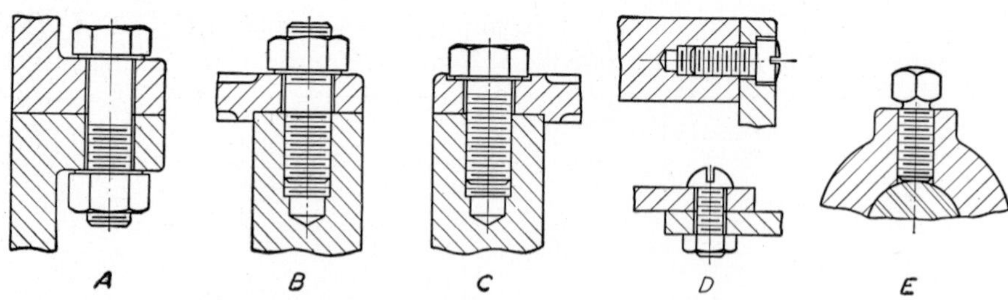

FIG. 13·22—Common types of fastenings.

A machine screw, Fig. 13·22*D*, is a small fastening, used with a nut to function in the same manner as a bolt; or without a nut, to function as a cap screw.

A setscrew, screws into a tapped hole in an outer part, often a hub, and bears with its point against an inner part, usually a shaft.

13·20 American Standard bolts and nuts. The former United States Standard for the sizes of boltheads and nuts is now replaced by the "American Standard Wrench-head Bolts and Nuts and Wrench Openings," first approved in 1927, revised in 1933 and again in 1941.

The Standard includes three series as follows:

Regular series boltheads and nuts. Regular boltheads and nuts are for general use. The dimensions and the resulting strengths of these boltheads and nuts are based on the theoretical analysis of the stresses and on results of numerous tests.

Heavy series boltheads and nuts. Heavy boltheads and nuts are for use where greater bearing surface is necessary; that is, where a large clearance between the bolt and hole or a greater wrench-bearing surface is considered essential.

Light series nuts. Light nuts have smaller dimensions across flats than regular series nuts. They are used where an extreme saving in weight and material is desired.

13·21 Classes of finish. The ASA specifies three classes of boltheads and nuts in both the regular and heavy series. These are (1) unfinished, (2) semifinished, and (3) finished.

Unfinished boltheads and nuts are, except for the threads, not machined on any surface.

Semifinished boltheads and nuts are machined or otherwise formed to provide a smooth bearing surface. For boltheads this will be either a washer-faced or a plain bearing surface, and for nuts a washer-faced or a circular bearing surface made by chamfering the edges.

Finished boltheads or nuts are the same as semifinished except that the surfaces other than the bearing surface are machined for accuracy and appearance. The finish desired on all nonbearing surfaces of finished boltheads and nuts should be specified by the purchaser.

13·22 Bolt information. Of the many forms of fastenings, the bolt, illustrated in pictorial form in Fig. 13·23, occurs most frequently. This

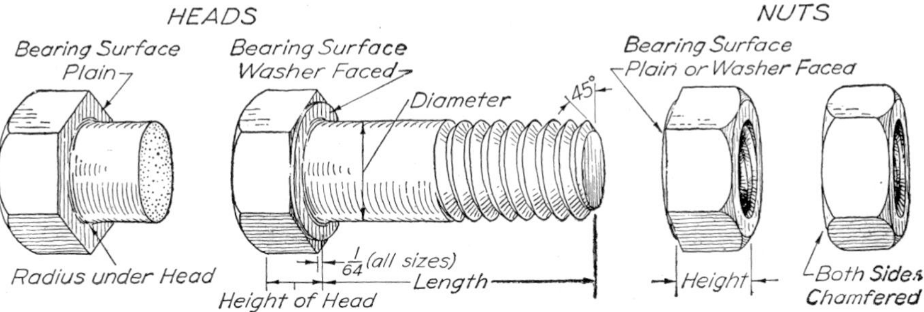

FIG. 13·23—American Standard bolt.

familiar fastening is used, with a nut, to hold two pieces together by passing through clear holes in each. The body is a cold-drawn mild steel. The head may be completely formed by a series of upsetting and shearing operations, or a combination of upsetting, shearing, and machining, to secure a desired finish. The threads are either cut or rolled. The nuts are sheared from hexagonal bars and forged into shape, the holes punched, and the threads tapped on automatic machines. Another method of manufacture is to machine the bolts and the nuts from hexagonal bars.

The draftsman must be thoroughly familiar with the following items concerning bolts and nuts:

General. *Diameter.* The size of the shaft on which the threads are cut.

Body length. The distance from under the head to the extreme end. Length increments vary with the diameter. See Appendix. The thread end is flat and chamfered. The angle of chamfer is drawn 45° and the depth of chamfer is to the root of the thread.

Thread length. This depends on the diameter, and the length of the bolt. See Appendix. The thread lengths shown in this table are not a part of the standard but show the usual practice followed by manufacturers when American Standard bolts are ordered and apply to both regular and heavy series.

Radius of fillet under head. The maximum radius for bolts 1/4″ to 1/2″ is 1/32″; for bolts 9/16″ to 1″ is 1/16″; for bolts 1 1/8″ to 2″ is 1/8″; for bolts 2 1/4″ to 3″ is 3/16″. In general, the filleted corner may be accommodated to the bolt hole by burring the rim of the hole and may be omitted on the drawing except in very large sizes.

Washer face. The washer face is a circular base, turned or otherwise formed on the bearing surface of a bolthead or nut, to make a smooth bearing surface. The diameter is equal to the distance across flats. The thickness is 1/64″ for all fastenings. A circular bearing surface may be obtained on a nut by chamfering the corners. The angle of chamfer with the bearing face is 30°, and the diameter of the circle is the width across flats.

Boltheads. *Form.* The head form is square or hexagonal in the unfinished, regular, and heavy series. All other heads are hexagonal only.

Bearing surfaces. The bearing surfaces of the heads are either plain or washer-faced.

Tops of heads. The tops of the heads are flat and chamfered. The angle of chamfer with the top surface is 25° (drawn 30°) for hexagonal heads. The diameter of the top circle is the width across flats, with a tolerance of minus 15 per cent.

Height of head. The height of head is the distance from the top to the bearing surface, and thus for washer-type heads includes the thickness of the washer.

Nuts. *Form.* The nut is square or hexagonal in the unfinished, regular, and heavy series. All others are hexagonal only.

Bearing surfaces. The bearing surfaces of nuts are plain, washer-faced, or chamfered.

Tops of nuts. The tops of nuts are flat, or chamfered, or (except in jam nuts) washer-crowned. For flat and chamfer nuts, the angle of chamfer with the top surface is 25° (drawn 30°) for square and 30° for hexagonal nuts; the diameter of the top circle is the width across flats with a tolerance of minus 15 per cent.

Thickness of nuts. The thickness of a nut is the over-all distance from the top to the bearing surface, and thus includes the washer face.

13·23 The drawing of fastenings is a tedious time-consuming task. Under some conditions they must be accurately drawn to scale, using exact dimensions from tables. Often, however, their representation may be approximate and symbolic, limited to a description that identifies them.

Two methods are given for drawing fastening heads and nuts, the first resulting in true over-all dimensions; the second, resulting in approximate over-all dimensions, is more of a symbol and requires less drawing time.

Beginning students should limit their practice to the true-size methods.

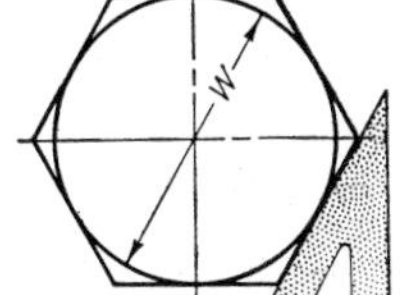

END VIEWS OF HEXAGONAL BOLTHEADS

Draw a circle of diameter W and then draw the hexagon with T square and 30°–60° triangle. (These views not needed for drawing the face views of head.)

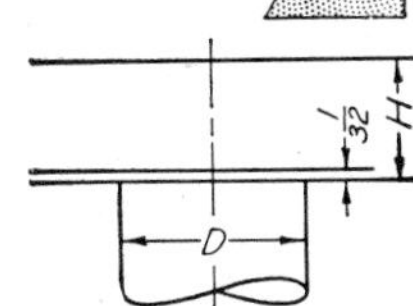

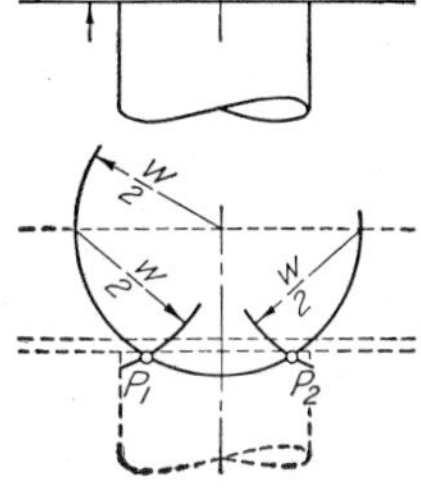

FACE VIEWS OF HEXAGONAL BOLTHEADS

1. Establish the diameter, height of head, and washer-face thickness. The actual thickness of the washer face for all fastenings is 1/64″ but may be increased up to 1/32″ for the drawing.

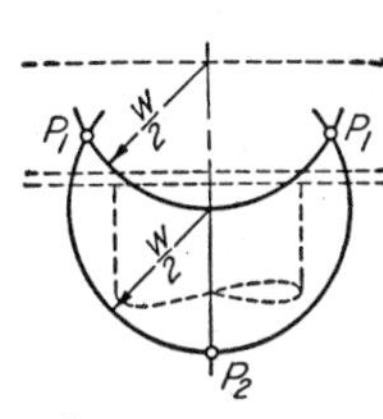

2. Set compass to radius of $W/2$ and draw the circle arcs locating centers P_1 and P_2.

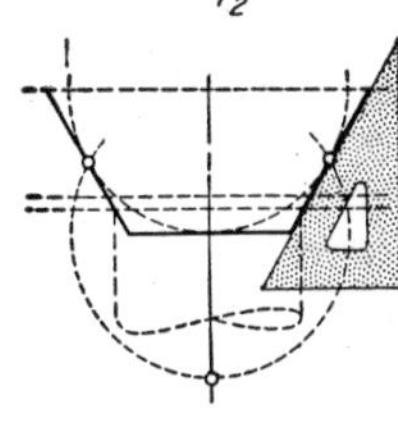

3. Draw tangents to circle arc with 30°–60° triangle and T square to locate edges of faces. (This stage is omitted if the end view is drawn.)

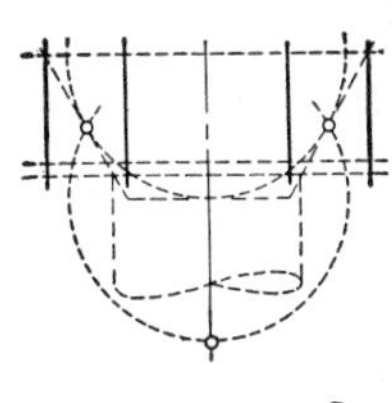

4. Draw, lightly, the vertical edges of the faces.

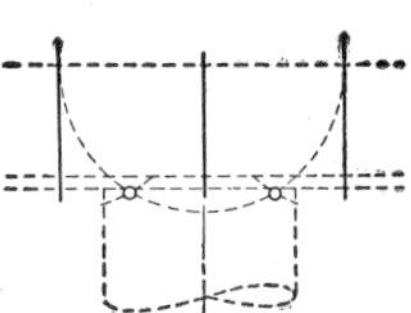

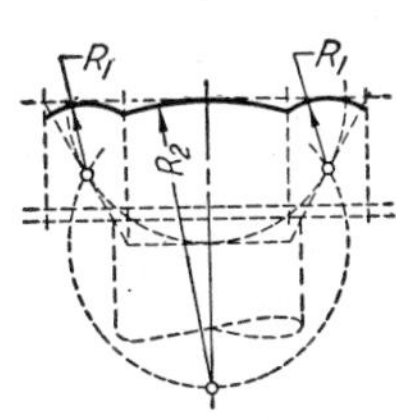

5. Draw chamfer curves as circle-arc approximations to the actual curves, which are hyperbolas, using radii and centers as shown.

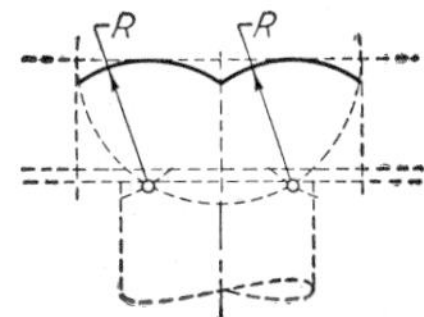

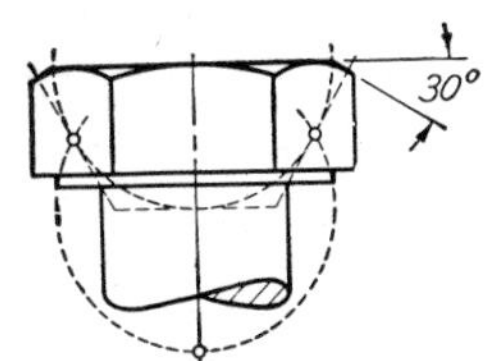

6. Complete the views. Show washer-face diameter equal to W. For across-corners view, show 30° chamfer.

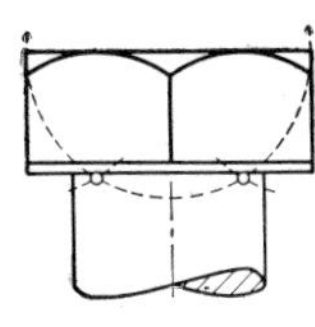

FIG. 13·24—Stages in drawing a hex head.

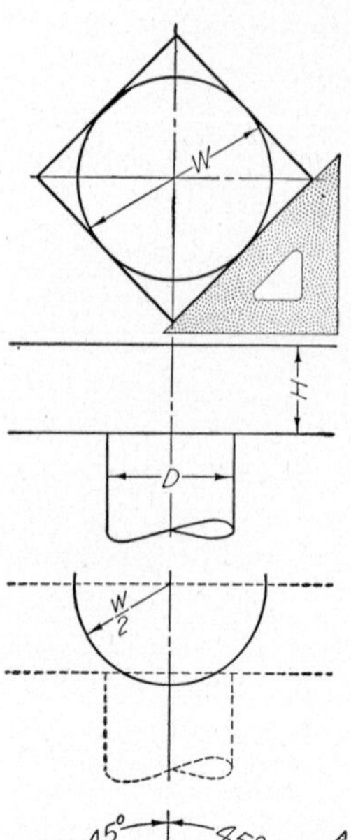

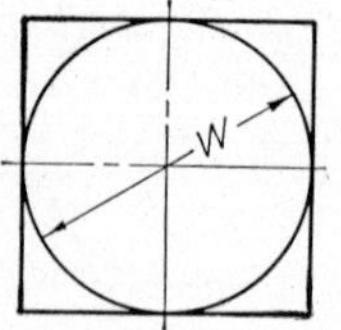

END VIEWS OF SQUARE BOLTHEADS

Draw a circle of diameter W and then draw the square with T square and 45° triangle. (These views not needed in drawing the face views of head.)

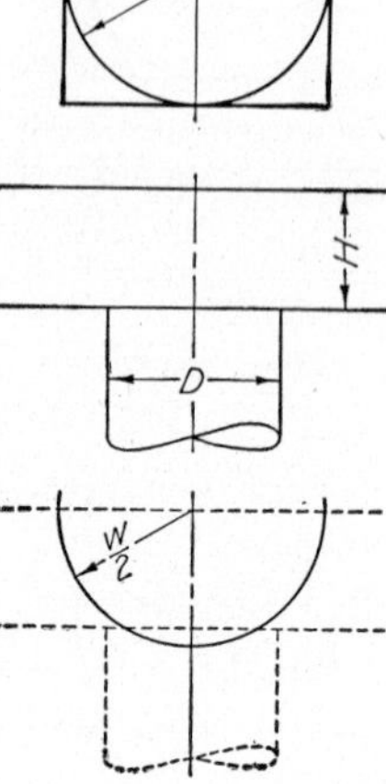

FACE VIEWS OF SQUARE BOLTHEADS

1. Establish the diameter and the height of head.

2. Set compass to radius of $W/2$ and draw the circle arc.

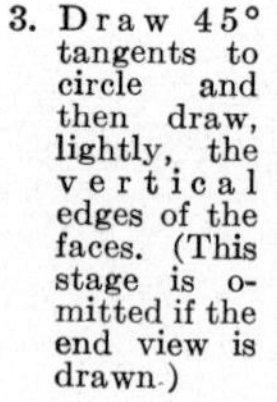

3. Draw 45° tangents to circle and then draw, lightly, the vertical edges of the faces. (This stage is omitted if the end view is drawn.)

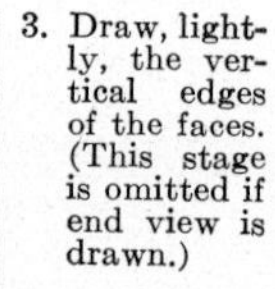

3. Draw, lightly, the vertical edges of the faces. (This stage is omitted if end view is drawn.)

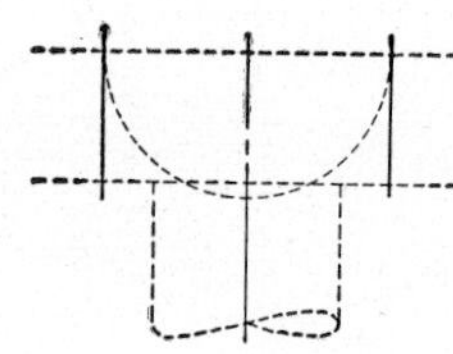

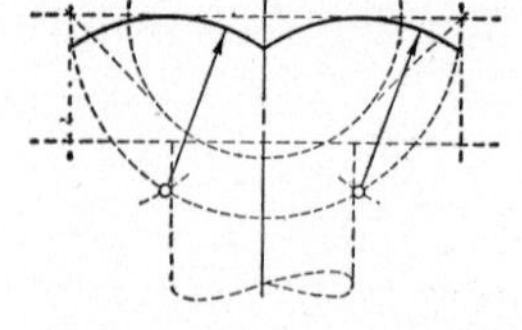

4. Set compass to radius of $C/2$ and draw the circle arcs locating centers P_1 and P_2.

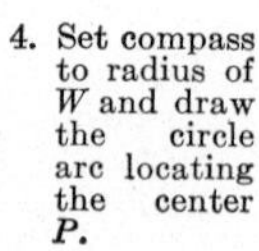

4. Set compass to radius of W and draw the circle arc locating the center **P**.

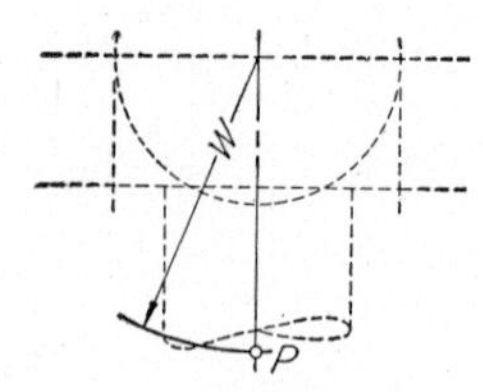

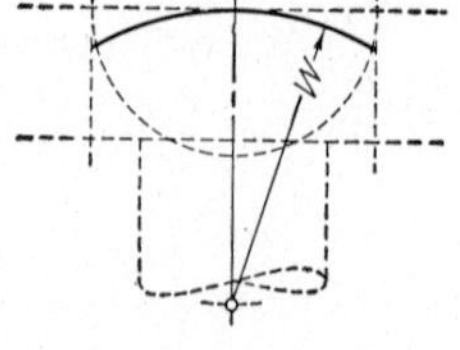

5. Draw chamfer curves as circle-arc approximations to the actual curves, which are hyperbolas, using radii and centers as shown.

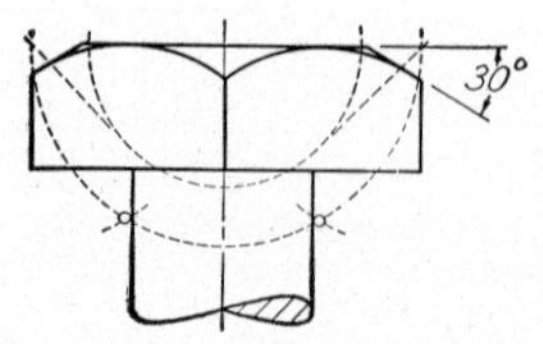

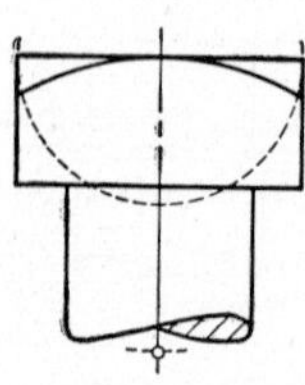

6. Complete the views. Show 30° chamfer on across-corners view.

FIG. 13·25—Stages in drawing a square head.

The shorter approximate method may be used after an understanding of the form and proportions of the fastenings has been acquired.

13·24 To draw an American Standard bolt and nut, true-size method, the following information must be known: (1) the diameter, (2) the length, (3) the series, (4) the type of head and nut, and (5) the class of finish. Using this information, additional data, *H* (height of head), *T* (thickness of nut), *W* (width across flats), and *L* (length of thread) is obtained from tables of bolt dimensions. All of this information and data should be tabulated before starting the drawing. Boltheads and nuts are always shown across corners on all views showing the faces unless there is some special reason for showing them across flats. Figure 13·24 shows the stages in drawing a hexagonal bolthead.

Since the head and nut in like series and finishes differ only in thickness, time can be saved by carrying similar steps together. Figure 13·25 shows the stages in drawing a square bolthead. Here also the only difference between the head and nut in like series is the thickness.

The methods of Figs. 13·24 and 13·25 apply as well for drawing square and hexagonal heads or nuts of other fastenings. Figure 13·26 shows a regular semifinished bolt and nut, drawn by the method of Fig. 13·24, show-

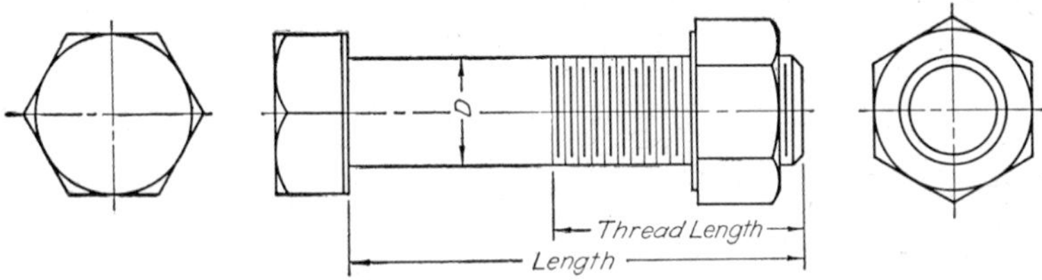

FIG. 13·26—American Standard regular semifinished bolt.

ing the hexagonal head across flats and the hexagonal nut across corners. The length of thread is obtained from manufacturers' tables in the Appendix. Other views of bolts and the notes for their specification are shown in Figs. 13·29 to 13·32.

13·25 To draw an American Standard bolt and nut, approximate method. Where many fastenings are to be drawn and the exact head size, for clearance, is not necessary, this method is quite satisfactory. The following information is needed: (1) diameter, (2) length, and (3) the type of head or nut. Drafting time is saved in establishing the width (*W*), height (*H*), or thickness (*T*), of a head or nut by observation directly from the diameter of the fastening. By using one set of proportions for the regular series and another set for the heavy, the resulting views are very close to the actual head and nut dimensions. After these values (*W*, *H*, *T*) are established, the stages in drawing are identical with the true-size method.

The stages for drawing a regular series hexagonal bolthead and nut across corners are shown in Fig. 13·27. This method closely approximates the formula of values in the regular series for $W = 1\frac{1}{2}D$, $H = \frac{2}{3}D$, and $T = \frac{7}{8}D$. The same values may be used for both square and hexagon forms in either the across-corners or across-flats views. Figure 13·28 shows the stages for drawing a heavy-series hexagonal bolthead and nut across corners. This approximates very closely the formula of values in the heavy

1. Establish the diameter D of the fastening.
2. By eye, locate mark P midway between the center line and the outside diameter. Use the distance shown for $W/2$.
3. By eye, divide the space from mark P to the center line into three equal parts. Use the distance shown for H (height of head).
4. By eye, divide the space from mark P to the outside diameter into two equal parts. Use the distance shown for T (thickness of nut).
5. Bolt is drawn using the same stages as in the *true-size* method. Length of thread for drawing purposes equals $2D + \frac{1}{4}''$.

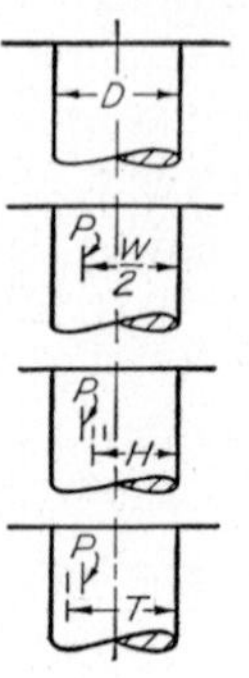

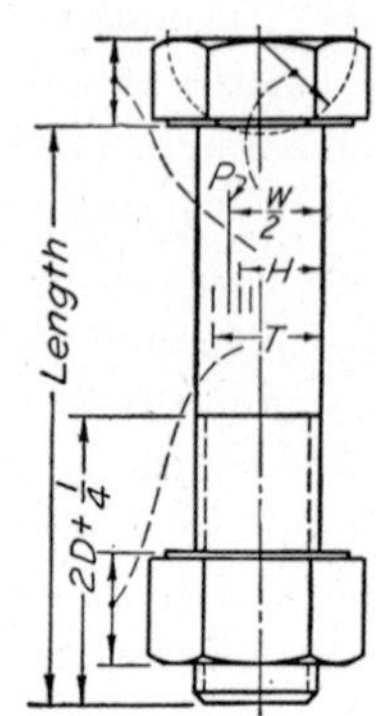

FIG. 13·27—Stages in drawing a regular series hex bolthead and nut across corners (approximate method).

1. Establish the diameter D. Use this distance for T (thickness of nut).

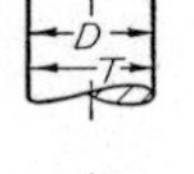

2. By eye, locate mark P midway between the center line and the outside diameter. Use the distance shown for H (height of head).

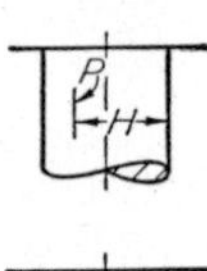

3. By eye, divide the space from mark P to outside diameter into two equal parts. Use the distance shown for $W/2$.
4. Bolt is drawn using the same stages as in the *true-size* method.

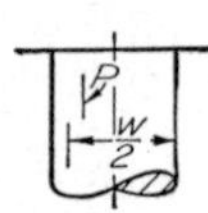

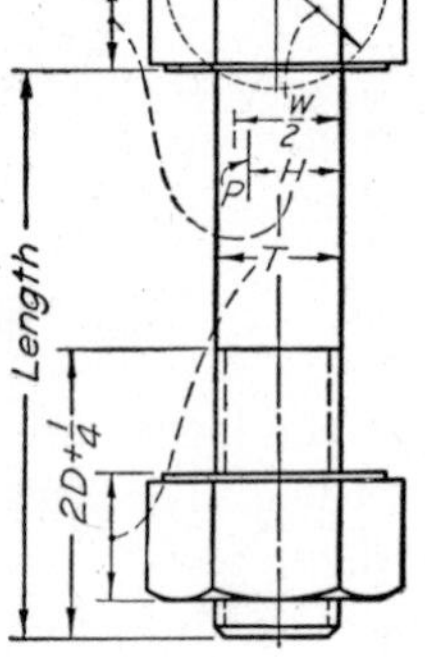

FIG. 13·28—Stages in drawing a heavy series hex bolthead and nut across corners (approximate method).

series for $W = 1\frac{1}{2}D + \frac{1}{8}$, $H = \frac{3}{4}D$, and $T = D$. The same values may be used for both square and hexagon forms in either the across-corners or the across-flats views.

No short methods are suggested for cap screws and other fastenings. They occur in only one series and finish, so little confusion results in obtaining head and nut dimensions directly from the tables.

13·26 Dimensioning and specifying an American Standard bolt. It is recommended that bolts be completely specified by note with the various items in the following definite order: (1) diameter and length; (2) material, if other than steel; (3) class of finish; (4) series (omitted if bolt is regular); (5) type of head; (6) type of nut if different from head; (7) thread specifications.

Example: ½″ × 4″ copper unfinished heavy square-headed bolt; steel, semifinished heavy hexagonal nut, ½″-13 NC-2.

This is abbreviated as follows:

½″ × 4″ Copper Unfin Heavy Sq Hd Bolt;
Steel Semifin Heavy Hex Nut, ½″-13 NC-2.

If bolt is steel and regular, and head and nut are like, the specification reads:

½″ × 4″ Semifin Hex Hd Bolt and Nut, ½″-13 NC-2.

Figures 13·29 to 13.32, inclusive, show the form of notes to be used for specifying various bolts and nuts.

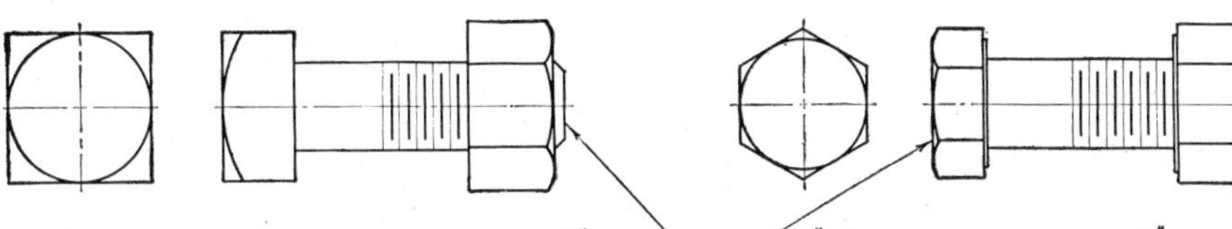

FIG. 13·29—American Standard unfinished heavy bolt.

FIG. 13·30—American Standard semifinished regular bolt.

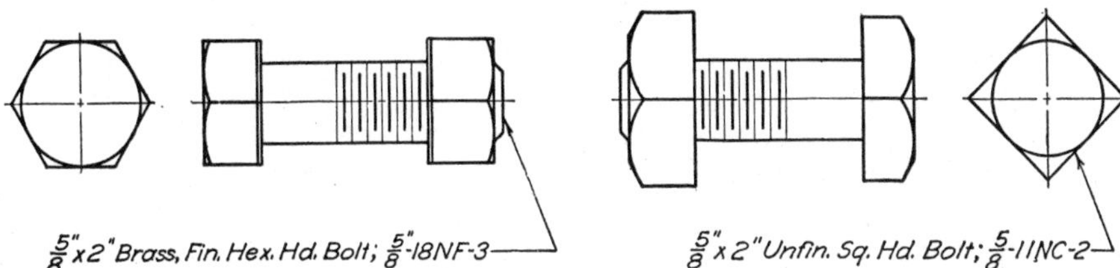

FIG. 13·31—American Standard finished regular bolt.

FIG. 13·32—American Standard unfinished regular bolt.

13·27 Studs. Fig. 13·33. The stud, a rod threaded on both ends, is used when through bolts are not suitable, for parts that must be removed frequently, such as cylinder heads, chest covers, etc. One end is screwed tightly into a tapped hole, and the projecting stud guides the removable piece to position. The end to be screwed permanently into position is called the "stud end" and the opposite end the "nut end." The stud end is sometimes identified by leaving a projection on it. Studs have not yet been standardized by the ASA. The length of thread on the stud end is governed by the material tapped, see Fig. 13·21. The threads should jam at the top of the hole to prevent the stud from turning out when the nut is removed.

The length of thread on the nut end should be such that there is no danger of the nut binding before the parts are drawn together. The name "stud bolt" is often applied to a stud used as a through fastening with a nut on each end. The stud and nut are usually specified by note on assembly drawings, as shown in Fig. 13·33*A*, with the various items in the following order: (1) diameter and length; (2) material if other than steel; (3) thread specification and length of thread on nut end; (4) type of nut; (5) thread specification and length of thread on stud end.

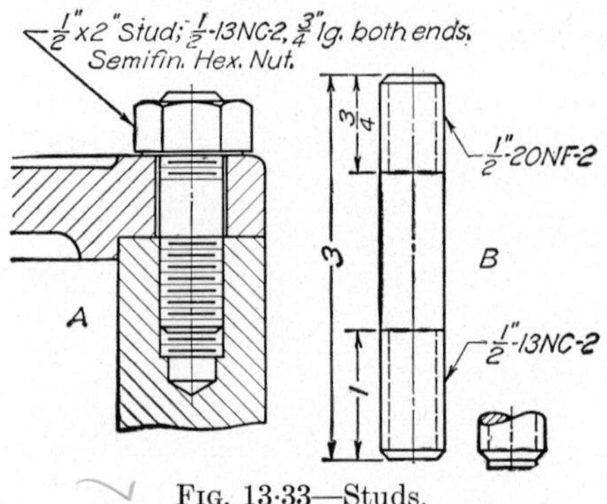

FIG. 13·33—Studs.

Example: ½″ × 4″ Brass Stud; ½″-20 NF-2, 1″ Lg with Semifin Hex Nut and ½″-13 NC-2, ¾″ Lg. If threads on both ends are alike and material is steel, the note reads: ½″ × 4″ Stud; ½″-13 NC-2, ¾″ Lg both ends; with Semifin Hex Nut.

The stud is usually specified on a detail drawing, as shown in Fig. 13·33*B*.

13·28 Cap screws, Fig. 13·34, differ from bolts in that they are used for fastening two pieces together by passing through a clear hole in one and screwing into a tapped hole in the other. Cap screws are used on machine tools and other products requiring close dimensions and finished appearances. Threads are class 3 fit, coarse

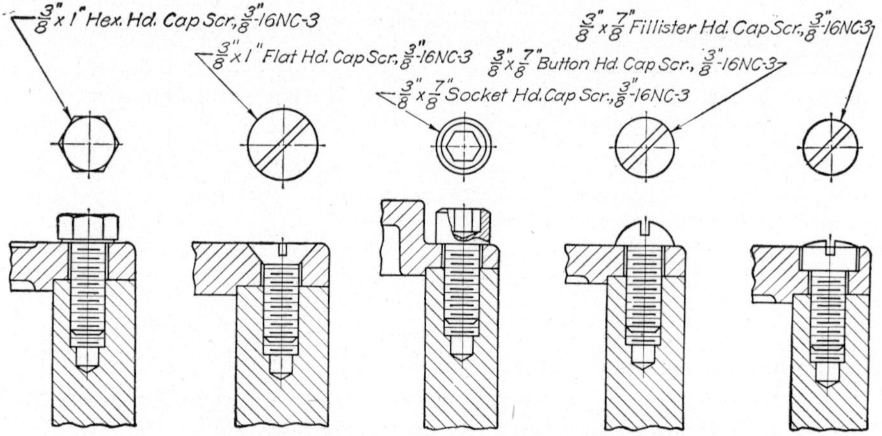

FIG. 13·34—American Standard cap screws.

or fine series. Full-finished cap screws are accurately made to proportions set up by the ASA. The semifinished screws do not always conform to the exact basic formulas.

The five types of heads shown in Fig. 13·34 are standard. Detail proportions and dimensions are given in the Appendix.

The steps in drawing a hex head are the same as for hex-head bolts. For other types of heads see Fig. 13·34 and obtain their sizes from tables in the Appendix. On the drawing it is not necessary to show clearance between the fastening and machine parts. However, clearance must be provided in the dimensioning.

Cap screws are specified by note, with the several items in the following order: (1) diameter and length; (2) material if other than steel; (3) type of head; (4) thread specifications.

Example: 3/8″ × 1½″ Brass Hex Hd Cap Screw, 3/8″-16 NC-3.

13·29 Machine screws are similar in appearance to cap screws. The heads have like names with the exception of the semielliptical shape, which is "round head" for machine screws and "buttonhead" for cap screws. The four standard shapes of heads are shown in Fig. 13·35. Numerous other shapes are available for special uses. All heads are slotted as a protection to the screw. Threads are either coarse or fine series. Diameters are nominal except in three fractional sizes of 1/4″, 5/16″, and 3/8″. Machine screws are specified by note giving in order: (1) diameter; (2) threads per inch; (3) length; (4) material if other than steel; (5) type of head.

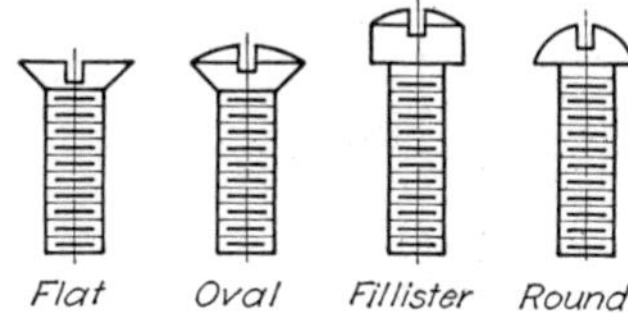

FIG. 13·35—American Standard machine screws.

Example: No. 10-24 × ½″ Brass Fillister-head Machine Screw.

The American Standard dimensions for the standard heads and sizes are given in Appendix.

13·30 Setscrews made of hardened steel are used for holding two parts in relative position, being screwed through one part and having the point set against the other. The American Standard square-headed and some forms of headless screws are shown in Fig. 13·36. Types of points are shown in Fig. 13·37. Dimensions for drawing purposes are given in the Appendix.

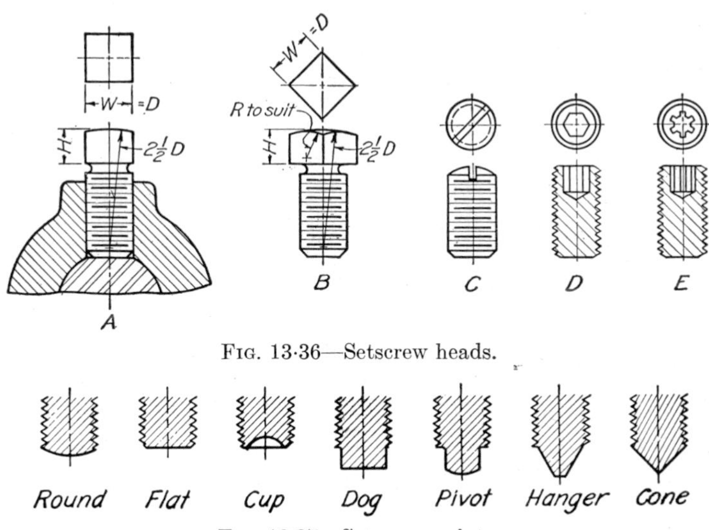

FIG. 13·36—Setscrew heads.

FIG. 13·37—Setscrew points.

Headless setscrews are made to comply with the safety code of factory inspection laws, which are very strict regarding the use of projecting screws on moving parts. Setscrews are specified by giving in order: (1) diameter; (2) length; (3) type of head; (4) type of point; (5) thread specification.

Example: ¼" × ¾" Sq Hd Cone-pointed Setscrew, ¼"-20 NC-2.

13·31 Standard forms of special-purpose nuts. *Jam nuts.* American Standard jam nuts provide the commonest form of locking device, Figs. 13·38 and 13·39. They have the same dimensions as corresponding full nuts, except thickness, and are made in regular, heavy, and light series, semifinished and (except light series) unfinished. The tops in all series and finishes are flat and chamfered. Bearing surfaces are plain on the unfinished, and washer-faced or chamfered on the semifinished. The form is hexagonal only. For detail dimensions, see Appendix.

Slotted nuts, Figs. 13·38 and 13·39, are used principally in automotive work. They are made in regular, heavy, light, and light-thick series, semifinished only. Tops in all series are flat and chamfered. Bearing surfaces are washer-faced or chamfered. Slots have square or round bottom, at the option of the manufacturer. For detail dimensions see Appendix.

Light-thick nuts, Fig. 13·38, have the same dimensions, except thickness, as the corresponding sizes in the light series. See Appendix. They are made only in hexagonal form, semifinished. Tops are flat and chamfered. Bearing surfaces are washer-faced or chamfered.

Light castle nuts, Fig. 13·38, are similar in use to slotted nuts. Bearing surfaces are washer faces or chamfered. Bottoms of slots are square or round. See Appendix for detail dimensions.

Machine-screw nuts, Fig. 13·38, are hexagonal. The tops are flat and chamfered. Bearing surfaces are plain, washer-faced, or chamfered. Sizes are by number except three fractional sizes. See Appendix.

Stove-bolt nuts, Fig. 13·38, are square, and the tops and bottoms are flat without chamfer. The width across flats and the thickness is the same as hexagonal machine-screw nuts. Two forms of threads are in use: the American Standard with coarse and fine series and the Tap and Die Manufacturer's Standard in which the width of the crest and root has been increased. The two are not interchangeable. The American Standard provides for nuts in the numbered sizes, but most manufacturers list stove bolts in fractional sizes from ⅛" to ½".

13·32 Lock nuts and locking devices. Fig. 13·39. Many different locking devices are used to prevent nuts from working loose. A screw thread holds securely unless the parts are subject to impact and vibration, as in a railroad track joint or an automobile engine. A common device is the *jam nut, A.* American Standard jam nuts have the same dimensions as corresponding full nuts except the thickness. *Slotted nuts* to be held with cotter or wire, used largely in automotive work, are shown at L, and *castellated nuts* as used with fine and extra-fine threads on light tubular sections in aeronautical work, at M. At B is shown a *round nut* locked by means of a setscrew. A brass plug is placed under the setscrew to prevent damage to the thread. This is a common type of adjusting nut used in machine-tool practice. C is

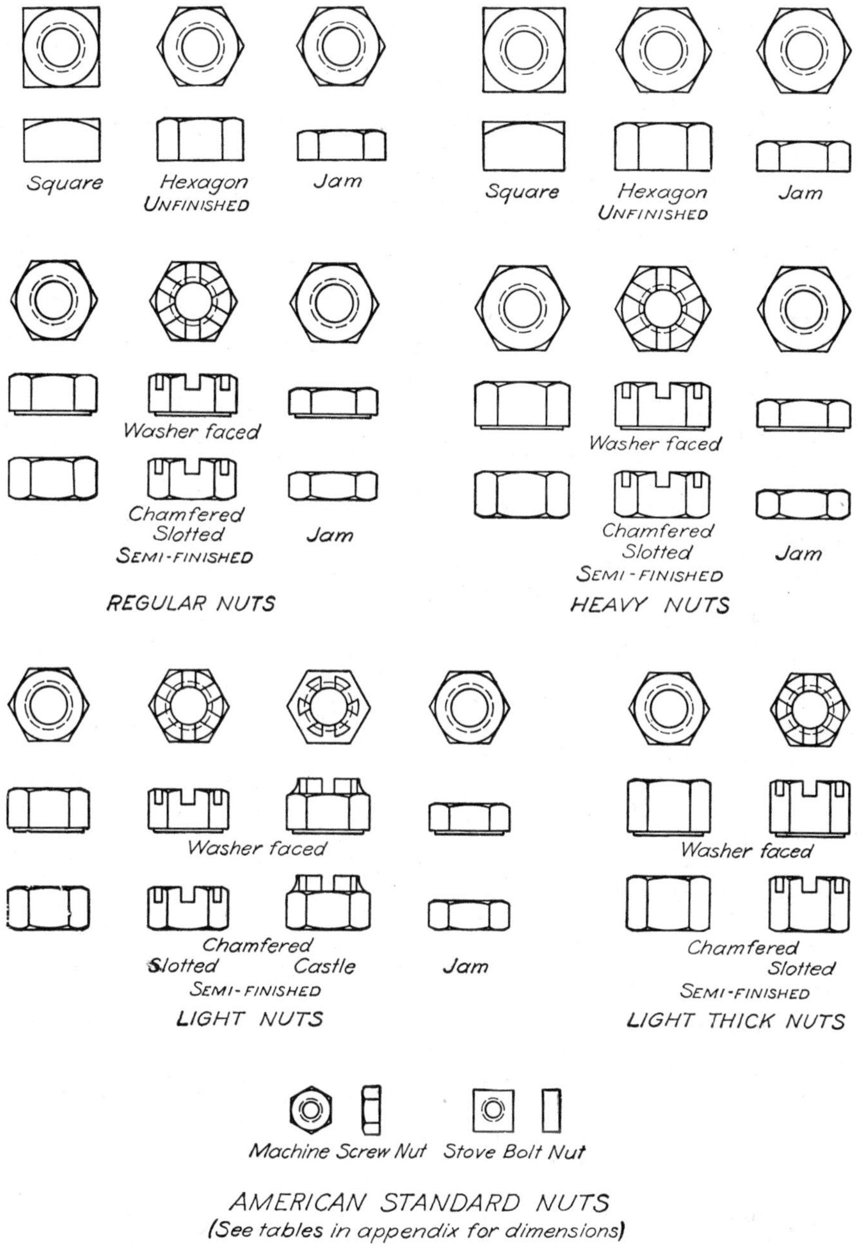

Square Hexagon Jam
UNFINISHED

Square Hexagon Jam
UNFINISHED

Washer faced

Chamfered
Slotted Jam
SEMI-FINISHED

REGULAR NUTS

Washer faced

Chamfered
Slotted Jam
SEMI-FINISHED

HEAVY NUTS

Washer faced

Chamfered
Slotted Castle Jam
SEMI-FINISHED
LIGHT NUTS

Washer faced

Chamfered
Slotted
SEMI-FINISHED
LIGHT THICK NUTS

Machine Screw Nut Stove Bolt Nut

AMERICAN STANDARD NUTS
(See tables in appendix for dimensions)

FIG. 13·38—Various American Standard nuts.

a lock nut, in which the threads are deformed after cutting. Patented spring washers such as are shown at *D*, *E*, and *F* are common devices. There are three standard SAE spring lock washers: SAE Light, SAE Standard, and

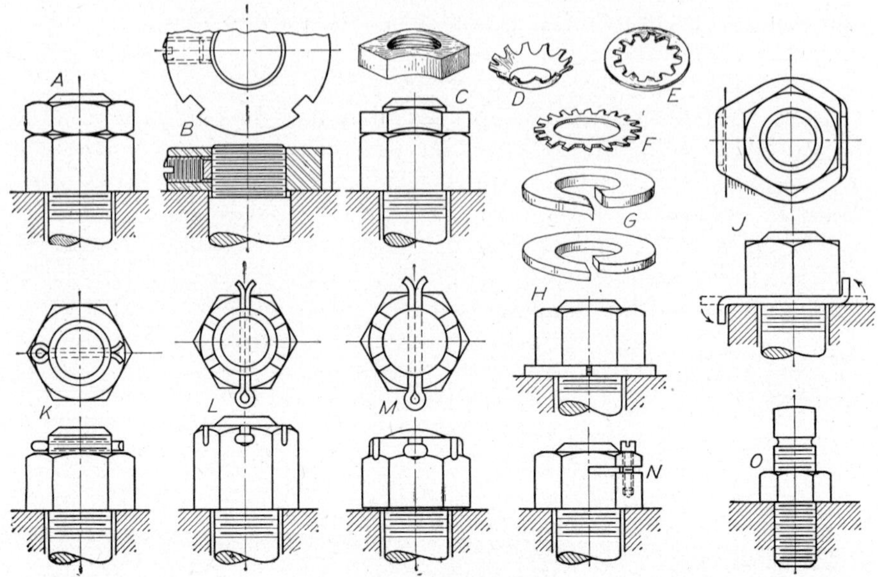

FIG. 13·39—Locking devices.

SAE Heavy; these are shown at *G* and *H* and are specified by giving nominal diameter and weight.

Example: ½″ SAE Heavy Lock Washer.

If special, give nominal diameter with width and thickness of steel section.

Example: ½ × 3⁄16 × 3⁄32 SAE Lock Washer (see Appendix).

J is typical of a number of lock washers which are bent after the nut is in place. *Spring cotters* are used as at *K*. *N* and *O* are self-explanatory. These illustrate only a few of the many locking devices available.

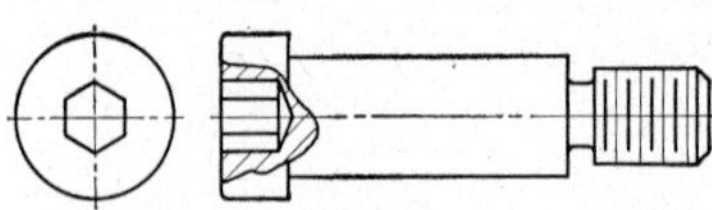

FIG. 13·40—Stripper bolt or shoulder screw.

13·33 Stripper bolts or shoulder screws. Fig. 13·40. This fastening was formerly used almost exclusively in die work for attaching strippers to punches. It is now widely used for holding machine parts together, such as cam attachments, links, levers, and oscillating parts. Four diameters in lengths from 1 to 7 inches are standard with manufacturers. Threads are coarse series. Detail dimensions are in the Appendix.

13·34 American Standard unslotted round-head bolts are used only as through fastenings. In this group are included carriage bolts, step bolts, buttonhead bolts, and countersunk bolts. Several of the forms are for wood construction, having square sections, ribs, or fins under the head to prevent the fastening from turning. Threads are American Standard coarse series with the threads cut or rolled. A table in the Appendix shows the form of heads and proportions suitable for drawing purposes. Exact dimensions may be obtained from ASA Pamphlet 18.5-1939.

13·35 United States Standard bolts and nuts. Before the adoption of the American Standard, the United States Standard was in general use, and in some places it has not yet been superseded by the regular series of the American Standard. The proportions of the United States Standard are $W = 1\frac{1}{2}D + \frac{1}{8}''$; height of head, $W/2$; thickness of nut, D. Thus it will be noted the United States Standard is virtually the same as the heavy series of the American Standard, except that the angle of chamfer on the hexagon is 45° instead of 30°, as in the American Standard. The "unfinished heavy" table may therefore be used as a table for the old United States Standard.

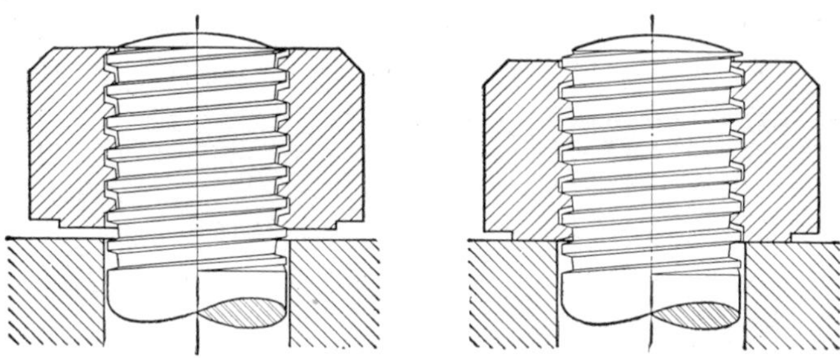

FIG. 13·41—Dardelet thread, unlocked and locked.

13·36 Dardelet screw thread. The Dardelet self-locking thread is a special thread requiring no auxiliary locking devices to hold the nut under vibration. Its profile, Fig. 13·3, is quite similar to the Acme thread, but the roots of the external thread and the crests of the internal thread are tapered about 6° to the axis. The nut screws on very easily until the bearing surface comes to rest, then the wrench torque forces the two tapered surfaces into binding contact. Figure 13·41 shows the nut in unlocked and locked positions. In drawing Dardelet bolts and nuts, the heads have the same proportions as the American Standard regular series. The nuts are the same except in thickness. For drawing purposes the thickness may be made $1\frac{1}{8}D$.

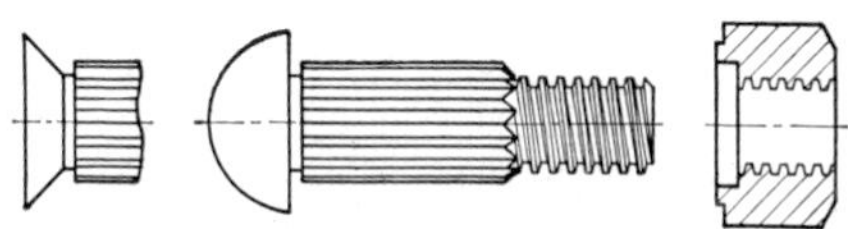

FIG. 13·42—Dardelet rivet bolt.

13·37 Dardelet self-locking rivet bolts, Fig. 13·42, combine the principles of both a rivet and a bolt. Head dimensions are ABA (American Boiler Makers Association) standards. The nut conforms to the American Standard heavy series proportions with the exception of thickness, which is

$\frac{3}{16}''$ to $\frac{1}{4}''$ greater, to provide for a counterbore $\frac{3}{32}''$ larger in diameter than the major thread diameter. Surrounding the body are a number of triangular-shaped ribs extending axially from head to threaded end. Because no upsetting is involved, material high in shear and tensile strength is used for the bolt. Among the many advantages over field-driven rivets are elimination of noise, body-bound fit, and high shear and tensile values.

Dardelet rivet bolts are carried in stock by licensed manufacturers and distributors in principal cities, from whom complete dimensions and specifications may be obtained.

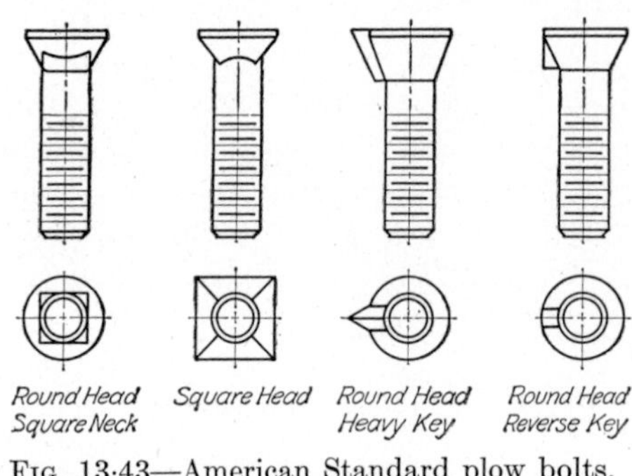

FIG. 13·43—American Standard plow bolts.

13·38 Plow bolts. Fig. 13·43. Four types of plow bolts from 182 varieties in use have been standardized by the ASA. For their particular uses, proportions, etc., see ASA Bulletin B18f-1928.

13·39 Parker-Kalon hardened self-tapping screws. Fig. 13·44. Recent years have seen the development and wide use of a group of fastenings with a special hardened thread, which form their own internal threads in the material when driven into a hole of the proper size. They do not offer the

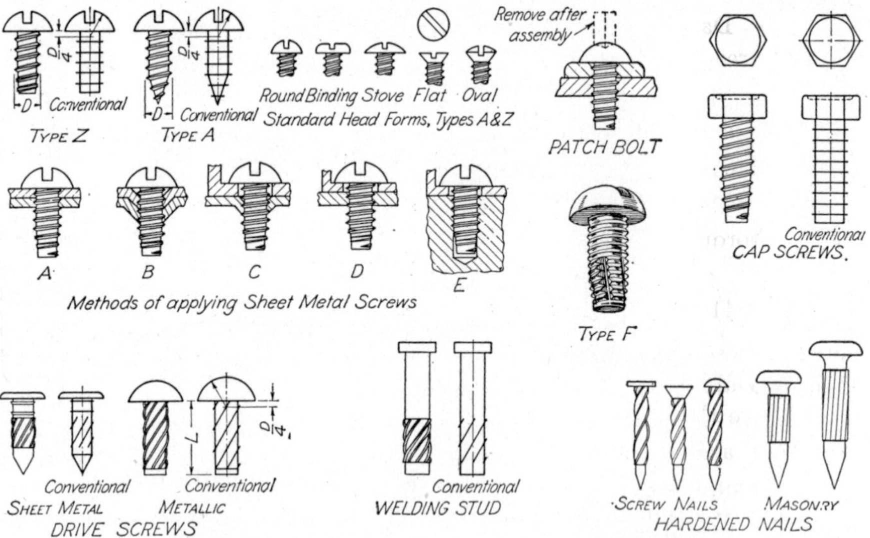

FIG. 13·44—Parker-Kalon hardened self-tapping screws.

best means of making every fastening and cannot replace bolts, machine screws, rivets, etc., under all conditions. However, under many conditions these screws give a combination of speed, security, and ease of working that make them the preferred fastening. Many factors, such as size of fastening, size of holes, amount of engagement, kind of material, etc., affect satisfactory results. Data sheets from the manufacturers giving this detailed information are available to instructors of engineering drawing, machine design, etc., for classroom use. Parker-Kalon self-tapping *cap screws* are for light and heavy assemblies; for fastenings to sheet metal, steel plate, and structural shapes up to ½″ thick; to brass, aluminum, and die castings; to slate, asbestos, etc. This screw is used by drilling a hole of the specified diameter and turning the fastening into it. No tapping is necessary, and the screw may be removed and replaced in the same hole without affecting the holding power. Threads are special, and the drill size is important. See tables in Appendix.

Hardened self-tapping sheet-metal screws are made with two types of points known commercially as type *A* and type *Z*. The essential difference is that type *A* has a gimlet point, while *Z* has a blunt point. Standard head forms are shown in Fig. 13·44. Many special head forms are available. They may be driven with hand or power screw drivers or with automatic feed machines. The different methods of applying Fig. 13·44 are

At *A*. Two sheets of light-gage sheet metal are drilled or clean-punched the same size in both sheets.

At *B*. Two sheets of light-gage sheet metal are punched together so that the burrs are nested. This gives a stronger fastening than at *A*.

At *C*. A part with clearance holes is fastened to light-gage sheet metal. The sheet metal should be pierced, providing a greater thread engagement.

At *D*. A part with clearance holes is fastened to heavy-gage sheet metal. The sheet metal should be drilled or clean punched.

At *E*. A part is fastened to a solid section of aluminum, die casting, etc. Clearance holes should be provided in the part to be fastened, to permit the parts to be drawn tightly together.

Hardened self-tapping screws known commercially as *type F* are used in materials of a crumbling or granular nature, such as cast and malleable iron, plasters, bakelite, etc. The tap-fluted pilot cuts a thread in the material as it is turned in. The threads are American Standard coarse and fine series and may be used with a nut or replaced with a standard machine screw if necessary. This screw is used by first drilling a hole of suitable diameter and turning in the fastening. Drill size and maximum and minimum penetration factors are important for satisfactory results, and should be obtained from manufacturers' catalogues.

Hardened metallic drivescrews are for making permanent fastenings to iron, brass, aluminum castings, steel, plastics, etc. They may be hammered in or driven with a press. The material into which they are driven should have a thickness not less than the body diameter of the screw.

Sheet-metal drivescrews are used by automotive manufacturers, body builders, and trim shops for attaching upholstering, trim pads, windlace, etc., to metal bodies. Severe vibration does not cause these screws to back out.

To use, hammer the screws into drilled, clean-punched, or pierced holes of the proper size. They may be driven with a hopper-feed press without drilling or punching holes in the metal.

Self-tapping patch bolts are used for making repairs to steel plate and structural shapes up ½″ thick, in railroad, ship, and bridge work. To use, make a hole of the proper size and turn in the bolt with a socket or end wrench. Cut off the square-headed shank (which is not hardened) and dress the head with a file. For satisfactory results the hole sizes are important and differ for materials of different thicknesses. Consult manufacturers' catalogues for recommended sizes.

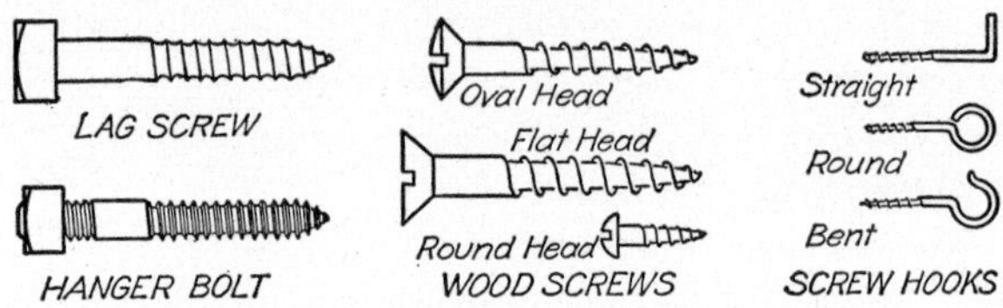

FIG. 13·45—Wood screws.

Welding studs are used in making welds on heavy iron castings. They are used by drilling holes of proper size and driving in the studs. As the studs are driven into place, their hardened spiral thread forms a thread in the casting that provides a combination of wedge and screw which results in a perfect bond between the casting and the weld.

Hardened masonry nails are used by sheet-metal workers, roofers, plumbers, electrical contractors, sign makers, etc., for making fastenings to masonry. To use, drill holes of the proper size and drive in the nails with a hammer. In comparatively soft masonry, such as mortar, cinder concrete, stucco, etc., the masonry nails ordinarily may be driven without drilling holes.

Sheet-metal screw nails are used to fasten sheet metal to wood. They combine the easy application of a nail and the holding property of a screw. They are driven directly through the metal in light gages and through pre-punched holes in heavier gages. They are available in a variety of sizes and head forms.

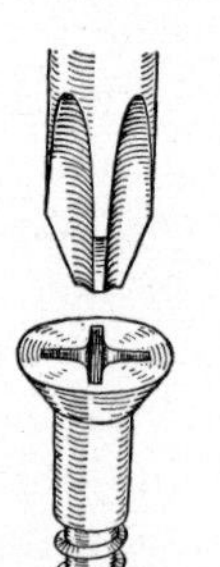

FIG. 13·46—Phillips' recessed head.

13·40 Wood screws have the threads proportioned to the relative holding strength of wood and metal. Three types of head—round, flat, and oval—are standard, Fig. 13·45. Many kinds of finish are available, such as steel, blued, chromium, nickel plated, etc. Wood screws are made with the regular screw-driver slot in the head or in a special form known as the "Phillips' recessed head," Fig. 13·46. This form has many advantages over the regular type. It is self-centering and the driver cannot slip out of the head. This permits the use of power drivers on operations that previously required careful hand driving. The Phillips' head is also being adapted to all fastenings that formerly used the slotted head. Wood-screw diameters are designated by number. Other forms of wood fastenings are lag screws, hanger bolts, and screw hooks, Fig. 13·45.

13·41 Other forms of fastenings. Figure 13·47 illustrates the method of representing various other bolts and screws.

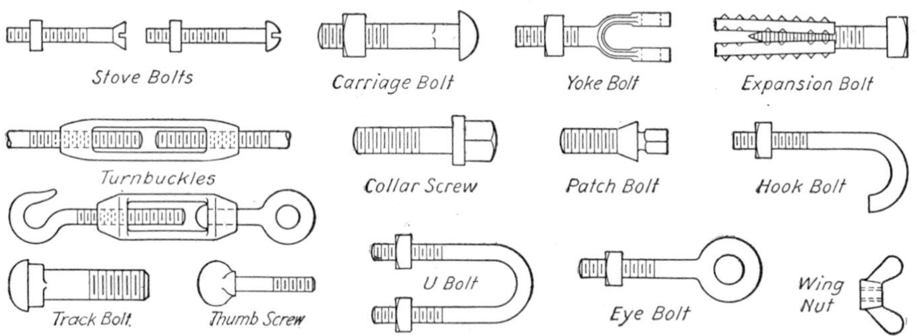

FIG. 13·47—Miscellaneous bolts and screws.

13·42 Aero thread. In the aero-thread system a coil-spring insert is used in the tapped hole, Fig. 13·48. This makes it possible to use high-strength cap screws and studs in comparatively soft material such as aluminum and magnesium alloys. The insert is assembled in the tapped hole and provides a smooth hard bearing surface for the screw. The thread in the tapped hole has the same form as the American Standard screw thread. The screw has a shallow circular form. Special dies for cutting the thread and a special tool for assembling the insert are necessary.

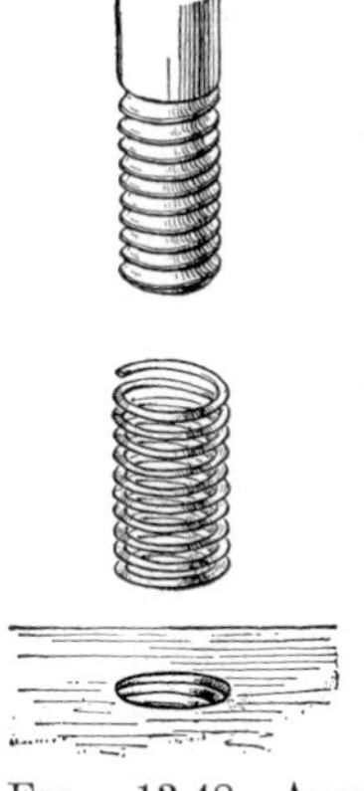

FIG. 13·48—Aero thread.

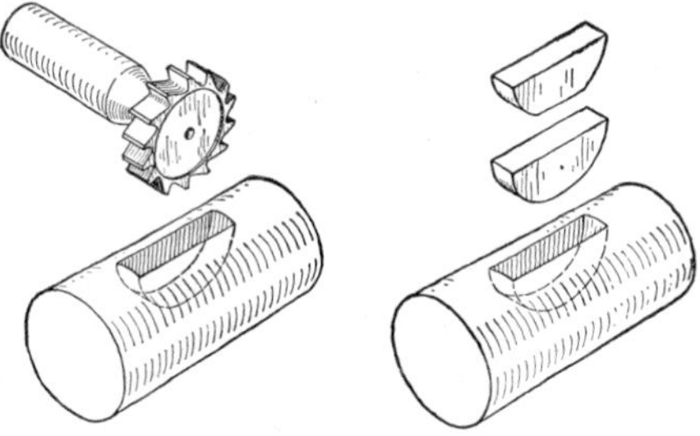

FIG. 13·49—Woodruff keys.

13·43 Keys. In machine drawing there is frequent occasion for representing keyed fastenings used in securing wheels, cranks, etc., to shafts. One of the commonest forms is the Woodruff key, a flat segmental disk with either round or flat bottom, as shown in Fig. 13·49. These are specified by number, and a table of standard sizes is given in the Appendix.

A good basic rule for proportioning a Woodruff key to a given shaft is to have the width of the key one-fourth the diameter of the shaft and its radius equal to the radius of the shaft, selecting the standard key that comes nearest to these proportions. In drawing Woodruff keys, care should be taken to place the center for the arc above the top of the key to a distance equal to one-half the thickness of the saw used in splitting the blank. This amount is given in column E of the table in the Appendix.

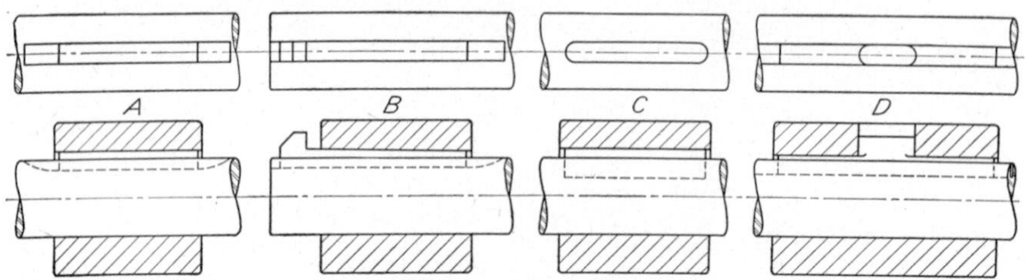

FIG. 13·50—Square and flat keys.

Square and flat keys, both plain and tapered, have a variety of applications. Figure 13·50 shows at A a square key and at B a gib-head taper key. Square- and flat-stock keys and taper-stock keys have been standardized by the ASA, and a table of sizes for use with various diameters of shafts is given in the Appendix. At C is a Pratt and Whitney key made with round ends. A *feather* is a straight key which allows a piece to slide lengthwise on a shaft while preventing rotation on the shaft. A sliding feather sometimes has a gib on each end and sometimes is made with one or more projections, as at D. With these the keyway must, of course, extend to one end of the shaft.

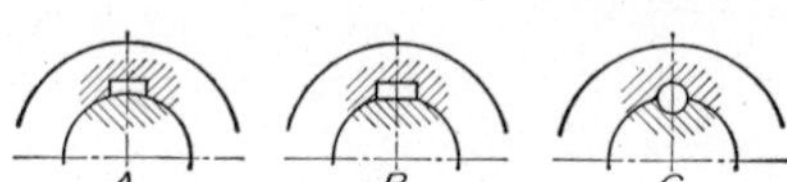

FIG. 13·51—Keys for light duty.

Figure 13·51 shows three keys for light duty: the saddle key, the flat key, and the pin or Nordberg key, which is used at the end of a shaft, as, for example, in fastening a handwheel. A taper pin is driven into a tapered hole made by drilling and reaming the shaft and hub together. The material of both pieces should be the same, for machining reasons.

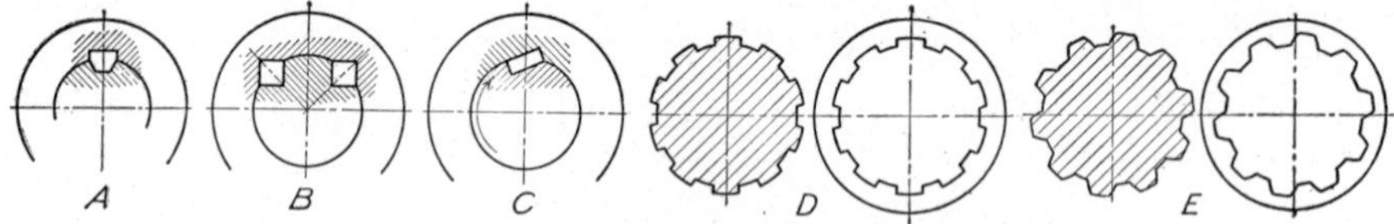

FIG. 13·52—Keys for heavy duty.

Figure 13·52 shows some forms of heavy-duty keys. A is the Barth key, an improvement on the flat spline, B is the Kennedy key, and C the Lewis key for driving in one direction. In the latter two the line of shear is on the diagonal. D and E are two forms of splined shaft, widely used instead of keyed shafts. E is the newer ASA involute spline (B5.15 1946).

13·44 Specification of keys. Keys are specified by note or number depending upon the type.

Square and flat keys are specified by a note giving the width, height, and length.

Examples: ½ Square key 2½ Lg.
½ × ⅜ Flat key 2½ Lg.

Woodruff keys are specified by number. See Appendix, page 650.

Example: Woodruff key No. 808.

Pratt and Whitney keys are specified by number. See Appendix, page 649.

Example: Pratt and Whitney key No. 6.

Dimensions and specifications of other keys are given in handbooks or manufacturers' catalogues.

Keyways and keyseats may be specified nominally by note as shown in Fig. 13·53. An alternate method, desirable for interchangeable manufacture, is illustrated in Fig. 13·54.

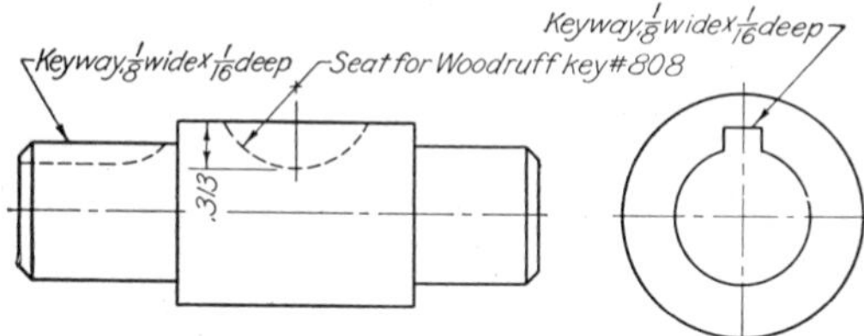

FIG. 13·53—Nominal dimensions.

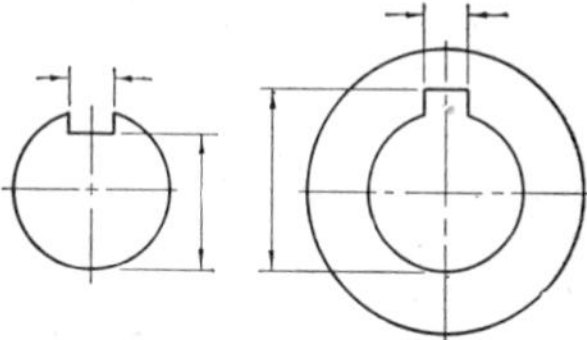

FIG. 13·54—Dimensions for interchangeable manufacture.

13·45 Rivets. Rivets are used for making permanent fastenings, generally between pieces of sheet or rolled metal. They are round bars of steel or wrought iron with a head formed on one end, and are often put in place red hot so that a head may be formed on the other end by pressing or hammering. Rivet holes are punched, punched and reamed, or drilled larger than the diameter of the rivet, and the shank of the rivet is made just long enough to give sufficient metal to fill the hole completely and make the head.

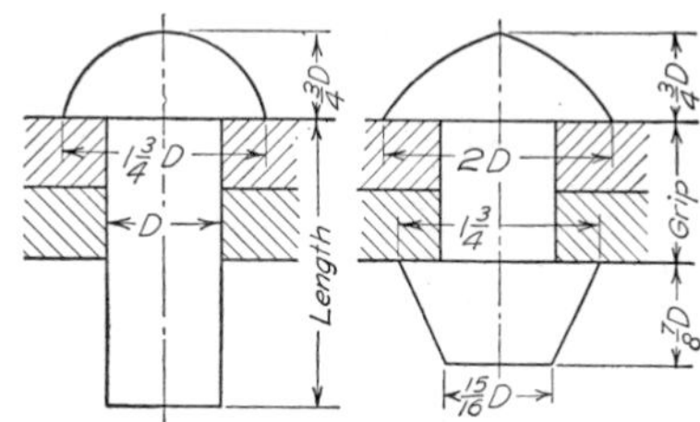

FIG. 13·55—Boiler and tank rivets.

It is not within our scope to consider the design of riveted joints, but we are concerned with the methods of representation. Large rivets are used in structural-steel construction and in boiler and tank work. Small rivets are used for fabricating light structural shapes and sheet metal. In structural work, only two kinds of heads are needed: buttonheads and countersunk heads. The standard symbols used in structural work are given on page 572.

For boiler and tank work, pressure against the head as well as shear must be considered, and the heads shown in Fig. 13·55 are used.

Plates are connected by either lap joints or butt joints. Single- and double-riveted lap joints and single and double straps are illustrated in Fig. 13·56. The American Standard proportions for the heads of small rivets are shown in Fig. 13·57.

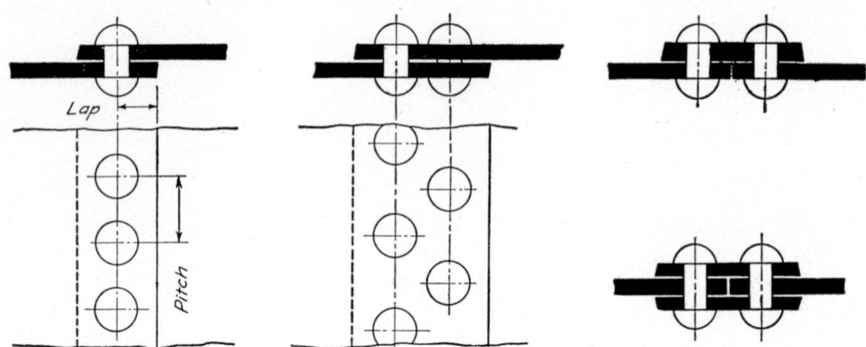

FIG. 13·56—Lap joints and butt joints.

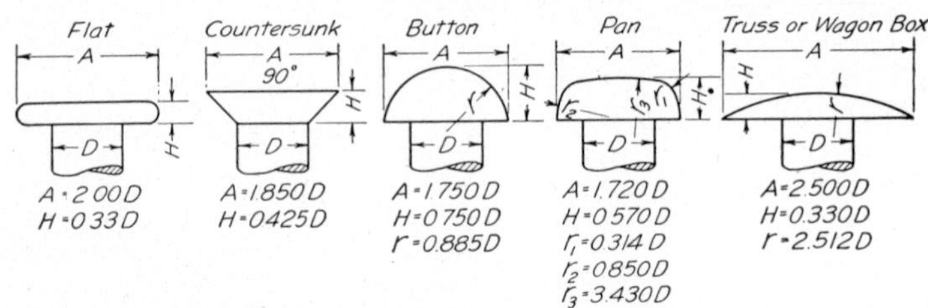

FIG. 13·57—American Standard small rivet heads.

13·46 Blind riveting. In aircraft and similar work, it is often necessary to resort to blind riveting under conditions where "backing up" the rivet is difficult or impossible. The following are common types.

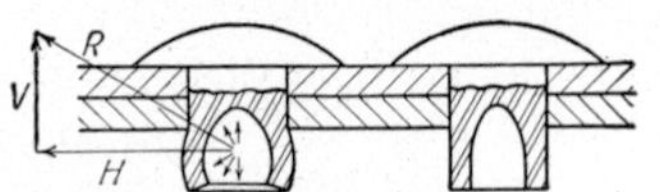

FIG. 13·58—Du Pont explosive-type rivet.

The du Pont rivet, Fig. 13·58, has a small cavity filled with an explosive charge which is fired by the application of an electrically heated tool to the head. Manufacturers' specifications should be followed closely in sizes of drilled holes and allowable grips. In aluminum alloys, properly expanded rivets have 85 to 90 per cent of the strength of corresponding rivets of the conventional type.

The Cherry blind rivet is made in two types: the self-plugging and the hollow. Figure 13·59 shows the self-plugging type before and after setting.

The rivet is hollow and has a mandrel extending from both ends. This mandrel is drawn into the rivet from the outside with a pneumatic or hand-operated gun, so that the body of the rivet is enlarged, completely filling the hole, and at the same time forming a head on the shank end. The pull is continued until the stem breaks; then the stem is trimmed off flush with the outside of the head. In the hollow type the stem may be pulled completely through. In some cases, the stem may break in two parts with the two ends falling free of the rivet.

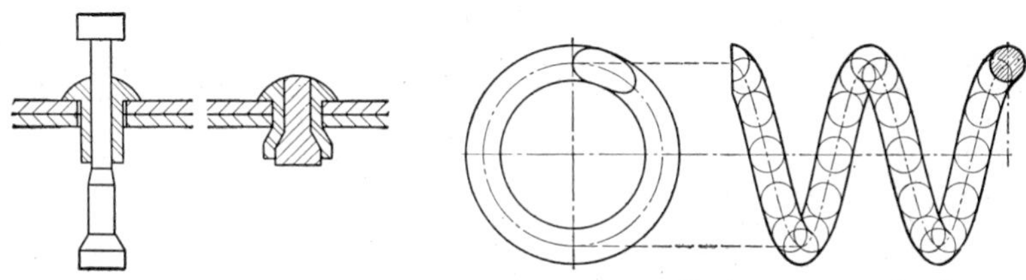

FIG. 13·59—Cherry blind rivet.

FIG. 13·60—Spring, true projection.

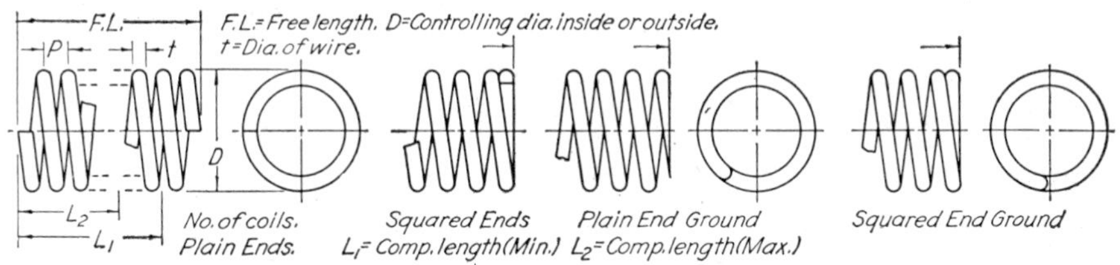

FIG. 13·61—Representation and dimensioning of compression springs.

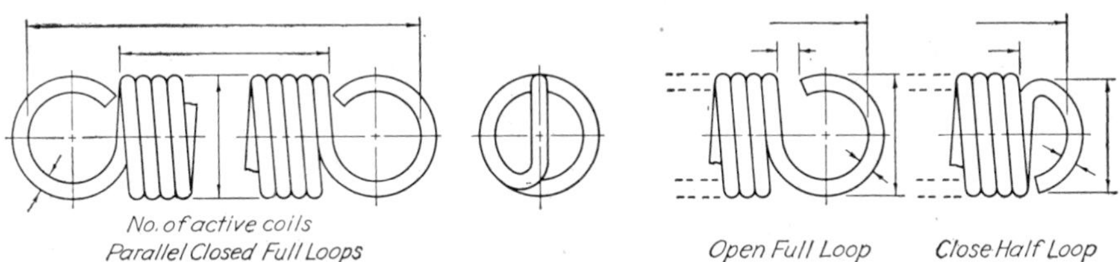

FIG. 13·62—Representation and dimensioning of tension springs.

13·47 Springs. Springs may be classified by the form of the material from which they are made, as *wire springs* and *flat springs*. Wire springs are either helical or spiral and are wound from round, square, or special section wire. Flat springs (such as stampings, snap rings, and spring washers) are made from either flat or strip material.

Figure 13·60 shows the method of drawing the true projection of a helical spring with round section, by constructing the helix of the center line of the section, drawing on it a number of circles of the diameter of the wire, and drawing an envelope curve tangent to the circles. This is known geometrically as a "serpentine." On working drawings, springs are drawn with straight lines and, when in small size, with single-line representation. Figure 13·61 shows how compression springs are drawn, how the ends may be prepared, and gives the method of specification. Helical springs should have their line of action coincide with the axis; hence com-

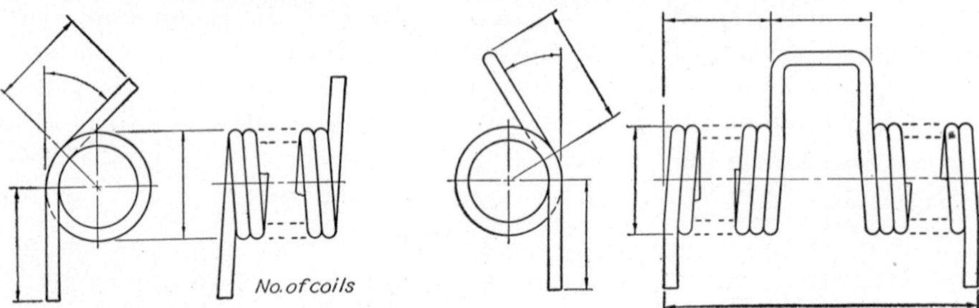

FIG. 13·63—Representation and dimensioning of torsion springs.

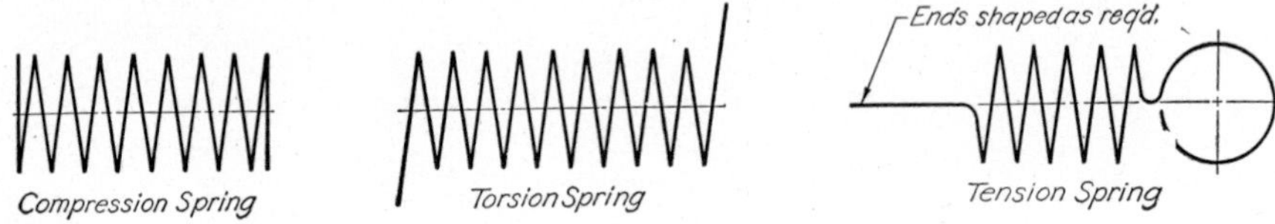

FIG. 13·64—Single-line representation of springs.

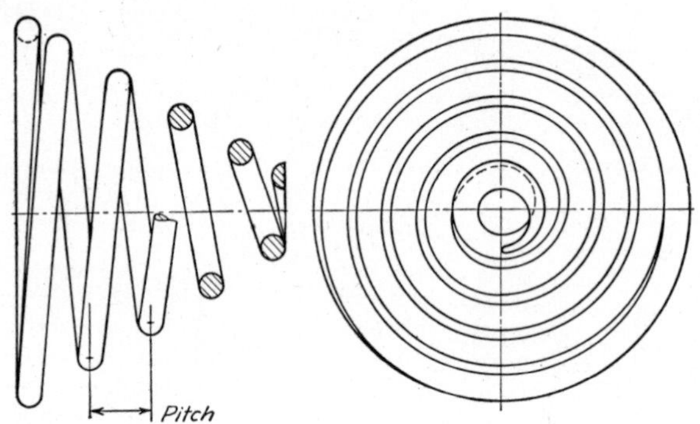

FIG. 13·65—Conical spring.

pression springs have ends "squared," "plain end ground" or "squared and ground." By squared is meant that the last coil has its lead gradually reduced to zero, thus touching the previous coil at the end of the last turn; then the end is ground flat, giving approximately 50 to 80 per cent bearing area, upon which the spring can stand unsupported with its axis vertical. Figures 13·62 and 13·63 show tension and torsion springs and indicate the information needed for dimensioning and specifying. Figure 13·64 shows single-line representation of compression, tension, and torsion springs. Figure 13·65 shows a conical spring. The top view is often omitted but may be drawn, if desired, as a four-center or two-center involute.

PROBLEMS

Group I. Helices

1. Draw three complete turns of a helix, diameter 3″, pitch 1¼″.

2. Draw three complete turns of a conical helix, top and front views, with 1½″ pitch, whose large diameter is 4″ and small diameter 1½″.

Group II. Screw threads

3. Fig. 13·66. Minimum working space 10½″ × 15″. Complete the views of the objects and show screw threads, tapped holes and other details as follows: *Upper left*, on center line *A-A* show in section a ¾″-10 NC-2 tapped hole, 1½″ deep, with tap-drill hole 2½″ deep. At *B* show a 1¾″-8 N8-2 external thread in section. At *C* show a

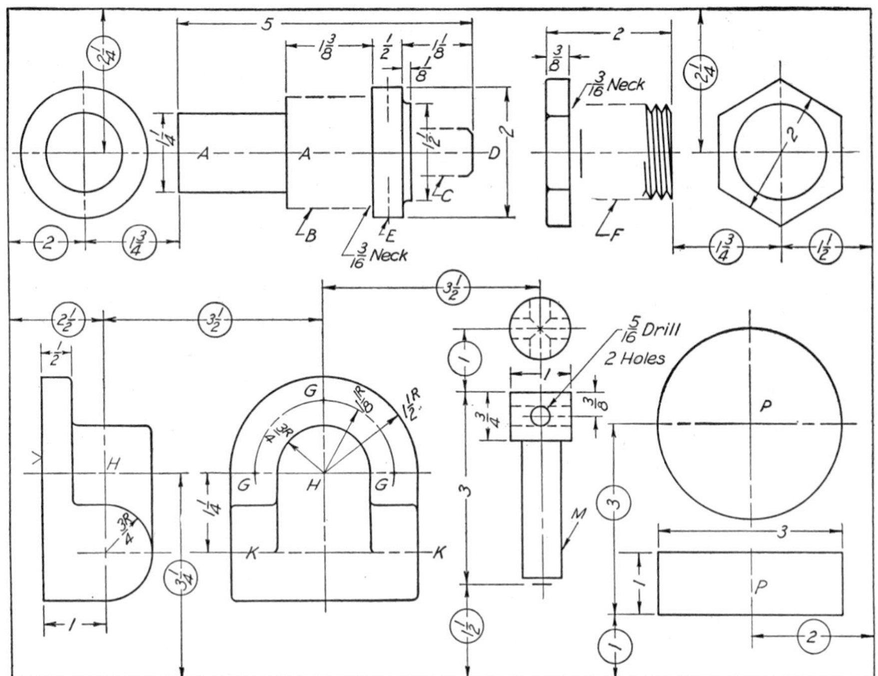

Fig. 13·66—Screw threads.

¾″-10 NC-2 external thread in section. From *D* on center line *A-A* show a ¼″ drilled hole extending to the tap-drill hole. At *E* show six ¼″ drilled holes ¼″ deep equally spaced for spanner wrench. *Upper right*, at *F* show a 1½″-6 NC-2 external thread. *Lower left*, at *G* show (three) ⅜″-16 NC-2 through tapped holes. At *H* show a ⅞″-9 NC-2 tapped hole 1⅛″ deep with the tap-drill hole going through the piece. On center line *K-K* show a ⅞″-14 NF-3 through tapped hole. *Lower center*, at *M* show a ⅝″-18

NF-3 external thread 1¾″ long. *Lower right,* on center line *P* show a 2″-4½ NC-2 tapped hole in section. Completely specify all threads and tapped holes.

4. Fig. 13·67. Complete the views of the offset support by showing tapped holes as follows: At *A* tap 1⅜″-6 NC-2. At *B*, tap ½″-13 NC-2. At *C*, tap ⅝″-18 NF-3. *A* and *C* are through holes. *B* is a blind hole to receive a stud. Material is cast iron. Specify the tapped holes and dimension the object.

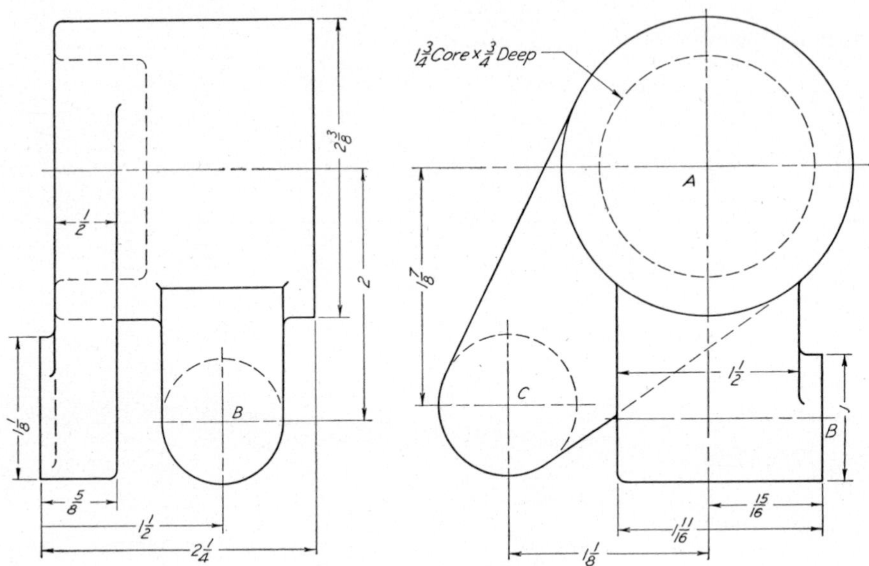

FIG. 13·67—Offset support.

5. Draw two views of a square-thread screw and a section of the nut, separated; diameter 2½″, pitch ¾″, length of screw 3″. Nut American Standard semifinished hex (except threads).

6. Same as Prob. 5 but for V thread with ½″ pitch.

7. Draw in section the following forms of screw threads, 1″ pitch: American Standard; Acme; Whitworth: square.

8. Draw screws 2″ diameter and 3½″ long: single square thread, pitch ½″; single V thread, pitch ¼″; double V thread, pitch ½″; left-hand double square thread, pitch ½″.

9. Draw the complete views of the valve ring, Fig. 13·68, showing one view as a section *A-A*. Material, cast steel.

10. Complete the views of the cast-steel rocker, Fig. 13·69, showing screw threads and tapped holes as follows: on center line *A-A*, tap, 2″-8 N8-2; on center line *B-B*, for cap screw, ½″-13 NC-2; on center line *C-C*, 2¾″-12 N12-2; on center line *D-D*, ⅞″-14 NF-3.

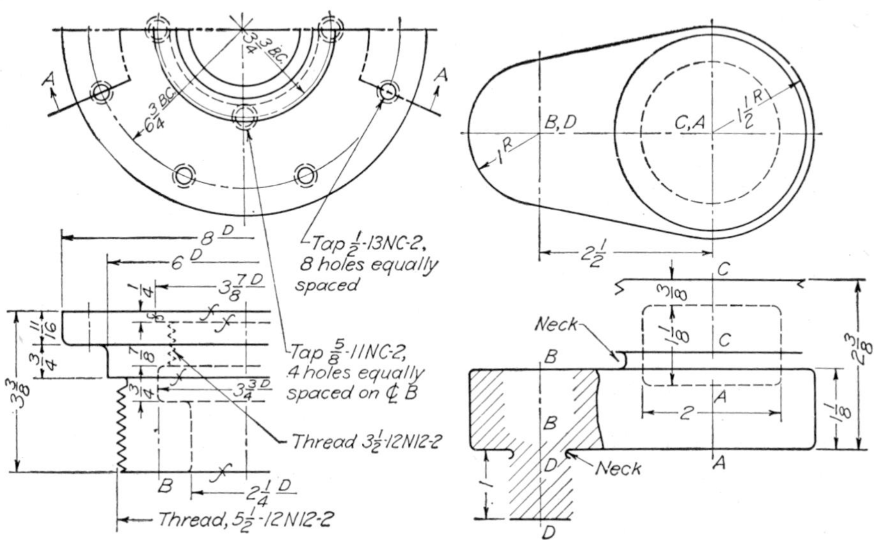

Fig. 13·68—Valve ring.

Fig. 13·69—Rocker.

Group III. Fastenings

11. Draw one view of an American Standard, regular, semifinished, hex-head bolt and nut across corners. Diameter 1″, length 5″. See table in Appendix for length of thread.

12. Same as Prob. 11 for an unfinished bolt and nut.

13. Same as Prob. 11 for a square-headed unfinished bolt and nut, heavy series.

14. Draw four ½″ × 1½″ cap screws, each with a different kind of head. Name and specify each.

15. Fig. 13·70. Fasten the pieces together on center line *E-E* with a ¾″ American Standard hex-head cap screw and lock washer. On center line *A-A* show a ⅝″ × 1¼″ stripper bolt.

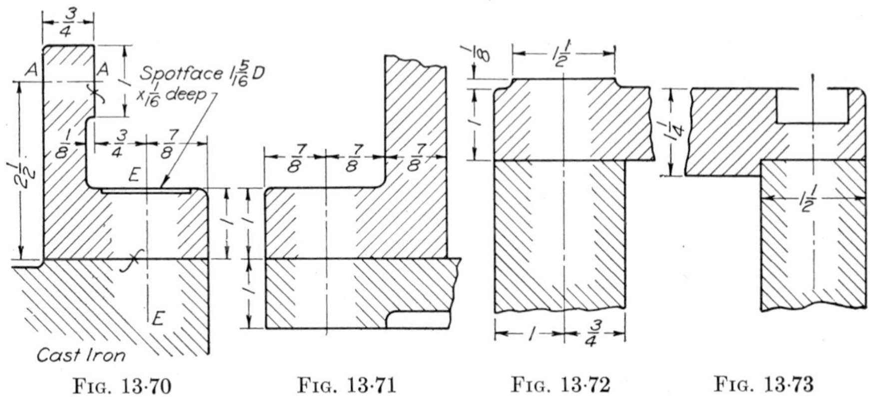

Fig. 13·70 Fig. 13·71 Fig. 13·72 Fig. 13·73

16. Fig. 13·71. Fasten pieces together with a ¾″ heavy, semifinished, hex-head bolt and nut.

17. Fig. 13·72. Fasten pieces together with a ¾″ stud and regular semifinished hex nut.

18. Fig. 13·73. Fasten pieces together with a $\frac{3}{4}''$ fillister-head cap screw.

19. Fig. 13·70. Fasten pieces together with a $\frac{3}{4}''$ stud and regular semifinished hex nut and $\frac{3}{4}''$ regular semifinished jam nut. On center line *A*-*A* show a $\frac{3}{4}'' \times 1''$ stripper bolt.

20. Fig. 13·71. Fasten pieces together with a 1″ American Standard hex-head cap screw.

21. Fig. 13·72. Fasten pieces together with a $\frac{3}{4}''$ socket-head cap screw.

22. Fig. 13·73. Fasten pieces together with a $\frac{7}{8}''$ socket-head cap screw.

23. Draw one view of an American Standard square-neck carriage bolt. Diameter 1″, length 5″, with American Standard regular unfinished square nut. See Appendix for proportions.

24. Draw one view of an American Standard rib-neck carriage bolt. Diameter $\frac{3}{4}''$, length 4″, with American Standard regular unfinished square nut. See Appendix for proportions.

25. Draw two views of a stripper bolt. Diameter $\frac{3}{4}''$, shoulder length 5″. See Appendix for proportions of stripper bolts, or shoulder screws.

26. Draw two views of an American Standard socket-head cap screw; diameter $1\frac{1}{4}''$, length 6″.

27. Fig. 13·74. Draw the stuffing box and gland, showing the required fastenings. Dimension fastenings only. On CL's *A* show $\frac{1}{2}''$ hex-head cap screws (six required). On CL's *B* show $\frac{1}{2}''$ studs and standard hex nuts. Supply missing dimensions.

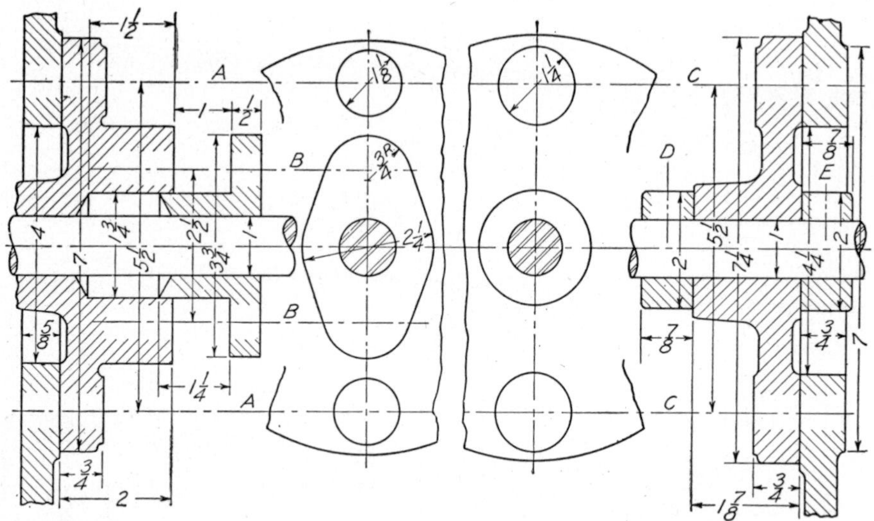

FIG. 13·74—Stuffing box and gland.

FIG. 13·75—Bearing plate.

28. Fig. 13·75. Draw the bearing plate, showing the required fastenings. On CL's *C* show $\frac{1}{2}''$ hex bolts and nuts (four required). On CL *D* show $\frac{1}{2}''$ safety setscrew. On CL *E* show $\frac{1}{2}''$ American Standard square-headed setscrew. Setscrews to have cone points. Supply missing dimensions.

Problems 27 and 28 may be drawn together on an $11'' \times 17''$ sheet, or on separate sheets, showing full diameter of flanges.

29. Fig. 13·76. Draw the ball-bearing head, showing the required fastenings. On CL's *A* show $\frac{1}{2}'' \times 1\frac{3}{4}''$ finished hex-head bolts and nuts (six required), with heads to left and shown across flats. Note that this design prevents the heads from turning. On CL's *B* show $\frac{5}{16}'' \times \frac{3}{4}''$ fillister-head cap screws (four required). On CL *C* show a

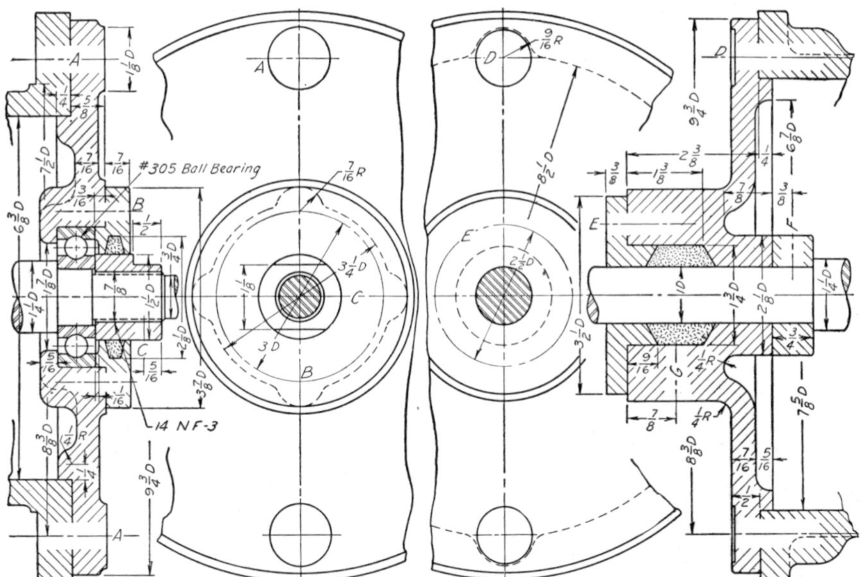

FIG. 13·76—Ball-bearing head. FIG. 13·77—Plain-bearing head.

$\frac{3}{8}'' \times \frac{1}{2}''$ cone-pointed, safety setscrew. Spot shaft with nut in position. Supply missing dimensions.

30. Fig. 13·77. Draw the plain-bearing head, showing the required fastenings. On CL's *D* show $\frac{1}{2}'' \times 2''$ studs and nuts (six required). Spot face $1''$ $D \times \frac{1}{16}''$ deep. On CL's *E* show $\frac{3}{8}'' \times 1''$ hex-head cap screws (four required). On CL *F* show a $\frac{7}{16}'' \times \frac{7}{8}''$ American Standard cone-pointed setscrew. On CL *G* show a $\frac{29}{64}''$ drilled hole plugged with a $\frac{1}{4}''$ pipe plug. This is for gun-packing the gland. Supply missing dimensions.

Problems 29 and 30 may be drawn together on an $11'' \times 17''$ sheet, or on separate sheets, showing full diameter of flanges.

Group IV. Keys and rivets (key sizes will be found in Appendix)

31. Fig. 13·78. Draw hub and shaft as shown, with a Woodruff key in position.

32. Fig. 13·79. Draw hub and shaft as shown, with a square key $2''$ long in position.

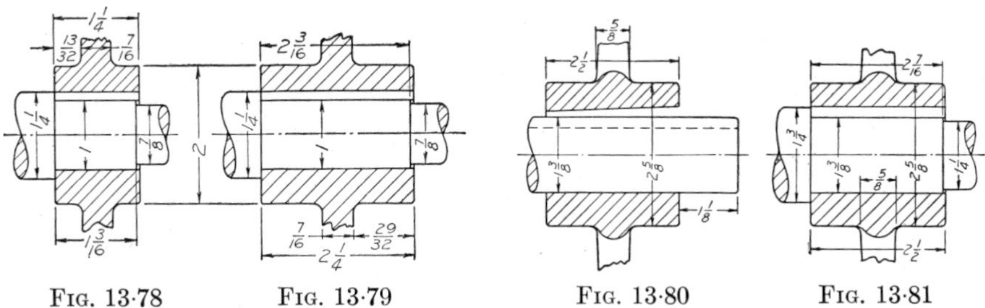

FIG. 13·78 FIG. 13·79 FIG. 13·80 FIG. 13·81

33. Fig. 13·80. Draw hub and shaft as shown, with a gib-head key in position.

34. Fig. 13·81. Draw hub and shaft as shown, with a Pratt and Whitney key in position.

35. Fig. 13·82. Draw top view and section of single-riveted butt joint 10⅝″ long. Pitch of rivets 1¾″.

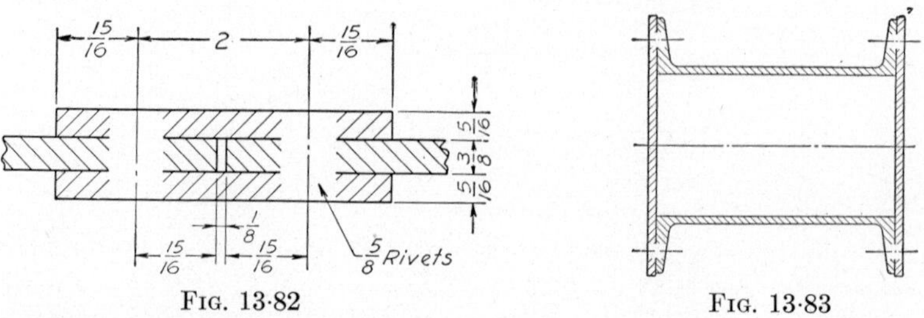

FIG. 13·82

FIG. 13·83

36. Fig. 13·83. Draw a column section made of 15″ × 33.9-lb. channels with cover plates as shown, using ⅞″ rivets (dimensions from the handbook of the American Institute of Steel Construction).

Group V. Springs

37. Draw four complete turns, two in section and two in full view, of a helical spring made of ⅜″ square stock. Outside diameter 3½″, pitch 1½″.

38. Draw a helical spring 4″ long made of ½″ round stock. Outside diameter 3″, pitch 1″.

39. Draw and dimension the helical spring (plain ends ground), piece No. 11 of the Corliss-engine dashpot, Fig. 15·78.

40. Draw and dimension the conical spring of the pump valve, Fig. 15·81. If desired, draw top view as a four-center involute.

41. Draw and dimension a tension spring made from ¼″ round stock. Outside diameter 2″, active coils 15, one closed full loop and one open full loop.

Chapter 14

PIPING DRAWINGS

14·1 A familiarity with pipe and pipe fittings is necessary not only for making piping drawings but because pipe is often used as a material of construction. Standard pipe of steel or wrought iron up to 12″ in diameter is designated by its nominal inside diameter, which differs somewhat from the actual inside diameter. Early pipe manufacturers made the walls in the smaller sizes much too thick and in correcting this error in design took the excess from the inside to avoid changing the sizes of fittings. Three weights of pipe—standard, extra strong, and double extra strong—are in common use. In the same nominal size all three have the same outside diameter, that of standard weight pipe, the added thickness for the extra and double extra strong being on the inside. Thus the outside diameter of 1″ pipe in all three weights is 1.315″, the inside diameter of standard 1″ pipe is 1.05″, of 1″ extra strong 0.951″, and of XX, 0.587″.

Many other weights of pipe are in more or less general use and are known by trade names, such as hydraulic pipe, merchant casing, API (American Petroleum Institute) pipe, etc. The American Standards Association in Bulletin ASA, B36.10-1939 gives a means of specifying wall thicknesses by a series of schedule numbers which indicate approximate values for the expression $1{,}000 \times (P/S)$, where P is pressure and S the allowable stress. Recommended values for S may be obtained from the ASME Boiler Code, the American Standard Code for Pressure Piping (ASA, B31.1), etc. The designer computes the exact value of wall thickness as required for a given condition and selects from the schedule numbers the one nearest to the computed values. In the ASA system pipe is designated by giving nominal pipe size and wall thickness, or nominal pipe size and weight per foot.

All pipe over 12″ in diameter is designated as OD (outside diameter) pipe and is specified by its outside diameter and thickness of metal. Boiler tubes in all sizes are known by their outside diameters.

Seamless flexible metal tubing is used for conveying steam, gases, and liquids in all types of equipment such as locomotives, diesel engines, hydraulic presses, etc., where vibration is present, where outlets are not in alignment, and where there are moving parts.

Lead pipe and lead-lined pipe are used in chemical work. Cast-iron pipe is used for water and gas in underground mains and for drains in buildings.

Copper tubing is available in nominal diameters of ⅛″ to 12″ and in four weights known in the trade as types K, L, M, and O. Type K is extra-heavy hard, type L is heavy hard, type M is standard hard, and type O is light hard. American Standards specifications designate different weights as *class K, L,* and *M* instead of *type K, L,* and *M*.

Brass and copper pipe have the same nominal diameters as iron pipe but have thinner wall sections. There are two standard weights: regular and extra strong. Commerical lengths are 12 ft., with longer lengths made to order.

14·2 Pipe threads. Pipe is usually threaded on the ends for the purpose of screwing into fittings and making connections. The ASA, in its tentative revision of May, 1940, provides two types of pipe thread: tapered and straight. The normal type employs a taper internal and taper external thread. This thread (originated in 1882 as the Briggs Standard) is illustrated in Fig. 14·1. The threads are cut on a taper of $\frac{1}{16}''$ per inch, measured on the diameter, thus fixing the distance a pipe enters a fitting and ensuring a tight joint. Taper threads are recommended by the ASA for all

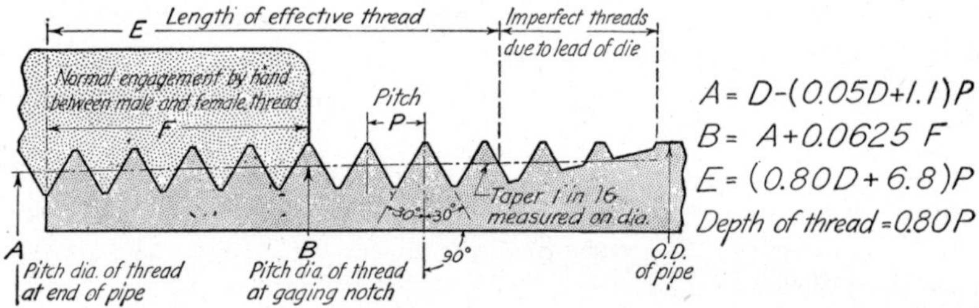

FIG. 14·1—American Standard taper pipe thread.

uses with the exception of the following five types of joints: type 1, pressure-tight joints for pipe couplings; type 2, pressure-tight joints for grease-cup, fuel, and oil fittings; type 3, free-fitting mechanical joints for fixtures; type 4, loose-fitting mechanical joints with lock nuts; type 5, loose-fitting mechanical joints for hose coupling. For these joints straight pipe threads may be used. The number of threads per inch is the same in taper and straight pipe threads. Actual diameters vary for the different types of joints. When needed they may be obtained from the ASA bulletins. A common practice is to use a taper external thread with a straight internal thread, on the assumption that the materials are sufficiently ductile to allow the threads to adjust themselves to the taper thread. All pipe threads are assumed to be tapered unless otherwise specified.

There is a great quantity of material now used which is generally classified as "oil country tubular goods." This material is so diversified that manufacturers' catalogues or API bulletins should be consulted for methods of specifying pipe, valves, fittings, and casing threads. All API threads, with the exception of drill-pipe threads, are identical in form with the American Standard pipe thread. The difference between the two systems is in the length of thread engagement, with the API having added length at the small end. API drill-pipe threads have a rounded crest and root similar to the Whitworth thread.

Pipe threads are represented by the same conventional symbols as bolt threads. The taper is so slight that it does not show unless exaggerated. It need not be indicated unless it is desired to call attention to it, as in Fig. 14·2. In plan view, as at *C*, the dotted circle should be the actual outside diameter of the pipe specified. The length of effective thread is $E = (0.80D + 6.8)P$, Fig. 14·1.

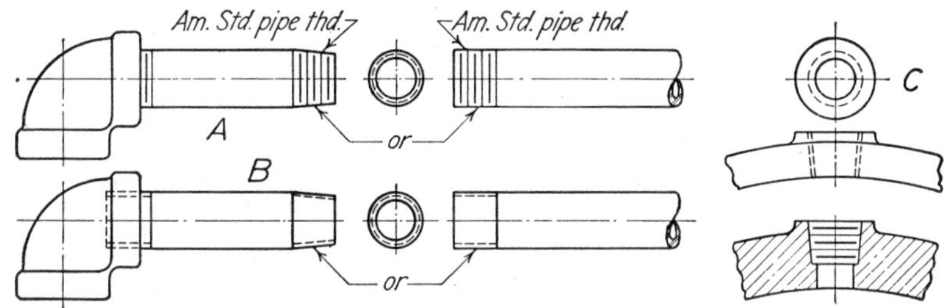

Fig. 14·2—Conventional pipe threads.

14·3 Pipe fittings. Pipe fittings are the parts used in connecting and "making up" pipe. They are usually cast iron or malleable iron, except couplings, which are wrought or malleable iron. Brass and other alloys are employed for special uses. Pipe fittings are *screwed fittings*, Fig. 14·3; *butt-welding fittings*, Fig. 14·4; and *soldered-joint fittings*, Fig. 14·5. Tube couplings, Fig. 14·6, are usually patented arrangements, in general requiring the flaring of the ends of the tubing. Manufacturers' catalogues should be consulted for details and methods of specifying.

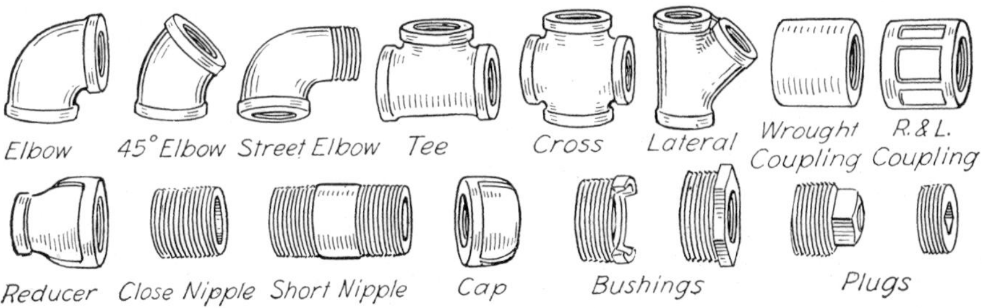

Fig. 14·3—Screwed fittings.

Straight sections of pipe are made in 12- to 20-ft. lengths and are connected by *couplings*. These are short cylinders, threaded on the inside. A right-hand coupling has right-hand threads at both ends. To close a system of piping, although a union is preferable, a *right-and-left coupling* is sometimes used. It is readily distinguished by the ribs on the outside, which are four in number on sizes up to 1 inch and six on sizes larger than one inch. Pipes are also connected by screwing them into cast-iron flanges and bolting the flanges together. Unless the pressures are very low, flanged fittings are recommended for all systems requiring pipe over 4 inches in diameter.

Nipples are short pieces of pipe threaded on both ends. If the threaded portions meet, the fitting is a *close nipple;* if there is a short unthreaded por-

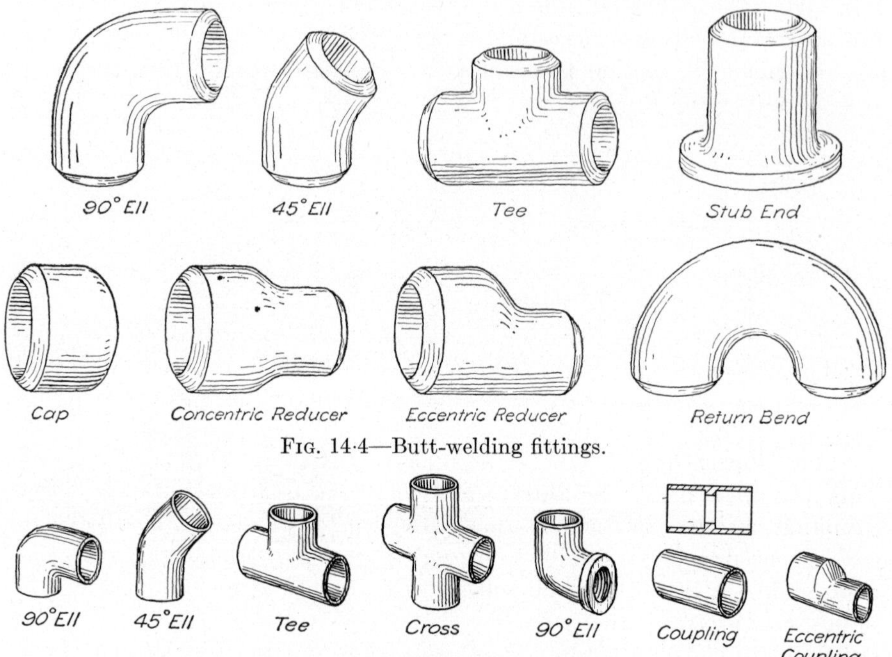

FIG. 14·4—Butt-welding fittings.

FIG 14·5—Soldered-joint fittings.

tion, it is a *short nipple.* Long and extra-long nipples range in length up to 12 inches.

A *cap* is used to close the end of a pipe. A *plug* is used to close an opening in a fitting. A *bushing* is used to reduce the size of an opening.

Formerly each manufacturer had his own sizes of elbows, tees, and other fittings, but now, to the great advantage of all pipe users, the ASA has standardized both screwed and flanged fittings.

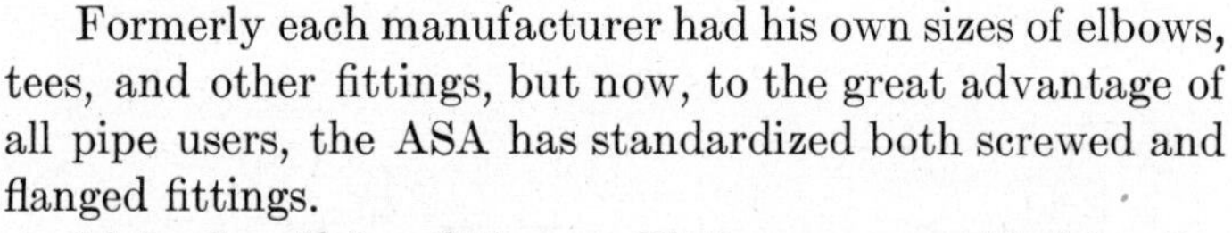

FIG. 14·6—A tube fitting.

14·4 Specifying fittings. Fittings are specified by the name, nominal pipe size, and the material. When they connect more than one size of pipe the size of the largest run opening is given first, followed by the size at the opposite end of the run. The diagrams of Fig. 14·7 show the order of specifying reducing fittings. The word "male" must follow the size of the opening if an external thread is wanted.

14·5 Unions are used to close systems and to connect pipes that are to be taken down occasionally. A screwed union, Fig. 14·8, is composed of three pieces, two of which, *A* and *B*, are screwed firmly on the ends of the pipes to be connected. The third piece *C* draws them together, the gasket *D* forming a tight joint. Unions are also made with ground joints or with special metallic joints instead of gaskets. Other forms of

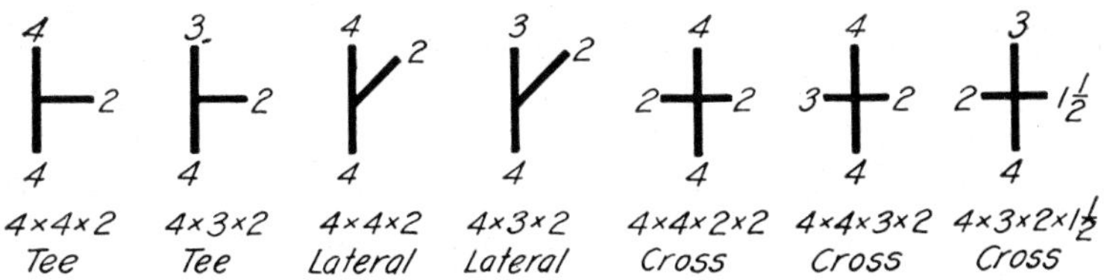

FIG. 14·7—Order of specifying openings of reducing fittings.

screwed unions and union fittings are shown in Fig. 14·9. Flange unions in a variety of forms are used for large sizes of pipe.

14·6 Valves. Figure 14·10 shows a few types of valves used in piping. *A* is a gate valve, used for water and other liquids, as it allows a straight flow. *B* is a plug valve, opened and closed with a quarter turn; *C* a ball check valve, and *E* a swing check valve permitting flow in one direction. For heavy liquids the ball check valve is preferred. *D* is a globe valve, used for throttling steam or other fluids; *F* is a butterfly valve, opened and closed with a quarter turn, but not steamtight, and used only as a check or damper.

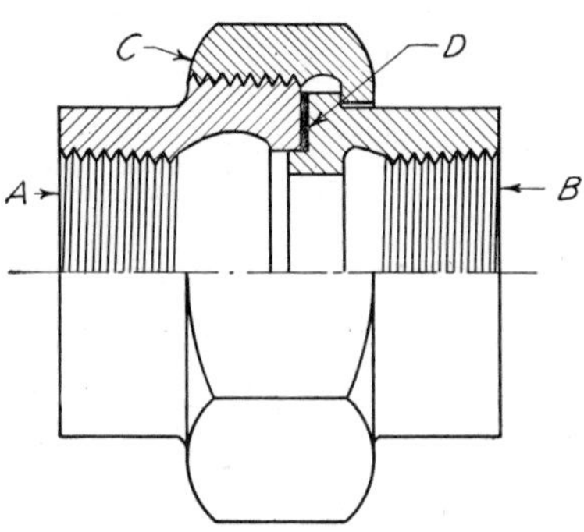

FIG. 14·8—Screwed union.

14·7 Piping drawings. When drawn to large scale, piping is represented as in Fig. 14·11. On small-scale drawings or in sketches the fittings are shown by conventional symbols and the runs of pipe by a single line, regardless of the pipe diameters, Fig.

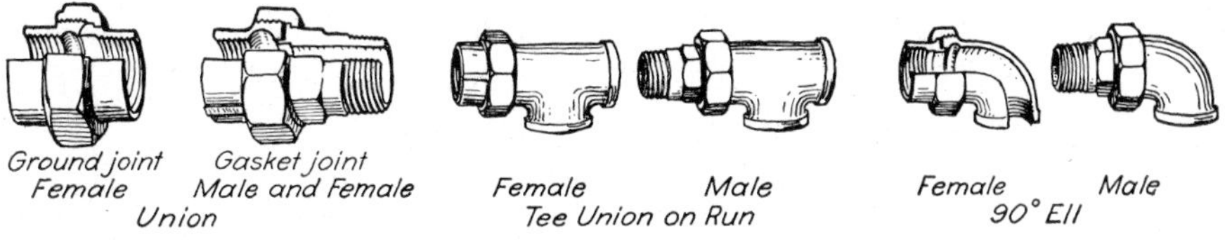

FIG. 14·9—Screwed unions and union fittings.

14·12. The single line should be made heavier than the other lines of the drawing.

The arrangement of views is generally in orthographic projection, Fig. 14·13*A*. Sometimes, however, it is clearer to swing all the piping into one plane and make only one "developed view" as at *B*. Isometric and oblique

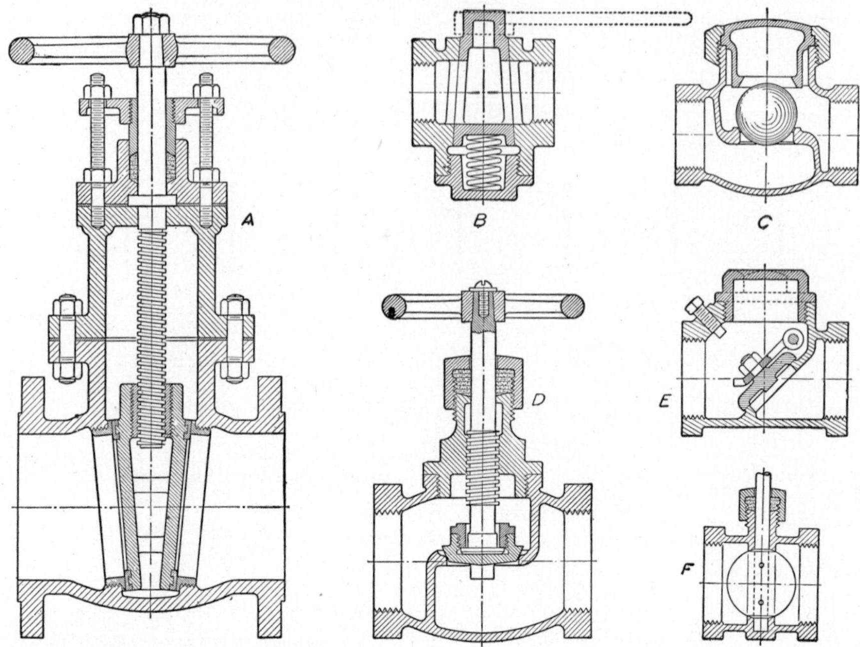

FIG. 14·10—Sections of valves.

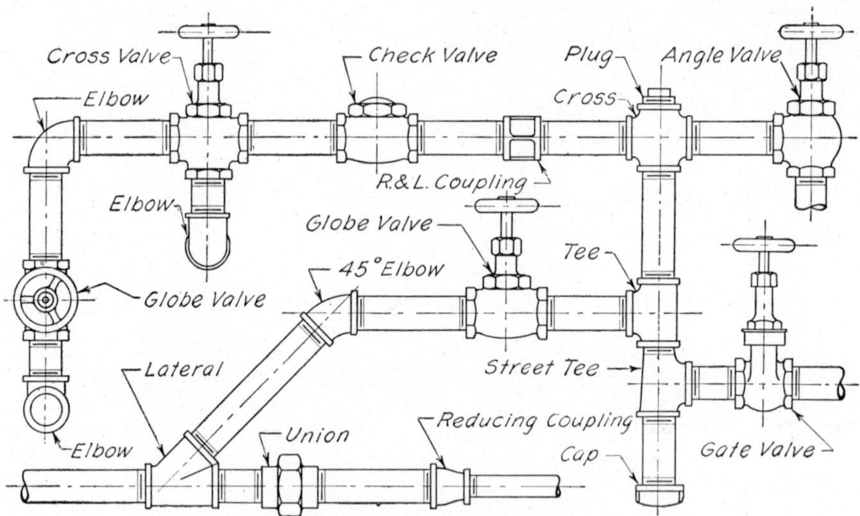

FIG. 14·11—Piping drawing, to scale.

diagrams, used either alone or in conjunction with orthographic or developed make-up drawings, are very often employed in representing piping, as at C.

14·8 Dimensions. The dimensions on a piping drawing are principally *location* dimensions, all of which are made to center lines, both in single-line diagrams and in double-line representation. Valves and fittings are located by measurements to their centers, and the allowances for make-up left to the pipe fitter. In designing a piping layout, care should be taken to locate valves so that they are easily accessible and have ample clearance at the

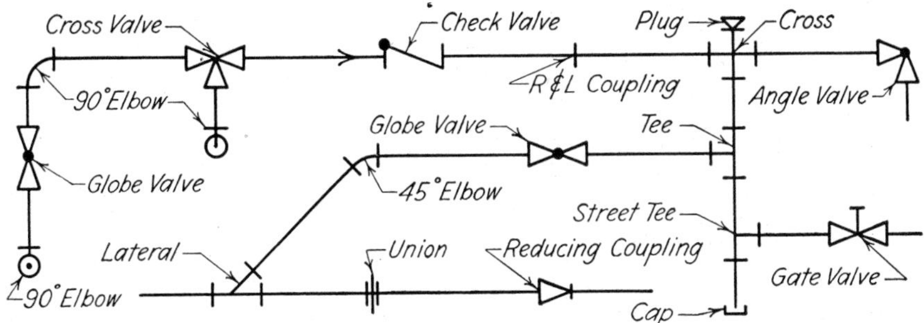

FIG. 14·12—Piping drawing, diagrammatic.

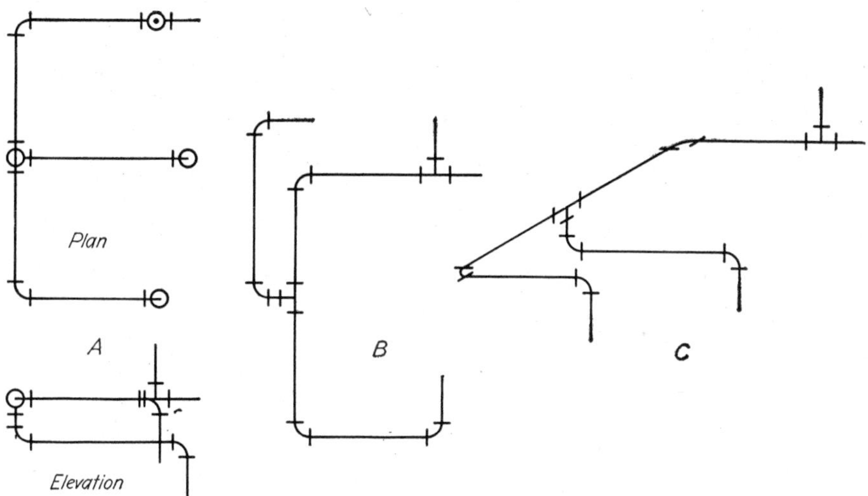

FIG. 14·13—Piping in orthographic, developed, and pictorial views.

handwheels. The *sizes* of pipe should be specified by notes telling the nominal diameters, never by dimension lines on the drawing of the pipes. Very complete notes are an important essential of all piping drawings and sketches.

Dimensions for standard pipe and for various fittings are given in the Appendix.

PROBLEMS

1. Pipe fittings. Make a complete developed layout of piping (full size), with necessary dimensions and specifications, showing the following: angle valve, globe valve, cross, 90° ell, 45° ell, Y, street tee, tee, screwed union, cap, and plug. Place angle valve in one of the upper corners of the sheet. Add extra pipe and nipples, but no extra fittings, to close the system. Use 1½″ pipe and fittings throughout.

2. Pipe fittings. In the upper left-hand corner of sheet draw a 2″ tee, (full size). Plug one outlet. In the second, place a 2″ × 1½″ bushing; in remaining outlet use a 2″

close nipple and on it screw a 2″ × 1½″ reducing coupling. Lay out remainder of sheet so as to include the following 1½″ fittings: coupling, globe valve, R&L coupling, angle valve, 45° ell, 90° ell, 45° Y, cross, cap, three-part union, flange union. Add extra pipe, nipples, and fittings so the system will close at the reducing fitting first drawn.

3. Make a one-view drawing of a 1½″ globe valve. 8½″ × 11″ sheet. See Appendix for proportions.

4. Same as Prob. 3 for a 1½″ angle globe valve.

5. Same as Prob. 3 for a 1¼″ gate valve.

6. Fig. 14·14. Draw the separator and fittings as specified, arranging them in the order given:

At *A*. Tap 6″ pipe cap for ¼″ × 2″ nipple; ¼″ ell opening to the left; ¼″ × 10″ pipe; ¼″ ell opening downward; ¼″ × 24″ pipe; ¼″ cock; ¼″ pipe, length to suit.

At *B* and *D*. ¾″ flange, welded; ¾″ × 2″ nipple; ¾″ union; ¾″ pipe, length to suit.

At *C*. Tap for ½″ × 2″ nipple; ½″ × 125# brass globe valve; ½″ pipe, length to suit. 11″ × 17″ sheet; scale 3″ = 1′-0″.

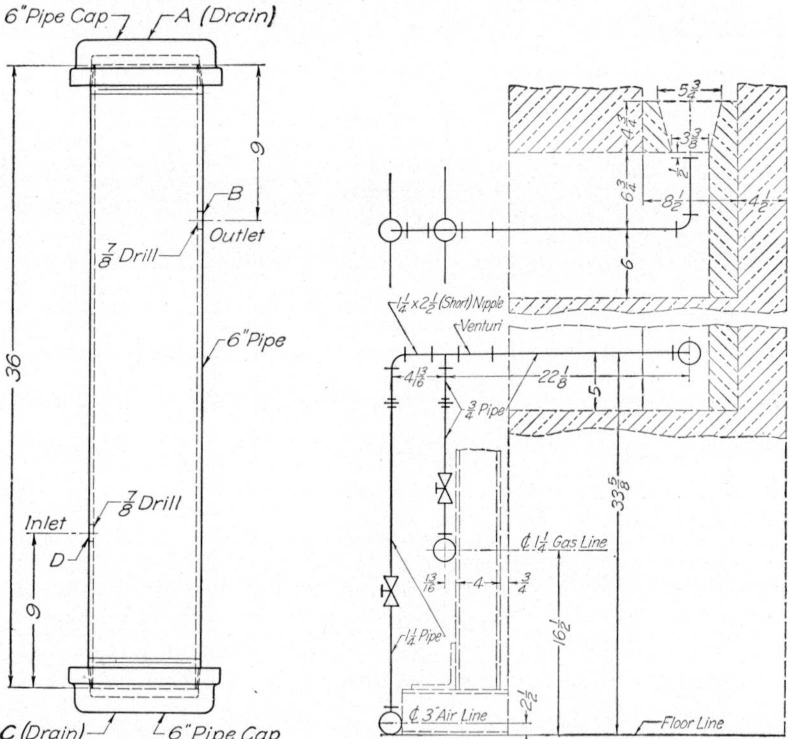

FIG. 14·14—Separator.

FIG. 14·15—Gas-burner installation.

7. Fig. 14·15. Make a detail (double-line) piping drawing of the gas-burner installation. Specify fittings and give CL dimensions. Use 11″ × 17″ sheet; scale 3″ = 1′-0″.

8. Fig. 14·16. Make a detail (double-line) piping drawing, to suitable scale, of the fuel-oil-burner installation. All pipe and fittings are ¼″. Name and specify all fittings. Pipe lengths to suit.

9. Fig. 14·17. Make a detail (double-line) piping drawing of Grinnell Industrial Heating Unit, Type 90-L, closed return, gravity system. Use CL distances and placement of fittings as shown in diagram. 3″ supply main; 2″ pipe and fittings to unit; ¾″ pipe and fittings from unit to return main; 2″ return main. Add all necessary notes and dimensions. 11″ × 17″ sheet; scale 3″ = 1′-0″.

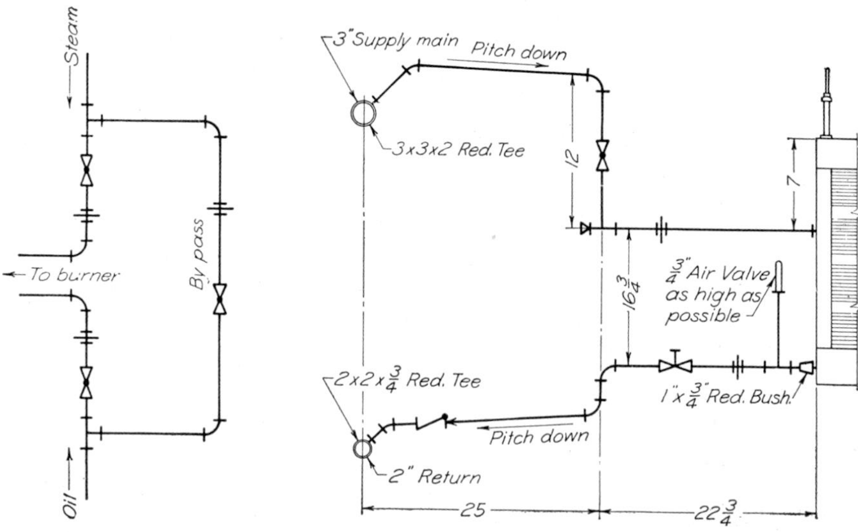

FIG. 14·16—Fuel-oil-burner installation.

FIG. 14·17—Grinnell Industrial Heating Unit.

10. Fig. 14·18. A is a storage tank for supplying the mixing tanks B, C, and D and is located directly above them. The capacities of the mixers are in the ratios of 1, 2, and 3. Design (in one view) a piping system with sizes such that, neglecting frictional losses, the three tanks will fill in approximately the same time. So arrange the piping that any one of the tanks can be cut out or removed for repairs without disturbing the others. Use single-line conventional representation. Dimension to center lines and specify the names and sizes of fittings.

11. Same as Prob. 10 except in the arrangement of the tanks. In plan the tanks B, C, and D are placed at the points of an equilateral triangle whose sides are 12 feet long. The center of tank A is in line with the centers of B and C, and 20 feet from the center of B, the nearer one. Draw plan and developed elevation of the piping system, with single-line representation. Dimension to center lines and specify fittings.

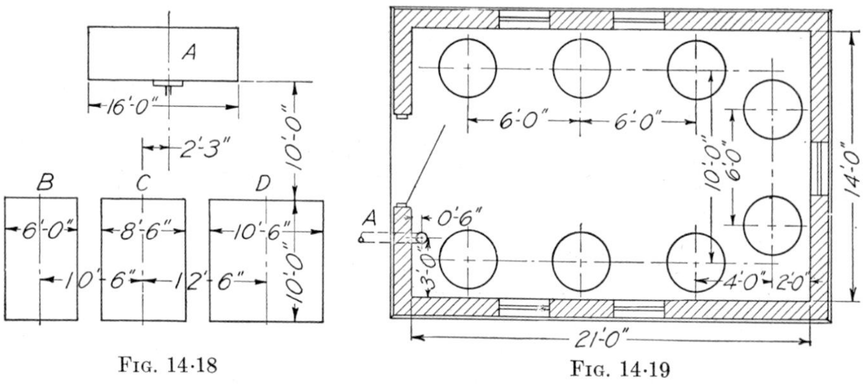

FIG. 14·18

FIG. 14·19

12. Figure 14·19 shows the arrangement of a set of mixing tanks. Make an isometric drawing of an overhead piping system to supply water to each tank. Water supply enters the building through a 2½″ main at point A, 3 feet below floor level. Place all pipe 10 feet above floor level, except riser from water main and drops to tanks, which are to end with globe valves 5 feet above floor level. Arrange the system to use as little pipe and as few fittings as possible. Neglecting frictional losses, sizes of pipe used should be such that they will deliver approximately an equal volume of water to each tank if all were being filled at the same time. The pipe size at the tank should not be less than ¾″. Dimension and specify all pipe and fittings.

13. Make a drawing of the system of Prob. 12. Show the layout in a developed view, using double-line conventional treatment. Dimension from center to center and specify all pipe and fittings.

14. Make a list of the pipe and fittings to be ordered for the system of Prob. 12. Arrange the list in a table, heading the columns as below:

Size	Pipe lengths	Valves		Fittings		Material	Remarks (make, kind of threads, etc.)
		Number	Kind	Number	Kind		

15. Make an oblique drawing of a system of piping to supply the tanks in Fig. 14·19. All piping except risers shall be in a trench 1 foot below floor level. Risers should not run higher than 6 feet above floor level. Other conditions as in Prob. 12.

16. Make a drawing of the system of Prob. 12. Show the layout in a developed view, using single-line conventional treatment. Dimension from center to center and specify all pipe and fittings.

17. Figure 14·20 shows the outline of the right-hand half of a bank of eight heat-treating furnaces. *X* and *Y* are the lead-ins from the compressed-air and fuel mains. Draw the piping layout, using single-line representation, to distribute the air and fuel to the furnaces. The pipe sizes should be reduced proportionately as the oven leads are taken off. Each tail pipe should be removable without disturbing the other leads or closing down the other furnaces. Dimension the piping layout and make a bill of material for the pipe and fittings.

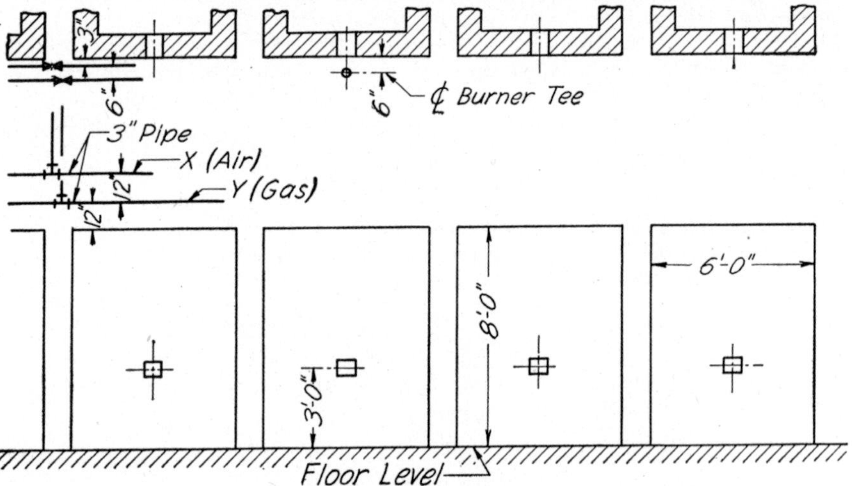

FIG. 14·20—Heat-treating furnace.

18. From memory, make a sketch of three kinds of valves.

19. From memory, make a sketch of eight different pipe fittings.

Chapter 15

WORKING DRAWINGS

15·1 Definition. A working drawing is any drawing used to give information for purposes of manufacture, construction, or erection of a machine or structure. Complete knowledge for the production of a machine or structure is given by a *set* of working drawings conveying all the facts fully and explicitly, so that further instruction is not required.

The description given by the set of drawings will thus include:

1. The full graphical representation of the shape of each part (shape description).
2. The figured dimensions of all parts (size description).
3. Explanatory notes, general and specific, on the individual drawings, giving the specifications of material, heat-treatment, finish, etc. Often, particularly in architectural and structural work, the notes of explanation and information concerning details of materials and workmanship are too extensive to be included on the drawings and so are made up separately in typed or printed form and called the *specifications;* thus the term "drawings and specifications."
4. A descriptive title on each drawing.
5. A description of the relationship of each part to the others (assembly).
6. A parts list or bill of material.

A set of drawings will include, in general, two classes: (1) *detail drawings* giving the information included in items 1 to 4, inclusive, and (2) an *assembly drawing,* item 5, giving the location and relationship of the parts.

15·2 Engineering procedure. In designing a new machine or structure, the first drawings are usually in the form of freehand sketches on which the original ideas, scheming, and inventing are worked out. These are either accompanied or followed by calculations to prove the suitability of the design. Working from the sketches and calculations, the design department produces a *design assembly* (also called a "design layout" or "design drawing"), Fig. 15·1. This is a preliminary pencil drawing on which more details of the design are worked out. It is accurately made with instruments, full size if possible, and shows the shape and position of the various parts, but little attempt is made to show all of the intricate detail. Only the essential dimensions, such as basic calculated sizes, are given. On the drawing, or separately as a set of written notes, will be the designer's general specifications for materials, heat-treatments, finishes, clearances or interferences, etc., and any other information needed by the draftsman in making up the individual drawings of the separate parts.

Working from the design drawing and notes, a draftsman (detailer) then makes up the individual detail drawings, illustrated by the detail drawing of Fig. 15·2, taken from the design drawing of Fig. 15·1. On the detail

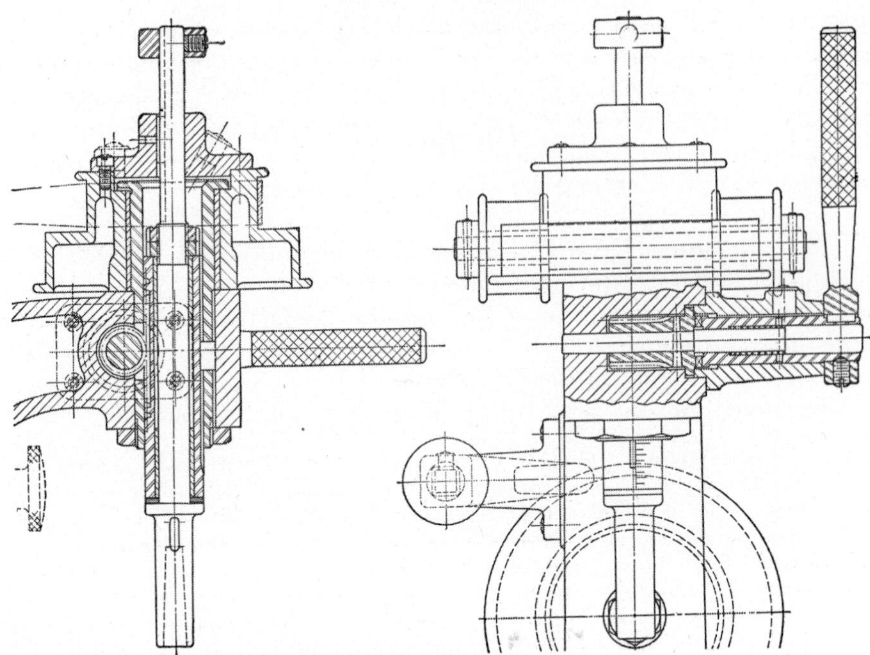

FIG. 15·1—A portion of a design drawing.

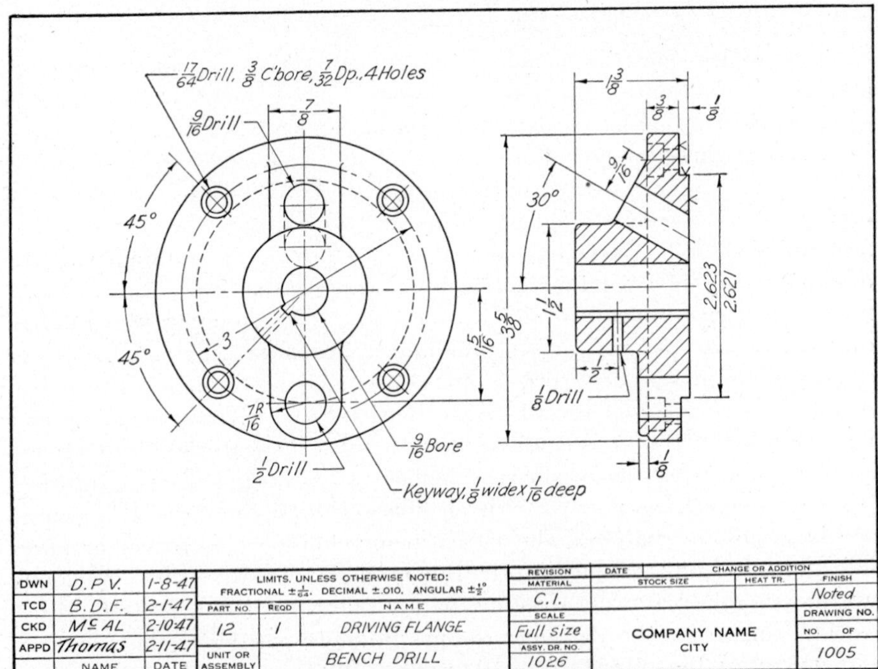

FIG. 15·2—A detail drawing.

drawing, all the views necessary for complete shape description are provided, and all of the necessary dimensions and manufacturing directions are given. Dimensions for nonmating surfaces are obtained by scaling the design drawing, and the more critical sizes are had from the design notes and from drafting-room standards. The detailer will correlate the dimensions of mating parts and give all necessary manufacturing information.

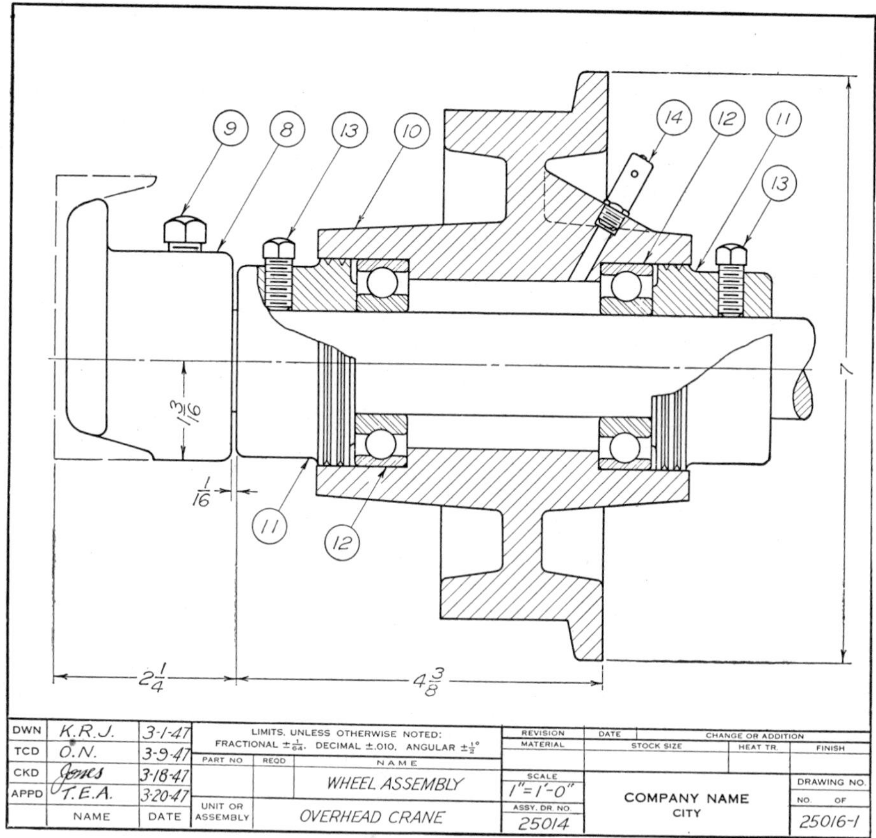

FIG. 15·3—A unit assembly.

The set of drawings is completed by making an assembly drawing and a parts list or bill of material.

If the machine is to be quantity-produced, "operation" or "job" sheets will be made up describing the separate manufacturing steps required and indicating the use and kind of special tools, jigs, fixtures, etc. The tool-design group, working from the detail drawings and the operation sheets, designs and makes the drawings for the special tools needed.

15·3 Assembly drawings. An assembly drawing is, as its name implies, a drawing of the machine or structure put together, showing the relative positions of the different parts. The term "construction drawing" is sometimes used. Its views may be either exterior or sectional.

Under the term "assembly drawings" are included preliminary design drawings and layouts, piping plans, unit assembly drawings, installation diagrams, and final complete drawings used for assembling or erecting the machine or structure.

The *design drawing*, as already indicated, is the preliminary layout on which the scheming, inventing, and designing are accurately worked out.

The *assembly drawing* is in some cases made by tracing from the design drawing. More often it is drawn from the dimensions of the detail drawings. This makes a valuable check on the correctness of the detail drawings.

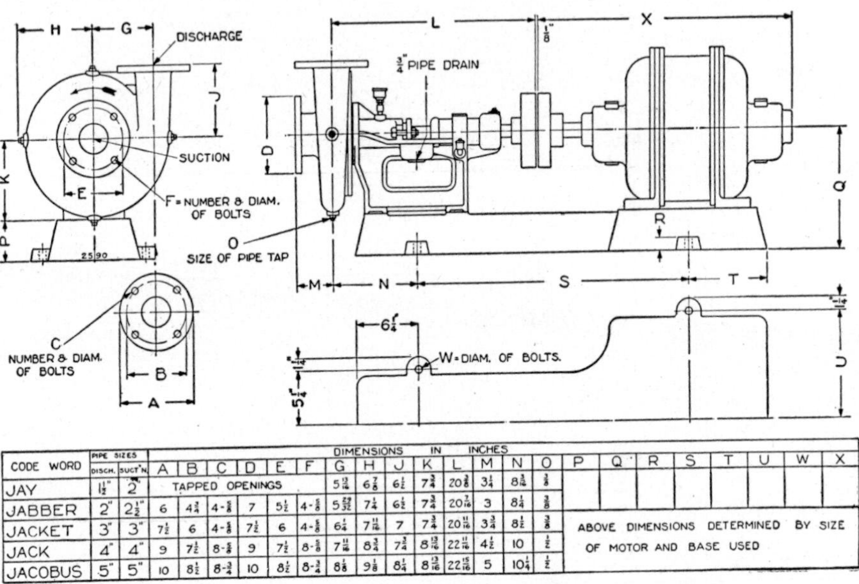

CODE WORD	PIPE SIZES		DIMENSIONS IN INCHES																						
	DISCH.	SUCT'N	A	B	C	D	E	F	G	H	J	K	L	M	N	O	P	Q	R	S	T	U	W	X
JAY	1 1/2"	2"	TAPPED OPENINGS						5 13/16	6 7/8	6 1/2	7 3/4	20 3/8	3 1/4	8 3/16	3/8								
JABBER	2"	2 1/2"	6	4 3/4	4-5/8	7	5 1/2	4-5/8	5 29/32	7 1/4	6 1/2	7 3/4	20 7/16	3	8 1/4	3/8								
JACKET	3"	3"	7 1/2	6	4-5/8	7 1/2	6	4-5/8	6 1/4	7 11/16	7	7 3/4	20 11/16	3 3/4	8 1/2	3/8	ABOVE DIMENSIONS DETERMINED BY SIZE OF MOTOR AND BASE USED							
JACK	4"	4"	9	7 1/2	8-5/8	9	7 1/2	8-5/8	7 11/16	8 3/4	7 3/4	8 13/16	22 11/16	4 1/2	10	1/2								
JACOBUS	5"	5"	10	8 1/2	8-3/4	10	8 1/2	8-3/4	8 1/8	9 1/8	8 1/4	8 13/16	22 15/16	5	10 1/4	1/2								

FIG. 15·4—An outline assembly drawing, tabular.

The assembly drawing may give the over-all dimensions and the distances between centers or from part to part of the different pieces, thus fixing the relation of the parts to each other and aiding in the erection of the machine. It should not be overloaded with detail, particularly invisible detail. Unnecessary hidden lines should not be used on any drawing, least of all on an assembly drawing.

Assembly drawings often have reference letters or numbers designating the different parts. These "piece numbers," sometimes enclosed in circles (called "balloons" by draftsmen), Fig. 15·3, with a leader pointing to the piece, are used in connection with the details and bill of material.

A *unit assembly drawing* or subassembly, Fig. 15·3, is a drawing of a related group of parts used for showing the assembly of complicated machinery where it would be practically impossible to show all of the features on one drawing. Thus, in the drawing of a lathe, there would be included unit assemblies of such groups of parts as the headstock, tailstock, gearbox, etc.

An *outline assembly drawing* is used to give a general idea of the exterior shape of a machine or structure and contains only the principal dimensions, Fig. 15·4. When it is made for catalogue or other illustrative purposes, dimensions are often omitted. These drawings are frequently used to give the information required for the installation or erection of equipment and are then called *installation drawings.*

An *assembly working drawing* gives complete information for producing a machine or structure on one drawing. This is done by providing adequate orthographic views together with dimensions, notes, and descriptive title. Figure 15·62 may be considered an example.

A *diagram drawing* is an assembly showing the erection or installation of equipment. Erection, piping, and wiring diagrams are examples. Diagram drawings are often made in pictorial form.

15·4 Detail drawings. A detail drawing is the drawing of a single piece, giving a complete and exact description of its form, dimensions, and construction. A successful detail drawing will tell the workman *simply* and *directly* the shape, size, material, and finish of each part; what shop operations are necessary; what limits of accuracy must be observed; the number of parts wanted, etc. It should be so exact in description that, if followed, a satisfactory part will result. Figure 15·5 illustrates a commercial detail drawing.

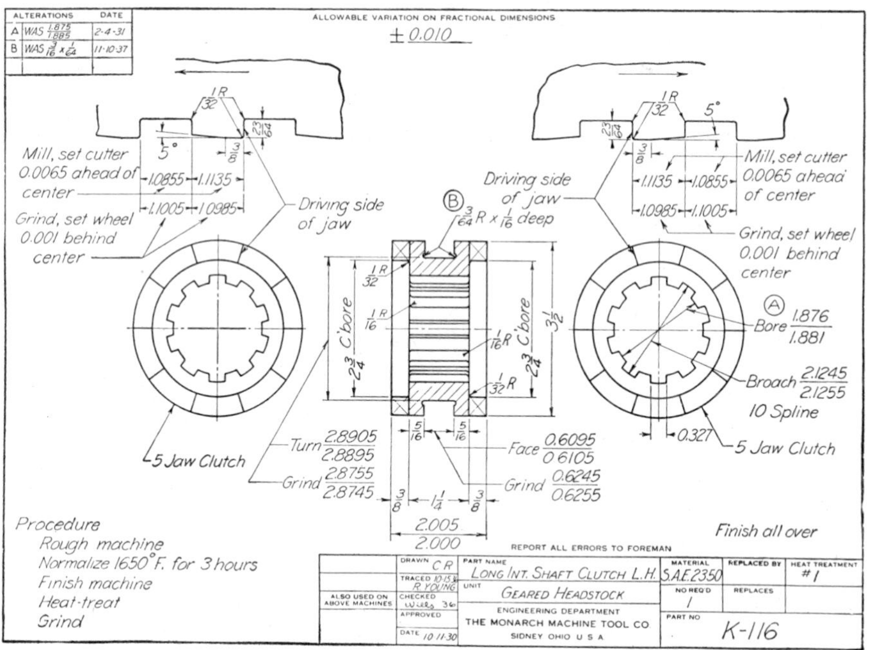

FIG. 15·5—A detail drawing.

Detailing practice will vary somewhat according to the industry and the requirements of the shop system. For example, structural details are often grouped together on one sheet, while modern mechanical practice uses a separate sheet for each part.

If the parts are grouped on one sheet, the detailed pieces should be set, if possible, in the same relative position as on the assembly and, to facilitate reading, placed as nearly as possible in natural relationship. Often, parts of the same material or character are grouped together as, for example, forgings on one sheet and shafts and similar parts on another. A subtitle must be made for each part, giving the part number, material, number required, etc.

The accepted and best system in mechanical work is to have each piece, no matter how small, on a separate sheet. As described in paragraph 10·3, if the single-drawing system is followed, one drawing will be used by all shops. If the multiple system is used, a separate drawing must be made for each shop; thus there may be a *pattern drawing*, a *casting drawing*, and a *machining drawing* for a single part. A detail drawing should be a complete unit for the purpose intended and should not be dependent in any way upon any other detail drawing.

15·5 Tabular drawings. A tabular drawing, either assembly or detail, is one on which the dimension lines are given reference letters, an accompanying table on the drawing listing the corresponding dimensions for a series of sizes of the machine or part, thus making one drawing serve for the range covered. Some companies manufacturing parts in a variety of sizes use this tabular system of size description, but a serious danger with it is the possibility of misreading the table. Figure 15·4 illustrates a tabular assembly drawing.

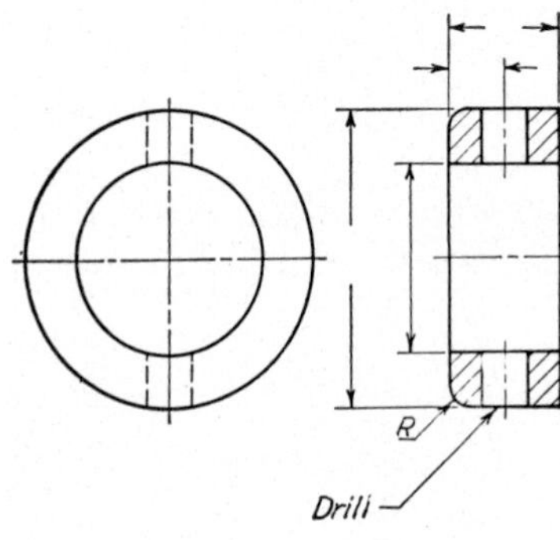

FIG. 15·6—A standard drawing.

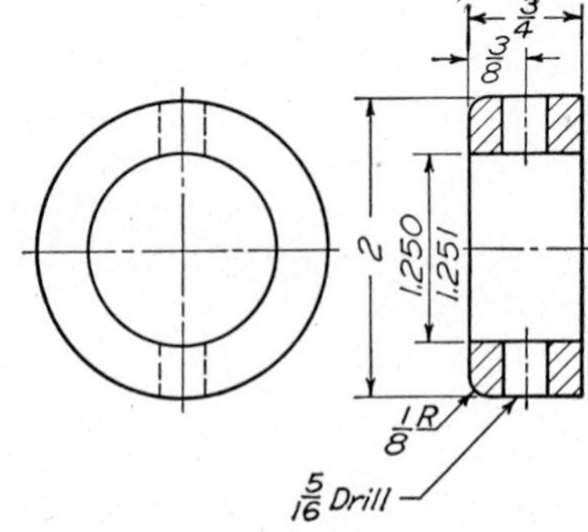

FIG. 15·7—A standard drawing filled in.

15·6 Standard drawings. To avoid the difficulties experienced with tabular drawings, some companies are now making a "standard drawing" complete except for the actual figured dimensions. This drawing is reproduced by offset printing or black-and-white reproduction on vellum paper, and the reproductions are dimensioned separately for the various sizes of parts. This method gives a separate, complete drawing for each size of part, and when a new size is needed the drawing is easily and quickly made. Figure 15·6 shows a standard drawing, and Fig. 15·7 the completed working drawing.

15·7 Plant layouts. In laying out the positions of machine tools and equipment in a plant, generally a drawing of the building is made and the machines are located by making scale drawings of them, cutting them out, and shifting them around on the building plan to get the best arrangement. When the final positions are decided upon, a drawing is made showing the machines and the "route lines" for materials and products. The Ford Motor Co. saves some of the drawing time required for this work by making the building drawing on beaverboard, attaching the machine cutouts to the drawing with a paper-stapling machine, and then photostating the complete assembly. The photostat is made to half the scale of the "master board" and is used as any plant layout drawing would be. The master boards are filed away in special cases so that when changes are necessary the machines may be relocated and a new photostat made.

15·8 Chemical engineering drawing. The study of drawing in preparation for chemical engineering involves all the basic principles considered in this and previous chapters. The chemical engineer should be informed on piping and on the various forms of equipment used in industrial chemistry, such as mixing, grinding, filtering, drying, and conveying machinery.

15·9 Electrical engineering drawing. Electrical engineers need the basic equipment in the language of drawing as do mechanical or other engineers. In its application in their profession it may be divided into two general classes: working drawings, as of electrical machinery; and diagrammatic or symbolic drawings, such as wiring diagrams, etc.

In electrical working drawings the principles and conventions of this chapter are all applicable. Figure 15·99 is an example of an erection working drawing.

Diagrammatic drawings, using conventional symbols for electrical equipment and connections, form an important class of electrical drawings. Electrical symbols, wiring symbols, and radio symbols are given in the Appendix. An example of a diagrammatic drawing is shown in Fig. 15·8.

15·10 The bill of material, or parts list, is a tabulated statement, usually placed on a separate sheet in the case of quantity production (as in Fig. 15·51), or on the assembly drawing in other cases, as illustrated in Fig. 15·76. This table gives the piece number, name, quantity, material, stock size of raw material, and sometimes the weight of each piece. A final column is usually left for remarks. The term "bill of material" is usually used in structural and architectural drawing. The term "parts list" more accurately applies in machine drawing practice. In general, the parts are listed in the order of their importance with the larger parts first and ending with the standard parts such as screws, pins, etc.

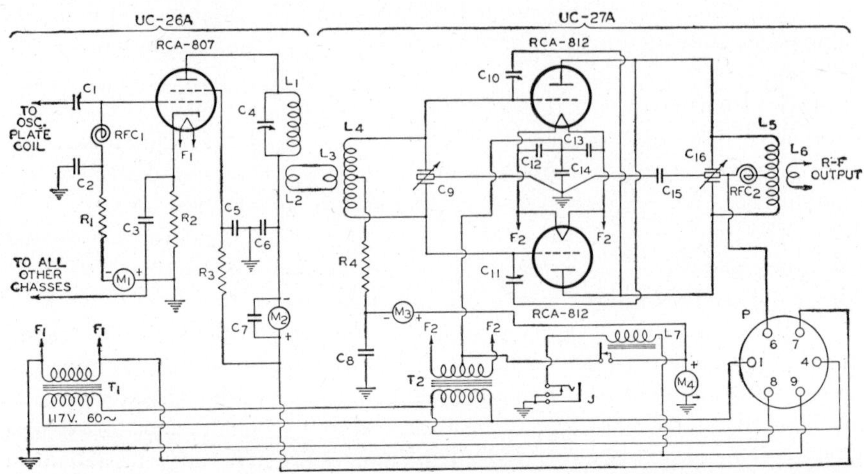

FIG. 15·8—A schematic diagram of a PM transmitter final amplifier unit. (*Courtesy of RCA.*)

The blank ruling for a bill of material should not be crowded. Lines should never be spaced closer than 1/4 inch; 5/16 or 3/8 inch is better, with the height of the lettering not more than half the space and centered between lines. Instead of being lettered, bills of material are frequently typed on forms printed on thin paper. Intensifying the impression by carbon paper on the back increases the opacity of the typing, and a clear blueprint will result.

15·11 Set of drawings. A *complete set* of working drawings consists of detail sheets and assembly sheets, the former giving all necessary information for the manufacture of each of the individual parts which cannot be purchased, and the latter showing the parts assembled as a finished unit or machine. The set includes the bill of material or parts list and may also contain special drawings for the purchaser, such as foundation plans or oiling diagrams.

15·12 Title blocks. The title of a working drawing is usually located in the lower right-hand corner of the sheet, the size of the space varying with the amount of information to be given. The spacing and arrangement are designed to provide the information most helpful in a particular line of work.

In general, the title of a machine drawing should contain the following information:

1. Name of company and its location.
2. Name of machine or unit.
3. Name of part (if a detail drawing).
4. Drawing number.
5. Part number (if a detail drawing).
6. Number of parts required (for each assembly).
7. Scale.
8. Assembly drawing number (given on a detail drawing to identify the part in assembly).
9. Drafting-room record: names or initials of draftsman, tracer, checker, approving authority; each with date.

To these, depending upon the need of the information, may be added:

10. Material.
11. Stock size.
12. Heat-treatment.
13. Finish.
14. Name of purchaser, if special machine.
15. Drawing "supersedes" and "superseded by."

Form of title. Every drafting room has its own standard form for titles. In large offices the blank form is often printed in type on the tracing paper or cloth. Figures 15·9 and 15·10 are characteristic examples.

THE HOOVER COMPANY
NORTH CANTON, OHIO

SCALE
DATE
DR. BY | TR. BY
CH. BY | APP. BY

CHG NO. | MADE BY CHKD BY | REQ NO. | DATE | CHANGE

FIG. 15·9—A printed title form.

HARRISON COUPLER CO.
ELECTRICAL DEPT. PHILADELPHIA
PATTERN NO. | MATERIAL | EST. WEIGHT | SUPERSEDES DWG.
TITLE:
ELECTRICAL ENGINEER | SUPT ELECTRICAL DEPARTMENT
DRAWN BY | DATE | TRACED BY | DATE
CHECKED BY
NO.

FIG. 15·10—A printed title form.

A form of title that is used to some extent is the *record strip,* a strip marked off across either the lower part or right end of the sheet, containing the information required in the title, and space for the record of orders, revisions, changes, etc., that should be noted, with date, as they occur. Figure 15·11 illustrates one form.

It is sometimes desired to keep the records of orders and other private information on the tracing but not to have them appear on the print. In such cases a record strip is put outside the border and trimmed off the print before sending it out.

			REVISION	DATE	CHANGE OR ADDITION
UNIT			NAME OF PIECE		
DR.	DATE	SYMBOL OF MACHINES USED ON	SUPERSEDES DRAW.	STOCK CASTING DROP FORGING	
CH.					
TR.		THE LODGE & SHIPLEY MACHINE TOOL CO.	SUPERSEDED BY DRAW.	MATERIAL	PIECE No.
TR. CH.		Form 795 CINCINNATI, OHIO. U. S. A.			

FIG. 15·11—A strip title.

To draw a title. The title should be lettered freehand in single-stroke capitals, either vertical or inclined, but not both styles in the same title. Write out the contents on a separate piece of paper, then refer back to paragraph 4·17 where full instructions have been given.

15·13 Standard parts. Purchased or company standard parts may be specified by name and size or by number, and consequently will not need to be detailed. All standard parts, such as bolts, screws, antifriction bearings, etc., are shown on the assembly drawing and are given a part number. The complete specifications for their purchase are given in the parts list.

Sometimes, however, a part is made by altering a standard or previously produced part. In this case a detail drawing is made showing and specifying the original part with complete dimensioning for the alterations.

15·14 Choice of views. Although pictorial drawings are used to some extent in special cases, the basis of all working drawing is orthographic projection. Thus, to represent an object completely, at least two views are necessary, often more. The only general rule is, *make as many views as are necessary to describe the object clearly,* **and no more.** Instances may occur in which the third dimension is so evident as to make one view sufficient, as, for example, in the drawing of a shaft or bolt. In other cases perhaps a half-dozen views might be required to describe a piece completely.

As previously stated, select for the front view the face showing the largest dimension, preferably the obvious front of the object when in its functioning position, and then decide what other views are necessary. A vertical cylindrical piece, for example, would require only a front and a top view; a horizontal cylindrical piece only a front and a side view. Determine which side view to use, or whether both are needed. The one with the fewest hidden lines should be preferred. See whether an auxiliary view or a note will save one or more other views and whether a section will be better than an exterior view. One statement may be made with the force of a rule: *If anything in clearness can be gained by violating a principle of projection violate it.*

Paragraphs 9·16 to 9·20, Chap. 9, give a number of examples of conventions that are in violation of theoretical representation but are in the interest of clearness. The draftsman must remember that his responsibility is to the reader of the drawing and that he is not justified in saving himself any time or trouble at the expense of the drawing by making it less plain or easy to read. The time so saved by the draftsman may be lost to the company a hundredfold in the shop, where the drawing is used not once but repeatedly.

15·15 Making a working drawing—order of penciling. After the scheming, inventing, and calculating have been done, and the design drawing completed, the order of procedure for making the detail drawings is

1. Select a suitable standard sheet, or lay off a sheet to standard size, with the excess paper to the right, as a convenient space for making sketches and calculations, and block out the space for the title. *Or*, lay off the standard size very lightly and, after the drawing is finished, shift the border to balance the sheet.
2. Decide what scale is to be used, choosing one large enough to show all dimensions without crowding, and plan the arrangement of the sheet by making a little preliminary freehand sketch, estimating the space each view will occupy and placing the views to the best advantage for preserving, if possible, a balance in the appearance of the sheet.
3. Draw the center lines for each view and on these "block in" the views by laying off the principal dimensions and outlines, using *light, sharp, accurate* pencil lines. Center lines are drawn for the axes of symmetry of all symmetrical views or parts of views. Thus every cylindrical part should have a center line—the projection of the axis of the piece. Every circle should have two center lines intersecting at its center.
4. Finish the projections, putting in last the minor details such as fillets, rounded corners, etc. The different views should be carried on together, projecting a characteristic shape as shown on one view to the other views, not finishing one view before starting another.
5. Draw all necessary dimension lines; then put in the dimensions.
6. Draw guide lines for the notes and then letter them.
7. Lay out the title.
8. Check the drawing carefully.

As an aid in tracing, either in pencil or in ink, the finished outline or parts of it may, if necessary, be brightened by running over a second time with the pencil. The overrunning lines of the constructive stage should not be erased before tracing or inking. These extensions are often convenient in showing the stopping points. All unnecessary erasing should be avoided as it abrades the surface of the paper so that it catches dirt more readily.

As an aid in stopping tangent arcs in inking, it is desirable to mark the tangent point on the pencil drawing with a short piece of the normal to the curve at the point of tangency. Figure 15·12 illustrates the stages of penciling.

15·16 Drawings to be reproduced. Working drawings go to the shop in the form of blueprints, black-line prints, or other similar forms of reproduction, and the drawings must therefore be made on translucent material, either directly or as tracings. Pencil drawings may be made on tracing paper or on pencil cloth; inked drawings on tracing paper or on tracing cloth.

Tracing paper is a thin translucent material commonly called "vellum." Considerable time and expense may be saved by making the original pencil drawing on this material. Excellent prints may be had if the lines are of sufficient blackness and intensity.

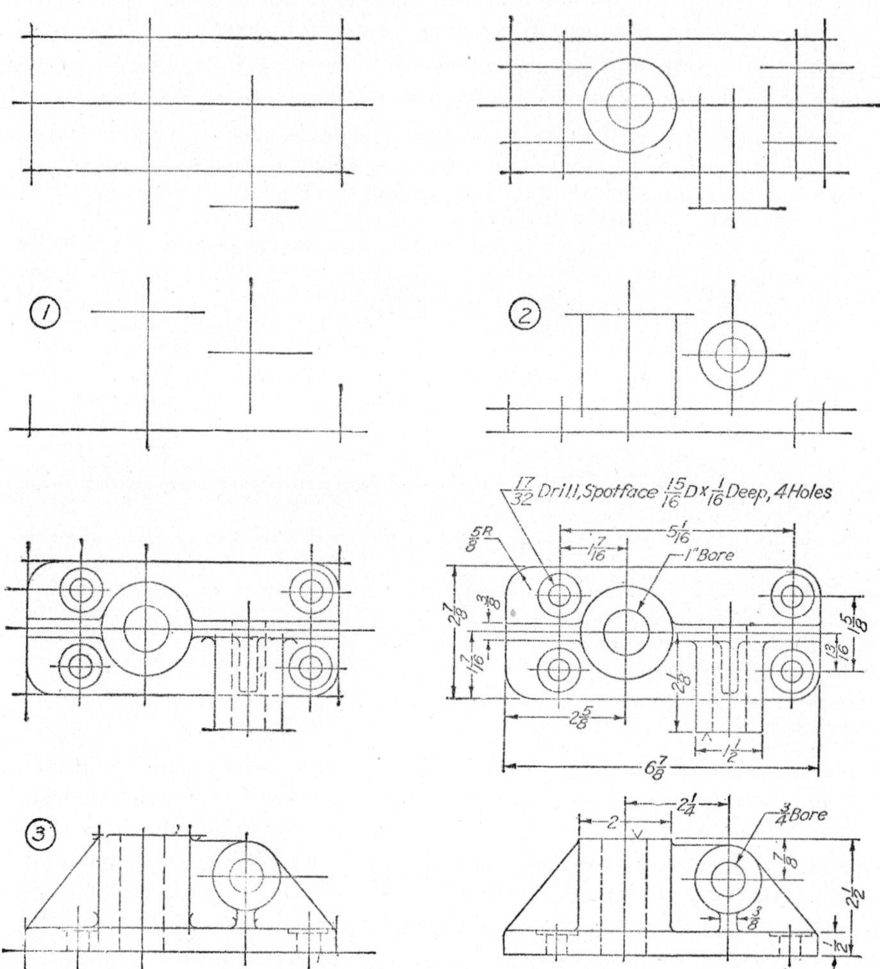

Fig. 15·12—Order of penciling.

Pencil cloth is a transparentized fabric with one or both sides of its surface prepared to take pencil, so that the original drawing may be made on it and prints made either from the pencil drawing or after it has been inked. Some of these newer cloths are moisture resistant, others are really waterproof. Pencil cloth is made for pencil drawings, and perfect blueprints can be made from drawings made on it with sharp, hard pencils. Ink lines, however, do not adhere well and have a tendency to chip or rub off in cleaning.

Tracing cloth is a fine-thread fabric sized and transparentized with a starch preparation. The smooth side is considered by the makers as the working side, but most draftsmen prefer to work on the dull side, which will take pencil marks. The cloth should be tacked down smoothly over the pencil drawing and its selvage torn off. To remove the traces of grease that sometimes prevent the flow of ink, it should then be dusted with chalk or prepared pounce (a blackboard eraser may be used) and rubbed off with a cloth.

15·17 Inked drawings. To ensure good printing, the ink should be perfectly black and the ruling pens in good condition. Red ink should not be used unless it is desired to have some lines conspicuous on the print. Blue ink will not print well. Sometimes, in maps, diagrams, etc., it is desirable to use colored inks on the tracing to avoid confusion of lines; in such cases, the addition of a little Chinese white will render them sufficiently opaque to print.

Ink lines may be removed from tracing cloth by rubbing with a pencil eraser, slipping a triangle under the tracing to give a harder surface. The rubbed surface should afterward be burnished with an ivory or bone burnisher or with the fingernail. In tracing a part that has been section-lined, a piece of white paper should be slipped under the cloth and the section lining done without reference to the section lines underneath.

Tracing cloth is very sensitive to atmospheric changes, often expanding overnight so as to require restretching. If the complete tracing cannot be finished during the day, some views should be finished and no figure left with only part of its lines traced.

In making a large tracing it is well to cut off the required piece from the roll and lay it exposed, flat, for a short time before tacking it down.

Water will ruin a tracing on starch-coated cloth, and moist hands or arms should not come in contact with it. The habit should be formed of keeping the hands off drawings. In both drawing and tracing on large sheets, it is a good plan to cut a mask of drawing paper to cover all but the view being worked on. Unfinished drawings should always be covered overnight.

Tracings may be cleaned of pencil marks and dirt by rubbing over with a cloth or waste dipped in benzine or carbon tetrachloride. To prevent smearing when using this method of cleaning, borders and titles, if printed from type on the tracing cloth, should be done in an ink not affected by benzine.

Order of inking

1. Ink all full-line circles, beginning with the smallest, then circle arcs.
2. Ink dotted circles and arcs in the same order as full-line circles.
3. Ink any irregular curved lines.
4. Ink straight full lines in this order: horizontal, vertical, and inclined.
5. Ink straight dotted lines in the same order.
6. Ink center lines.
7. Ink extension and dimension lines.

8. Ink arrowheads and dimensions.
9. Section-line all areas representing cut surfaces.
10. Letter notes and titles. (On tracings, draw pencil guide lines first.)
11. Ink the border.
12. Check the inked drawing.

Figure 15·13 shows the stages of inking.

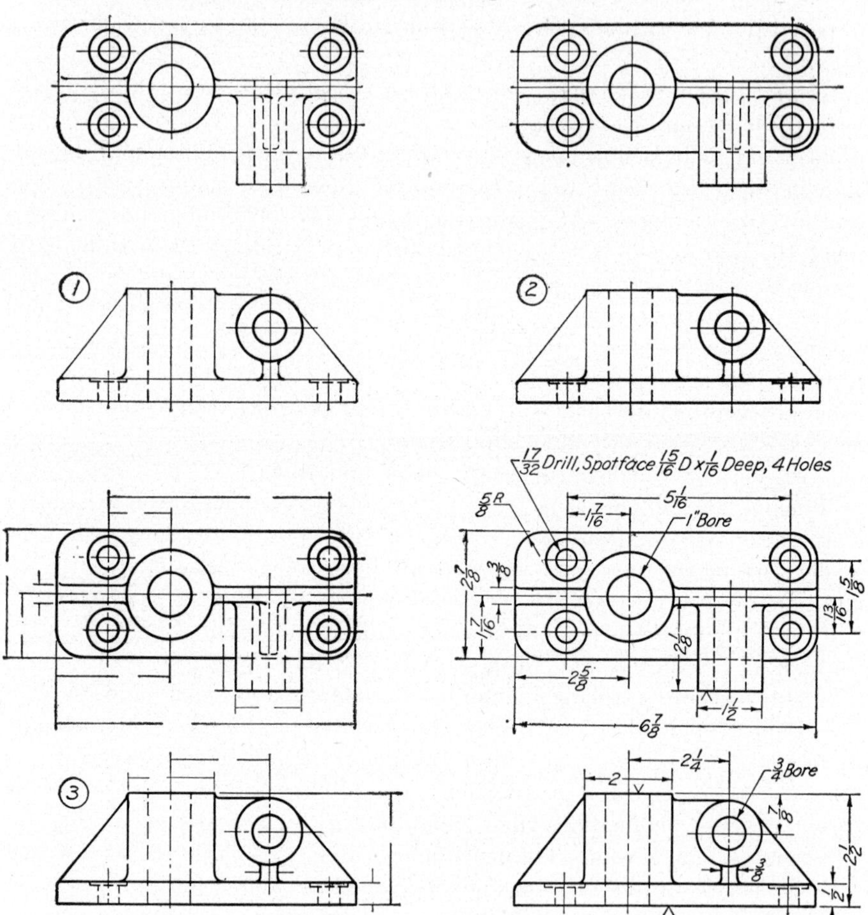

FIG. 15·13—Order of inking.

15·18 Checking. Before being sent to the shop, a working drawing is carefully checked for errors and omissions. A first check of the pencil drawing is made by the chief designer, who knows the price at which the machine is to be made and checks the design for soundness and economy, sees if existing patterns for any parts can be used, checks for adequate lubrication, for correct representation, and other points in the list following.

When the drawing is finished it is gone over by an experienced checker who, in signing his name to it, becomes responsible for any errors. This is the final "proofreading" and cannot be done by the one who has made the drawing nearly so well as by another person. In small offices all the work is checked by the chief draftsman, and draftsmen sometimes check each other's work; in large drafting rooms one or more checkers who devote all their time to this kind of work are employed. All notes, computations, and checking layouts should be preserved for future reference.

Students may gain experience in this work by checking each other's drawings.

To be effective, checking must be done in an absolutely systematic way and with thorough concentration.

15·19 To check a drawing, each of the following items[1] should be gone through separately, the checker allowing nothing to distract his attention from it. As each dimension or feature is verified, a check mark should be placed on or above it and corrections indicated with soft or colored pencil.

1. Put yourself in the position of those who are to read the drawing and find out if it is easy to read and tells a straight story. Always do this before checking any individual features; in other words, before you have had time to become accustomed to the contents.
2. See that each piece is correctly designed and illustrated and that all necessary views are shown but none that are not necessary.
3. Check all the dimensions by scaling and, where advisable, by calculation also. Preserve the calculations.
4. See that dimensions for the shop are given as required by the shop and that the shop is not left to do any adding or subtracting in order to get a needed dimension.
5. Check for tolerances. See that they are neither too "fine" nor too "coarse" for the particular conditions of the machine, so as neither to increase unnecessarily the cost of production nor, on the other hand, to impair accuracy of operation or duplication.
6. Go over each piece and see that finishes are properly specified.
7. See that every specification of material is correct and that all necessary ones are given.
8. Look out for "interferences." This means that each detail must be checked with the parts that will be adjacent to it in the assembled machine to see that proper clearances have been allowed.
9. When checking for clearances in connection with a mechanical movement, lay out the movement to scale, figure the principal angles of motion, and see that proper clearances are maintained in all positions, drawing small mechanisms to double size or larger.
10. See that all the small details: screws, bolts, pins, rivets, etc., are standard and that, where possible, stock sizes have been used.
11. Check every feature of the title, or record strip, and bill of material.
12. Review the drawing in its entirety, adding such explanatory notes as will increase its efficiency.

15·20 Style. There is a *style* in drawing, just as there is in literature, which indicates itself in one way by ease of reading. Some drawings stand out, while others which may contain all the information are difficult to decipher. Although dealing with mechanical thought, there is a place for

[1] Adapted from Follows' "Dictionary of Mechanical Drawing."

some artistic sense in mechanical drawing. The number, selection, and disposition of views; the omission of anything unnecessary, ambiguous, or misleading; the size and placement of dimensions and lettering; and the contrast of lines are elements concerned in the *style*.

15·21 Requirements of commercial practice. In commercial drafting, *accuracy* and *speed* are the two requirements. The drafting room is an expensive department, and time is thus an important element. The draftsman must therefore have a ready knowledge not only of the principles of drawing but of the conventional methods and abbreviations and of any device or system that will save time without sacrificing clearness.

The usual criticism of the student by the employer is the result of the former's lack of appreciation of the necessity for *speed*.

15·22 Alterations. Once a drawing has been printed and the prints released to the shop, any alterations or changes should be recorded on the drawing and new prints issued. If the changes are extensive, the drawing may be *obsoleted* and a new drawing made which *supersedes* the old drawing. Many drawing rooms have "change record" blocks printed in conjunction with the title, where minor changes are recorded, Fig. 15·9. The change is identified in the record and on the face of the drawing with a letter.

New designs may be changed so often that the alterations cannot be made fast enough to reach the shop when needed. In this case, sketches showing the changes are rapidly made, reproduced, and sent to the shop where they are fastened to each print of the drawing. These sketches, commonly known as "engineering orders," are later incorporated on the drawing.

Portions of a drawing may be canceled by drawing closely spaced parallel lines, usually at 45°, over the area to be voided.

15·23 Reproduction of drawings. As has already been indicated, working drawings go to the shop in the form of prints from the original drawings. Several different printing processes are in use, all of which give the best results from tracings inked on tracing cloth or paper. However, quite satisfactory prints may be obtained from pencil drawings on translucent paper when the penciling is done skillfully, with uniform opaque lines.

Blueprints. The simplest and most generally used copying process is the blueprinting process, in which the prints are made by exposing a piece of sensitized paper and a tracing in close surface contact with each other to sunlight or electric light in a printing frame or machine made for the purpose. This paper is a white stock free from sulphites, coated with a solution of citrate of iron and ammonia, and ferricyanide of potassium. On exposure to the light a chemical action takes place, which when fixed by washing in water gives a strong blue color. The parts protected from the light by the black lines of the tracing wash out, leaving the white paper. Blueprint paper is usually bought ready sensitized and may be had in different weights and different degrees of rapidity. When fresh, it is of a yellowish green color, and an unexposed piece should wash out perfectly white. With age or exposure to light or air it turns to a darker gray-blue color and spoils altogether in a comparatively short time.

Vandyke paper is a thin sensitized paper which turns dark brown when exposed to light and properly "fixed." It is fixed by first washing in water, then in hyposulphite of soda, and again thoroughly in water. A reversed negative of a tracing may be made on it by exposing it to light with the inked side of the drawing next to the sensitized side of the paper; then this negative can be printed on blueprint paper, giving a positive print with blue lines on white.

B W prints and Directo prints, have black lines on a white ground and are made directly from the original tracing, either in a blueprinting machine (and developed by hand) or in a special machine made for the purpose. They are used extensively when positive prints are desired.

Ozalid prints. This process is based on the chemical action of light-sensitive diazo compounds. It is a contact method of reproduction in which the exposure is made in either a regular blueprinting machine or an ozalid "whiteprint" machine, and the exposed print developed dry with ammonia vapors in a developing machine. Standard papers giving black, blue, and maroon lines on a white ground are available. Dry developing has the distinct advantage of giving prints without distortion, and it also makes possible the use of transparent papers, cloth, and foils to effect savings in drafting, as these transparent replicas can be changed by additions or erasures and prints made from them without altering the original tracing.

Photostat prints are extensively used by large corporations. By this method a print with white lines on a dark background is made directly from any drawing or tracing, to any desired reduction or enlargement, through the use of a large specially designed camera. This print may be again photostated, giving a brown-line print with a white ground. This method is extremely useful to engineers for drawings to be included in reports and for matching drawings of different scales which may have to be combined into one.

Duplicating tracings. Tracings having all the qualities of ordinary inked ones are made photographically from pencil drawings by using a sensitized tracing cloth.

Lithoprinting. When a number of copies of a drawing (fifty or more) are needed, they may be reproduced by lithoprinting, a simplified form of photolithography, at comparatively small cost.

Copying methods, such as those of the mimeograph, ditto machine, and other forms of the hectograph or gelatin pad are often used for small drawings.

15·24 Drawing sizes. Drawing paper and cloth are available in rolls of various widths and in standard trimmed sizes. Most drafting rooms use standard sheets, printed with border and title block. The ASA recommends the following sizes, based on multiples of $8\frac{1}{2}'' \times 11''$, which permits the filing of prints in a standard letter file.

Size *A*—$8\frac{1}{2} \times 11$
Size *B*—11×17
Size *C*—17×22
Size *D*—22×34
Size *E*—34×44

Figure 15·14 illustrates the ASA trimmed sizes. Larger drawings may be made on rolled stock of standard width, with the length as a multiple of 11 inches.

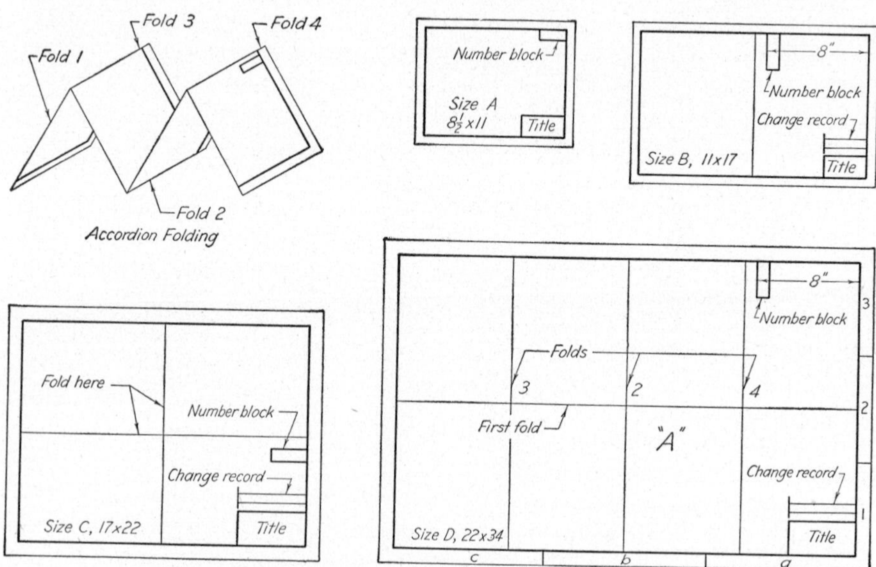

FIG. 15·14—ASA trimmed sizes of paper and cloth.

For drawings made in the metric system of units, or for foreign correspondence, the following metric standard trimmed sheet sizes, based on a width-to-length ratio of 1 to $\sqrt{2}$, may be used.

*A*0—841×1189 mm
*A*1—594×841 mm
*A*2—420×594 mm
*A*3—297×420 mm
*A*4—210×297 mm
*A*5—148×210 mm
*A*6—105×148 mm

15·25 Zoning. As an aid in locating some item on a large drawing, the lower and right borders may be ruled and marked as shown on the *D* size drawing of Fig. 15·14. Item *A* would be located in zone *b*2. A separate column in the change record block is often used to indicate the position of each drawing change.

15·26 Filing and storing of drawings. Drawings are filed in steel or wooden cabinets made for the purpose. Valuable drawings are often stored in fireproof vaults, and never removed except for making alterations or for printing. Microfilm[1] copies (35-mm photographic copy) are sometimes made as a separate permanent record. Drawings are always filed flat or rolled. Prints, however, are folded for filing or mailing. The usual method is the "accordion" fold illustrated in Fig. 15·14. To aid in the filing of accordion folded prints, a supplementary number block may be added, as shown.

PROBLEMS

15·27 The first part of any working-drawing problem consists of the selection of views, the choice of suitable scales, and the arrangement of the sheet. In classwork a preliminary sketch layout should be submitted for approval before the drawing is commenced.

In dimensioning these problems the principles given in Chaps. 11 and 12 should be followed carefully. Before applying finish marks, study the problem to determine which surfaces should be so marked. On parts that are to fit accurately, the class of fit is to be assumed or assigned, and limit dimensions are to be figured from the nominal sizes given, using the ASA tables of allowances and tolerances in the Appendix. The illustration for the problem is to be taken as the preliminary sketch from which to make the actual working drawings for the shop. Because of restricted space, the illustrations are often crowded; do not, therefore, follow them as examples of good spacing or of the best placing of dimensions.

Group I. Detail drawings

Problems 1 to 28, Figs. 15·15 to 15·42

This group includes problems involving sectional views, auxiliaries, double auxiliaries, and conventional representation.

Group II. An assembly drawing from the details

Problems 29 to 40, Figs. 15·43 to 15·53

Group III. Detail drawings from the assembly

Problems 41 to 73, Figs. 15·54 to 15·79

Group IV. A set of drawings from a pictorial assembly

Problems 74 to 83, Figs. 15·80 to 15·89

Group V. A set of drawings from the design drawing

Problems 84 to 89, Figs. 15·90 to 15·95

Group VI. Electrical problems

Problems 90 to 99, Figs. 15·96 to 15·99

[1] Graflex Corporation, Rochester, N.Y.

Group I. Detail drawings

1. Fig. 15·15. Working drawing of support bearing. Three views, full size.
2. Fig. 15·16. Working drawing of centering-yoke base. Three views, full size.

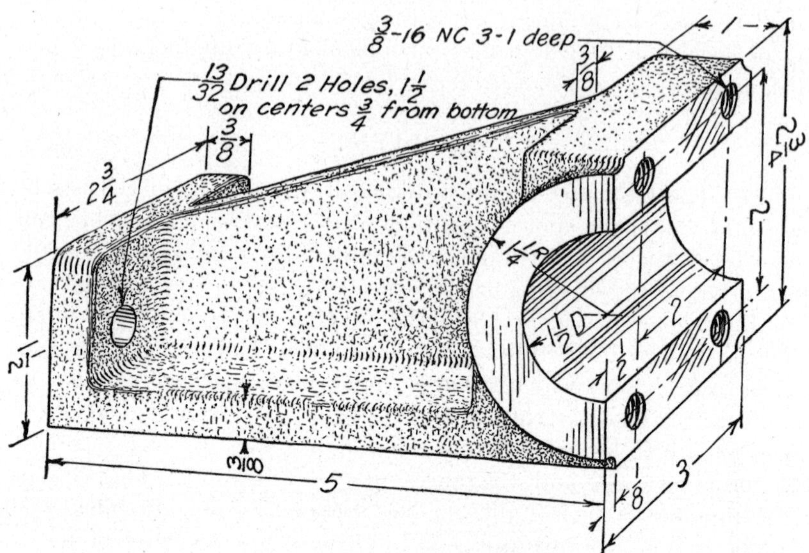

FIG. 15·15—Support bearing.

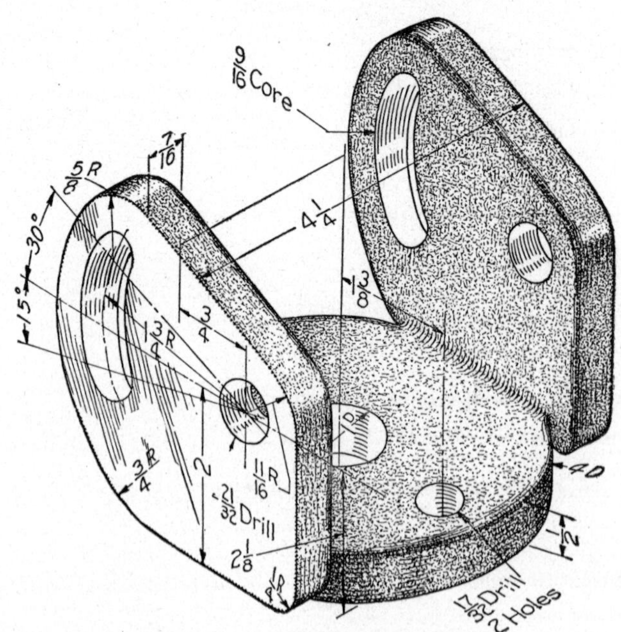

FIG. 15·16—Centering-yoke base.

3. Fig. 15·17. Make complete working drawing with necessary sectional views.
4. Fig. 15·18. Working drawing of drawbar pivot. Full size.

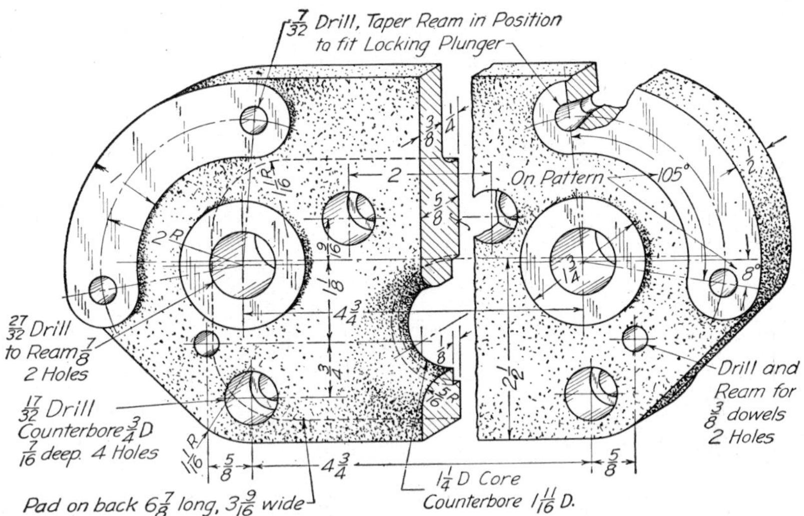

FIG. 15·17—Gear-shifter bracket.

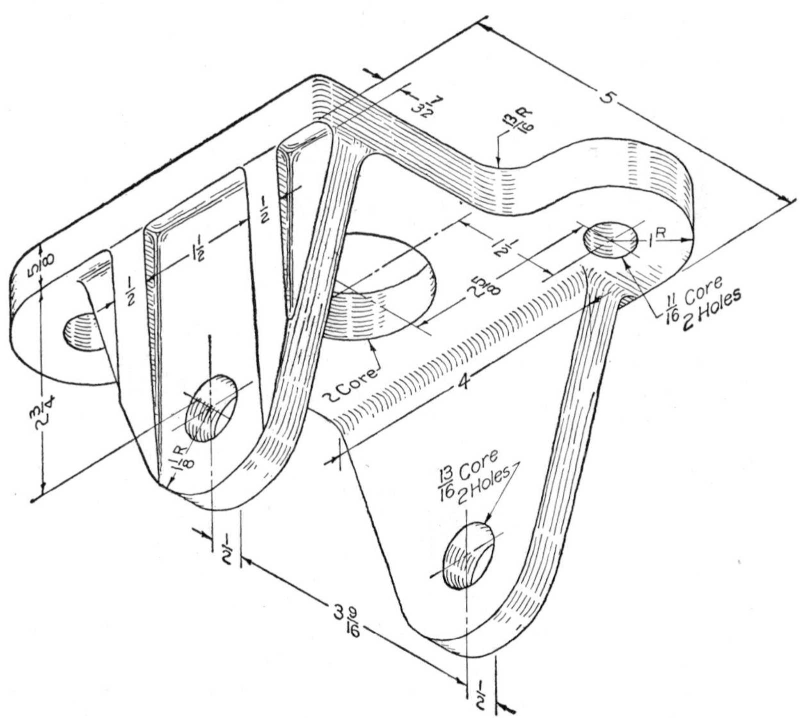

FIG. 15·18—Drawbar pivot.

5. Fig. 15·19. Working drawing of compound-gear arm.
6. Fig. 15·20. Working drawing of fan bracket.
7. Fig. 15·21. Working drawing of friction shaft bearing.
8. Fig. 15·22. Working drawing of crossover link.

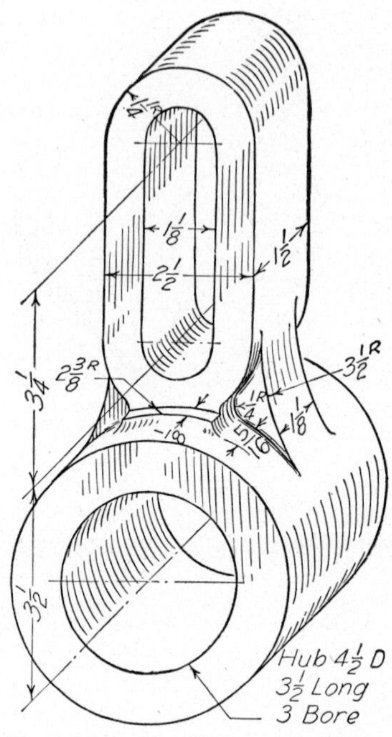

FIG. 15·19—Compound-gear arm.

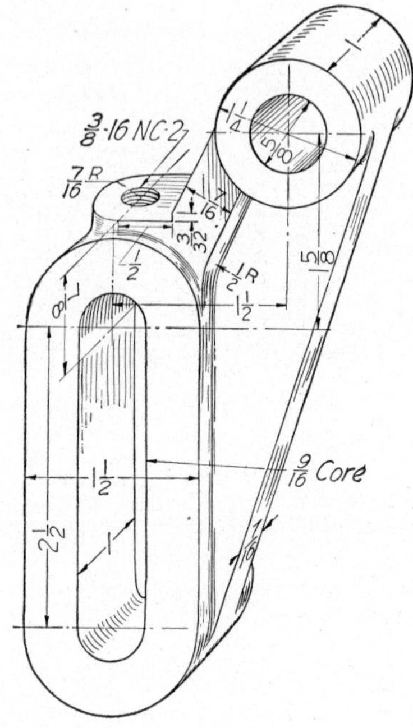

FIG. 15·20—Fan bracket.

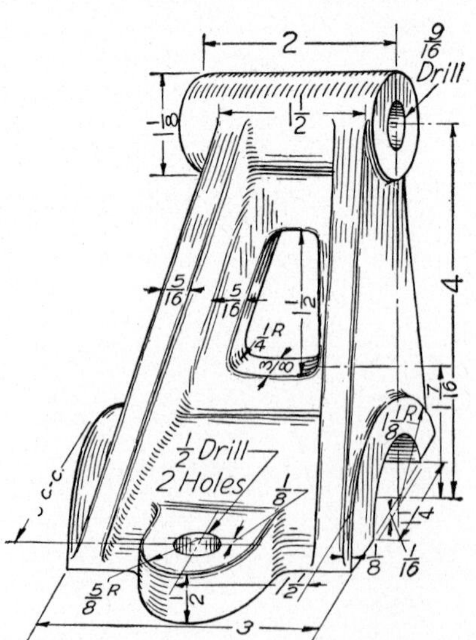

FIG. 15·21—Friction shaft bearing.

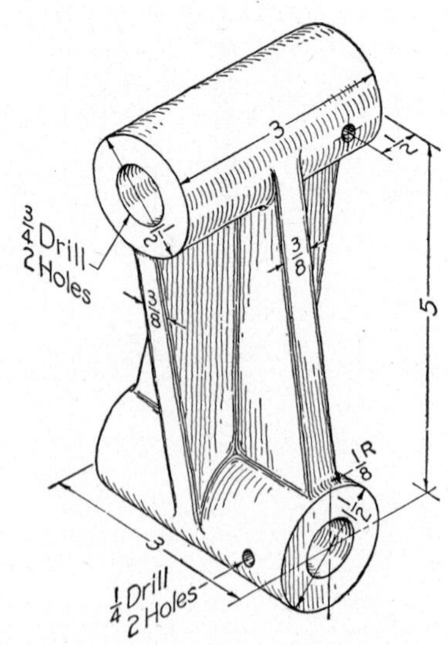

FIG. 15·22—Crossover link.

9. Fig. 15·23. Working drawing of adjustable base.
10. Fig. 15·24. Working drawing of bed bracket.

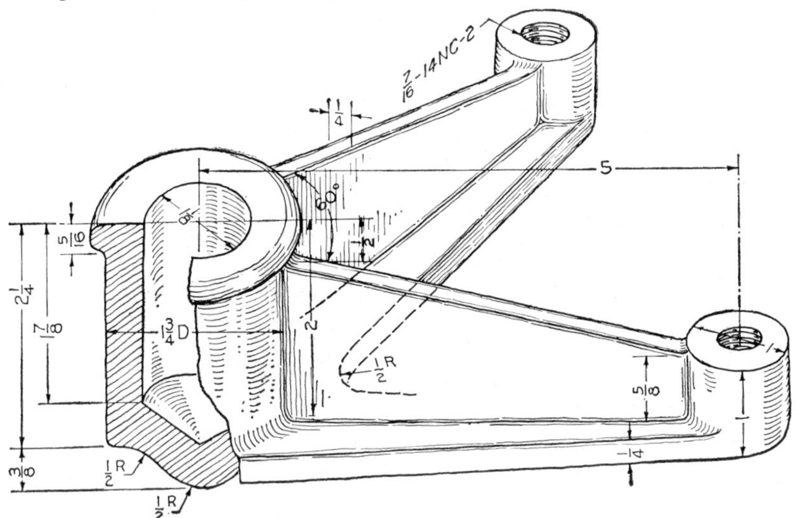

Fig. 15·23—Adjustable base.

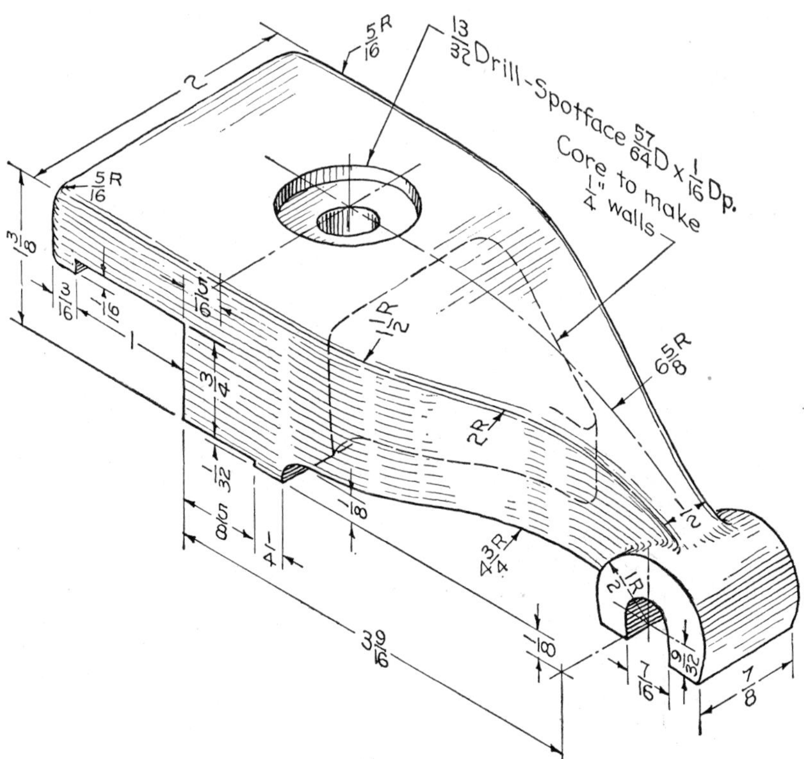

Fig. 15·24—Bed bracket.

11. Fig. 15·25. Working drawing of valve seat.
12. Fig. 15·26. Working drawing of supply head.

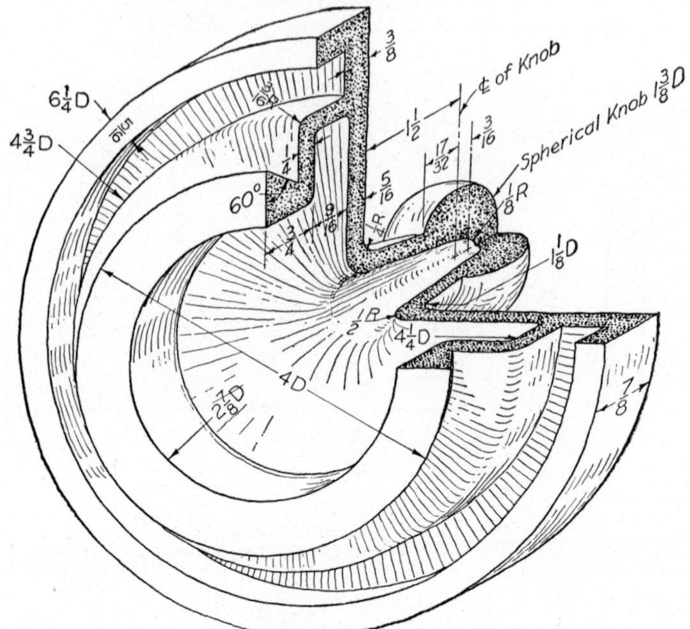

FIG. 15·25—Valve seat.

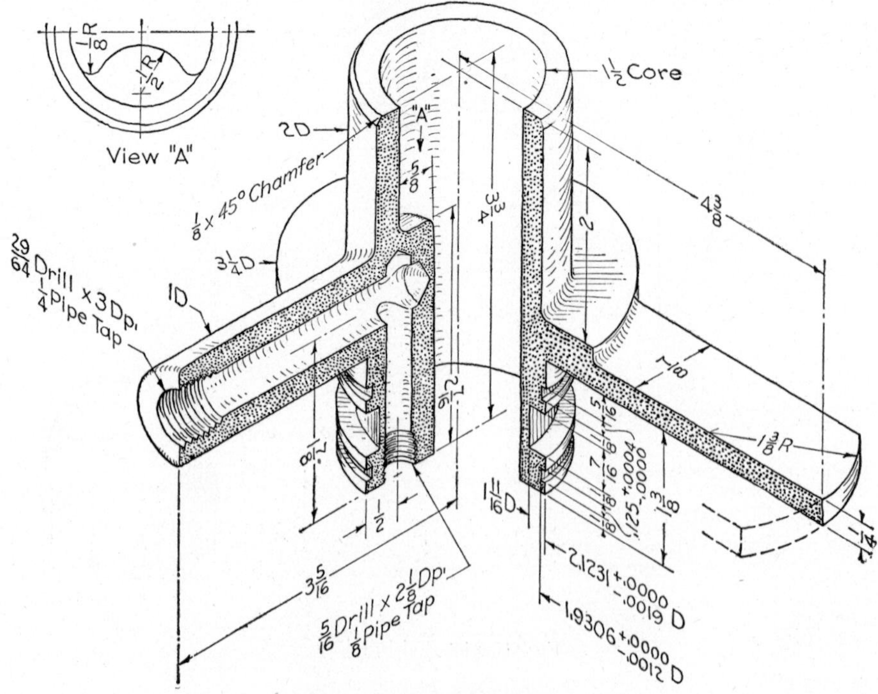

FIG. 15·26—Supply head.

13. Fig. 15·27. Working drawing with right or left auxiliary.
14. Fig. 15·28. Working drawing with front auxiliary.
15. Fig. 15·29. Working drawing with right auxiliary.
16. Fig. 15·30. Working drawing with partial auxiliary.

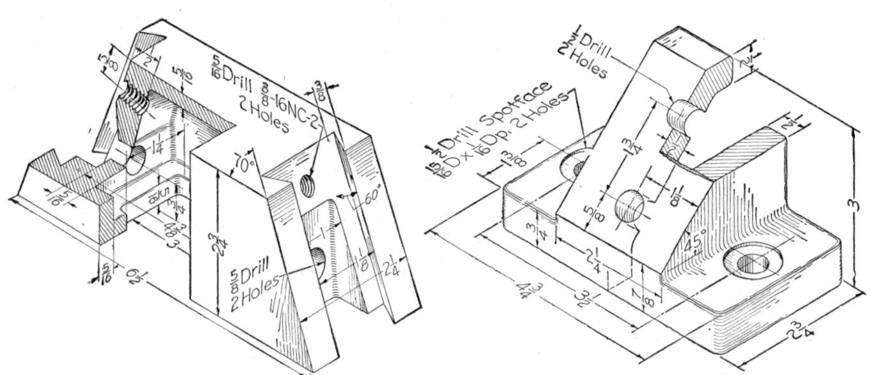

Fig. 15·27—Slide base. Fig. 15·28—Idler bracket.

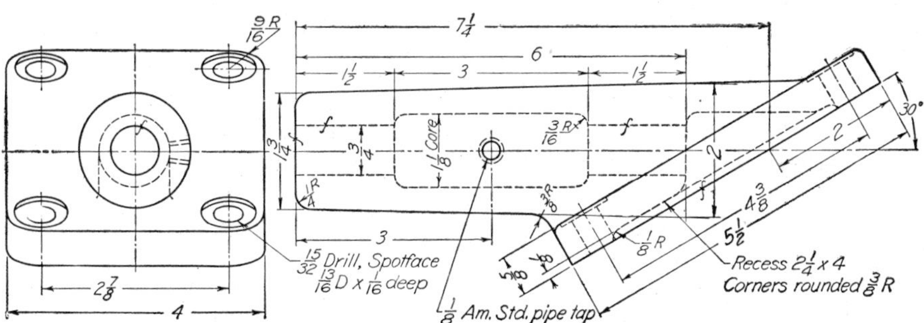

Fig. 15·29—Angle bracket.

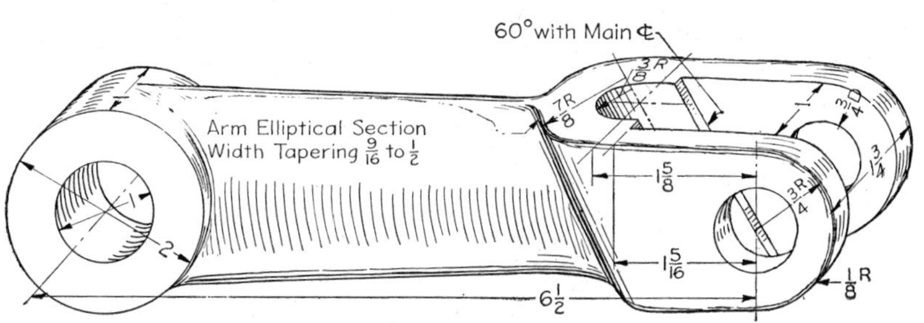

Fig. 15·30—Pawl carrier.

17. Fig. 15·31. Working drawing with auxiliary elevation.
18. Fig. 15·32. Working drawing with partial auxiliary.

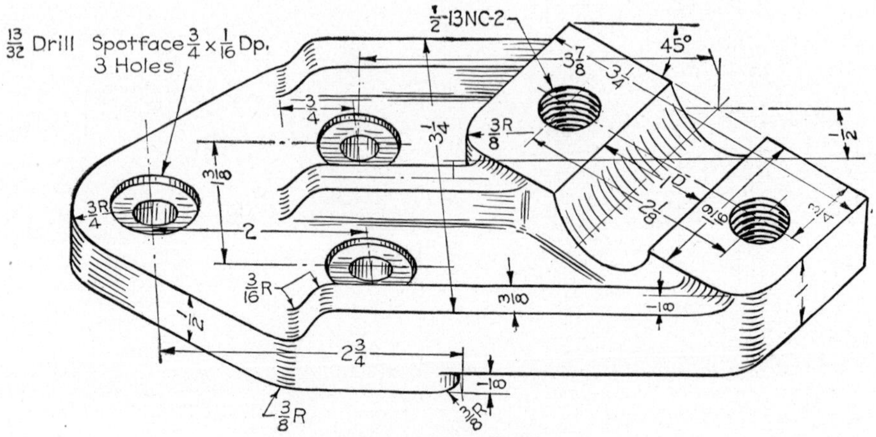

Fig. 15·31—Hinge base.

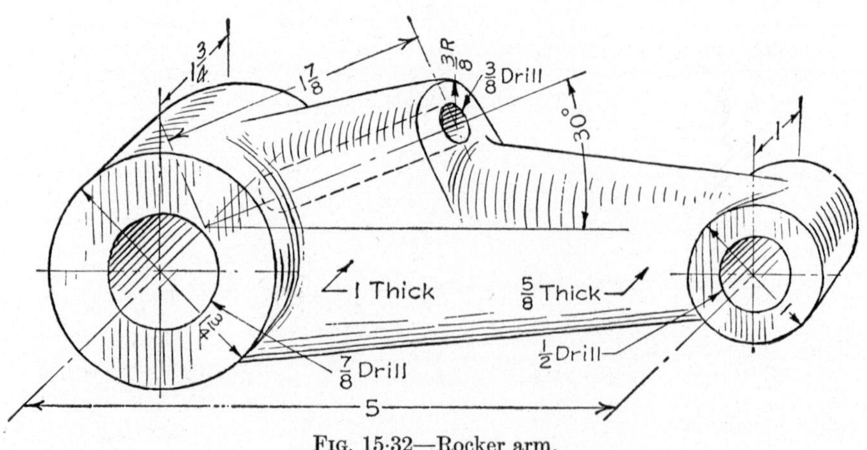

Fig. 15·32—Rocker arm.

19. Fig. 15·33. (*a*) Make detail working drawings on same sheet, one for *rough forging* and one for *machining* or, (*b*) make one detail drawing for forging and machining.

20. Fig. 15·34. Working drawing of fan-type meter case. Molded bakelite.

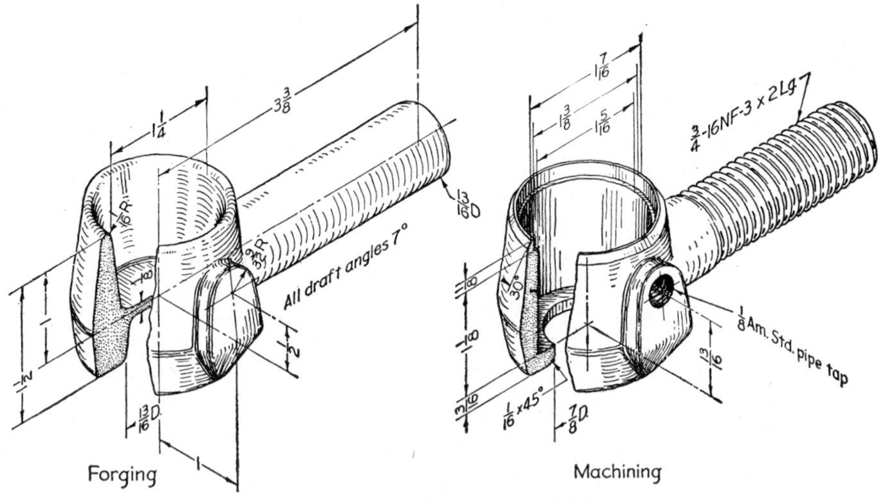

FIG. 15·33—Steering knuckle.

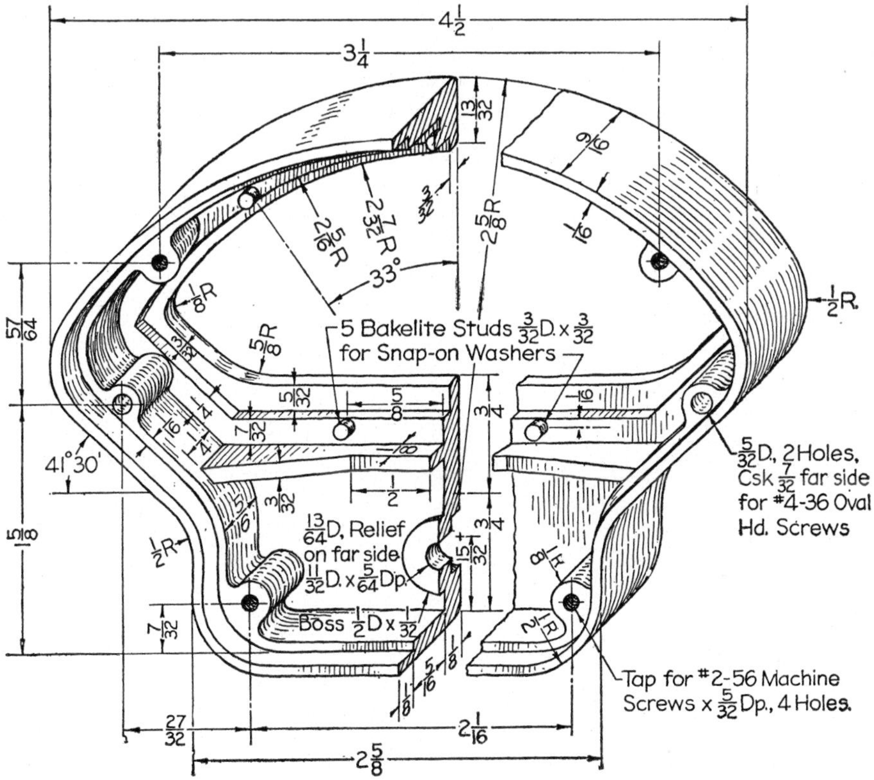

FIG. 15·34—Meter case.

21. Fig. 15·35. Working drawing of torque-tube support. Forged aluminum. (*a*) Make two detail drawings, one for forging and one for machining or, (*b*) make one drawing for both forging and machining.

22. Fig. 15·36. Working drawing of slotted spider.

23. Fig. 15·37. Working drawing of valve cage.

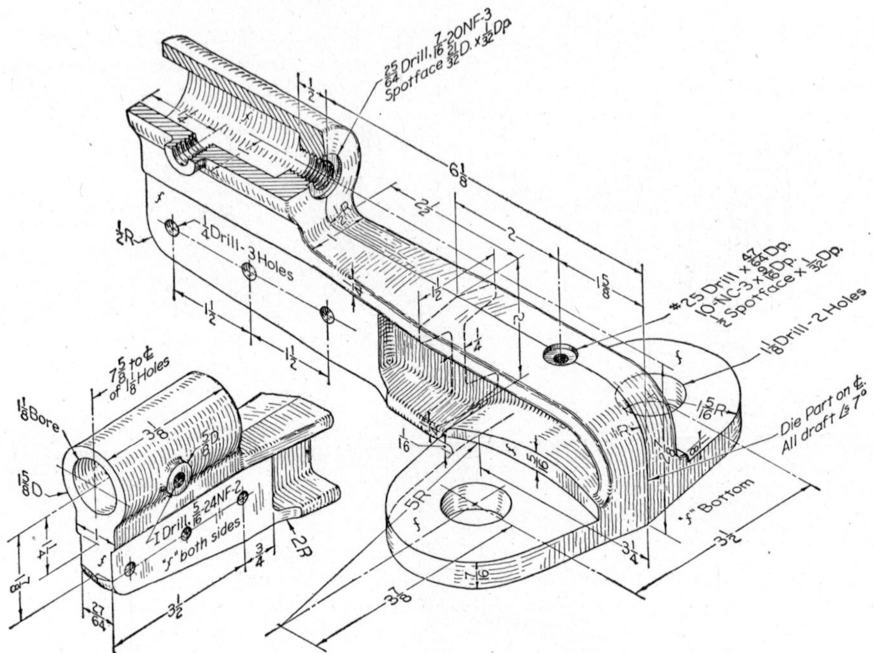

FIG. 15·35—Torque-tube support.

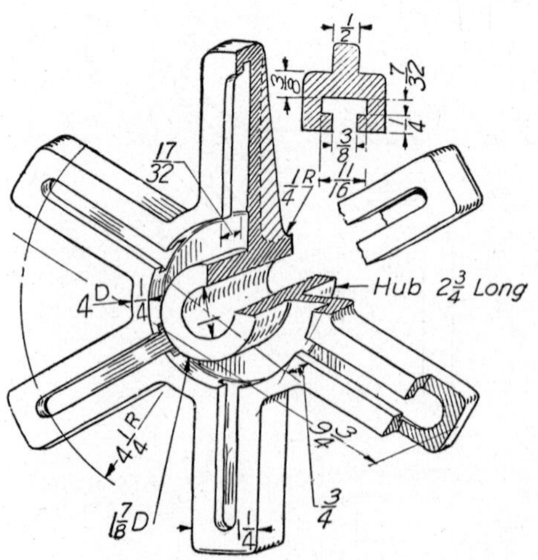

FIG. 15·36—Slotted spider.

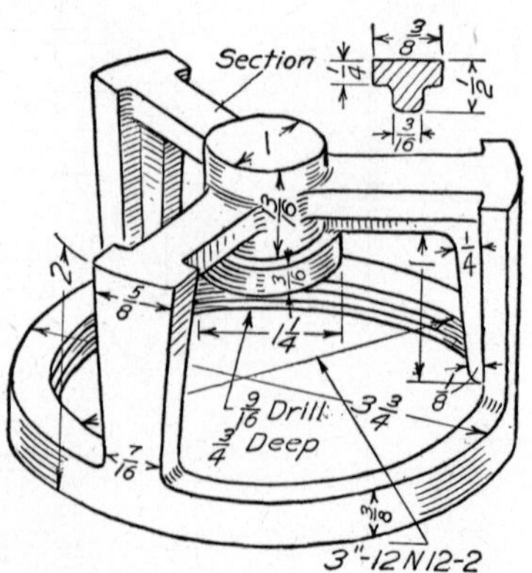

FIG. 15·37—Valve cage.

24. Fig. 15·38. Working drawing of water-pump cover.

25. Fig. 15·39. Working drawing of stuffing-box seat.

26. Fig. 15·40. Working drawing of valve flange. The three 1¼″ bosses are equispaced. Use top view, partial right-side view, and front view as a conventional section.

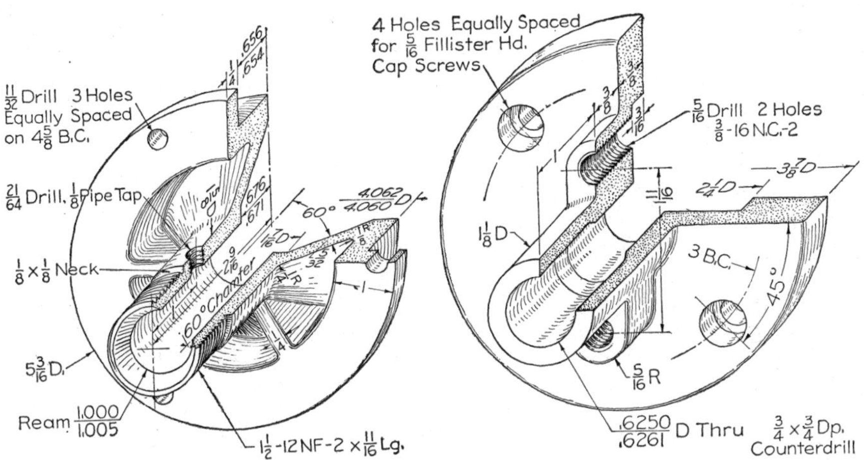

Fig. 15·38—Water-pump cover.

Fig. 15·39—Stuffing-box seat.

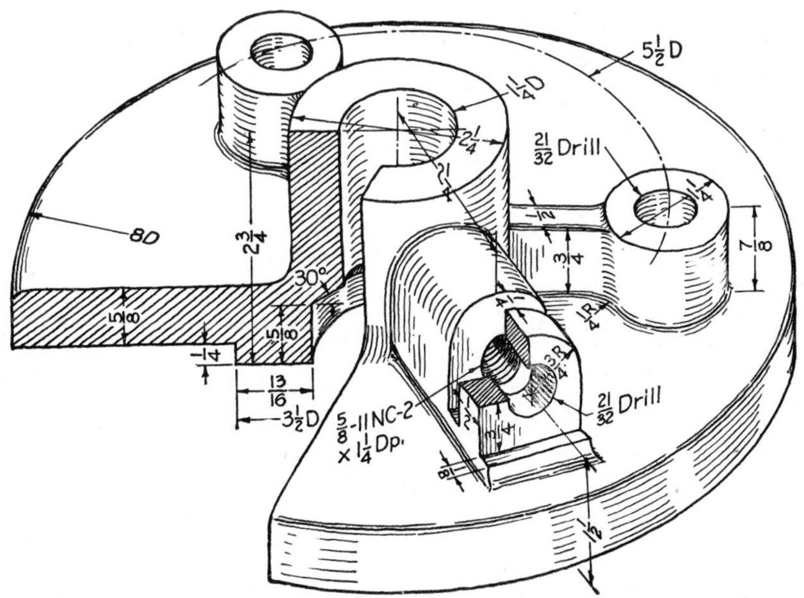

Fig. 15·40—Valve flange.

27. Fig. 15·41. Working drawing of stake socket. Use top view, partial front view, and auxiliary elevation.

28. Fig. 15·42. Working drawing of automobile piston. Make sectional views as indicated.

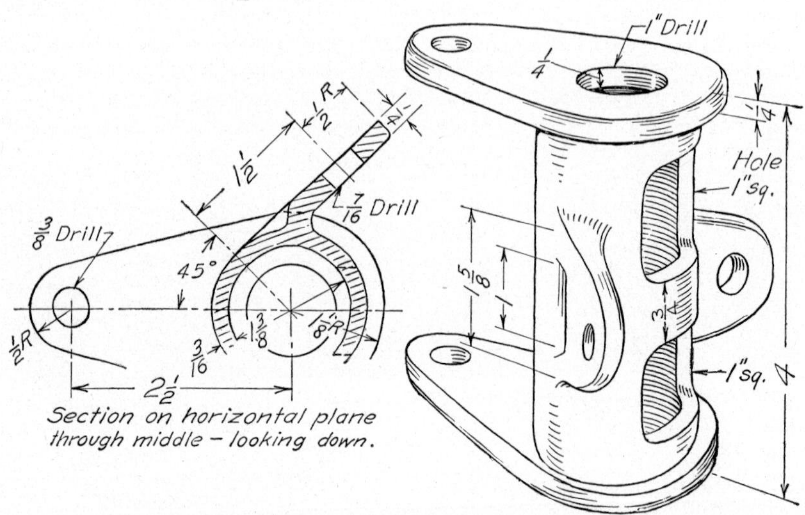

FIG. 15·41—Stake socket.

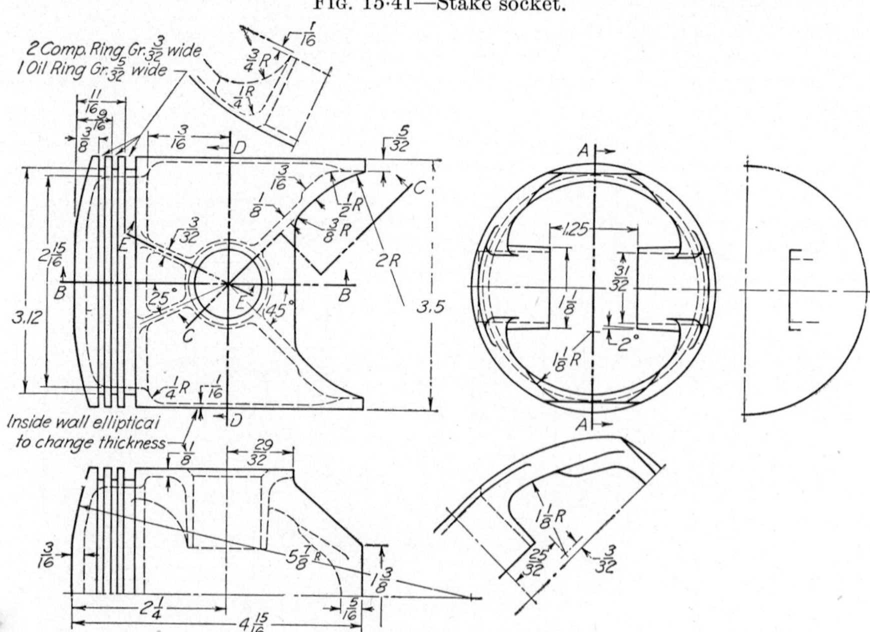

FIG. 15·42—Automobile piston (Chevrolet).

Group II. An assembly drawing from the details

29. Fig. 15·43. Make an assembly drawing of the Boyle union, from details given. The pictorial sketch, as well as the identified pieces and bill of material, will assist in identifying the parts for the assembly. The two flanges are screwed on the pipes to be joined, and the sleeve and two packing rings are placed between the flanges. Then bolts are placed and nuts tightened to hold the assembly together and ensure a tight joint. Use two views, end and longitudinal, with longitudinal view in full section. Use conventional symbols for sectioning the different materials. The dimensions of the pipe thread are given in the Appendix.

30. Fig. 15·44. Make an assembly drawing of the crane hook from details given. Standard parts 7 to 10, inclusive, are not detailed; see Appendix or handbook for sizes.

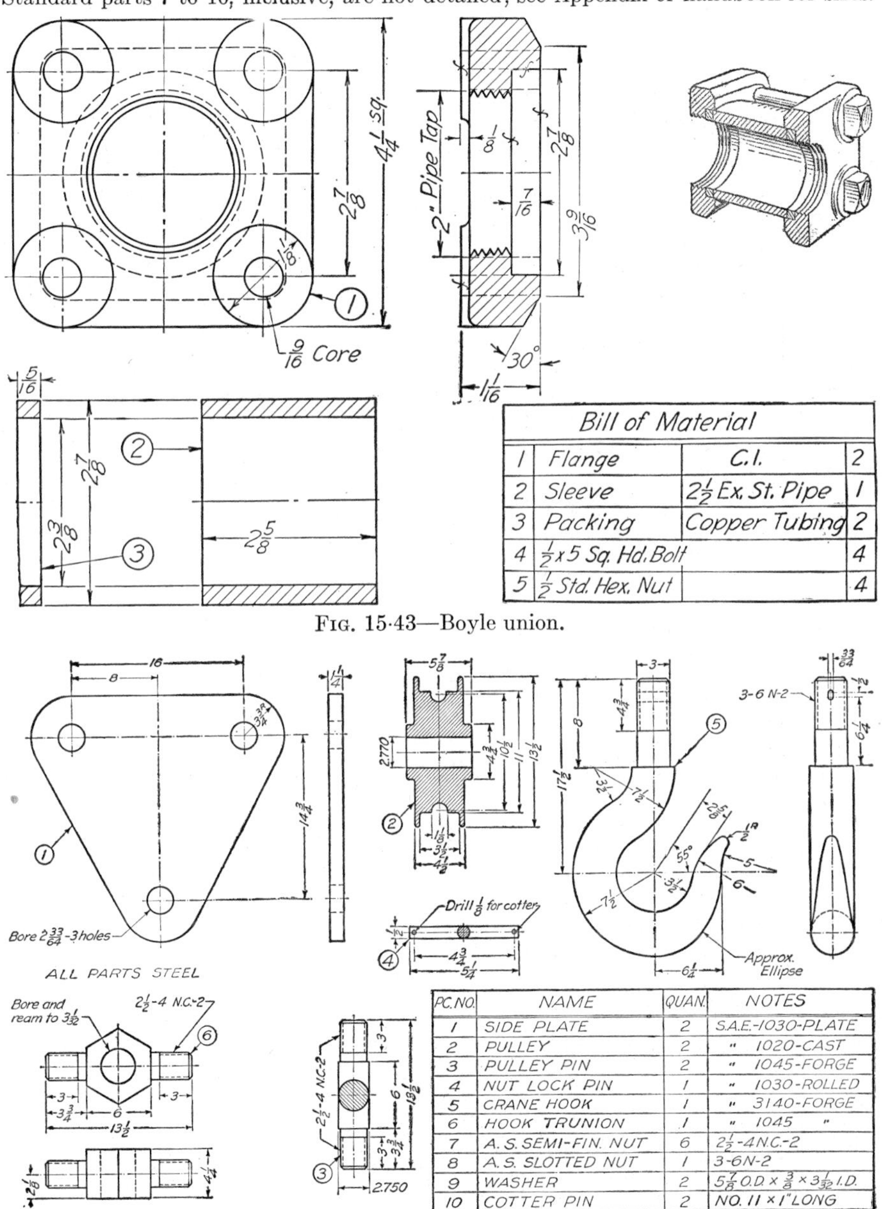

	Bill of Material		
1	Flange	C.I.	2
2	Sleeve	2½ Ex. St. Pipe	1
3	Packing	Copper Tubing	2
4	½ x 5 Sq. Hd. Bolt		4
5	½ Std. Hex. Nut		4

FIG. 15·43—Boyle union.

PC. NO.	NAME	QUAN.	NOTES
1	SIDE PLATE	2	S.A.E.-1030-PLATE
2	PULLEY	2	" 1020-CAST
3	PULLEY PIN	2	" 1045-FORGE
4	NUT LOCK PIN	1	" 1030-ROLLED
5	CRANE HOOK	1	" 3140-FORGE
6	HOOK TRUNION	1	" 1045 "
7	A. S. SEMI-FIN. NUT	6	2½-4N.C.-2
8	A. S. SLOTTED NUT	1	3-6N-2
9	WASHER	2	5⅞ O.D. x ⅜ x 3 1/32 I.D.
10	COTTER PIN	2	NO. 11 x 1" LONG

FIG. 15·44—Crane hook.

31. Fig. 15·45. Make an assembly drawing, front view in section, of caster.

32. Fig. 15·45. Redesign caster for ball-bearing installation.

33. Fig. 15·46. Make an assembly drawing of the ball-bearing live center from details given. The "live" type of center is used on machine tools of various types in

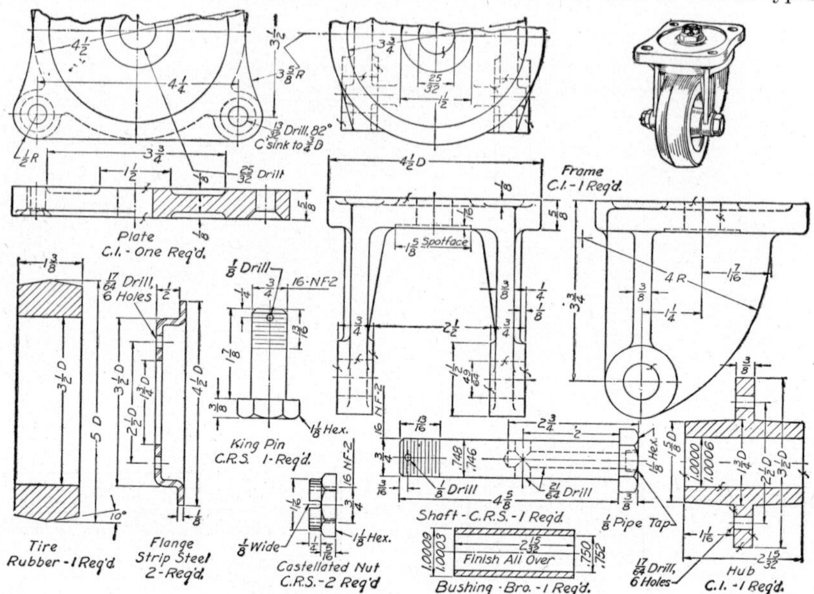

FIG. 15·45—Caster.

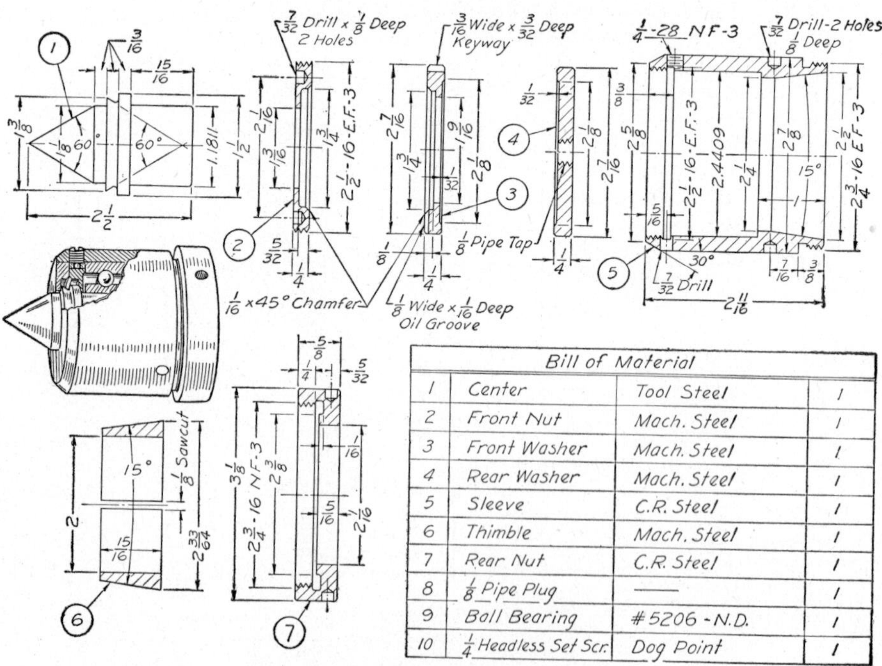

	Bill of Material		
1	Center	Tool Steel	1
2	Front Nut	Mach. Steel	1
3	Front Washer	Mach. Steel	1
4	Rear Washer	Mach. Steel	1
5	Sleeve	C.R. Steel	1
6	Thimble	Mach. Steel	1
7	Rear Nut	C.R. Steel	1
8	$\frac{1}{8}$ Pipe Plug	——	1
9	Ball Bearing	#5206 - N.D.	1
10	$\frac{1}{4}$ Headless Set Scr.	Dog Point	1

FIG. 15·46—Ball-bearing live center.

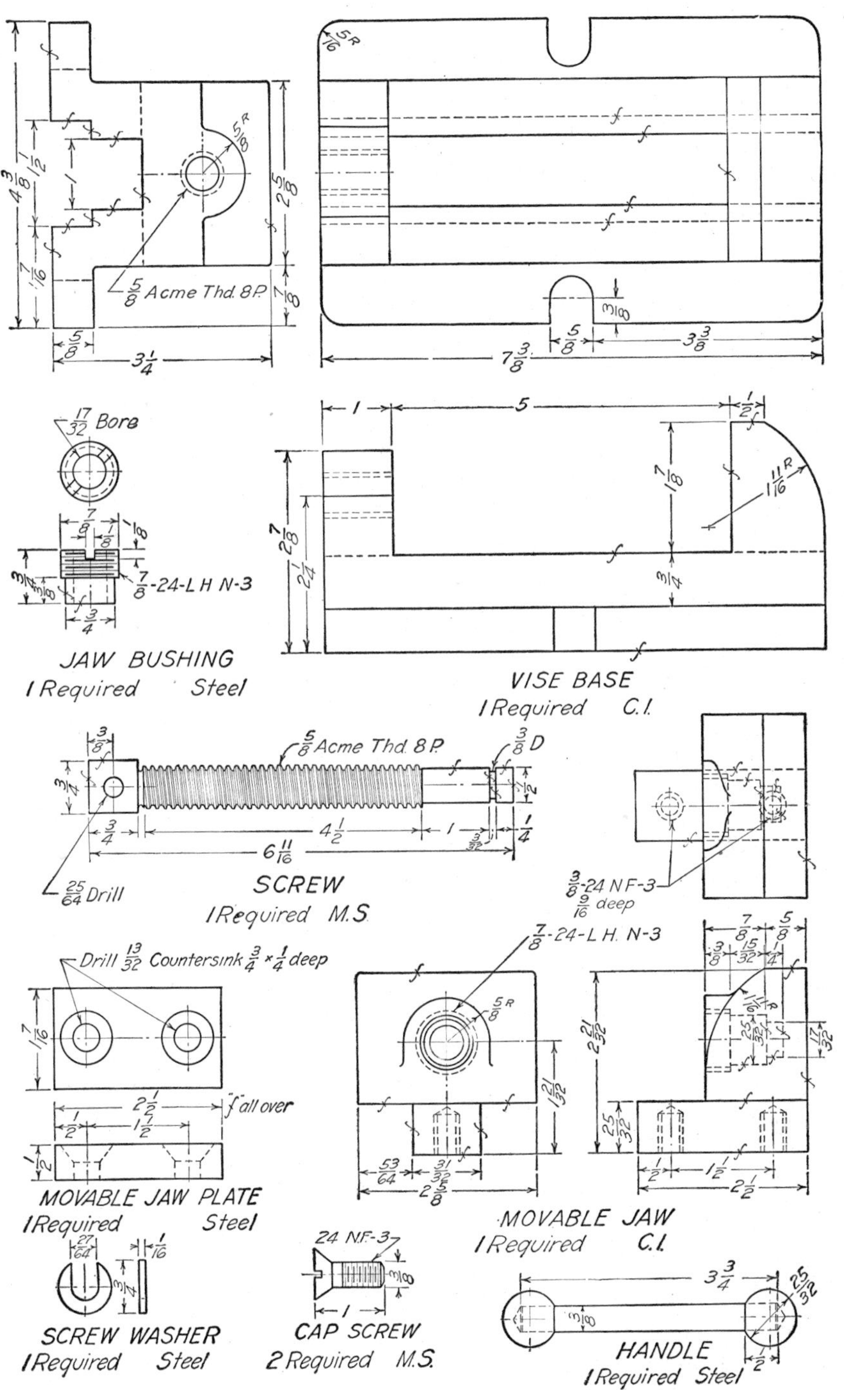

FIG. 15·47—Drill-press vise.

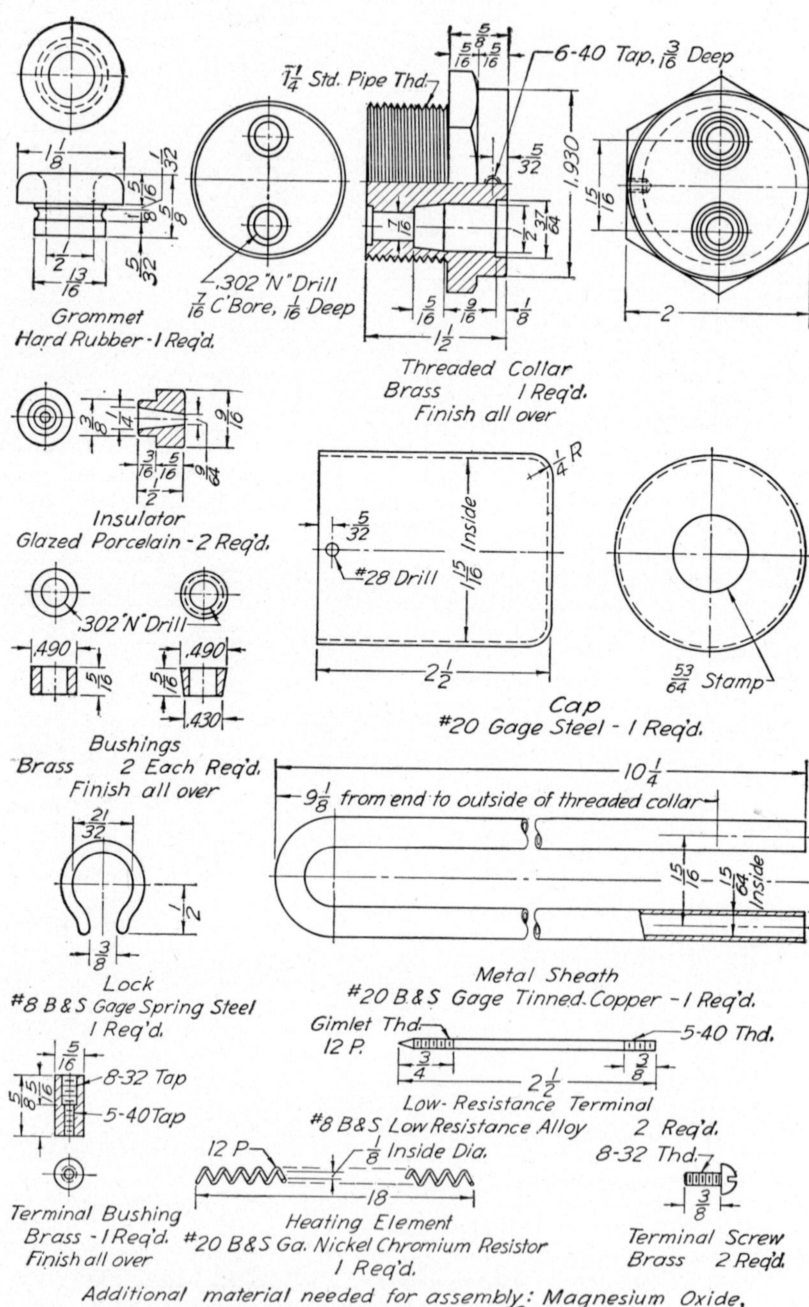

FIG. 15·48—Details of immersion heater.

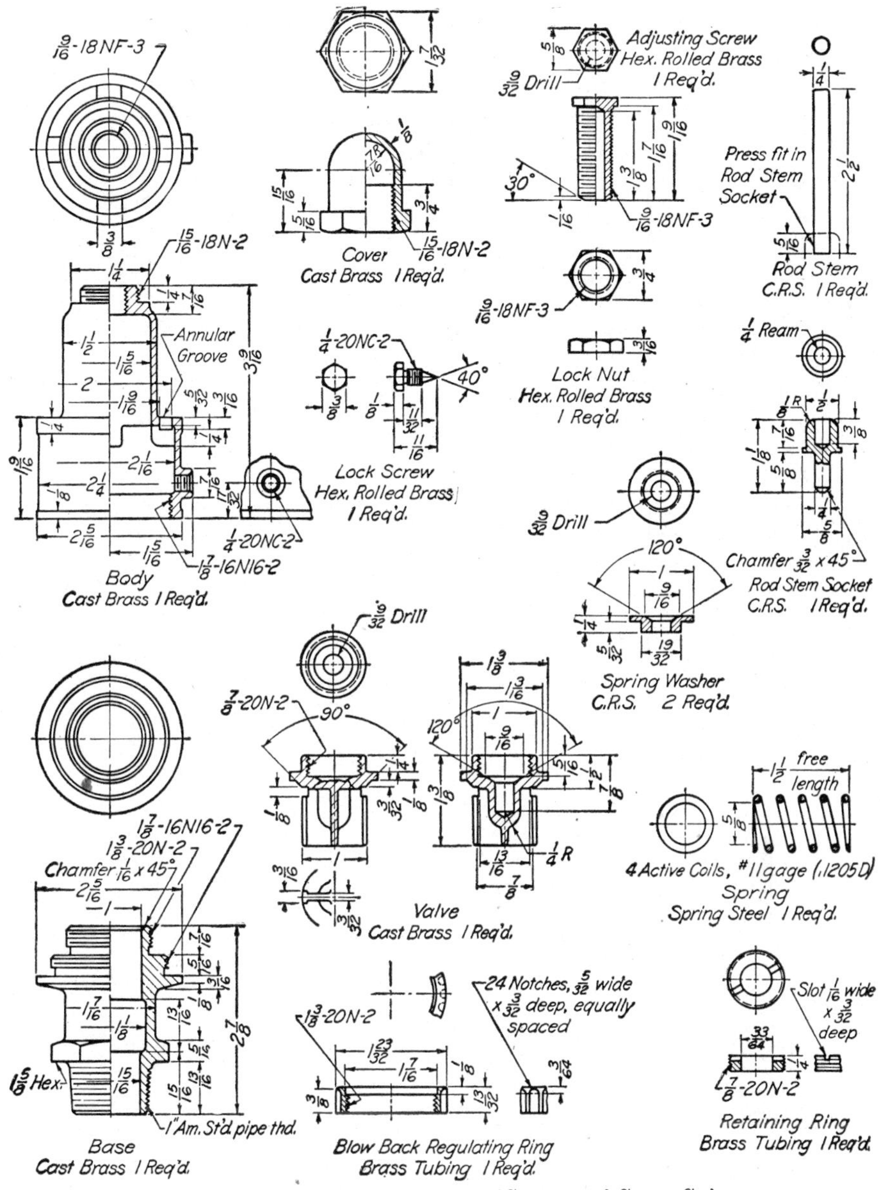

FIG. 15·49—Brass relief valve. (*Courtesy of Crane Co.*)

operations where high speed of the moving part held by the center would cause excessive heating if the stationary or "dead" center were used. The parts may be oriented in the assembly by checking the dimensions of one part against those of another to find mating pieces. The pictorial sketch and the bill of material will also assist. The detail dimensions of the ball bearing may be obtained from the manufacturer's catalogue. Draw both end views and a longitudinal view in section.

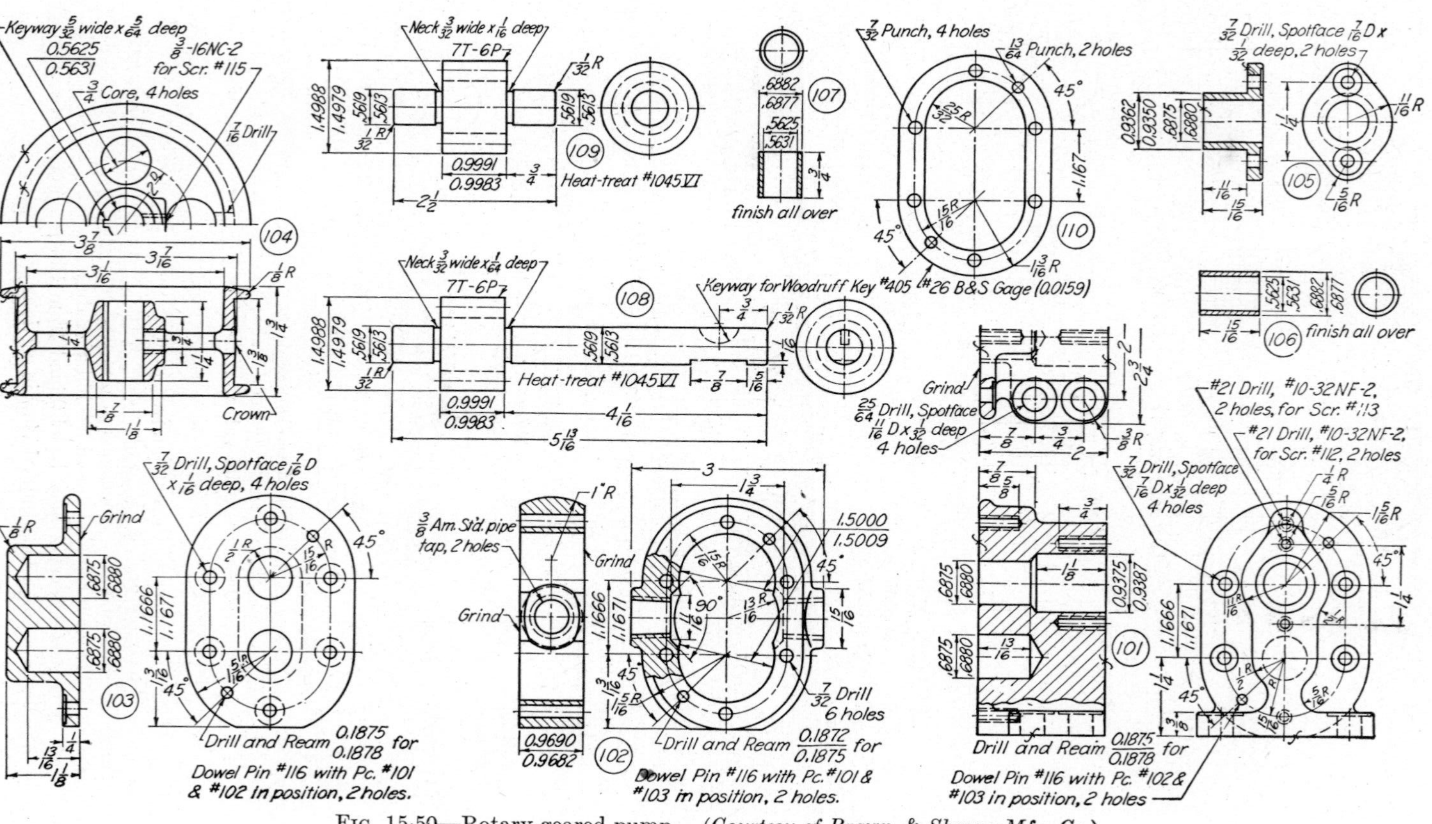

Fig. 15·50—Rotary geared pump. (Courtesy of Brown & Sharpe Mfg. Co.)

PARTS LIST BROWN AND SHARPE No. 1 ROTARY GEARED PUMP									
PC. NO	DRAW. SIZE	NAME	QUAN	MAT.	STOCK		USED ON		REMARKS
					DIA.	LENG	NAME	PC. NO	
101		Base	1	C.I.					
102		Body	1	C.I.					
103		Cover	1	C.I.					
104		Pulley	1	C.I.					
105		Gland	1	C.I.					
106		Gland Bushing	1	Bro.					
107		Gear Bushing	4	Bro.					
108		Driving Gear	1	S.A.E. #1045	1 9/16	5 7/8			
109		Driven Gear	1	S.A.E. #1045	1 9/16	2 9/16			
110		Gasket	2	Sheet Copper			Body	102	#26 B&S Gage (0.0159)
111		#10-32 x 1 5/8 Slotted Hex. Hd. Mach. Scr. & Nut	4				Cover	103	
112		#10-32 x 1 5/8 Slotted Hex. Hd. Cap Scr.	2				Cover	103	
113		#10-32 x 7/8 Slotted Hex. Hd. Cap Scr.	2				Gland	105	
114		Woodruff Key #405	1				Driving Gear	108	
115		3/8 x 3/8 Headless Set Scr., 3/8-16NC-2	1				Pulley	104	
116		3/16 x 1 7/16 Dowel Pin	2	C.R.S.			Cover	103	
		Packing	To Suit						Garlock Rotopac #239

FIG. 15·51—Parts list for rotary geared pump.

34. Fig. 15·47. Make an assembly drawing of the drill-press vise. Show maximum opening of jaws with alternate position lines.

35. Fig. 15·48. From the details given, make an assembly drawing of the immersion heater, adding such dimensions and notes as would make the drawing useful as a descriptive illustration.

36. Fig. 15·49. Make an assembly drawing of the brass relief valve from details given. The parts may be oriented in the assembly by checking the dimensions of one part against those of another to find mating pieces. The thread specifications given will also aid materially in locating the parts that are screwed together. Use two views, front and top, with front view in section. Indicate part numbers and make a bill of material.

37. Fig. 15·50. Make an assembly drawing of the Brown and Sharpe rotary geared pump, with top view, longitudinal section, and side view. Show direction of rotation of shafts and flow of liquid with arrows. Give dimensions for base holes to be used in setting; also give distance from base to center of driving shaft and size of shaft and key. Refer to Chap. 17 for method of drawing the teeth of the gears, pieces 108 and 109. For parts not detailed, see bill of material, Fig. 15·51.

38. Fig. 15·51. Letter bill of material on separate sheet to accompany Prob. 37.

39. Fig. 15·52. From detail sketches, make assembly and detail drawings of Unipump centrifugal pump, as made by the Weinman Pump Mfg. Co., in which the pump casing is mounted directly on a driving motor, making a compact and efficient design. Cross sections of the volute taken at intervals of 45° should be shown by removed sections, either successive or superimposed, and similar sections should be made through the impeller. At 3,425 rpm this pump delivers 520 gal per min against a head of 160 ft.

40. Fig. 15·53. Make assembly drawing of telescopic screw jack, with front view in section. Make a bill of material on a separate sheet. Show jack partially opened and give dimensions from base to top of cap for lowest and highest positions. Handle and handle shaft may be shown broken in order to save space and reduce the sheet size. Refer to Chap. 17 for the method of drawing the teeth of the bevel gears.

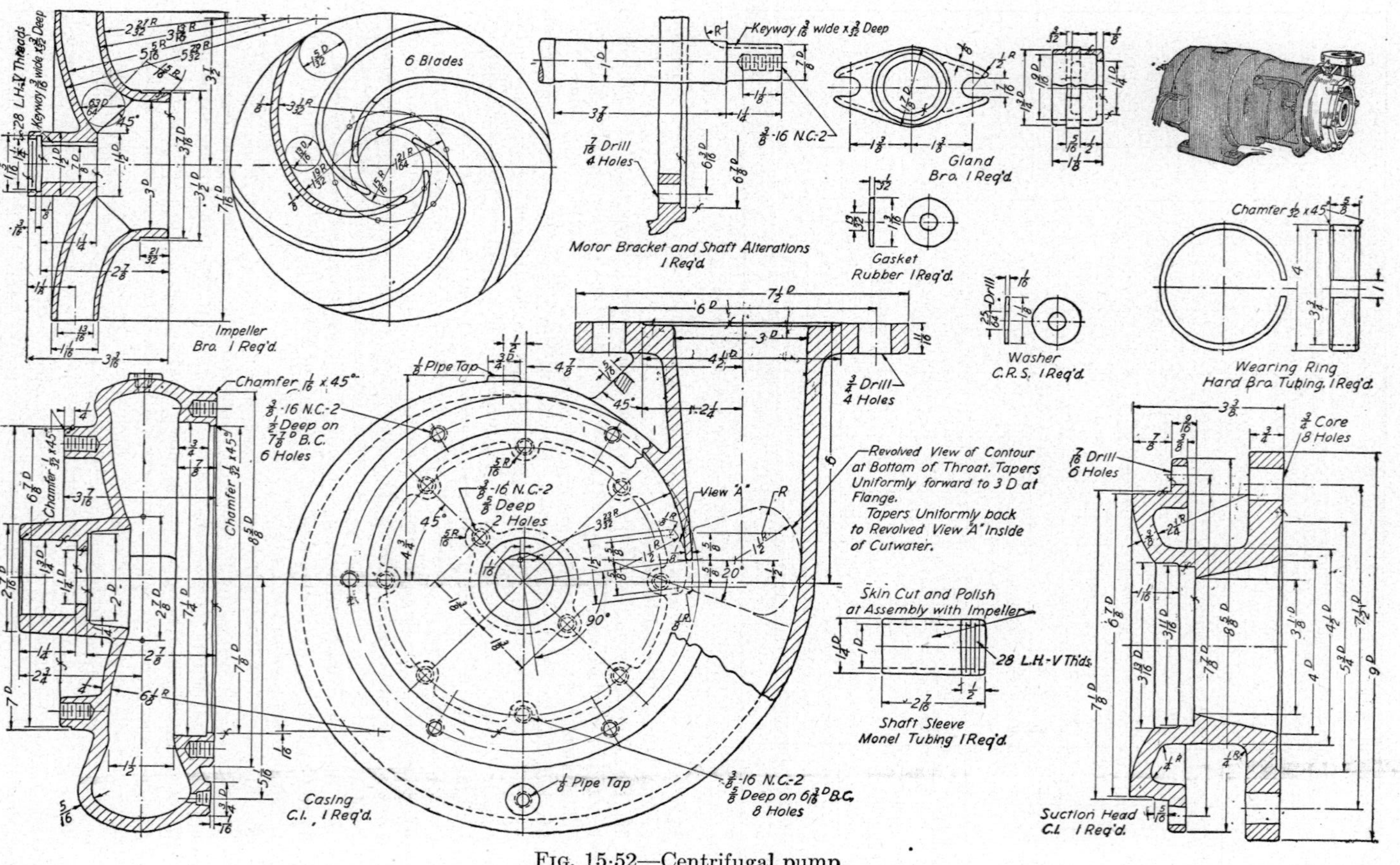

FIG. 15·52—Centrifugal pump.

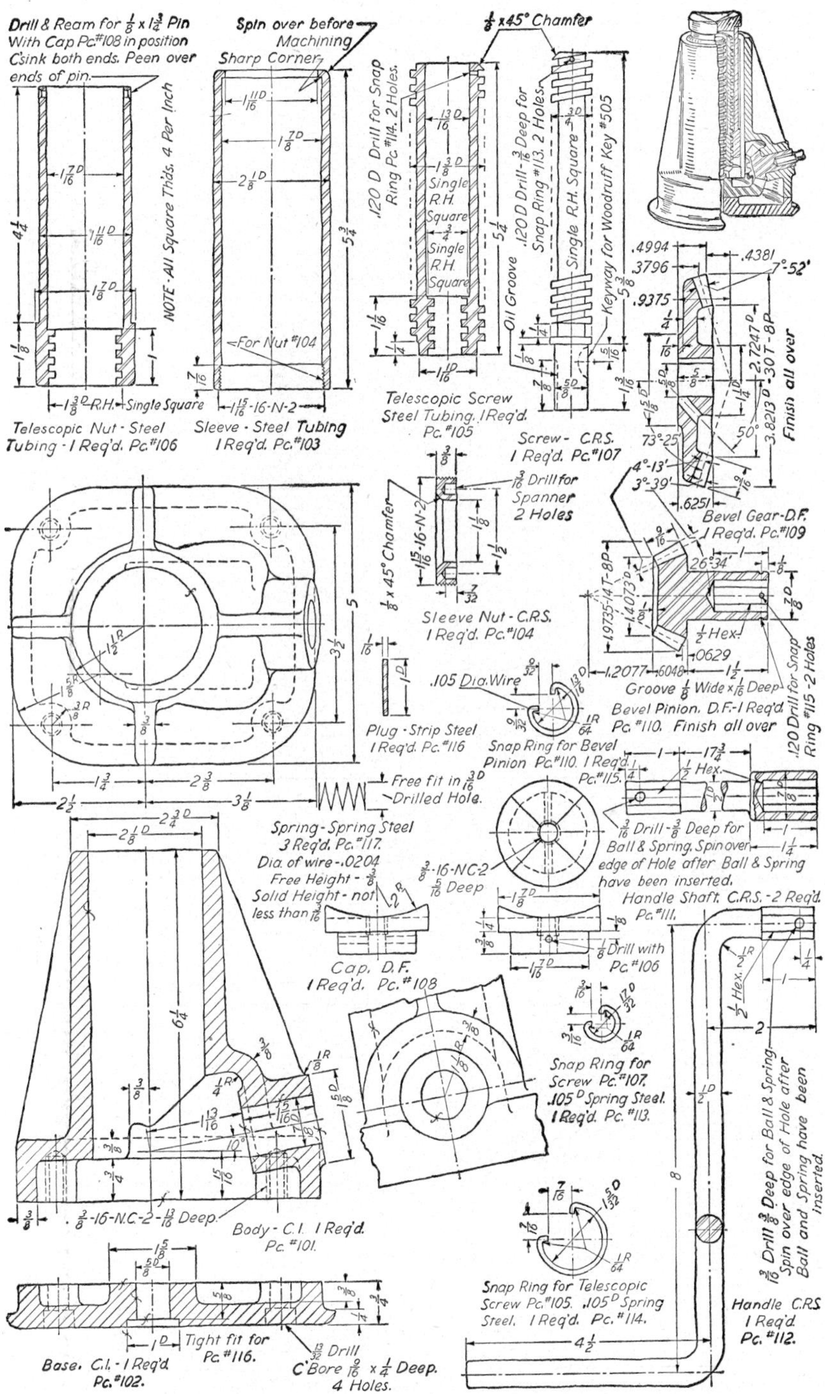

FIG. 15·53—Telescopic screw jack.

Group III. Detail drawings from the assembly

41. Fig. 15·54. Make detail drawings of jig table.

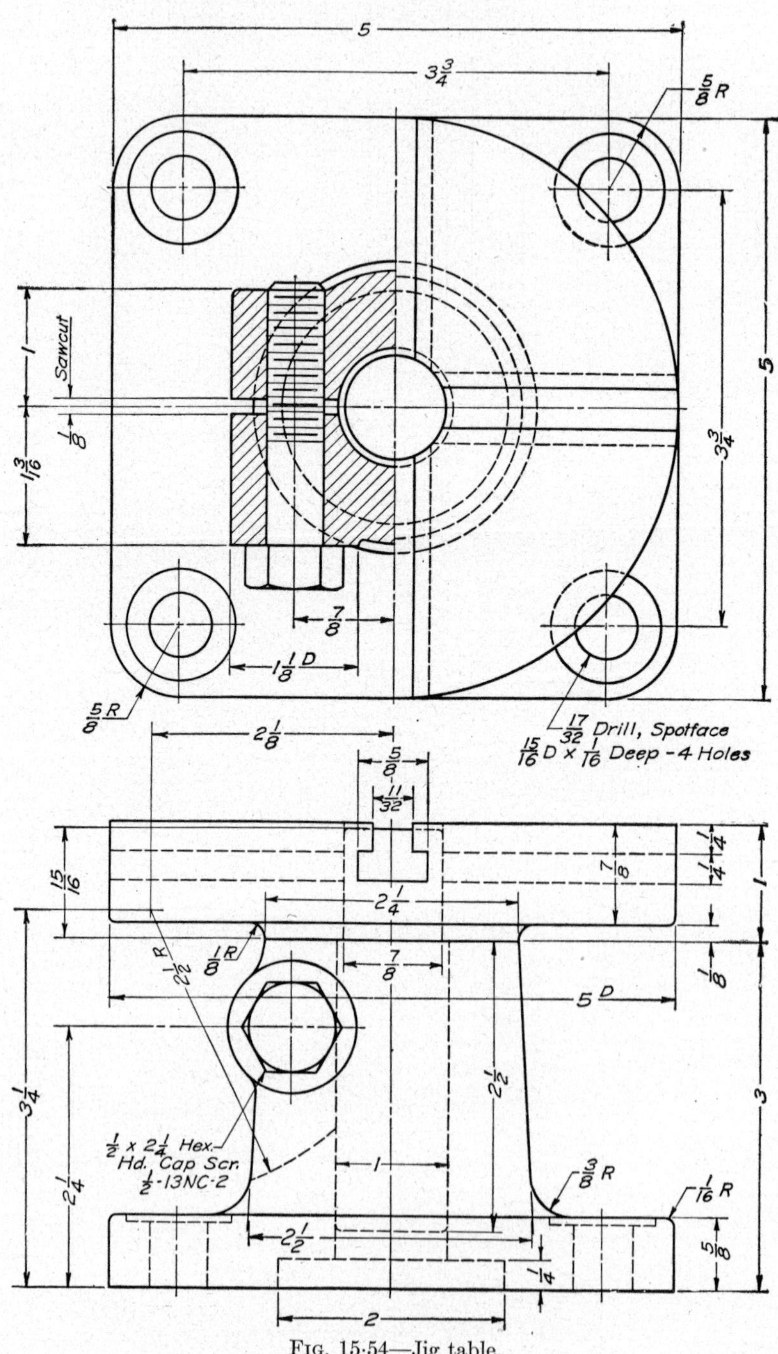

FIG. 15·54—Jig table.

42. Fig. 15·55. Make working drawings, assembled. Size to be assigned.
43. Fig. 15·56. Make detail drawings of screw-end ball joint.

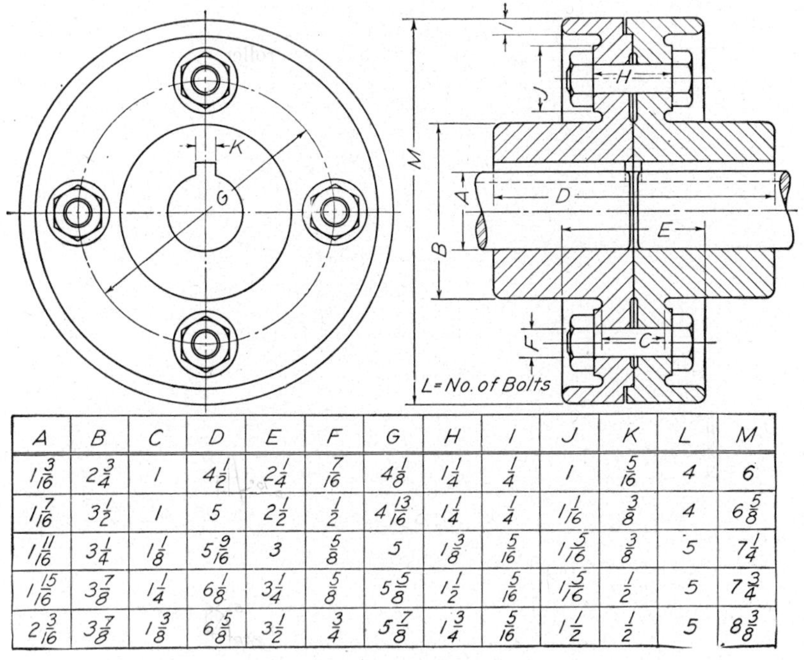

A	B	C	D	E	F	G	H	I	J	K	L	M
1 3/16	2 3/4	1	4 1/2	2 1/4	7/16	4 1/8	1 1/4	1/4	1	5/16	4	6
1 7/16	3 1/2	1	5	2 1/2	1/2	4 13/16	1 1/4	1/4	1 1/16	3/8	4	6 5/8
1 11/16	3 1/4	1 1/8	5 9/16	3	5/8	5	1 3/8	5/16	1 5/16	3/8	5	7 1/4
1 15/16	3 7/8	1 1/4	6 1/8	3 1/4	5/8	5 5/8	1 1/2	5/16	1 5/16	1/2	5	7 3/4
2 3/16	3 7/8	1 3/8	6 5/8	3 1/2	3/4	5 7/8	1 3/4	5/16	1 1/2	1/2	5	8 3/8

Fig. 15·55—Flange coupling.

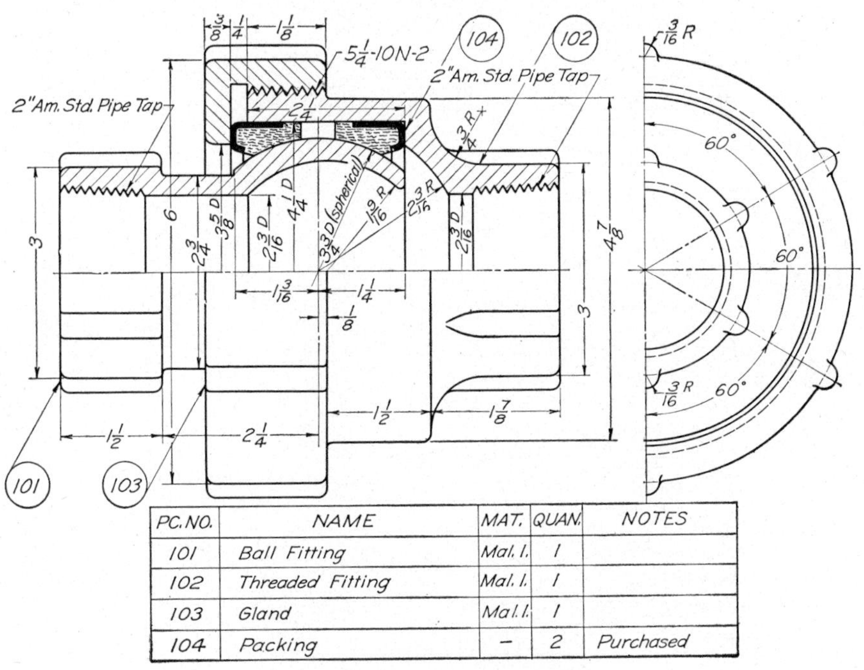

PC. NO.	NAME	MAT.	QUAN.	NOTES
101	Ball Fitting	Mal. I.	1	
102	Threaded Fitting	Mal. I.	1	
103	Gland	Mal. I.	1	
104	Packing	–	2	Purchased

Fig. 15·56—Screw-end ball joint.

44. Fig. 15·57. Make detail drawings of adjustable roller stand.
45. Fig. 15·58. Make detail drawings of the eccentric and strap.

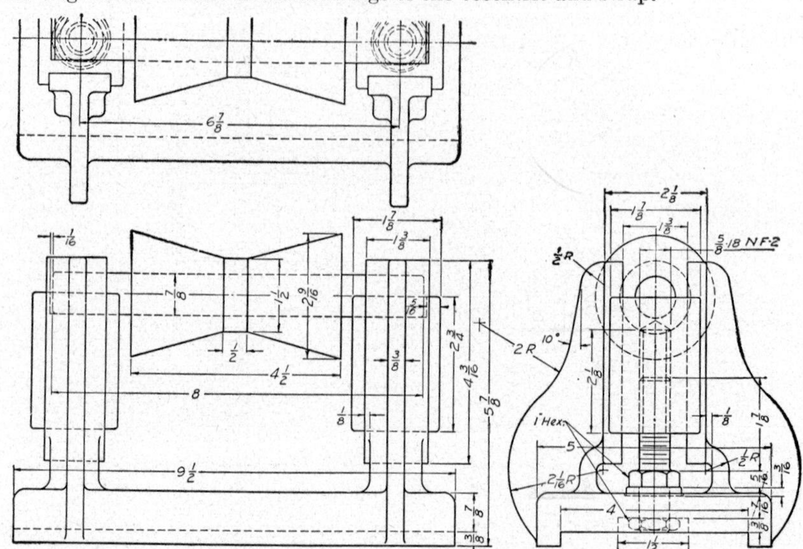

FIG. 15·57—Adjustable roller stand.

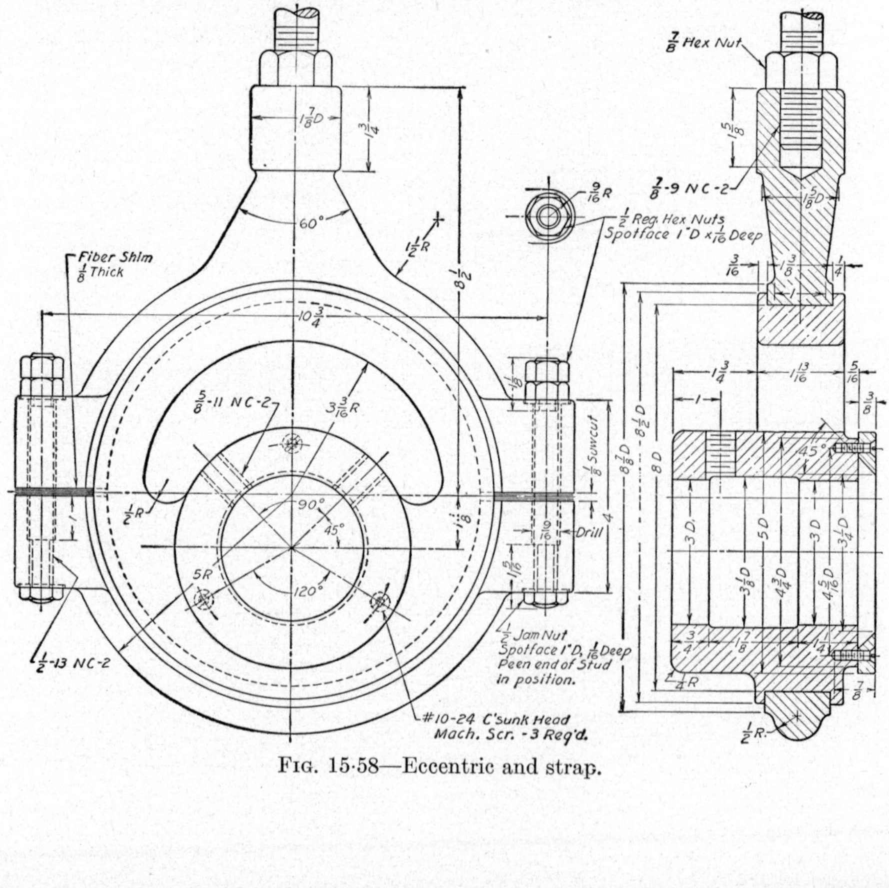

FIG. 15·58—Eccentric and strap.

46. Fig. 15·59. Make detail drawings of swing table.

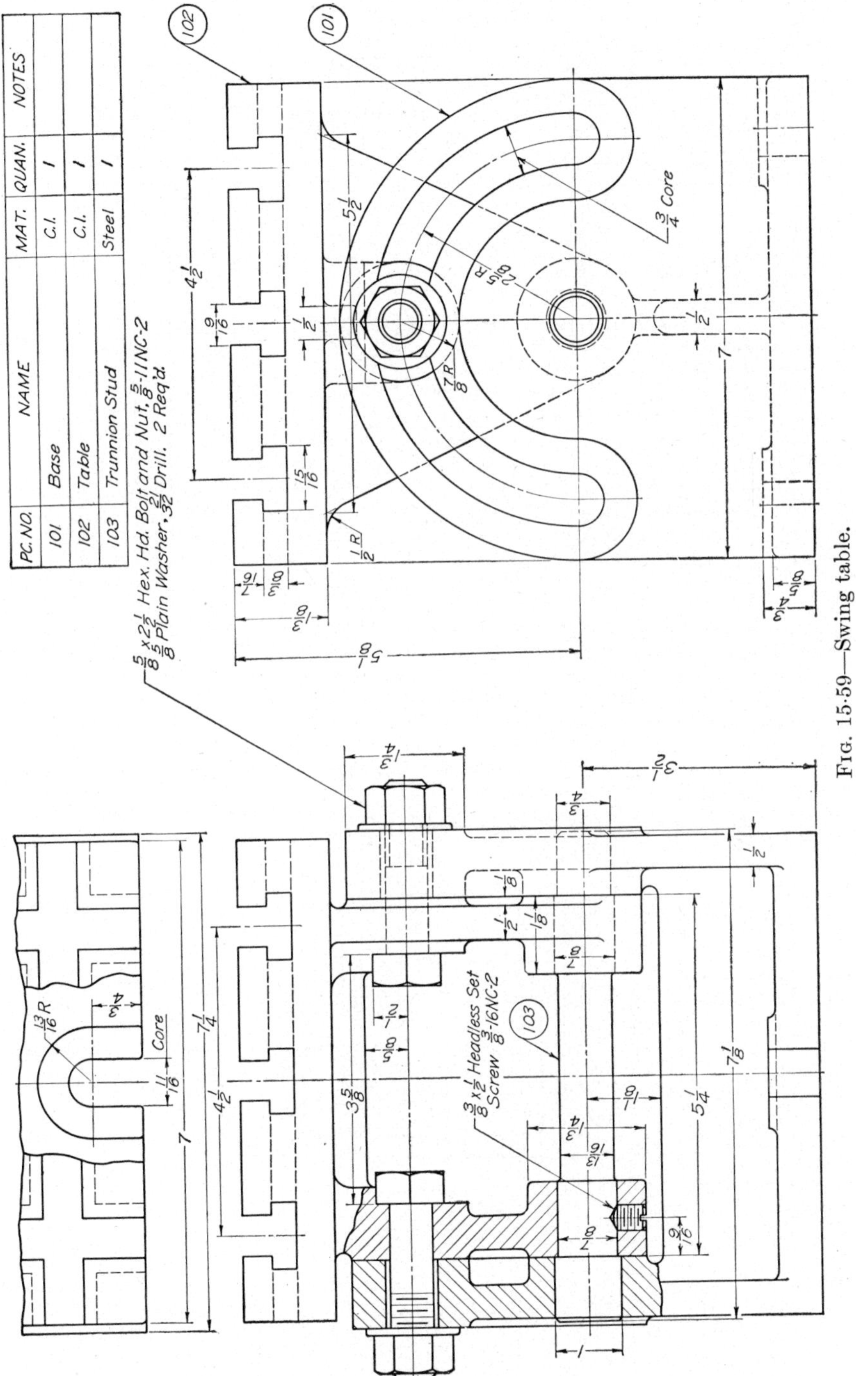

PC. NO.	NAME	MAT.	QUAN.	NOTES
101	Base	C.I.	1	
102	Table	C.I.	1	
103	Trunnion Stud	Steel	1	

FIG. 15·59—Swing table.

47. Fig. 15·60. Make detail drawings of belt drive.

48. Fig. 15·61. Make detail drawings of valve and seat.

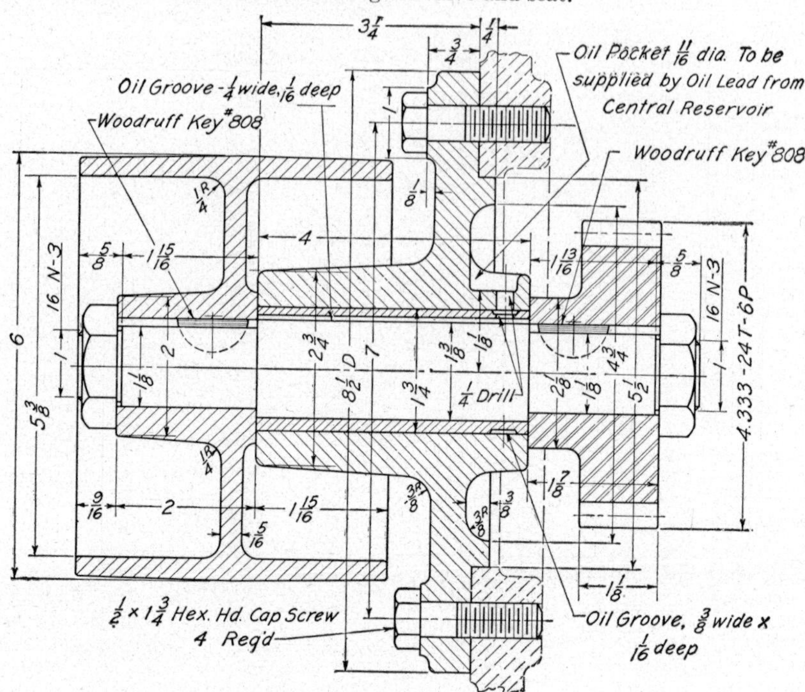

Fig. 15·60—Belt drive.

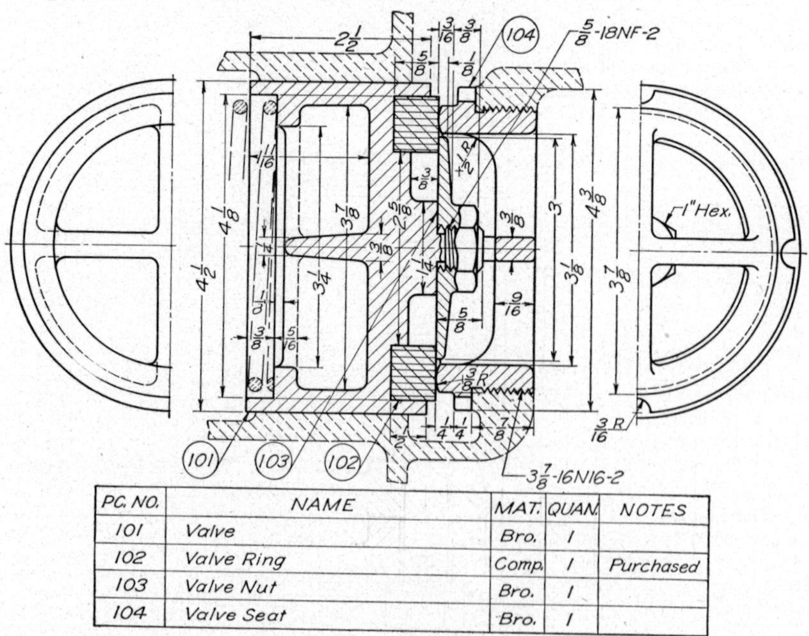

PC. NO.	NAME	MAT.	QUAN.	NOTES
101	Valve	Bro.	1	
102	Valve Ring	Comp.	1	Purchased
103	Valve Nut	Bro.	1	
104	Valve Seat	Bro.	1	

Fig. 15·61—Valve and seat.

49. Fig. 15·62. Make detail drawings of sealed ball joint.
50. Fig. 15·63. Make detail drawings of belt tightener.

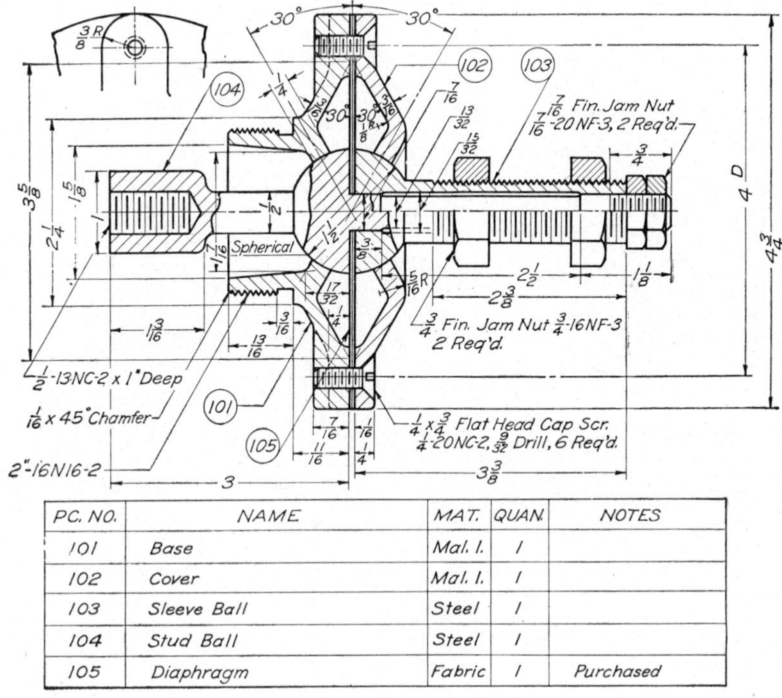

PC. NO.	NAME	MAT.	QUAN.	NOTES
101	Base	Mal. I.	1	
102	Cover	Mal. I.	1	
103	Sleeve Ball	Steel	1	
104	Stud Ball	Steel	1	
105	Diaphragm	Fabric	1	Purchased

FIG. 15·62—Sealed ball joint.

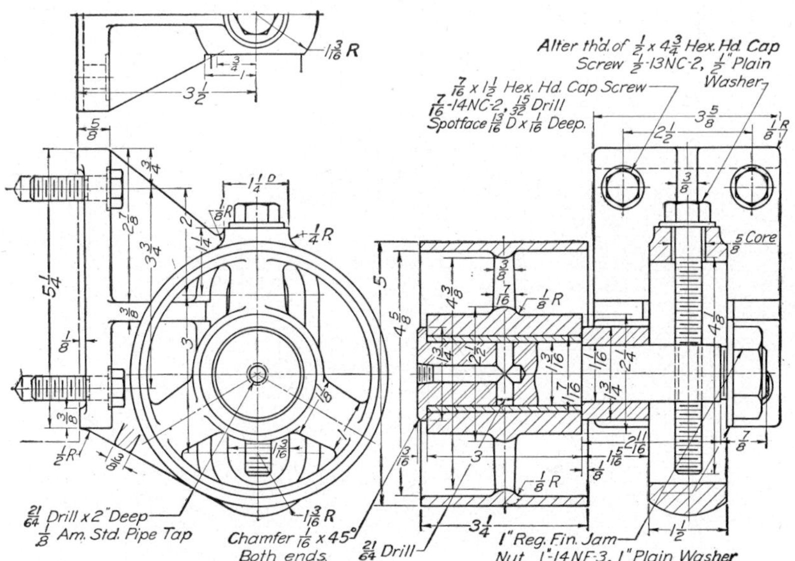

FIG. 15·63—Belt tightener.

51. Fig. 15·64. Make detail drawings of lubricant pump. Note that on the end view, shown with cover removed, the gears are represented conventionally.

2 Circular Holes in Pulley Flange
1/2 Pipe Tap
1 5/8 D
1/4 Dowels 2 Req'd.
1/4-20 NC-2-6 Holes.
1/4-20 NC-2- 2 Holes
1/2 Drill
3/8 Hal's Set Screw
1/8 Woodruff Key #406
8T. 4P.
Slip Fit
Drive
15/32 Drill C'bore 5/8 D x 19/64 deep - 2 Holes

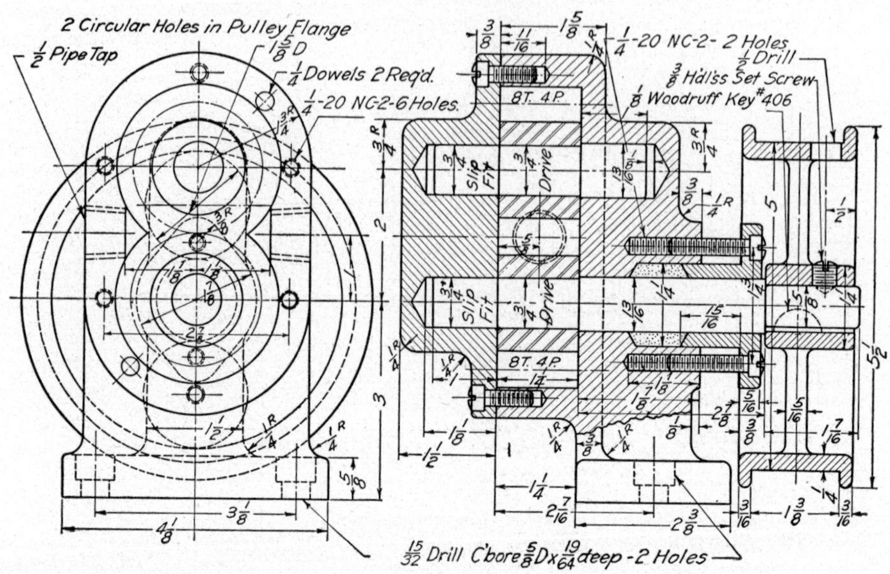

FIG. 15·64—Lubricant pump.

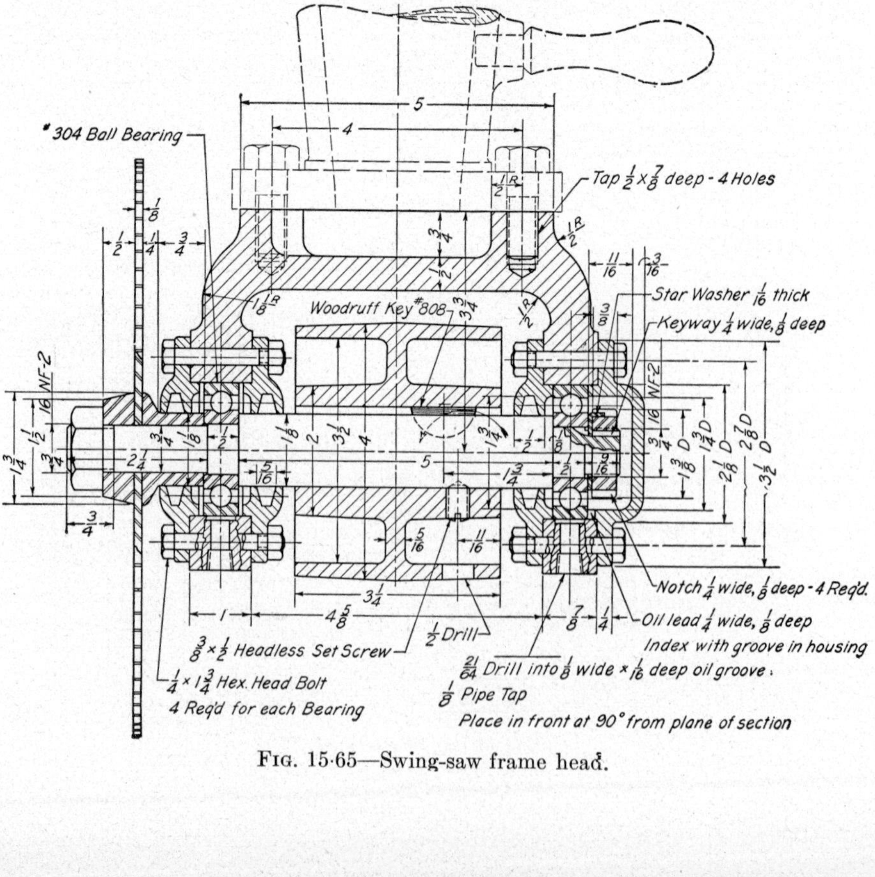

#304 Ball Bearing
Tap 1/2 x 7/8 deep - 4 Holes
Woodruff Key #808
Star Washer 1/16 thick
Keyway 1/4 wide, 1/8 deep
NF-2
Notch 1/4 wide, 1/8 deep - 4 Req'd.
Oil lead 1/4 wide, 1/8 deep
Index with groove in housing
3/8 x 1/2 Headless Set Screw
1/2 Drill
21/64 Drill into 1/8 wide x 1/16 deep oil groove
1/8 Pipe Tap
Place in front at 90° from plane of section
1/4 x 1 3/4 Hex. Head Bolt
4 Req'd for each Bearing

FIG. 15·65—Swing-saw frame head.

52. Fig. 15·65. Make detail drawings and parts list for swing-saw frame head. The bearing sizes may be obtained from a ball-bearing catalogue. For belt clearance make base elliptical, 5″ × 4″.

53. Fig. 15·66. Make detail drawings of compensating nut. The purpose of this device is to take up the wear resulting from heavy duty imposed on a feed screw. To adjust the nut, the cap screw at the left is loosened and the nut on the draw screw is tightened, the wedging action pushing the loose nut to the left until all lost motion is taken up.

54. Fig. 15·67. Make detail drawings of adjustable mid-bearing.

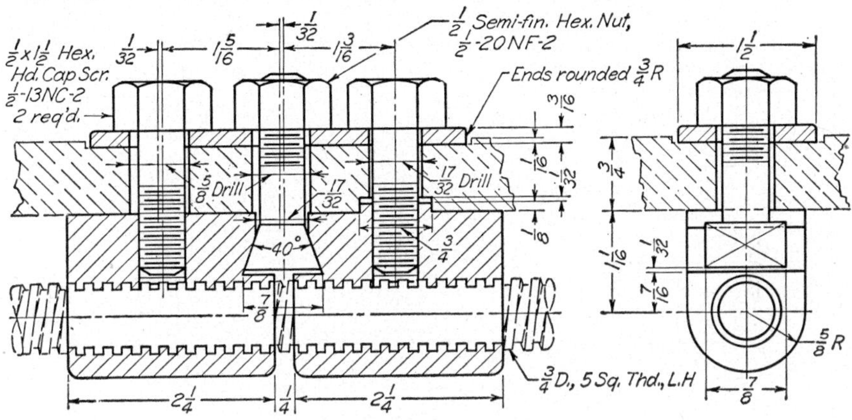

Fig. 15·66—Compensating nut.

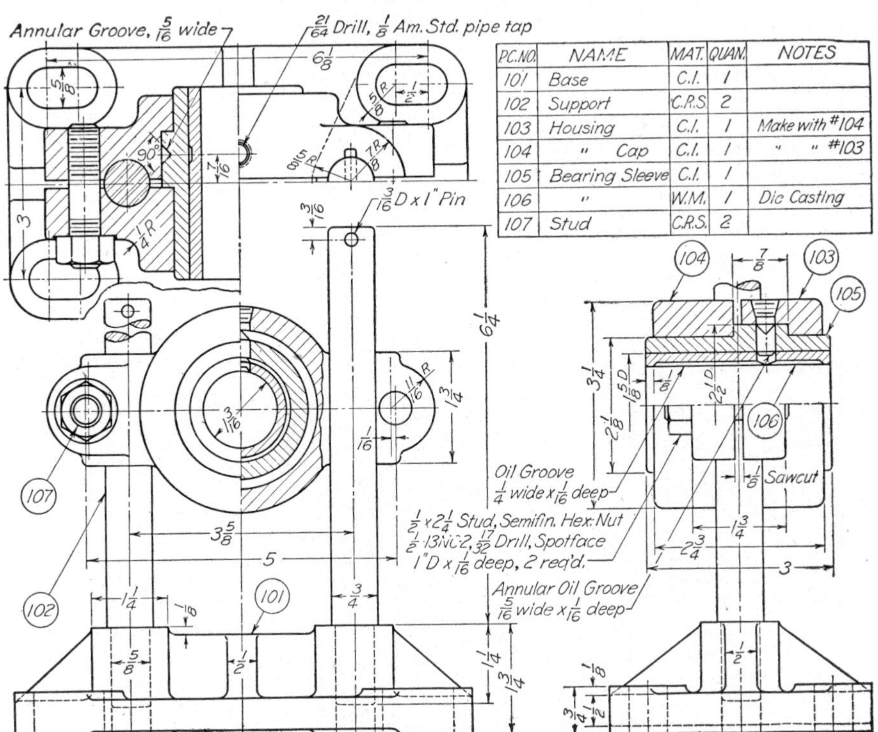

PC. NO.	NAME	MAT.	QUAN.	NOTES
101	Base	C.I.	1	
102	Support	C.R.S.	2	
103	Housing	C.I.	1	Make with #104
104	" Cap	C.I.	1	" " #103
105	Bearing Sleeve	C.I.	1	
106	"	W.M.	1	Die Casting
107	Stud	C.R.S.	2	

Fig. 15·67—Adjustable mid-bearing.

55. Fig. 15·68. Make detail drawings of the signal-tower bracket.
56. Fig. 15·69. Make detail drawings of ball-bearing idler pulley.

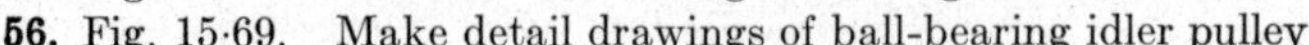

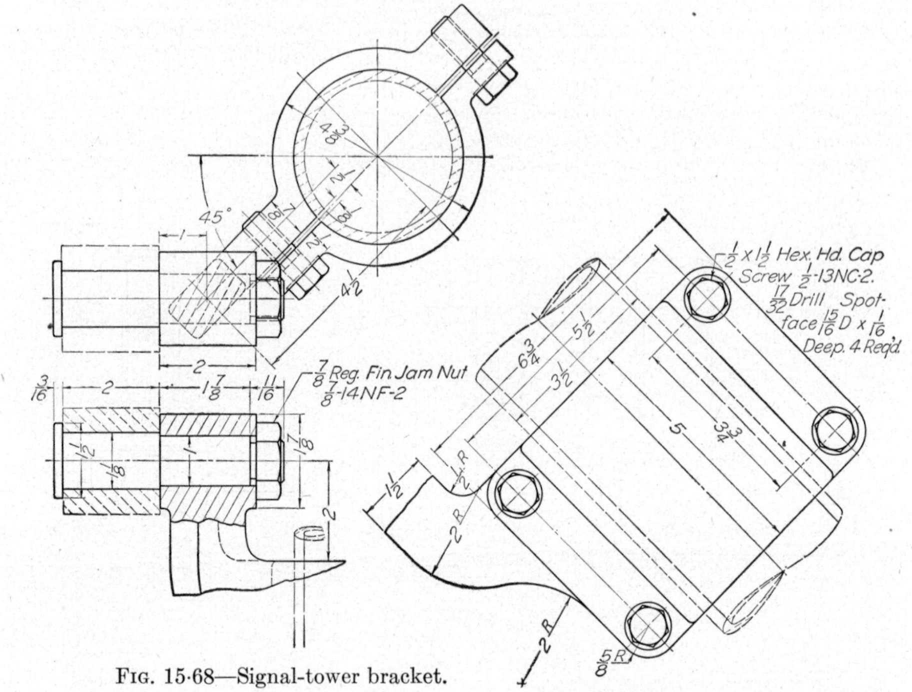

FIG. 15·68—Signal-tower bracket.

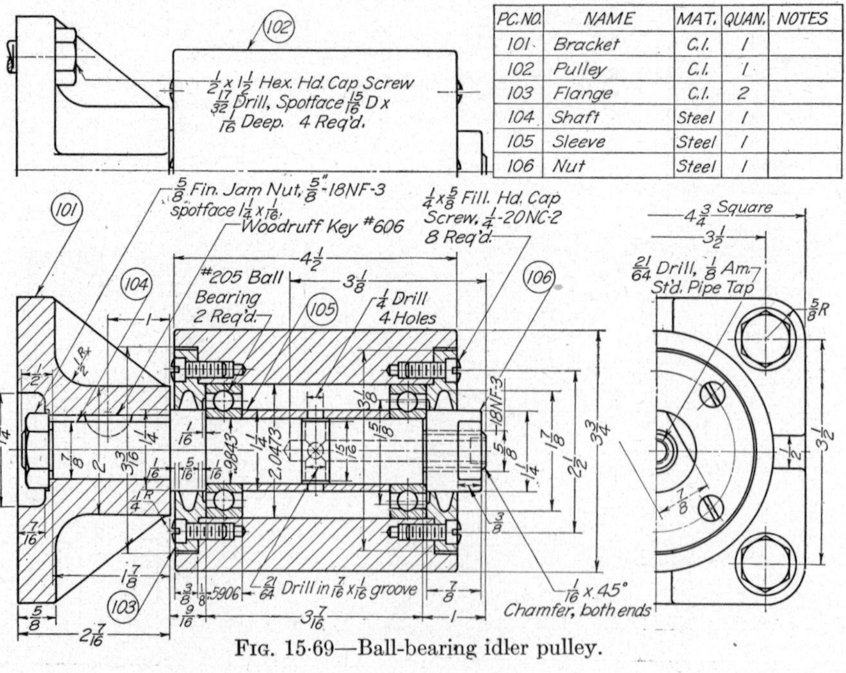

PC.NO.	NAME	MAT.	QUAN.	NOTES
101	Bracket	C.I.	1	
102	Pulley	C.I.	1	
103	Flange	C.I.	2	
104	Shaft	Steel	1	
105	Sleeve	Steel	1	
106	Nut	Steel	1	

FIG. 15·69—Ball-bearing idler pulley.

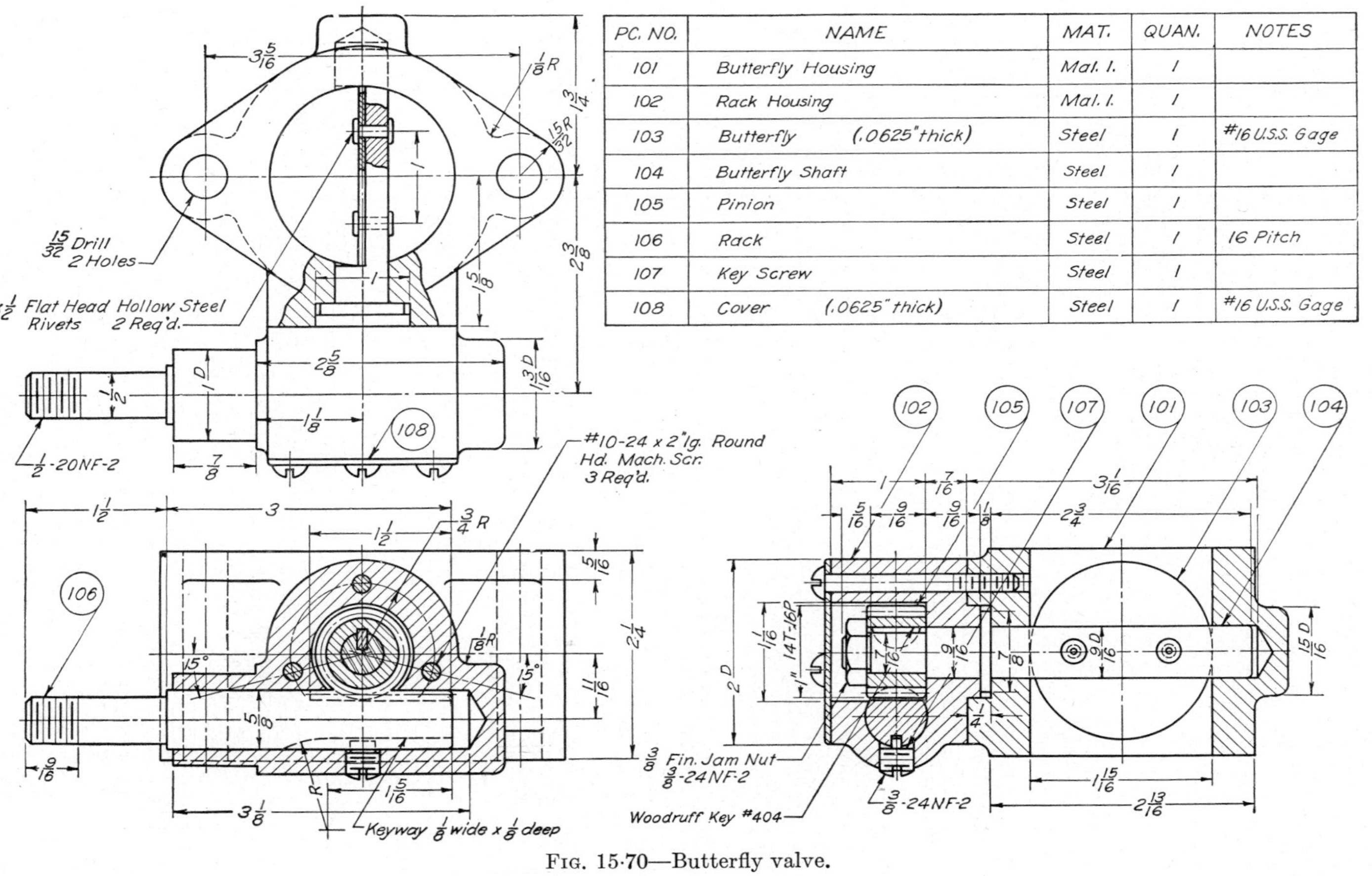

PC. NO.	NAME	MAT.	QUAN.	NOTES
101	Butterfly Housing	Mal. I.	1	
102	Rack Housing	Mal. I.	1	
103	Butterfly (.0625" thick)	Steel	1	#16 U.S.S. Gage
104	Butterfly Shaft	Steel	1	
105	Pinion	Steel	1	
106	Rack	Steel	1	16 Pitch
107	Key Screw	Steel	1	
108	Cover (.0625" thick)	Steel	1	#16 U.S.S. Gage

Fig. 15·70—Butterfly valve.

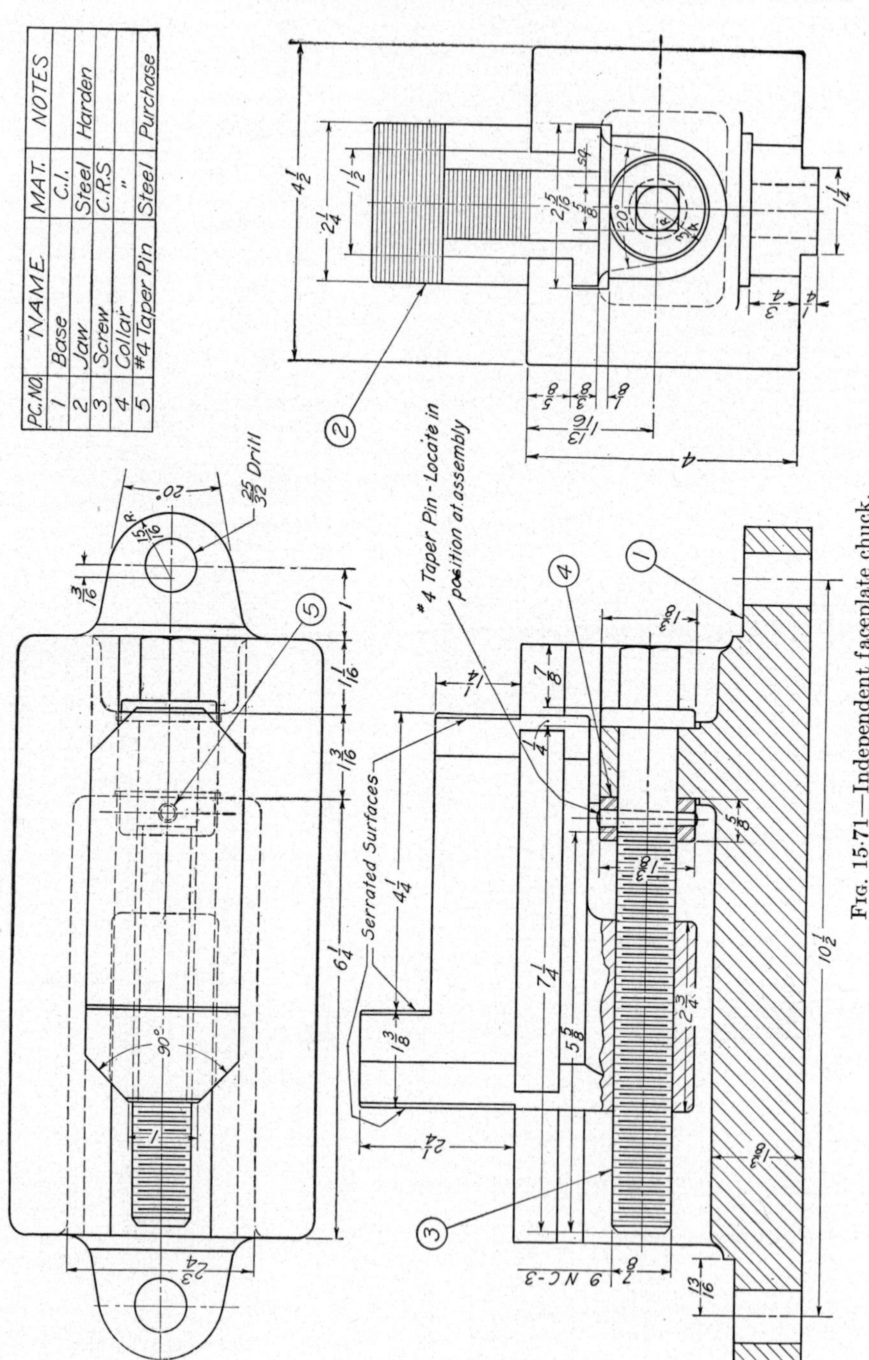

PC.NO.	NAME	MAT.	NOTES
1	Base	C.I.	
2	Jaw	Steel	Harden
3	Screw	C.R.S	
4	Collar	"	
5	#4 Taper Pin	Steel	Purchase

FIG. 15·71—Independent faceplate chuck.

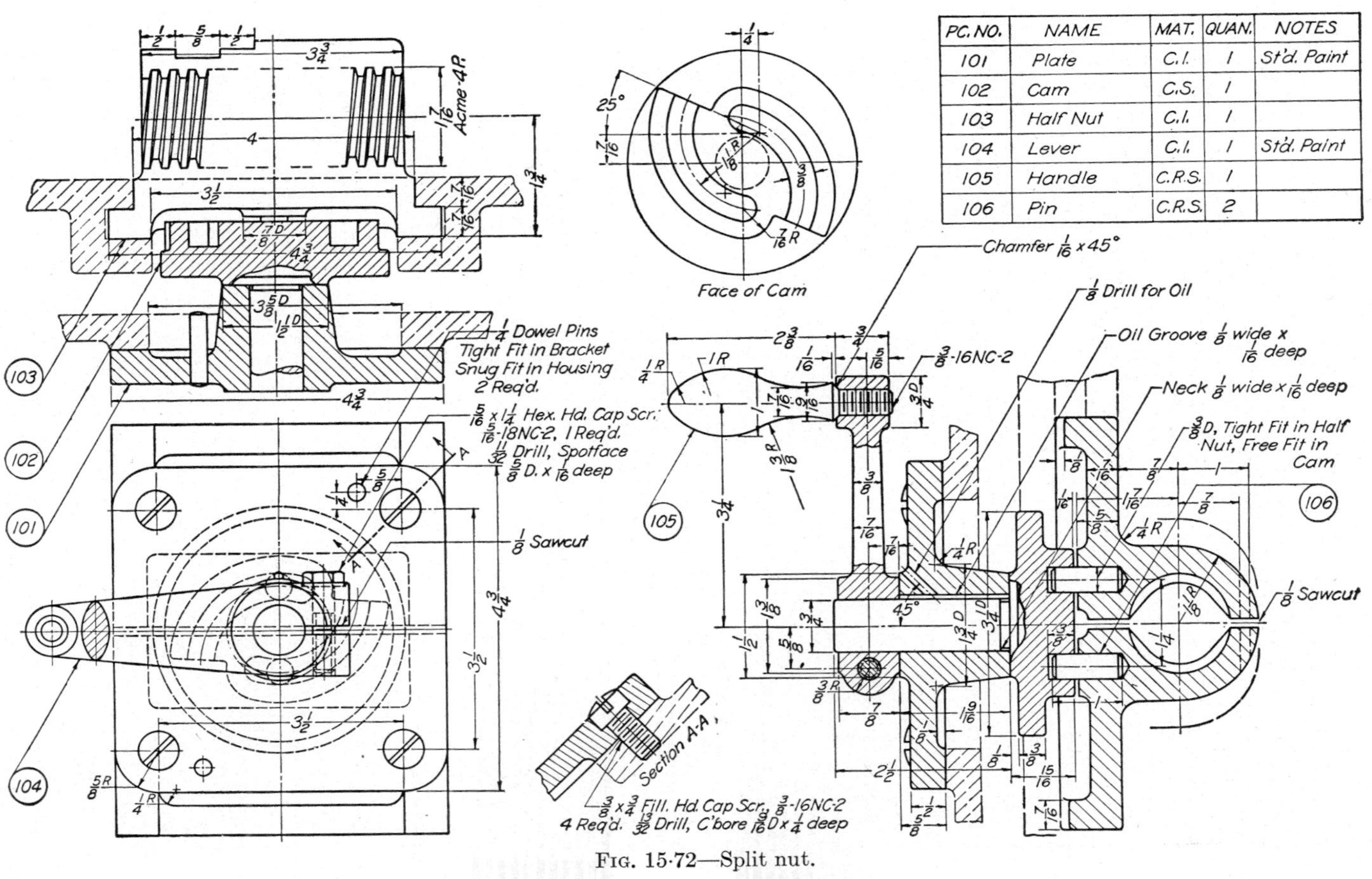

PC. NO.	NAME	MAT.	QUAN.	NOTES
101	Plate	C.I.	1	St'd. Paint
102	Cam	C.S.	1	
103	Half Nut	C.I.	1	
104	Lever	C.I.	1	St'd. Paint
105	Handle	C.R.S.	1	
106	Pin	C.R.S.	2	

FIG. 15·72—Split nut.

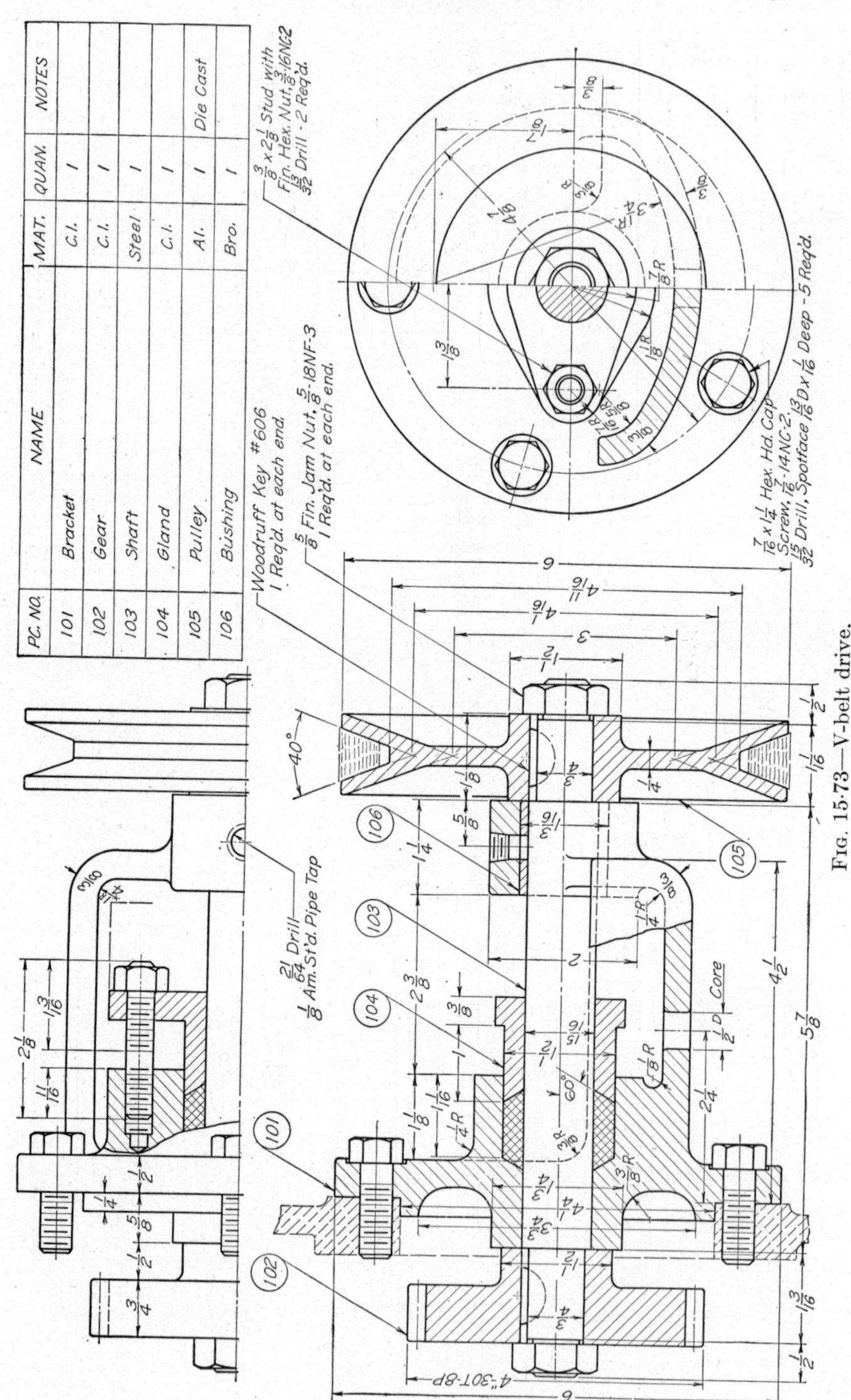

PC. NO.	NAME	MAT.	QUAN.	NOTES
101	Bracket	C.I.	1	
102	Gear	C.I.	1	
103	Shaft	Steel	1	
104	Gland	C.I.	1	
105	Pulley	Al.	1	Die Cast
106	Bushing	Bro.	1	

FIG. 15·73—V-belt drive.

57. Fig. 15·70. Make detail drawings of butterfly valve. Refer to Chap. **17** for method of detailing gear and rack.

58. Redesign Fig. 15·70, making butterfly $2\frac{1}{4}''$.

59. Fig. 15·71. Make detail drawings of independent faceplate chuck.

60. Fig. 15·72. Make detail drawings for split nut. This well-known mechanism provides for engagement and disengagement of a nut on a screw while the screw is in motion. A 90° movement of the hand lever actuates the two pins in the half nuts by means of the milled slots in the cam, thus raising or lowering the half nuts.

61. Fig. 15·73. Make detail drawings of V-belt drive.

62. Fig. 15·74. Make detail drawings of swivel base.

63. Fig. 15·75. Make detail drawings of rail-transport hanger. Rail is 10-lb ASCE.

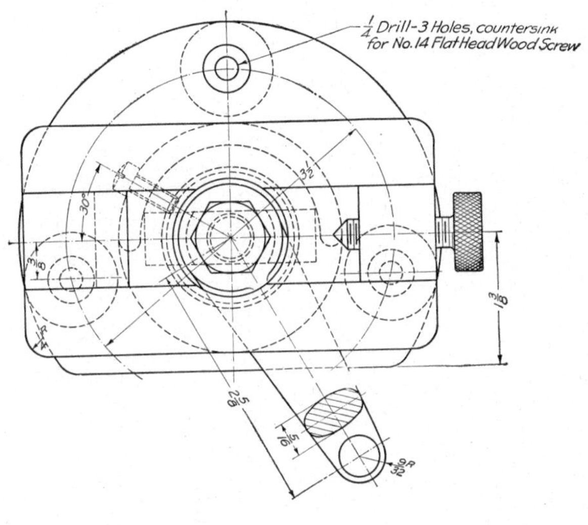

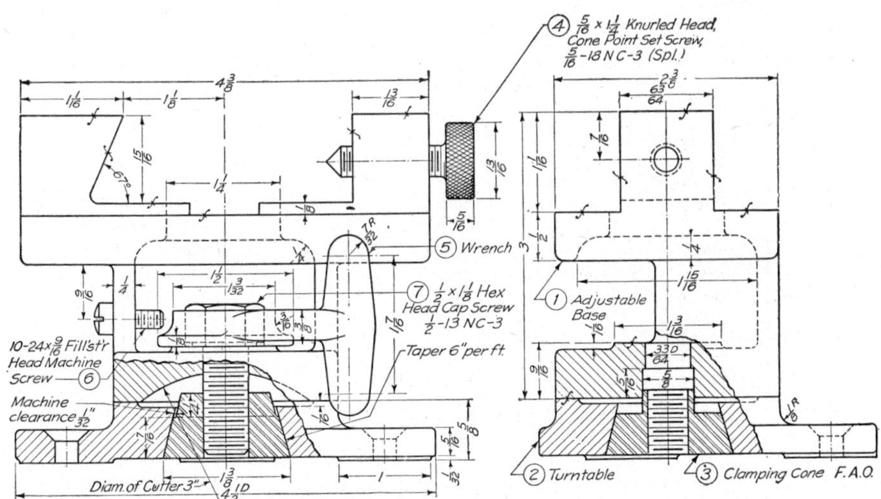

Fig. 15·74—Swivel base.

64. Redesign Fig. 15·75 for 21-lb ASCE rail. Use standard 2½″ pipe for support.

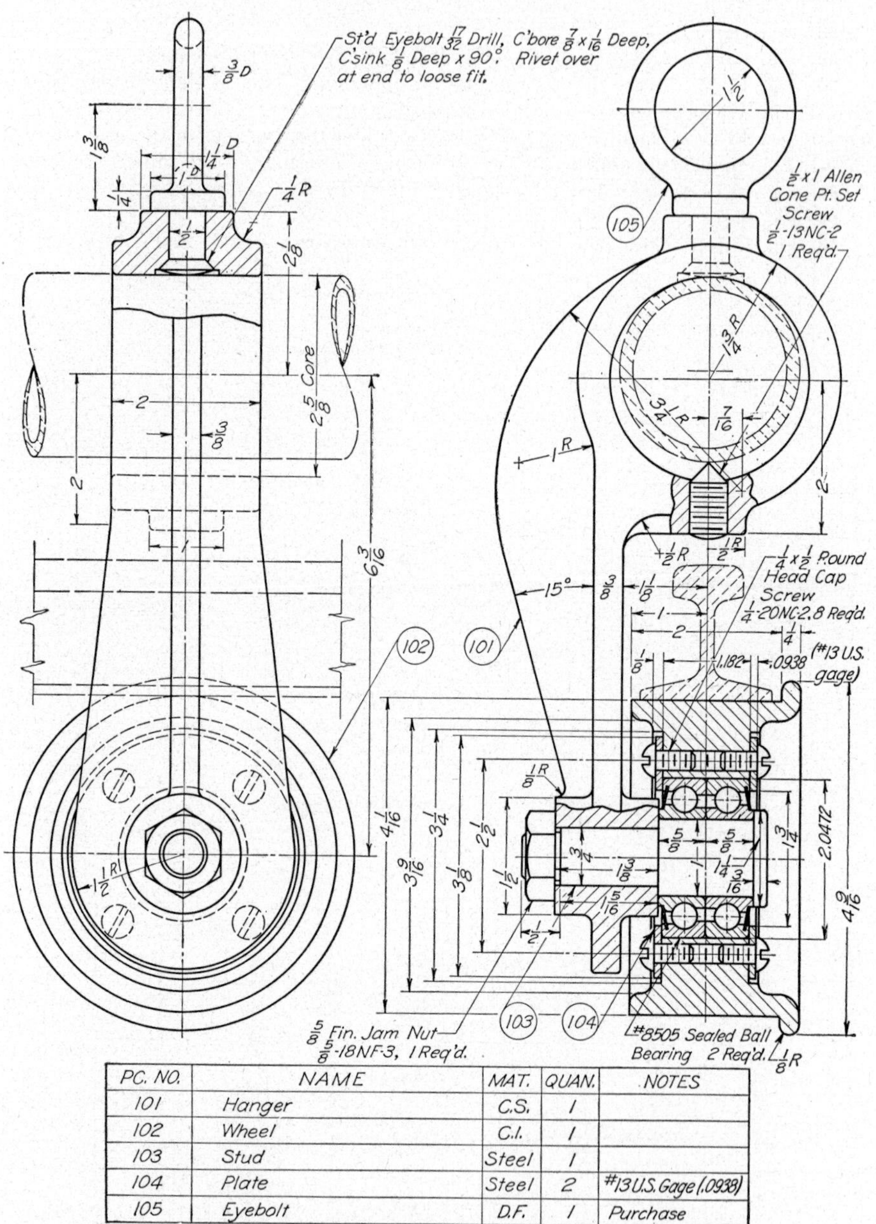

PC. NO.	NAME	MAT.	QUAN.	NOTES
101	Hanger	C.S.	1	
102	Wheel	C.I.	1	
103	Stud	Steel	1	
104	Plate	Steel	2	#13 U.S. Gage (.0938)
105	Eyebolt	D.F.	1	Purchase

FIG. 15·75—Rail-transport hanger.

65. Fig. 15·76. Make detail drawings of double-acting air cylinder. Length of stroke to be assigned. Fix length of cylinder to allow for clearance of 1″ at ends of stroke. Note that pieces 101 and 102 are identical except for the extra machining of the

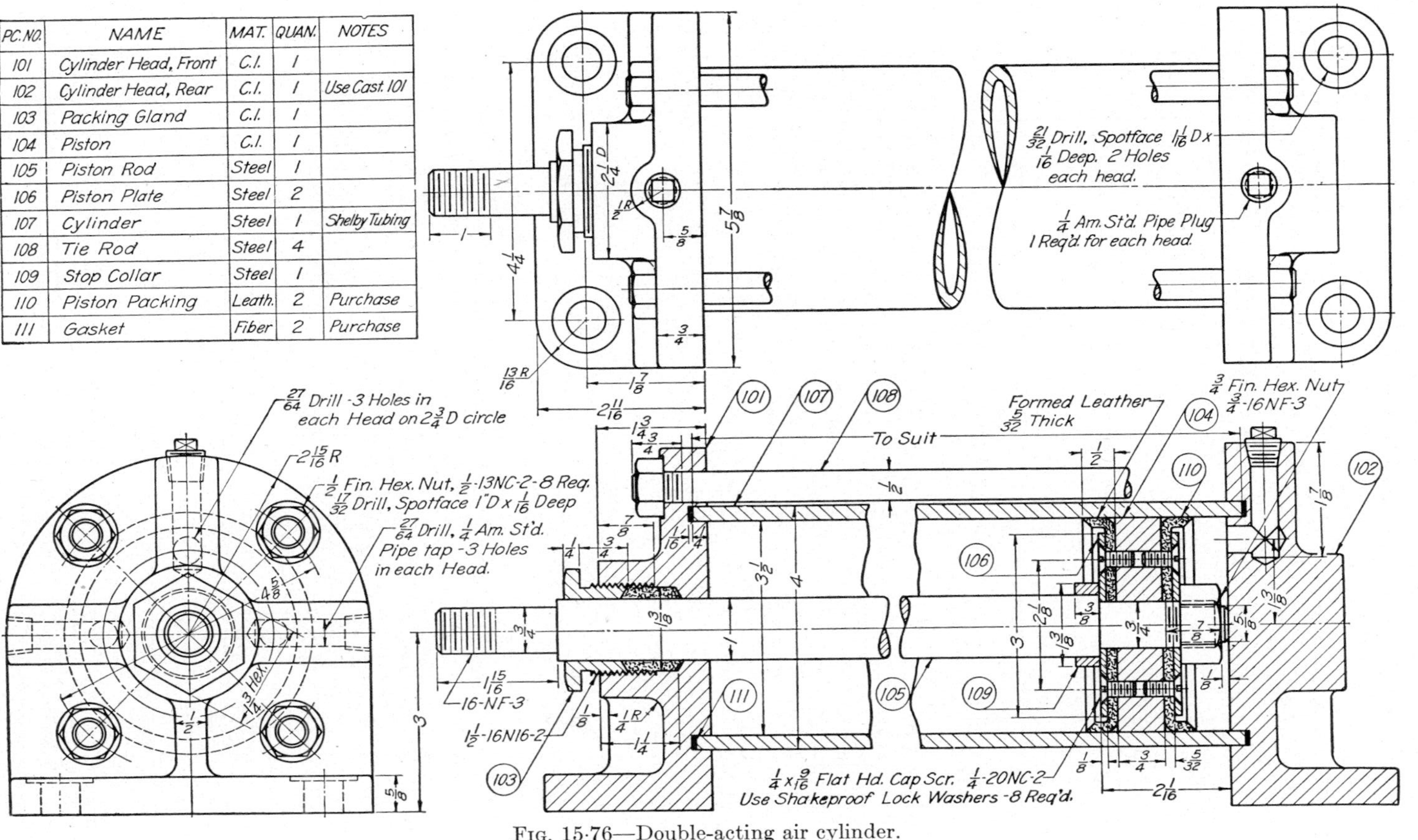

PC. NO.	NAME	MAT.	QUAN.	NOTES
101	Cylinder Head, Front	C.I.	1	
102	Cylinder Head, Rear	C.I.	1	Use Cast. 101
103	Packing Gland	C.I.	1	
104	Piston	C.I.	1	
105	Piston Rod	Steel	1	
106	Piston Plate	Steel	2	
107	Cylinder	Steel	1	Shelby Tubing
108	Tie Rod	Steel	4	
109	Stop Collar	Steel	1	
110	Piston Packing	Leath.	2	Purchase
111	Gasket	Fiber	2	Purchase

FIG. 15·76—Double-acting air cylinder.

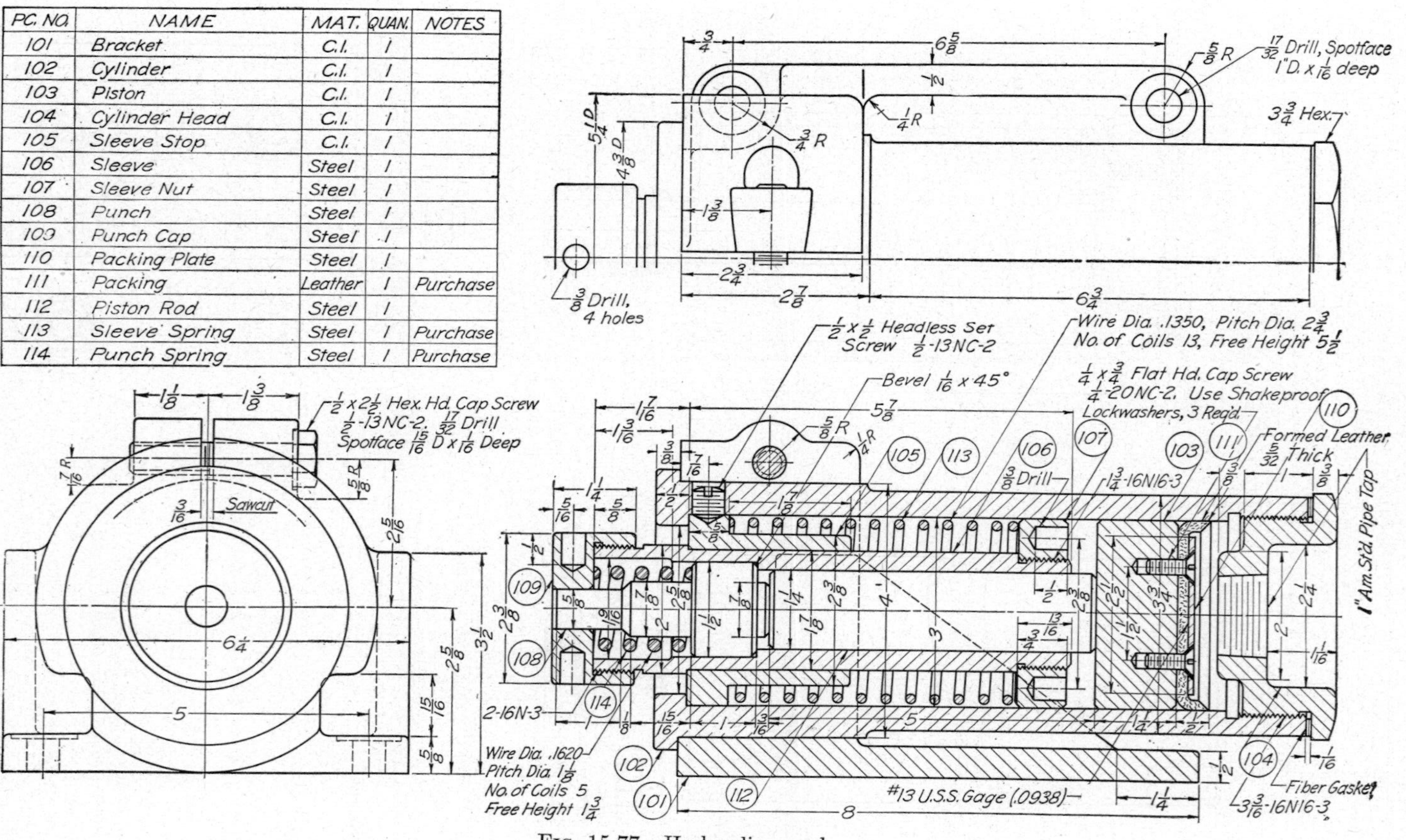

PC. NO.	NAME	MAT.	QUAN.	NOTES
101	Bracket	C.I.	1	
102	Cylinder	C.I.	1	
103	Piston	C.I.	1	
104	Cylinder Head	C.I.	1	
105	Sleeve Stop	C.I.	1	
106	Sleeve	Steel	1	
107	Sleeve Nut	Steel	1	
108	Punch	Steel	1	
109	Punch Cap	Steel	1	
110	Packing Plate	Steel	1	
111	Packing	Leather	1	Purchase
112	Piston Rod	Steel	1	
113	Sleeve Spring	Steel	1	Purchase
114	Punch Spring	Steel	1	Purchase

FIG. 15·77—Hydraulic punch.

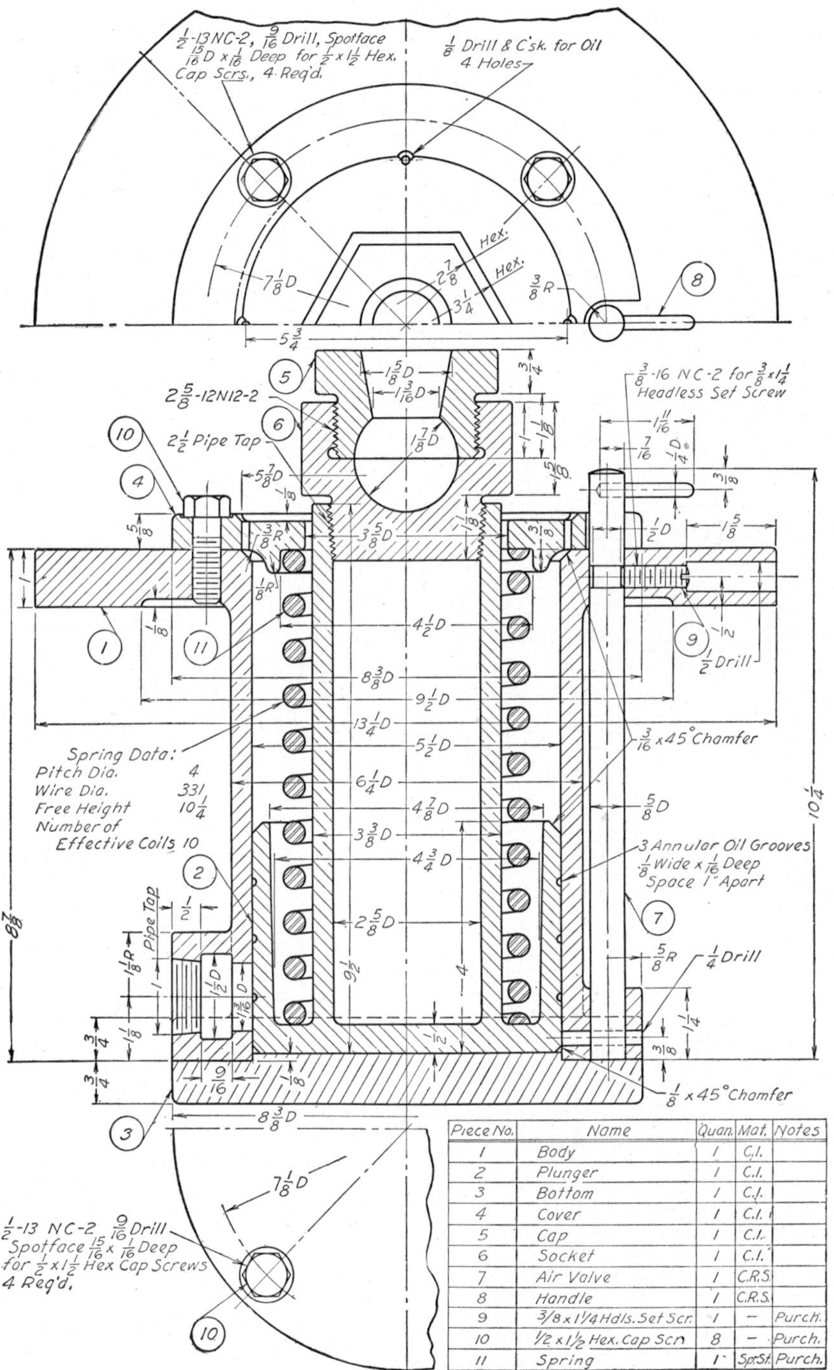

Piece No.	Name	Quan.	Mat.	Notes
1	Body	1	C.I.	
2	Plunger	1	C.I.	
3	Bottom	1	C.I.	
4	Cover	1	C.I.	
5	Cap	1	C.I.	
6	Socket	1	C.I.	
7	Air Valve	1	C.R.S.	
8	Handle	1	C.R.S.	
9	3/8 x 1 1/4 Hdls. Set Scr.	1	—	Purch.
10	1/2 x 1 1/2 Hex. Cap Scr.	8	—	Purch.
11	Spring	1	Sp. St.	Purch.

FIG. 15·78—Corliss-engine dashpot.

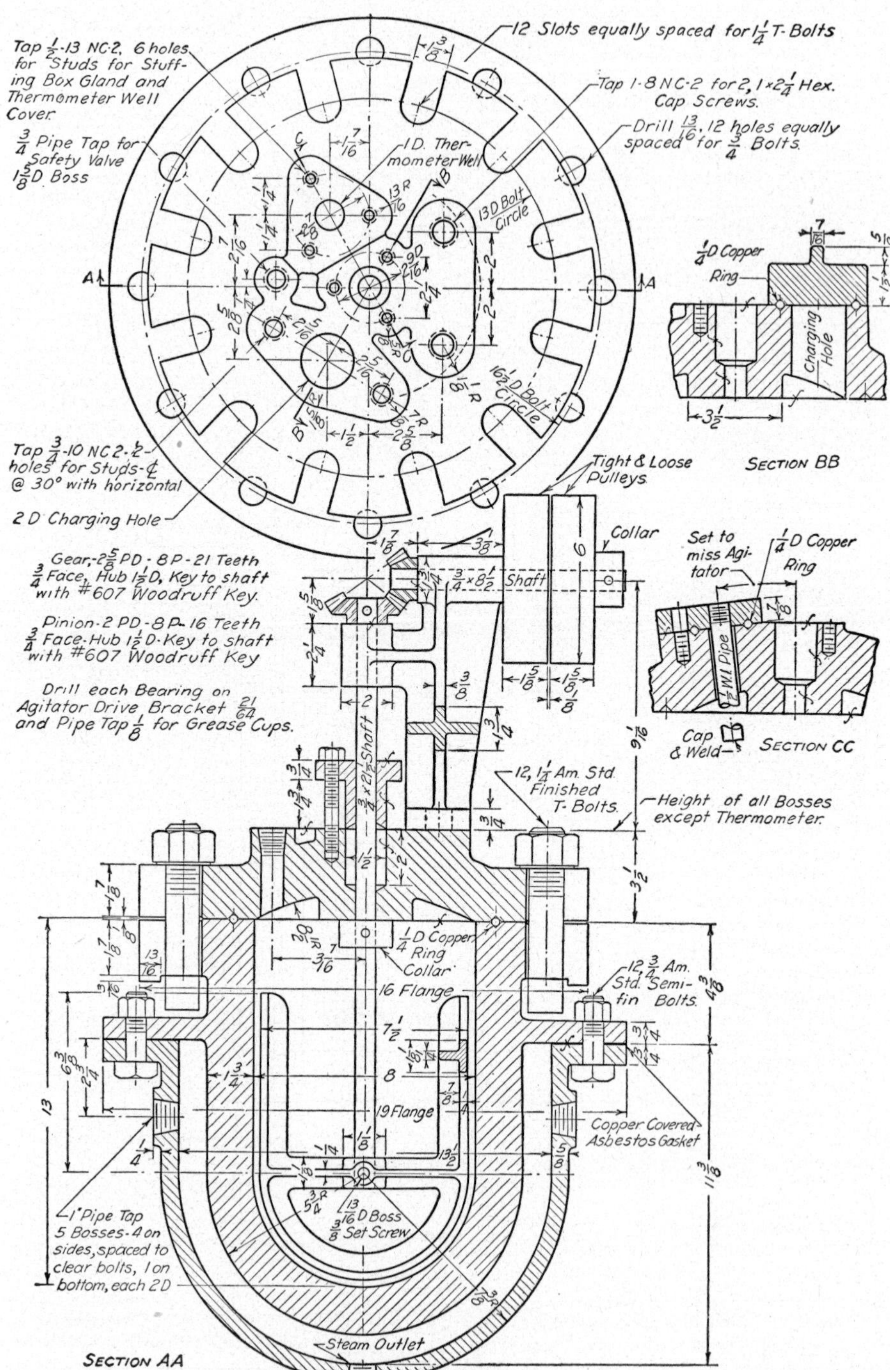

FIG. 15·79—Steam-jacketed autoclave.

central hole in piece 101 for the shaft, packing, and gland. Make separate drawings for this piece, one for the pattern shop, and two for the machine shop.

66. Fig. 15·77. Make detail drawings of hydraulic punch. In action, the punch assembly proper advances until the cap, piece 109, comes against the work. The assembly (piece 106 and attached parts) is then stationary and the tension of the punch spring (piece 114) holds the work as the punch advances through the work and returns.

67. Redesign Fig. 15·77 for a punch diameter ¾″ and stroke 1½″.

68. Fig. 15·78. Make detail drawings of Corliss-engine dashpot. This is the spring type as made by the Allis-Chalmers Mfg. Co. The high efficiency of the Corliss engine is obtained by what is known as the "trip-cut-off Corliss gear," a mechanism that opens the valve and then automatically disengages. The valve is then closed by the action of the dashpot, which, through a connecting link to the valve gear, pulls the linkage back to the closed position. Thus the spring (piece 11) is compressed when the valve is open and extends to close the valve. The air valve (piece 7) is regulated to cushion the fall of the plunger (piece 2) and also to create a partial vacuum in the cylinder, thereby amplifying the action.

69. Fig. 15·79. Make detail drawings for steam-jacketed laboratory autoclave. An autoclave is a piece of chemical apparatus used where chemical action under pressure is required. It may be built with a steam jacket as in Fig. 15·79, or without. Stirring devices may or may not be provided, depending on the use. The autoclave shown has a 2-gal capacity and is designed for 800-lb working pressure.

70. Design an autoclave of 10-gal capacity. Provide an agitator to revolve at 125 rpm driven from motor running at 1,200 rpm. Calculate size of pulley and bevel gears. Figure wall thickness for 900-lb pressure. On steam-jacket shell add three lugs for supporting legs. Provide openings in cover for safety valve, pressure gage, and thermometer well. Use T bolts, calculating area and referring to handbook for corresponding bolt size. Make complete assembly drawing.

71. Make detail drawings of autoclave from Prob. 70, including design of supporting legs.

72. Design an autoclave of 15-gal capacity. Use welded construction for body and steam jacket. Use 600-lb pressure. Use eye bolts for fastening cover to body. Motor-driven agitator to turn at 125 rpm. Provide openings in the cover for safety valve pressure gage and thermometer well. Use three supporting legs. Make complete assembly drawing.

73. Make complete detail drawings of autoclave from Prob. 72.

Group IV. A set of drawings from a pictorial assembly

74. Fig. 15·80. Make a complete set of drawings for pivot hanger, including detail drawings, assembly drawing, and parts list. All parts are steel. This assembly is comprised of a yoke, base, collar, and standard parts.

75. Fig. 15·81. Make a complete set of drawings for pump valve. The valve seat, stem, and spring are brass; the disk is hard-rubber composition. In operation, pressure of a fluid upward against the disk raises it and allows flow. Pressure downward forces the disk tighter against the seat and prevents flow.

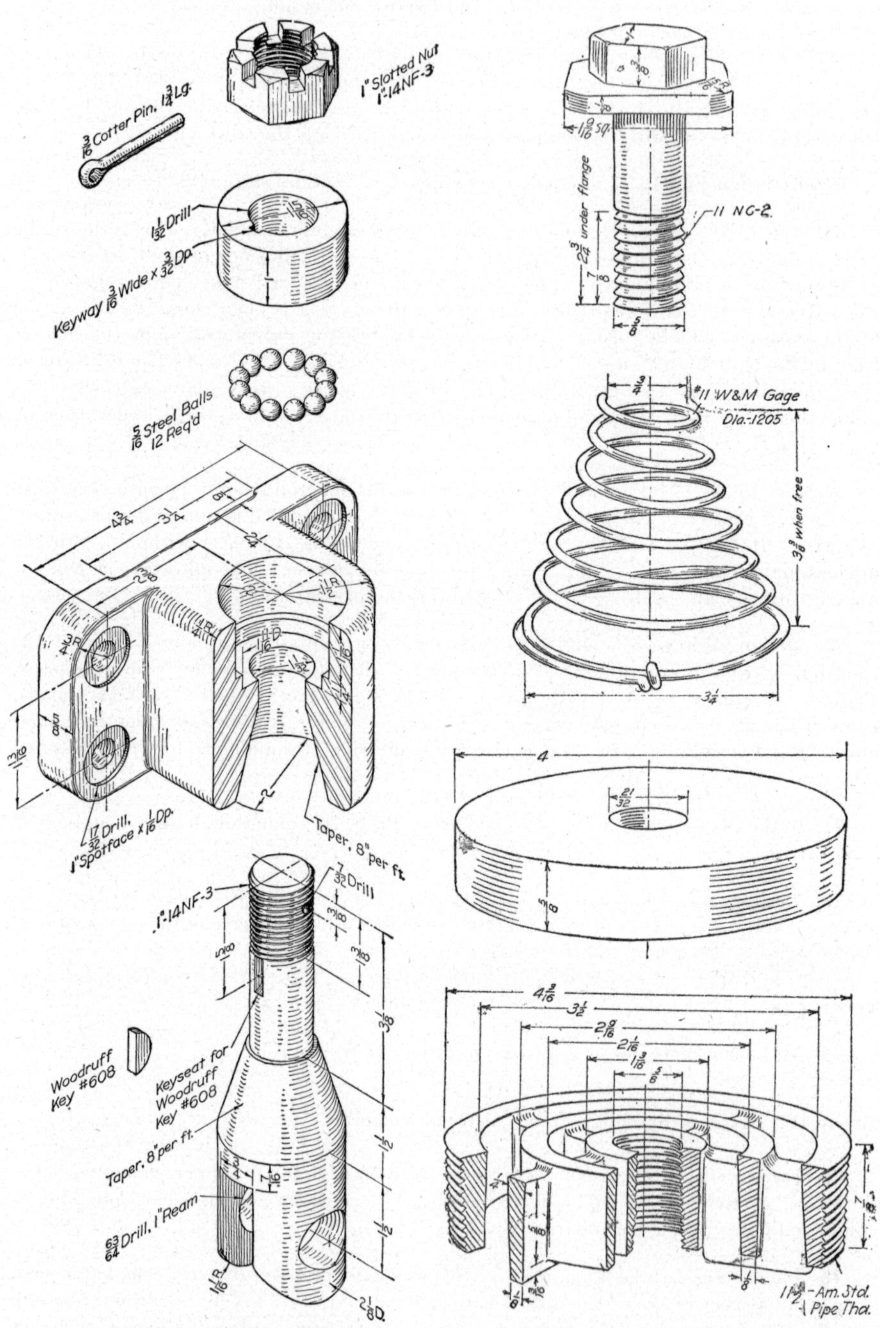

FIG. 15·80—Pivot hanger.

FIG. 15·81—Pump valve.

76. Fig. 15·82. Make a complete set of drawings for antivibration mount.

77. Fig. 15·83. Make a complete set of drawings for pop-off valve. All parts brass, except spring.

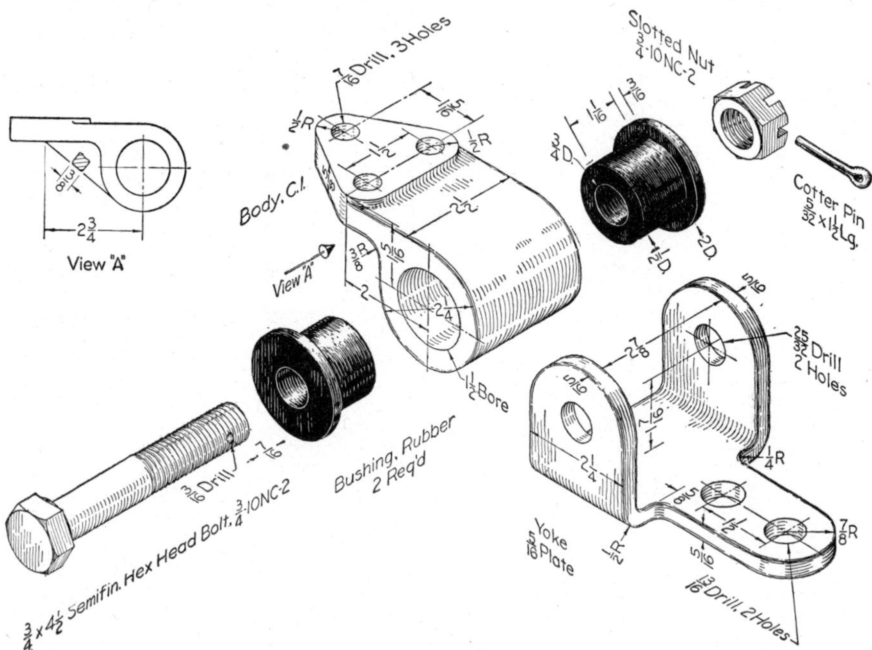

FIG. 15·82—Antivibration mount.

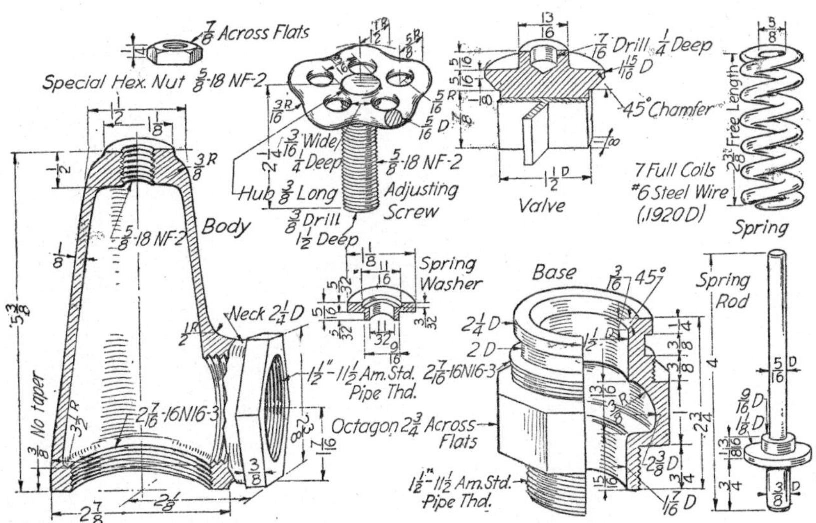

FIG. 15·83—Detail sketches of pop-off valve.

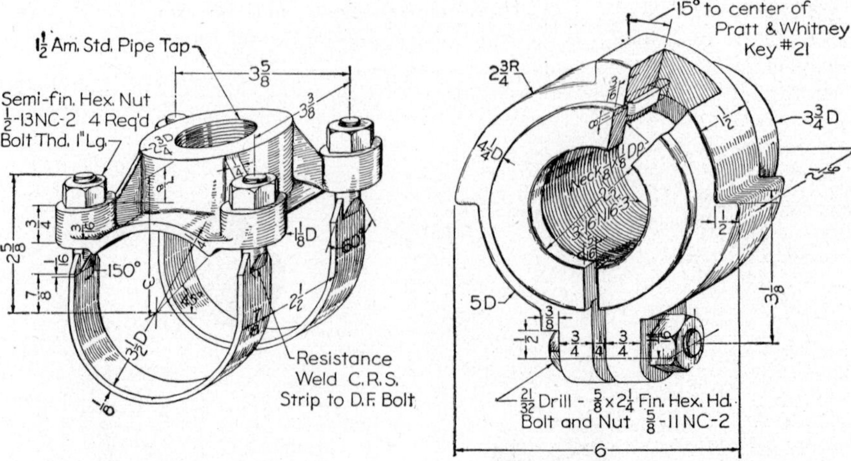

FIG. 15·84—Pipe clamp. FIG. 15·85—Drill-head clamp.

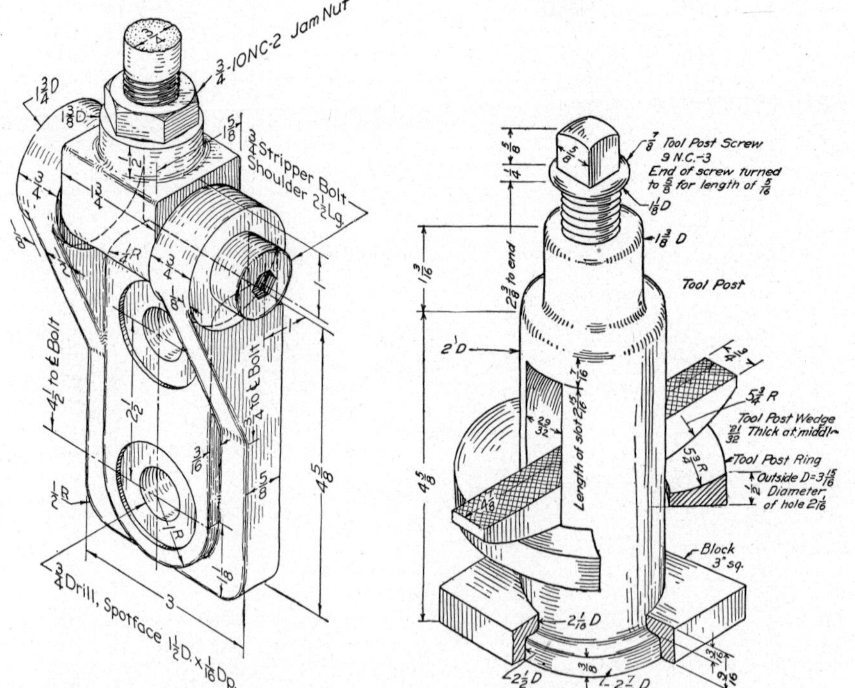

FIG. 15·86—Stay-rod pivot. FIG. 15·87—Tool post.

78. Fig. 15·84. Make a complete set of drawings for pipe clamp. Detail the strap and bolt together and use resistance-welding symbols and specifications.

79. Fig. 15·85. Make assembly and detail drawings of drill-head clamp. The assembly consists of two pieces, split nut and clamp, with Pratt and Whitney key and bolt as purchased parts. The dimensions of Pratt and Whitney keys are given in the Appendix.

80. Fig. 15·86. Make a complete set of drawings for stay-rod pivot. Bracket and pivot block are cast steel.

81. Fig. 15·87. Make a complete set of drawings for tool post.

82. Fig. 15·88. Make detail drawings of the insulator fitting. The buttonhead terminal openings in the body slope inward to prevent them from pulling out of the body when strain is applied.

83. Fig. 15·89. Make assembly and details of automotive thermostat to double size. In detailing the bimetallic spring, use a development to show the shape before coiling. The width changes uniformly from 1½″ at the base to 7⁄16″ at the end.

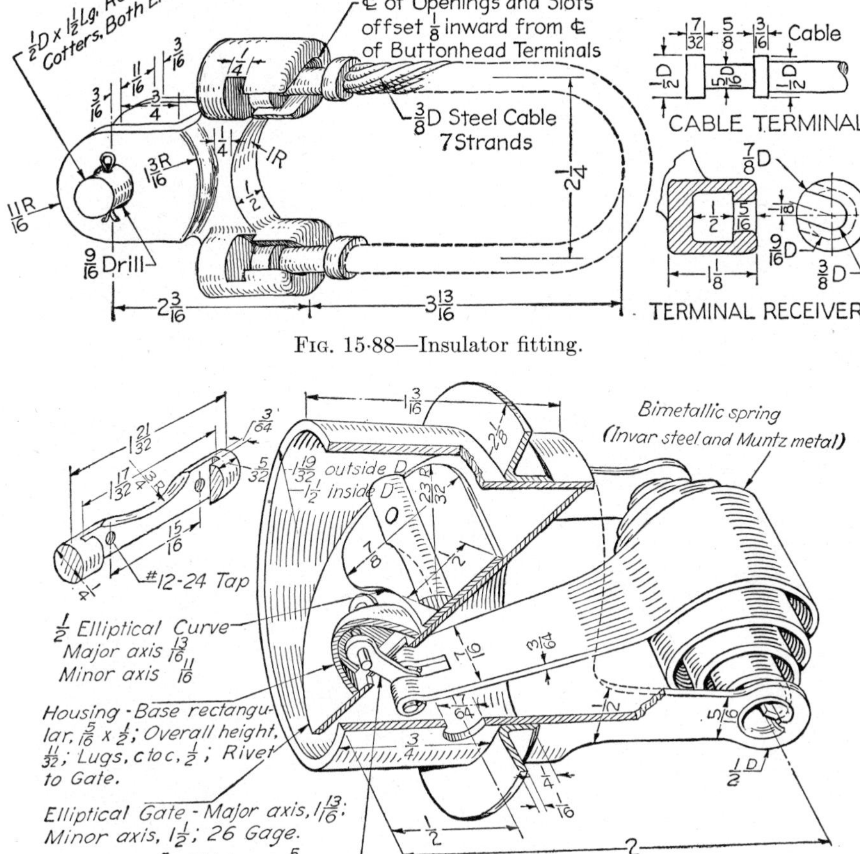

Fig. 15·88—Insulator fitting.

Fig. 15·89—Automotive thermostat.

Group V. A set of drawings from the design drawing

84. Fig. 15·90, fan. From design drawing, make complete set of drawings, including details, parts list, and assembly. Design drawing is shown one-half size. Base is plastic molding, with threaded brass inserts. Frame guard is steel, welded construction, chromium plated; detail as a unit. Motor is to be purchased with cord and switch and has plastic case; detail in outline only, giving over-all dimensions, location of threaded holes, etc., for manufacturer. Fan proper is to be purchased.

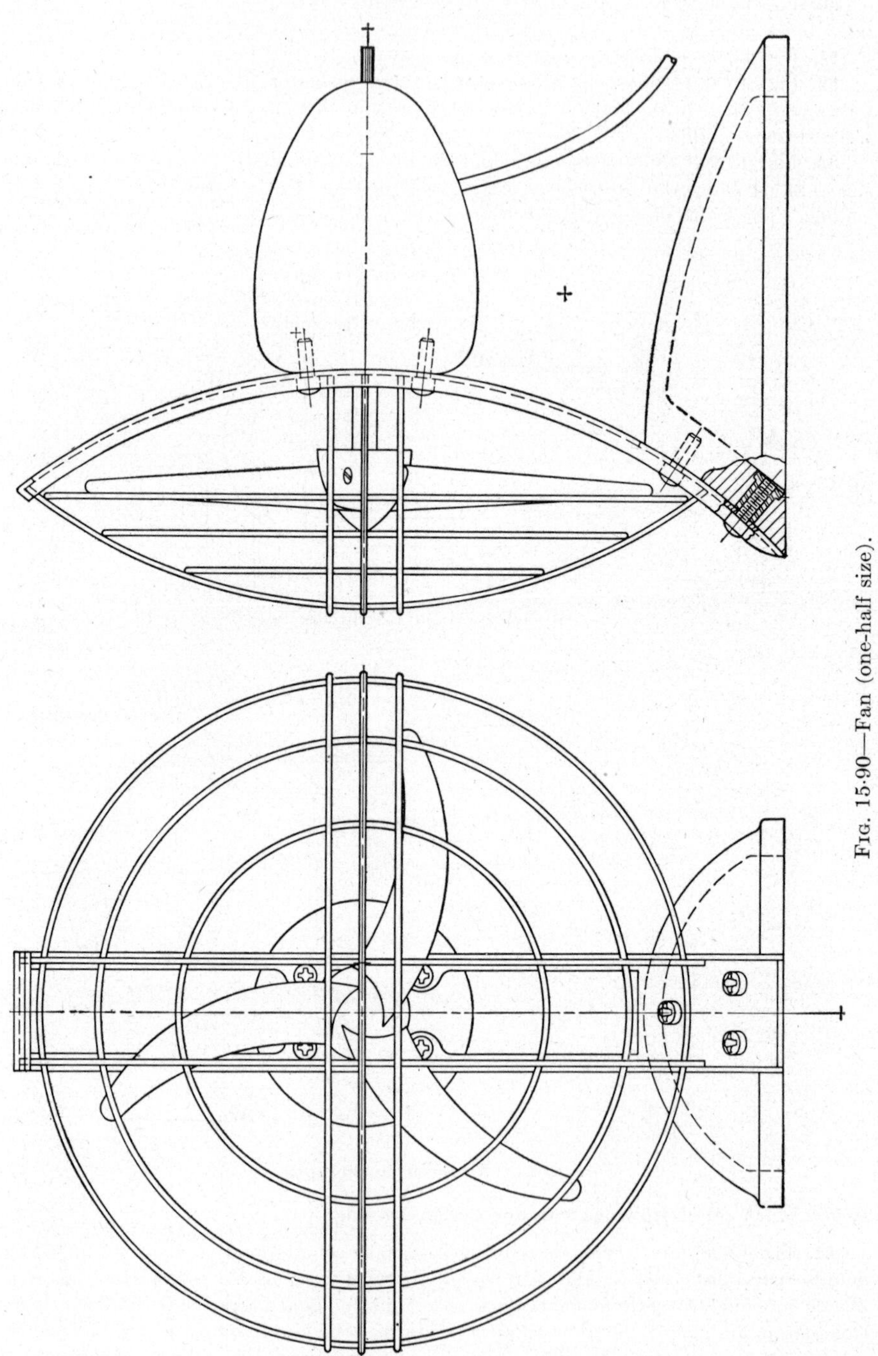

Fig. 15·90—Fan (one-half size).

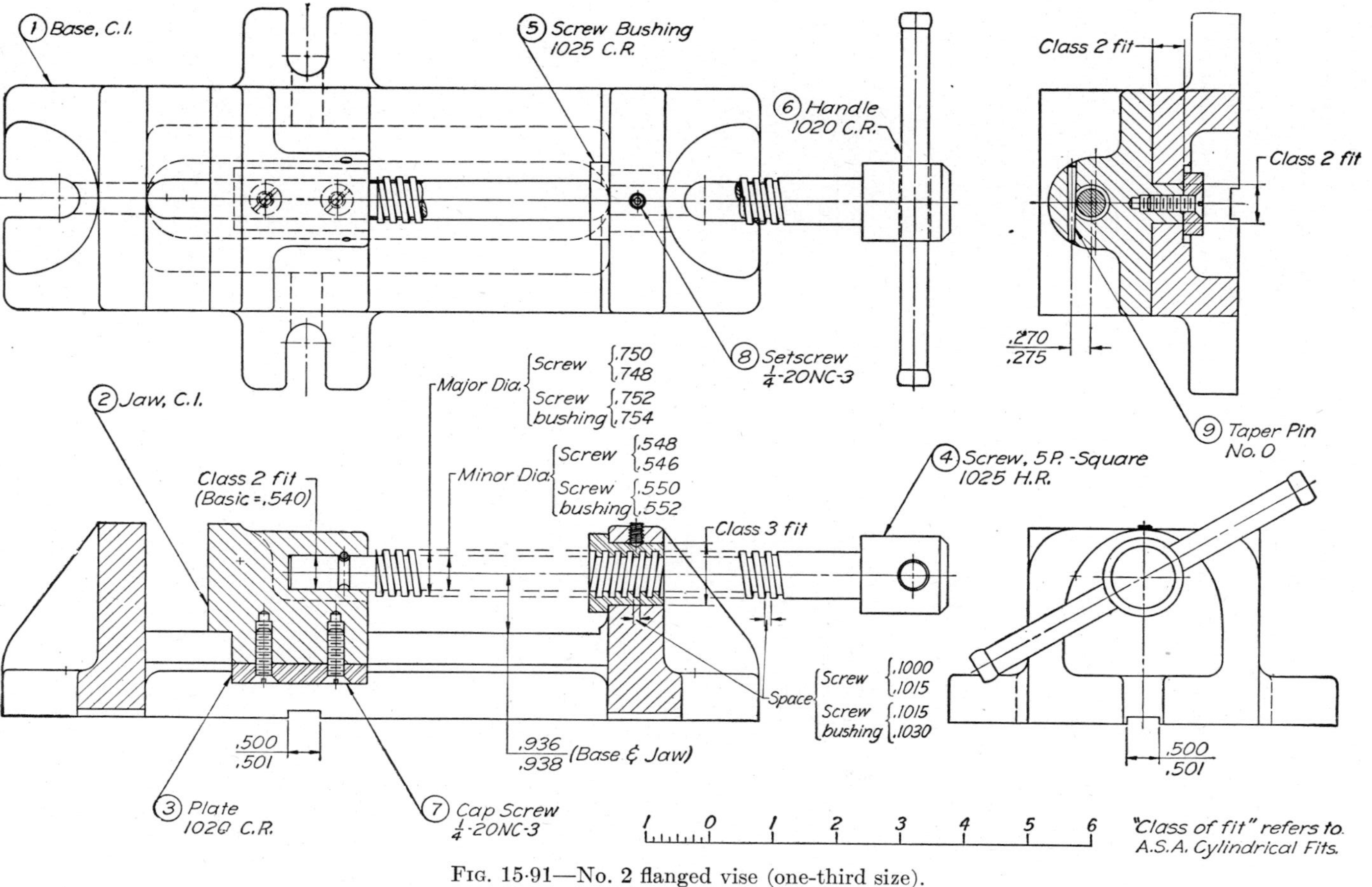

Fig. 15·91—No. 2 flanged vise (one-third size).

85. Fig. 15·91, No. 2 flanged vise. From design drawing, make complete set of drawings, including details, parts list, and assembly. Design drawing is shown one-third size. All necessary information is given on the design drawing.

86. Fig. 15·92, saw-hole punch. From design drawing, shown one-half size, make complete set of drawings. Frame is 1035 steel drop forging. Screw is 1025 CRS. Screw handle is 1020 CRS, ends upset. Punch and die are 1085 HR, heat-treat SAE No. 66.

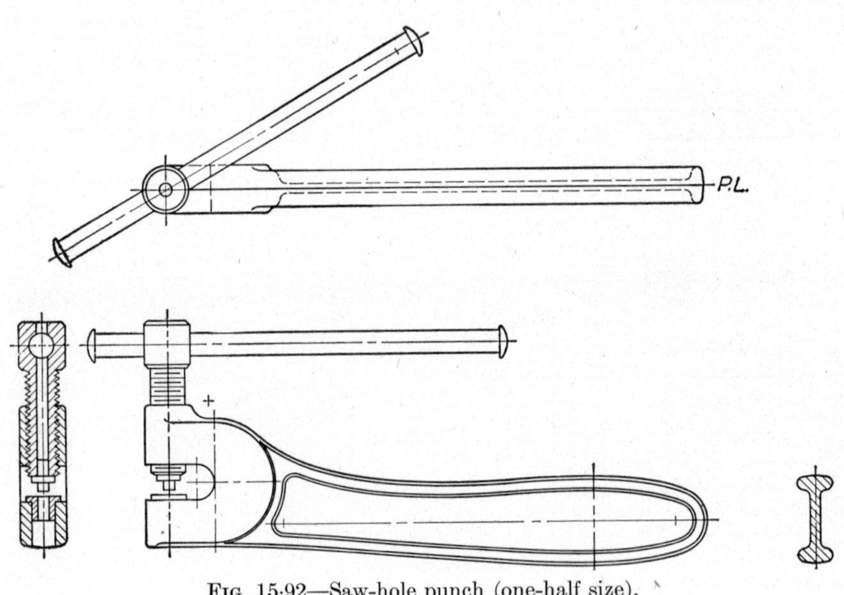

FIG. 15·92—Saw-hole punch (one-half size).

87. Fig. 15·93, marking machine. From design drawing, shown half-size, make complete set of drawings. Base, piece 1, is malleable-iron casting. Frame, piece 2, is cast iron. Ram, piece 3, is 1020 HR, bushing piece 4 is 1020 cold-drawn tubing; heat-treatment for both is: carburize at 1650° to 1700° F, quench direct, temper at 250° to 325° F. Spring piece 5, is piano wire, No. 20 (0.045) gage, six coils, free length 2″, heat-treatment is "as received." Marking dies and holders are made up to suit objects to be stamped.

88. Fig. 15·94, arbor press. From design drawing, shown one-quarter size, make complete set of drawings. All necessary information is given on the design drawing.

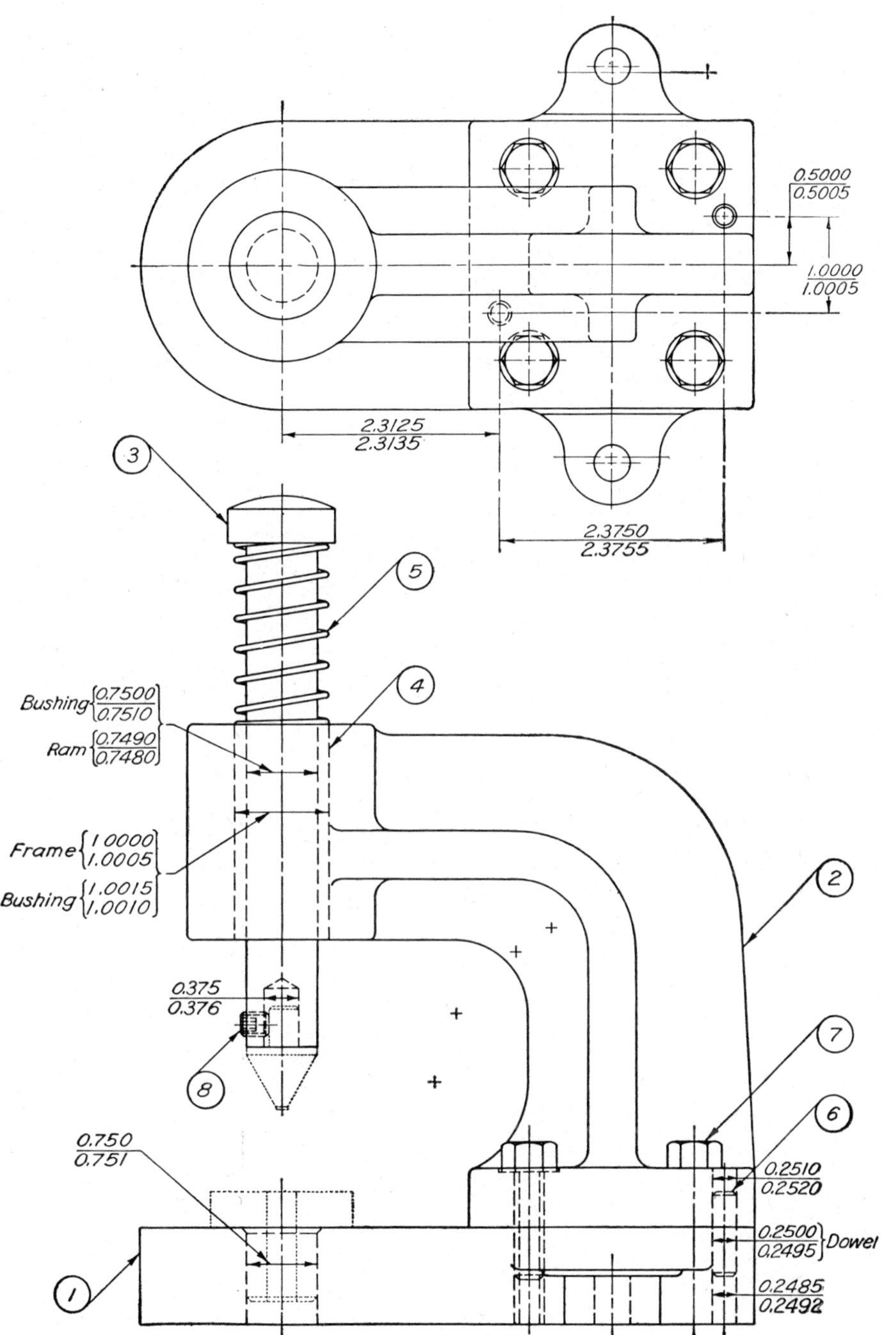

FIG. 15·93—Marking machine (one-half size).

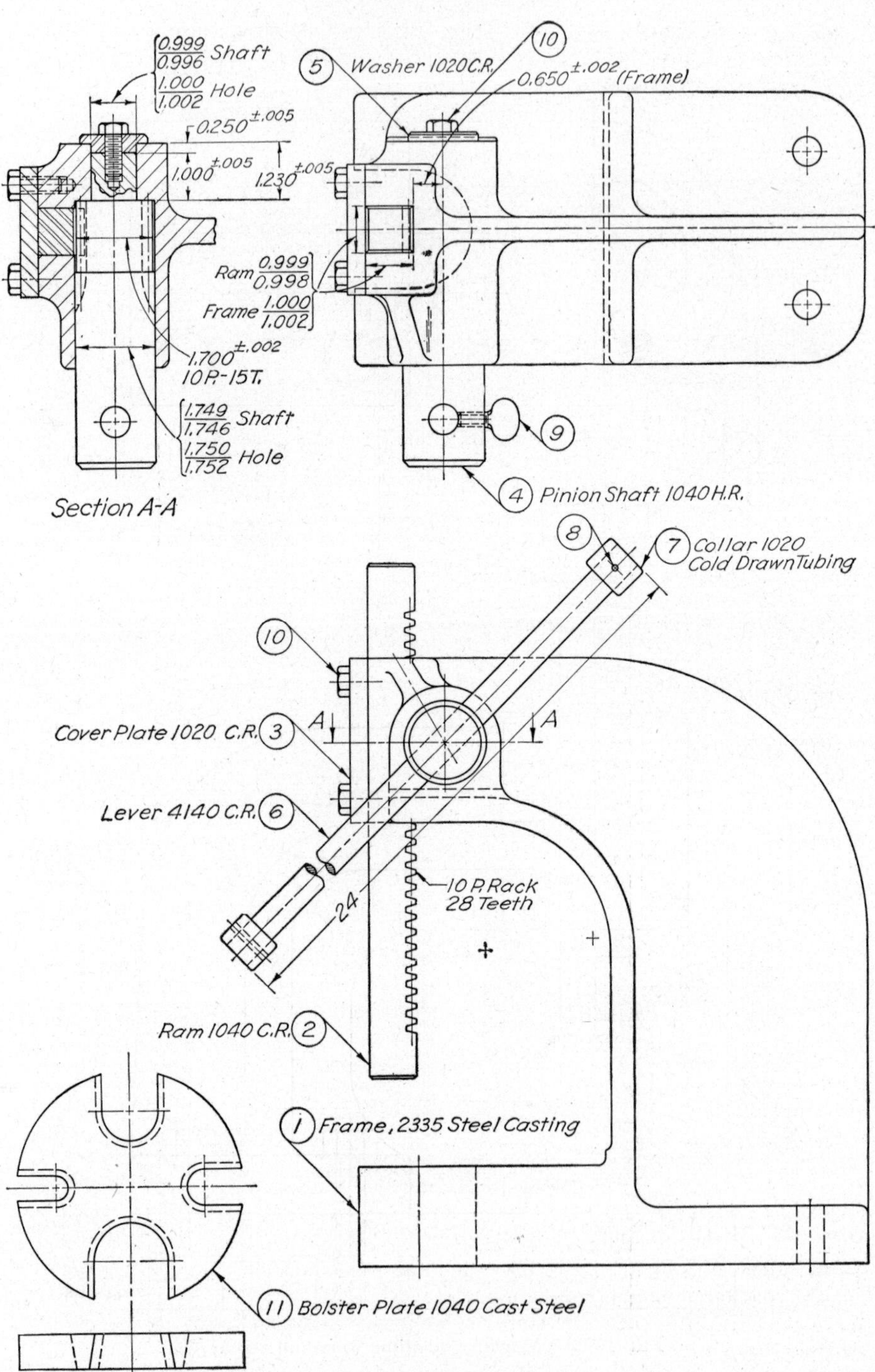

FIG. 15·94—One-ton arbor press (one-quarter size).

89. Fig. 15·95. Make a complete set of drawings from design sketch of drill press: design drawing, details, assembly, and parts list.

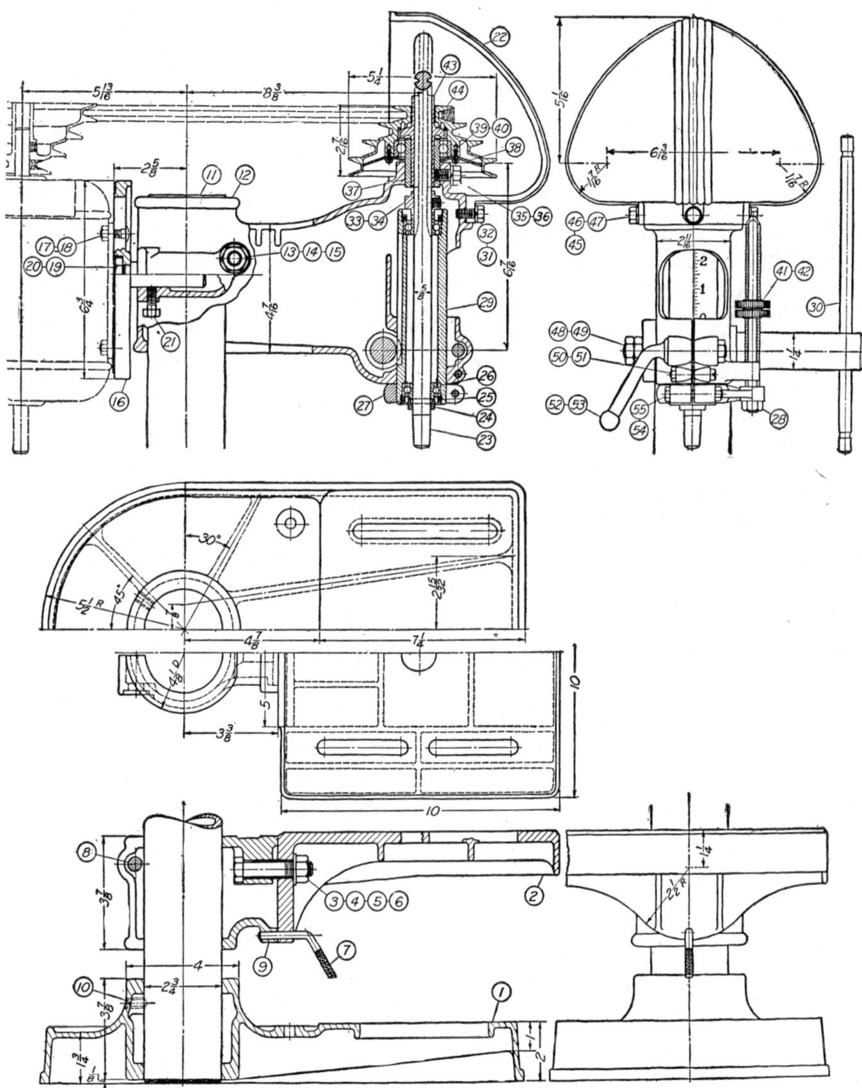

Fig. 15·95—Design sketch of drill press.

Group VI. Electrical problems

90. Make a diagrammatic sketch from information given in a catalogue of electrical control equipment for the installation of a thermostat bulb in a bearing retainer of a machine. Arrange so that the bulb will actuate a relay and disconnect power to the driving source if the bearing overheats.

91. Make a diagrammatic sketch from information given in a catalogue of electrical control equipment for the installation of an overcurrent relay in the supply line to elec-

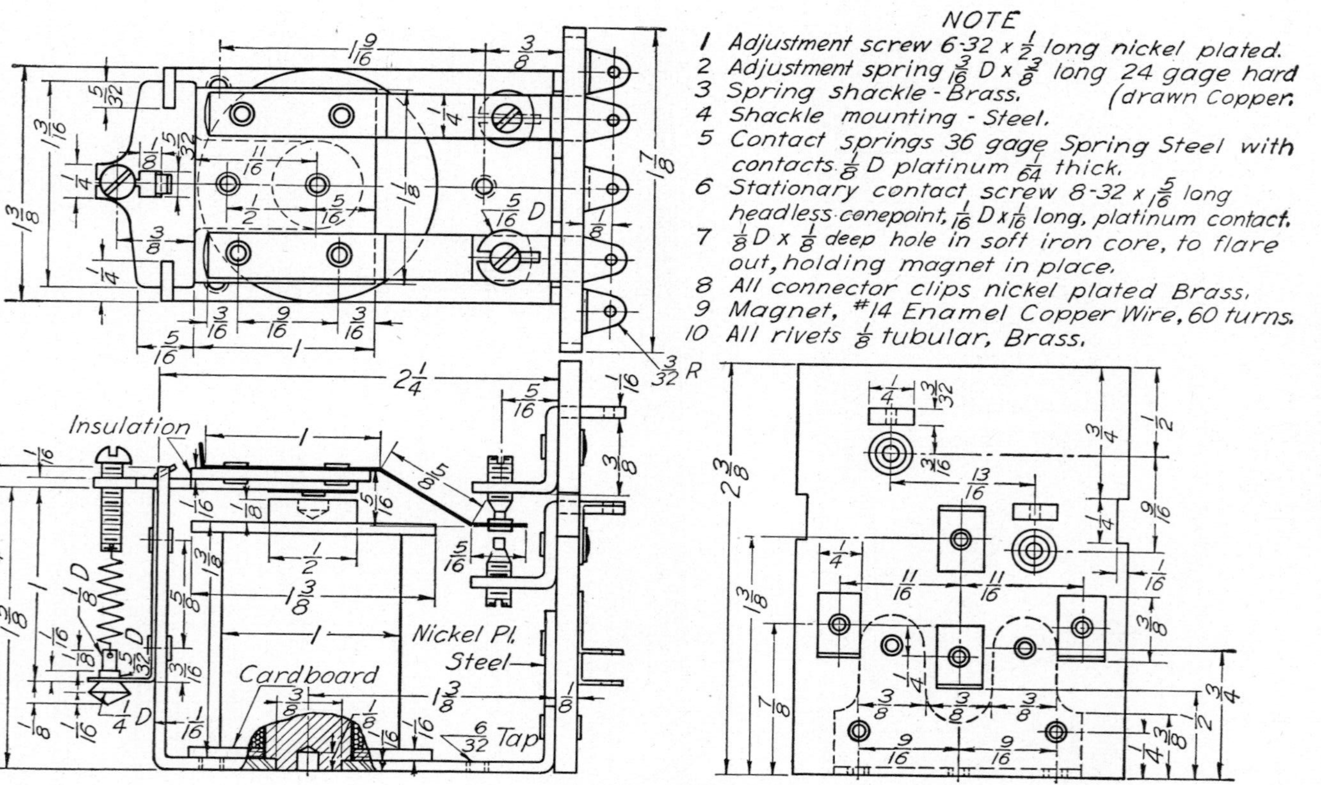

Fig. 15·96—Relay assembly.

trical equipment. Arrange so that the relay will actuate the trip coil of a circuit breaker when the current reaches a dangerous value for continuous operation.

92. Fig. 26·3. Make outline plan drawings of the house, scale ¼″ = 1′-0″. Add the wiring plan, using standard wiring symbols. The current is single phase, three wire, 110 volt, entering overhead at the rear.

93. Make a material list for Prob. 92. Use BX cable throughout.

94. Same as Prob. 92, but for one of the houses of Figs. 26·21 to 26·24.

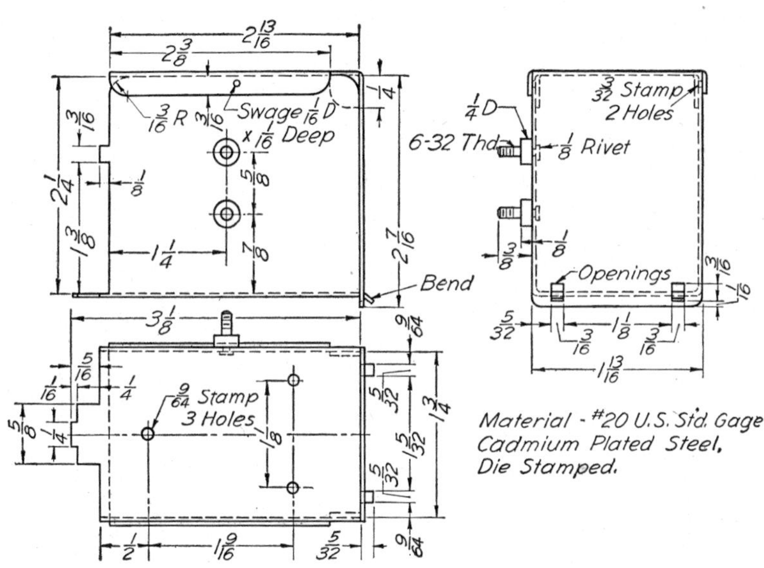

Fig. 15·97—Case for relay.

95. Select a popular radio receiver circuit and make a complete wiring diagram, using symbols shown in the Appendix.

96. Fig. 15·96. Make detail working drawings of all parts of the relay. All metal parts are die-stamped; hence developed views can be used to advantage in showing these parts.

97. Fig. 15·97. Make a developed working drawing of the relay case. Add on the sheet a bill of material for the complete relay and case, and a drawing of the panel to show connections needed.

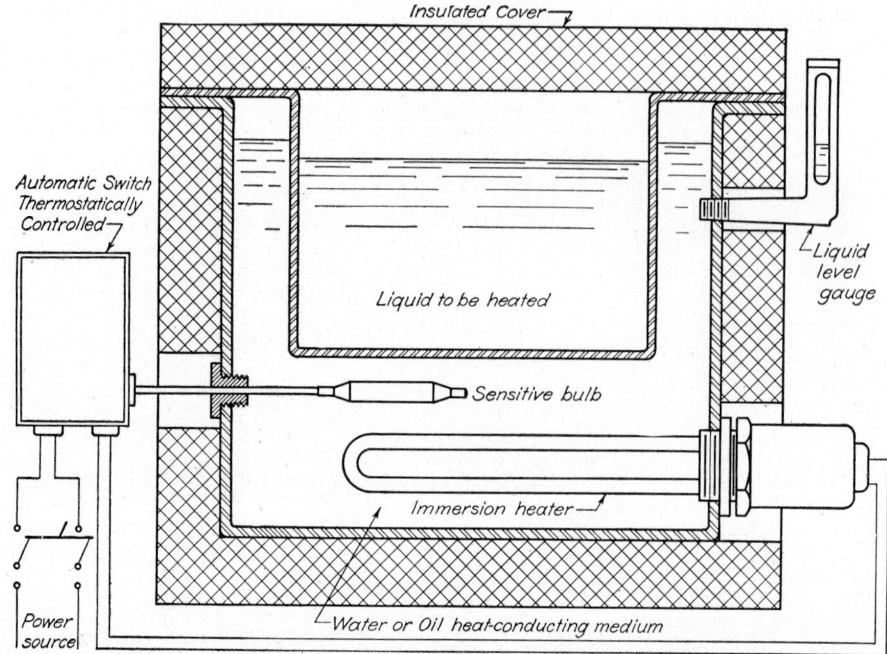

FIG. 15·98—Installation of immersion heater.

98. Fig. 15·98. Make an assembly drawing in section showing tanks in position, with the heating unit installed in the tank wall. Equip the unit with a liquid-level gage for the conducting medium and with a sensitive bulb as part of a thermostat controlling a contactor in the 115-volt line. Include also a dropping resistor in the a-c line to the thermostat. Show the contactor and a fused line switch to the 115-volt line.

Immersion heaters offer one of the most economical means of heating liquids in tanks, kettles, metal barrels, etc. They are of substantial construction and high efficiency, utilizing the Calrod sheath wire. The screw-in type is easily installed, the only requirement being a hole with standard pipe thread in the container. Figure 15·98 shows a typical installation of a Calrod heater. In this unit an oil-conducting medium is heated, and in turn heats a second tank which may contain a heavy viscous liquid or other liquid that would carbonize easily. Tank 1 for liquid to be heated is 9″ square by 6″ deep, inside, and of No. 2 Brown and Sharpe gage sheet copper with a lip 3¾″ all around, measured from inside. Tank 2 for water or oil bath, 12″ square by 9″ deep inside, and 0.2500-inch steel plate with a lip 2¼″ all around, measured from inside. The outer tank is covered on all sides, top and bottom, with insulating material.

99. Fig. 15·99. Miniature switchboard. A miniature switchboard is used to control the larger main switchboard and equipment in a power station or substation. Draw a floor plan of a substation using three miniature switchboards each 24″ wide, 48″ deep, and 90″ high and arranged in one unit so as to control 18 main switchboards. Show lighting, windows, doors, and any other features necessary on the floor plan, making the floor space adequate for inspection of the rear of the main switchboards. Building to be of reinforced concrete and brick fireproof construction.

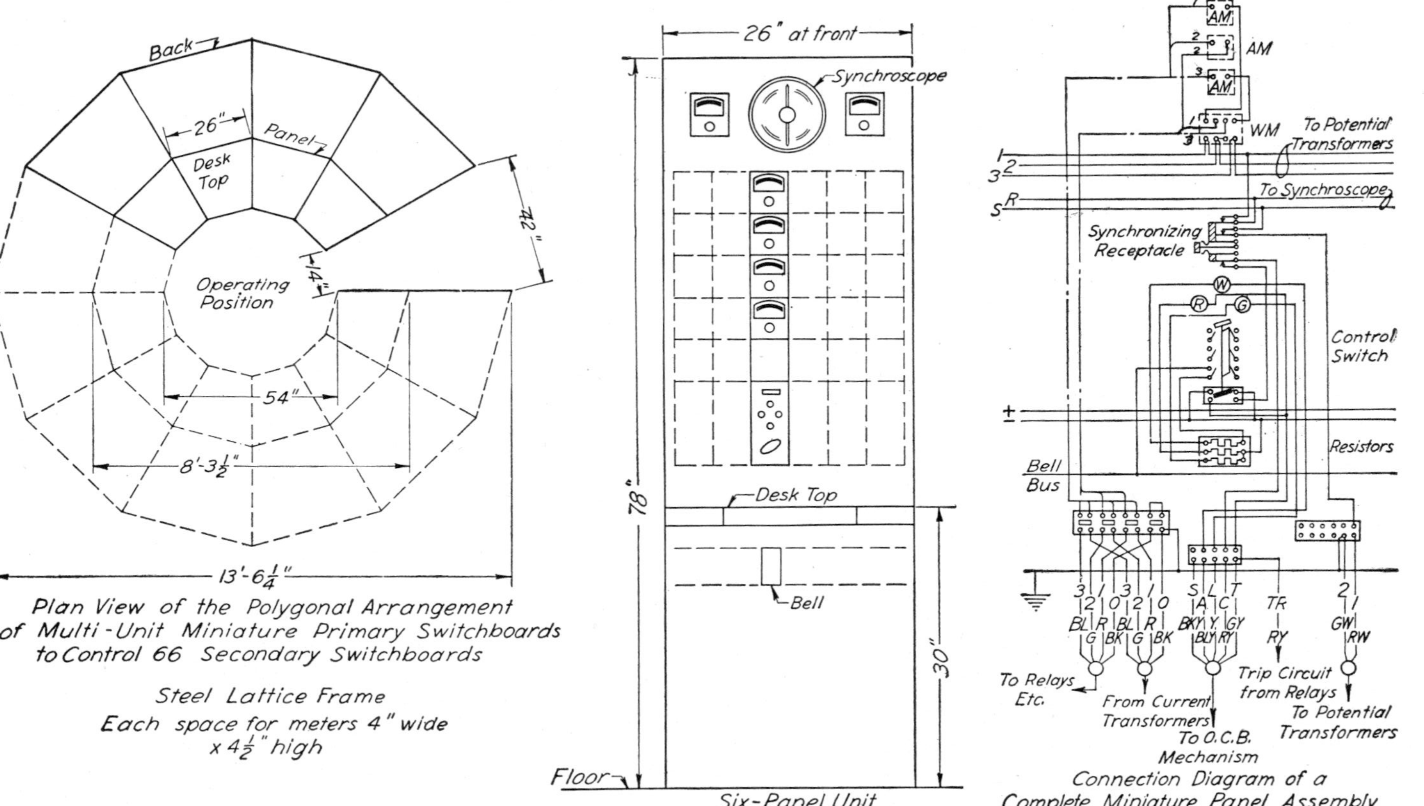

Fig. 15·99—Miniature primary switchboard.

Chapter 16

WELDING DRAWINGS

16·1 The subject of welding is of particular interest to the draftsman for two reasons. First, welding is being used more and more extensively for permanent fastenings in places where formerly rivets or bolts were employed, and the draftsman must know not only what type of joint to use but also how to specify it with the standard code of symbols. Second, the method of designing and fabricating welded machine parts that have heretofore been made as castings or forgings is gaining rapidly in favor. A wide variety of parts such as machinery bases, frames, and brackets are built up of standard steel shapes and plates joined by arc or oxyacetylene welding.

Since steel is approximately 6 times as strong in tension as cast iron and 2½ times as stiff, it is apparent that, by using steel, greater strength and rigidity may be secured with less weight of metal. Designing for welded-steel construction requires ingenuity but is in reality simpler than designing complicated cast parts. The strength and weight of rolled-steel shapes are standard, complete detailed information is readily available, and the computations for sizes of members are therefore greatly simplified.

As to the strength of welded connections, it is possible to make a welded joint stronger than the members joined.

16·2 Welding drawings. A welding drawing shows a unit or part made of several pieces of metal, with each welded joint described and specified. The first welding drawings carried a general note as, "to be welded throughout," or, "to be completely welded." A later system indicated the weld by a series of cross marks with an informative note either on the symbol or elsewhere on the drawing. The American Welding Society in October, 1940, recommended its final draft of a complete system of specification by means of ideographic symbols, and the basic system has been adopted by the American Standards Association. Figure 16·1 shows the detail drawing of a part made of cast iron, and Fig. 16·2 shows a part identical in function, but made up by welding. A comparison of the two drawings shows the essential differences both in construction and in drawing technique. Note the absence of fillets and rounds in the welding drawing. Note also that all the pieces making up the welded part are dimensioned so that they may be cut easily from standard stock.

All joints between the individual pieces of the welded part must be shown, even though the joint would not appear as a line on the completed part. The lines marked *A* in Fig. 16·3 illustrate this principle. Each individual piece should be identified by number, Fig. 16·2.

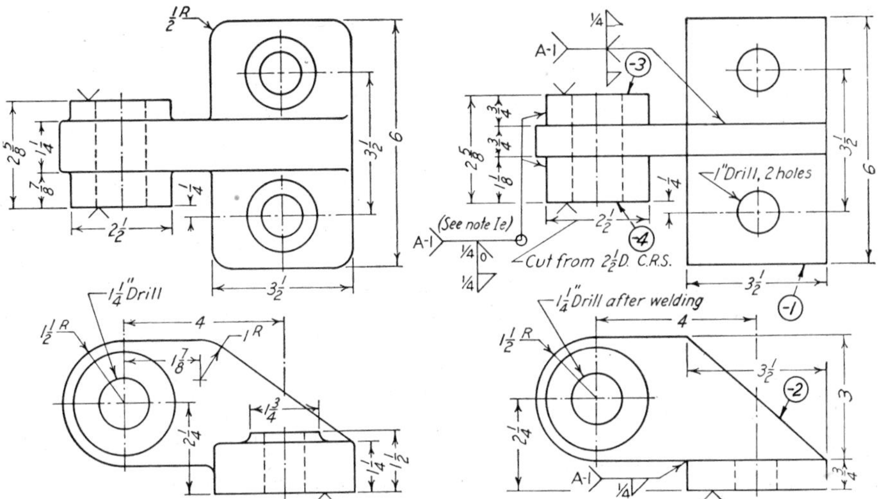

FIG. 16·1—Detail drawing of casting.

FIG. 16·2—Detail drawing, welded construction.

16·3 Welding processes are classified according to the manner in which the welded joint is completed, (1) pressure welding (forging) and (2) nonpressure welding (fusion and brazing). Actually all welding is a fusion process but, by long usage, fusion welding is understood to include the arc, gas, and thermit processes.

16·4 Classification of welded joints. Figure 16·4 shows the types of joints, which are classified by the method of assembly of the parts, and may be further differentiated by the way in which the parts are prepared for welding.

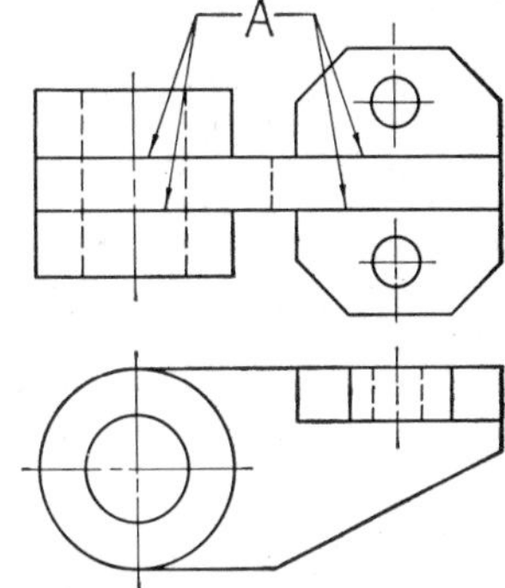

FIG. 16·3—Joint lines shown.

16·5 Types of welds. Figure 16·5 shows in cross section the fundamental types of welds. For bead and fillet welds, the pieces are not prepared by cutting, chipping, or grinding before making the weld, and the essential difference in V, bevel, U, and J welds is in the preparation of the parts joined. Pairs of the fundamental welds such as double-V, double-bevel, etc., make a further variety. Almost any combination is possible for complicated connections.

FIG. 16·4—Classification of welded joints.

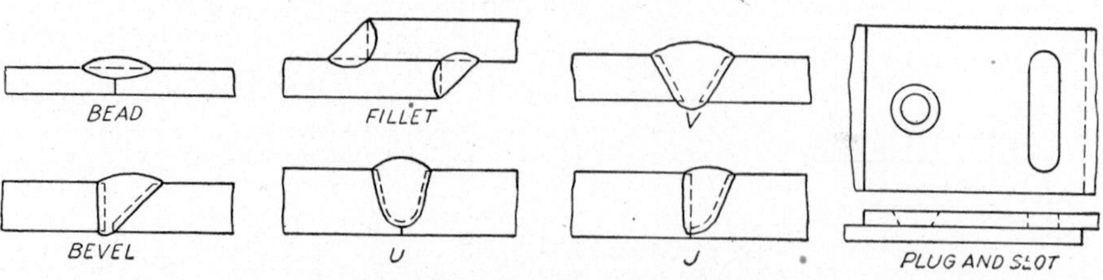

FIG. 16·5—Fundamental welds.

16·6 The individual basic symbols originate either from the preparation of the pieces making up the joint or, where no preparation is necessary, from the section shape of the weld. Figure 16·6 shows the fundamental welds and the basic symbols specifying these welds.

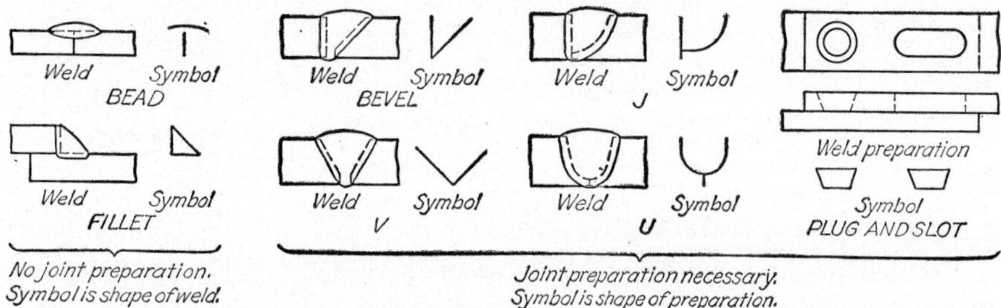

FIG. 16·6—Fundamental welds and individual basic symbols.

16·7 The basic form of the symbol. Figure 16·7 shows the basic form of the welding symbol and gives the position of the various marks and dimensions.

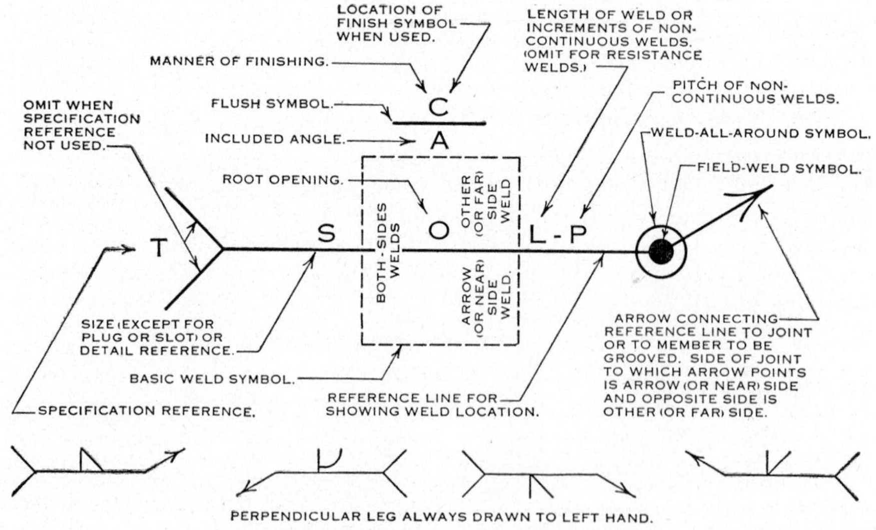

FIG. 16·7—Basic form of the welding symbol.

The arrow points to the grooved member at a point near the weld, Fig. 16·8. The side of the weld pointed to is always called the arrow side (or near side). The tail of the arrow is used to hold a symbol only when specification of strength, type of rod, etc., are to be given.

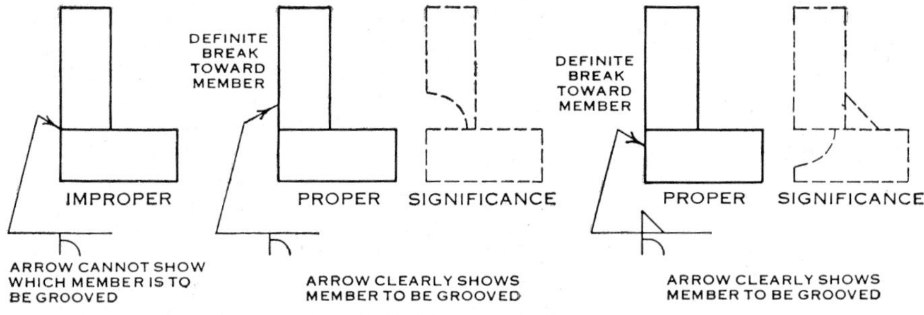

FIG. 16·8—Placement of arrow.

Figure 16·9 illustrates the placement of the symbol and shows arrow sides and other sides of the weld on some fundamental types.

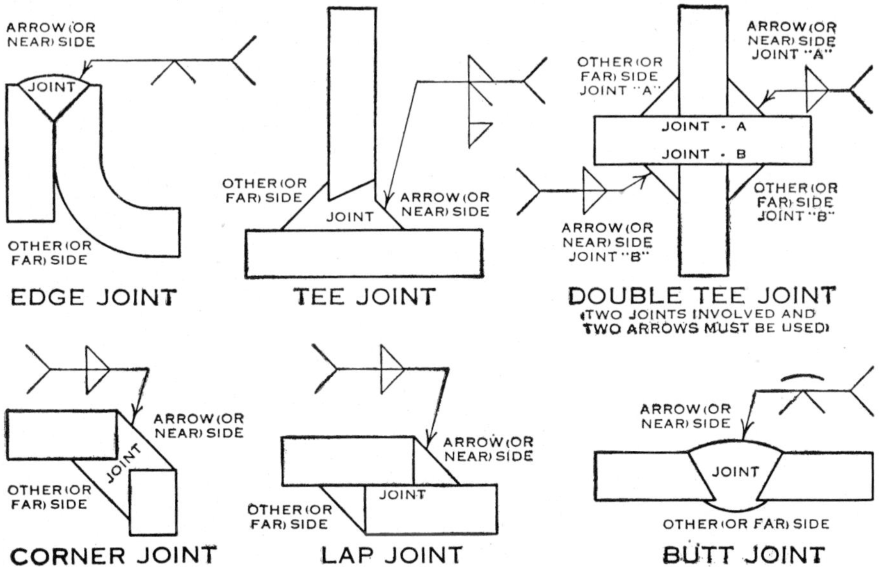

FIG. 16·9—Arrow sides and other sides.

16·8 Specification and size of welds. The information necessary to specify the weld, including all sizes of the weld proper, is placed on the body of the leader as indicated in Fig. 16·7. Figure 16·10 shows weld sizes. The dimensions of root opening, depth of weld, and included angle are the important sizes to specify for grooved welds. The size of a 45° fillet weld is the dimension shown. Unequal-leg fillet welds are specified by giving the size of both legs, as described in II3*j*, page 388.

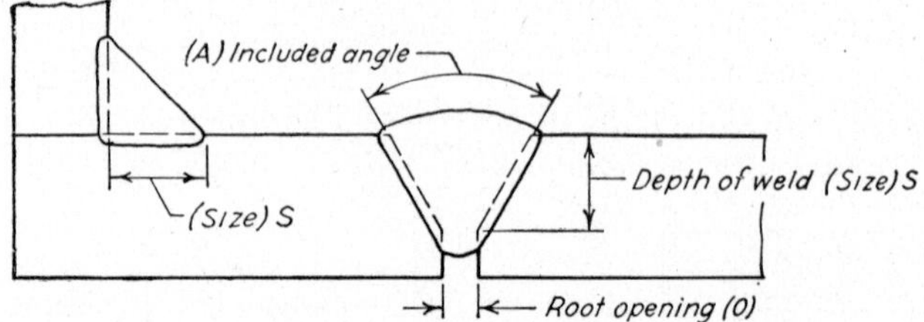

FIG. 16·10—Weld sizes.

16·9 The symbols. Figure 16·11 shows arc- and gas-welding (fusion) symbols and illustrates their use. The individual basic symbols are placed on the basic form to describe any possible combination of welds for a

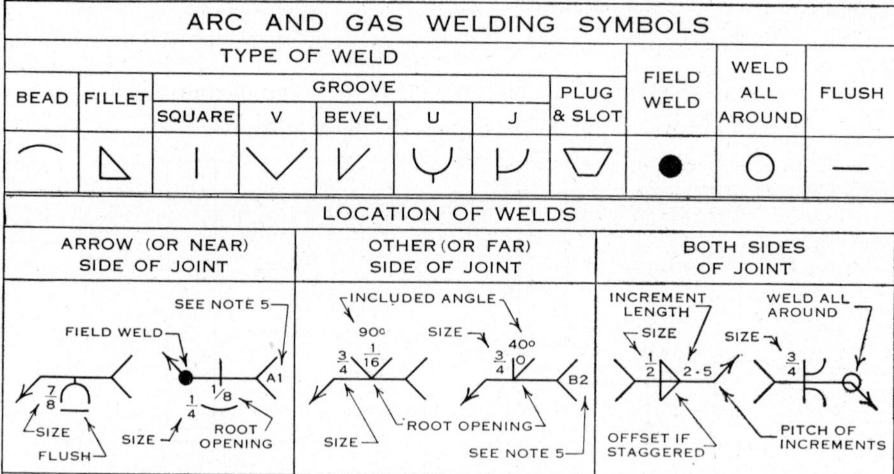

FIG. 16·11—American Standard fusion-welding symbols.

complete joint. Every simple weld that is a part of the complete joint must be specified. The symbol describes a given weld in less space than would be required for dimensions and notes, and requires much less drawing time.

A comparison is made in Fig. 16·12 between the information given by the symbol, the joint dimensioned, and a complete note. Study each part of the symbol carefully in connection with the dimensioned sketch and the note.

Interpretation of Symbol

Double-fillet-welded, partially grooved, double-J, tee joint with incomplete penetration. (Type of joint shown by drawing.) Grooves of standard proportions (which are ½ in. R, 20° included angle, edges in contact before welding), ¾ in. deep for other- (or far-) side weld and 1¼ in. deep for arrow- (or near-) side weld. ⅜ in. continuous other- (or far-) side fillet weld and ½-in. intermittent arrow- (or near-) side fillet weld with increments 2 in. long, spaced 6 in. center to center. All fillets standard 45° fillets. All welding done in field in accordance with welding specification number *A*2 (which requires that weld be made by manual d-c shielded metal-arc process, using high-grade, covered, mild-steel electrode; that root be unchipped and welds unpeened, and that joint be preheated before welding).

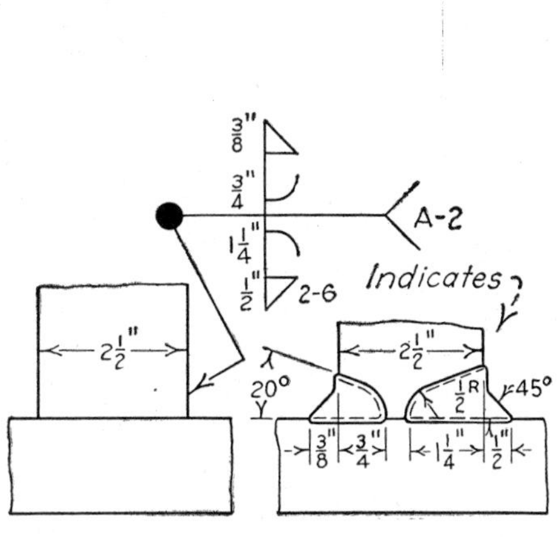

FIG. 16·12—A comparison.

Figure 16·13 classifies some typical joints and gives the welding symbols for each.

16·10 Use of the symbols. The following instructions should be followed for placement and form of the symbols. Some practices to avoid are also given.

INSTRUCTIONS FOR USE OF WELDING SYMBOLS

I. General.

a. Do not use the word "weld" as a symbol on drawings.

b. Symbols may or may not be made freehand as desired.

c. Inch, degree, and pound marks may or may not be used as desired.

d. The symbol may be used without specification references or tails to designate the most commonly used specification when the following note appears on the drawing:
"Unless otherwise designated, all welds to be made in accordance with welding specification No. —."

e. When specification references are used, place in tail, thus: A1 BB2

f. Symbols apply between abrupt changes in direction of joint or to extent of hatching or dimension lines (except where all-around symbol is used). See IV *d* and *e*.

g. Faces of welds assumed to have user's standard contours unless otherwise indicated.

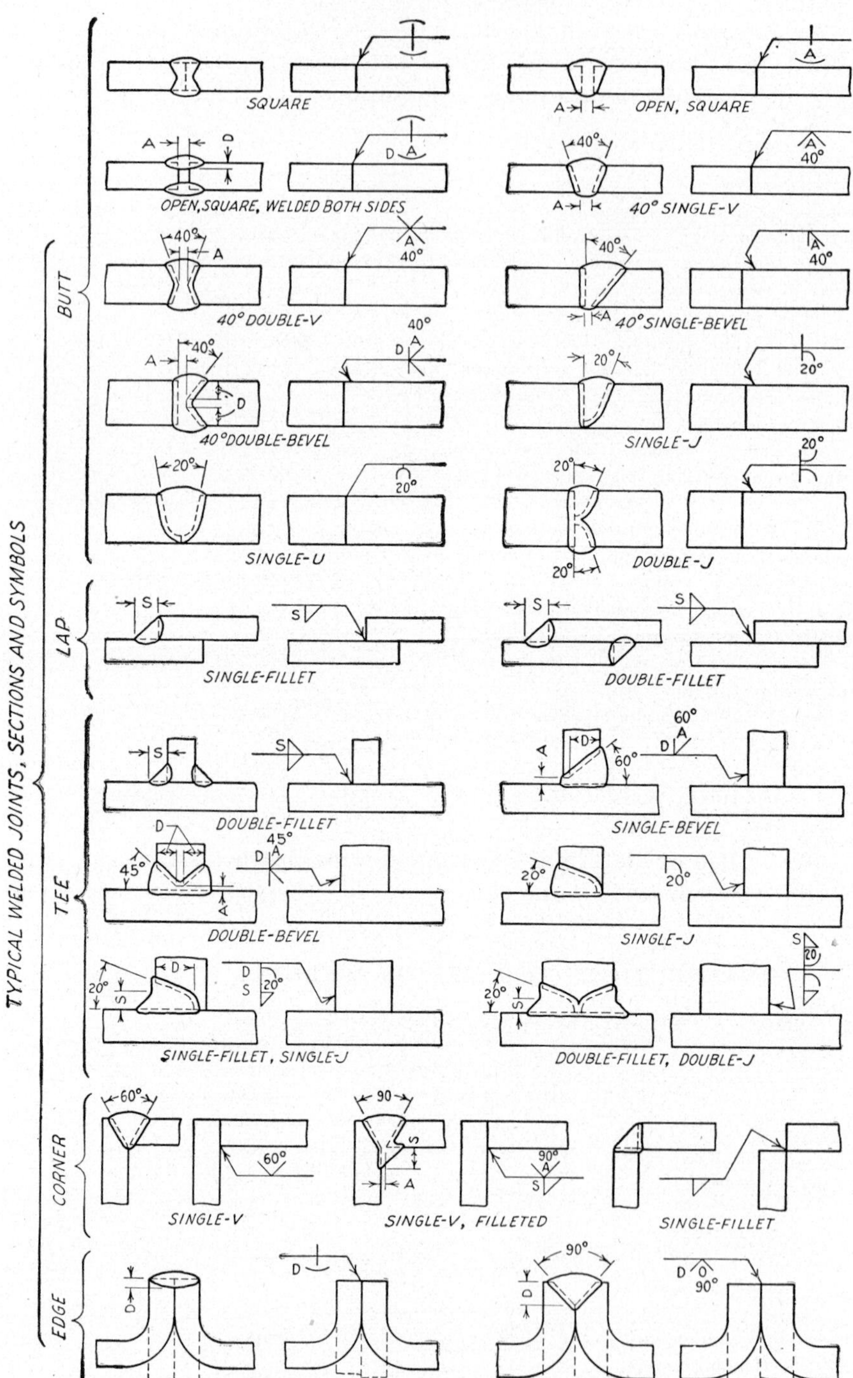

FIG. 16·13—Classification of welded joints.

h. Faces of welds assumed not to be finished other than cleaned unless otherwise indicated.

i. All except plug, spot, and projection welds assumed continuous unless otherwise indicated.

II. Arc and gas welds.

1. General.

a. Do not put symbol directly on lines of drawing; place symbol on reference line and connect latter to joint with arrow, thus:

b. For welds on arrow (or near) side of joint show symbol on near side of reference lines, face toward reader, thus:

c. For welds on other (or far) side show symbol on far side of reference line, face away from reader, thus:

d. For welds on both sides of joint show symbols on both sides of reference line, faces toward and away from reader, thus:

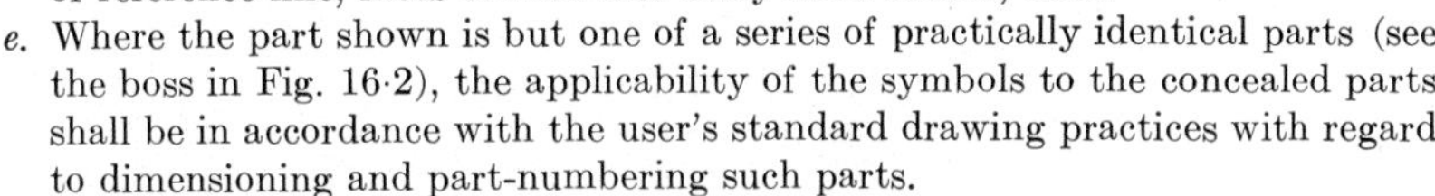

e. Where the part shown is but one of a series of practically identical parts (see the boss in Fig. 16·2), the applicability of the symbols to the concealed parts shall be in accordance with the user's standard drawing practices with regard to dimensioning and part-numbering such parts.

f. Where one member only is to be grooved, show arrow pointing unmistakably to that member. See Fig. 16·8.

g. Read symbols from bottom and right-hand side of drawing in the usual manner and place numerical data on vertical reference lines so that reader will be properly oriented, thus:

h. Show symbol for each weld in joints composed of more than one weld, thus:
(Give numerical data in proper location with regard to each symbol.)

i. In complicated joints requiring large compound symbols, two separate sets of symbols may be used if desired.

j. Show dimensions of weld on same side of reference line as symbol, thus:

k. Show dimensions of one weld only when welds on both sides of the joint are of the same type and size, thus: (If size of undimensioned fillets is governed by a note on the drawing, all weld sizes different from that covered in the note must be given.)

l. Show dimensions for welds on both sides of the joint, when the arrow-side and other-side welds are different, thus:

m. Indicate specific lengths of welds in conjunction with dimension lines, thus:

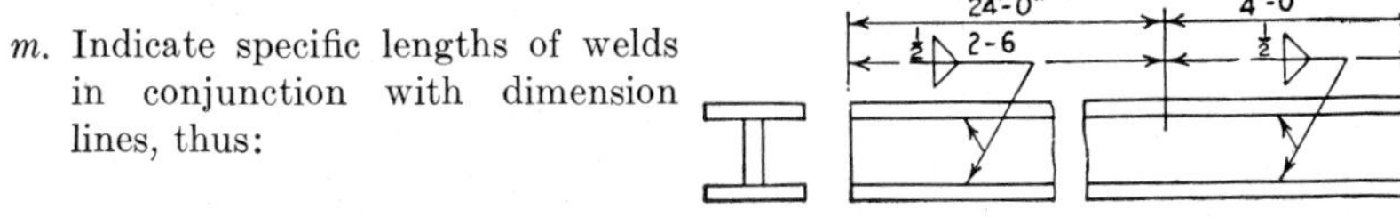

n. Show the welding between abrupt changes in the direction of the weld, thus (except when all-around symbol is used; see IV *d* and *e*):

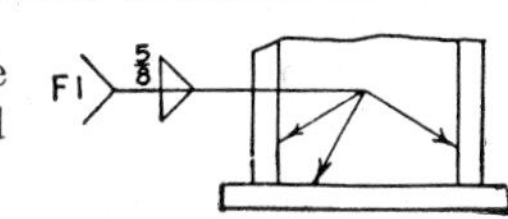

o. When it is desired to show extent of welds by hatching, use one type of hatching with definite end lines, thus:

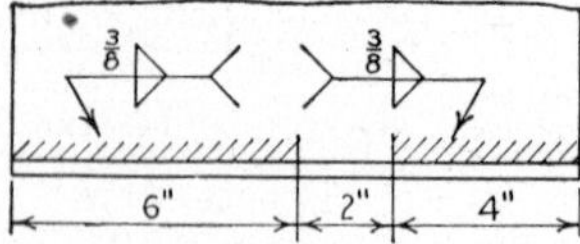

p. If actual outlines of welds are drawn in section or end elevation, basic symbol is not necessary to show type and location; size or other numerical details only need to be given, thus:

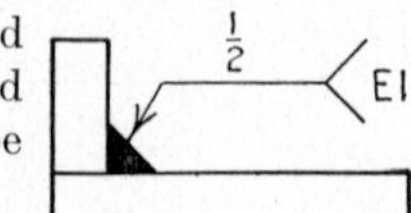

q. Show fillet, bevel- and J-groove weld symbols with perpendicular leg always to the left hand, thus:

2. Bead welds.

a. Show bead welds used in building up surfaces (size is minimum height of pad), thus:

b. When a small but no specific minimum height of pad is desired, show thus:

3. Fillet welds.

a. Show size of fillet weld to the left of the perpendicular leg, thus:

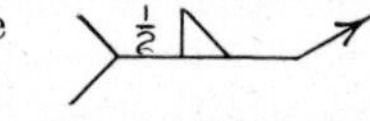

(Incorrect)

b. Show specific length of fillet weld or increment after size so that data read from left to right, thus:

c. Show center-to-center pitch of increments of intermittent fillet welds after increment length so that data read from left to right, thus:

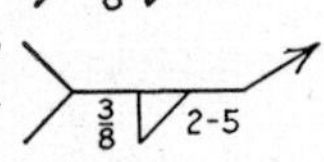

d. Use separate symbol for each weld when intermittent and continuous fillet welds are used in combination.

e. Show two intermittent fillet welds with increments opposite each other (chain), thus:

f. Show two intermittent fillet welds with increments not opposite each other (staggered), thus:

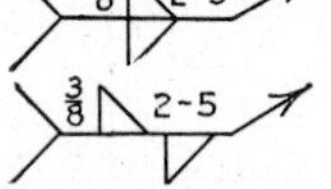

g. Measure pitch of intermittent fillet welds between centers of increments on one side of member.

h. Increments and not spaces assumed to be at ends of all intermittent welds and over-all length dimensions govern to ends of those increments, thus:

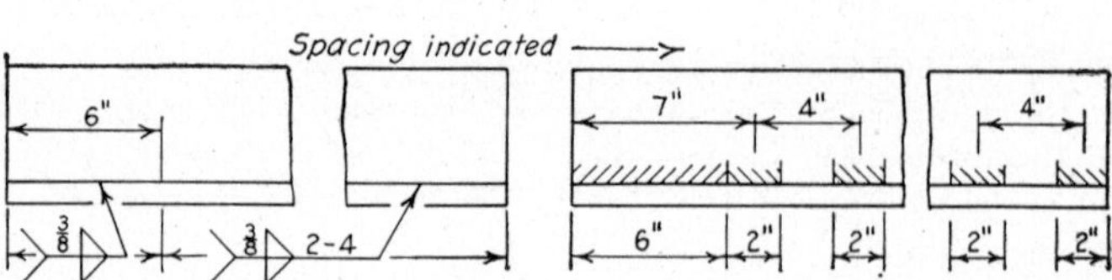

i. Faces of fillet welds assumed to be at 45° from legs unless otherwise indicated

j. When the face of a fillet weld is to be at any other angle than 45°, two dimensions are necessary to designate fully the size of the weld. Place these dimensions in parentheses so that the two dimensional size data will be a single entity and will not be confused with length of increment and spacing data.

Show on drawings, positions of legs relative to members.

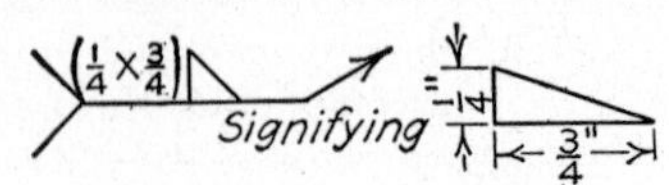

4. Groove welds.
   a. Show side from which square-groove weld is made by bead or flush symbols, thus (see III, 4*a*; IV *h*; and IV *j* and *k*):

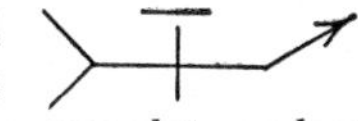

   b. Total penetration of square-groove welds assumed to be complete unless otherwise indicated.
   c. Show size of square-groove welds (depth of penetration) when penetration is less than complete, thus:
   d. Show root opening of open, square-groove welds inside symbol, thus:

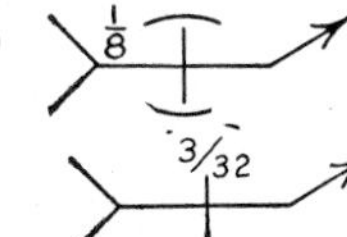

   e. Total depth of V and bevel grooves before welding assumed to be equal to thickness of member unless otherwise indicated.
   f. Show size of V- and bevel-groove welds (depth of single groove before welding) when grooving is less than complete, thus:

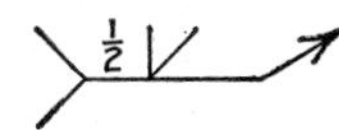

   g. Total depth of penetration of V- and bevel-groove welds assumed complete unless, with usual welding processes, depth of grooving is such that complete penetration is not possible, when depth of penetration is assumed to be depth of groove plus normal penetration. When using welding processes giving abnormal penetration, give information on latter by detail or note (see IV *j*).
   h. Root opening of V- and bevel-groove welds assumed to be user's standard unless otherwise indicated.
   i. Show root openings of V- and bevel-groove welds when not user's standard, inside symbol, thus:

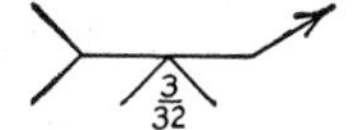

   j. Included angle of V- and bevel-groove welds assumed to be user's standard unless otherwise indicated.
   k. Show included angle of V- and bevel-groove welds when not user's standard inside symbol, thus:

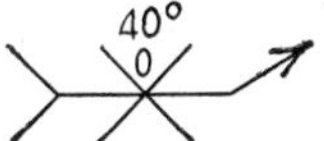

   l. Proportions of U- and J-groove welds assumed to be user's standard unless otherwise indicated.
   m. Show size of U- and J-groove welds (depth of single groove before welding) having user's standard proportions but incomplete penetration, thus:

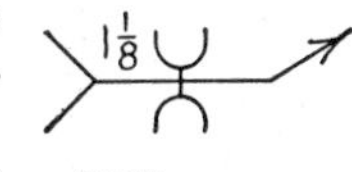

   n. When proportions of U- and J-groove welds are not user's standard, show weld by detail or reference drawing and use reference symbol, thus (see IV *o*):

NOTE 16

   o. Show welding done from root side of single-groove welds with bead-weld symbol, thus:

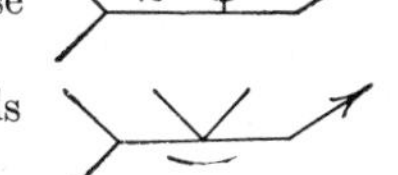

5. Plug and slot welds.
   a. Show size of plug and slot welds (root opening and root length), thus:
   (Root opening equals root length for plug welds.)

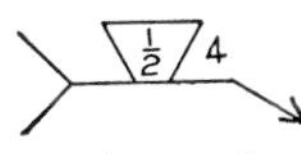

   b. Included angle of bevel of plug and slot welds assumed to be user's standard unless otherwise indicated.
   c. Show included angle of bevel of plug and slot welds when not user's standard, thus:
   d. Show pitch of plug and slot welds in row, thus:

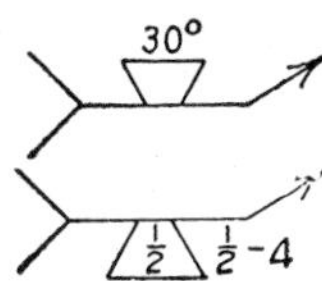

   e. Show fillet-welded holes and slots with proper fillet-weld symbols and not with plug-weld symbols.

III. Resistance welds.

1. General.

a. Center resistance-welding symbols for spot and seam welds on reference line because these symbols have no arrow-side or other-side (near- and far-side) significance (see Fig. 16·14 and also refer to IV *m*), but do not center projection-welding symbols, because the latter have such significance.

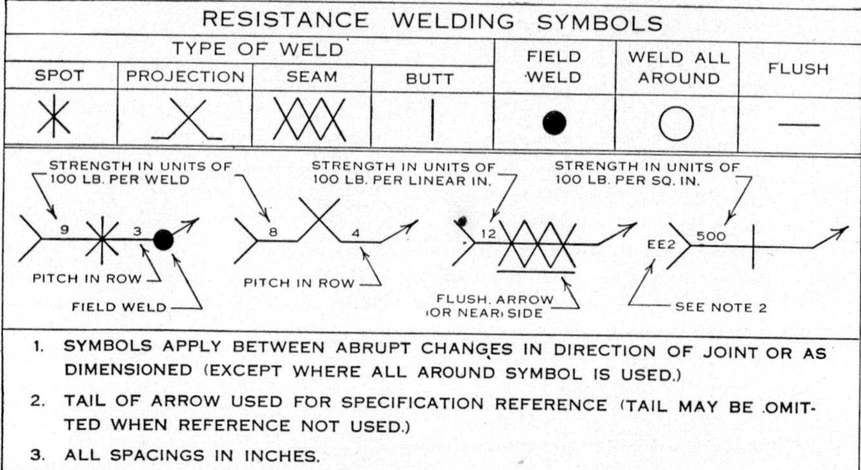

RESISTANCE WELDING SYMBOLS

TYPE OF WELD				FIELD WELD	WELD ALL AROUND	FLUSH
SPOT	PROJECTION	SEAM	BUTT			

1. SYMBOLS APPLY BETWEEN ABRUPT CHANGES IN DIRECTION OF JOINT OR AS DIMENSIONED (EXCEPT WHERE ALL AROUND SYMBOL IS USED.)
2. TAIL OF ARROW USED FOR SPECIFICATION REFERENCE (TAIL MAY BE OMITTED WHEN REFERENCE NOT USED.)
3. ALL SPACINGS IN INCHES.

FIG. 16·14—American Standard resistance-welding symbols.

b. Designate resistance welds by strength rather than size (because of impracticability of determining latter).

c. Spot- and seam-weld symbols may be used directly on drawings, thus; but projection-weld symbols should not.

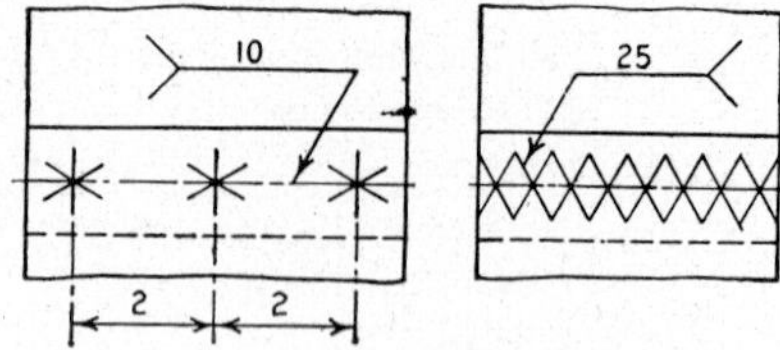

d. When not used on lines of drawing, connect reference line to center line of weld or rows of welds with arrow, thus:

e. Show welds of extent less than between abrupt changes in direction of joint, thus:

f. When tension, impact, fatigue or other properties are required, use reference symbol, thus (see IV *o*):

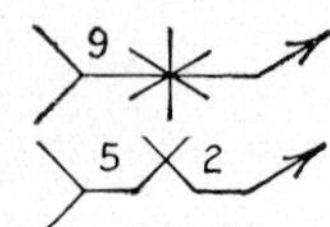

2. Spot and projection welds.

a. Show strength of spot and projection welds in single shear in units of 100 pounds per weld, thus:

b. Show strength and center-to-center spacing of spot and projection welds in row, thus:

c. Proportions of projections assumed given on drawing.

d. In a projection-welded joint parallel, or nearly so, to the plane of the paper, show whether the arrow- (or near-) side or other- (or far-) side member is to be embossed by placing the projection-weld symbol on the arrow (or near) or the other (or far) side of the reference line, thus:

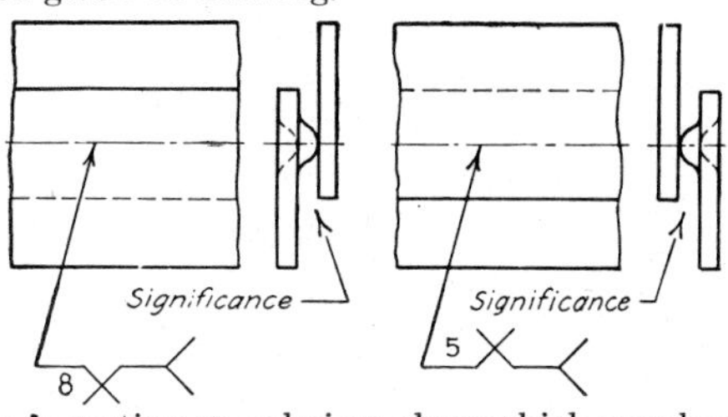

e. In a projection-welded joint shown in section or end view, show which member is to be embossed by pointing arrow to that member, thus:

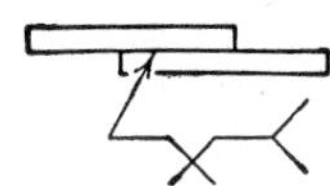

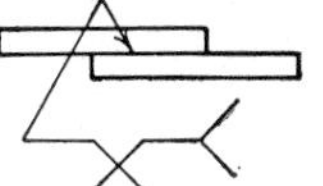

3. Seam welds.
   a. Seam welds assumed to be of overlapping or tangent spots. If any spacing exists between spots, welds are considered to be a series of spot welds, and spot symbol should be used.
   b. Show shear strength of seam welds in units of 100 pounds per linear inch, thus

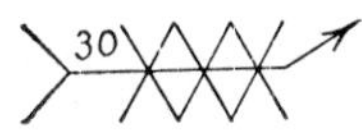

4. Butt welds.
   a. Show resistance butt welds without bead-weld symbol, signifying that weld is not made from any side, but all at once, thus (see II, 4*a*):

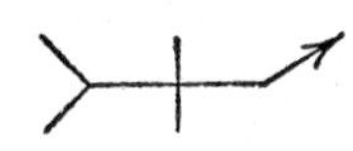

   b. Resistance butt welds assumed to be equal to strength of base metal in tension unless otherwise indicated.
   c. When a different strength is desired, show strength of butt welds in tension in units of 100 pounds per square inch, thus:

IV. Supplementary symbols.
   a. Show "field" welds (any weld not made in shop), thus:

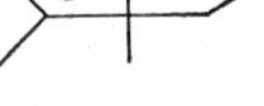

   b. Show "all-around" welds, and weld-encircling joint (or joints) in so far as is possible, thus:

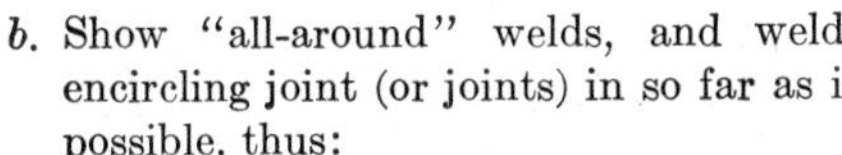

   c. When the weld encircles the joint but there is no abrupt change in the direction of the joint or parts of the joint (changes in the direction of rolled structural sections are considered abrupt even though there are fillets in the corners), the all-around symbol may or may not be used as desired, thus:

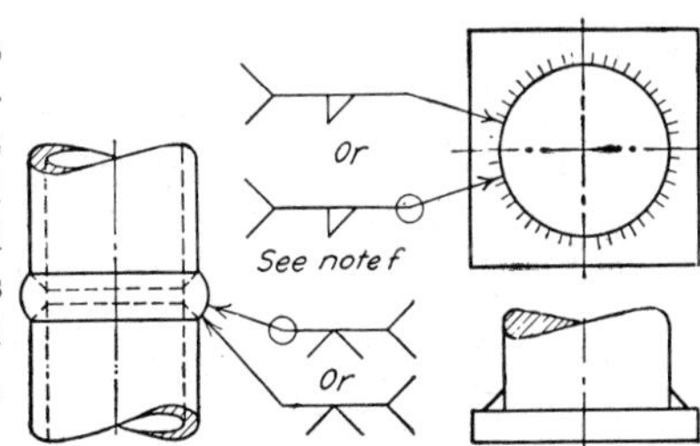

   d. The all-around symbol extends control of the welding symbol beyond abrupt changes in the direction of one joint, or parts of one joint, to encirclement of the complete joint in so far as is possible, thus:

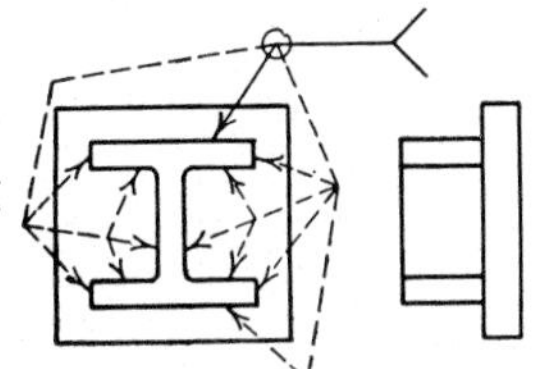

e. The all-around symbol extends the control of the welding symbol not only beyond abrupt changes in the direction of one joint, but to two or more joints to the encirclement of the joints in so far as is possible, thus:

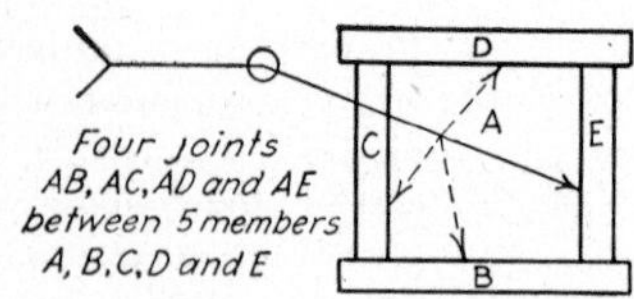

f. When the use of an arrow-side or other-side symbol, together with an all-around symbol, results in a weld on both sides of the joint as a whole, it is advisable to use the both-sides symbol even though a one-side symbol may be strictly correct (see *g* below), thus:

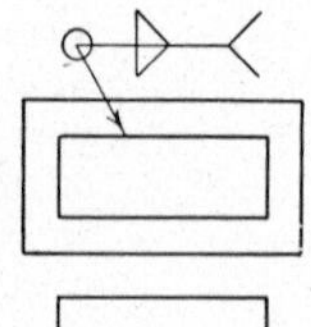

g. When the member involved is hollow or annular, when there is more than one encircling weld, and when there is likelihood of confusion existing as to whether or not a both-sides symbol would refer to a part of the joint or to the joint as a whole, show each encircling weld with a separate arrow, thus:

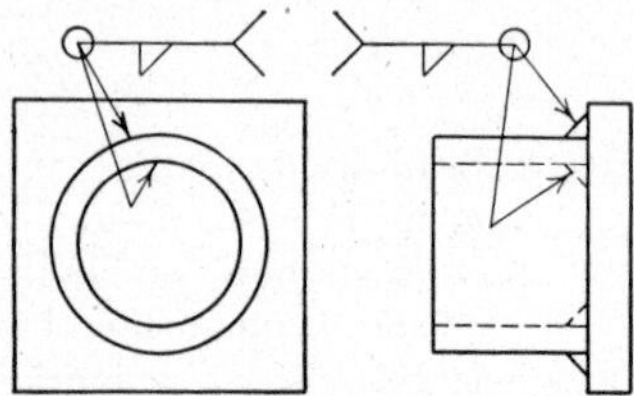

h. The locations of the flush and finish symbols have the usual arrow- and other- (near- and far-) side significance and govern only the sides on which they are shown.

i. Finish marks govern faces of welds only and not base metal either before or after welding.

j. Show arc and gas welds made flush without recourse to any kind of finishing, thus:

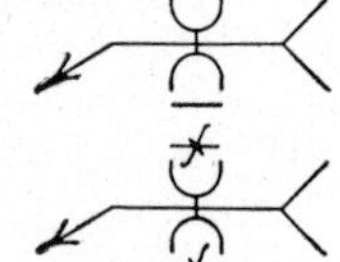

k. Show arc and gas welds made flush by mechanical means with both flush and user's standard finish symbols, thus:

The following letters are suggested for indicating finishing processes:

C—Chip G—Grind M—Machine

l. Show finishing on face of arc and gas welds, which need not be flush, with user's standard finish symbols on bead symbol, thus:

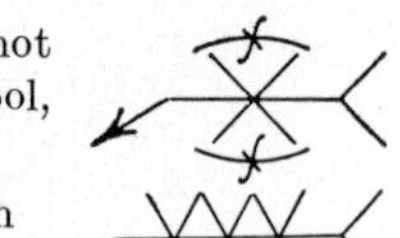

m. Show spot, seam, or projection welds made practically flush (with minimum indentation), thus:

n. Show resistance butt welds, finished by mechanical means, without flush symbol, thus:

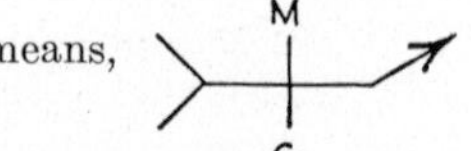

o. Show special welds not covered by any of the above symbols by a detailed section or reference drawing, or give any supplementary information by means of a note and refer weld to section, drawing, or note by a reference symbol. Reference symbol has usual location significance, thus:

PROBLEMS

The draftsman should be so thoroughly familiar with the welding symbols that he can write and read them without hesitation. Problems 1 and 2 give practice in reading, 3 and 4 in writing. Problems 5 to 9 give practice in the use of the symbols on working drawings.

1, 2. Figs. 16·15, 16·16. Make full-size cross-sectional sketches (similar to Figs. 16·17 and 16·18) of the joints indicated. Dimension each sketch.

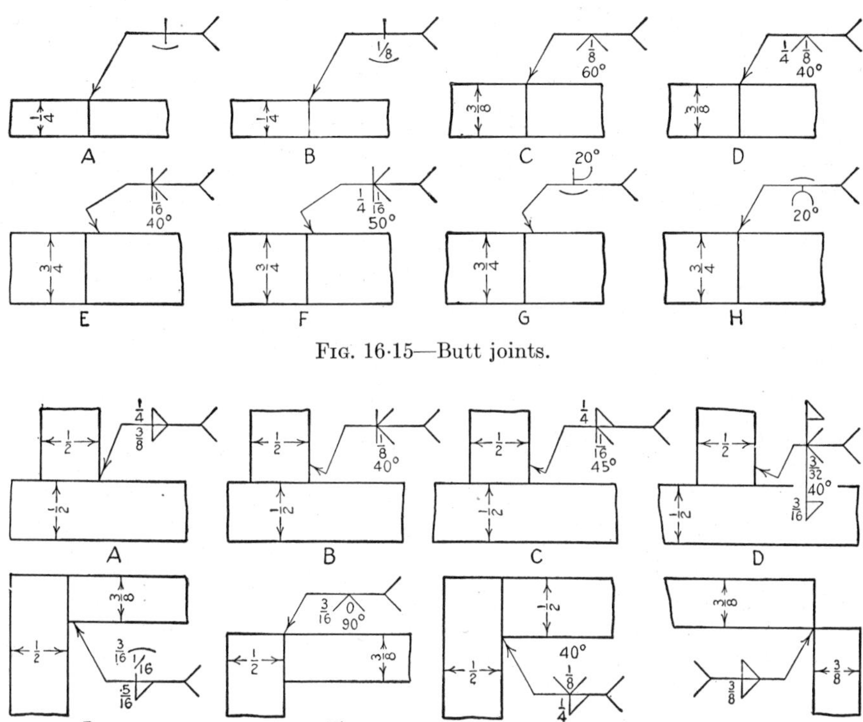

Fig. 16·15—Butt joints.

Fig. 16·16—Tee and corner joints.

3, 4. Figs. 16·17, 16·18. Sketch members and show welding symbol for each complete joint. Estimate weld size from plate thickness.

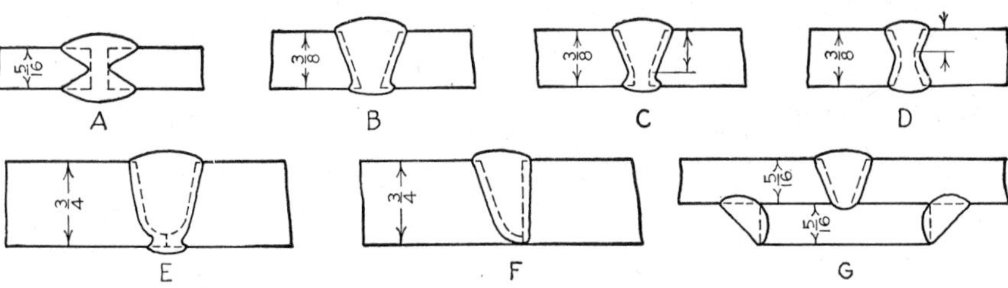

Fig. 16·17—Butt joints.

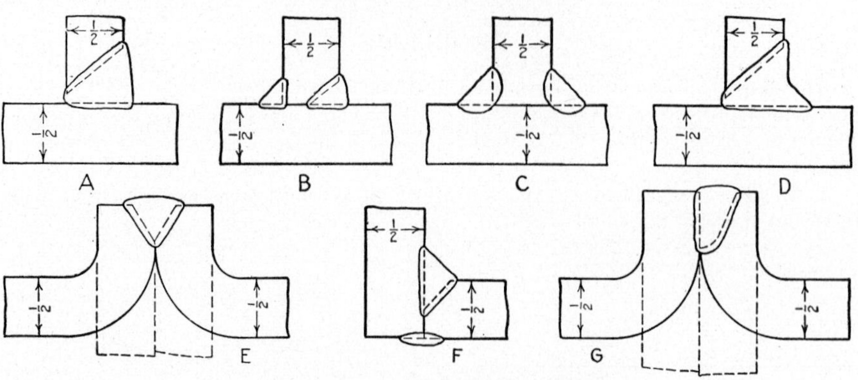

FIG. 16·18—Tee, corner, and edge joints.

5, 6. Figs. 16·19, 16·20. Make complete welding drawing for each object. These problems are printed quarter size. Draw full size by scaling or transferring with dividers.

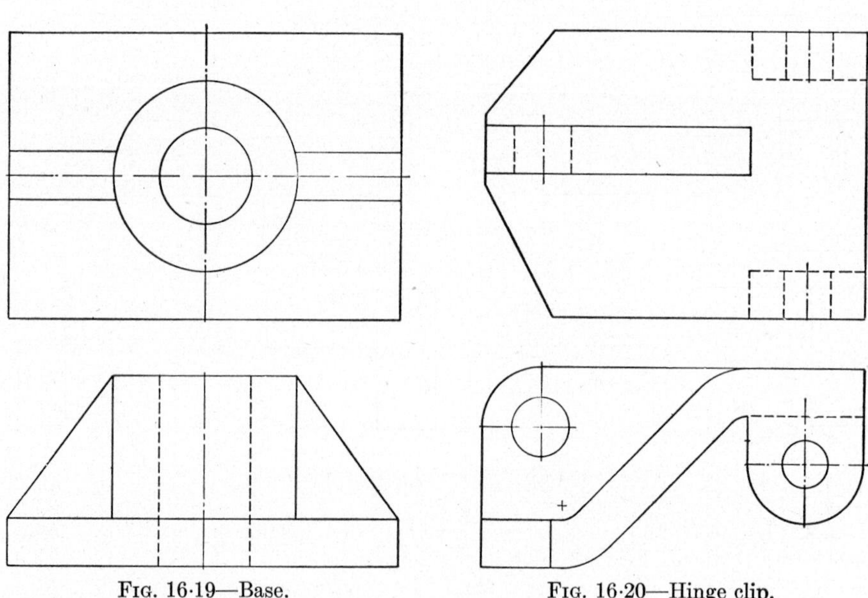

FIG. 16·19—Base.

FIG. 16·20—Hinge clip.

7. Fig. 16·21. Draw the views given; add welding symbols, dash numbers for identification of the individual pieces, and complete the materials list.

8. Fig. 16·22. Draw the views given and add welding symbols and dash numbers. Make a materials list similar to the one used in Prob. 7. Determine stock length of material to form slotted piece by using the formula for bend allowance, page 538.

DASH NO.	MAT'L	STOCK SIZE

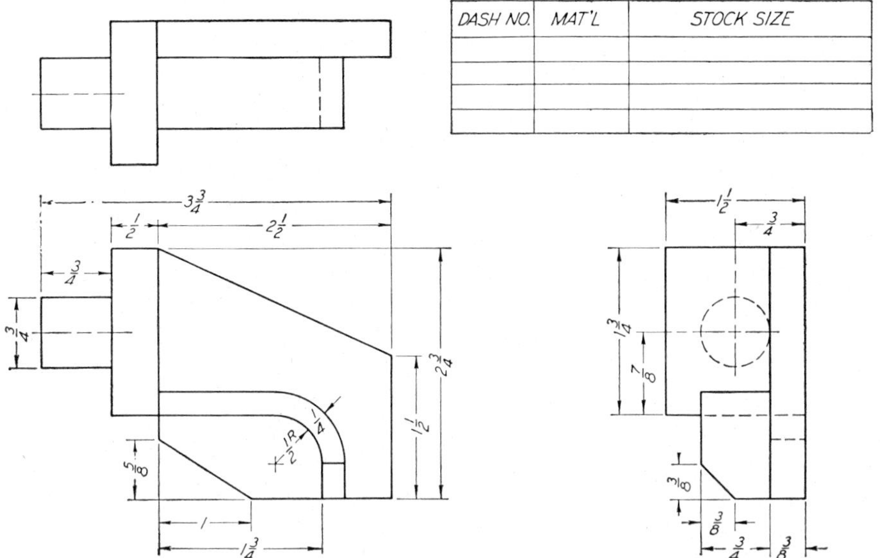

Fig. 16·21—Pivoted spacer.

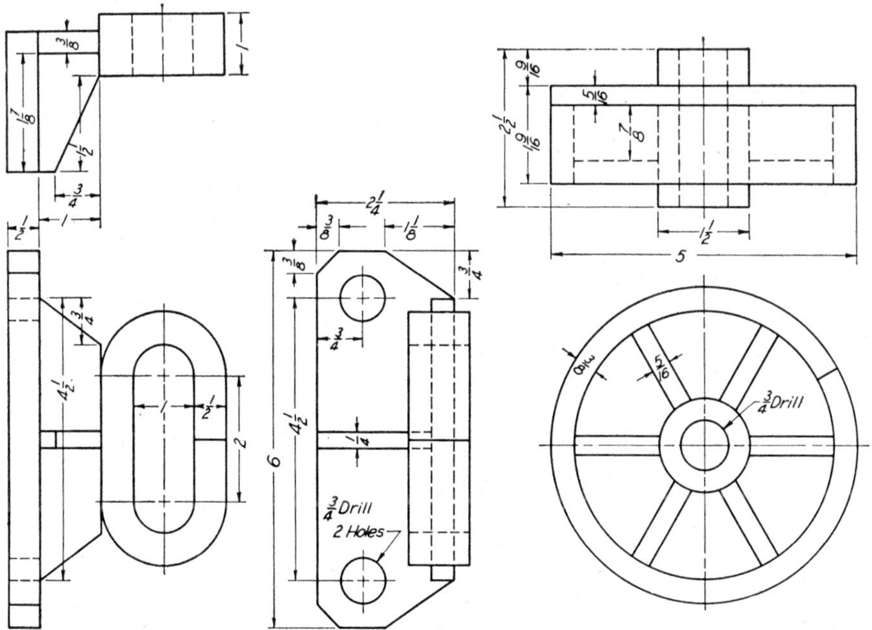

Fig. 16·22—Belt-tightener bracket. Fig. 16·23—Ribbed disk wheel.

9. Fig. 16·23. Draw the views given and add welding symbols and dash numbers. Make a materials list. Determine length of material for rim by using the formula for bend allowance, page 538.

Chapter 17

GEARS AND CAMS

17·1 Gears. The theory of gearing belongs to the study of mechanism, but the representation and specification of gears are of such common occurrence that the proportions and nomenclature should be familiar to the young engineer.

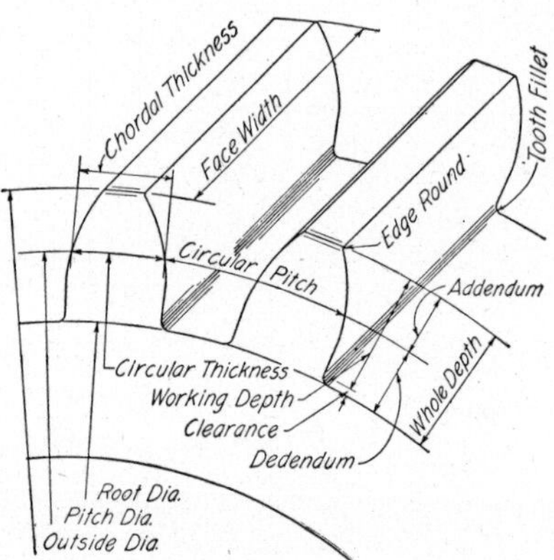

Fig. 17·1—Gear nomenclature.

Briefly, gears are a substitute for rolling cylinders and cones, designed to ensure positive motion. There are numerous kinds of gears, of which the most common forms are *spur gears* for transmitting power from one shaft to another parallel shaft, and *bevel gears* for two shafts whose axes intersect, usually at right angles. When one gear of a pair is much smaller than the other, it is called a "pinion."

Some of the terms in the American Standard nomenclature of gearing are given in Fig. 17·1. In the calculations concerning gears the following standardized terms and abbreviations are used:

N = number of teeth = $DP \times PD$.

DP = diametral pitch = number of teeth in the gear for each inch of pitch diameter = N/PD.

PD = diameter of pitch circle = N/DP.

CP = circular pitch = the distance on the circumference of the pitch circle between corresponding points of adjacent teeth = $\pi PD/N = \pi/DP$.

CTh = circular thickness = the thickness of the tooth on the pitch circle = $CP/2$.

CT = chordal thickness = length of the chord subtended by the circular thickness arc = $PD \sin (90/N)$.

A = addendum = radial distance between the pitch circle and the top of the teeth = constant/DP (= for standard involute teeth $1/DP$).

D = dedendum = radial distance between the pitch circle and the bottom of the tooth space = constant/DP (= for standard involute teeth $1.157/DP$).

C = clearance = radial distance between the top of a tooth and the bottom of the mating tooth space = constant/DP (= for standard involute teeth $0.157/DP$).

WD = whole depth = radial distance between outside circle and root circle = $A + D$.

WDe = working depth = greatest depth to which a tooth of one gear extends into the tooth space of a mating gear = $2A$.

OD = outside diameter = the diameter of the greatest circle which contains the tops of the teeth $= PD + 2A$.

RD = root diameter = the diameter of the root circle $= PD - 2D$.

FW = face width = width of pitch surface.

ER = edge round = radius of the circumferential edge of a gear tooth (to break the corner)

TFi = tooth fillet = curved line joining the tooth flank and the bottom of the tooth space.

The necessary information concerning a gear may be found by counting the number of teeth and measuring the outside diameter.

Example: Given N and OD. To find DP. $OD = PD + 2A$

Substitute in terms of DP,

$$OD = \frac{N}{DP} + \frac{2}{DP} \qquad \text{Then} \qquad OD = \frac{N+2}{DP'} \qquad \text{and} \qquad DP = \frac{N+2}{OD}$$

In a similar way any required dimensions may be found by the solution of the proper equation.

In working drawings of gears and toothed wheels, not all the teeth are drawn. For cast gears, the pitch circle, outside circle, root circle, and the full-sized outline of one tooth are drawn. For cut gears the blank is drawn and a note added concerning the number of teeth and pitch.

17·2 To draw a spur gear. Fig. 17·2. To draw the teeth of a standard involute-toothed spur gear by an approximate circle-arc method, lay off the

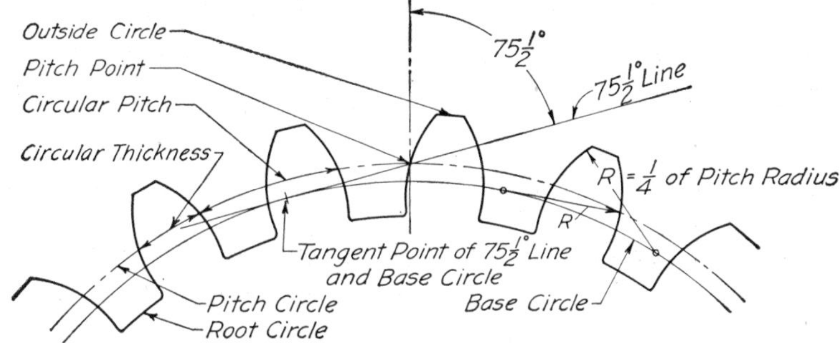

FIG. 17·2—To draw an involute spur gear, approximate method.

pitch circle, root circle, and outside circle. Start with the pitch point and divide the pitch circle into distances equal to the circular thickness. Through the pitch point draw a line of 75½° with the center line (for convenience the draftsman uses 75°). Draw the base circle tangent to the 75° line. With compasses set to a radius equal to one-fourth the radius of the pitch circle, describe arcs through the division points on the pitch circle, keeping the needle point on the base circle. Darken the arcs for the tops of the teeth and bottoms of the spaces and add the tooth fillets. For 16 or fewer teeth the radius value of one-fourth pitch radius must be increased to suit, in order to avoid the appearance of excessive undercut. For stub teeth the 75½° line is changed to 70°.

This method of drawing gear teeth is useful on display drawings, but on working drawings the tooth outlines are not drawn. Figure 17·3 illustrates the method of indicating the teeth and dimensioning a working drawing of a spur gear.

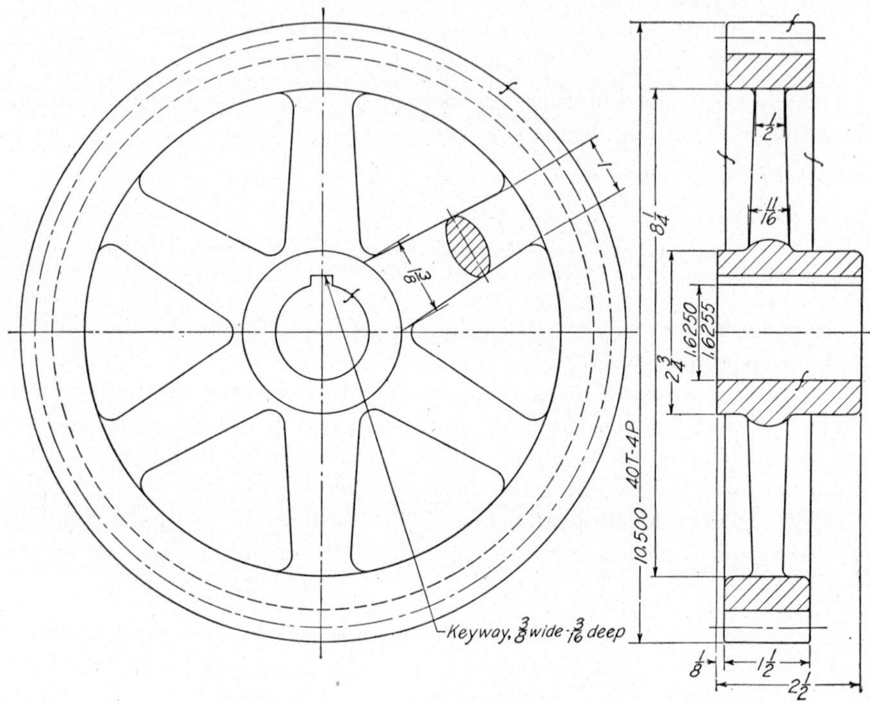

FIG. 17·3—Working drawing of a spur gear.

The dimensions necessary for the teeth of cut gears are: outside diameter, number of teeth, diametral pitch, and width of face.

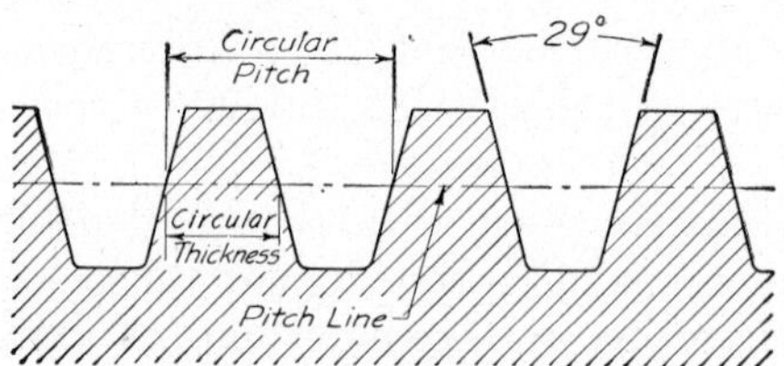

FIG. 17·4—Involute rack.

17·3 To draw a rack. Fig. 17·4. To draw the teeth of a standard involute rack by an approximate method, draw the pitch line and lay off the addendum and dedendum distances. Divide the pitch line into spaces equal to the circular thickness of the mating gear. Through these points of division draw the tooth faces at 14½° (15° is used by draftsmen). Draw tops and bottoms and add the tooth fillets. For stub teeth use 20° instead of 14½°. Specifications of rack teeth (to be given on a detail drawing) are: linear pitch (equal to circular pitch of the mating gear), number of teeth, diametral pitch, whole depth.

17·4 To draw a bevel gear. Fig. 17·5. To draw the teeth of an involute-toothed bevel gear by an approximate method (the Tredgold method). Draw the center lines, intersecting at *O*. Across the center lines

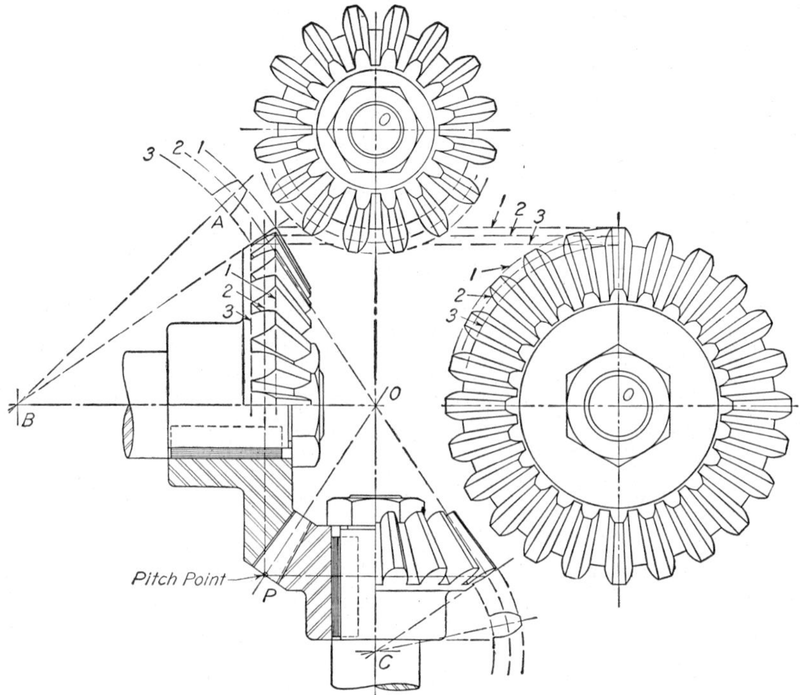

FIG. 17·5—To draw involute bevel gears, approximate method.

lay off the pitch diameters and project them parallel to the center lines until the projectors intersect at the pitch point *P*. From the pitch point, draw the pitch-circle diameters for each gear and from their extremities the "pitch cones" to the vertex or "cone center" *O*. Lay off the addendum and dedendum distances for each gear on lines through the pitch points perpendicular to the cone elements. Extend one of these normals for each gear to intersect the axis, as at *B* and *C*, making the "back cones." With *B* as center, swing arcs 1, 2, and 3 for the top, pitch line, and bottom, respectively, of a developed tooth. On a radial center line *AB*, draw a tooth, by the method of Fig. 17·2. Start the plan view of the gear by projecting points 1, 2, and 3 across to its vertical center line and drawing circles through the points. Lay off the radial center lines for each tooth. With dividers take the circular thickness distances from *A* and transfer them to each tooth. This will give three points on each side of each tooth through which a circle arc, found by trial, will pass, giving the foreshortened contour of the large end of the teeth in this view. From this point the drawing becomes a problem in projection drawing. Note that in every view the lines converge at the cone center *O*, and that by finding three points on the contour of each tooth, circle arcs can be found by trial which will be sufficiently close approximations to give the desired effect.

This method is used for finished display drawings. Working drawings for cut bevel gears are drawn without tooth outlines and are dimensioned as shown in Fig. 17·6. For a cast gear the tooth outline must be given for the patternmaker.

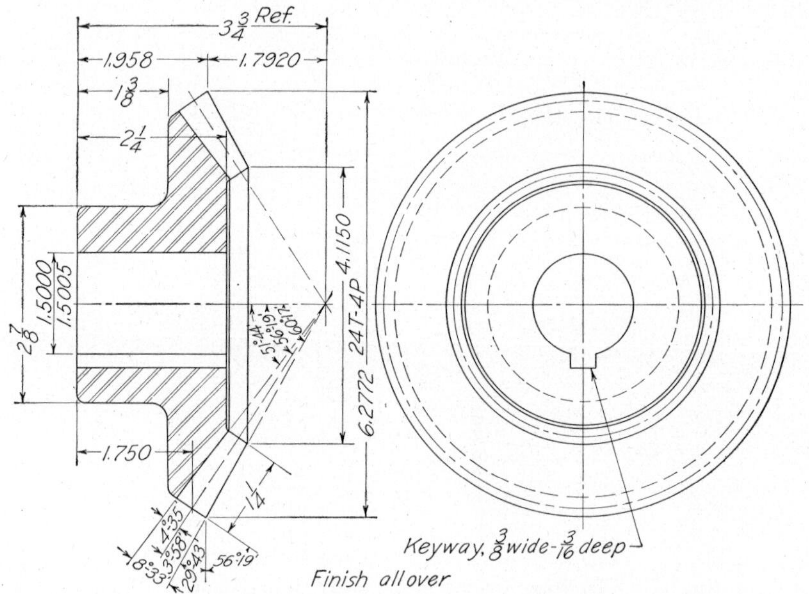

FIG. 17·6—Working drawing of a bevel gear.

17·5 Cams. A cam is a machine element with surface or groove formed to produce special or irregular motion in a second part, called a "follower." The shape of the cam is dependent upon the motion required and the type of follower that is used. The type of cam is dictated by the required relationship of the parts, and the motions of both.

17·6 Types of cams. The direction of motion of the follower with respect to the cam axis determines two general types, as follows: (1) radial or disk cams, in which the follower moves in a direction perpendicular to the cam axis, and (2) cylindrical or end cams, in which the follower moves parallel to the cam axis. Figure 17·7 shows at *A* a *radial cam*, with a roller follower held against the cam by gravity or by a spring. As the cam revolves the follower is raised and lowered. Followers are also made with pointed ends and with flat ends. *B* shows a *face cam*, with a roller follower at the end of an arm or link, the follower oscillating as the cam revolves.

When the cam itself oscillates, the *toe* and *wiper* are used, as at *C*. The toe, or follower, may also be made in the form of a swinging arm.

A *yoke* or *positive-motion cam* is shown at *D*, the enclosed follower making possible the application of force in either direction. The sum of the two

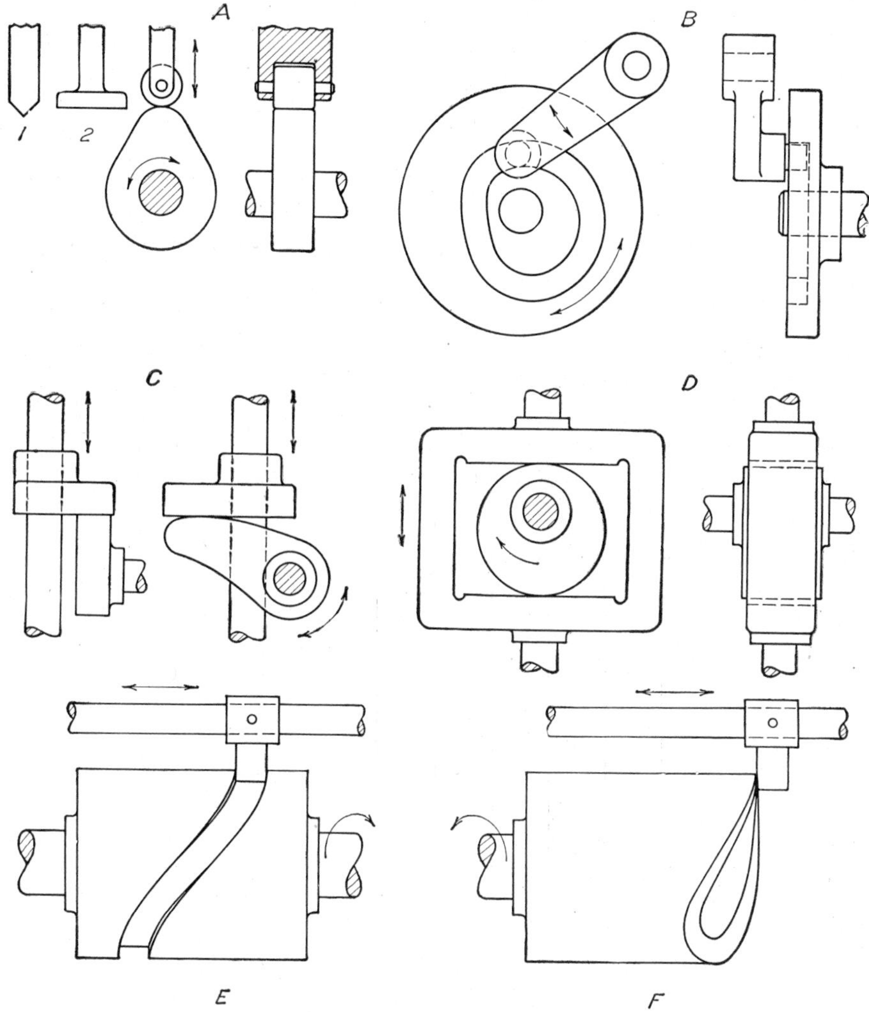

FIG. 17·7—Types of cams.

distances from the center of the cam to the points of contact must always be equal to the distance between the follower surfaces. The cylindrical *groove cam* at *E* and the *end cam* at *F* both move the follower parallel to the cam axis, force being applied to the follower in both directions with the groove cam, and in only one direction with the end cam.

17·7 Kinds of motion. Cams may be designed to move the follower with constant velocity, acceleration, or harmonic motion. In many cases, combinations of these motions, together with surfaces arranged for sudden rise or fall, or to hold the follower stationary, go to make up the complete cam surface.

17·8 Cam diagrams. In studying the motion of the follower, a diagram showing the height of the follower for successive cam positions is useful and is

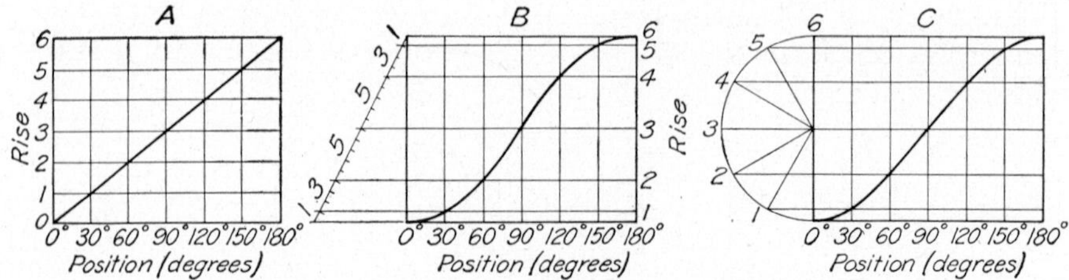

FIG. 17·8—Methods of plotting cam diagrams; three kinds of motion.

frequently employed. The cam position is shown on the abscissa, the full 360° rotation of the cam being divided, generally, every 30° (intermediate points may be used if necessary). The follower positions are shown on the ordinate, divided into the same number of parts as the abscissa. These diagrams are generally made to actual size.

Constant velocity gives a uniform rise and fall, and may be plotted as at *A*, Fig. 17·8, by laying off the cam positions on the abscissa, measuring the

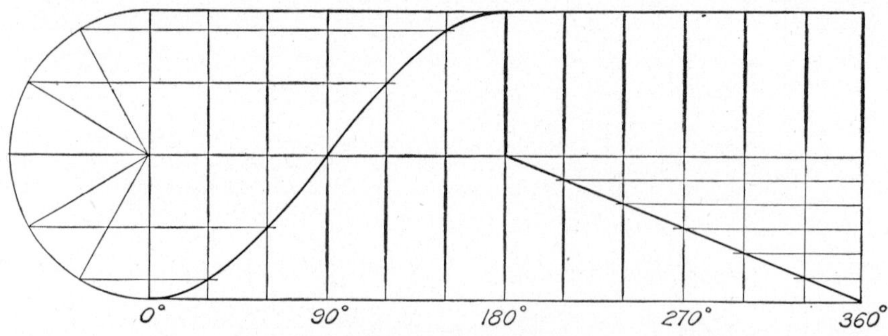

FIG. 17·9—A cam diagram.

total follower movement on the ordinate and dividing it into the same number of parts as the abscissa. As the cam moves one unit of its rotation, the follower likewise moves one unit, producing the straight line of motion shown.

With constant acceleration, the distance traveled is proportional to the square of the time, or the total distance traveled is proportional to 1, 4, 9, 16, 25, etc., and if the increments of follower distance are made proportional to 1, 3, 5, 7, etc., the curve may be plotted as shown at *B*. Using a scale, divide the follower rise into the same number of parts as the abscissa, making the first part 1 unit, the second 3 units, and so on. Plot points at the intersection of the coordinate lines, as shown. The curve at B accelerates and then decelerates to slow up the follower at the top of its rise.

Harmonic motion (sine curve) may be plotted as at C by measuring the rise and drawing a semicircle, dividing it into the same number of parts as the abscissa and projecting the points on the semicircle as ordinate lines. Points are plotted at the intersection of the coordinate lines, as shown.

Figure 17·9 is the cam diagram for the cam of Fig. 17·11. The follower rises with harmonic motion in 180°, drops halfway down instantly, and then returns with uniform motion to the point of beginning.

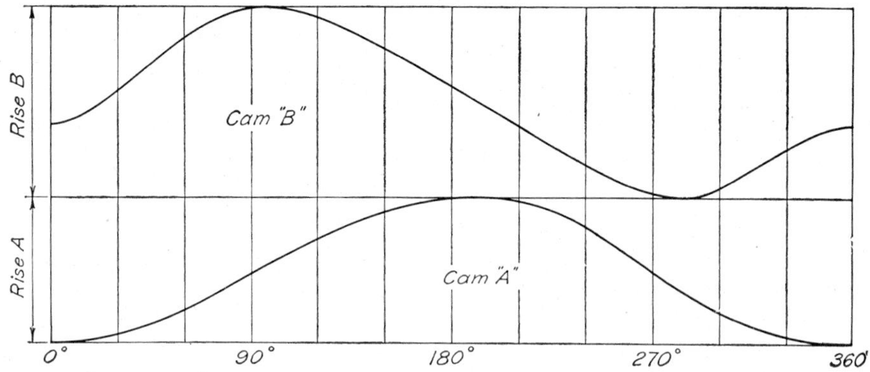

FIG. 17·10—A timing diagram.

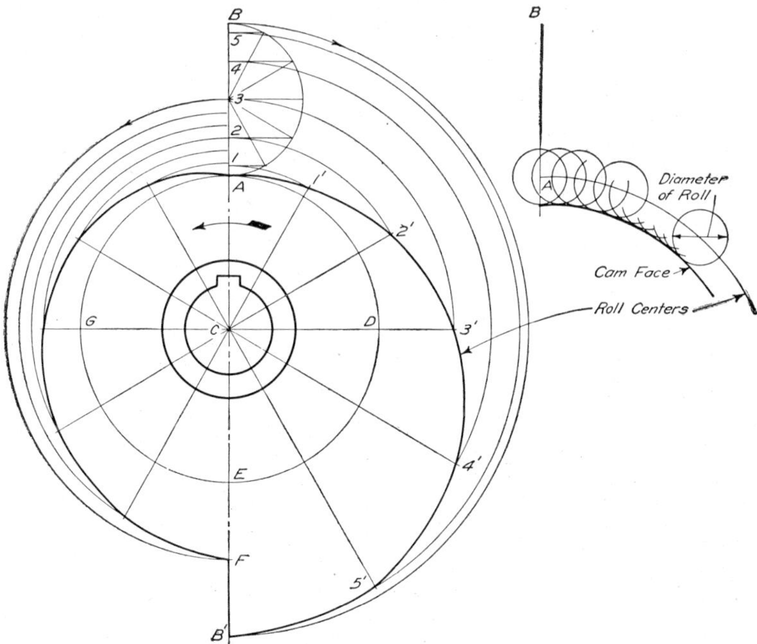

FIG. 17·11—Layout of plate cam.

17·9 Timing diagrams. When two or more cams are used on the same machine and their functions are dependent on each other, the "timing" and relative motions of each may be studied by means of a diagram showing each follower curve. The curves may be superimposed, but a better method is to place one above the other as in Fig. 17·10.

17·10 To draw a plate cam. The principle involved in drawing a cam is the same for all types. Illustrating with the cam of Fig. 17·11, for which the diagram of Fig. 17·9 was made, the point *C* is the center of the shaft, and *A* is the lowest and *B* the highest position of the center of the roller follower.

Divide the rise into six parts harmonically proportional. Divide the semicircle *ADE* into as many equal parts as there are spaces in the rise and draw radial lines. With *C* as center and radius *C*1, draw an arc intersecting the first radial line at 1′. In the same way locate points 2′, 3′, etc., and draw a smooth curve through them. If the cam is revolved in the direction of the arrow, it will raise the follower with the desired harmonic motion.

Draw *B′F* equal to one-half *AB*. Divide *A*3 into six equal parts and the arc *EGA* into six equal parts. Then for equal angles the follower must fall equal distances. Circle arcs drawn as indicated will locate the required points on the cam outline.

This outline is for the center of the roller; allowance for the roller size may be made by drawing the roller in its successive positions and then drawing a tangent curve as shown in the auxiliary figure.

17·11 To draw a cylindrical cam. The drawing of a cylindrical cam differs somewhat from that of a plate cam, as, in addition to the regular views, it generally includes a developed view, from which a template is made. Assume that the follower is to move upward 1½″ with harmonic motion in 180°, and then return with uniform acceleration. Top and front views of

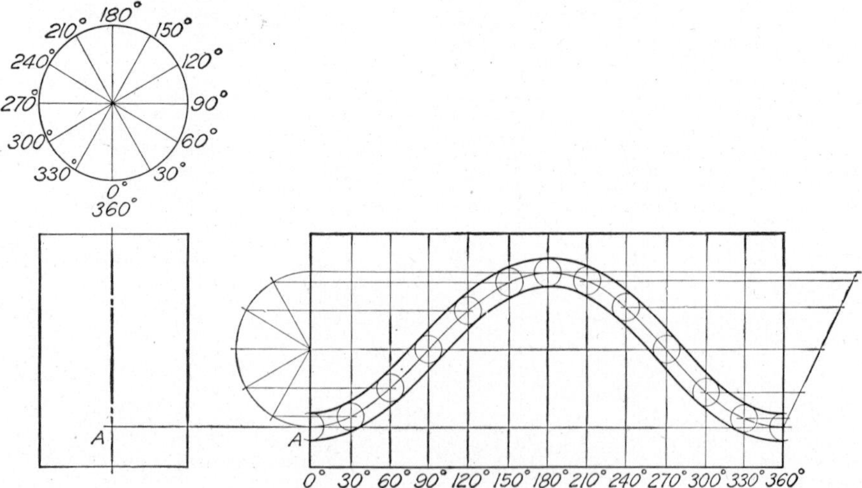

FIG. 17·12—Layout of cylindrical cam.

the cylinder are drawn, Fig. 17·12, and the development of the surface laid out. Divide the surface as shown, also the top view to show the positions of points plotted. Divide the rise for harmonic motion by drawing the semicircle and projecting the points. Refer to Fig. 17·8*C*. Divide the return for acceleration as shown. Refer to Fig. 17·8*B*. The curve thus obtained is for the center of the follower. Curves drawn tangent to circles representing positions of the follower will locate the working surfaces of the cam. The development made as described is the drawing used to make the cam.

PROBLEMS

Group I. Gears

1. A broken spur gear has been measured and the following information obtained: number of teeth, 33; outside diameter, 4⅜″; width of face, 1″; diameter of shaft, ⅞″; length of hub, 1¼″. Make drawing of gear blank with all dimensions and information necessary for making a new gear. Dimensions not given above may be made to suit as the drawing is developed.

2. Make a drawing for a spur gear. The only information available is as follows: root diameter, 7.3372″; outside diameter, 8.200″; width of face, 1⅞″; diameter of shaft, 1⅜″; length of hub, 2″.

3. Make an assembly drawing of a pair of spur gears, from the following information: On an 11″ × 17″ sheet locate centers for front view of gear *B* 4½″ from right border and 3½″ from bottom border. Gear *A* is to the left of gear *B*. Center distance between gears is 5.250″. Gear *A* revolves 300 rpm and has four spokes, elliptical in cross section, 1″ major and ½″ minor axes; inside flange diameter 4⅜″; hub 2″ diameter, 1½″ long. Gear *B* revolves 400 rpm and is disk type with ½″ web; inside flange diameter 3¼″; hub 2″ diameter, 1½″ long. Material is cast steel; face width 1″; *DP* = 4; shaft diameters 1″, ¼″ Woodruff keys. Draw front view and sectional top view.

4. Fig. 17·13. Make an assembly drawing of gear train, as follows: *A* and *B* are bevel gears, ⅞″ face width, 6 *DP*. *A* has 3″ *PD*, revolves 150 rpm. *B* revolves 100 rpm. *C* and *D* are spur gears 8 *DP*, 1″ face width. *C* engages *D*, which revolves 40 rpm. All shafts 1″. Draw *A* in full section, *B* with lower half in section, *C* and *D* in full section, quarter end view of gear *B* in space indicated, and end views of *C* and *D*.

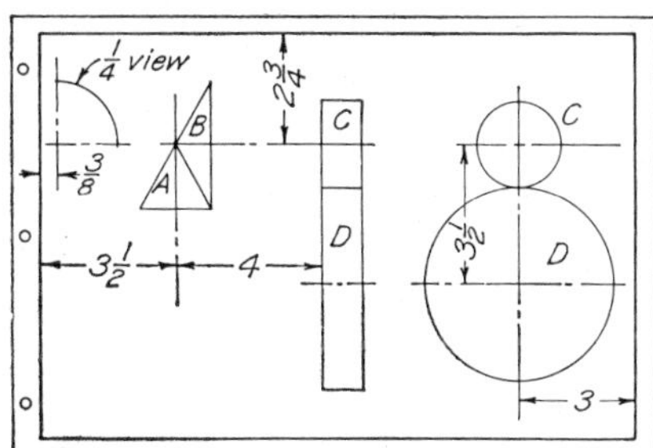

Fig. 17·13

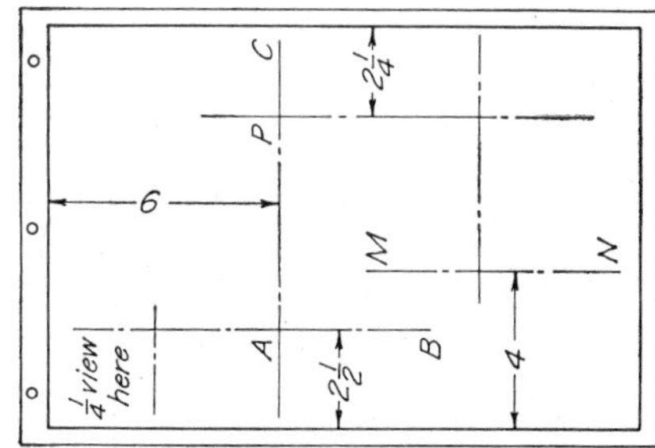

Fig. 17·14

5. Fig. 17·14. A 3″-*PD* 3-*DP* bevel gear *R* on shaft *AB* running 1,120 rpm drives another bevel gear *S* on shaft *AC* at 840 rpm. On shaft *AC* centered at *P*, an 8″-*PD* 4-*DP* spur gear *T* drives a pinion *U* at 1,680 rpm. All shaft diameters 1″, face widths 1″. Hub diameters of *R* and *S*, 1¾″. Gear *C* has four spokes, elliptical, ⅝″ × 1″; hub 1⅞″ diameter; thickness of flange ½″. Draw gear *R* with upper half in section; *S*, *T*, and *U* in full section. Put quarter-end view of R in space indicated, and end views of T and U on center line M-N.

6. Fig. 17·15. Make complete detail drawings of reversing mechanism, with bill of material and title. The purpose of this device is to drive a shaft in either direction from a shaft at right angles to it which always revolves in the same direction. In the design shown, either shaft may be driver, the gear ratios being 3 to 2.

The two bevel pinions, piece 6, are keyed to clutches, piece 4, which are bushed, piece 5, and run free on the splined shaft. These bevel pinions are always in mesh with the gear, piece 7, and, being on opposite sides of it, revolve on the splined shaft in opposite directions. The clutch, piece 3, is splined to its shaft and is free to shift axially into mesh with either of the two clutches, piece 4. This movement is controlled by the shifter arrangement, pieces 11, 12, 13, 14, 15, and 16. Three reamed tapered holes are provided in the pad on the top of the housing for the locking plunger, piece 15. This ensures positive retention of the clutch in either neutral or driving positions.

7. Fig. 17·15. Make assembly drawing of reversing mechanism, with title and piece numbers.

8. Fig. 17·15. Redesign reversing mechanism for complete ball-bearing installation.

9. Fig. 17·15. Redesign reversing mechanism with gear ratio 7 to 4 instead of 3 to 2.

10. Fig. 17·15. Redesign reversing mechanism as follows: Gear ratios 7 to 5 instead of 3 to 2; all thrust requirements to be met by ball-bearing installation. Spline shaft diameters to be 1″ instead of 1¼″. Keyed shaft to be 1⅛″ instead of 1⅜″. Use one centralizing oiling system for the whole mechanism.

11. Fig. 17·15. Redesign reversing mechanism for splash lubrication. Provision must be made for retaining the oil at cover joint and where shafts enter the box. Do not neglect to provide filling and draining plugs and an oil-level gage.

12. Fig. 17·15. Redesign reversing mechanism as follows: Make pieces 3, 4, and 6 in one piece, and spline to shaft as in present design. This will dispense with the two bushings, piece 5, and also the clutch teeth. This new piece is called a "double-bevel gear" and should be made long enough to be shifted axially in and out of mesh with gear, piece 7. Be sure to provide a neutral position. This design requires the thrust of the bevel gears to be taken by the shifter fork, which should be redesigned to take this load. It is suggested that a double fork of bronze be used with a strengthened locking plunger.

13. Fig. 17·16. Four-speed machine-tool transmission box. The power comes in on shaft A at a constant rate and leaves on shaft B at a rate depending on the positions of the sliding gears. Only the top view and end in section are given. The detail drawing of the gear-shifter bracket is shown in Fig. 15·17. Make a complete assembly drawing showing the front, top, and end views.

14. Fig. 17·16. Make complete working details with bill of material from the design of Prob. 13.

15. Fig. 17·16. Redesign Prob. 13 for ball-bearing installation.

16. Fig. 17·16. Redesign Prob. 13 for speed ratios 1 to 1, 1 to 1.228, 1 to 1.437, and 1 to 1.776, making pieces 1 and 6 duplicates. Shaft centers are to remain as in Prob. 13. Note that in the required set of speeds the ratio between each successive speed is approximately a constant (1.2).

17. Fig. 17·16. Redesign Prob. 13, using gears ¾″ wide, shafts A and B to be 1⅜″ in diameter. Omit center bearing for jack shaft but leave the shaft diameter unchanged.

Group II. Cams

18. Make a drawing for a plate cam to satisfy the following conditions: On a vertical center line a point A is ⅞″ above a point O, and a point B is 1¾″ above A. With center at O, revolution clockwise, the follower starts at A and rises to B with uniform motion during one-third revolution, remains at rest one-third revolution, and drops with uniform motion the last one-third revolution to the starting point. Diameter of shaft ¾″; diameter of hub 1¼″; thickness of plate ½″; length of hub 1¼″; diameter of roller ½″.

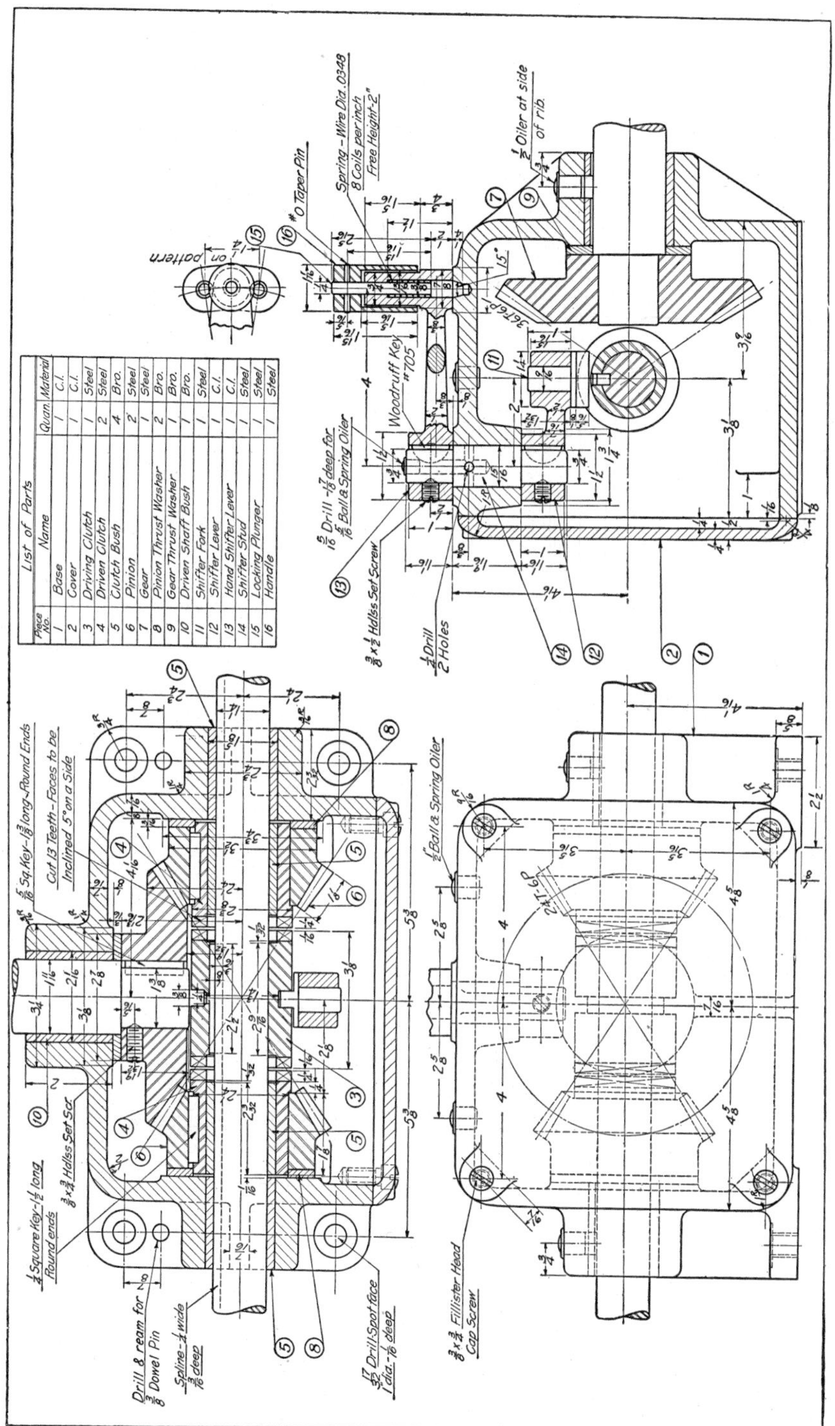

List of Parts

Piece No.	Name	Quan.	Material
1	Base	1	C.I.
2	Cover	1	C.I.
3	Driving Clutch	1	Steel
4	Driven Clutch	2	Steel
5	Clutch Bush	4	Bro.
6	Pinion	2	Steel
7	Gear	1	Steel
8	Pinion Thrust Washer	2	Bro.
9	Gear Thrust Washer	1	Bro.
10	Driven Shaft Bush	1	Bro.
11	Shifter Fork	1	Steel
12	Shifter Lever	1	C.I.
13	Hand Shifter Lever	1	C.I.
14	Shifter Stud	1	Steel
15	Locking Plunger	1	Steel
16	Handle	1	Steel

FIG. 17.15—Reversing mechanism.

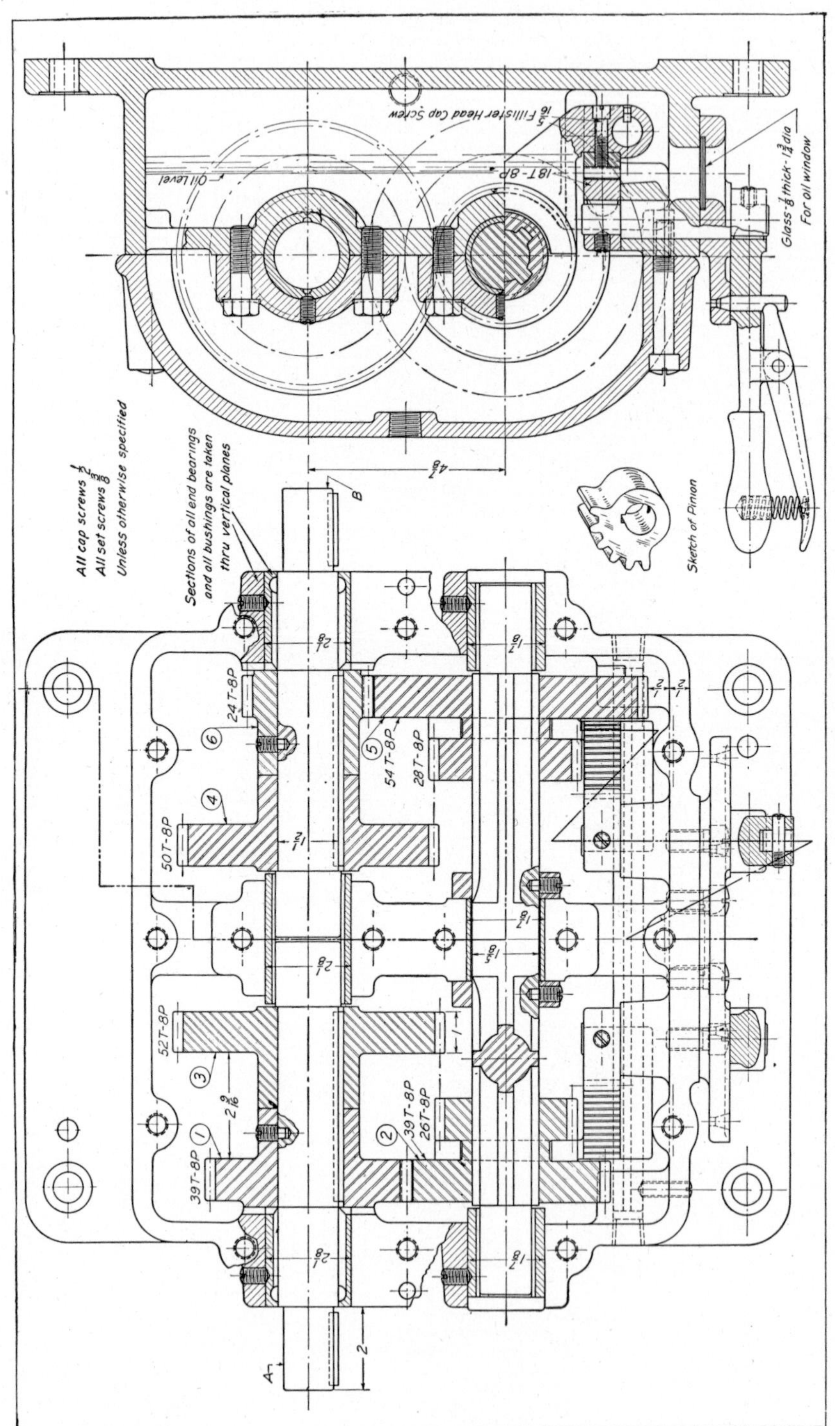

FIG. 17·16—Transmission box.

19. Make a drawing for a face cam using the data of Prob. 18.

20. Make a drawing for a toe-and-wiper cam. The toe shaft is vertical, ¾″ in diameter. Starting at a point 1″ directly above center of wiper shaft, the toe is to move upward 2″ with simple harmonic motion, with 135° turn of the shaft. Wiper has 1¼*D* hub, 1¼″ long; ¾″ diameter shaft. Design toe to suit.

21. Make a drawing for a positive-motion cam. Starting at a point 1″ above center of cam shaft, upper follower surface is to move upward 1″ with simple harmonic motion in 180° turn of cam. Return is governed by necessary shape of cam. Follower ½″ thick on ½″ vertical shaft. Cam ½″ thick, on ¾″ diameter shaft; hub 1¼″ *D*, 1¼″ long.

22. Make a drawing, with development, for a cylindrical cam. The ½″ *D* roller follower is to move 2″ leftward with constant velocity in 180° turn of cylinder and return with simple harmonic motion. Cam axis horizontal, cylinder 4″ *D*, 4″ long on 1″ shaft. Follower pinned to ⅝″ shaft 3″ *c* to *c* from cylinder.

Chapter 18

JIGS AND FIXTURES

18·1 Jigs and fixtures are devices for holding the work and guiding the tools for machining operations on pieces made in interchangeable quantity production. Their use makes possible more rapid as well as more accurate manufacturing at a reduction of cost. In general the distinction between a jig and a fixture is that a jig clamps or is clamped to the work and guides the various tools into position, while a fixture is fastened to the machine and holds the piece in a definite position but does not guide the cutting tool. The object to be machined, usually termed "the production," or "the subject," may, for example, require the drilling of several holes or their drilling and tapping, drilling and counterboring, or drilling and reaming. The particular jig designed to aid in these operations would be called a "drill jig," "drill-and-tap jig," "drill-and-counterbore jig," or "drill-and-ream jig." If the operation to be performed is to face the end of a cylinder, the device for holding the production would be called a "facing fixture." If the production is to be held while a hole is bored in it on a lathe, the holding device would be a "boring fixture."

18·2 Production cost. Whether or not to use a jig depends on two items: first, the number of pieces to be machined and, second, the accuracy demanded. The cost of producing the part individually should be figured carefully and compared to the cost of producing with a jig, in each case measuring time from the starting of one piece to the starting of the next piece, and using the current wage scale of the kind of operators required. The estimated cost of making the jig will then answer the question. In the same way the saving in time by the use of a more expensive jig over a cheaper one should be studied.

18·3 Jig borers. When relatively few pieces are to be drilled, it may be cheaper to machine them individually, either on a drill press or, very much more accurately, on a jig borer, Fig. 18·1. If many are required, such as parts for automobiles and similar large-quantity work, a jig is indispensable for accuracy, speed, interchangeability, and reduction of cost. The correct procedure, therefore, is to use the jig borer to construct a jig (the purpose for which the jig borer was designed), and use the jig for accurate, interchangeable products done on machines cheaper and speedier than the jig borer and operated by almost unskilled labor.

In a job shop making parts to be cast and finished but assembled at another place, orders might call for from ten to a hundred or a thousand machines, with repeat orders later, and the jigs would assure the same degree of accuracy in all the production pieces.

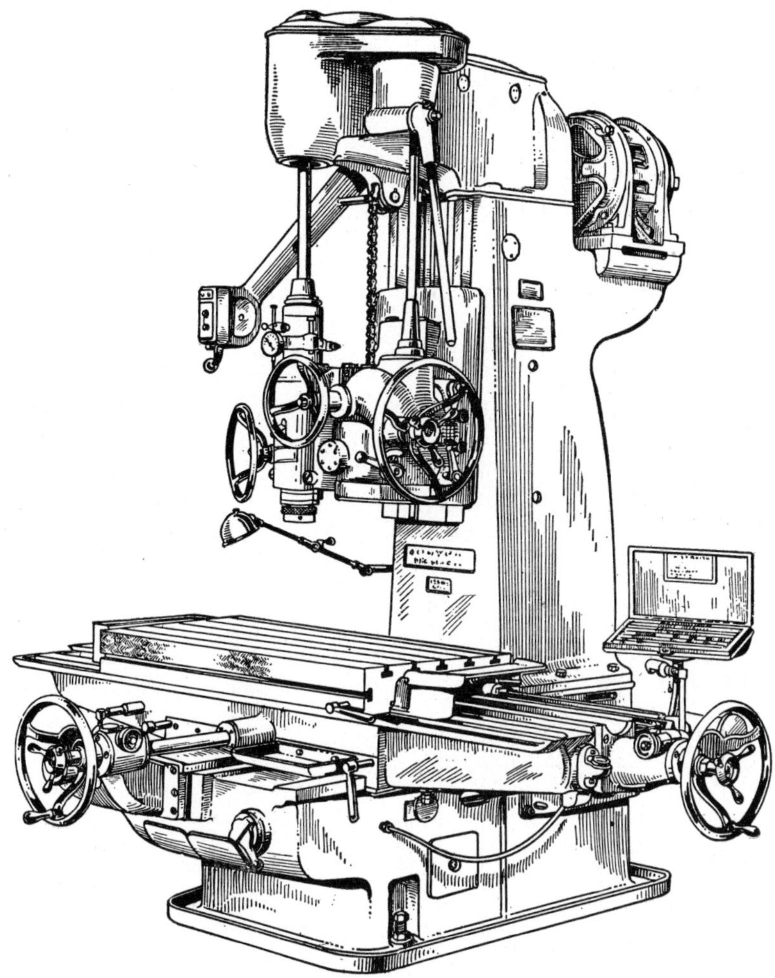

FIG. 18·1—Jig borer. (*Courtesy of Pratt and Whitney.*)

18·4 Principles of design. To illustrate some of the principles of jig design, a simple jig for drilling two $\frac{3}{4}''$ holes and reaming one $1''$ hole in the pawl carrier of Fig. 15·30 is shown in Fig. 18·2. These principles, which should be followed as far as possible, are

1. The production must go into the jig easily and quickly.
2. The production must be located accurately.
3. The bushings must be accessible to the operator.
4. The production must be securely clamped in the jig.
5. The production must be removable easily and quickly.

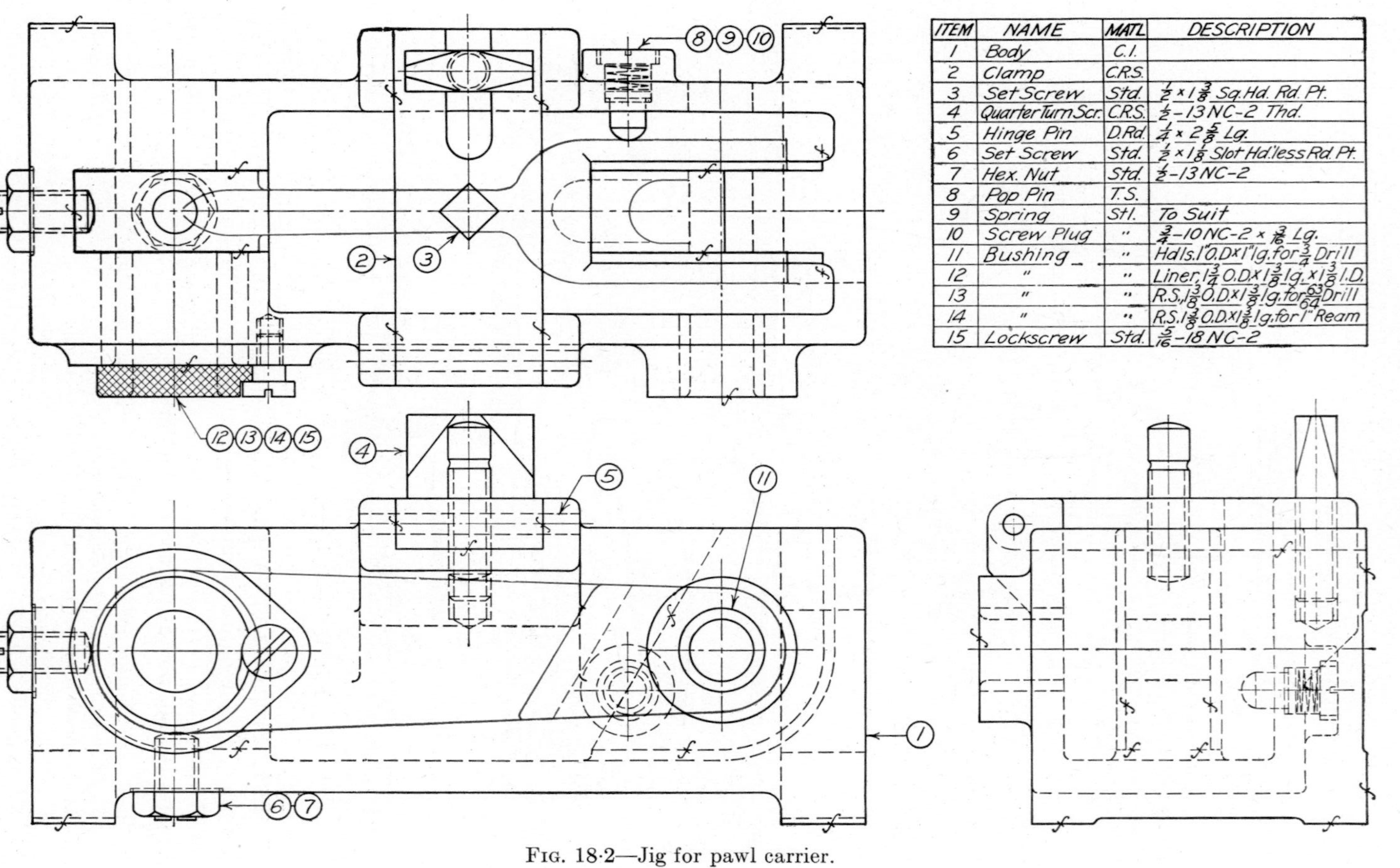

ITEM	NAME	MATL	DESCRIPTION
1	Body	C.I.	
2	Clamp	C.R.S.	
3	Set Screw	Std.	$\frac{1}{2} \times 1\frac{3}{8}$ Sq. Hd. Rd. Pt.
4	Quarter Turn Scr.	C.R.S.	$\frac{1}{2}$–13 NC-2 Thd.
5	Hinge Pin	D. Rd.	$\frac{1}{4} \times 2\frac{5}{8}$ Lg.
6	Set Screw	Std.	$\frac{1}{2} \times 1\frac{1}{8}$ Slot Hd'less Rd. Pt.
7	Hex. Nut	Std.	$\frac{1}{2}$–13 NC-2
8	Pop Pin	T.S.	
9	Spring	Stl.	To Suit
10	Screw Plug	"	$\frac{3}{4}$–10 NC-2 × $\frac{3}{16}$ Lg.
11	Bushing	"	Hdls. 1" O.D. × 1" lg. for $\frac{3}{4}$ Drill
12	"	"	Liner, $1\frac{3}{4}$ O.D. × $1\frac{3}{8}$ lg. × $1\frac{3}{8}$ I.D.
13	"	"	R.S. $1\frac{3}{8}$ O.D. × $1\frac{3}{8}$ lg. for $\frac{63}{64}$ Drill
14	"	"	R.S. $1\frac{3}{8}$ O.D. × $1\frac{3}{8}$ lg. for 1" Ream
15	Lockscrew	Std.	$\frac{5}{16}$–18 NC-2

Fig. 18·2—Jig for pawl carrier.

Note incidentally that it is universal practice in jig drawing to show the production in *red*, while the jig itself, in *black*, is drawn, as to visibility, as if the production was not in place.

In this example, and in all other designs, four main points of design involved in the above principles must be observed. Briefly these are

1. Locating the production.
2. Clamping the production.
3. Selecting bushings of correct style and size.
4. Designing the jig body to accommodate the production and satisfy the principles.

By following these four cardinal points, a drill jig can be designed that will satisfy the requirements of commercial production. Each point involves careful study to decide upon the most suitable of many methods to use in combination with the others. Several types in each division will be discussed, but the reader will understand that he is not confined to these only, in designing some particular piece of work.

18·5 Locating the production. The shape of the production, previous milling and finishing before drilling, and other points of design will influence

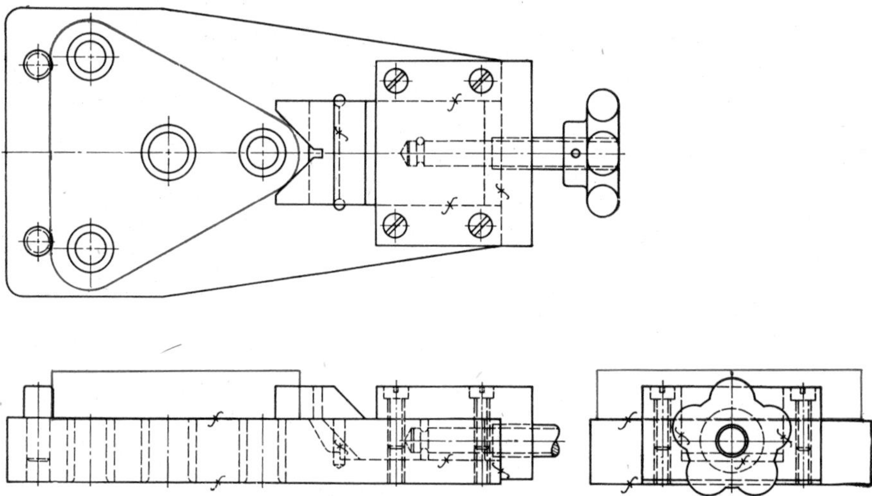

FIG. 18·3—Jig for cover plate.

the type of locator best suited for the production. Location must be thoroughly considered, as it is perhaps the most important of the four points, from the standpoint of accuracy in the jig.

Finished surfaces are often used to locate—a finished surface of the production is placed against a finished surface of the jig; or, when necessary, even an unfinished surface of the production is placed against a finished surface of the jig. Location surfaces may take the form of pads, counterbores, or two finished surfaces at right angles to each other.

Pins give an easy and relatively inexpensive method of location and at the same time a very accurate one. A finished or an unfinished surface of the production is held against a pin and a finished surface, or against either two or three pins, by a clamp or screws, Fig. 18·3.

In the jig of Fig. 18·6, two pins, one circular and the other flattened, are used to locate. Both pins are accurate to the size necessary to fit into two previously drilled or reamed holes in the production. (One pin must be flattened because the center-to-center distances of the holes may vary

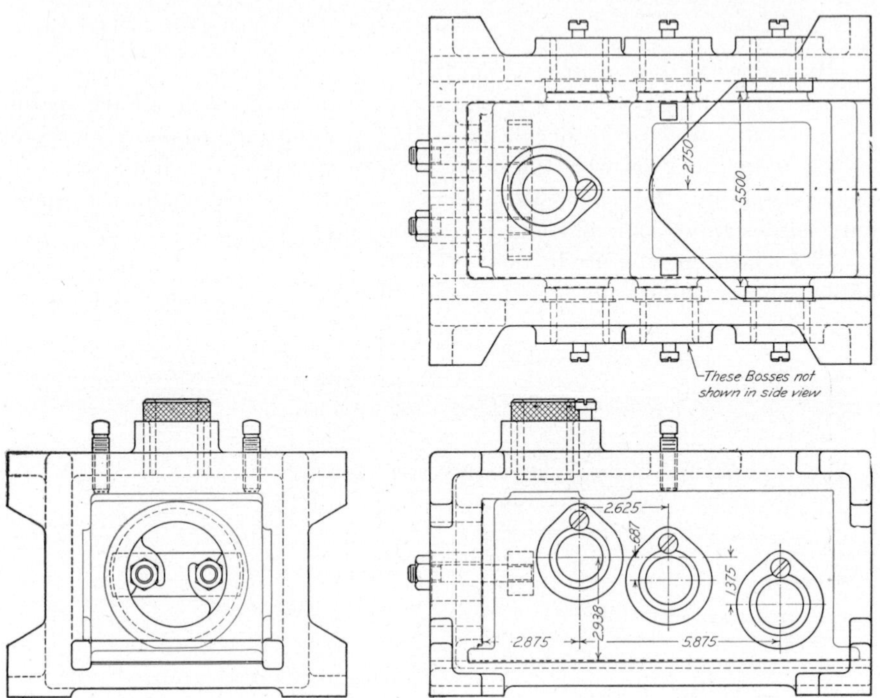

Fig. 18·4—Drill-and-ream jig for gear case.

enough to make a fit impossible with two round pins.) The round pin locates along the line of centers, and both pins locate at right angles to the line of centers, since the flats of the flattened pin are always placed perpendicular to the line of centers. Note that the pins are made so that they can be pressed into the fixture only up to the shoulder. The ends are chamfered, preferably at 30 degrees, to allow easy entry into the production.

Small pins are usually made of tool steel, hardened and ground. Large pins may be made of cold-rolled steel, pack-hardened, and ground. They should not be cyanided, as this does not give sufficient depth of hardening, and the grinding of a cyanided piece is not successful. The shoulder of the pin is pressed against a finished surface or into a light spot face or counterbore to a suitable depth.

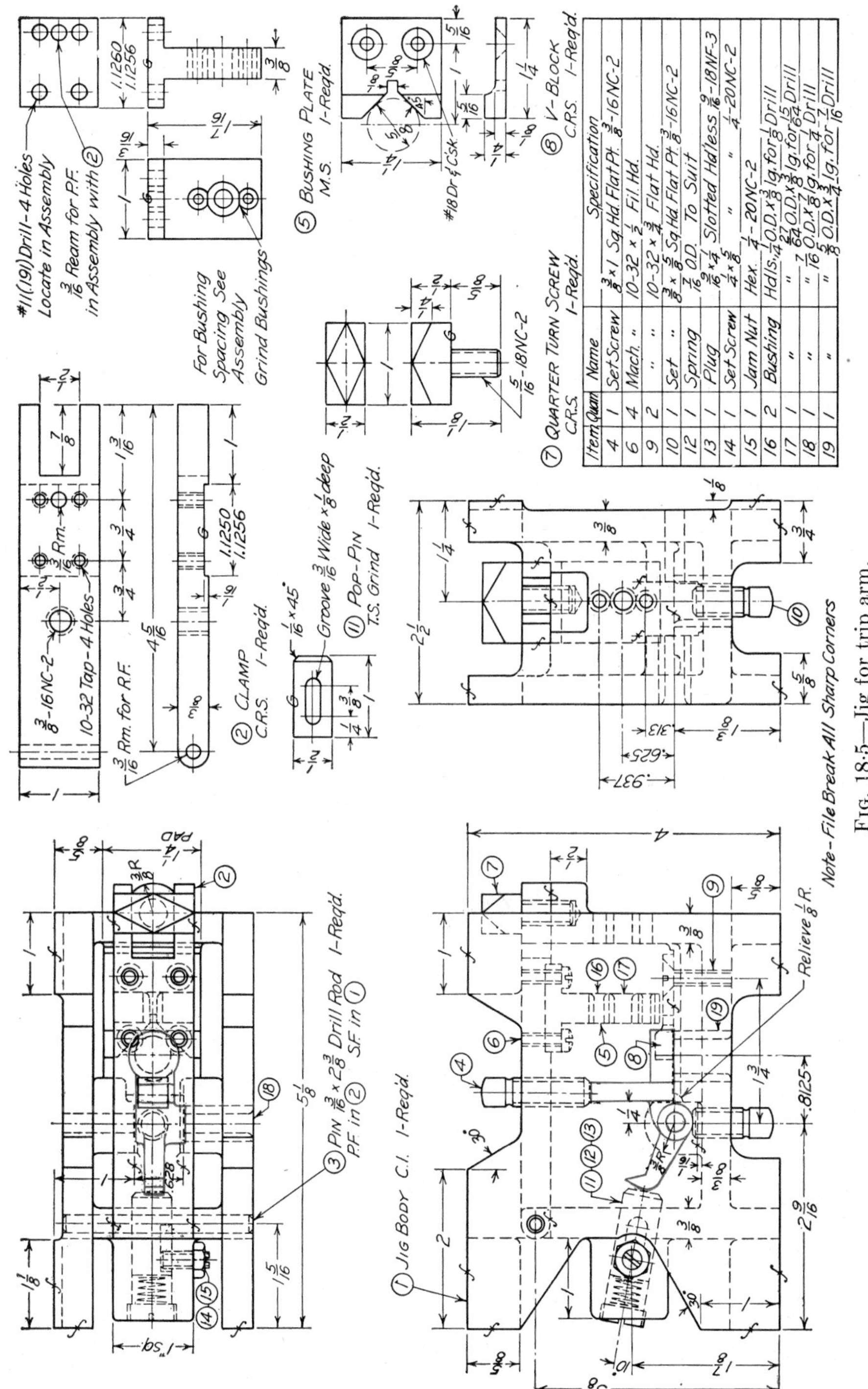

Item	Quan.	Name	Specification
4	1	Set Screw	3/8 × 1 Sq. Hd. Flat Pt. 3/8-16NC-2
6	4	Mach. "	10-32 × 1/2 Fil. Hd.
9	2	" "	10-32 × 3/4 Flat Hd.
10	1	Set "	3/8 × 5/8 Sq. Hd. Flat Pt. 3/8-16NC-2
12	1	Spring	7/16 O.D. To Suit
13	1	Plug	9/16 × 1/4 Slotted Hdless 9/16-18NF-3
14	1	Set Screw	1/4 × 5/8 " " 1/4-20NC-2
15	1	Jam Nut	Hex. 1/4-20NC-2
16	2	Bushing	Hdls. 1/4 O.D. × 3/8 lg. for 1/8 Drill
17	1	"	" 27/64 O.D. × 3/8 lg. for 15/64 Drill
18	1	"	" 7/16 O.D. × 7/8 lg. for 1/4 Drill
19	1	"	" 5/8 O.D. × 3/4 lg. for 7/16 Drill

FIG. 18·5—Jig for trip arm.

Bushings serve as locators in certain designs, as illustrated in Fig. 18·4. This jig is to serve in drilling and reaming holes in a gear case, on which the out-to-out distance between bosses is an accurate dimension with limits; hence the surfaces of these bosses provide good points for location, and the accurately located shoulder bushings are designed to come to contact with them. Location of the subject in the other directions is by using finished surfaces, against which it is clamped by screws and a bar clamp.

V blocks are often used in jig design, both as locators and as clamps. An example was seen in Fig. 18·3. The jig of Fig. 18·5 employs a V whose purpose is mainly for location, though it also serves as a "backstop" in clamping, while the setscrews are the clamps proper. A V block is more easily made as a separate piece, secured to the body of the jig by screws and dowel pins. Fastening the V block without dowel pins, by using slotted holes for the cap screws, might be necessary in case the circular boss on the production varied considerably in diameter with different castings.

Accurate holes for pins. A small plate jig is often used to drill a recurring series of holes in making a large jig, Fig. 18·6, or in a production itself.

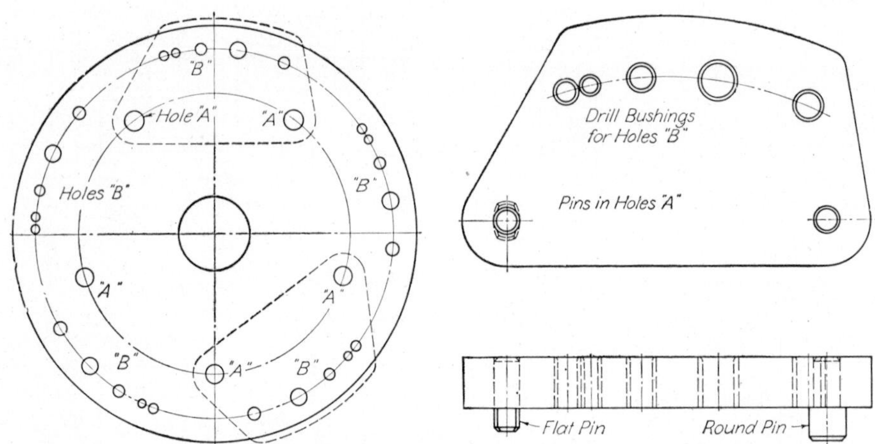

Fig. 18·6—Jig for making a jig.

The small jig carries two locating pins, one round and the other flattened for reasons already mentioned in paragraph 18·5. On the large jig the holes marked *A* have been previously drilled and reamed, either with the jig borer or on a radial boring machine, to match the pins of the small jig, through whose use the series of holes may then be drilled with far more accuracy and speed than if each hole had to be located individually.

Center locators. The jig of Fig. 18·7 uses a center locator. If the hole in the production is of such size that it has been bored on a lathe and the piece faced at the same time, this method of locating is indicated. The shank for locating is of such diameter that the hole is a slip fit over it.

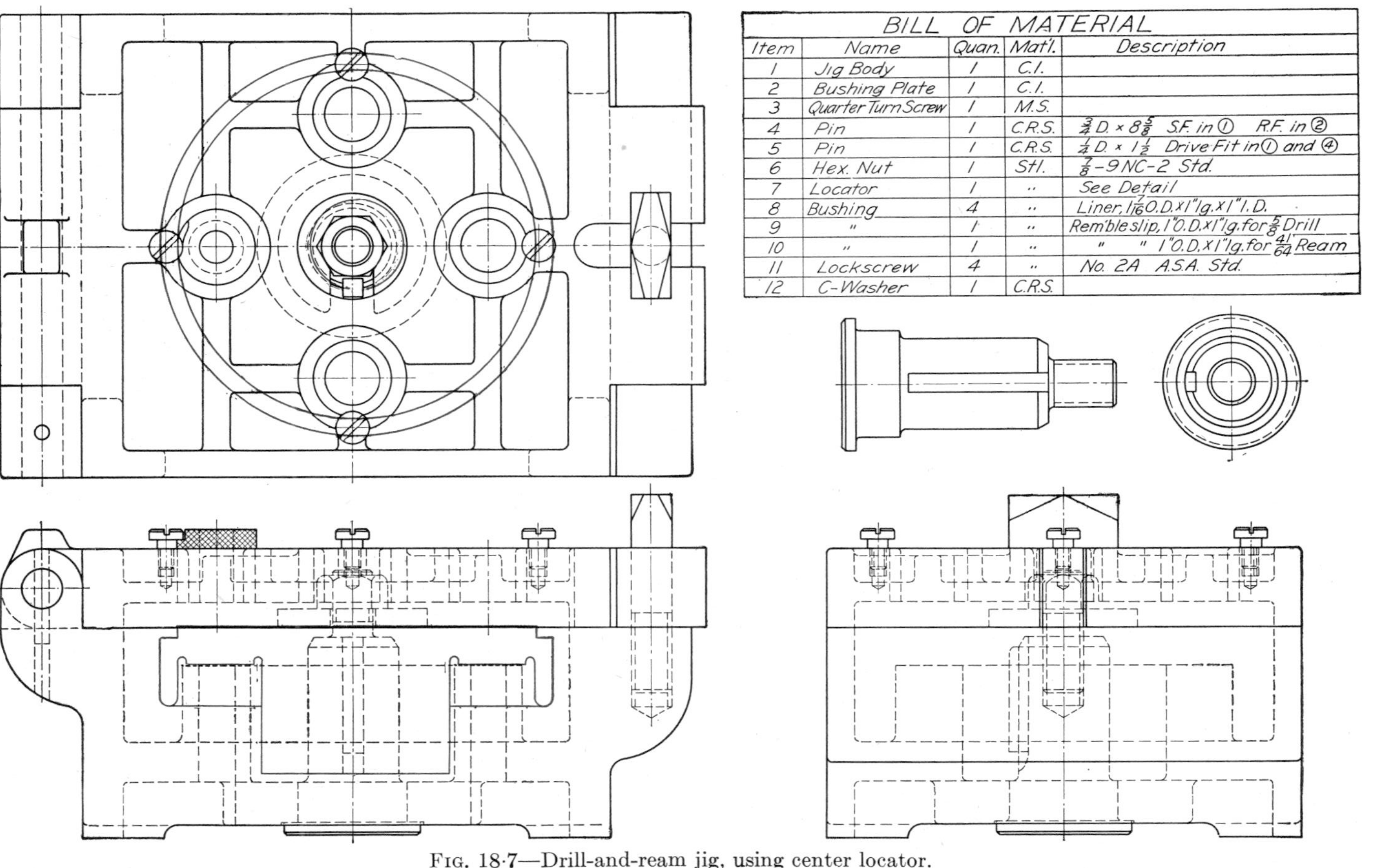

BILL OF MATERIAL

Item	Name	Quan.	Mat'l.	Description
1	Jig Body	1	C.I.	
2	Bushing Plate	1	C.I.	
3	Quarter Turn Screw	1	M.S.	
4	Pin	1	C.R.S.	$\frac{3}{4}$ D. × $8\frac{5}{8}$ S.F. in ① R.F. in ②
5	Pin	1	C.R.S.	$\frac{1}{4}$ D. × $1\frac{1}{2}$ Drive Fit in ① and ④
6	Hex. Nut	1	Stl.	$\frac{7}{8}$-9 NC-2 Std.
7	Locator	1	"	See Detail
8	Bushing	4	"	Liner, $1\frac{7}{16}$ O.D. × 1" lg. × 1" I.D.
9	"	1	"	Rem'ble slip, 1" O.D. × 1" lg. for $\frac{5}{8}$ Drill
10	"	1	"	" " 1" O.D. × 1" lg. for $\frac{41}{64}$ Ream
11	Lockscrew	4	"	No. 2A A.S.A. Std.
12	C-Washer	1	C.R.S.	

FIG. 18·7—Drill-and-ream jig, using center locator.

Either a class 2 or 3 ASA fit could be used, depending upon the accuracy of drilling required.

Keyways serve as locators in cases where it is necessary to drill holes that must be in a particular position. In a jig designed for the coupling of Fig. 15·55, where the holes must be in the center of the bosses and at the same time be located with respect to the keyway, the center locator would include a key to slip into the keyway of the subject.

18·6 Clamps and clamping. Some of the more commonly used clamps for fastening the subject securely in the jig are the following:

1. Bar clamp.
2. Slotted clamp.
3. Setscrews and studs.
4. C washer.
5. V slide.
6. Spiral-rise cam.
7. Star knob and stud.
8. Adjustable pins.
9. Hydraulic piston.

The jigs illustrated in this chapter show several of these methods of clamping. The important point to observe is that *the clamp must not distort the production, as such distortion introduces inaccuracy in the drilled holes upon release of the clamping pressure. Clamping must be applied at a point on the production that will withstand the strain introduced,* and as close as possible to the point drilled. This last cannot always be made to apply, but it should be considered carefully.

Clamps suffer the most wear of any part of a jig, and cyanide hardening is advisable. When there is a possibility of marring a finished surface, a soft-nosed clamp should be employed.

Slotted clamps are widely used. To get proper action they should have the stud at the center or closer to the production than to the tail of the clamp. Studs and nuts are preferred over cap screws, as they do not wear out the body of the jig and may be replaced cheaply.

Setscrews are cheap and highly efficient as a means of holding the production securely, Fig. 18·5. In clamping four sides of an object, the setscrews on two sides will have lock nuts, and those on the other two sides will be used for locking and unlocking the piece.

Use may be made of a stud and nut in combination with a C washer in cases where the production slips over the stud or a locating pin, Fig. 18·7.

V slide. The principal precaution in the use of the V slide in clamping is to see that its length is at least equal to its width, to avoid having an unstable action. Its thickness depends upon the production and whether the slide is fixed or movable. In the latter case the size of the control screw will have a bearing on the thickness.

Spiral-rise cam clamps are useful in quantity production where quick clamping and unclamping with little thought required from the operator are the prime requisites. The maximum variation in the production pieces at the point of clamping must be known, from which the rise of the cam is computed, in order that the cam face will clamp the production with a 90°

turn of the handle. Figure 18·8 shows two types of locking cams which give locking action in either of two directions from the axis.

Star knobs and studs are an adaptation of the setscrew principle for hand operation.

Adjustable pins are used to support fragile sections of the production. Correct designs are shown in Fig. 18.9. They should be locked into position by a setscrew.

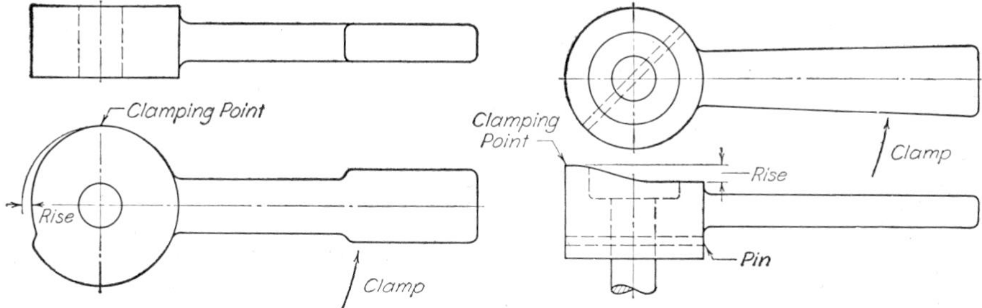

FIG. 18·8—Spiral-rise cam clamps.

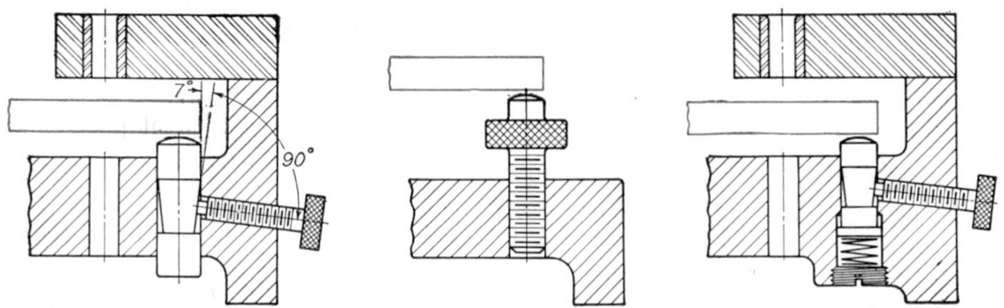

FIG. 18·9—Three methods of supporting fragile sections.

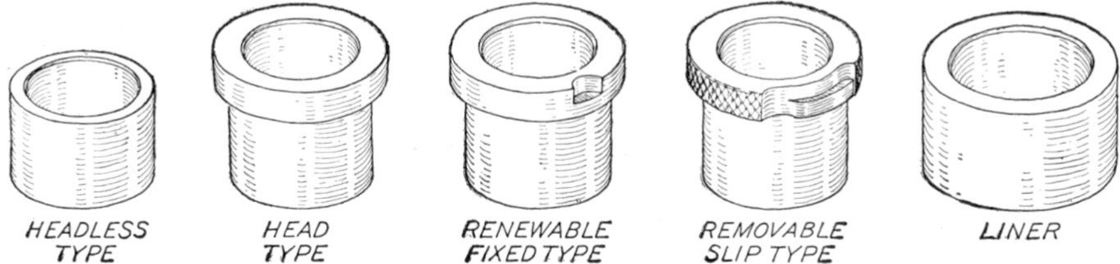

FIG. 18·10—ASA standard jig bushings.

Hydraulic pistons are for heavy work and work requiring special clamping. Their design is of too specialized a nature to be included here.

18·7 American Standard bushings. Drill bushings are standardized items, made in five different styles, Fig. 18·10. They are available in six to eight lengths in each style for use with all the numbered, lettered, and fractional drill sizes up to 2 inches.

The plain stationary press-fit bushings, used when the bushing is expected to last during the life of the jig, are made in two types: the *headless* and the *head type.* The headless type is used when the center distance of holes is too close for a bushing with a head and when it is desirable to have the top of the bushing flush with the top of the jig plate. Both are used without liners.

Renewable bushings, with liners, are used in cases either where the bushing will wear enough for replacement or where it is necessary to interchange bushings in one hole. There are two types: the *renewable fixed* and the *renewable slip*[1] type. Renewable fixed bushings are used for one operation only. Renewable slip bushings are used where two or more operations, requiring different inside diameters, are performed in a single jig without removing the production from the jig, such as where drilling is followed by reaming, spot facing, counterboring, tapping, etc. They should be used in combination with a liner and lock screw unless the design cannot possibly allow the additional space required by the liner.

Bushings are specified by giving in order: (1) type, (2) outside diameter, (3) length, (4) drill size.

For correct installation, design drawings should show clearly the bell-mouthed end of the bushing as the entry end for the drill. For accurate drilling the other end should be not more than one drill diameter from the production. The thickness of the production, type of material being drilled, and the design of the jig will all influence the minimum distance between the end of the bushing and the production. Chip clearance must be considered to avoid drill binding and the creation of unusual pressures. Sometimes the bushing is designed to touch the production, and the chips are carried up and out at the top.

Some shops prefer to use the type of bushings that have $\frac{1}{64}''$ grinding stock on the outside diameter, for fitting the bushing to the hole.

Bushings for special work should be described by following the tables of standard wall thicknesses, size of head, etc., and specifying the proper finish and heat-treatment.

18·8 The jig body. Jig bodies are of two general classes: the open body and the closed or box type. In general, open jigs have drill bushings in the same plane, parallel to one another. The second, box-shaped type is for drilling holes from various planes and directions. Occasionally there may be an overlap in the nomenclature of the two general types.

On account of the required rigidity, cast iron has been the usual material for jig bodies, but welded steel is now being used successfully.

Judgment should be given to the weight of the body. For ease of handling it should have no excess weight but must not be lightened at any expense of the stiffness and rigidity necessary for accuracy. It is often possible, however, to core out metal in various places without decreasing strength. For the comfort and safety of the operator, corners should be rounded and all burrs and sharp edges removed by filing. For convenience

[1] Also called *removable slip* type.

in moving, small jigs may be equipped with handles, and large ones with hooks for handling with a crane.

Finished feet should be provided on the sides opposite the drill bushings. For proper machining, small lugs are often placed on other sides to act as stops. The jig feet are generally part of the casting but in some cases are inserts. Four should always be used in preference to three, because with four feet any unevenness in setting, such as a chip under one foot, will at once draw the attention of the operator, by rocking.

On the inside of the jig and at other places where machining is to be done, particular care should be taken to allow proper clearance for the machining tools. Points of location should, if possible, be visible to the operator.

Small jigs do not need to be clamped to the table, but large jigs and all fixtures should be provided with means of clamping securely to the machine on which they are used.

18·9 Summary. Fourteen points in jig design.

1. Provide best method of locating.
2. Provide best method of clamping.
3. Select correct types of bushings.
4. Have bushings accessible to operator.
5. Design for quick loading and unloading.
6. Design for ability to withstand abuse without affecting accuracy.
7. Keep in mind the safety of the operator.
8. Provide clearance for drills after passing through the work.
9. Provide for chip clearance and easy removal of chips.
10. Design so that cheaper parts wear out first.
11. See that finished surfaces will not be marred by clamping devices.
12. Provide means for lifting heavy jigs.
13. If loose parts are unavoidable, chain them to the body of the jig.
14. Consider the cost of materials and labor, but do not attempt to cut the cost of the jig at the expense of efficiency of the design.

18·10 Making a jig drawing. The drafting-room procedure in designing a jig or fixture should follow approximately this order:

1. Sketch the design freehand, to get the proper choice of views and an idea of space requirements. This original sketch will take into account previously finished surfaces of the production.
2. Allowing ample space between views, carefully draw the production in red in its several views.
3. Build the jig around the production, following the correct principles of location, clamping, bushings, and body design.
4. Dimension the drawing of the jig, using decimal dimensions for all locators and bushings, following the system of base-line dimensioning, from zero coordinate axes. See Fig. 12·19.
5. Give each part an item number.
6. Prepare a bill of material of all items in sequence.
7. Check the drawing.

18·11 Fixtures. Two examples are given here to illustrate the many uses of fixtures in quantity production. Figure 18·11 is a fixture to aid in boring the hole and facing the projection and bottom of the flange of Fig. 9·45. The flange locates over the pins. The center clamp is removed, and slotted clamps are used while the hole and projection are being machined. To complete the finishing of the bottom, the clamps are slid back and the center clamp is put in place.

Figure 18·12 is a fixture for holding the toggle-shaft support of Fig. 7·122 in boring the hole and facing the end. The bracket locates over two pins and is held in place by the clamp.

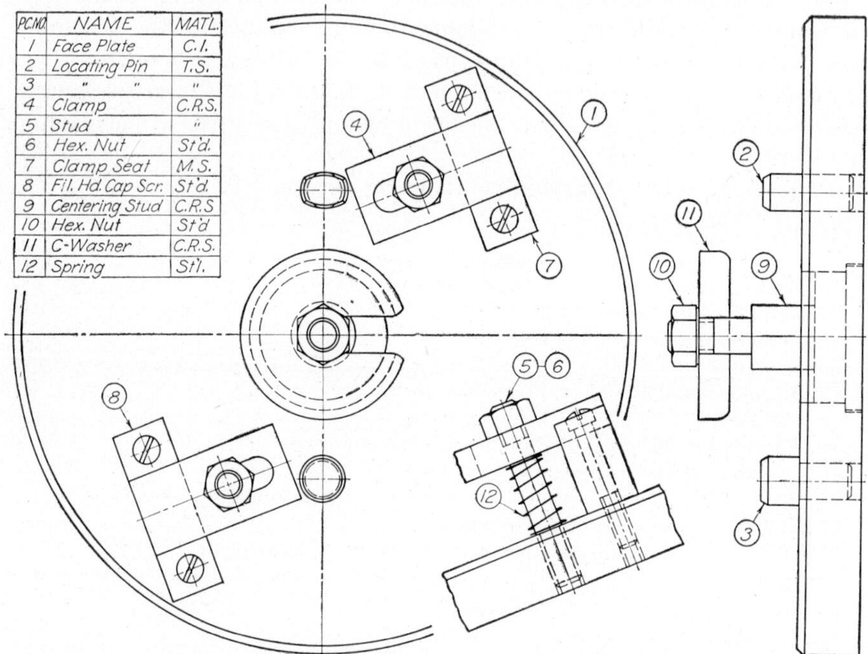

FIG. 18·11—Lathe fixture for boring and facing.

Both these fixtures clamp to the faceplate of the lathe, the entire fixture and production rotating. Being unbalanced, the offset bracket fixture requires a counterbalance to reduce vibration and aid in accuracy of work. To compute the size of the counterbalance, the center of gravity and the moment of the fixture and production together about the working center must be found. From this the area and thickness of counterbalance and its working distance from the center may be calculated to find an equivalent moment to balance that on the opposite side of center. Common practice is to provide a slightly oversize counterbalance thickness, which allows the shop to complete the balance by removal of metal. This is a timesaver and permits slight changes that may take place in some parts used in the fixture.

In designing fixtures for milling, slotting, saw cutting, and similar operations the same principles of location and clamping as those given for jig designing are followed. To obtain secure clamping, finished bases should be provided with two square keys for aligning the fixture with the T slots in the milling table, as well as with slots at each end for T bolts.

If a previous operation has been performed on the subject, a gaging surface should be provided, if at all possible, to which the cutter may be set, thus obtaining accurately the required distance between the two finished surfaces.

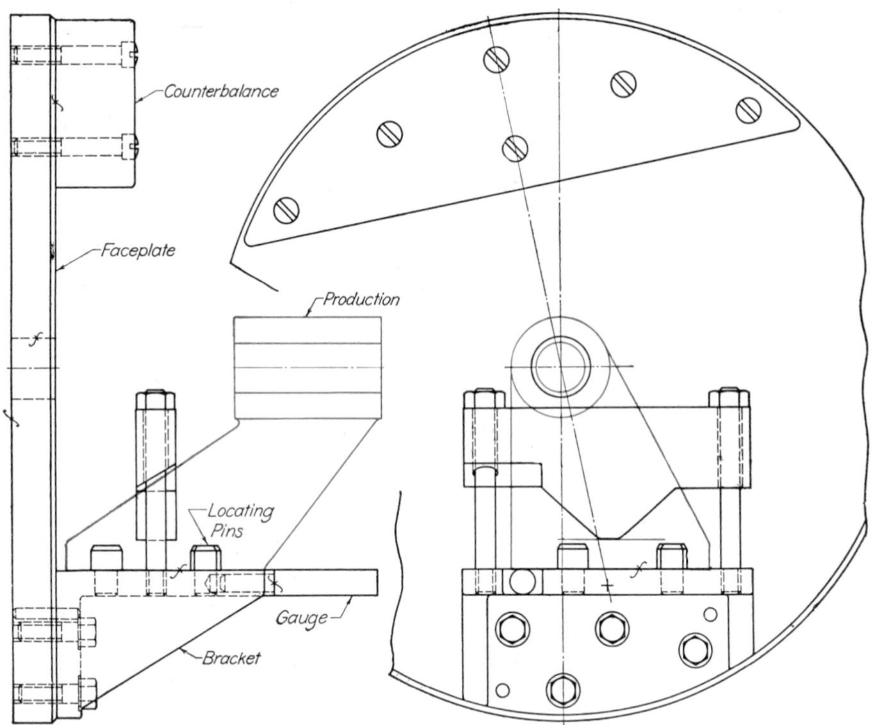

FIG. 18·12—Counterbalanced boring-and-facing fixture.

PROBLEMS

18·12 The "tooling-up" procedure in machining a casting from its unfinished state to the finished product has an important bearing on the total cost and requires careful thought as to the proper sequence of operations. In the following problems consider the entire casting as rough, and prepare a shop procedure schedule, listing the tools in their successive order, so that each operation may have a direct relationship to the preceding one. Give the tools the progressive numbers *T*-1; *T*-2; etc.

1. Design a drill-and-ream jig for Fig. 11·21. Locate on a finished pad the lug in a finished slot and the finished end of the cylinder, 4″ long, against a finished boss of the jig. Clamp from the top and back with one setscrew each. Provide plain bushings for the base holes in the pad, and two liners with removable drill-and-ream bushings for the larger holes. Two lengths of removable bushings will be required, the longer being to reach into within a drill diameter of the cylinder 2¾″ long. Design a box-type body with feet opposite the sides in which bushings are placed. The right side of the body will be open to permit loading. Spot-face the holes outside the jig.

2. Design a drill jig for special nut, Fig. 12·28*A*. Locate over a center locator on a finished pad through the 1⅛″ hole, the locator reducing in size sufficiently to use a nut and C washer for clamping on the 1¾″ diameter end. Nut should be small enough to clear the hole when loading and unloading. Provide bushings in an open-type body.

Alternative method. Use the same method of locating but provide only one drill bushing and an index pin 90 degrees from the bushing. Drill one hole, index this hole to the pin, drill the next hole, etc.

3. Design a drill-and-ream jig for the base plate, Fig. 12·20. The body may consist of two rectangular plates somewhat larger than the production, separated ⅝″ more than the thickness of the production. This thickness may be taken as ½″. Locate against three pins, two on the flat side and one at the left end, the pins being in the top plate and located in the jig at the time of locating the bushing holes on the jig borer. Clamp in place against the pins and down to the finished surface upon which the production rests. Provide the proper bushings in the top plate of the jig.

4. Fig. 15·16. Design a drill-and-ream jig for all holes in the centering-yoke base. Assume that the base and sides have been finished. Locate between finished surfaces of the jig, on a pad, with the side of the 4″ diameter base against a setscrew with lock nut. Clamp down to the pad and against the setscrew. Provide spring-backed pins or an equivalent means of holding the vertical sides of the casting against deflection upon application of the drilling pressure. Drill two holes for each slotting operation; all the remaining holes are to be drilled only, except the central base hole, which is to be reamed.

5. Fig. 15·23. Drill and ream the 1⅛″ hole, and drill for tapping the 7/16-14 NC-2 holes. Since the tops of the bosses have been finished before drilling, locate on them by means of two stationary V blocks and a movable V slide against the central cylinder. Use a bar clamp inside the 60-degree arms of the subject, placed approximately in the center of the triangle formed by the bosses.

6. Fig. 15·32. Design a drill-and-ream jig for the holes in the rocker arm, locating with V blocks. The jig body will contain a bushing along the center line of the ⅜″ hole, which will make it necessary to provide feet on the side opposite the bushing.

7. Fig. 15·60. Design a drill jig for the ¼″ oilhole. Locate on a horizontal locator through the large center hole of the production, using a nut and C washer for removal. Index the production with a pin through one of the cap-screw holes, so that the drill will enter the oil reservoir in the casting at the proper place.

8. Fig. 9·45. Design a boring-and-facing fixture for flange. Refer to the design shown in Fig. 18·11. Assume that the top flat surface has been finished and the ¾″ holes reamed prior to the operation of boring and facing in this fixture. For boring the 2⅝″ and 2″ diameter holes, use the two clamps, the center stud and washer being removed. For facing, remove or slip the clamps out of place and use the centering stud with washer and nut. On a production line, two fixtures could be made using those parts necessary for successive operations in each fixture.

9. Fig. 7·120. Design a boring-and-facing fixture for plunger bracket. Refer to the design shown in Fig. 18·12. Assume that the base is finished and the base holes reamed to size. Use these for locating over two pins, one flat and one round, and clamp down to the projecting shelf with a clamp as shown, or equivalent. This fixture should be counterbalanced to reduce vibration and obtain greater accuracy.

10. Design a drill-and-ream jig for a piece illustrated in one of the following figures: 15·17, 15·40, 15·64, 15·65, 15·80, or 15·86.

Chapter 19

TECHNICAL SKETCHING

19·1 Facility in making a freehand orthographic drawing is an essential part of the equipment of every engineer. So necessary is this training in freehand sketching that it might almost be said that the preceding 18 chapters have all been in preparation for this one. Such routine men as tracers and detailers may get along with skill and speed in mechanical execution, but the designer must be able to *sketch* his ideas with a sure hand and clear judgment. In all inventive mechanical thinking, in all preliminary designing, in all explanation and instructions to draftsmen, freehand sketching is the mode of expression. Its mastery means the mastery of the language, and it is gained only after full proficiency in drawing with instruments is acquired. It is the mastery which the engineer, inventor, designer, chief draftsman, and contractor, with all of whom time is too valuable to spend in mechanical execution, must have. It is the chief engineer's method of design.

The use and value of sketching are not confined to the engineering staff. A serviceman, for example, out on a trouble-giving machine may have to make a sketch, or a salesman in his daily report may need to send back sketches, perhaps of a customer's product, or even of some point of advantage in a competitor's machine.

Training in sketching develops accuracy of observation. It may be necessary to go a long distance from the drawing room to get some preliminary information, and the record thus obtained would be valueless if any detail were missing or obscure. Mistakes or omissions that would be discovered quickly in making an accurate scale drawing may easily be overlooked in a freehand sketch, and constant care must be exercised to prevent their occurrence.

Sometimes, if a piece is to be made but once, a sketch is used as a working drawing and afterward filed.

19·2 Kinds of technical sketches. Sketches may be divided into two general classes: first, those made before the structure is built and, second, those made after the structure is built. In the first class are included the sketches made in connection with the designing of the structure, which may be classified as (1) *scheme* or *idea* sketches, used in studying and developing the arrangement and proportion of parts; (2) *computation sketches,* made in connection with the figured calculations for motion and strength; (3) *executive sketches,* made by the chief engineer, inventor or consulting engineer, to give instructions for special arrangements or ideas which must be embodied in the design; (4) *design sketches*, used in working up the schemes and ideas into such form that the design drawing can be started; and (5) *working sketches*, made as substitutes for working drawings.

The second class includes (1) *detail sketches*, drawn from existing parts, with complete notes and dimensions, from which duplicate parts may be constructed directly, or from which working drawings may be made, Fig. 19·1; (2) *assembly sketches*, made from an assembled machine to show the relative positions of the various parts, with center and location dimensions, or sometimes for a simple machine, with complete dimensions and specifica-

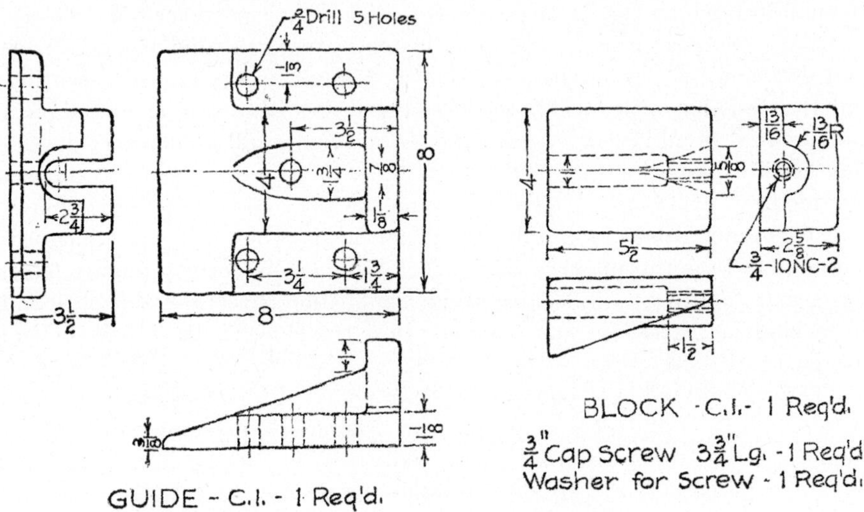

FIG. 19·1—A detail sketch (leveling block).

tions; and (3) *outline* or *diagrammatic sketches*, generally made for the purpose of location; sometimes, for example, to give the size and location of pulleys and shafting, piping, or wiring, that is, information for use in connection with the setting up of machinery; sometimes to locate a single machine, giving the over-all dimensions, sizes, and center distances for foundation bolts, and other necessary information.

19·3 Materials. The only necessary materials for sketching are a pencil (F or H) sharpened to a long conical point, not too sharp, a pencil eraser, to be used sparingly, and paper—notebook, pad, or single sheet clipped on a board.

In making working sketches from objects a 2-foot rule or flexible steel rule and calipers will be needed to obtain dimensions. Other machinists' tools may be required, such as a try square, surface gage, depth gage, thread gage, and, for accurate measurements, a micrometer caliper. Sometimes a plumb line is of service. Much ingenuity is often required to get dimensions from an existing machine.

19·4 Technique. The pencil should be held with freedom and not close to the point. Vertical lines are drawn downward with a finger movement in a series of overlapping strokes, with the hand somewhat in the position of Fig. 19·2. Horizontal lines are drawn with the hand shifted to the position of Fig. 19·3, using a wrist motion for short lines and a forearm motion for longer ones. In drawing any straight line between two points, keep the eyes on the point to which the line is to go rather than on the point of the pencil. Do not try to draw the whole length of a line in a single stroke. It may be an aid to draw a *very* light line first, then to sketch the finished line,

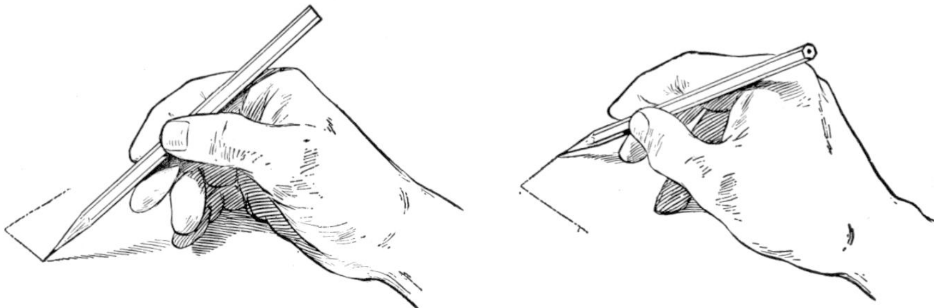

FIG. 19·2—Sketching a vertical line.

FIG. 19·3—Sketching a horizontal line.

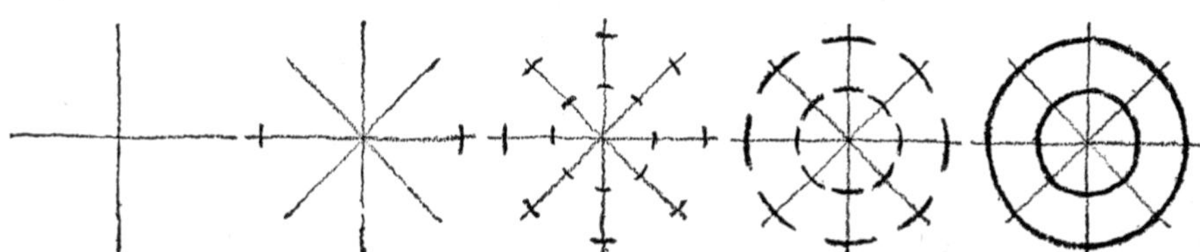

FIG. 19·4—Method of sketching circles.

correcting the direction of the light line without rubbing it out. Do not be disturbed by any nervous waviness. Accuracy of direction is more important than smoothness of line.

It is legitimate in technical sketching to draw long vertical or horizontal lines by using the little finger as a guide along the edge of the pad or clip board.

Steep inclined lines running downward from right to left are drawn easily with the same movement as vertical lines, but those running downward from left to right are much harder to draw (except for left-handed persons). They may be drawn by turning the paper and drawing them as horizontal lines. The three important things about a straight line are (1) that it be essentially straight, (2) that it be the right length, and (3) that it go in the right direction.

Circles may be drawn by marking the radius on each side of the center lines, or, more accurately, by drawing two diagonals in addition to the center lines and marking points equidistant from the center of the eight radii. At these points draw short arcs perpendicular to the radii, then complete the circle, as shown in Fig. 19·4. A modification is to use a slip of paper as a trammel. Large circles can be done very smoothly, after a little practice, by using the third or fourth finger as a pivot, holding the pencil stationary and rotating the paper under it, or by holding two pencils and using one as a pivot about which to rotate the paper. Another way of drawing a circle is to sketch it in its circumscribing square.

19·5 Practice. The best preliminary training for this work of technical sketching is the drawing taught in the public schools, training as it does the hand and eye to see and represent form and proportion. Those who have not had this preparation should practice drawing lines with the pencil until the hand obeys the eye to a reasonable extent.

The best practice is obtained by sketching from castings, machine parts, or simple machines and making working drawings from those sketches, without further reference to the object. In classwork a variation may be introduced by exchanging the sketches so that the working drawing is made by another student. This will emphasize the necessity of putting down all the information and not relying on memory to supply what is missing. It is helpful to work with the idea that the object is not to be seen after the sketch is made. A most valuable training in observing details is sketching, from memory, a piece previously studied. It is an excellent training in sureness of touch to make sketches directly in ink, perhaps with a fountain pen.

19·6 Making a sketch. In making an orthographic sketch the principles of projection and the rules of practice for working drawings are to be remembered and applied. A systematic order should be followed for both idea sketches and sketches from objects, as listed below:

1. Visualize the object.
2. Determine the views.
3. Determine the size of the sketch.
4. Locate the center lines.
5. Block in the main outlines.
6. Complete the detail.
7. Add dimension lines and arrowheads.
8. Put on the dimensions.
9. Letter notes and title, with date.
10. Check the drawing.

Before a good graphical description of an object or idea can be developed, it is essential that the mental image of it be definite and clear. The clearness of the sketch is a direct function of this mental picture. Hence the first step is to concentrate on visualization. This leads directly to the second step, determination of the necessary views and part views. These will probably not be just the same as would be made in a scale drawing. For example, a note in regard to thickness or shape of section will often be used to save a view, Fig. 19·5; thus one view of a piece circular in cross section would

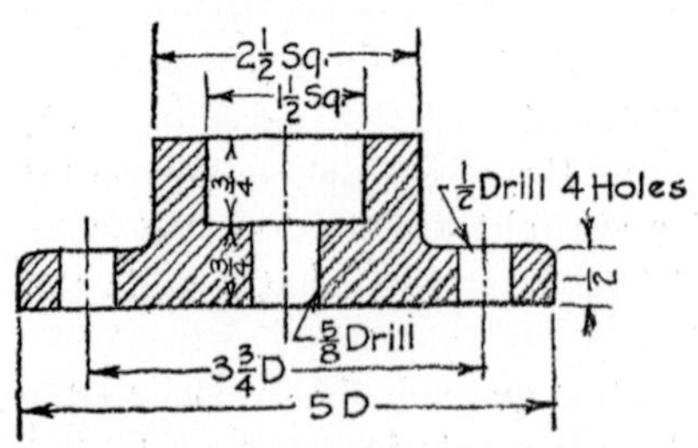

FIG. 19·5—A one-view sketch.

be sufficient. In other cases additional part views and extra sections may be sketched rather than complicate the regular views with added lines that might confuse the sketch, although the same lines might be perfectly clear in a measured drawing. The third step is to proportion the size of the sketch to the sheet. Have it large enough to show all detail clearly, but allow plenty of room for dimensions, notes, and memoranda. Small parts may be sketched larger than full size. Do not try to crowd all the views on one sheet of paper. Use as many sheets as may be required, but name each view, indicating the direction in which it is taken. Sometimes one view alone will require a whole sheet.

In beginning a sketch, always start by locating the center lines or datum lines, and remember that the view showing the contour or characteristic shape should be drawn first. This is generally the view showing circles if there are any. Block in the main outlines, watching proportions carefully, selecting one edge as a unit from which to estimate the proportionate lengths of the other edges. When the main outlines are satisfactory, add the details, again watching proportions. One of the commonest faults in sketching is in getting details out of scale.

In drawing on plain paper, the location of the principal points, centers, etc., should be so marked that the sketches will fit the sheet, and the whole sketch, with as many views, sections, and auxiliary views as are necessary to describe the piece, will be drawn in as nearly correct proportion as the eye can determine, *without taking any measurements.*

A machine should, of course, be represented right side up, in its natural working position. If symmetrical about an axis, often one-half only need be sketched. If a whole view cannot be made on one page, it may be put on two, each part being drawn up to a break line used as a datum line.

19·7 Dimension lines. After the sketching of a piece is finished, it should be gone over, and dimension lines for all the dimensions needed for the construction added, drawing extension lines and arrowheads carefully and checking to see that none is omitted but still *making no measurements.*

19·8 Measuring and dimensioning. Up to this stage the object has not been handled, and consequently the drawing has been kept clean. The measurements for the dimensions indicated on the drawing may now be added. A flexible rule or steel scale will serve for getting most of the dimensions. Never use a draftsman's scale for measuring castings, as it will be soiled and have its edges marred. The diameter of cylindrical shapes or the distance between outside surfaces may be measured by using outside calipers and scale, Fig. 19·6, and the sizes of holes or internal surfaces, by using inside calipers. Figure 19·7 illustrates the inside transfer caliper, used when a projecting portion prevents removing the ordinary caliper. The outside transfer caliper is used for a similar condition, occurring with an outside measurement. The depth of a hole is easily measured with the depth gage, Fig. 19·8*A*. Screw threads are measured by calipering the body diameter and either counting the number of threads per inch or gaging with a screw-pitch gage, Fig. 19·8*B*. A fillet-and-round gage measures radii by fitting the gage to the circular contour, Fig. 19·8*C*. It is often necessary to lay a

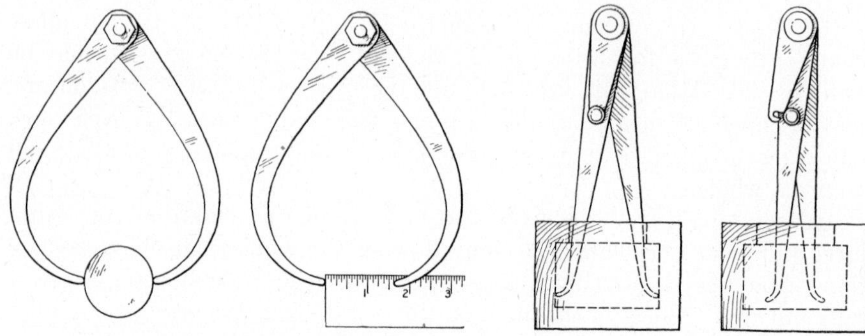

FIG. 19·6—Outside caliper.

FIG. 19·7—Inside transfer caliper.

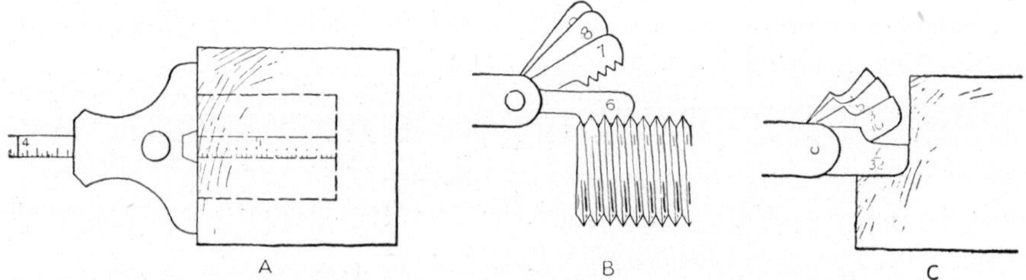

FIG. 19·8—*A*, depth gage; *B*, screw-pitch gage; *C*, fillet-and-round gage.

straightedge across a surface, as in Fig. 19·9. This type of measurement could be made conveniently with a combination square, or with a surface gage. The combination square uses two different heads, the regular 90°-45°

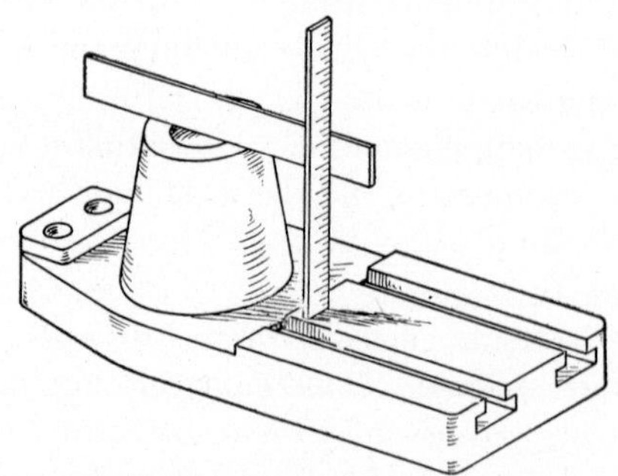

FIG. 19·9—Taking a measurement.

head, Fig. 19·10*A*, for a variety of measurements, or the protractor head, Fig. 19·10*B*, for measuring or laying out angles. For accurate measurements, outside or inside micrometer calipers are necessary. The outside type is illustrated in Fig. 19·11. Readings to 0.001″ are easily obtained.

Accurate measurements of holes may be made with a telescopic gage in conjunction with an outside micrometer.

A variety of gages made for special purposes, as a wire gage, gage for sheet metal, etc., may be used as occasion demands. With some ingenuity, measurements can often be made with the simpler instruments when special ones are not available.

Always measure from finished surfaces, if possible. Judgment must be exercised in measuring rough castings so as not to record inequalities.

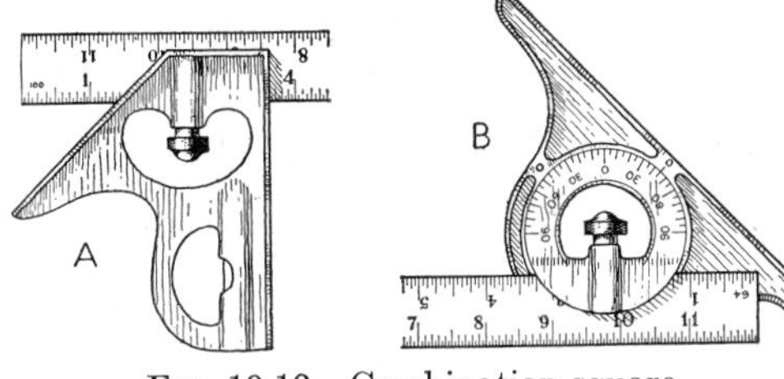

FIG. 19·10—Combination square.

FIG. 19·11—Outside micrometer caliper.

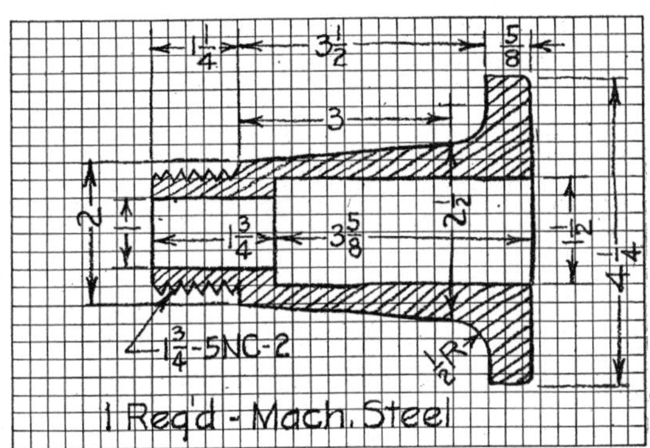

FIG. 19·12—A sketch on coordinate paper.

In finding the distance between centers of two holes of the same size, measure from the edge of one to the corresponding edge of the other. Curves are measured by coordinates or offsets, as shown in Fig. 11·39. A curved outline may be recorded by laying a sheet of paper on it and making a rubbing.

Add all remarks and notes that may seem to be of possible value.

The title should be written or lettered on the sketch, and for class sketches a statement of the amount of time spent on it.

Always date a sketch. Valuable inventions have been lost through inability to prove priority, because the first sketches had not been dated. In commercial work the draftsman's notebook with sketches and calculations is preserved as a permanent record, and its sketches should be made so as to stand the test of time and be legible after the details of their making have been forgotten.

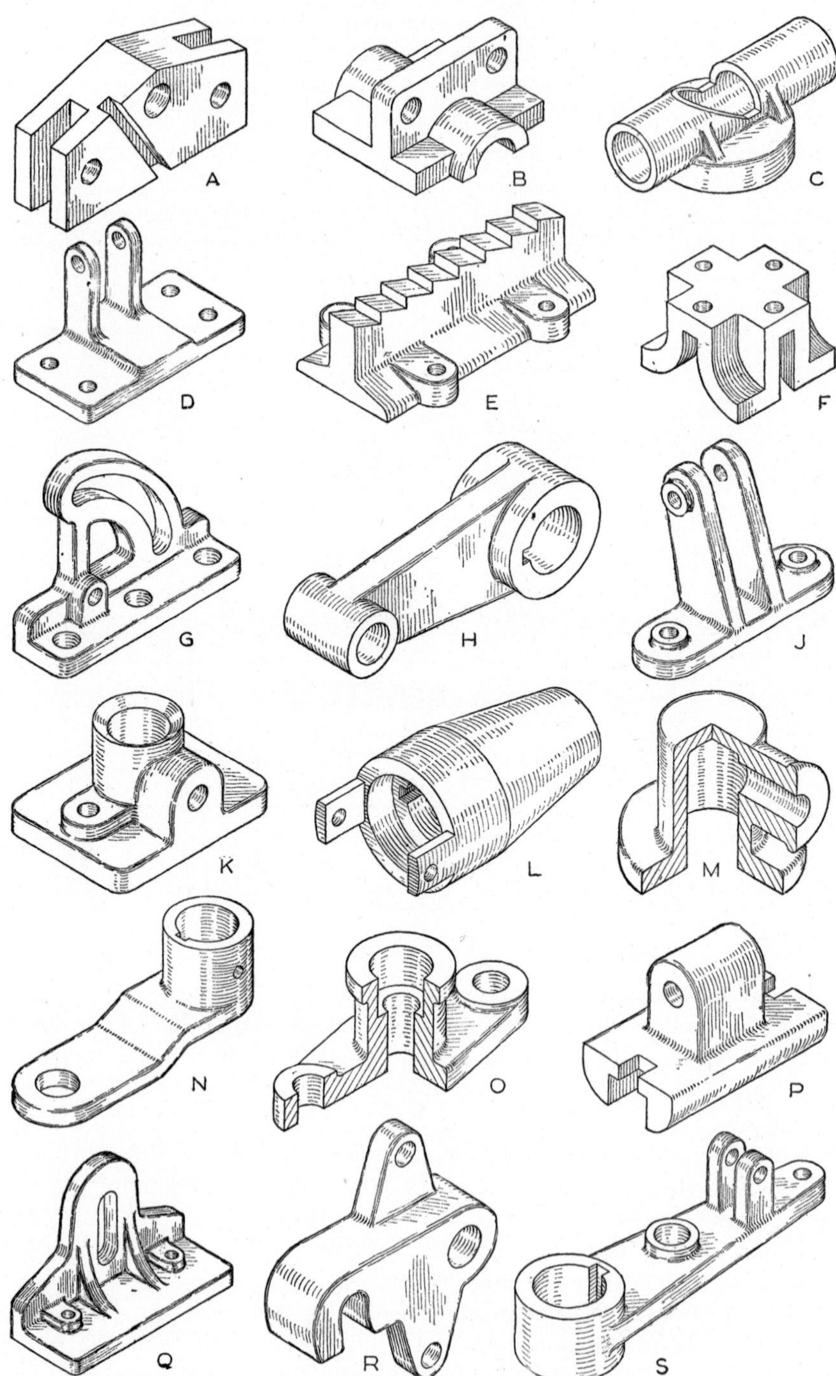

FIG. 19·13—Sketching problems.

The final step is to check the sketch. It is a curious fact that when a beginner omits a dimension it is usually a basic, vital one, as that of the center height of a machine or the rise of an arch.

19·9 For gaining skill through practice, sketches should be made entirely freehand. However, in commercial work the engineer often saves time by making a hybrid sketch, drawing circles with the compasses, or even with a coin from his pocket, ruling some lines with a pocket scale or a triangle, and making some freehand, but always keeping a workmanlike quality and good proportion.

Cross-section paper. Sketches are often made on coordinate paper ruled faintly in sixteenths, eighths, or quarters of an inch, used either simply as an aid in drawing straight lines and judging proportions, or for drawing to approximate scale by assigning suitable values to the unit spaces. The latter use is more applicable to design sketches than to sketches from the object, Fig. 19·12.

PROBLEMS

19·10 Sketching problems may be made in great variety from pictorial views and from castings or models. The following are suggested:

Group I. Preliminary line practice

1. Draw Fig. 3·35 to 3·38 without measurement in squares of about 6-inch sides.

Group II. Orthographic sketches of details

2. Sketch the necessary orthographic views, without dimensions, of the pieces shown in Fig. 19·13.

3. Make orthographic sketches of selections from Figs. 7·66 to 7·101, adding the necessary dimensions according to the order of dimensioning, paragraph 11·32.

4. From the assembly drawings, Figs. 15·54 to 15·79, select a single piece and make a detail sketch of it.

Group III. Sketches from machine parts

5. Obtain a casting, forging, or machined part such as a gear, pulley, etc., from the shop. Make a working sketch of the part selected.

Group IV. Sketches from assembled machines

6. In the mechanical, industrial, or electrical engineering laboratories, select an accessible part on one of the machines and make a working sketch.

Group V. Memory sketching

7. Look at one of the pieces of Fig. 19·13 with concentration for 15 seconds. Close the book and make its three views.

Chapter 20

DEVELOPED SURFACES AND INTERSECTIONS

20·1 Surfaces. A surface may be considered to be generated by the motion of a line: the generatrix. Surfaces may thus be divided into two general classes: (1) those which can be generated by a moving *straight* line and (2) those which can be generated only by a moving *curved* line. The first are called *ruled surfaces;* the second, *double-curved surfaces.* Any position of the generatrix is called an *element* of the surface.

Ruled surfaces may be divided into (*a*) the *plane,* (*b*) *single-curved surfaces,* and (*c*) *warped surfaces.*

The *plane* may be generated by a straight line moving so as to touch two other intersecting or parallel straight lines or a plane curve.

Single-curved surfaces have their elements either parallel or intersecting. In this class are the cylinder and the cone and also a third surface, which we shall not consider, known as the "convolute," in which consecutive elements intersect two and two.

Warped surfaces have no two consecutive elements either parallel or intersecting. There is a great variety of warped surfaces. The surface of a screw thread and that of the pilot of a locomotive are two examples.

Double-curved surfaces are generated by a curved line moving according to some law. The commonest forms are *surfaces of revolution,* made by revolving a curve about an axis in the same plane, as the sphere, torus, or ring, ellipsoid, paraboloid, hyperboloid, etc. Illustrations of various surfaces may be found in Fig. 5·69.

20·2 Development. In some kinds of construction, full-size patterns of some of the faces or of the entire surface of an object are required, as, for example, in stonecutting, a template or pattern giving the shape of an irregular face; or in sheet-metal work, a pattern to which a sheet may be cut so that when rolled, folded, or formed it will make the object.

The complete surface laid out in a plane is called the *development* of the surface.[1]

Surfaces about which a thin sheet of flexible material (as paper or tin) can be wrapped smoothly are said to be developable; these include objects made up of planes and single-curved surfaces only. Warped and double-curved surfaces are nondevelopable and, when patterns are required for their construction, they can be made only by methods that are approximate; but,

[1] The full theoretical discussion of surfaces, their classification, properties, intersections, and development may be found in any good descriptive geometry.

assisted by the ductility or pliability of the material, they give the required form. Thus, while a ball cannot be wrapped smoothly, a two-piece pattern developed approximately and cut from leather may be stretched and sewed on in a smooth cover, or a flat disk of metal may be die-stamped, formed, or spun to a hemispherical or other required shape.

We have learned the method of finding the true size of a plane surface by projecting it on an auxiliary plane. If the true size of all the plane faces of an object made of planes are found and joined in order at their common edges so that all faces lie in a common plane, the result will be the developed surface. Usually this may be done to the best advantage by finding the true length of the edges.

The development of a right cylinder is evidently a rectangle whose width is the altitude, and length the rectified circumference, Fig. 20·1; and the

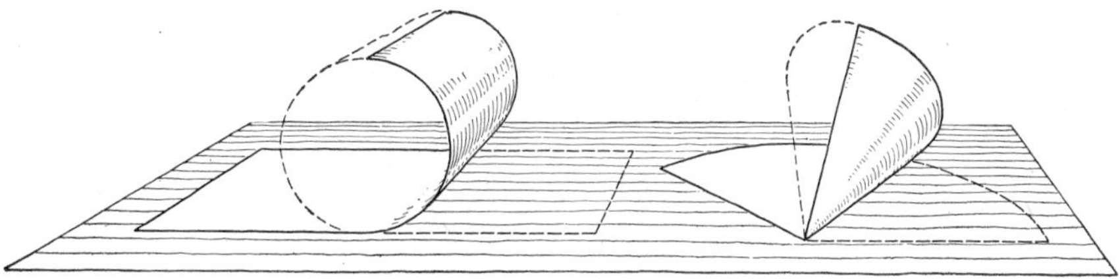

FIG. 20·1—Development of a cylinder and a cone.

development of a right circular cone is a circular sector with a radius equal to the slant height of the cone, and an arc equal in length to the circumference of its base, Fig. 20·1.

As illustrated in Fig. 20·1, developments are drawn with the inside face up. This is primarily the result of working to inside rather than outside dimensions of ducts. This procedure also facilitates the use of fold lines, identified by punch marks at either end, along which the metal is folded in forming the object.

In the laying out of real sheet-metal designs, an allowance must be made for seams and lap and, in heavy sheets, for the thickness and crowding of the metal; there is also the consideration of the commercial sizes of material, as well as the question of economy in cutting, in all of which some practical shop knowledge is necessary. Figure 20·17 and paragraph 20·18 illustrate and explain the usage of some of the more common joints, although the developments in this chapter will be confined to the principles alone.

20·3 Prisms. A prism is a polyhedron whose bases or ends are equal parallel polygons and whose lateral faces are parallelograms. A right prism is one whose lateral faces are rectangles; all others are called oblique prisms. The axis of a prism is a straight line connecting the centers of the bases. A truncated prism is that portion of a prism lying between one of its bases and a plane which cuts all its lateral edges.

20·4 To develop a truncated hexagonal prism. Fig. 20·2. First draw the projections of the prism: (1) a normal view of a right section (a section or cut obtained by a plane perpendicular to the axis) and (2) a normal view of the lateral edges. The base, *ABCDEF*, is a right section shown in true size in the bottom view. Lay off on line *AA* of the development the perimeter of the base. This line is called by sheet-metal workers the "stretchout" or "girth" line. At points *A*, *B*, *C*, etc., erect perpendiculars called "measuring lines" or "bend lines," representing the lateral edges along which the pattern is folded to form the prism. Lay off on each of these its

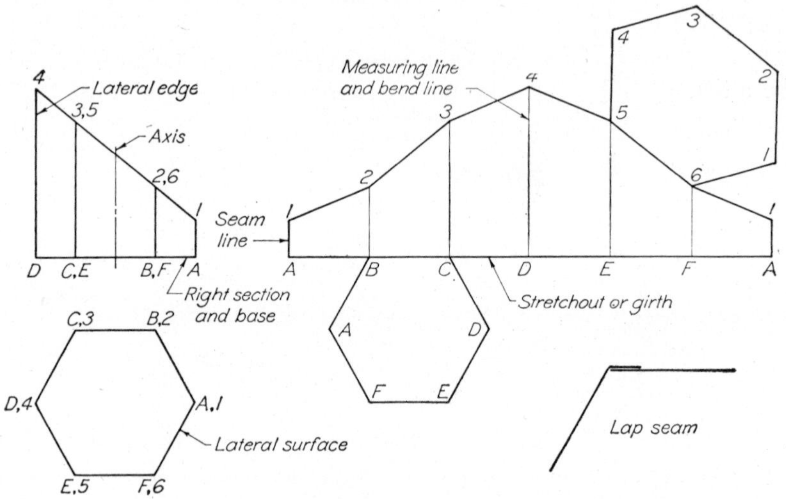

FIG. 20·2—Development of a truncated hexagonal prism.

length *A*1, *B*2, *C*3, etc., as given on the front view. Connect the points 1, 2, 3, etc., in succession, to complete the development of the lateral surfaces. Note on the pattern that the inside of the lateral faces is toward the observer. For the development of the entire surface in one piece, attach the true sizes of the upper end and the base as shown, finding the true size of the upper end by an auxiliary view as described in paragraph 8·9. For economy of solder or rivets and time it is customary to make the seam on the shortest edge or surface. In seaming along the intersection of surfaces whose dihedral angle is other than 90°, as in the case here, the lap seam lends itself to convenient assembling. The flat lock could be used if the seam were made on one of the lateral faces.

20·5 Cylinders. A cylinder is a single-curved surface generated by the motion of a straight-line generatrix remaining parallel to itself and constantly intersecting a curved directrix. The various positions of the generatrix are elements of the surface. It is a right cylinder when the elements are perpendicular to the bases; an oblique cylinder when they are not. A truncated cylinder is that portion which lies between one of its bases and a cutting plane which cuts all the elements. The axis is the line joining the centers of the bases.

20·6 To develop a truncated right cylinder. Fig. 20·3. The development of a cylinder is similar to the development of a prism. Draw the projections of the cylinder: (1) a normal view of a right section and (2) a normal view of the elements. In rolling the cylinder out on a tangent plane, the base or right section, being perpendicular to the axis, will develop into a straight line. For convenience in drawing, divide the normal view of the base, here shown in the bottom view, into a number of equal parts by points

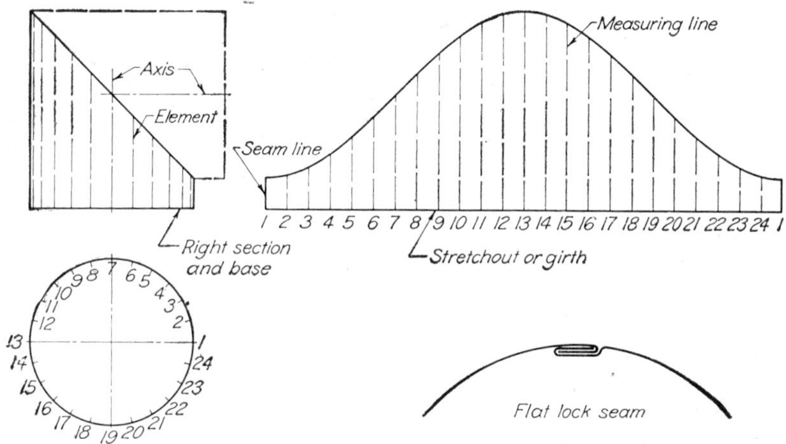

FIG. 20·3—Development of a truncated right cylinder.

that represent elements. These divisions should be spaced so that the chordal distances closely enough approximate the arc to make the stretchout practically equal to the periphery of the base or right section. Project these elements up to the front view. Draw the stretchout and measuring lines as in Fig. 20·2, the cylinder now being treated as a many-sided prism. Transfer the lengths of the elements in order, either by projection or with dividers, and join the points thus found by a smooth curve, sketching it in very lightly, freehand, before fitting the french curve to it. This development might be the pattern of one-half of a two-piece elbow. Three-piece, four-piece, or five-piece elbows may be drawn similarly, as illustrated in Fig. 20·4. As the base is symmetrical, only one-half of it need be drawn. In these cases the intermediate pieces as *B*, *C*, and *D* are developed on a stretchout line formed by laying off the perimeter of a right section. If the right section is taken through the middle of the piece, the stretchout line becomes the center line of the development.

Evidently any elbow could be cut from a single sheet without waste if the seams were made alternately on the long and short sides. The flat lock seam is recommended for Figs. 20·3 and 20·4, although other types could be used.

The octagonal dome, Fig. 20·5, illustrates an application of the development of cylinders. Each piece is a portion of a cylinder. The elements are parallel to the base of the dome and show in their true lengths in the top

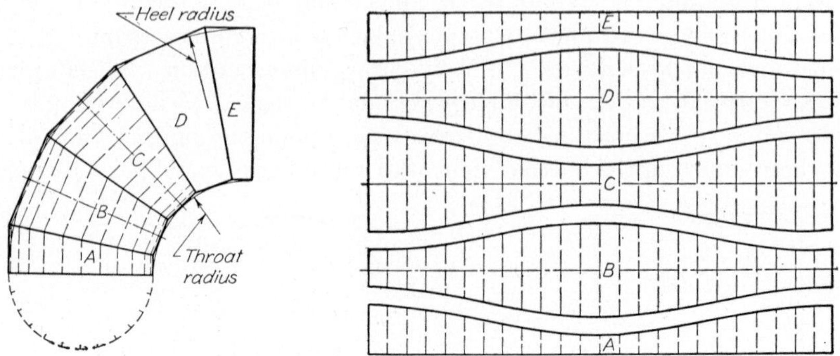

FIG. 20·4—Development of a five-piece elbow.

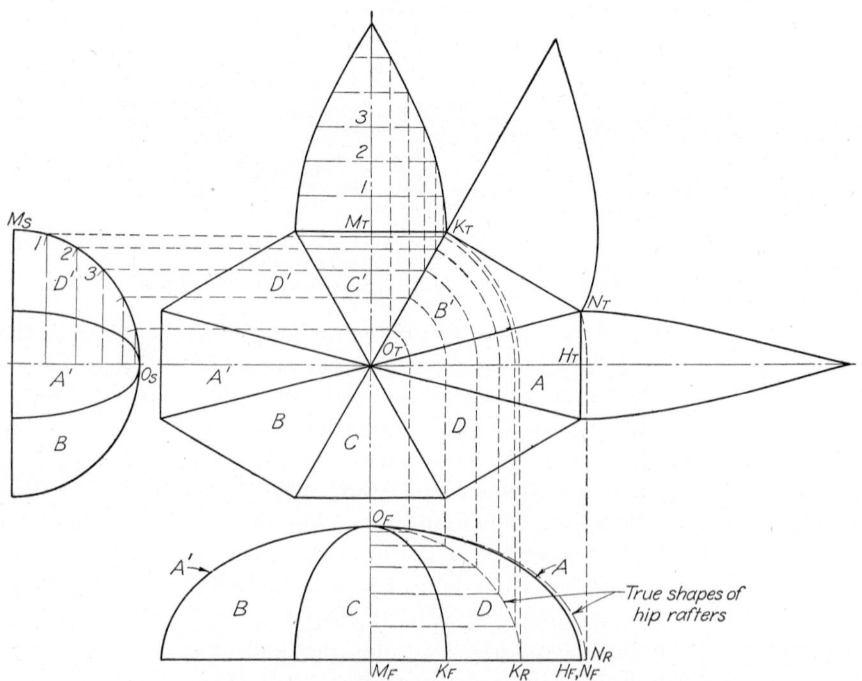

FIG. 20·5—Development of an octagonal dome.

view. The true length of the stretchout line for sections A and A' shows in the front view at O_FH_F. By considering O_TH_T as the edge of a plane cutting a right section, the problem is identical with the preceding problem.

Similarly, the stretchout line for sections B, B', D, and D' shows in true length at O_FK_R in the front view, and for section C and C' at O_SM_S in the side view.

The true shape of a hip rafter is found by revolving it until it is parallel to the frontal plane, in the same manner as in finding the true length of any line. A sufficient number of points should be taken to give a smooth curve.

20·7 Pyramids. A pyramid is a polyhedron whose base is a polygonal plane and whose other surfaces are triangular planes meeting in a point called the "vertex." The axis is a line passing through the vertex and the mid-point of the base. The altitude is a perpendicular from the vertex to the base. A pyramid is *right* if the altitude coincides with the axis; it is *oblique* if they do not coincide. A truncated pyramid is that portion lying between the base and a cutting plane which cuts all the lateral edges. The frustum of a pyramid is that portion lying between the base and a parallel cutting plane cutting all the lateral edges.

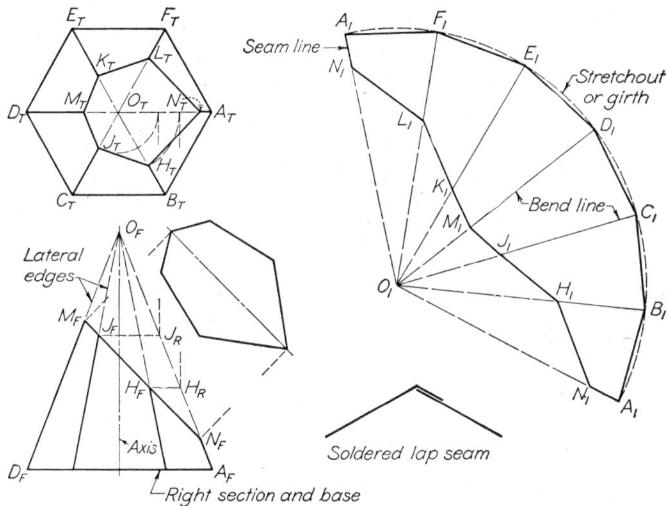

FIG. 20·6—Development of a truncated right hexagonal pyramid.

20·8 To develop a truncated right pyramid. Fig. 20·6. Draw the projections of the pyramid which show (1) a normal view of the base or right section and (2) a normal view of the axis. Lay out the pattern for the pyramid and then superimpose the pattern of the truncation.

Since this is a portion of a right regular pyramid, the lateral edges are all of equal length. The lateral edges OA and OD are parallel to the frontal plane and consequently show in their true length on the front view. With center O_1, taken at any convenient place, and a radius O_FA_F, draw an arc which is the stretchout of the pattern. On it step off the six equal sides of the hexagonal base, obtained from the top view, and connect these points successively with each other and with the vertex O_1, thus forming the pattern for the pyramid.

The intersection of the cutting plane and lateral surfaces is developed by laying off the true length of the intercept of each lateral edge on the corresponding line of the development. The true length of each of these intercepts, such as OH, OJ, etc., is found by revolving it about the axis of the pyramid until they coincide with O_FA_F, as explained in paragraph 8·14. The path of any point, as H, will be projected on the front view as a horizontal line. To obtain the development of the entire surface of the truncated pyramid, attach the base; also find the true size of the cut face and attach it on a common line.

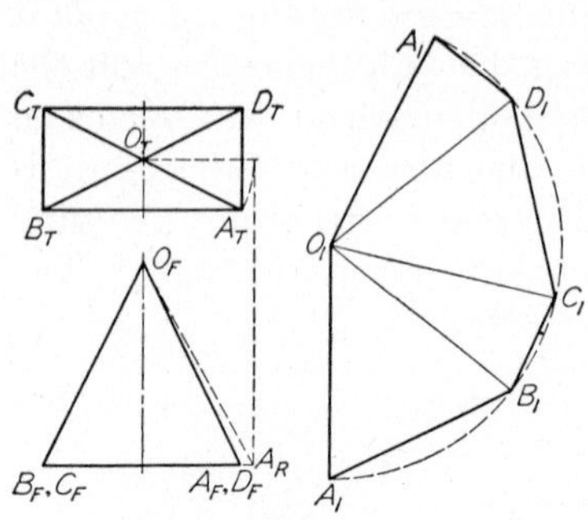

FIG. 20·7—Development of a right rectangular pyramid.

The lap seam is suggested for use here for the same reason that was advanced in paragraph 20·4.

The right rectangular pyramid, Fig. 20·7, is developed in a similar way, but as the edge OA is not parallel to the plane of projection it must be revolved to O_FA_R to obtain its true length.

20·9 To develop an oblique pyramid. Fig. 20·8. Since the lateral edges are unequal in length, the true length of each must be found separately by revolving it parallel to the frontal plane as explained in paragraph 8·14. With O_1 taken at any convenient place, lay off the seam line O_1A_1 equal to

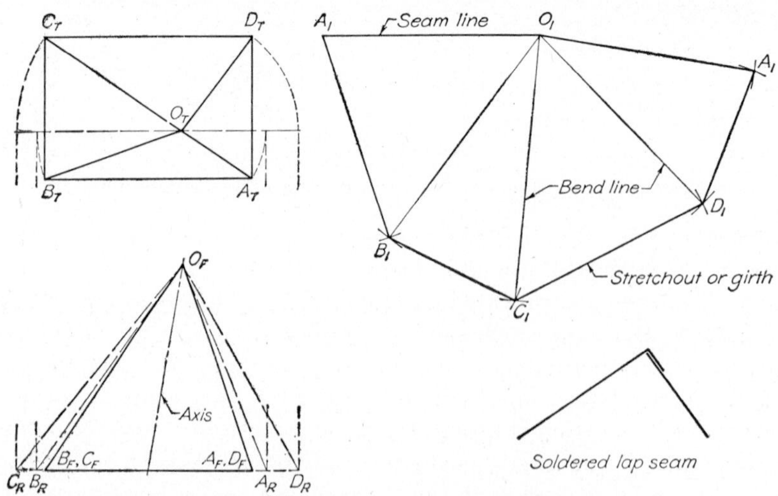

FIG. 20·8—Development of an oblique rectangular pyramid.

O_FA_R. With A_1 as center and radius A_1B_1 equal to A_TB_T, describe an arc. With O_1 as center and radius O_1B_1 equal to O_FB_R, describe a second arc intersecting the first in vertex B_1. Connect the vertices O_1, A_1, B_1, thus forming the pattern for the lateral surface OAB. Similarly lay out the patterns for the remaining three lateral surfaces, joining them on their common edges. The stretchout is equal to the summation of the base edges. If the complete development is required, attach the base on a common line. The lap seam is suggested as the most suitable for the given conditions.

20·10 Cones. A cone is a single-curved surface generated by the movement, along a curved directrix, of a straight-line generatrix, one point of which is fixed. The directrix is the base, and the fixed point the vertex of the cone. Each position of the generatrix is an element of the surface. The axis is a line connecting the vertex and the center of the base. The altitude is a perpendicular dropped from the vertex to the base. A cone is

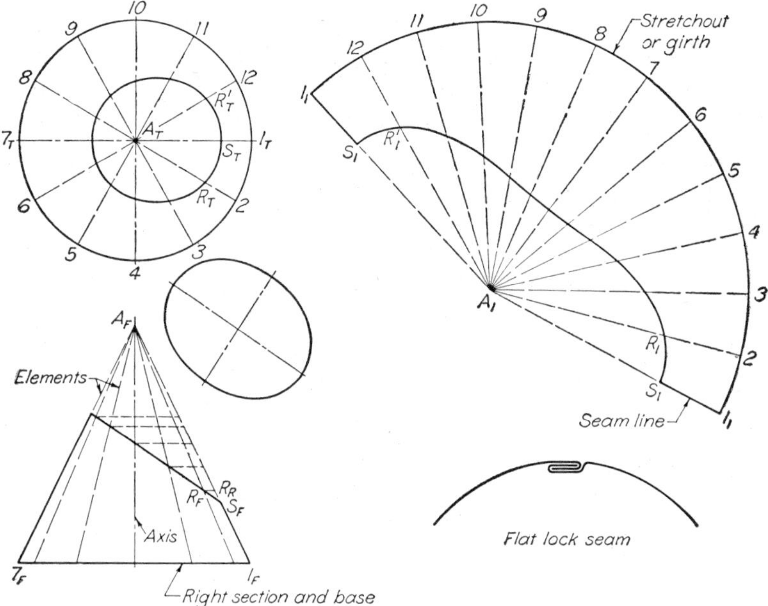

FIG. 20·9—Development of a truncated right circular cone.

right if the axis and altitude coincide; it is *oblique* if they do not coincide. A truncated cone is that portion lying between the base and a cutting plane which cuts all the elements. The frustum of a cone is that portion lying between the base and a parallel cutting plane which cuts all the elements.

20·11 To develop a truncated right circular cone. Fig. 20·9. Draw the projections of the cone which will show (1) a normal view of the base or right section and (2) a normal view of the axis. First develop the surface of the complete cone and then superimpose the pattern for the truncation.

Divide the top view of the base into a sufficient number of equal parts so that the sum of the resulting chordal distances will closely approximate the periphery of the base. Project these points to the front view and draw front views of the elements through them. With center A_1 and a radius equal to the slant height A_F1_F, which is the true length of all the elements, draw an arc, which is the stretchout, and lay off on it the chordal divisions of the base, obtained from the top view. Connect these points 1_1, 2_1, 3_1, etc., with A_1, thus forming the pattern for the cone. Find the true length of each element from vertex to cutting plane by revolving it to coincide with the contour element A_1, and lay off this distance on the corresponding line of the development. Draw a smooth curve through these points. The pattern for the cut surface is obtained from the auxiliary view. The flat lock seam is recommended here, although other types could be employed.

20·12 Triangulation. Nondevelopable surfaces are developed approximately by assuming them to be made of narrow sections of developable sur-

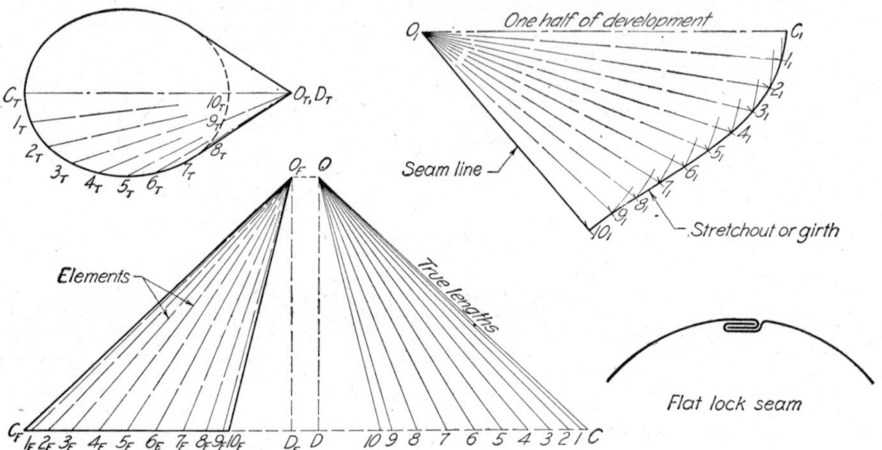

FIG. 20·10—Development of an oblique cone by triangulation.

faces. The commonest and best method for approximate development is that of triangulation, that is, the surface is assumed to be made up of a large number of triangular strips or plane triangles with very short bases. This method is used for all warped surfaces and also for oblique cones, which, although single-curved surfaces and capable of true theoretical development, can be developed much more easily and accurately by triangulation.

The principle is extremely simple. It consists merely in dividing the surface into triangles, finding the true lengths of the sides of each, and constructing them one at a time, joining these triangles on their common sides.

20·13 To develop an oblique cone. Fig. 20·10. An oblique cone differs from a cone of revolution in that the elements are all of different lengths. The development of the right circular cone is practically made up of a number of equal triangles meeting at the vertex, whose sides are elements and whose bases are the chords of short arcs of the base of the cone. In the oblique cone, each triangle must be found separately.

If possible, draw views of the cone showing (1) a normal view of the base and (2) a normal view of the altitude. Divide the true size of the base, here shown in the top view, into a sufficient number of equal parts, so that the sum of the chordal distances will closely approximate the arc. Project these points to the front view of the base. Through these points and the vertex draw the elements in each view. Since this cone is symmetrical about a frontal plane through the vertex, the elements are shown only on the front half of it. Also, only one-half of the development is drawn. With the seam on the shortest element, the element OC will be the center line of the development and may be drawn directly at O_1C_1, as its true length is given at O_FC_F. Find the true length of the elements by revolving them until parallel to the frontal plane, or by constructing a "true-length diagram." The true length of any element would be the hypotenuse of a triangle, one leg being the length of the projected element as seen in the top view, the other leg equal to the altitude of the cone. Thus, to make the diagram, draw the leg OD coinciding with or parallel to O_FD_F. At D and perpendicular to OD draw the other leg, on which lay off the lengths $D1$, $D2$, etc., equal to D_T1_T, D_T2_T, etc., respectively. Distances from O to points on the base of the diagram are the true lengths of the elements.

Construct the pattern for the front half of the cone as follows: With O_1 as center and radius $O1$, draw an arc. With C_1 as center and radius C_T1_T, draw a second arc intersecting the first at 1_1; then O_11_1 will be the developed position of the element $O1$. With 1_1 as center and radius 1_T2_T, draw an arc intersecting a second arc with O_1 as center and radius $O2$, thus locating 2_1. Continue this procedure until all the elements have been transferred to the development. Connect the points C_1, 1_1, 2_1, etc., with a smooth curve, the stretchout line, to complete the development. The flat lock seam is recommended for joining the ends of the pattern to form the cone.

20·14 A conical connection between two parallel cylindrical pipes of different diameters is shown in Fig. 20·11. The method used in drawing the

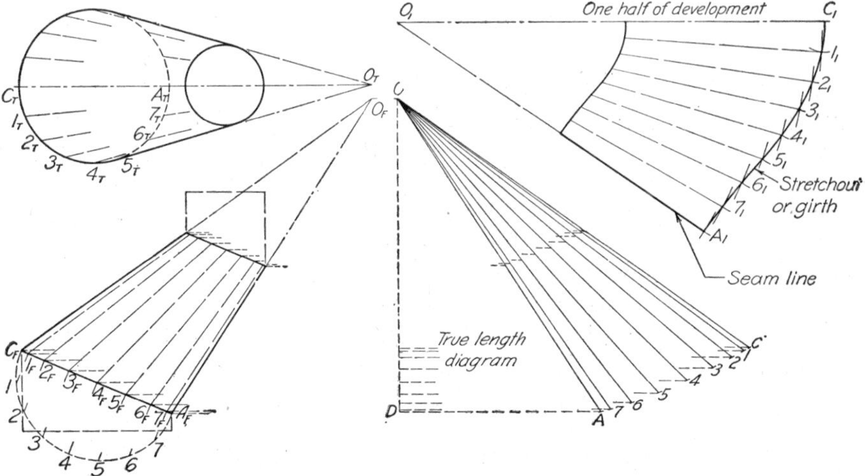

FIG. 20·11—Development of a conical connection.

pattern is an application of the development of an oblique cone. One-half of the elliptical base is shown in true size in an auxiliary view, here attached to the front view. Find the true size of the base from its major and minor axes; divide it into a number of equal parts so that the sum of these chordal distances closely approximates the periphery of the curve, and project these points to the front and top views. Draw the elements in each view through these points and find the vertex O by extending the contour elements until they intersect. The true length of each element is found by using the vertical distance between its ends as the vertical leg of the diagram and its horizontal projection as the other leg. As each true length from vertex to

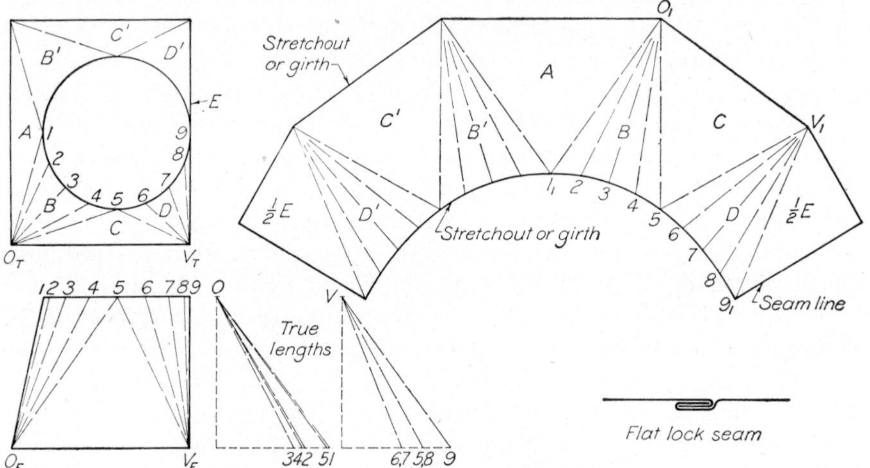

Fig. 20·12—Development of a transition piece.

base is found, project the upper end of the intercept horizontally across from the front view to the true length of the corresponding element to find the true length of the intercept. The development is drawn by laying out each triangle in turn, from vertex to base as in paragraph 20·13, starting on the center line O_1C_1, then measuring on each element its intercept length. Draw smooth curves through these points to complete the pattern. Join the ends of the development with a flat lock seam to form the connection.

20·15 Transition pieces are used to connect pipes or openings of different shapes of cross section. Figure 20·12, showing a transition piece for connecting a round pipe and a rectangular pipe with parallel axes, is typical. These are always developed by triangulation. The piece shown in Fig. 20·12 is, evidently, made up of four triangular planes whose bases are the sides of the rectangle, and four parts of oblique cones whose common bases are arcs of the circle and whose vertices are at the corners of the rectangle. To develop it, make a true-length diagram as in Fig. 20·10. The true length of $O1$ being found, all the sides of triangle A will be known. Attach the development of cones B and B', then those of triangles C and C', and so on.

Figure 20·13 is another transition piece joining a rectangular to a circular pipe whose axes are nonparallel. By using a partial right-side view of the round opening, the divisions of the bases of the oblique cones can be found (as the object is symmetrical, one-half only of the opening need be divided). The true lengths of the elements are obtained as in Fig. 20·11.

With the seam line the center line of the plane *E* in Figs. 20·12 and 20·13, the flat lock is recommended for joining the ends of the development.

20·16 Triangulation of warped surfaces. The approximate development of a warped surface is made by dividing it into a number of narrow

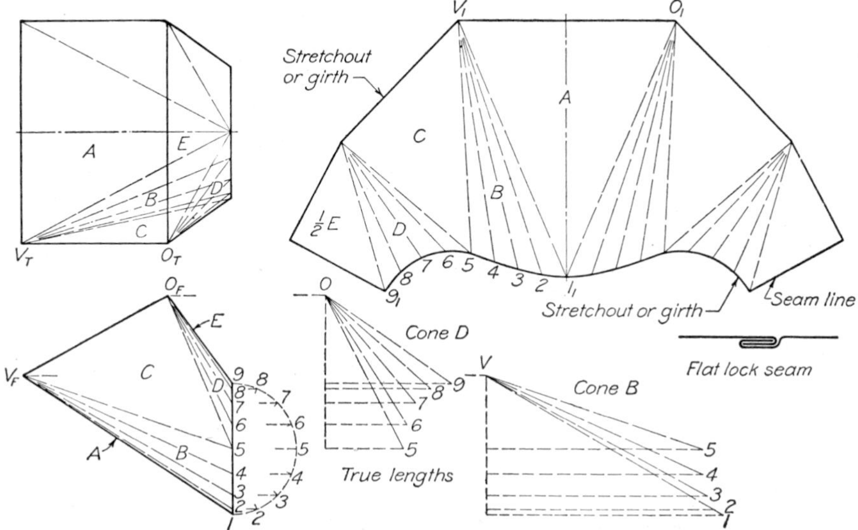

FIG. 20·13—Development of a transition piece.

quadrilaterals and then splitting each of these quadrilaterals into two triangles by a diagonal, which is assumed to be a straight line, although really a curve. Figure 20·14 shows a warped transition piece. Find the true size of one-half the elliptical base by revolving it, until horizontal, about an axis through 1, when its true shape will be seen on the top view. The major axis is 1, 7_R and the minor axis through 4_R equals 1, 7. Divide the semi-ellipse into a sufficient number of equal parts and project these to the top and front views. Divide the top semicircle into the same number of equal parts and connect similar points on each end, thus dividing the surface into approximate quadrilaterals. Cut each into two triangles by a diagonal. On true-length diagrams find the lengths of the elements and the diagonals, and draw the development by constructing the true sizes of the triangles in regular order. The flat lock seam is recommended for joining the ends of the development.

20·17 To develop a sphere. The sphere may be taken as typical of double-curved surfaces, which can be developed only approximately. It

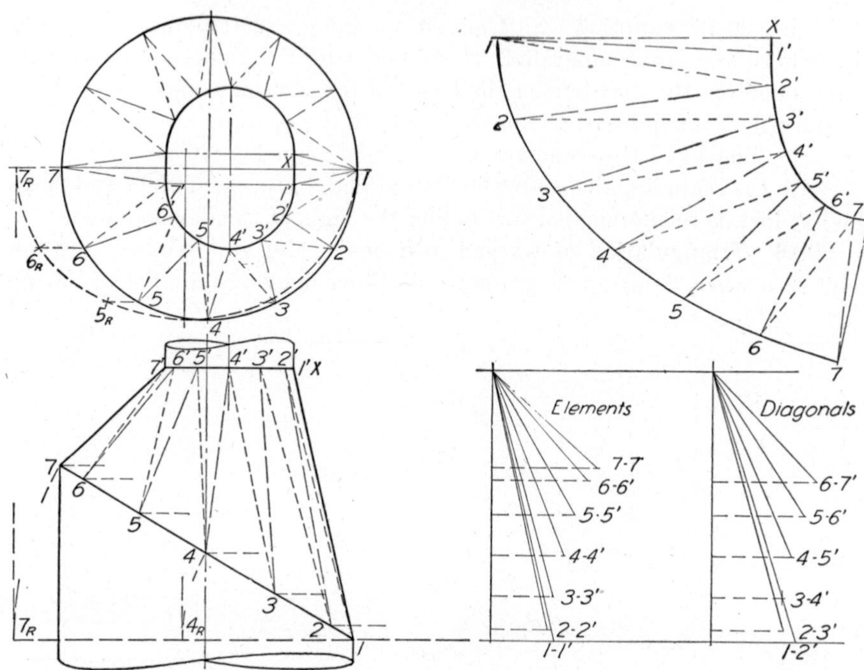

Fig. 20·14—Development of a warped transition piece.

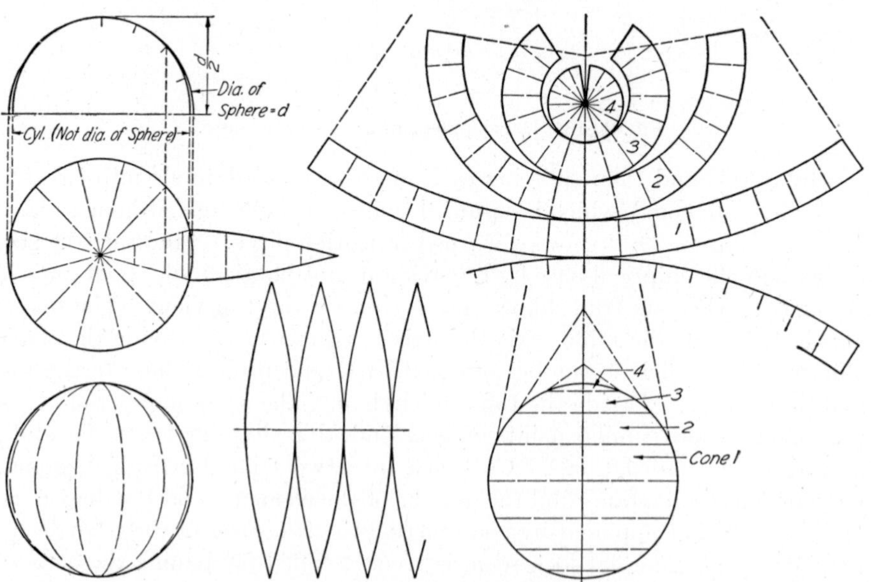

Fig. 20·15—Sphere, gore method.

Fig. 20·16—Sphere, zone method.

may be cut into a number of equal meridian sections, or lunes, as in Fig. 20·15, and these may be considered to be sections of cylinders. One of these sections developed as the cylinder in Fig. 20·15 will give a pattern for the others.

Another method is to cut the sphere into horizontal sections, or zones, each of which may be taken as the frustum of a cone whose vertex is at the intersection of the extended chords, Fig. 20·16.

20·18 Joints, connectors, and hems. There are numerous joints used in seaming sheet-metal ducts and in connecting one duct to another. Figure 20·17 illustrates some of the more common types, which may be formed by

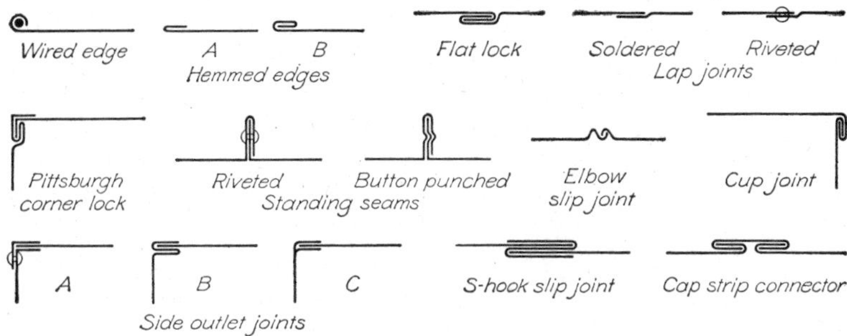

FIG. 20·17—Cross sections of joints and finished edges.

hand on a break, or by special seaming machines. No attempt to dimension the various seams and connections has been made here because of the variation in sizes for different gages of metal and in the forming machines of manufacturers.

The type of seam for longitudinal joints is selected according to conditions. For sheets from 20 to 28 gage, the flat lock seam is used more than any other. The hammered or Pittsburgh lock is used more for irregular duct work, such as transformers, where one edge can be made straight for bending in the break or special forming machine. Lap joints are usually used where the applications of the flat lock and hammered lock are not readily adaptable, such as metal heavier than 18 gage or corner joints other than 90 degrees.

For metals 18 gage and heavier, standing seams are generally employed for both longitudinal and cross seams. They serve the double purpose of seaming and stiffening large ducts.

The cap-strip or S-hook slip joints are used in connecting sections of prismatic ducts such as rectangular ones. The S hook is usually used on temporary ducts or those that must be removed occasionally. The cap strip is used as a permanent connector.

For fastening side outlets to the main duct, connectors illustrated at *A*, *B*, and *C* are used. Joints *A* and *B* are self-explanatory. At *C* the end of the side outlet is notched, and the resulting tabs are alternately lapped inside and outside the periphery of the hole in the main duct.

Hemming is used in finishing the raw edges of the end of the duct. In wire hemming an extra allowance of about 2½ times the diameter of the wire is made for wrapping around the wire. In flat hemming the end of the duct is bent over either once or twice to relieve the sharp edge of the metal.

20·19 The intersection of surfaces. When two surfaces intersect, the line of intersection, which is the line common to both, may be thought of as a line in which all the elements of one surface pierce the other. Nearly every line on a drawing is a line of intersection, generally the intersection of two planes, or of a cylinder and a plane, giving a circle. The term "intersection of surfaces" refers, however, to the more complicated lines that occur when geometrical surfaces such as cylinders, cones, prisms, etc., intersect each other.

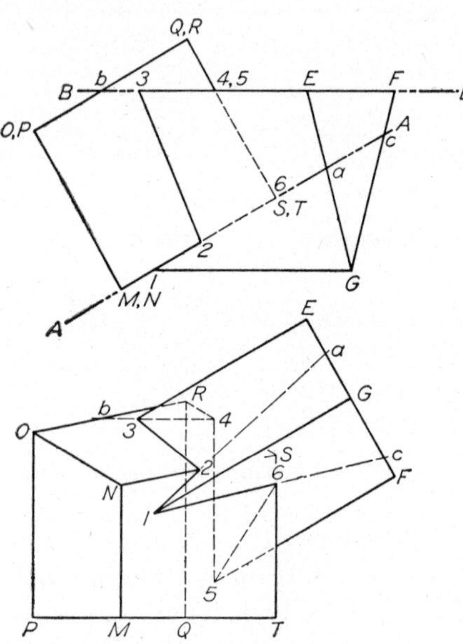

FIG. 20·18—Intersection of two prisms.

Two reasons make it necessary for the draftsman to be familiar with the methods of finding the intersections of surfaces: first, intersections are constantly occurring on working drawings and must be represented; second, in sheet-metal combinations the intersections must be found before the piece can be developed. In the first case it is necessary to find only a few critical points and "guess in" the curve; in the second case enough points must be determined to enable the development to be laid out accurately.

Any practical problem resolves itself into some combination of the geometrical type forms. In general the method of finding the line of intersection of any two surfaces is to pass a series of planes through them in such a way that each plane cuts from each surface the simplest lines. The intersection of the lines cut from each surface by a plane will give one or more points on the line of intersection. The following examples illustrate the method of using cutting planes in finding the line of intersection of various combinations encountered in practical work.

20·20 To find the intersection of two prisms. Fig. 20·18. In general, find the line of intersection of a surface on one prism with all surfaces on the other. Then take a surface adjacent to the first and find its intersections with the other prism. Continue in this manner until the complete line of intersection of the prisms is determined.

The method of locating end points on the line of intersection of two surfaces depends upon the position of the surfaces, as follows:

Both surfaces receding. Their intersection appears as a point in the view in which they recede. Project the intersection to an adjacent view, locating the two ends of the intersection on the edges of one or both intersecting surfaces so that they will lie within the boundaries of the other surface. The intersection of 4-5 of surfaces *QRST* and *EF*3 was obtained in this manner.

One surface receding, the other oblique. An edge of the oblique surface may appear to pierce the receding surface in a view in which these conditions exist. If, in an adjacent view, the piercing point lies on the edge of the oblique surface and within the boundaries of the other surface, then it is an

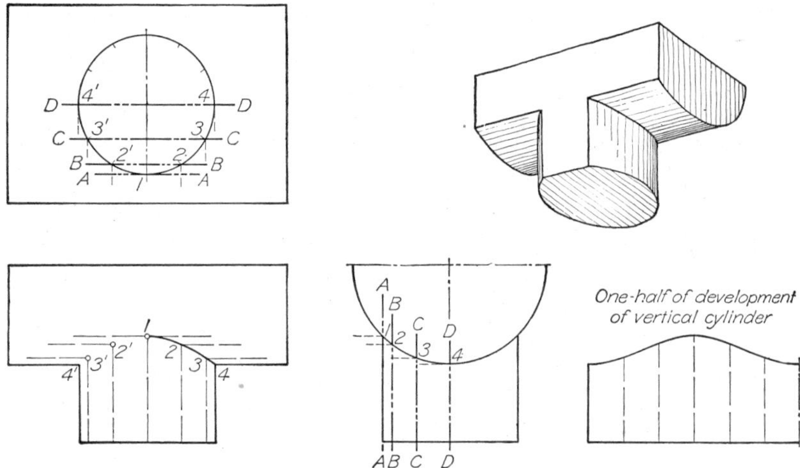

FIG. 20·19—Intersection of two cylinders.

end point on the intersection of the surfaces. Point 5 lying on edge *F*5 of the oblique surface *FG*1-5 and the surface *QRST* is located in the top view in this manner. Point 1 was similarly established.

Both surfaces oblique. Find the piercing point of an edge of one surface with the other surface, as follows: Pass a receding plane through an edge of one surface. Find the line of intersection of the receding plane and the other surface as explained above. The piercing point of the edge and surface is located where the line of intersection, just found, and the edge intersect. Repeat this operation to establish the other end of the line of intersection of the surfaces. Point 3, on the line of intersection 2-3 of the oblique surfaces *NORS* and *EG* 1-3, was found in this manner, by passing the receding plane *B-B* through edge *E*3; finding the intersection *b*4 of the surfaces and then locating point 3 at the intersection of *b*4 and *E*3.

20·21 To find the intersection of two cylinders. Fig. 20·19. Cutting planes parallel to the axis of a cylinder will cut straight-line elements from the cylinder. The frontal cutting planes *A*, *B*, *C*, and *D*, parallel to the axis of each cylinder, cut elements from each cylinder, the intersections of which are points on the curve. The pictorial sketch shows a slice cut by a plane from the object, which has been treated as a solid in order to illustrate the method more easily. The development of the vertical cylinder is evident from the figure.

When the axes of the cylinders do not intersect, as in Fig. 20·20, the same method is used, but judgment must be exercised in the choice of cutting

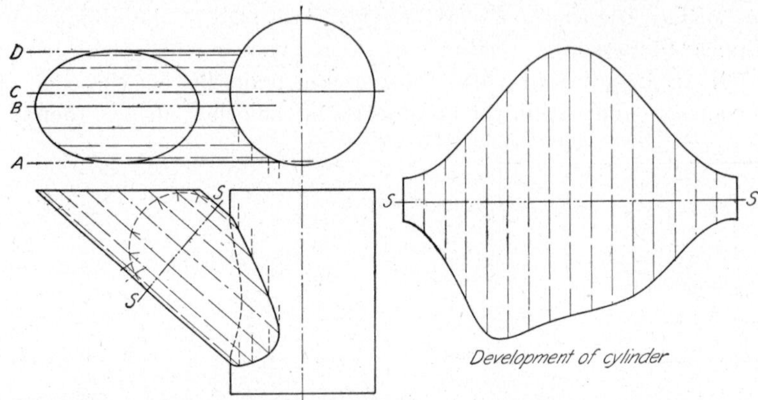

FIG. 20·20—Intersection of two cylinders, axes not intersecting.

planes. Certain "critical planes" give the limits and turning points of the curve. Such planes should always be taken through the contour elements. For the position shown, planes *A* and *D* give the depth of the curve, the plane *B* the extreme height, and the plane *C* the tangent or turning points on the contour element of the vertical cylinder. After the critical points have been determined, a sufficient number of other cutting planes are used to give an accurate curve.

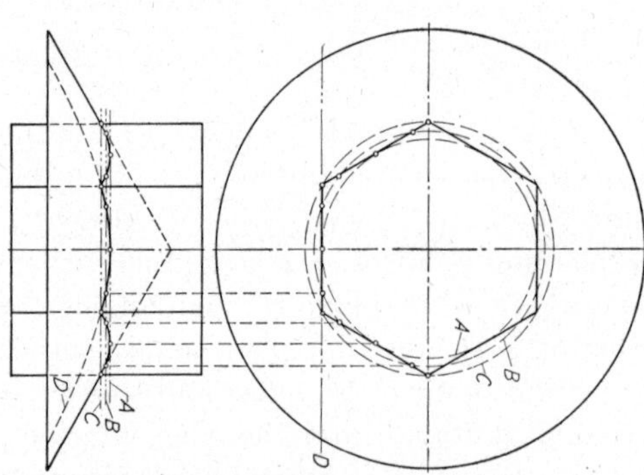

FIG. 20·21—Prism and cone.

To develop the inclined cylinder, a right section at *S-S* is taken, whose stretchout is a straight line equal in length to the circumference of the right section. If the cutting planes are taken at random, the elements will not be spaced uniformly. To simplify the development, other planes may be assumed by dividing the turned section into equal parts, as shown.

20·22 To find the intersection of a prism and a cone. Fig. 20·21. In this case the choice of cutting planes parallel to *H* is made. Thus each plane cuts a circle from the cone and a hexagon from the prism, whose intersections give points on the curve. The curve is limited between the plane *A*, cutting a circle whose diameter is equal to the short diameter of the hexagon, and the plane C, cutting a circle whose diameter is equal to the long diameter. As the prism is made up of six vertical planes, the entire line of intersection of cone and prism consists of the ends of six hyperbolas, three of which are visible, one showing its true shape, as cut by plane D, the two others foreshortened. This figure illustrates the true curve in a chamfered hexagonal bolthead or nut. In practice it is always drawn approximately, with three circle arcs.

20·23 To find the intersection of a cylinder and a cone. Fig. 20·22. Here the cutting planes may be taken so as to pass through the vertex of the cone and parallel to the axis of the cylinder, thus cutting straight-line elements from both cylinder and cone; or, with a right circular cone, they may be taken parallel to the base so as to cut circles from the cone. Both sys-

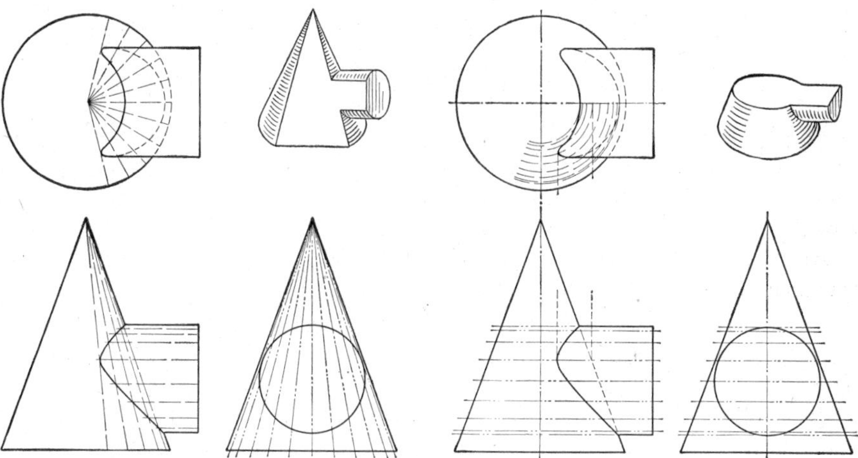

FIG. 20·22—Intersection of a cylinder and a cone.

tems of planes are illustrated in the figure. The pictorial sketches show slices taken by each plane through the objects, which have been treated as solids in order to illustrate the method more easily. Some judgment is necessary in the selection of both the direction and the number of cutting planes. More points need to be found at the places of sudden curvature or changes of direction of the projections of the line of intersections.

20·24 To find the intersection of a plane and a surface of revolution. Fig. 20·23. This problem depends on the principle that planes perpendicular to the axis of any surface of revolution will cut circles (right sections). Thus the line of intersection of a plane and a surface of revolution is found by passing a series of planes perpendicular to the axis of revolution. Each of these planes will cut a straight line from the given plane and a circle from the surface of revolution, the intersection of which will give two points on the curve. In Fig. 20·23 the diameter of the circle cut by the plane S-S has been projected across to the end view and the points at which the circle cuts the "flat" projected back to S-S to give points on the curve.

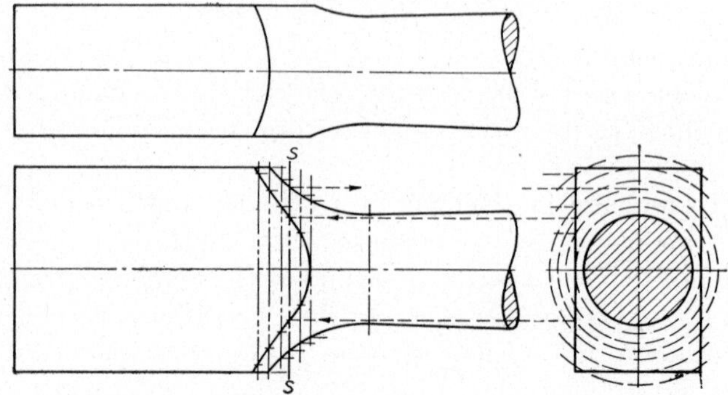

FIG. 20·23—Intersection of a surface of revolution and a plane.

PROBLEMS

20·25 Selections from the following problems may be made and the figures constructed accurately in pencil without inking. Any practical problem can be resolved into some combination of the "type solids," and the exercises given illustrate the principles involved in the various combinations.

An added interest in developments may be found by working the problems on suitable paper, allowing for fastenings and lap, and cutting them out. It is recommended that at least one or two models be constructed in this way.

In sheet-metal shops, development problems, unless very complicated, are usually laid out directly on the metal.

The following problems may be drawn on $8\frac{1}{2}'' \times 11''$ or $11'' \times 17''$ sheets. Assume the objects to be made of thin metal with open ends unless otherwise specified.

Group I. Prisms

1 to 6. Fig. 20·24. Develop lateral surfaces of the prisms.

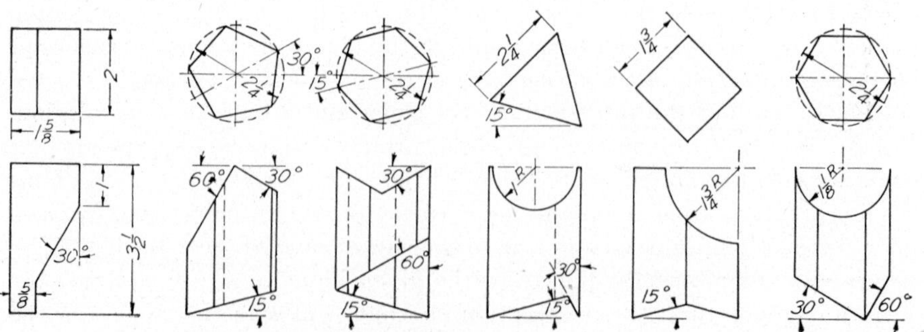

FIG. 20·24—Prisms (Probs. 1 to 6).

Group II. Cylinders

7 to 13. Fig. 20·25. Develop lateral surfaces of the cylinders.

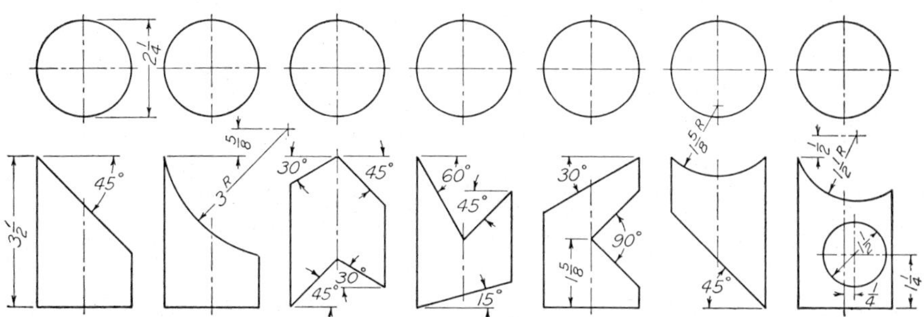

Fig. 20·25—Cylinders (Probs. 7 to 13).

Group III. Combinations of prisms and cylinders

14 to 16. Fig. 20·26. Develop lateral surfaces.

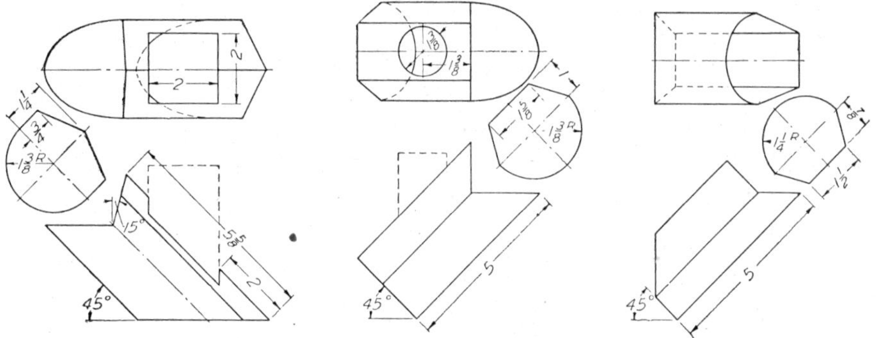

Fig. 20·26—Combination surfaces (Probs. 14 to 16).

Group IV. Pyramids

17 to 19. Fig. 20·27. Develop lateral surfaces of the hoppers.
20, 21. Fig. 20·27. Develop lateral surfaces of the pyramids.

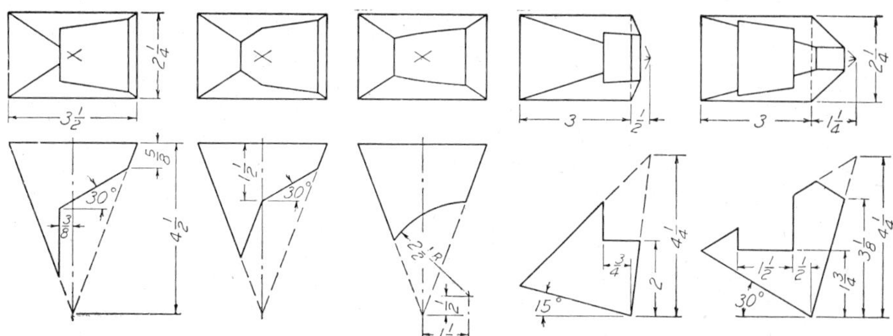

Fig. 20·27—Pyramids (Probs. 17 to 21).

Group V. Cones

22 to 26. Fig. 20·28. Develop lateral surfaces.

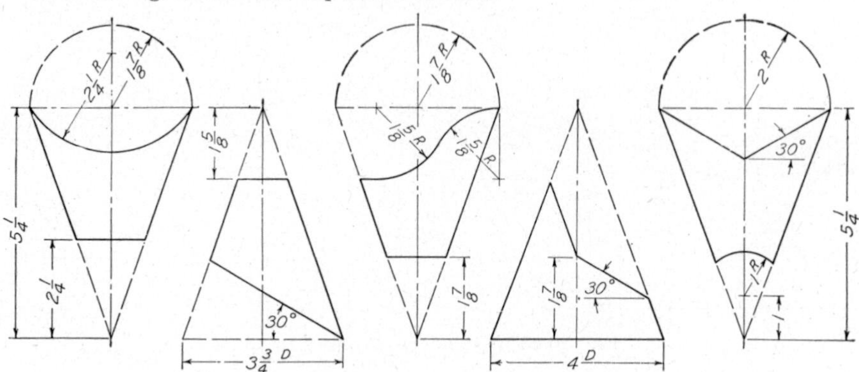

FIG. 20·28—Cones (Probs. 22 to 26).

Group VI. Developments

27 to 30. Fig. 20·29. Develop lateral surfaces of the objects. Note that 28 is a GI gutter, and 29 is a conical hood.

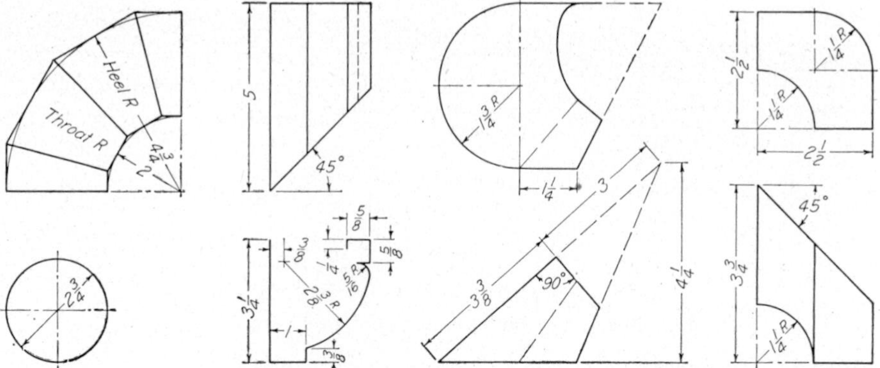

FIG. 20·29—Various surfaces (Probs. 27 to 30).

Group VII. Cones and transition pieces

31 to 34. Fig. 20·30. Develop lateral surfaces of the objects (one-half of Probs. 31, 32, 34).

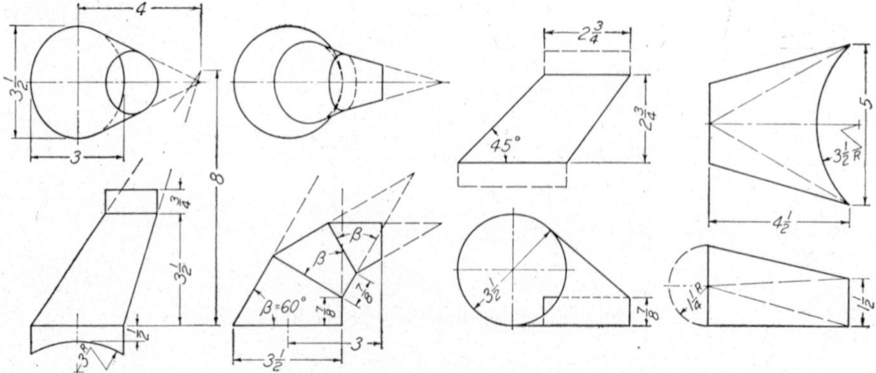

FIG. 20·30—Transition pieces (Probs. 31 to 34).

35 to 37. Fig. 20·31. Develop lateral surfaces of the objects (one-half).

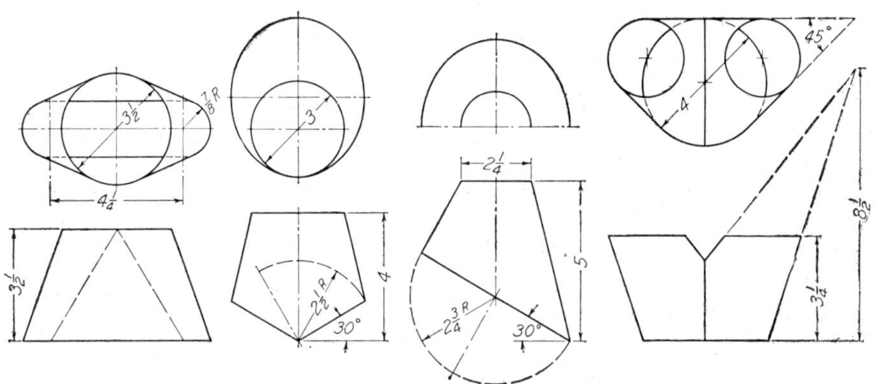

FIG. 20·31—Transition pieces (Probs. 35 to 38).

38. Fig. 20·31. Develop surface of one-half of Y connection.

Group VIII. Furnace-pipe fittings

39 to 46. Fig. 20·32. Develop surfaces and make paper models.

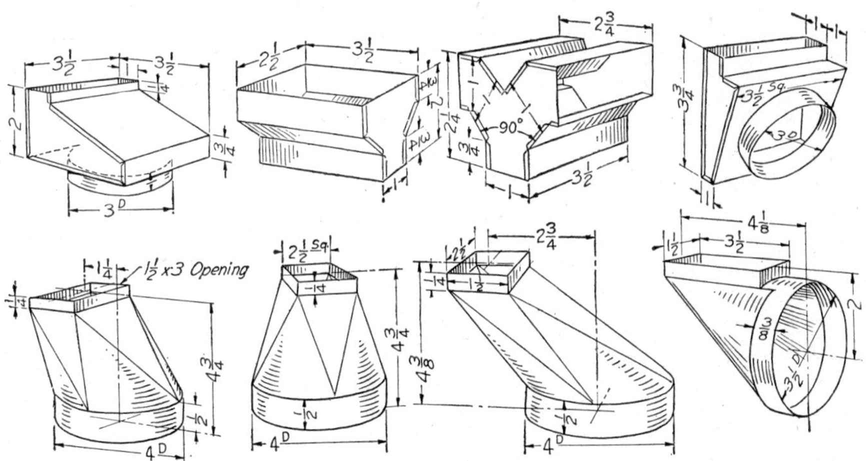

FIG. 20·32—Sheet-metal connections (Probs. 39 to 46).

Group IX. Intersections of prisms

47 to 49. Fig. 20·33. Find line of intersection, considering prisms as pipes opening into each other. Use particular care in indicating visible and invisible portions of line of intersection. On another sheet develop the surfaces.

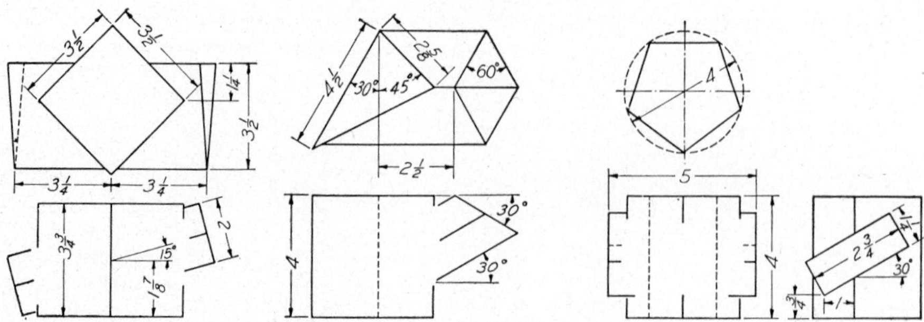

Fig. 20·33—Intersections of prisms (Probs. 47 to 49).

50 to 52. Fig. 20·34. Find line of intersection, indicating visible and invisible parts, and considering prisms as pipes opening into each other. Note that in Probs. 51 and 52 the vertical pipes must have heads cut out to fit inclined pipe.

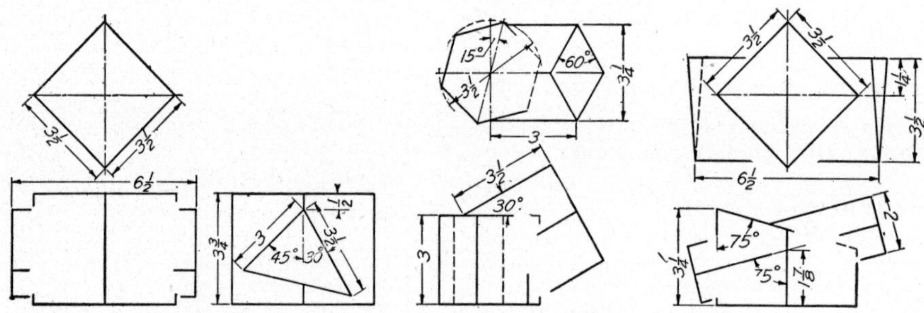

Fig. 20·34—Intersections of prisms (Probs. 50 to 52).

Group X. Intersections of cylinders

53 to 55. Fig. 20·35. Find line of intersection, indicating visible and invisible portions and considering cylinders as pipes opening into each other. On another sheet develop the surfaces of each cylinder.

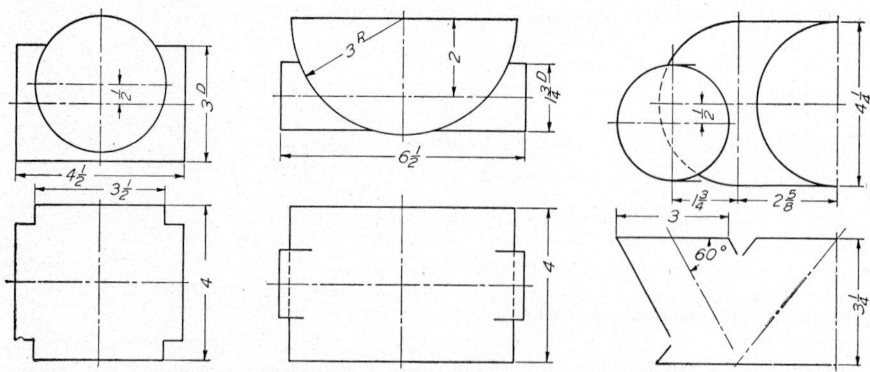

Fig. 20·35—Intersections of cylinders (Probs. 53 to 55).

Group XI. Intersections of surfaces

56 to 59. Fig. 20·36. Find lines of intersection.

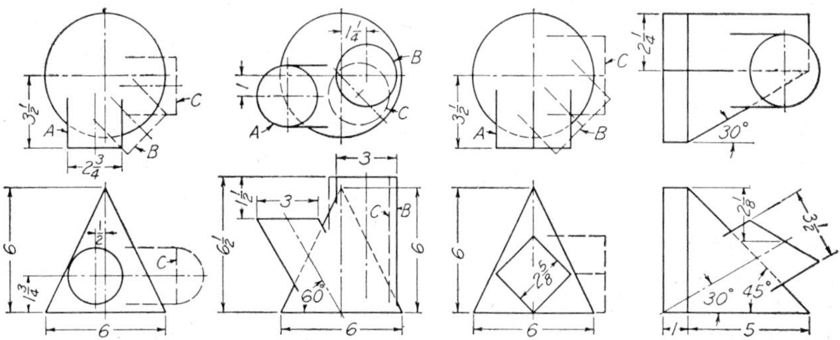

FIG. 20·36—Intersections (Probs. 56 to 59).

60 to 62. Fig. 20·37. Find lines of intersection and develop surfaces.

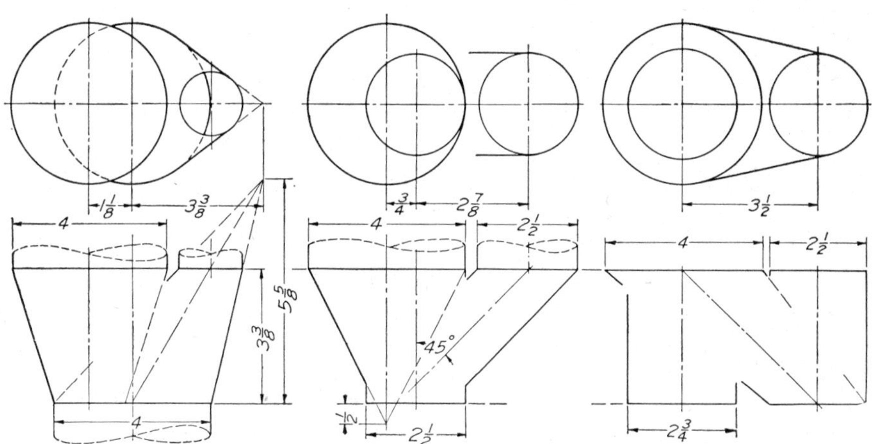

FIG. 20·37—Intersections (Probs. 60 to 62).

63 to 67. Fig. 20·38. Find the lines of intersection and develop surfaces.

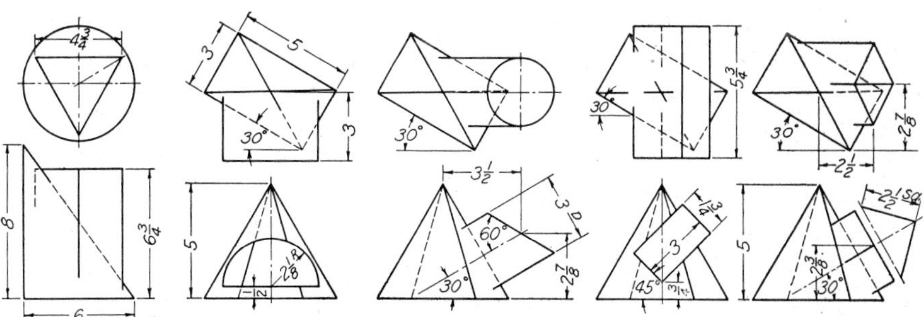

FIG. 20·38—Intersections (Probs. 63 to 67).

68 to 71. Fig. 20·39. Find lines of intersection and develop surfaces.

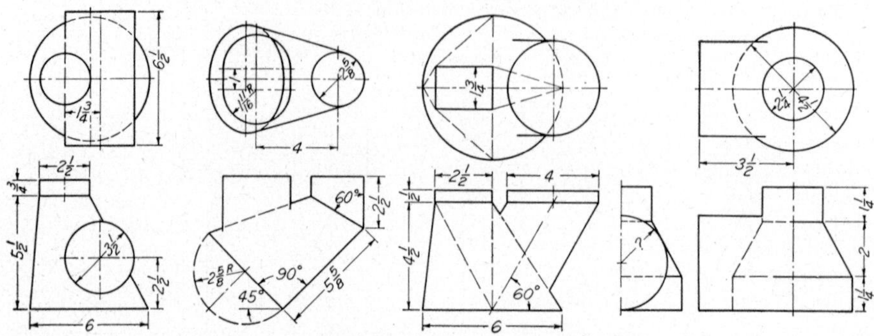

FIG. 20·39—Intersections (Probs. 68 to 71).

Group XII. Surfaces cut by planes

72 to 76. Fig. 20·40. Complete the views, finding lines of intersection. Make separate views of sections on planes indicated.

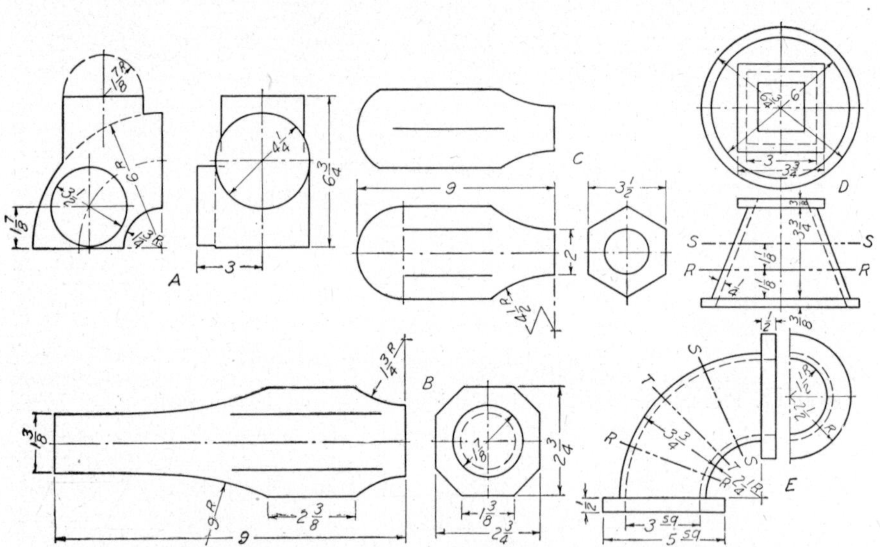

FIG. 20·40—Surfaces cut by planes (Probs. 72 to 76).

Chapter 21

PICTORIAL REPRESENTATION

21·1 In the study of the theory of projection in Chap. 6 it was found that perspective projection shows the object as it appears to the eye but that its lines cannot be measured directly, while orthographic projection, with two or more views, shows it as it really is in form and dimensions but requires a trained imagination to visualize the object from the views. To combine the pictorial effect of perspective drawing with the possibility of measuring the principal lines directly, several forms of one-plane projection or conventional picture methods have been devised, in which the third dimension is taken care of by turning the object in such a way that three of its faces are visible. Along with the advantages of these methods go some serious disadvantages which limit their usefulness. The distorted effect is often unreal and unpleasant; only certain lines can be measured; the execution requires more time, particularly if curved lines occur, and it is difficult to add many figured dimensions; but, even with their limitations, a knowledge of these methods is extremely desirable as they can often be used to great advantage. Mechanical or structural details not clear in orthographic projection may be drawn pictorially or illustrated by supplementary pictorial views. Technical illustrations, patent-office drawings, and the like are advantageously made in one-plane projection; layouts and piping plans may be drawn, as in Fig. 14·13, and many other applications will occur to draftsmen who can use these methods with facility. One of the most important reasons for learning them is that they are so useful in making freehand sketches, as already shown in Chap. 7.

21·2 Divisions. Aside from perspective drawing, there are two general divisions of pictorial projection: first, *axonometric,* with its divisions into isometric, dimetric, and trimetric; and, second, *oblique* projection, with several variations. Other methods not theoretically correct but effective are sometimes used.

21·3 Axonometric projection as shown in the tabular classification on page 91 is, theoretically, simply orthographic projection in which only one plane is used, the object being turned so that three faces show. Imagine a transparent vertical plane with a cube behind it, one face of the cube being parallel to the plane. The projection on the plane, that is, the front view of the cube, will be a square. Rotate the cube about a vertical axis through any angle less than 90°, and the front view will now show two faces, both foreshortened. From this position tilt the cube forward any amount less than 90°. Three faces will now be visible on the front view. Thus there can be an infinite number of axonometric positions, only a few of which are ever used for drawing. The simplest of these is the *isometric* (equal-measure) position, in which the three faces are foreshortened equally. This is the basis for the isometric system.

21·4 Isometric projection. If a cube in position I, Fig. 21·1, is rotated about a vertical axis through 45° as shown in II, then tilted forward as in III until the edge *AD* is foreshortened equally with *AB* and *AC*, the front view of the cube in this position is said to be an "isometric projection." (The cube has been tilted forward until the body diagonal through *A* is per-

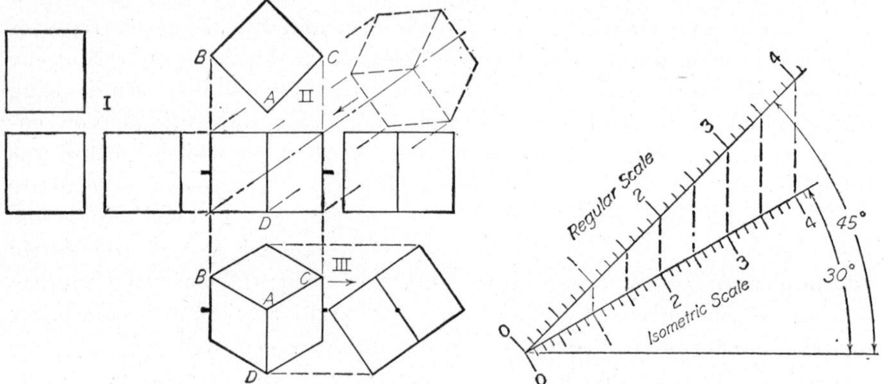

FIG. 21·1—The isometric cube.

FIG. 21·2—Isometric scale.

pendicular to the front plane. This makes the top face slope approximately 35°16′).[1] The projections of the three mutually perpendicular edges *AB*, *AC*, and *AD* meeting at the front corner *A* make equal angles, 120°, with each other and are called *isometric axes*. Since the projections of parallel lines are parallel, the projections of the other edges of the cube will be respectively parallel to these axes. Any line parallel to an edge of the cube, whose projection is thus parallel to an isometric axis, is called an *isometric line*. The planes of the faces of the cube and all planes parallel to them are called *isometric planes*.

In isometric projection the isometric lines have been foreshortened to approximately $^{81}/_{100}$ of their length, and an isometric scale to this proportion can be made graphically as shown in Fig. 21·2 if it becomes necessary to make an isometric projection to theoretical size.

21·5 Isometric drawing. In nearly all practical use of the isometric system this foreshortening of the lines is disregarded, and their full lengths

[1] In paragraph 8·12 the statement is made that the only difference between revolution and auxiliary projection is that in the former the object is moved and in the latter the plane is moved. Thus an auxiliary view on a plane perpendicular to a body diagonal of the cube in position II would be an isometric projection, as illustrated by the dotted view.

are laid off on the axes. This gives a figure of exactly the same shape but larger in the proportion of 1.23 to 1, linear, or, in optical effect 1.23^3 to 1.00^3, Fig. 21·3. Except when drawn beside the same piece in orthographic projection, the effect of increased size is usually of no consequence, and as the advantage of measuring the lines directly is of such great convenience, isometric drawing is used almost exclusively instead of isometric projection.

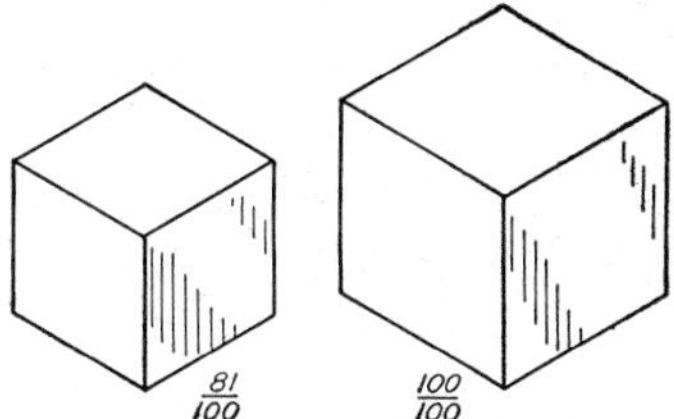

FIG. 21·3—Isometric projection and isometric drawing.

21·6 To make an isometric drawing. If the object is rectangular, start with a point representing a front corner and draw from it the three isometric axes 120° apart, one vertical, the other two with the 30° triangle, Fig. 21·4. On these three lines measure the height, width, and depth of the object, as indicated; through the points so determined draw lines parallel to the axes, completing the figure. To draw intelligently in isometric it is only necessary to remember the direction of the three principal isometric planes. Hidden lines are always omitted except when needed for the description of the piece.

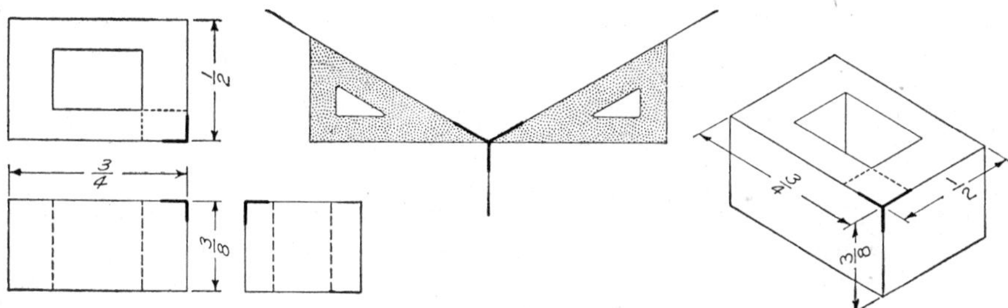

FIG. 21·4—Isometric axes, first position.

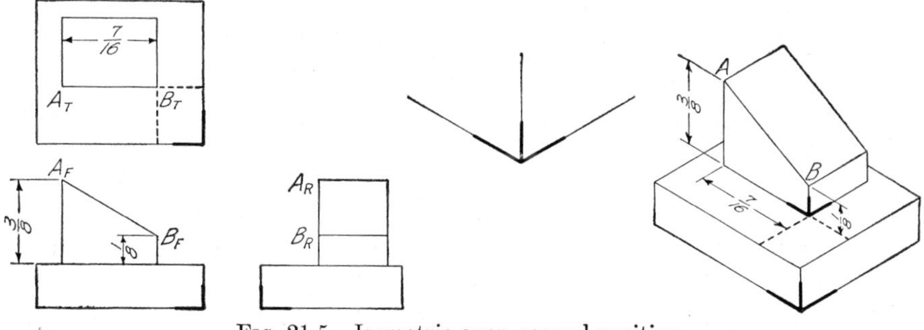

FIG. 21·5—Isometric axes, second position.

It is often more convenient to build up an isometric drawing from the lower front corner, as illustrated in Fig. 21·5, starting from axes in what may be called the "second position."

Edges whose projections or drawings are not parallel to one of the isometric axes are called "nonisometric lines." The one important rule is, *measurements can be made only on the drawings of isometric lines;* and, conversely, measurements cannot be made on the drawings of nonisometric lines. For example, the diagonals of the face of a cube are nonisometric lines and, although equal in length, their isometric drawings will not be at all of equal length on the isometric drawing of the cube.

21·7 Objects containing nonisometric lines. Since a nonisometric line does not appear in the isometric drawing in its true length, the isometric view of each end of the line must be located and the isometric view of the

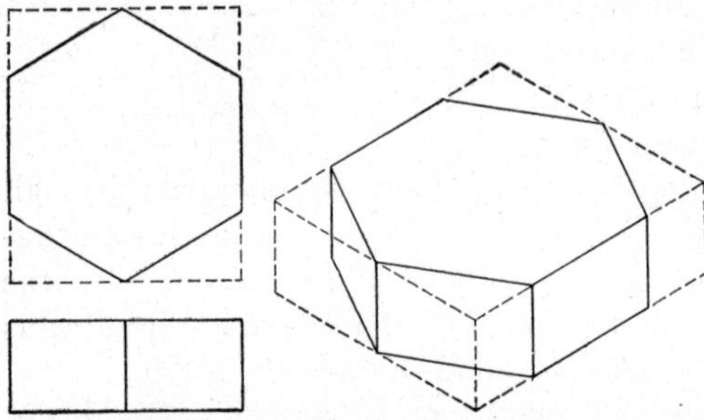

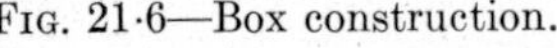

FIG. 21·6—Box construction.

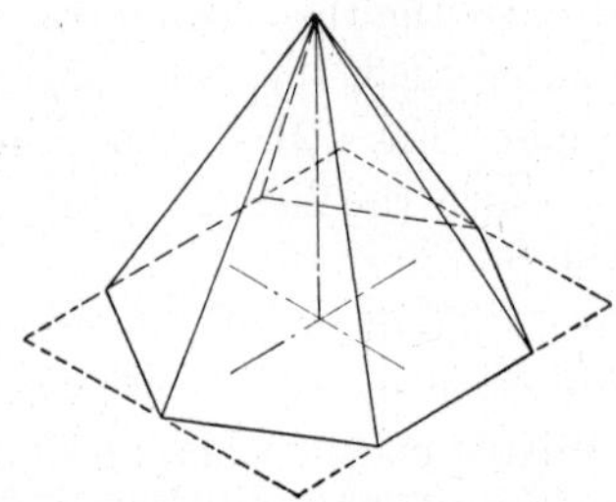

FIG. 21·7—Semibox construction

line found by joining these two points. In Fig. 21·5, AB is a nonisometric line whose true length could not be measured on the isometric drawing.

When the object contains many nonisometric lines, it is drawn either by the "boxing method" or the "offset method." In the first method the object is enclosed in a rectangular box, which is drawn around it in orthographic projection. The box is then drawn in isometric and the object located in it by its points of contact, as in Figs. 21·6 and 21·8. It should be

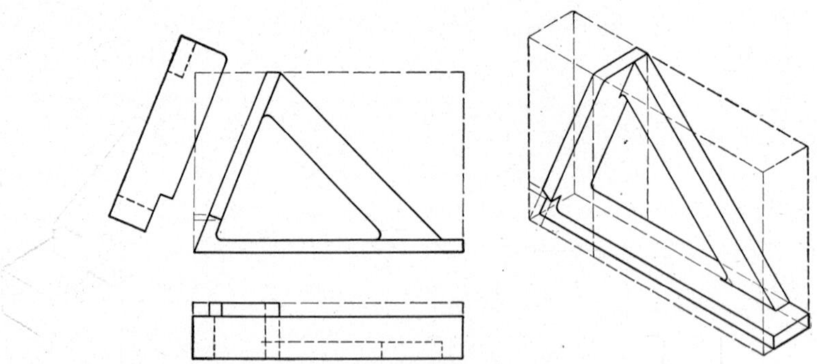

FIG. 21·8—Box construction.

noted that the isometric views of lines which are parallel on the object are parallel. Knowledge of this may often be used to save a large amount of construction, as well as to test for accuracy. Figure 21·6 might be drawn by putting the top face into isometric and drawing vertical lines equal in length to the edges downward from each corner. It is not always necessary actually to enclose the whole object in a rectangular "crate." The pyramid, Fig. 21·7, would have its base enclosed in a rectangle and the apex located by erecting a vertical axis from the center.

The object shown in Fig. 21·8 is composed almost entirely of nonisometric lines. In such cases the isometric cannot be drawn without first making the orthographic views necessary for boxing. In general the boxing

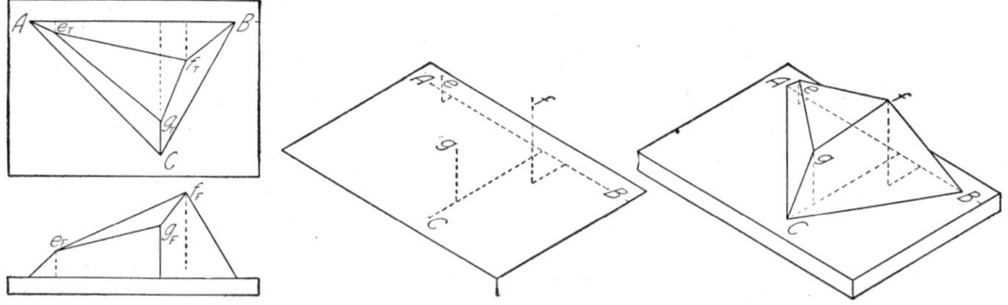

FIG. 21·9—Offset construction.

method is adapted to objects which have the nonisometric lines in isometric planes.

21·8 Offset method. When the object is made up of planes at a number of different angles, it is better to locate the ends of the edges by the offset

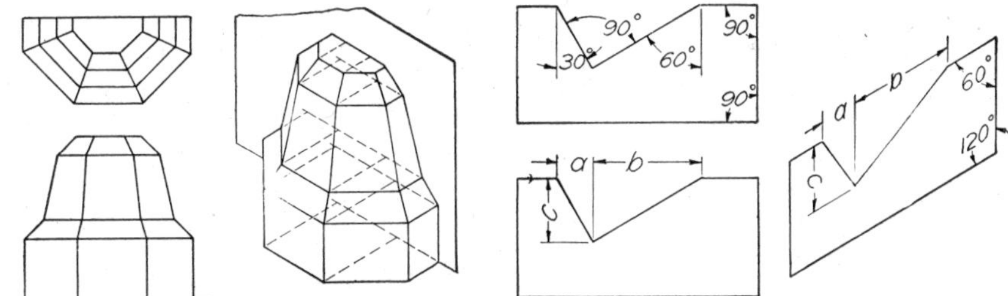

FIG. 21·10—Offset construction.

FIG. 21·11—Angles in isometric.

method. In this method, perpendiculars are dropped from each point to an isometric reference plane. These perpendiculars, which are isometric lines, are located on the drawing by isometric coordinates, the dimensions being taken from the orthographic views. In Fig. 21·9, line AB is used as a base line and measurements made from it as shown. Figure 21·10 is another example of offset construction, using a vertical plane as a reference plane.

Of course, angles in isometric drawing do not appear in their true sizes, thus it is necessary to locate the direction of the including sides by coordinates, as in Fig. 21·11. This is well illustrated also in Fig. 21·8.

21·9 Objects containing curved lines. It is obvious that a circle or any other curve on the face of a cube will not show in its true shape when the cube is drawn in isometric. A circle on any isometric plane will be projected as an ellipse.

Any curve may be drawn by plotting points on it from isometric reference lines, as in Fig. 21·12. A circle plotted in this way is shown in Fig. 21·13.

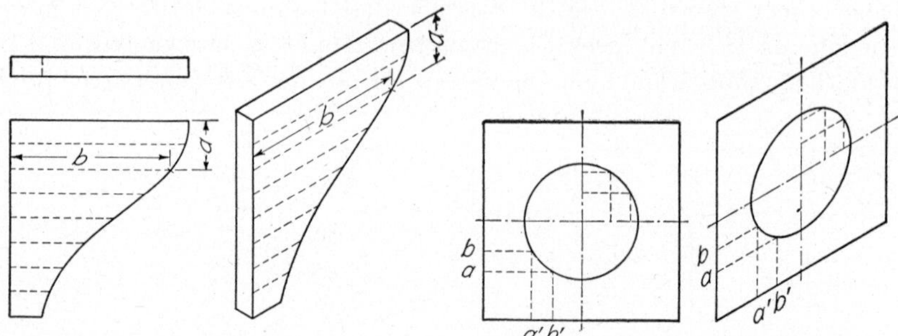

FIG. 21·12—Curves in isometric. FIG. 21·13—Circle, points plotted.

21·10 Isometric circles and circle arcs occur so frequently that they are usually drawn by a four-centered approximation, which is sufficiently accurate for all ordinary work. The center for any arc tangent to a straight line lies on a perpendicular from the point of tangency. If perpendiculars

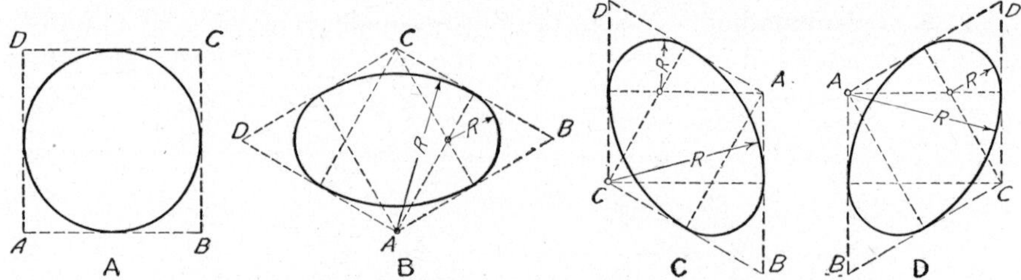

FIG. 21·14—Isometric circles, four-center approximation.

are drawn from the middle point of each side of the circumscribing square, the intersections of these perpendiculars will be centers for arcs tangent to two sides, Fig. 21·14*B*. Two of these intersections will evidently fall at the corners *A* and *C* of the square, as the perpendiculars are altitudes of equilateral triangles. The construction of Fig. 21·14*C* may thus be made by simply drawing 60° lines from the corners *A* and *C*.

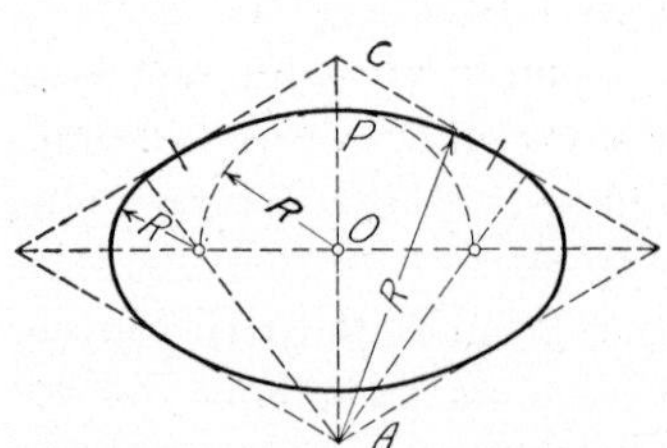

FIG. 21·15—The Stevens method.

If a true ellipse is plotted in the same square as this four-centered approximation, it will be a little longer and narrower and of much more pleasing shape but, in the great majority of drawings, the difference is not sufficient to warrant the extra expenditure of time required in execution. A little closer approximation may be made by the "Stevens method," a very simple four-centered method shown in Fig. 21·15. Draw the arcs from A and C as before, extending them a little past the tangent point. With O as center and radius OP, draw a semicircle intersecting the long diagonal in points which are to be used as centers for the end arcs.

21·11 Isometric arcs. To draw any circle arc, the isometric square of its diameter should be drawn in the plane of its face, with as much of the four-centered construction as is necessary to find centers for the part of the circle needed. The arc occurring most frequently is the quarter circle.

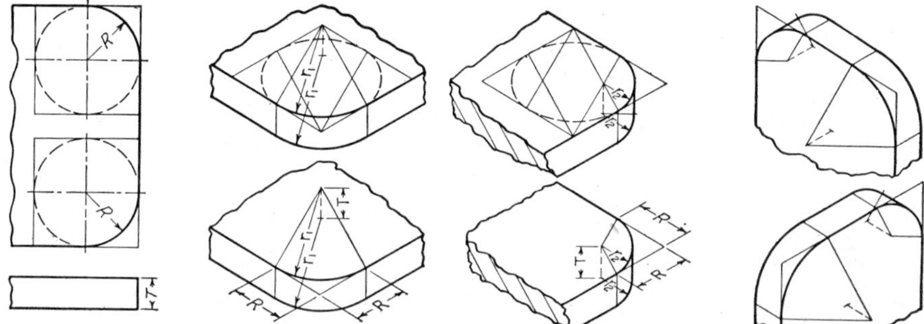

FIG. 21·16—Isometric quarter circles (approximate method).

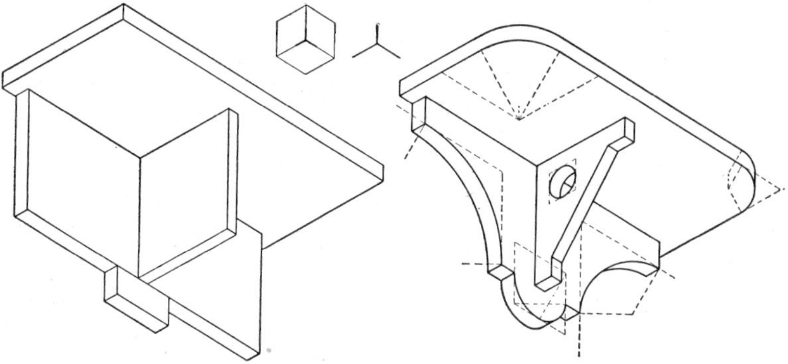

FIG. 21·17—Construction with reversed axes.

Note that only two construction lines are needed to find the center of a quarter circle in an isometric plane. Figure 21·16 illustrates this method. Measure the true radius of the circle from the corner on the two isometric lines and draw actual perpendiculars from these points. Their intersection will be the required center for the isometric quadrant.

The isometric drawing of a *sphere* is a circle with its diameter equal to the long axis of the ellipse inscribed in the isometric square of a great circle of the sphere. It would thus be 1.22/1.00 of the actual diameter (the isometric *projection* of a sphere would be a circle of the actual diameter of the sphere).

21·12 Reversed isometric. It is often desirable to show the lower face of an object by tilting it *back* instead of *forward,* thus reversing the usual position so as to show the underside. The construction is just the same but the directions of the principal isometric planes must be kept clearly in mind. Figure 21·17 shows the reference cube and the position of the axes as well as the application of reversed-isometric construction to circle arcs. A practical use of this construction is in the representation of such architectural features as are naturally viewed from below. Figure 21·18 is an example.

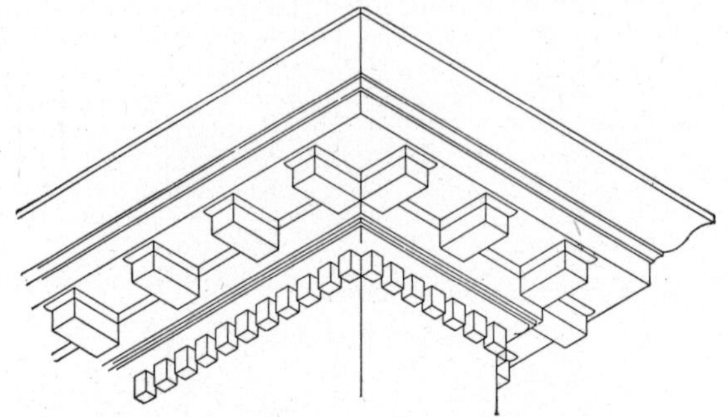

FIG. 21·18—An architectural detail on reversed axes.

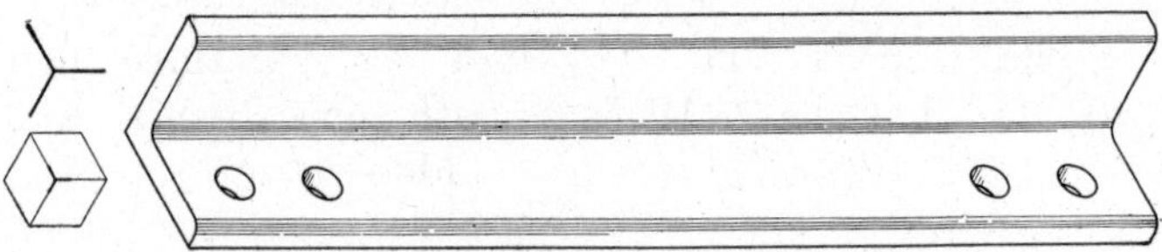

FIG. 21·19—Isometric with main axis horizontal.

Sometimes a piece may be shown to better advantage with the main axis horizontal, as in Fig. 21·19.

21·13 Isometric sections. Isometric drawings are, from their pictorial nature, usually outside views, but sometimes a sectional view may be employed to good advantage to show a detail of shape or interior construction. The cutting planes are taken as isometric planes and the section lining is done in a direction to give the best effect. As a general rule, a half section would be made by outlining the figure in full, then cutting out the front quarter by two isometric planes as in Fig. 21·20, while for a full section the cut face would be drawn first and the part of the object behind it added afterwards, Fig. 21·21.

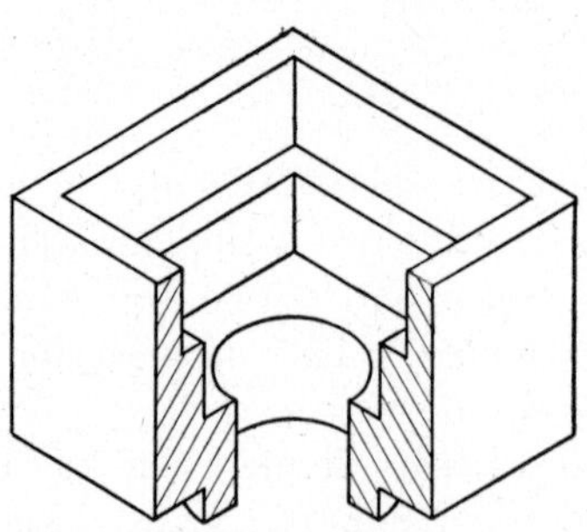

FIG. 21·20—Isometric half section.

21·14 Dimetric projection. The reference cube can be revolved into any number of positions in which two edges will be equally foreshortened, and the direction of axes and ratio of foreshortening for any one of these positions might be taken as a basis for a system of dimetric drawing. A simple dimetric position is one with the ratios 1 to 1 to ½. In this position the tangents of the angles are ⅛ and ⅞, making the angles approximately 7° and 41°. Figure 21·22 shows a drawing in this system.

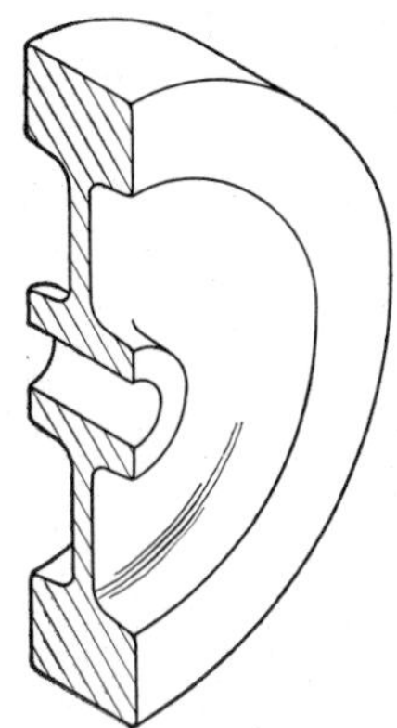

FIG. 21·21—Isometric full section.

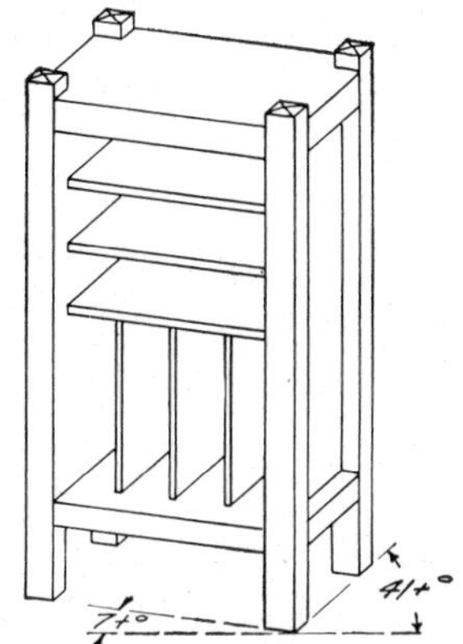

FIG. 21·22—Dimetric drawing.

21·15 Trimetric projection. Any position with three unequal axes would be called "trimetric." Although with some of these positions the effect of distortion might be lessened, the added time required makes trimetric drawing impractical, except when drawn by projection as explained in Chap. 24.

21·16 Oblique projection. When the projectors make an angle other than 90° with the picture plane, the resulting projection is called "oblique projection." Refer to paragraph 6·5 with tabular classification. The name

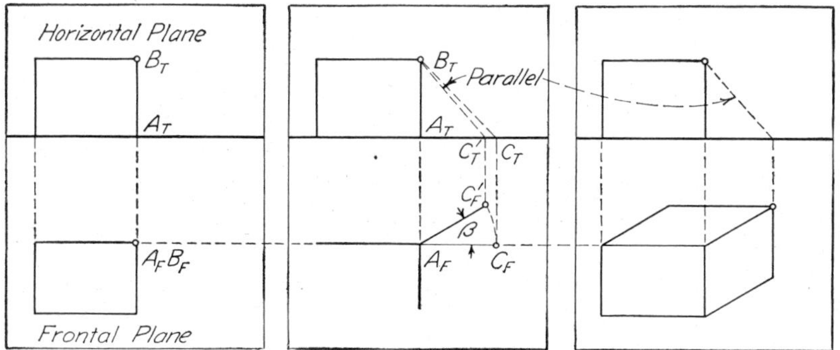

FIG. 21·23—Oblique projection and the picture plane.

cavalier projection is given to that special and most-used case of oblique projection in which the projectors make an angle of 45° with the plane of projection. It is often called by the general name *oblique projection,* or *oblique drawing.* The principle of it is as follows: Imagine a vertical plane with a rectangular block behind it, having its long edges parallel to the plane. Assume a system of parallel projecting lines in any direction making an angle of 45° with the picture plane (they could be parallel to any one of the elements of a 45° cone with its base in the picture plane). Then that face of the block that is parallel to the plane is projected in its true size, and the edges perpendicular to the plane are projected in their true length. Figure 21·23 illustrates this principle. The first panel shows the regular

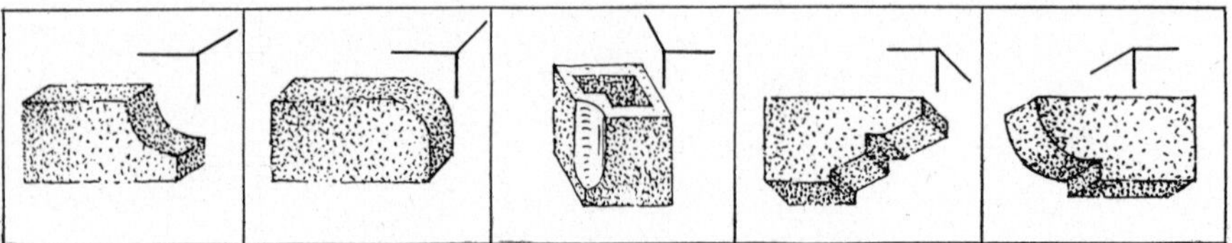

Fig. 21·24—Various positions of oblique axes.

orthographic projection of a rectangular block with its front face in the frontal plane. An oblique projector from the back corner B is the hypotenuse of a 45° right triangle of which AB is one side and the projection of AB on the plane is the other side. When this triangle is horizontal the projection on the plane will be AC. If the triangle is revolved about AB through any angle β, C will revolve to C' and A_FC_F will be the oblique projection of AB, since $A_FC_F = A_TC_T$, and $A_FC_F = AB$.

21·17 To make an oblique drawing. Oblique drawing is similar to isometric drawing in having three axes representing three mutually perpendicular edges, upon which measurements can be made. Two of the axes are always at right angles to each other, being in a plane parallel to the picture plane. The third or cross axis may be at any angle to the horizontal, 30° or 45° being generally used. It is thus more flexible than isometric drawing, Fig. 21·24. For a rectangular object, Fig. 21·25, start with a point representing a front corner and draw from it the three oblique axes, one vertical, one horizontal, and one at an angle. On these three axes measure the height, width, and depth of the object.

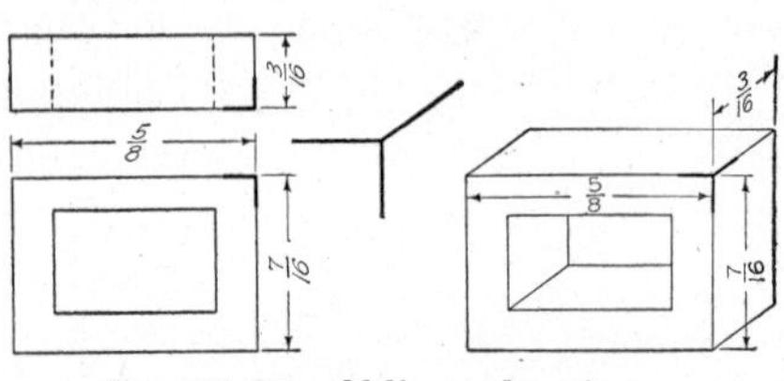

Fig. 21·25—Oblique drawing.

Any face parallel to the picture plane will evidently be projected without distortion, an advantage over isometric of particular value in the representation of objects with circular or irregular outline. The first rule for oblique projection is, *place the object with the irregular outline or contour parallel to the picture plane.* Note in Fig. 21·26 the distortion of B and C over that of A.

One of the greatest disadvantages in the use of either isometric or oblique drawing is the effect of distortion produced by the lack of convergence in the receding lines—the violation of perspective. In some cases, particularly with large objects, this becomes so painful as practically to preclude the use of these methods. It is perhaps even more noticeable in oblique than in isometric and, of course, increases with the length of the cross axis. Hence the **second rule:** *preferably, the longest dimension should be parallel to the picture plane.* In Fig. 21·27, *A* is preferable to *B*.

In case of conflict between these two rules, the first should always have precedence, as the advantage of having the irregular face without distortion

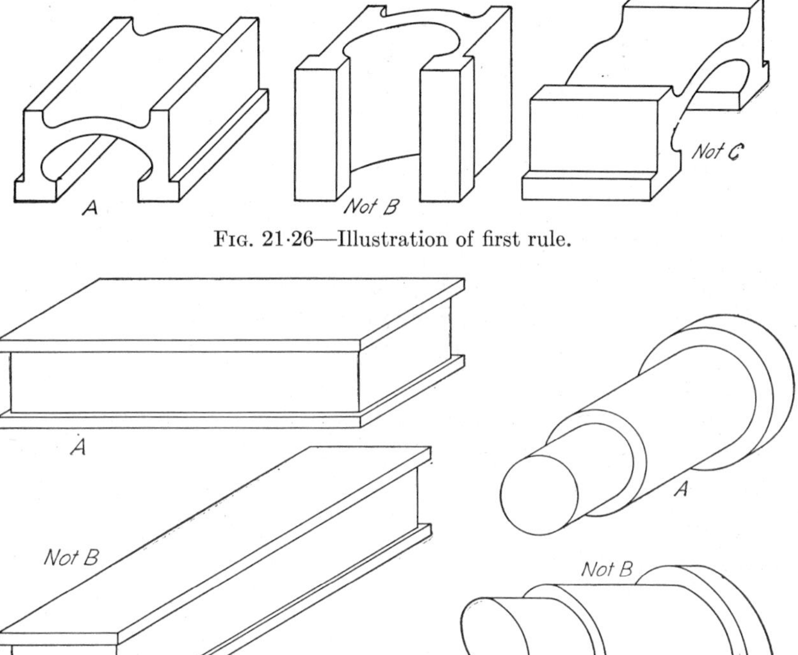

FIG. 21·26—Illustration of first rule.

FIG. 21·27—Illustration of second rule.

FIG. 21·28—Precedence of first rule.

is greater than that gained by the second rule, as illustrated in Fig. 21·28. The first rule should be given precedence even with shapes that are not irregular if, in the draftsman's judgment, the distortion can be lessened, as in the example of Fig. 21·29, where *B* is perhaps preferable to *A*.

21·18 Starting plane. It will be noted that so long as the front of the object is in one plane parallel to the plane of projection, the front face of the oblique projection is exactly the same as the orthographic. When the front is made up of more than one plane, particular care must by exercised in preserving the relationship by selecting one of these planes as the starting plane and working from it. In such a piece as the link, Fig. 21·30, the front bosses may be imagined as cut off on the plane *A*-*A*, and the front view, that is, the section on *A-A*, drawn as the front of the oblique projection. On cross axes through the centers *C* and *D*, the distances *CE* behind and *CF* in front of the plane *A-A* may be laid off. When an object has no face perpendicular to its base, it may be drawn in a similar way by cutting a right section and measuring offsets from it, as in Fig. 21·31. This offset method, previously illustrated in the isometric drawings of Figs. 21·9 and 21·10, will be found to be a most rapid and convenient way for drawing almost any figure, and it should be studied carefully.

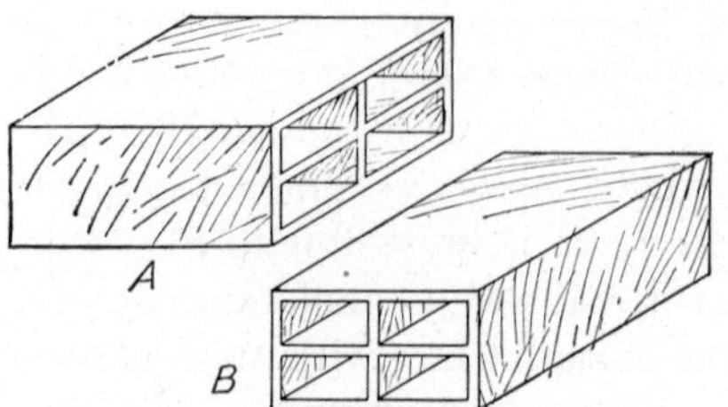

FIG. 21·29—Choice of position.

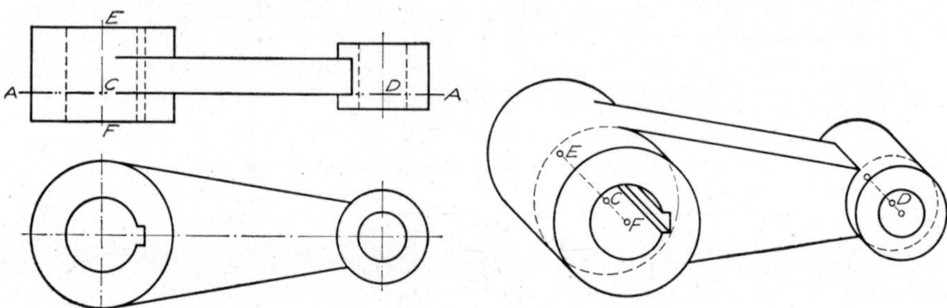

FIG. 21·30—Offsets from reference plane.

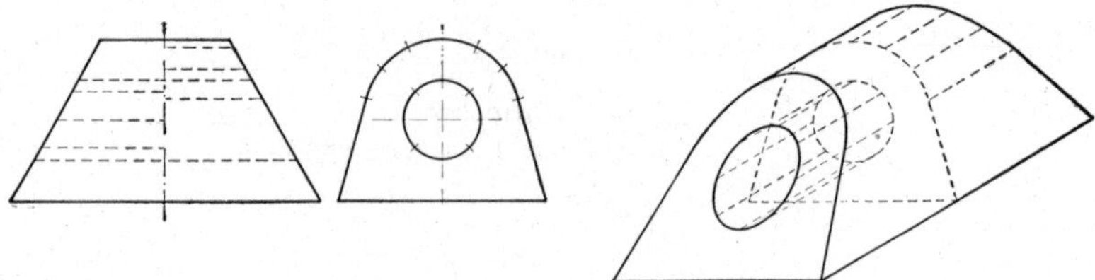

FIG. 21·31—Offsets from right section.

When it is necessary to draw circles that lie on oblique faces, they may be either plotted and drawn with the french curve or approximated, with circle arcs drawn with the compasses on the same principle as the four-centered isometric approximation shown in Fig. 21·14. In isometric it happens that two of the four intersections of the perpendiculars from the middle points of the containing square fall at the corner of the square, and advantage is taken of the fact. In oblique, the position of the corresponding points depends on the angle of the cross axis. Figure 21·32 shows three

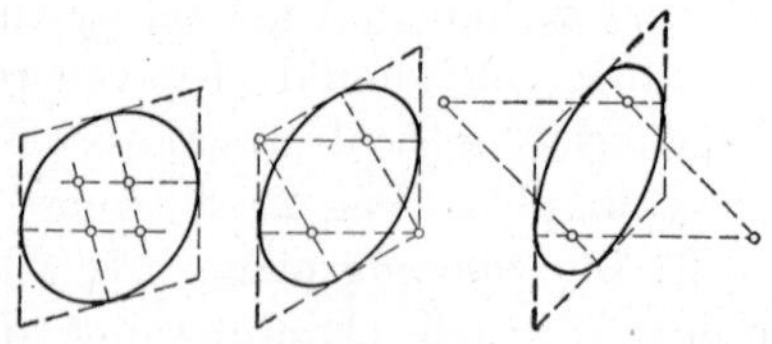

FIG. 21·32—Oblique circle construction.

squares in oblique positions at different angles and the construction of their inscribed circles.

21·19 Cabinet drawing is that case of oblique projection in which the parallel projectors make with the picture plane an angle of such a value that distances measured parallel to the cross axis are reduced one-half that of cavalier projection. The appearance of excessive thickness that is so disagreeable in cavalier projection is entirely overcome in cabinet projection. The cross axis may be at any angle with the horizontal but is usually taken either at 30° or 45°. The comparative appearances of isometric, cavalier, and cabinet drawing are illustrated in Fig. 21·33.

21·20 Other forms. Cabinet drawing, explained above, is popular because of the easy ratio, but the effect is often too thin. Other oblique drawing ratios, such as 2 to 3 or 3 to 4, may be used with pleasing effect.

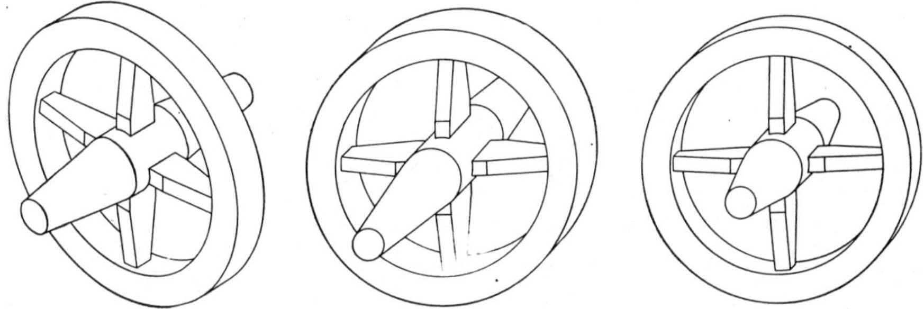

FIG. 21·33—Isometric, oblique, and cabinet drawing compared.

Pictorial drawings are sometimes made without reference to the theory of projection, on axis combinations of 15° and 30°, 15° and 45°, 15° and 15°, 20° and 20°.

21·21 Sketching. One of the valuable uses of pictorial methods is in making freehand sketches, either to illustrate some object or detail of construction or, dimensioned, to form working drawings. Chapter 23 discusses pictorial sketching, emphasizing the importance of such points as flattening the axes (the beginner's usual mistake is in drawing them too steep, thereby spoiling the appearance of his sketch), keeping parallel lines parallel and vertical lines vertical, always blocking in circumscribing squares before sketching circles, not confusing the drawing with dotted lines, etc.

PROBLEMS

21·22 The following problems are intended to serve two purposes: first, furnish practice in the various methods of pictorial representation; and, second, furnish practice in reading and translating orthographic projection.

In reading a drawing remember that a line on any view always means an edge or change in direction of the surface of the object, and that one must always look at another view to interpret the meaning of the line. Do not try or expect to read a whole drawing at a glance.

For convenience in selection and assignment the problems are arranged in groups. Figures from previous chapters may be used to give a further variety of problems.

Do not show hidden lines except where necessary to explain construction.

Group I. Isometric drawings

Problems 1 to 23. Figs. 21·34 to 21·56

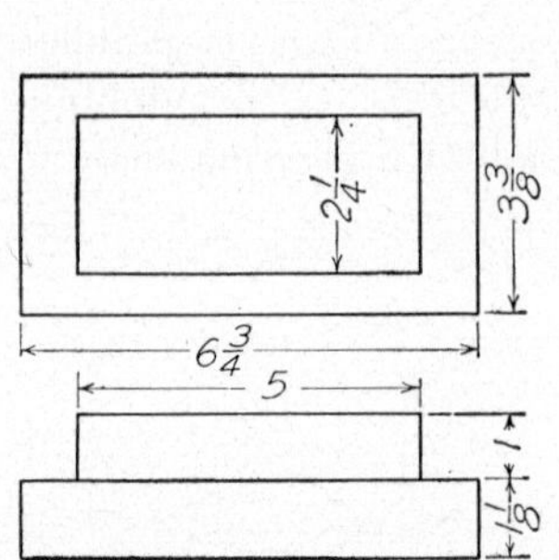

FIG. 21·34—Jig block.

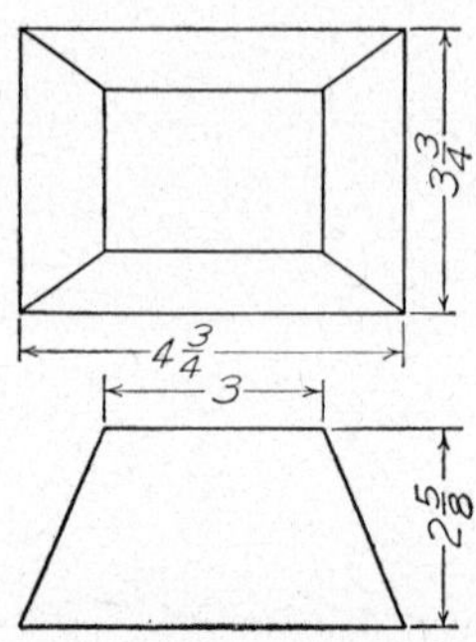

FIG. 21·35—Frustum of pyramid.

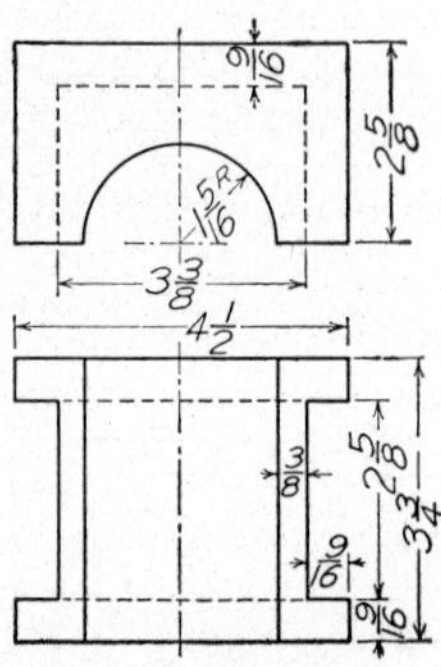

FIG. 21·36—Bearing brass.

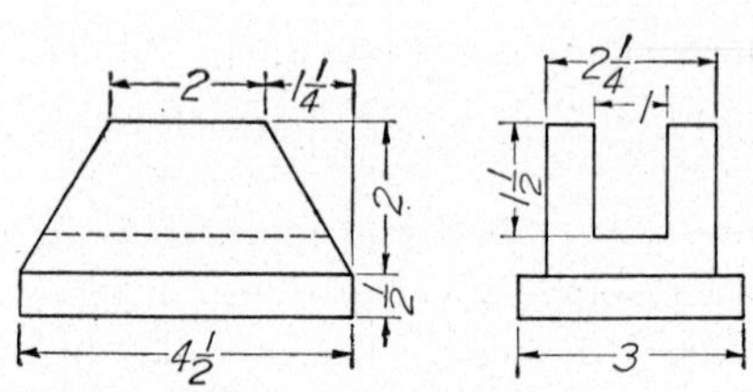

FIG. 21·37—Guide block.

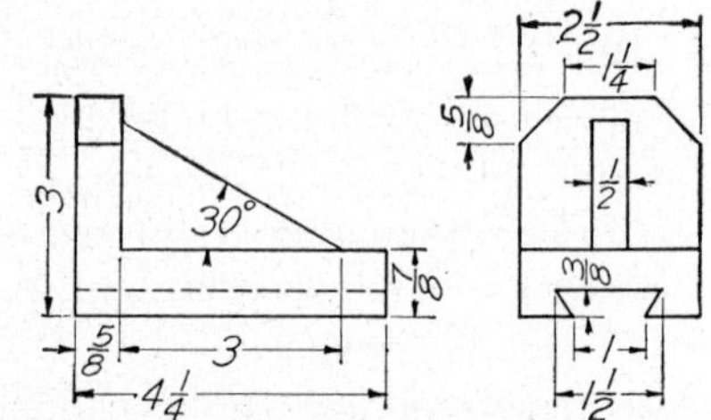

FIG. 21·38—Dovetail stop.

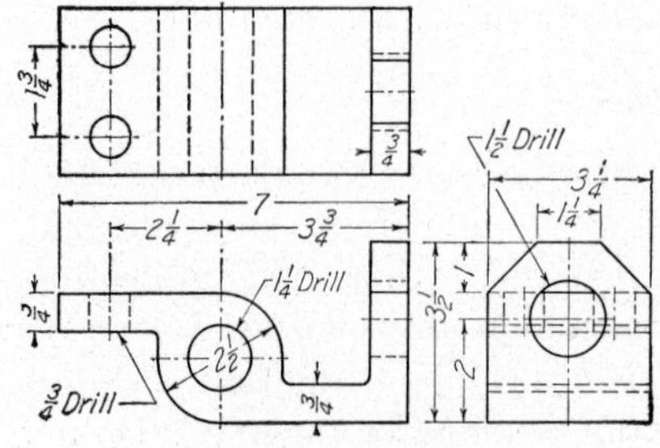

FIG. 21·39—Bracket.

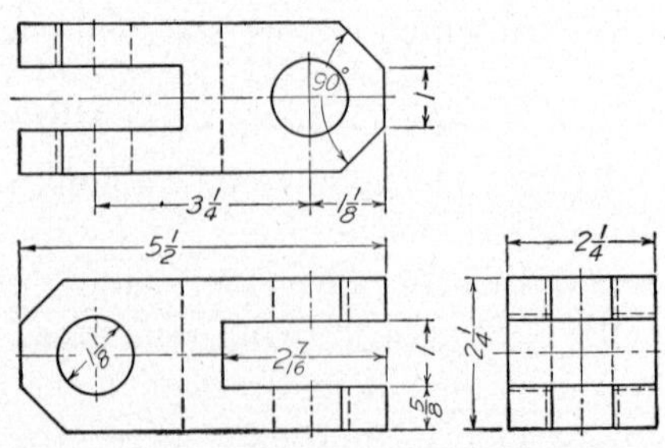

FIG. 21·40—Swivel block.

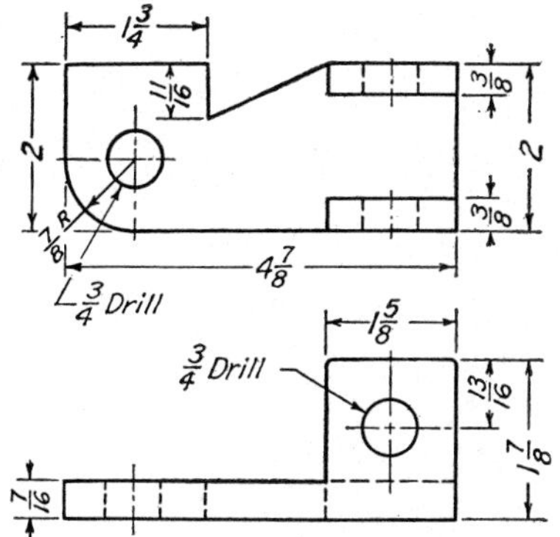

FIG. 21·41—Hinged catch.

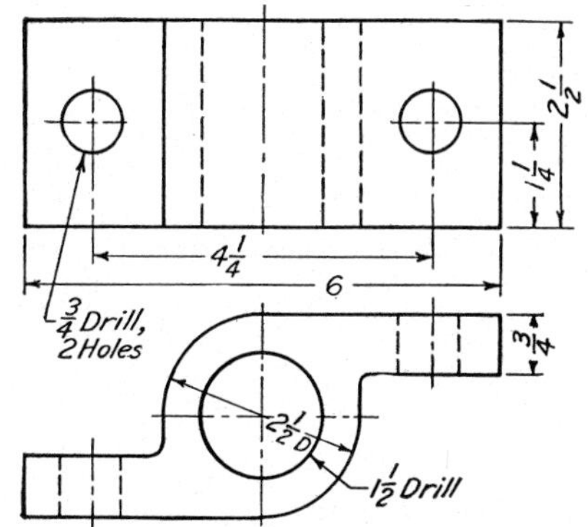

FIG. 21·42—Pivot plate.

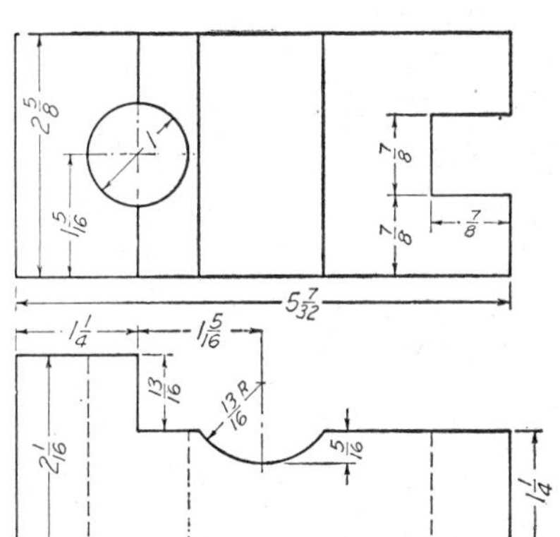

FIG. 21·43—Clip half.

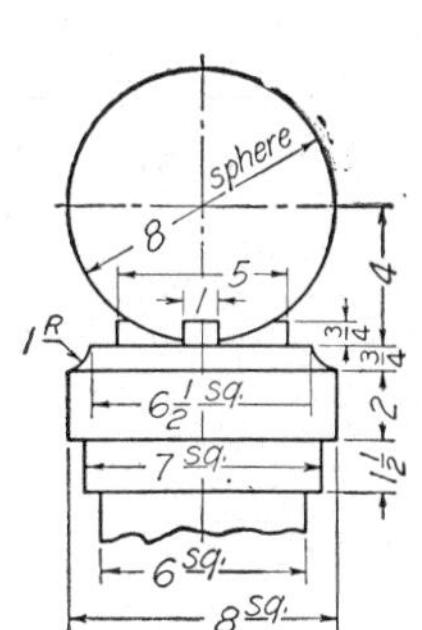

FIG. 21·44—Ball finial.

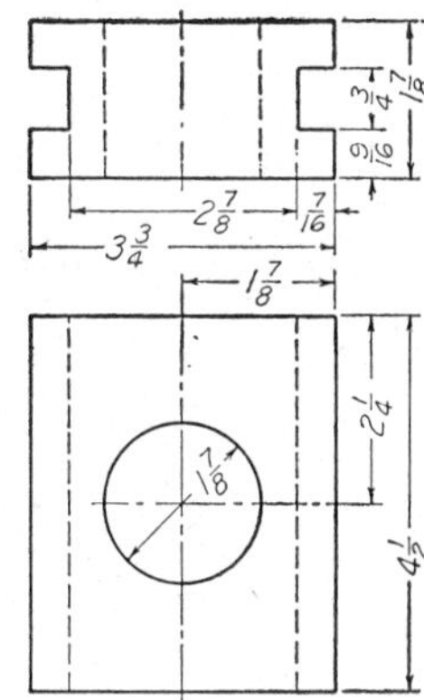

FIG. 21·45—Sliding shoe.

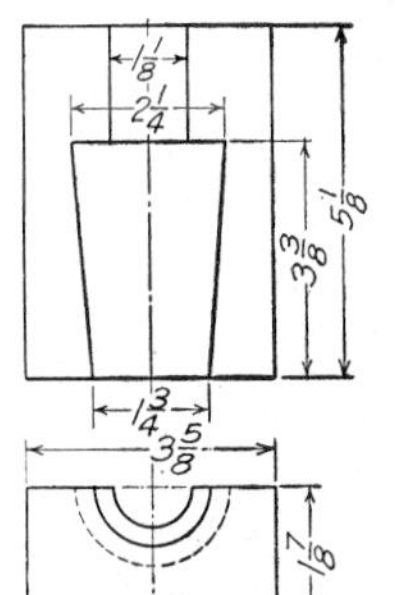

FIG. 21·46—Core box.

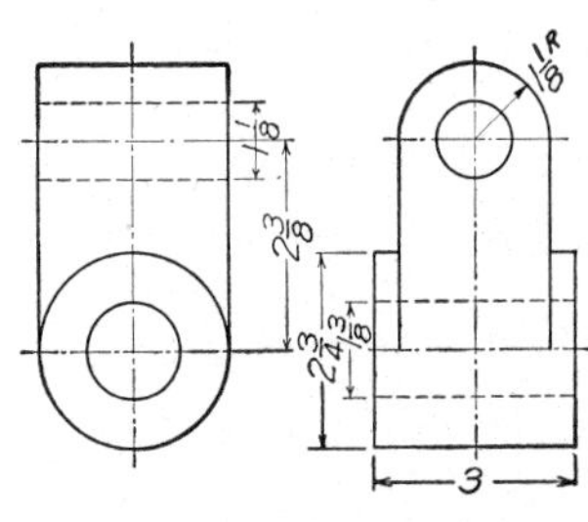

FIG. 21·47—Cross link.

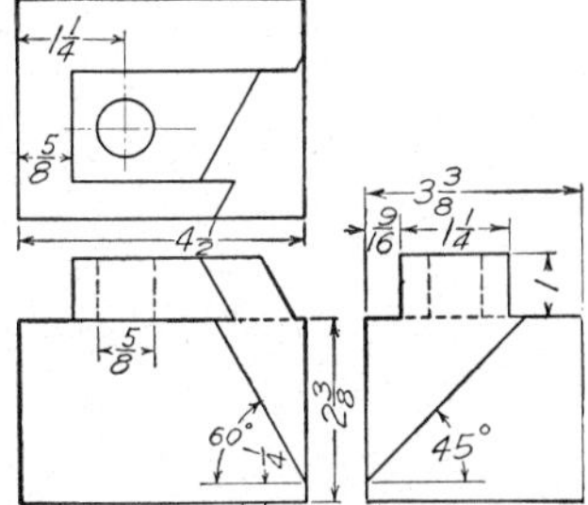

FIG. 21·48—Wedge block.

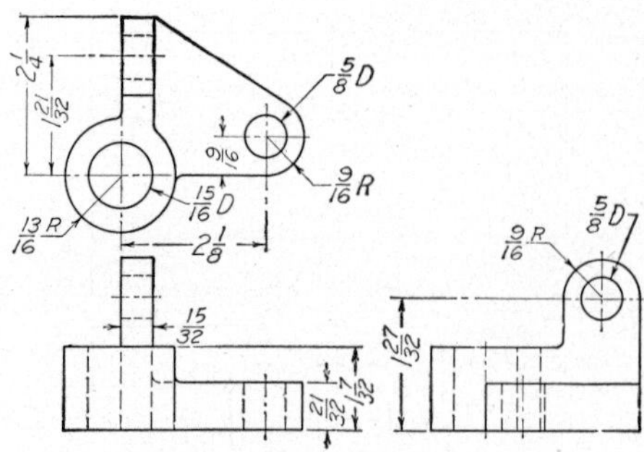

FIG. 21·49—Cable clip.

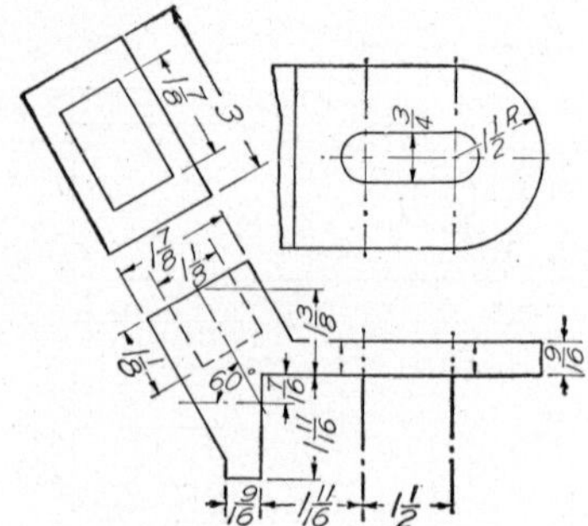

FIG. 21·50—Strut anchor.

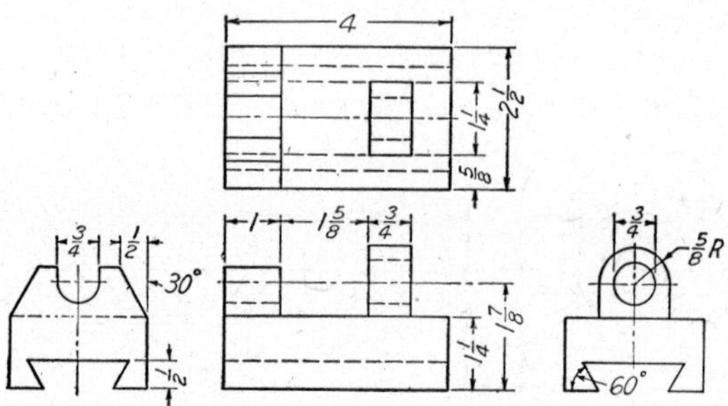

FIG. 21·51—Dovetail stop.

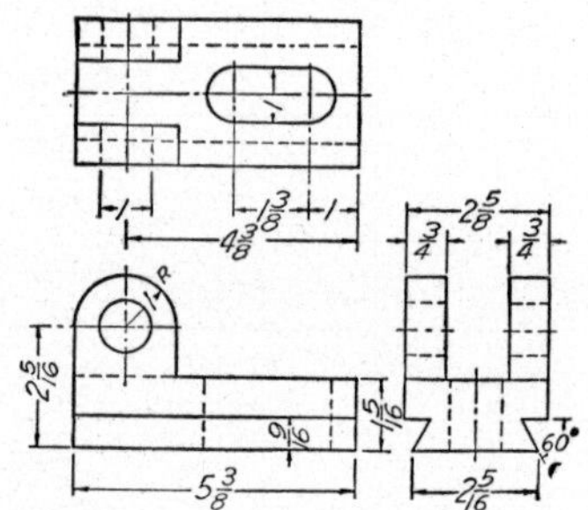

FIG. 21·52—Dovetail bracket.

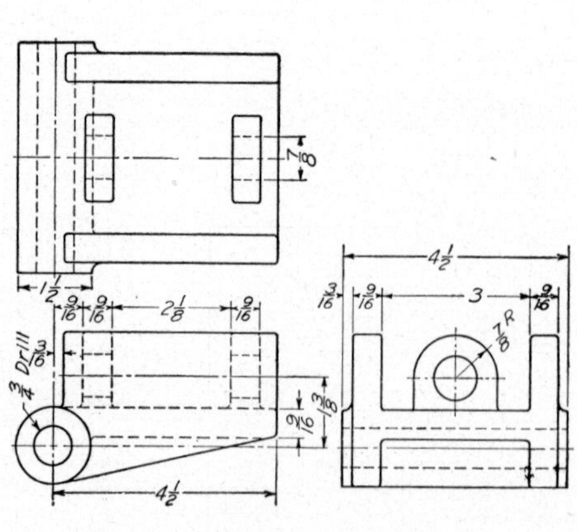

FIG. 21·53—Swing plate.

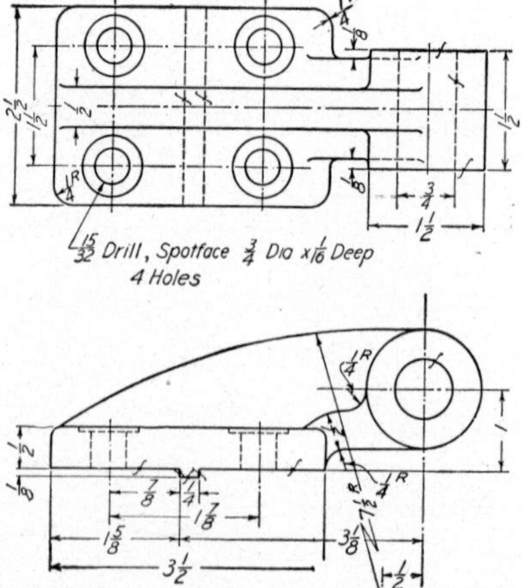

FIG. 21·54—Offset side bracket.

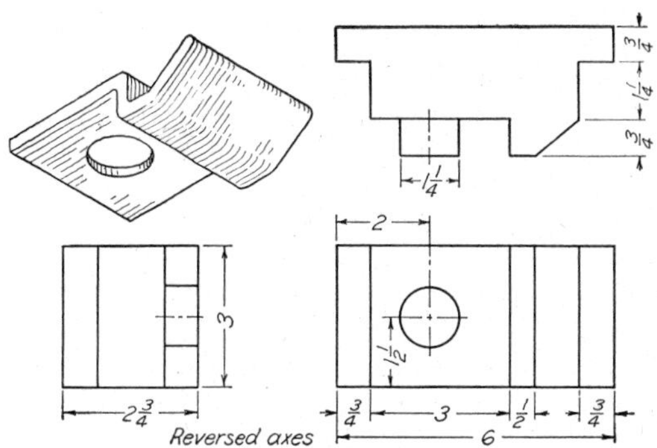

Fig. 21·55—Forming punch.

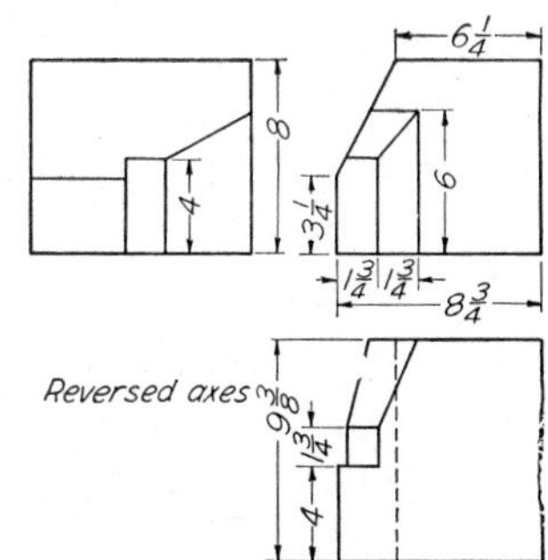

Fig. 21·56—Springing stone.

Group II. Isometric sections

Problems 24 to 33. Figs. 21·57 to 21·66

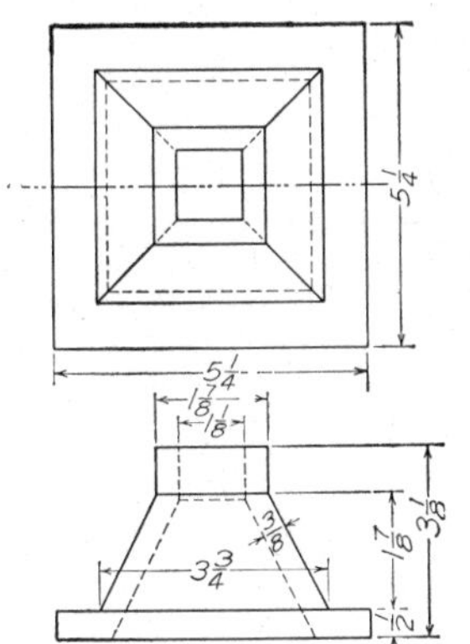

Fig. 21·57—Column base.

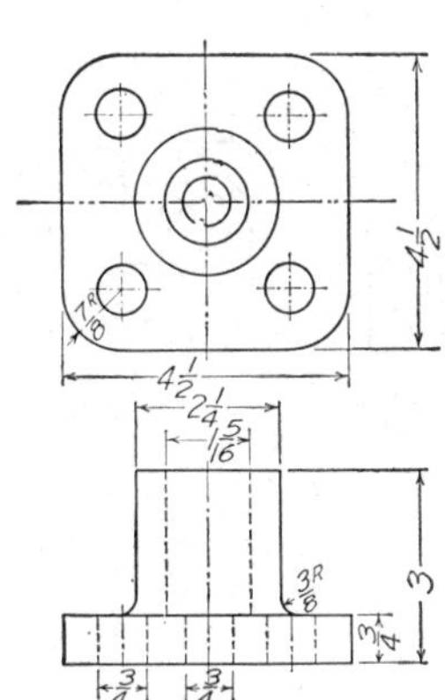

Fig. 21·58—Base plate.

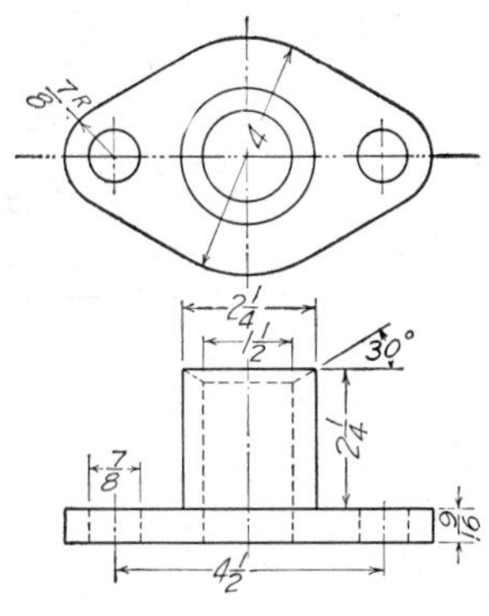

Fig. 21·59—Gland.

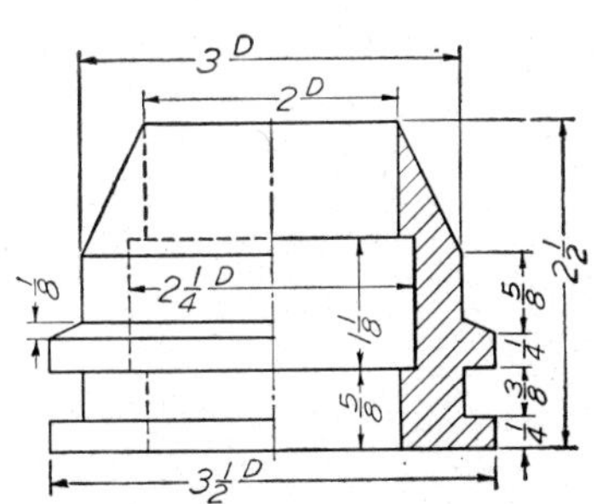

Fig. 21·60—Sliding cone.

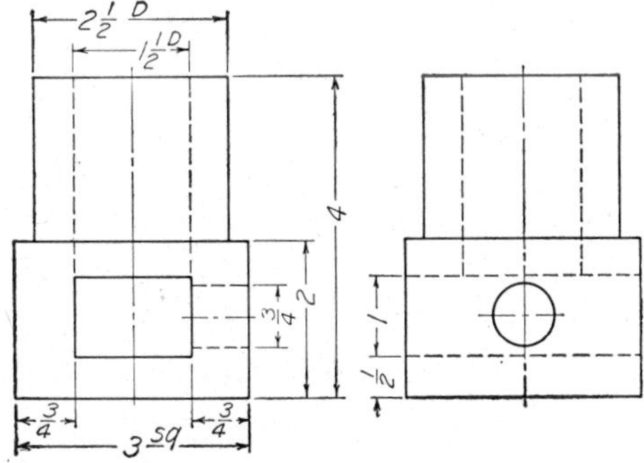

Fig. 21·61—Squared collar.

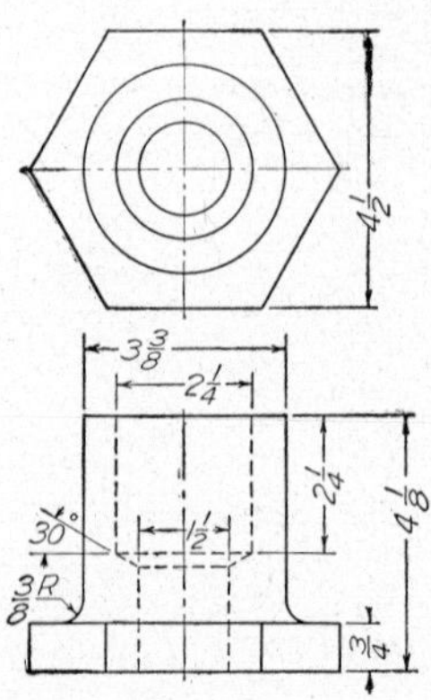

FIG. 21·62—Blank for gland.

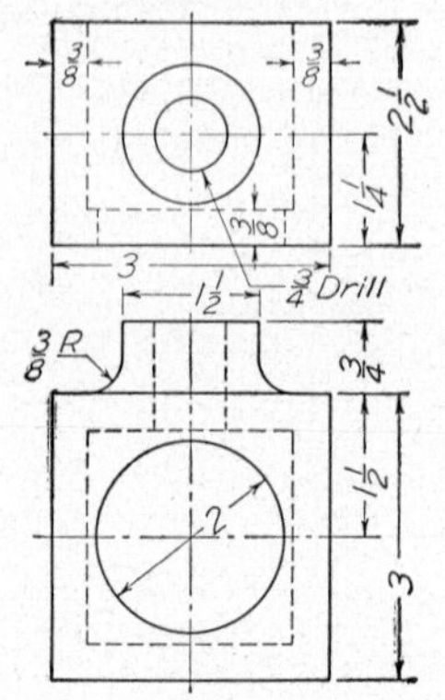

FIG. 21·63.—Sliding cover.

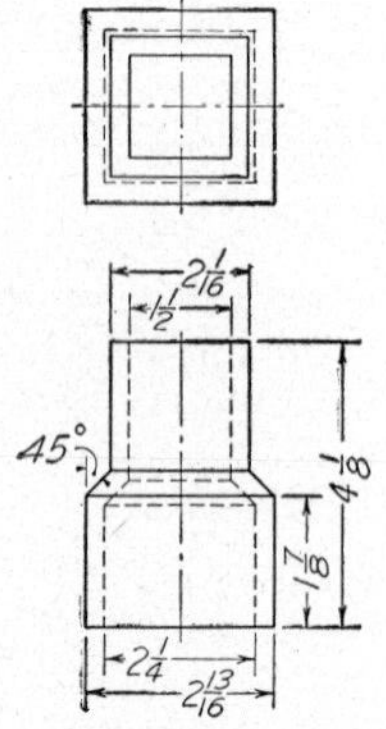

FIG. 21·64—Wrench socket.

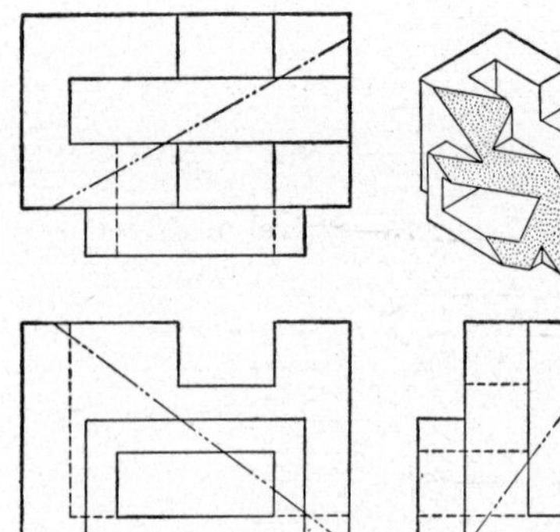

FIG. 21·65—Section study.

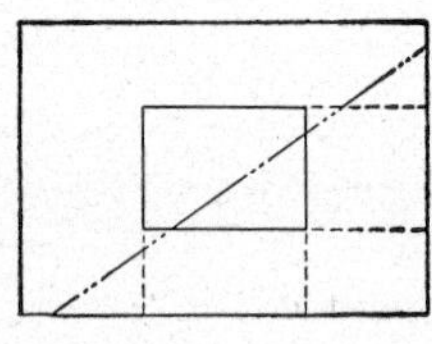

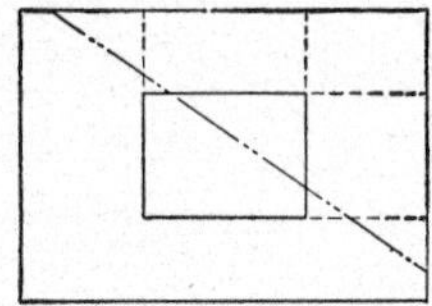

FIG. 21·66—Section study.

Group III. Oblique drawing

Problems 34 to 52. Figs. 21·67 to 21·85

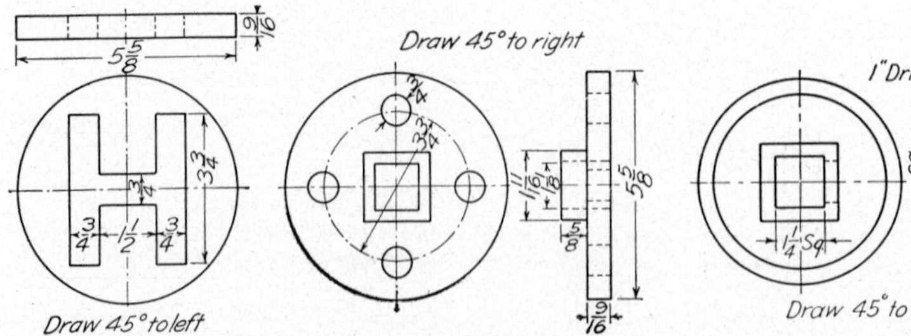

FIG. 21·67—Letter die.

FIG. 21·68—Guide plate.

FIG. 21·69—Brace base.

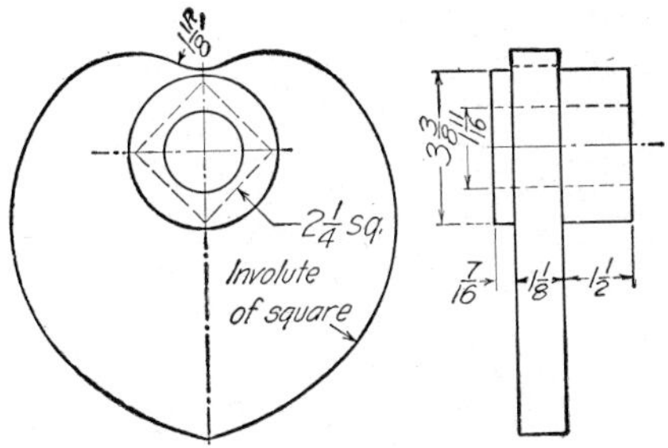

FIG. 21·70—Heart cam.

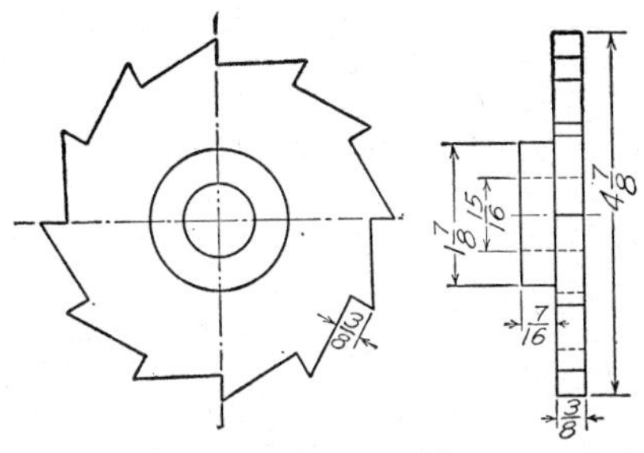

FIG. 21·71—Ratchet wheel.

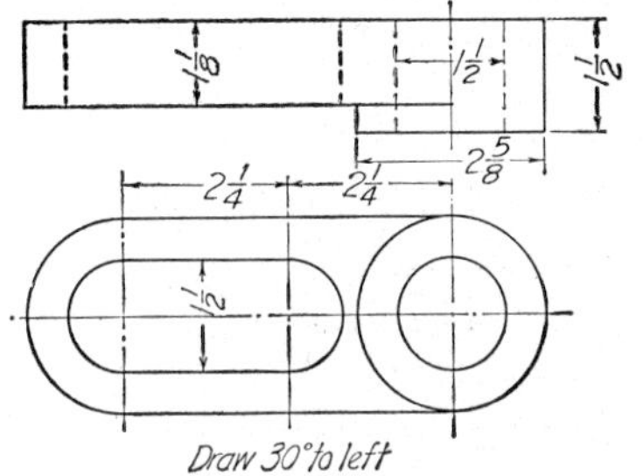

FIG. 21·72—Slotted link.

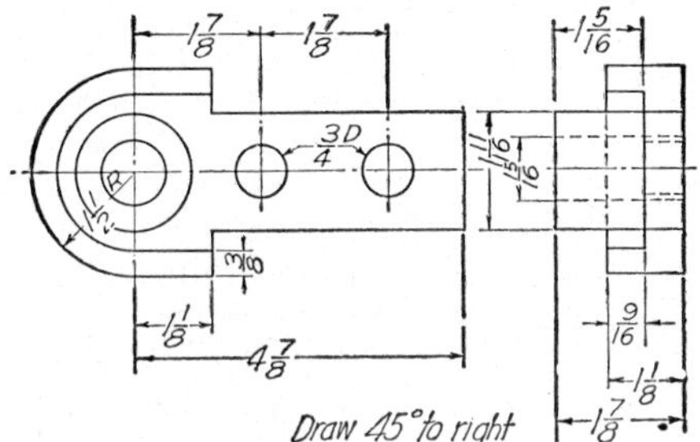

FIG. 21·73—Swivel plate.

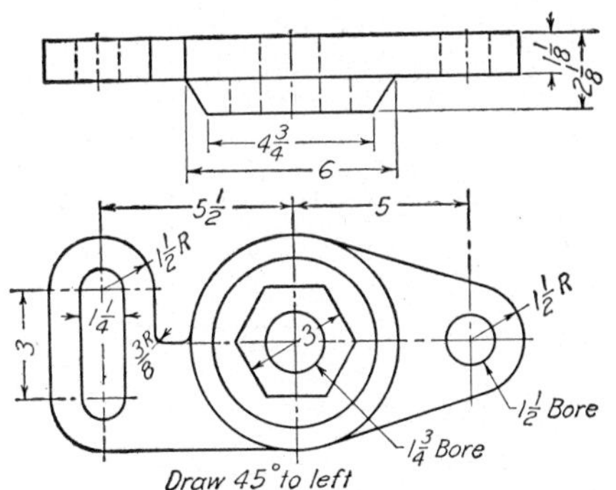

FIG. 21·74—Link.

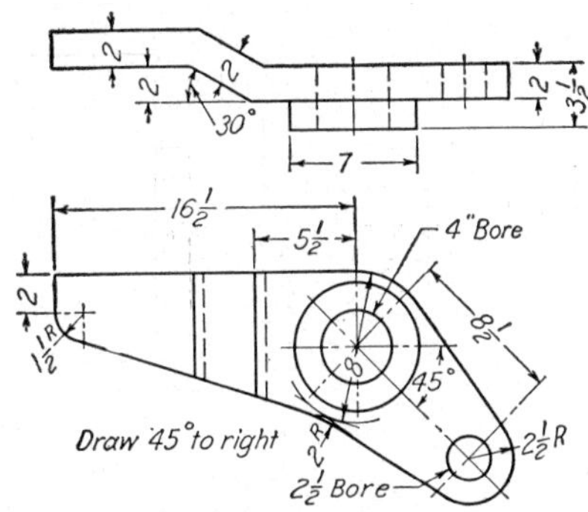

FIG. 21·75—Pawl.

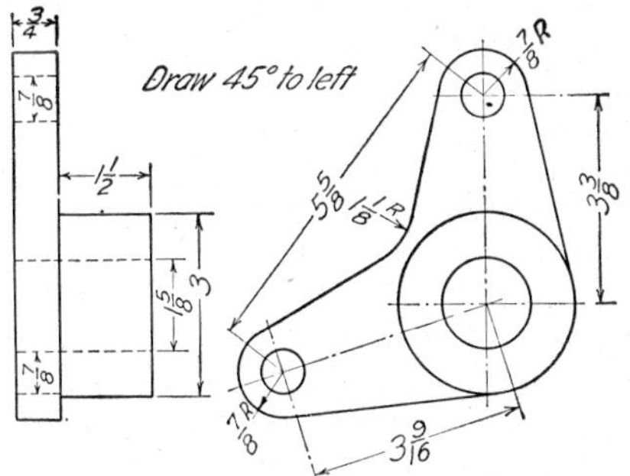

FIG. 21·76—Bell crank.

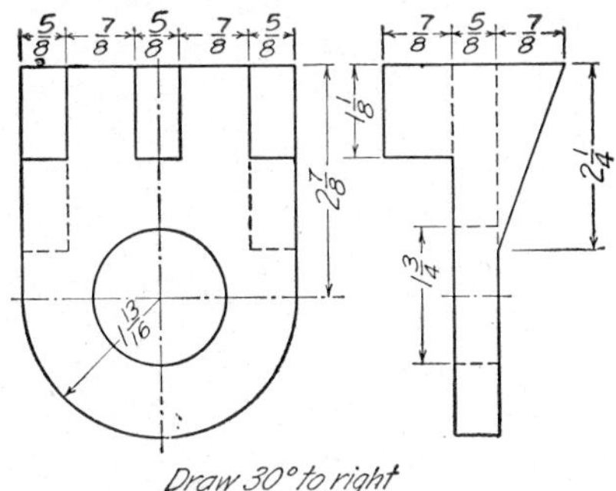

FIG. 21·77—Stop plate.

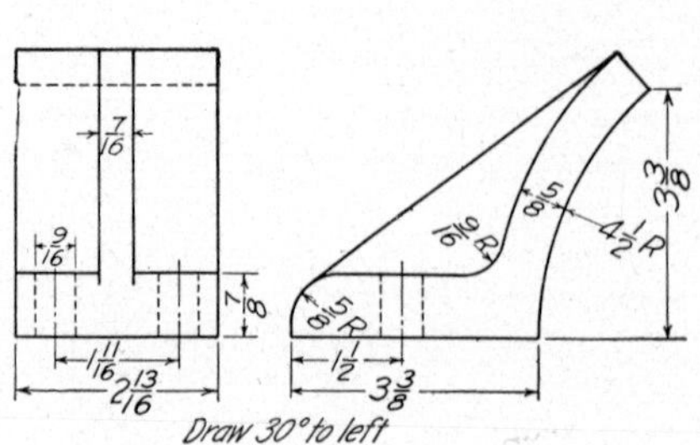

FIG. 21·78—Guard bracket.

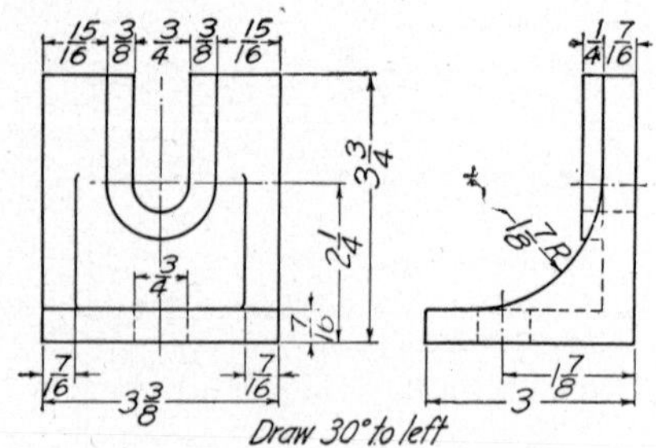

FIG. 21·79—Angle yoke.

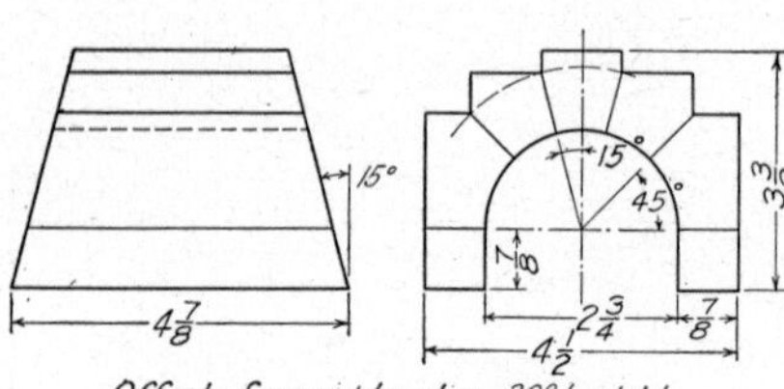

FIG. 21·80—Culvert model.

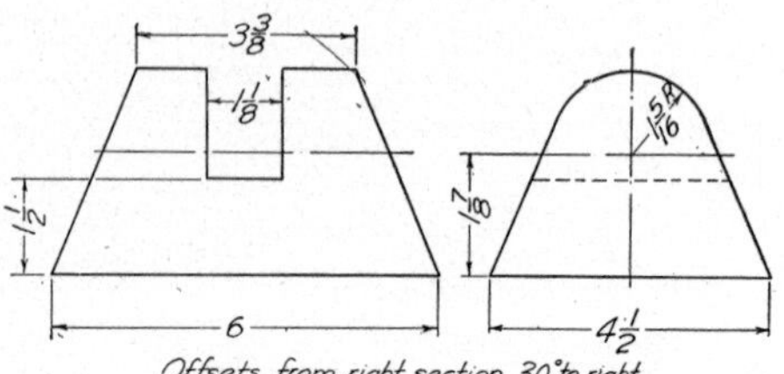

FIG. 21·81—Slotted guide.

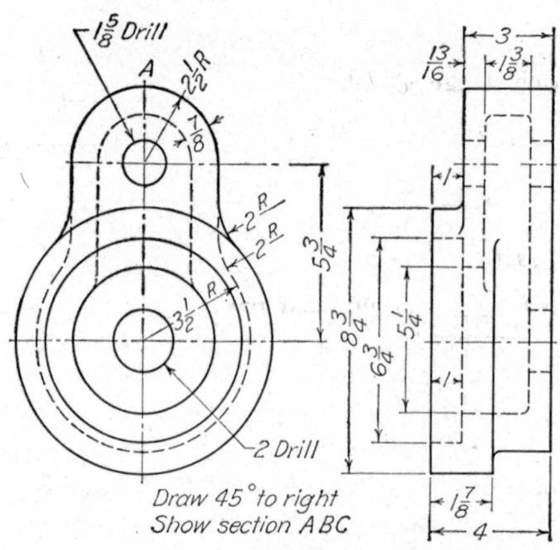

FIG. 21·82—Port cover.

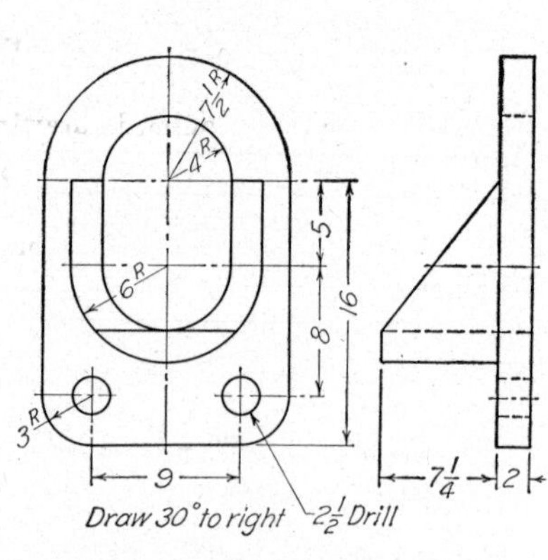

FIG. 21·83—Support bracket.

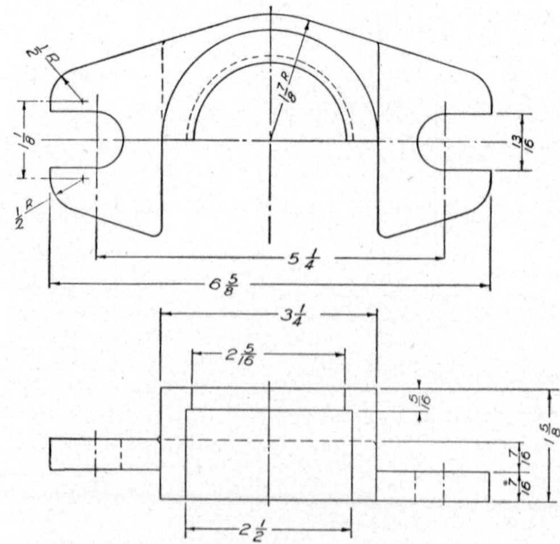

FIG. 21·84—Split gland.

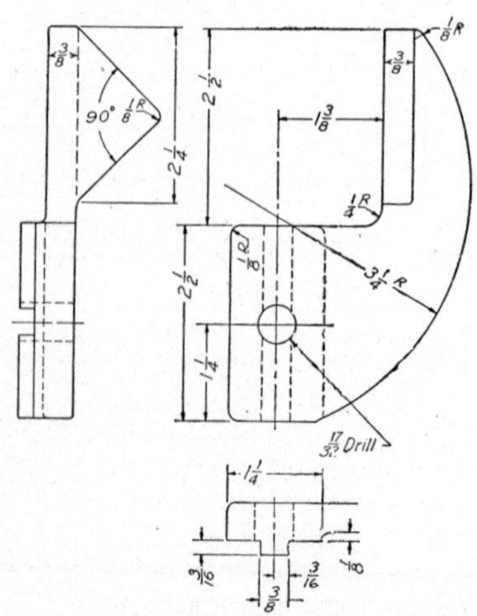

FIG. 21·85—Table dog.

Group IV. Oblique sections and half sections

53. Fig. 9·52. Oblique full section of pulley in pulley-bracket assembly
54. Fig. 9·33. Oblique half section of step pulley.
55. Fig. 9·52. Oblique full section of pulley bracket in pulley-bracket assembly.
56. Fig. 9·32. Oblique full section of flanged wheel.
57. Fig. 9·34. Oblique full section of flanged pulley.
58. Fig. 9·51. Oblique half section of step bearing.
59. Fig. 9·45. Oblique half section of pump flange.
60. Fig. 21·86. Oblique full section of wire-rope wedge socket.

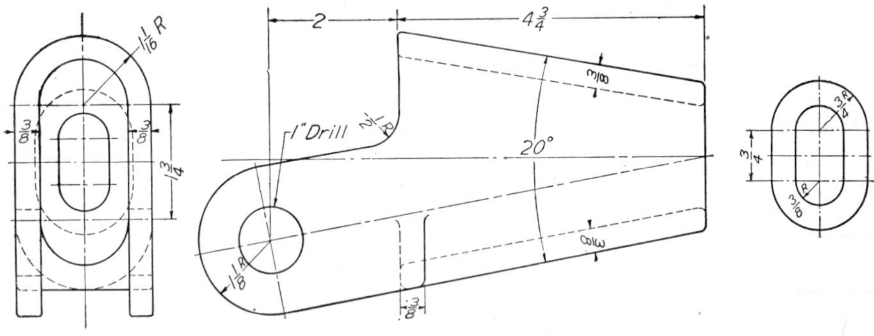

Fig. 21·86—Wire-rope wedge socket.

Group V. Cabinet and dimetric drawing

Problems 61 to 65. Figs. 21·34, 21·35, 21·37, 21·38, 21·57

Group VI. Pictorial drawings from machine parts

Machine parts, either rough castings and forgings or finished parts, offer valuable practice in making pictorial drawings. Choose pieces to give practice in isometric and oblique drawings, sections and half sections.

Group VII. Pictorial working drawings

Any of the problems in this chapter offer practice in making complete pictorial working drawings. Follow the principles of dimensioning given in Chap. 11. The form and placement of the dimension figures are given on page 221.

The following problems are suggested:

66. Fig. 21·37. Pictorial working drawing of guide block.
67. Fig. 21·41. Pictorial working drawing of hinged catch.
68. Fig. 21·43. Pictorial working drawing of clip half.
69. Fig. 21·58. Pictorial working drawing, in half section, of base plate.
70. Fig. 21·76. Pictorial working drawing of bell crank.
71. Fig. 21·86. Pictorial working drawing of wire-rope wedge socket.

Group VIII. Reading exercises. Figs. 21·87, 21·88, 21·89

These figures are to be sketched freehand in one of the pictorial systems, as a test of the ability to read orthographic projections. They may also be used as reading problems by requiring other orthographic views, particularly the figures with two views given. Note that *C*-4 has warped surfaces on the sides.

Find three solutions of figure *Y* and two solutions each for Z-1, Z-2, Z-3, and Z-4.

In the last row of Fig. 21·89, *A-A* to *E-E*, each problem has several solutions.

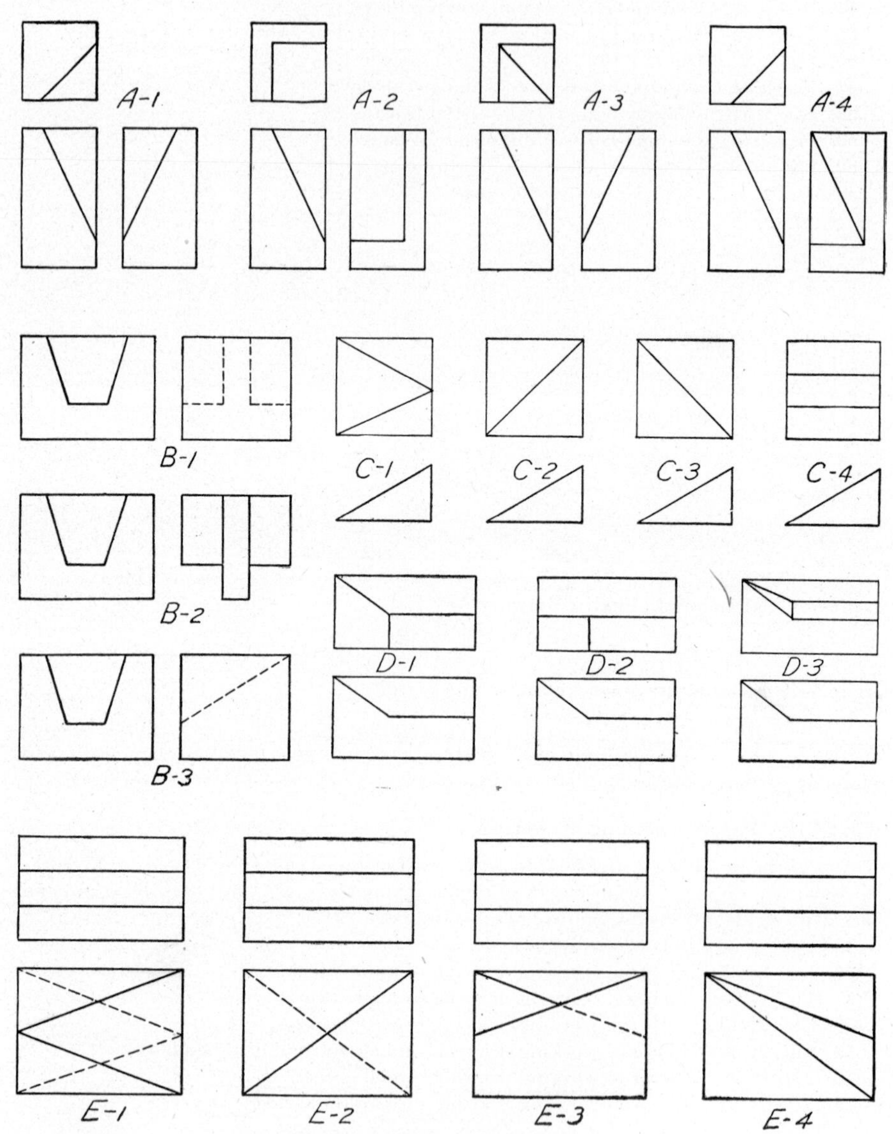

FIG. 21·87—Reading exercises.

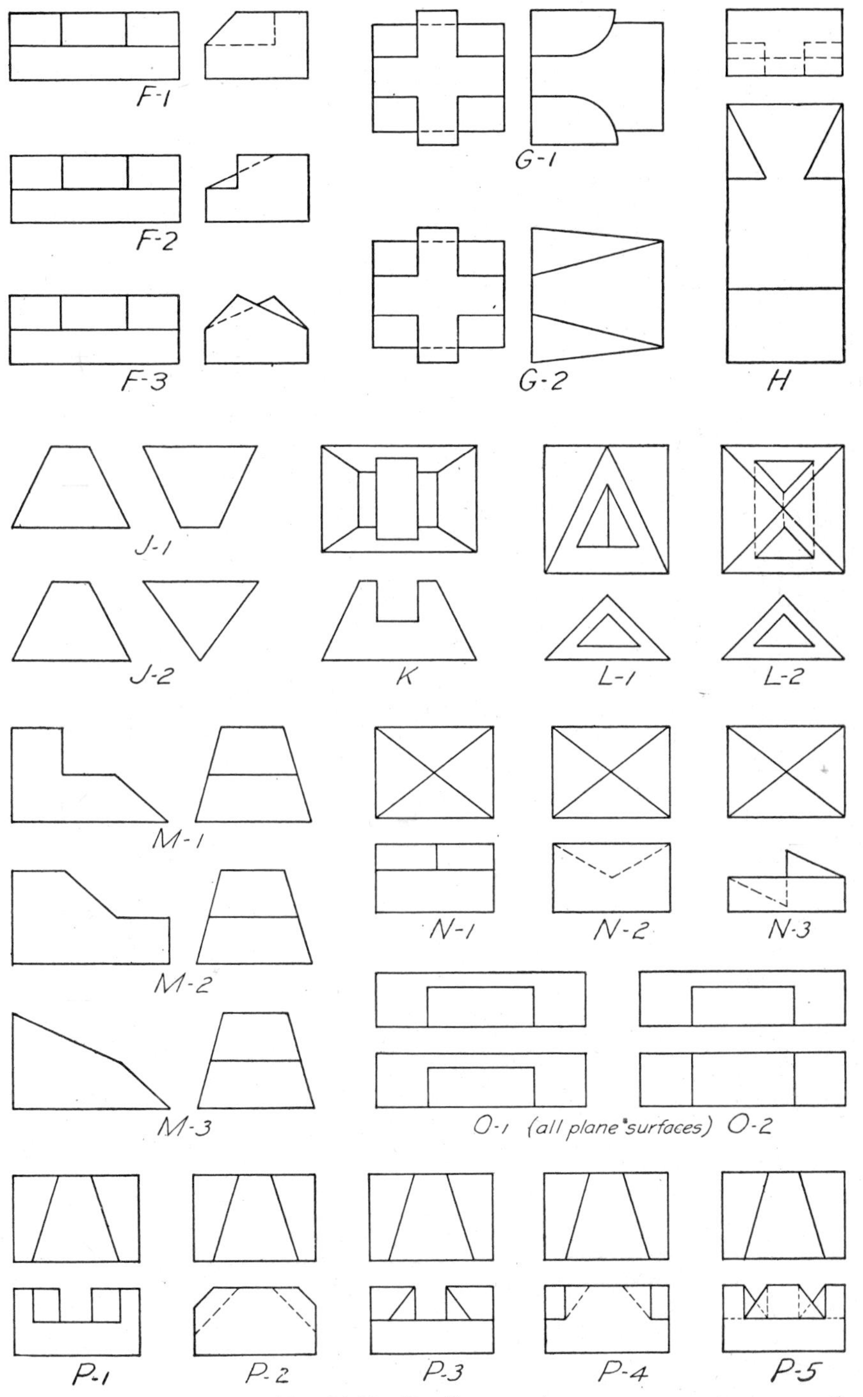

Fig. 21·88—Reading exercises.

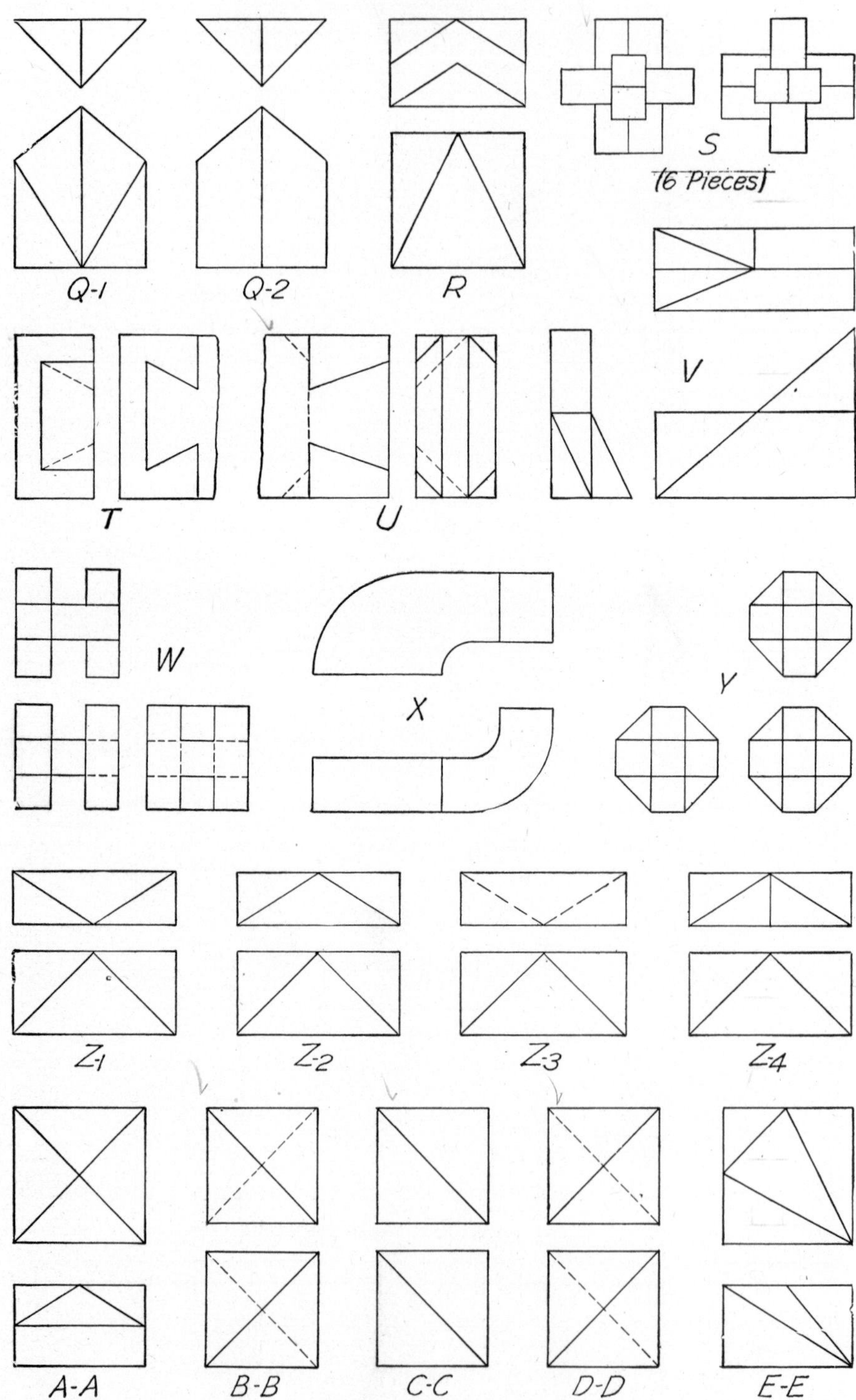

FIG. 21·89—Reading exercises.

Chapter 22

PERSPECTIVE DRAWING

22·1 Perspective drawing is the representation of an object as it appears to an observer stationed at a particular position relative to the object. Geometrically it is the figure resulting when visual rays from the eye to the object are cut by a picture plane. There is a difference between "artists' perspective" and "geometrical perspective" in that the artist draws the object as he sees it before him, or as he visualizes it through his creative imagination, while geometrical perspective is projected mechanically on a plane from views or measurements of the object represented. Projected geometrical perspective is, theoretically, very similar to the optical system in photography.

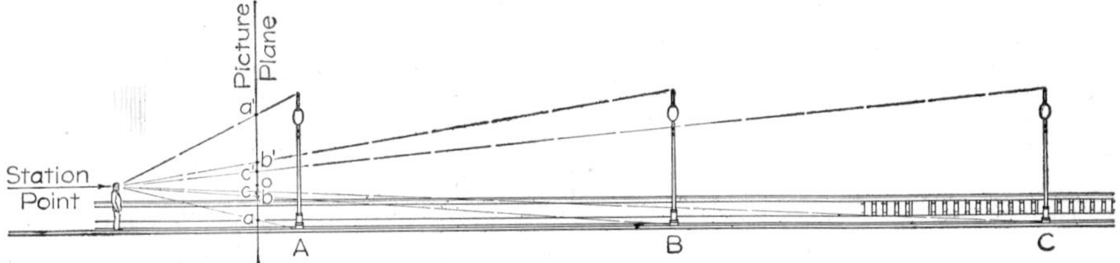

FIG. 22·1—The observer and the picture plane.

In a technical way, perspective is used more in architecture and in illustration than in other branches, but every engineer will find it of advantage to know the principles of the subject.

22·2 Fundamental concepts. Let one imagine himself standing on the sidewalk of a city street, as in Fig. 22·1, with the picture plane erected between him and the street scene ahead. Visual rays from the observer's eye to the ends of the lamppost *A* intercept a distance *aa'* on the picture plane. Similarly, rays from post *B* intercept *bb'*, a lesser distance than *aa'*. This apparent diminution in the size of like objects as the distance from the objects to the eye increases agrees with our everyday experience, and is the keynote of perspective drawing. It is evident from the figure that succeeding lampposts will intercept shorter distances on the picture plane than the preceding ones, and that a post at infinity would show only as a point ***o*** at the level of the observer's eye.

In Fig. 22·2, the plane of the paper is the picture plane, and the intercepts *aa'*, *bb'*, etc., show as the heights of their respective lampposts as they diminish in their projected size and finally disappear on the horizon. In a similar way the curbings and balustrade appear to converge at the same point O. Thus a system of parallel horizontal lines will vanish at a single point on the horizon, and all horizontal planes will vanish on the horizon. Verticals such as the lampposts and the edges of the buildings, being parallel to the picture plane, pierce the picture plane at an infinite distance and therefore show as vertical lines in the picture.

FIG. 22·2—The perspective.

22·3 Definitions and nomenclature. Figure 22·3 illustrates perspective theory and names the points, lines, and planes used. An observer in viewing an object selects his *station point* and thereby determines the *horizon plane* as the horizontal plane at eye level. This horizon plane is normally above the horizontal *ground plane* upon which the object is assumed to rest. The *picture plane* is usually located between the station point and the object being viewed and is ordinarily a vertical plane perpendicular to the horizontal projection of the line of sight to the object's center of interest. The *horizon line* is the intersection of the horizon plane and picture plane, and the *ground line* is the intersection of the ground plane and picture plane. The *axis of vision* is the line through the station point that is perpendicular to the picture plane. The piercing point of the axis of vision with the picture plane is the *center of vision.*

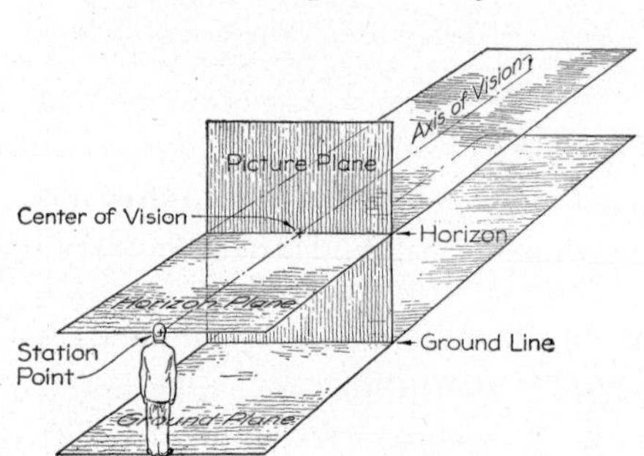

FIG. 22·3—Perspective nomenclature.

22·4 Selection of the station point. Care must be exercised in selecting the station point, for an indiscriminate choice may result in a distorted drawing. If the station point is placed to one side of the drawing, the same effect is had as when a theater screen is viewed from a position close to the front and well off to one side; heights are seen properly but not horizontal distances. Therefore, the *center of vision should be somewhere near the picture's center of interest.*

Wide angles of view will result in a violent convergence of horizontal lines and so should be avoided. The angle of view is the included angle θ between the widest visual rays, Fig. 22·4. Figure 22·5 shows the difference in perspective foreshortening for different lateral angles of view. In general, an angle of about 20° will give the most natural picture.

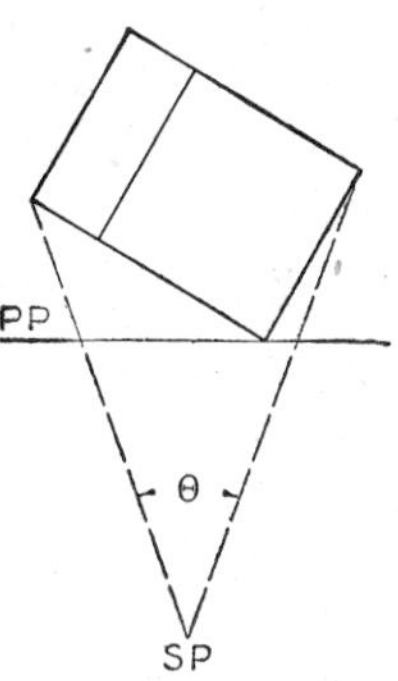

FIG. 22·4—Angle of view, lateral.

The station point should be located where the object will be seen to best advantage and, for this reason, on large objects such as buildings, etc., the station point is usually taken at a normal standing height of about 5 feet above the ground plane. For small objects, however, the best representation demands that the top, as well as the lateral surfaces, be seen, and the station point must be elevated accordingly. Figure 22·6 shows the angle of elevation Ω between the horizon plane and the widest visual ray. By contrasting several different angles of elevation (Ω), Fig. 22·7 shows the effect of elevation of the station point. In general, the best picturization is had at an angle of about 20° to 30°.

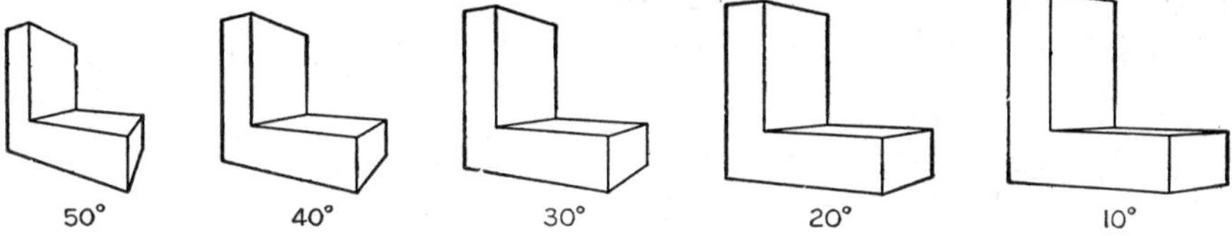

FIG. 22·5—Comparative lateral angles of view.

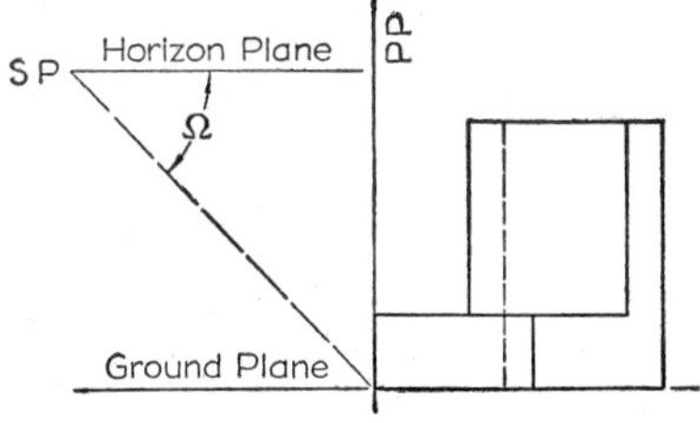

FIG. 22·6—Angle of view, elevation.

It may be established, therefore, that *the visual rays to the object should be kept within a right circular cone whose elements make an angle of not more than* 15° *with the cone axis.*

In choosing the station point, its position should always be offset to one side and also offset vertically from the exact middle of the object, or a rather stiff and awkward perspective will be had.

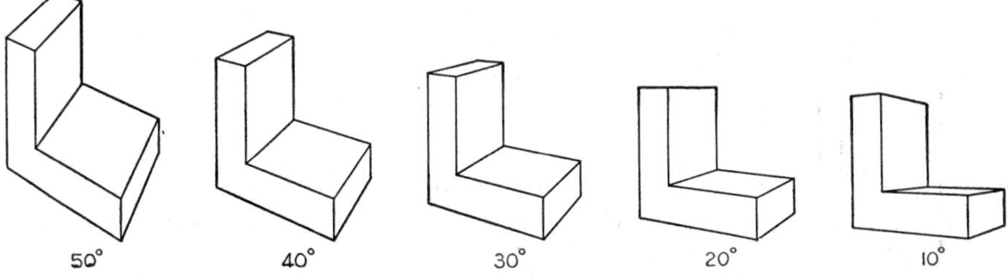

FIG. 22·7—Comparative elevation angles of view.

Similarly, in locating the object with reference to the picture plane, the faces should not make identical angles with the picture plane or the same stiffness will appear.

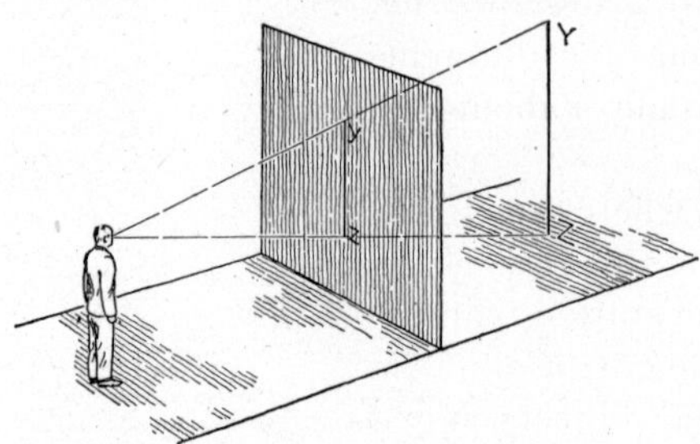

FIG. 22·8—Perspective of a line.

22·5 To draw a perspective. Perspective projection is based on the theory that visual rays from the object to the eye pierce the picture plane, and form an image of the object on the plane. Thus in Fig. 22·8, the image of line YZ is formed by the piercing points y and z of the rays. Several projective methods may be used. The simplest method, basically, but the most laborious to draw, is illustrated by the purely orthographic method of Fig. 22·9, in which the top and side views are drawn in orthographic. The picture plane (edge view) and the station point are located in each view. Assuming that the line YZ of Fig. 22·8 is one edge of the L-shaped block of Fig. 22·9, visual rays from Y and Z will intersect the picture plane in the top view, thus locating the perspective of the points laterally.

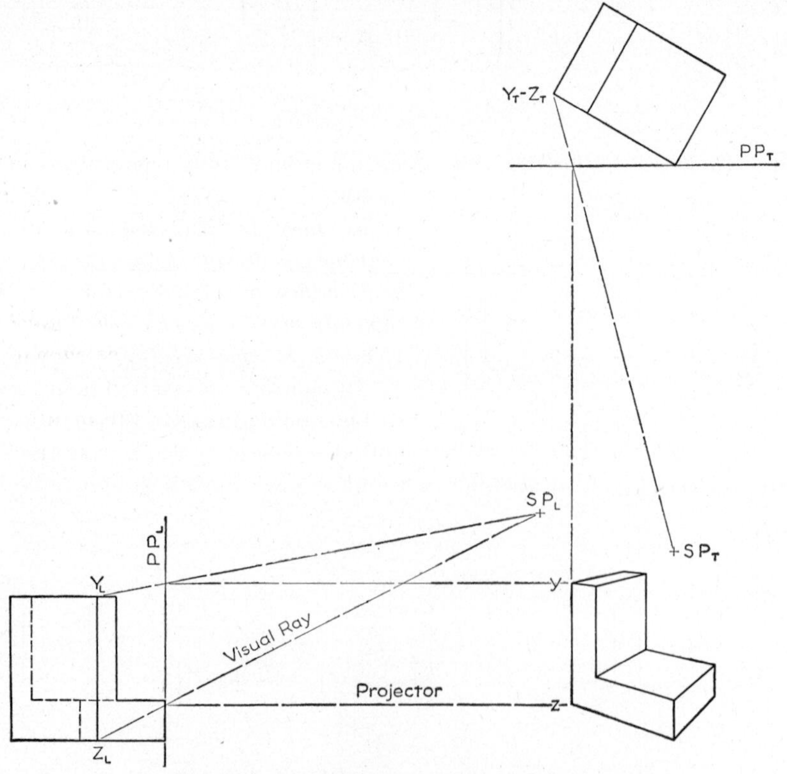

FIG. 22·9—Perspective drawing, orthographic method.

Similarly, the intersections of the rays in the side view give the perspective heights of Y and Z. Projection from the top and side views of the picture plane gives the perspective of YZ, and a repetition of the process for the other lines will complete the drawing.

22·6 The use of vanishing points and measuring lines will facilitate the projections. Let it be required to make a perspective of the sliding block of Fig. 22·10. The edge view of the picture plane (plan view) is drawn, Fig. 22·11, and behind it the top view of the object is located and drawn. In this case, one side of the object is oriented at 30° to the picture plane in order to emphasize the L shape more than the end of the block. The station point is located a little to the left of center and far enough in front of the picture plane to give a good angle of view. The ground line is then drawn and on it is placed the front view of the block from Fig. 22·10. The height of the station point is then decided—in this case well above the block so that the top surfaces will be seen—and the horizon line drawn at the station-point height.

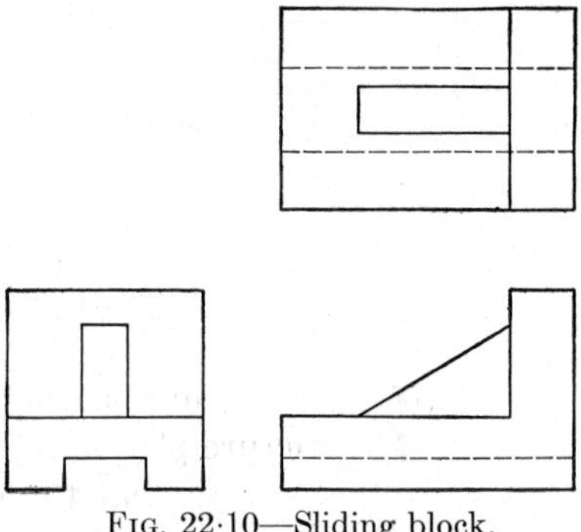

FIG. 22·10—Sliding block.

To avoid the labor of redrawing the top and front views in the positions just described, the views may be cut from the orthographic drawing, oriented in position, and fastened with tacks or tape.

The vanishing point for any horizontal line may be found by drawing a visual ray from the station point *parallel* to the horizontal line, and finding the piercing point of this visual ray with the picture plane. Thus, in Fig. 22·11, the line SP to R is parallel to the edge AB of the object, and R is the piercing point. Point R is then projected to the horizon line, locating VR, the vanishing point for AB and all edges parallel to AB. The vanishing point VL for AC and edges parallel to AC is found similarly, as shown.

In visualizing the location of a vanishing point, imagine that the edge, as for example AB, is moved to the right along the ground, still making the same angle with the picture plane; the intercept of AB will become less and less until, when A is in coincidence with R, the intercept will be zero. R then must be the top view of the vanishing point for all lines parallel to AB.

Point A lies in both the picture plane and the ground plane and will therefore be shown in the perspective at a, on the ground line, and in direct projection with the top view. The perspective of AB is determined by drawing a line from a to VR (the perspective *direction* of AB) and then projecting the intercept Z (of the visual ray SP to B) to the line, thus locating b.

All lines behind the picture plane are foreshortened in the picture, and only those lying in the picture plane will appear in their true length. For this reason, *all measurements must be made in the picture plane.* Since *AD* is in the picture plane, it will show in its actual height as *ad*.

A measuring line will be needed for any verticals such as *BF* that do not lie in the picture plane. If a vertical is brought forward to the picture plane along some established line, the true height can be measured in the picture plane. If, in Fig. 22·11, *BF* is imagined as moved forward along *ab* until *b* is in coincidence with *a*, the true height can be measured vertically from *a*.

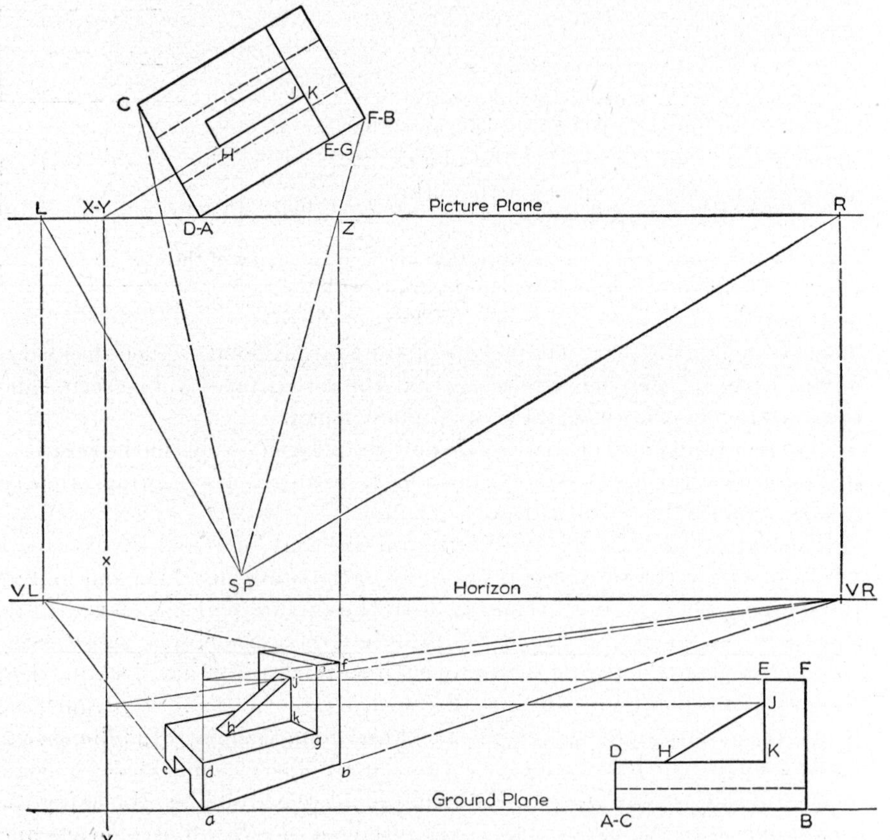

FIG. 22·11—Use of vanishing points and measuring lines.

This vertical line at *a* is then the measuring line for all heights in the vertical plane containing *a* and *b*. The height of *f* is measured from *a*, and from this height point a vanishing line is drawn to *VR*; then from *Z* (the piercing point in the picture plane of the visual ray to *F*) *f* may be projected to the perspective.

The measuring line may also be thought of as the intersection of the picture plane with a vertical plane that contains the distance to be found. Thus *ad*, extended, is the measuring line for all heights in surface *ABFEGD*. The triangular rib of Fig. 22·11 is located by continuing surface *HJK* until it intersects the picture plane at XY, thereby establishing xy as the measuring line for all heights in HJK. In the figure, the height of J is measured on the measuring line xy, and j is found as described for f.

Note that heights can either be measured with a scale on the measuring line or they can be projected from the front view as indicated in Fig. 22·11.

Summary

1. Draw the top view (edge of the picture plane).
2. Orient the object relative to the picture plane so that the object will appear to advantage, and draw the top view of the object.
3. Select a station point that will best show the shape of the object.
4. Draw the horizon and ground line.
5. Find the top view of the vanishing points for the principal horizontal edges by drawing lines parallel to the edges, through the station point, and to the picture plane.
6. Project from the top views of the vanishing points to the horizon line, thus locating the vanishing points for the perspective.
7. Draw the visual rays from the station point to the corners of the object in the top view, locating the piercing point of each ray with the picture plane.
8. Start the picture, building from the ground up, and from the nearest corner to the more distant ones.

22·7 Planes parallel to the picture plane. Objects having circles or other curves in a vertical plane may be oriented with their curved faces parallel to the picture plane. The curves will then appear in true shape. This method, often called "parallel perspective," is also suitable for interiors and for street vistas and similar scenes where considerable depth is to be represented.

The object of Fig. 22·12 has been placed so that the planes containing the circular contours are parallel to the picture plane. The horizontal edges parallel to the picture plane will appear horizontal in the picture and will have no vanishing point. Horizontals perpendicular to the picture plane are parallel to the axis of vision and will vanish at the center of vision CV. Except for architectural interiors, the station point is usually located above the object and either to the right or left, yet not so far in any direction as to cause unpleasant distortion. For convenience, one face of the object is usually placed in the picture plane and is therefore not reduced in size in the perspective.

In Fig. 22·12, the end of the hub is in the picture plane; thus the center o is projected from O in the top view, and the circular edges are drawn in their true size. The center line ox is vanished from o to CV. To find the perspective of center line MN, a vertical plane is passed through MN intersecting the picture plane in measuring line gh. A horizontal line from o intersecting gh locates m, and m vanished to CV is the required line.

By using the two center lines from o and m as a framework, the remaining construction is simplified. A ray from the station point to B pierces the picture plane at J, which, projected to mn, locates b. The horizontal line

bz is the center line of the front face of the nearer arm, and the intercept IJ gives the perspective radius ab. The circular hole having a radius CB has an intercept PJ, giving cb as the perspective radius. The arc qy has its center on ox at z. On drawing the tangents lq and ky, the face "F" is completed.

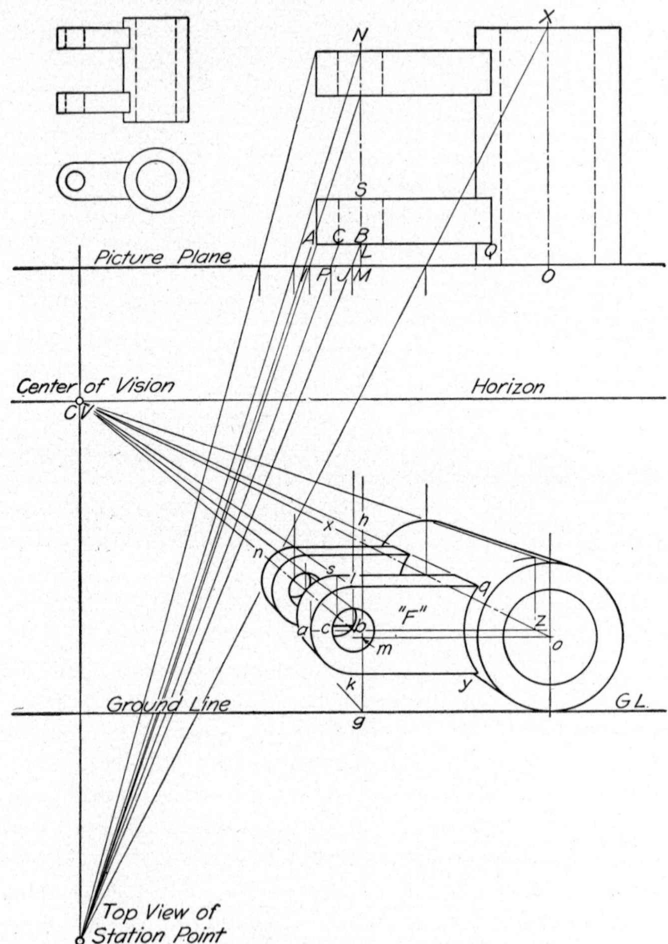

FIG. 22·12—Planes parallel to the picture plane.

The remaining construction for the arms is exactly the same as that for face "F." The centers are moved back on the center lines, and the radii are found from their corresponding intercepts on the picture plane.

22·8 Circles in perspective. The perspective of a circle is a circle only when its plane is parallel to the picture plane; the circle appears as a straight line when its plane is receding from the station point. In all other positions the circle projects as an ellipse whose axes are not readily determinable. The major axis of the ellipse will be at some odd angle except when a vertical circle has its center on the horizon plane; then the major axis will be vertical. Also, when a horizontal circle has its center directly above, below, or on the center of vision, the major axis will be horizontal. It should be noted that in all cases the center of the circle is not coincident with the center of the ellipse representing the circle, and that concentric circles are not represented by concentric ellipses. The major and minor axes of the ellipses for concentric circles are not even parallel except in special cases.

The perspective of a circle may be plotted point by point, but the most rapid solution is had by enclosing the circle in a square, as shown in Fig. 22·13, and plotting points at the tangent points and at the intersections of the diagonals. The eight points thus determined are usually sufficient to give an accurate curve. The square, with its diagonals, is first drawn in the perspective. From the intersection of the diagonals, the vertical and horizontal center lines of the circle are established; where these center lines cross the sides of the square are four points on the curve. In the orthographic view, the measurement X is made, then laid out *in the picture plane* and vanished, crossing the diagonals at four additional points.

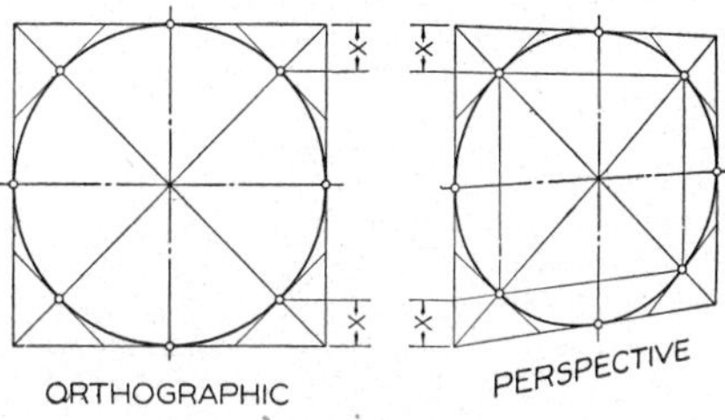

FIG. 22·13—Perspective of a circle.

It must be realized that the curve is tangent to the lines enclosing it, and that the *direction* of the curve is established by these tangent lines; if the lines completing the circumscribing octagon are projected and drawn, the direction of the curve is established at eight points.

22·9 Craticulation. The perspectives of irregular curves may be had by projecting a sufficient number of points to establish the curve, but, if the curve is complicated, the method of craticulation may be used to advantage.

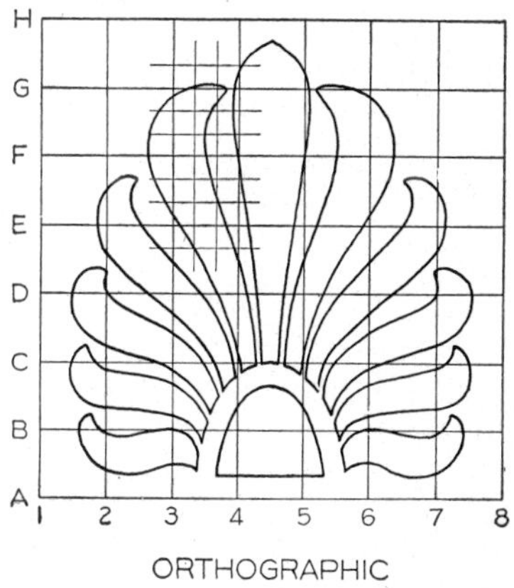

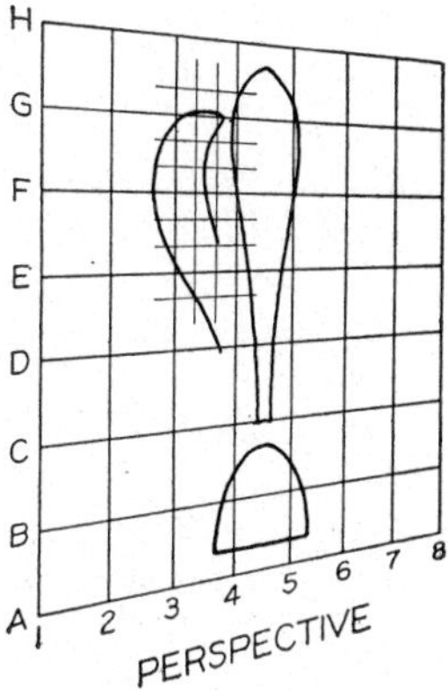

FIG. 22·14—Craticulation.

A square grid is overlaid on the orthographic view as shown in Fig. 22·14; then the grid is drawn in perspective, and the outlines of the curve transferred by inspection from the orthographic view.

22·10 Measuring points. It has been shown that all lines lying in the picture plane will be their own perspectives and may be scaled directly on the perspective drawing. The adaptation of this principle has an advantage in laying off a series of measurements, such as a row of pilasters, because it avoids a confusion of intercepts on the picture plane and the inaccuracies due to long projection lines.

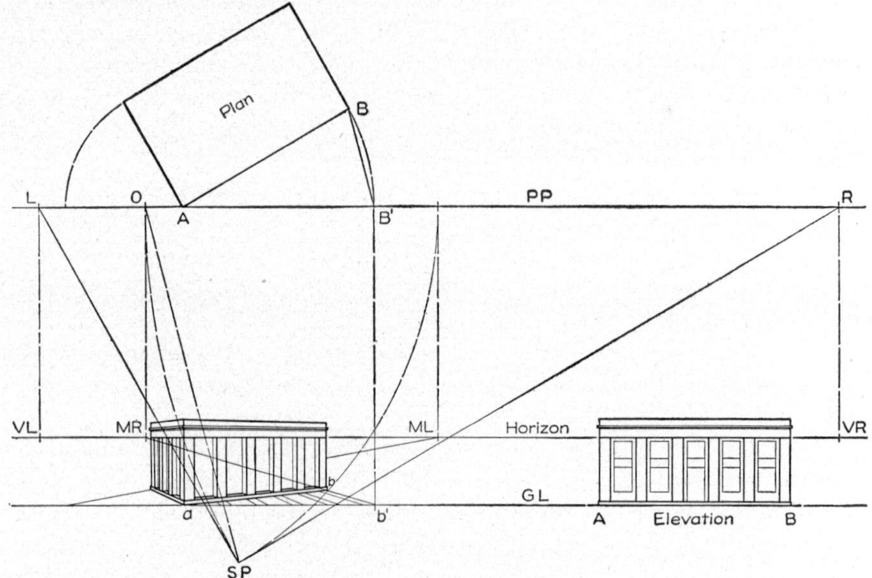

FIG. 22·15—Use of measuring points.

In the measuring-points method, a surface, such as the wall between *A* and *B* of Fig. 22·15, is revolved into the picture plane for the purpose of making measurements, as shown at *AB'*. While in the picture plane, the entire surface can be laid out directly to the same scale as the top view; therefore, *ab'* and other horizontal dimensions of the surface are established along the ground line as shown. The counterrevolution of the wall to its actual position on the building and the necessary projections in the perspective are based on the principle that the revolution has been made about a vertical axis, and that any point has traveled in a horizontal plane. By drawing, as usual, a line parallel to *BB'*, from the station point to the picture plane, and then projecting to the horizon, the vanishing point *MR* is found. This vanishing point is termed a *measuring point* and may be defined as the vanishing point for lines joining corresponding points of the actual and revolved positions of the face considered. The divisions on *ab'* are therefore vanished to *MR*; where this construction intersects *ab* (the perspective of

AB), the lateral position of the pilasters, in the perspective, is determined. Heights are scaled on the vertical edge through *a*, as this edge lies in the picture plane. The perspective of the wall between *A* and *B* is completed by the regular methods previously described. For work on the end of the building, the end wall is revolved as indicated, measuring point *ML* is found, and the projections continued as described for the front wall.

Measuring points may be more readily located if the draftsman will recognize that the triangles *ABB′* and *R O SP* are similar. Therefore, a measuring point is as far from its corresponding vanishing point as the station point is from the picture plane, measuring the latter parallel to the face concerned. *MR* can then be found by measuring the distance from the station point to *R* and laying off *RO* equal to the measurement, or by swinging an arc, with *R* as center, from the station point to *O*, as shown. The measuring point *MR* is then projected from *O*.

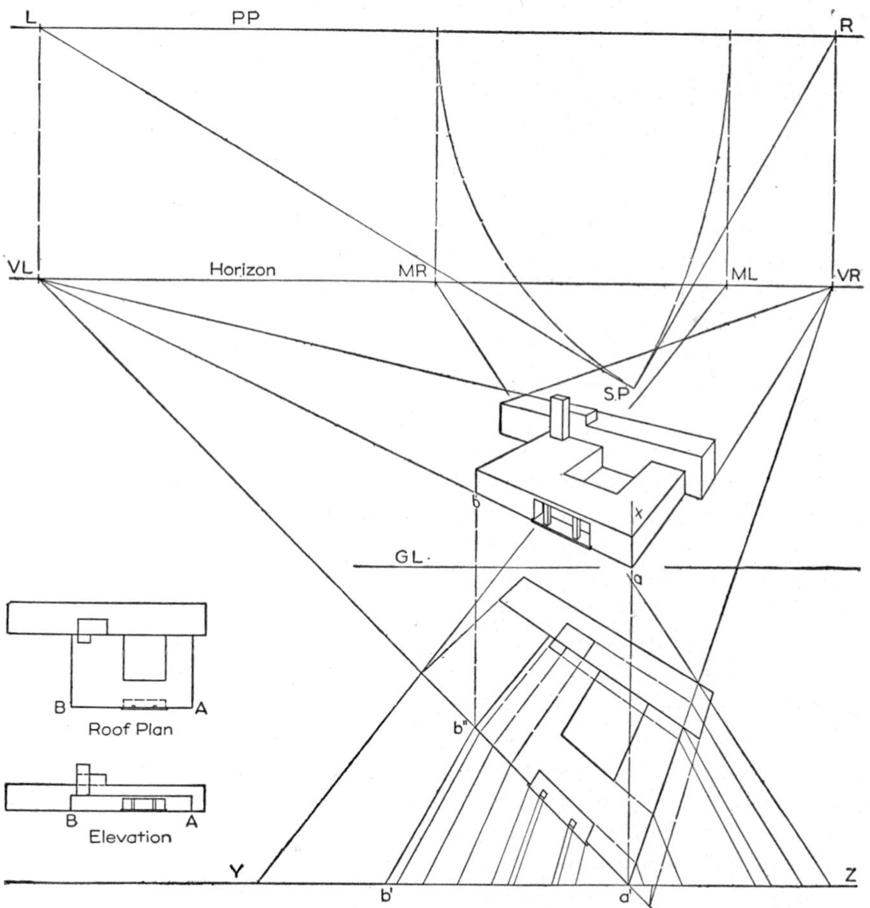

FIG. 22·16—Perspective plan.

22·11 The perspective-plan method. The orthographic views of an object are often drawn at a scale either too large or too small for direct use in drawing a perspective by the methods previously described. Considerable time may be required to redraw them at the desired scale, and instead, the drawing of a perspective plan will be found to be advantageous.

In Fig. 22·16, the roof plan (top view) and elevation (front view) of a building are already drawn in block outline. A perspective of this structure is required, drawn with the near corner of the building at a scale of twice that used for the orthographic views. The selection of the station point is made, and the top view of the picture plane, station point, vanishing points, and measuring points are all drawn at the required scale without drawing the top view of the structure. The horizon and ground lines are then drawn, and the vanishing points and measuring points located in the perspective. The perspective plan can now be started.

At a considerable distance below the ground plane, a horizontal plane is selected on which the perspective plan will be drawn. The perspective plan of corner A is placed at a'. As A has been placed in the picture plane, measuring lines for widths and depths are from a' toward Y and Z (parallel to the horizon). AB is then scaled from a' to b' and vanished to ML. In the perspective plan proper, AB vanishes from a' to VL, and the intersection of $a'VL$ with $b'ML$ determines the location of B in the perspective plan at b''. The perspective plan is completed by continuing this procedure.

In projection with the perspective plan, the required perspective is drawn, using the horizon and ground line already established. Corner a is located on the ground line in projection with a'. Then AB vanishes from a to VL and, in projection with b'' of the perspective plan, b is located in the perspective. Heights are measured on ax and on such other vertical measuring lines as are needed. The perspective is then completed in the usual manner.

22·12 The revolved-plan method. This method is based on the principle that the perspective of any point can be found by drawing the perspective of two lines through the point; specifically, the two lines are horizontal, one perpendicular and one at 45 degrees to the picture plane. Normally, the top and perspective views would overlap each other, and so to avoid this confusion, the top view is not drawn in the normal position, but is *revolved through 180 degrees and drawn in front of the picture plane in reversed form.* Figure 22·17 shows the perspective of a tiled floor. The phantom view $ABCD$ would be the normal top view; the revolved view is $AB'C'D$. Note that the revolution is made about the coincident picture plane and ground line, and that any line such as EF will revolve to $E'F'$, with the common intersection P. Two lines are then drawn through each point; lines perpendicular to the picture plane will vanish at CV, and the diagonals at 45° will vanish at VL. The other system of 45° lines will vanish at VR.

The perspective could be made without drawing the top view by measuring distances on the ground line. The length of *DC*, measured from *D* to *G* and vanished from *G* to *VL*, would locate the perspective of *C* by the intersection with *D CV*. Any other point may be located in a similar manner.

22·13 Inclined lines. Any line neither parallel nor perpendicular to either the picture plane or the horizon plane is termed an inclined line. Any line may have a vertical plane passed through it, and if the vanishing line of the plane is found, a line in the plane will vanish at some point on the vanishing line of the plane. Vertical planes will vanish on vertical lines, just as

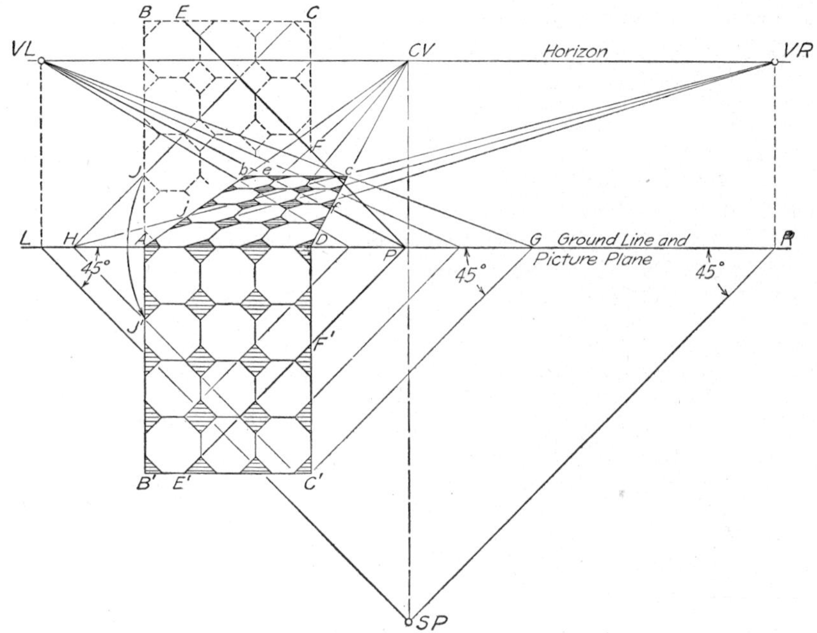

FIG. 22·17—Revolved plan.

horizontal planes vanish on a horizontal line, the horizon. In Fig. 22·18, the points *a*, *b*, *c*, *d*, and *e* have all been found by regular methods previously described. The vanishing point of the horizontal *ab* is *VR*. A vertical line through *VR* is the vanishing line of the plane of *abc* and all planes *parallel* to *abc*. This vanishing line is intersected by the extension of *de* at *UR*, thereby determining the vanishing point for *de* and all edges *parallel* to *de*.

The vanishing point for inclined lines may also be located on the theory that the vanishing point for any line may be determined by moving the line until it appears as a point, while still retaining its original angle with the picture plane. The vanishing point of *de* may therefore be located by drawing a line through the station point parallel to *DE* and finding its piercing point with the picture plane. This is done by laying out *SP T* at the angle β

to *SP R* and erecting *RT* perpendicular to *SP R*. Then *RT* is the height of the vanishing point *UR* above *VR*.

If measuring points are used for the initial work on the perspective, it will be an advantage to recognize which one of the measuring points was used for determining horizontal measurements in the parallel vertical planes containing the inclined lines; at that measuring point the angle β is laid out, either above or below the horizon depending upon whether the lines slope up or down as they go into the distance. Where this construction intersects the vanishing line for the vertical planes containing the inclined lines, the vanishing point is located.

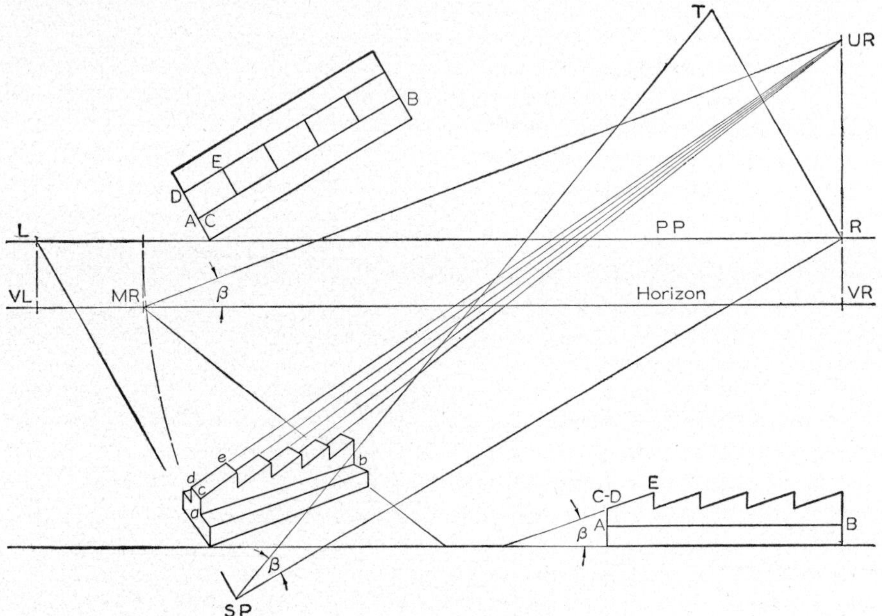

FIG. 22·18—Vanishing point of inclined lines.

22·14 Inclined planes. An inclined plane is any plane neither parallel nor perpendicular to either the picture plane or the horizon plane. The vanishing line for an inclined plane may be found by locating the vanishing points for any two systems of parallel lines in the inclined plane. For determining the vanishing line of plane *ABCD* of Fig. 22·19, the vanishing point *VL* of the horizontal edges *AD* and *BC* is one point, and the vanishing point *UR* for the inclined edges *AB* and *DC* gives a second point on the vanishing line *VL UR* for plane *ABCD*.

It is often necessary to draw the line of intersection of two inclined planes. The intersection will vanish at the point of intersection of the vanishing lines of both planes. The intersection *J* of the two vanishing lines of the roof planes of Fig. 22·19 is the vanishing point of the line of intersection of the two planes.

22·15 Inclined picture plane. In the majority of cases, the object or structure to be drawn is a shape that will give the desired result when pictured by ordinary perspective methods. Occasionally, however, for

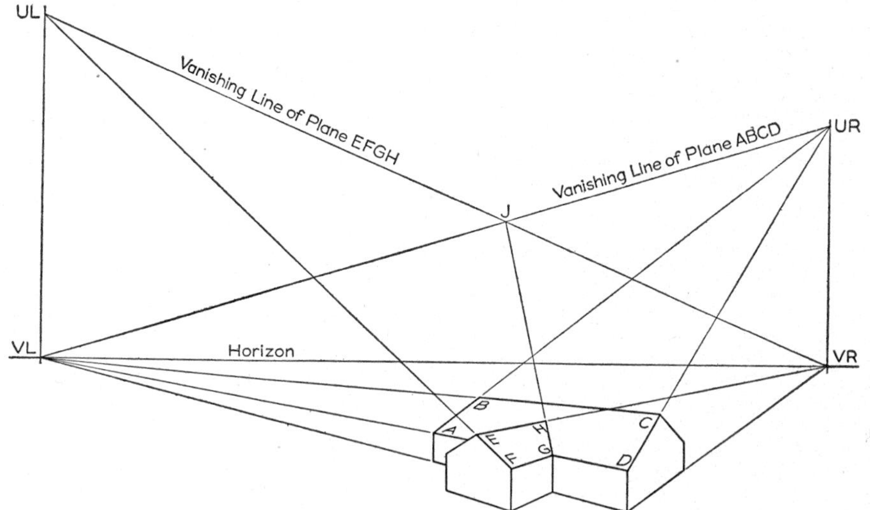

FIG. 22·19—Vanishing lines of inclined planes; vanishing point for intersection of two inclined planes.

some tall structure such as a skyscraper, it is desirable to show the vanishing effect of tall vertical edges. This effect becomes increasingly noticeable as the station point is brought nearer to the structure, and if, practically, the head must be tilted backwards to look up, the axis of vision and the picture plane are then inclined.

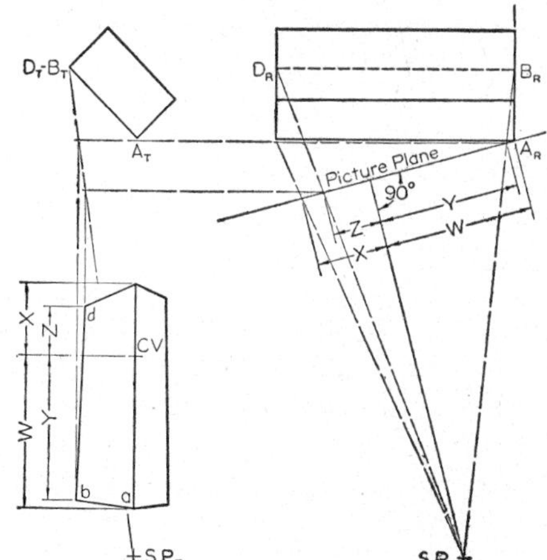

FIG. 22·20—Use of inclined picture plane, orthographic method.

Figure 22·20 illustrates the orthographic method of drawing a perspective on an inclined picture plane. The top view and right-side view (in alternate position) are drawn, the station point selected, and the inclined picture plane drawn in the side view. Since it is inclined, the picture plane will not appear as an edge in the top view. The piercing point of each visual ray is located in the side view and then projected to the corresponding visual ray in the top view; these points then are projected to the perspective, and "picture-plane heights" measured from the side view will locate the points for the perspective.

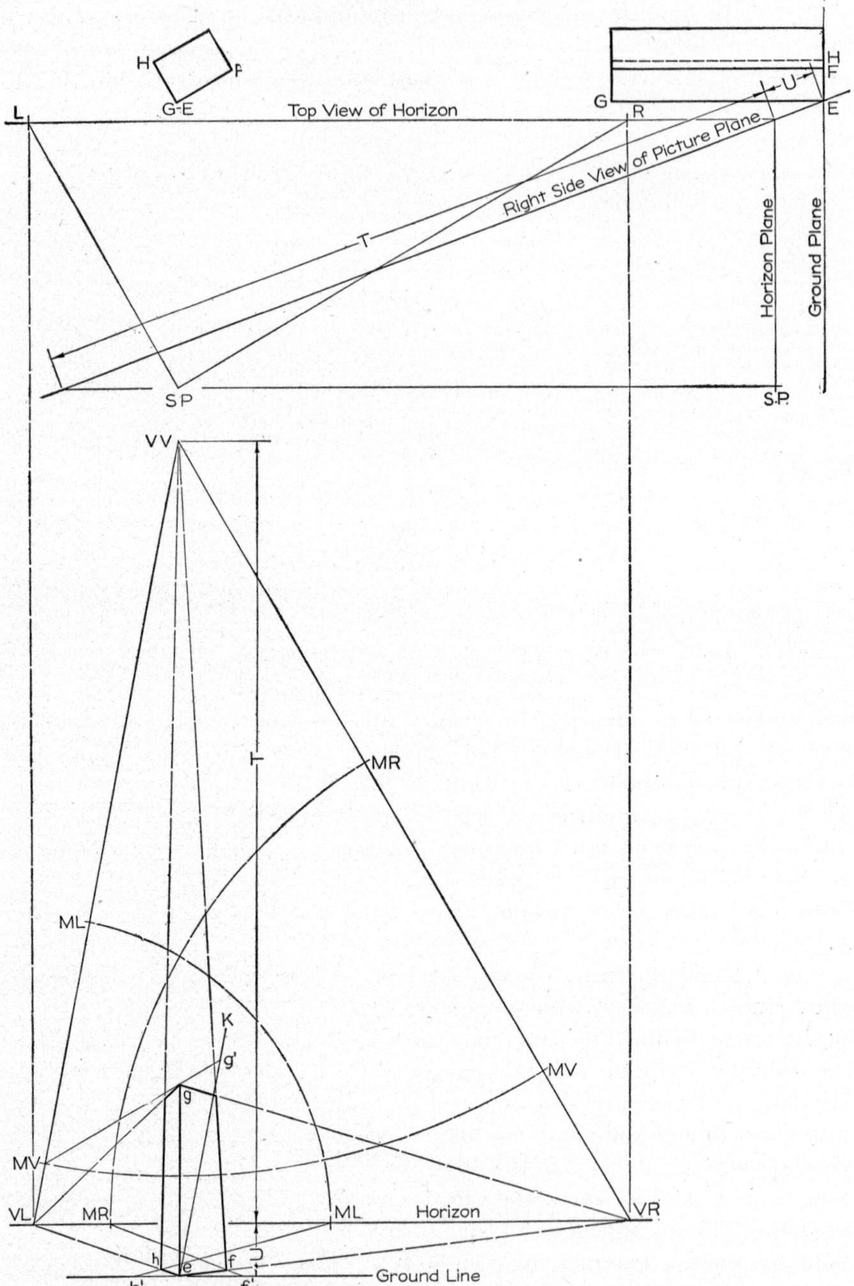

FIG. 22·21—Inclined picture plane, vanishing-points and measuring-points method.

A more inclusive solution is shown by Fig. 22·21, in which the vanishing and measuring points are located. As is the case when a vertical picture plane is used, the intersection of the horizon plane with the inclined plane is the horizon—the vanishing line of all horizontal planes. The vanishing point of any system of parallel edges is found by drawing a line parallel to the edges, through the station point, and to the picture plane. In Fig. 22·21 the intersection of the horizon plane and the picture plane appears as a point in the side view and is projected to the top view. Through the station point, parallel to *EH* and *EF*, lines are drawn until they pierce the picture plane at *L* and *R* on the horizon, thereby establishing the top view of the vanishing points for *EH* and *EF*; these are then projected to the perspective on the horizon, locating *VL* and *VR*.

The vanishing point for vertical edges is similarly found. A vertical line is drawn through the station point in the side view and its intersection with the picture plane is the distance *T* from the horizon; this distance is then laid off vertically, in projection with the station point, from the horizon in the perspective, thus locating *VV*, the vanishing point for vertical edges.

Point *e* (in the picture plane and on the ground line) is placed the distance *U* from the horizon and in projection with its top view. Note that the distances *T* and *U* are not vertical measurements.

The three vanishing points of the mutually perpendicular edges of the rectangular prism are the corners of a triangle whose sides are the vanishing lines for the object's surfaces. Measuring points are established by laying off the true distance of a vanishing point from the station point, along both vanishing lines containing the vanishing point, from the perspective of the vanishing point. Thus *ML* will be on the vanishing lines *VL VV* and *VL VR*, while *MR* will be on *VR VV* and *VR VL*, and *MV* will be on *VV VL* and *VV VR*. Edges that vanish to *VV* may then be measured in planes that vanish on either *VV VL* or *VV VR*. Measuring lines originating at some point in the picture plane are drawn parallel to the appropriate vanishing lines. The height of *EG*, measured in the side view, is scaled along measuring line *eK*, then vanished from *g′* to *MV* on *VL VV*. Where this construction intersects *eg*, vanishing from *e* to *VV*, *g* is located. The edge *EF* is scaled along measuring line *ef′* (the ground line), vanished to *MR* (on the horizon), and where this line intersects *ef*, vanishing to *VR*, is the location of *f*. In a similar way *h* is determined. The perspective is completed by vanishing edges to their proper vanishing points.

22·16 Cylindrical picture surface. Whenever the angle of vision is extremely wide, much distortion will result. A satisfactory method of eliminating the distortion is to use, instead of the regular picture plane, a cylindrical picture surface with the station point on the geometrical axis of the cylinder. If the angle of vision is wide horizontally, the cylinder axis must be vertical; if it is wide vertically, as with tall buildings, the cylinder axis must be horizontal.

The group of buildings of Fig. 22·22 gives a very wide angle horizontally, but very little comparative height. The plan view of the building group is drawn, and the station point and picture surface located. Elements of the cylinder are selected, and the perspective is laid out as a development

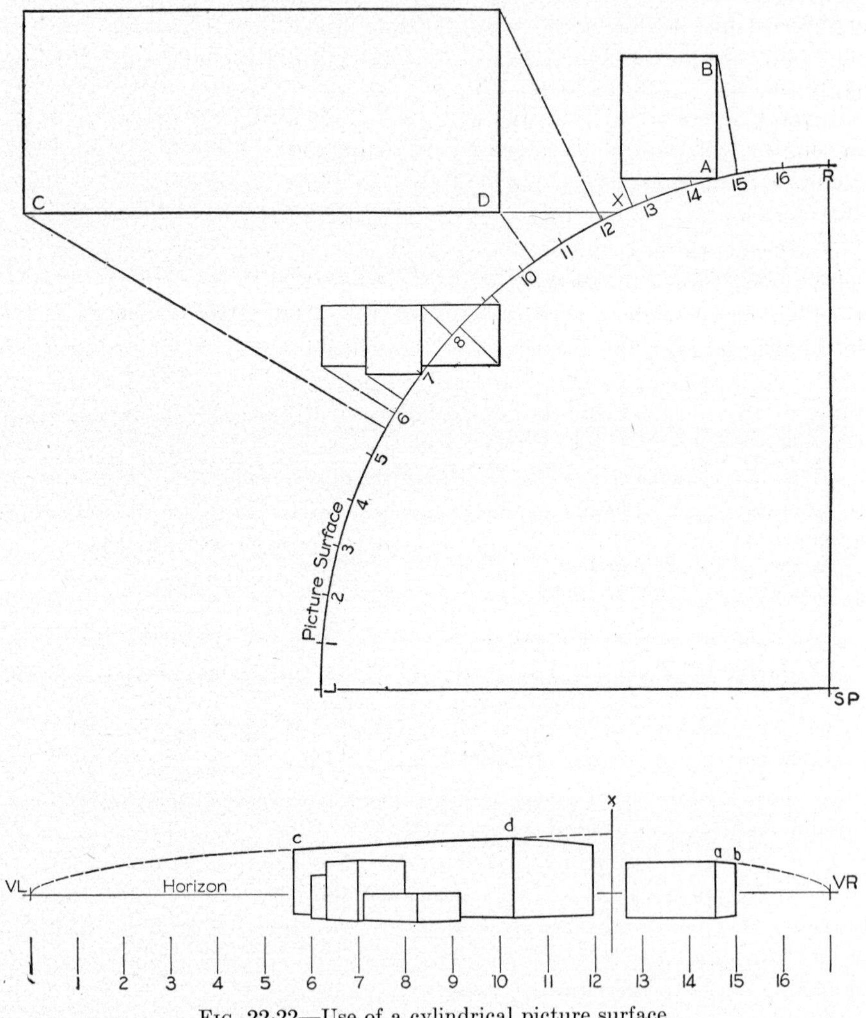

FIG. 22·22—Use of a cylindrical picture surface.

of the cylindrical surface. Visual rays are then drawn from the station point to the corners of the buildings, and the piercing points located, for lateral position, in the top view and on the developed or perspective view.

Heights are scaled in the picture surface and then vanished to their proper vanishing points. The vanishing lines on the cylindrical surface will be elliptical instead of straight and will have two vanishing points, the extremities of the major axis of its ellipse. However, edges, which are parallel to the axis of the picture surface or which are in a plane through the station point and perpendicular to the axis, will be straight lines.

When the picture surface is vertical, the major axis for all horizontal edges will be coincident with the horizon and will be equal in length to one-half the circumference of the cylinder. To determine the vanishing point of *ab*, a line is drawn through the station point, parallel to *AB*. The piercing point *R* of this line with the cylinder's surface is located in the developed view and is the required vanishing point *VR*. The ellipse that contains the perspective of *AB* will have its center a distance of *one-fourth* the cylinder's circumference to the left of *VR*. Corner *A* lies in the picture surface and its height may be scaled. A trammel is made for the ellipse containing the perspective of *AB* and is used to trace *ab* between the previously determined lateral limits of the edge. Where edges do not touch the picture surface, they are continued until they do so, as shown for edge *CD*. Then at *x* the vertical height may be measured, and the procedure just described then used to find the perspective of the edge.

PROBLEMS

The following give a variety of different objects to be drawn in perspective. A further selection may be made from the orthographic drawings in other chapters.

1. Fig. 22·23. Double wedge block.
2. Fig. 22·24. Notched holder.

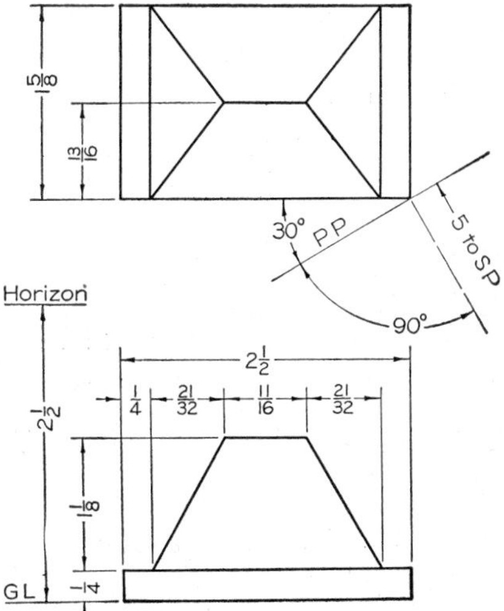

FIG. 22·23—Double wedge block.

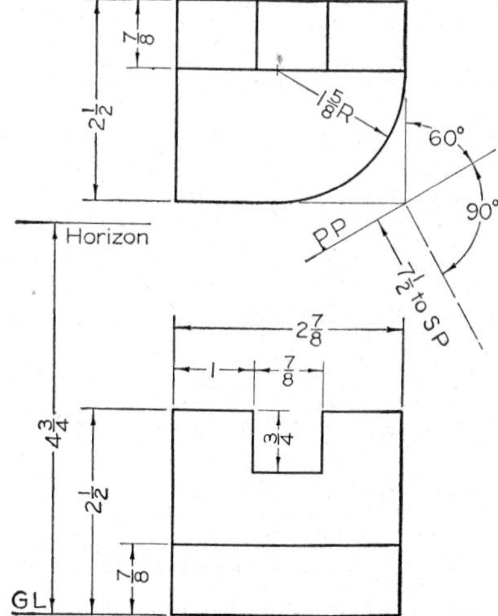

FIG. 22·24—Notched holder.

3. Fig. 22·25. Crank.
4. Fig. 22·26. Corner lug.

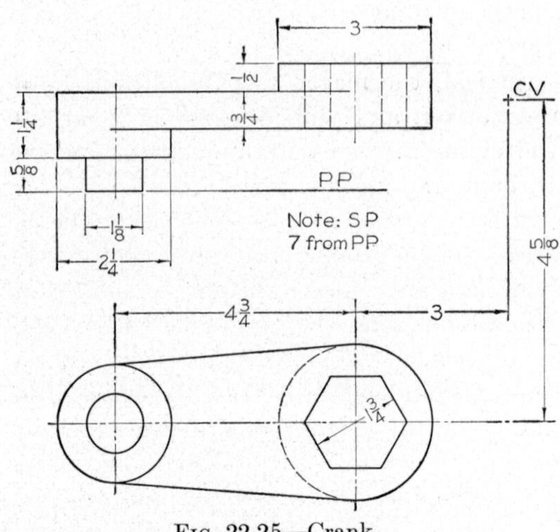

FIG. 22·25—Crank.

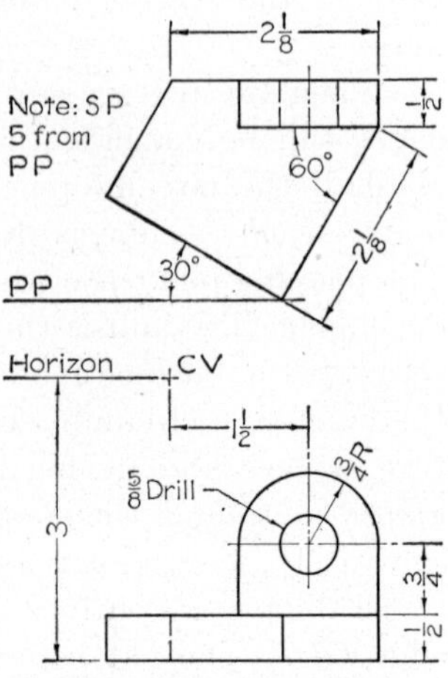

FIG. 22·26—Corner lug.

5. Fig. 22·27. House.
6. Fig. 22·28. Church.

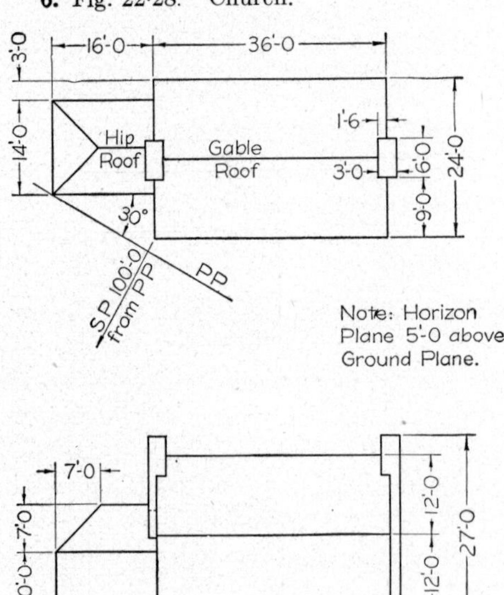

FIG. 22·27—House.

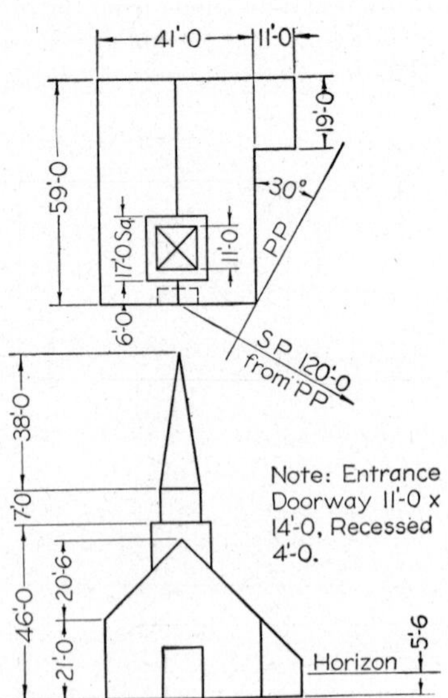

FIG. 22·28—Church.

Chapter 23

PICTORIAL SKETCHING

23·1 The necessity that the engineer be trained in freehand sketching was emphasized in Chap. 19. What was said there, however, referred particularly to sketching in orthographic projection; now let it be remarked that before the engineer can be said to be adequately equipped to use the graphic language, he must possess the ability to sketch *pictorially* with skill and facility.

In designing and inventing, the first ideas come into the mind in pictorial form, and preliminary sketches made in this form preserve the ideas as visualized. From this record the preliminary orthographic design sketches are made. A pictorial sketch of an object or of some detail of construction can often be used to explain it when the orthographic projection cannot be read intelligently by a client or a workman. If a working drawing is difficult to understand, one of the best ways of reading it is to start a pictorial sketch of it. Usually before the sketch is finished the orthographic drawing is perfectly clear. Often again, a pictorial sketch may be made more quickly and may serve as a better record than would orthographic views of the same piece. The young engineer should not be deterred by any fancied lack of "artistic ability." An engineer's sketch is a record of information, not a work of art. The one requirement for both is *good proportion.*

23·2 Methods. Although not an accurate classification, there may be said to be three pictorial methods: axonometric, oblique, and perspective. The mechanical construction of the first two has been explained in detail in Chap. 21, and the third in Chap. 22.

23·3 Axonometric sketching. After a clear visualization, the first step in the procedure is to select the best position from which to view the object and thus determine the direction of the axes. It will be remembered that there are an infinite number of positions for the three axes that represent three mutually perpendicular lines, and that the simplest is the isometric position. Sketches may be made on isometric axes, but, unless it is important to show some feature on the top, a much better effect is gained and the distortion greatly lessened by drawing the cross axes at a much smaller angle with the horizontal, Fig. 23·1. Since measurements are not made on sketches, the axes may be foreshortened until the proportion is satisfactory to the eye; moreover the effect of distortion may be overcome still further by slightly converging the receding lines. Objects of rectangular outline are best adapted to sketching in axonometric projection. Figure 19·13 shows examples of pictorial sketches.

A successful method of establishing the direction of the two horizontal axes, used by George J. Hood, is to sketch first a horizontal ellipse (with a little practice this can be done with a free sweep of the arm), Fig. 23·2. At some point, as A, draw a tangent. Through A and the center of the ellipse

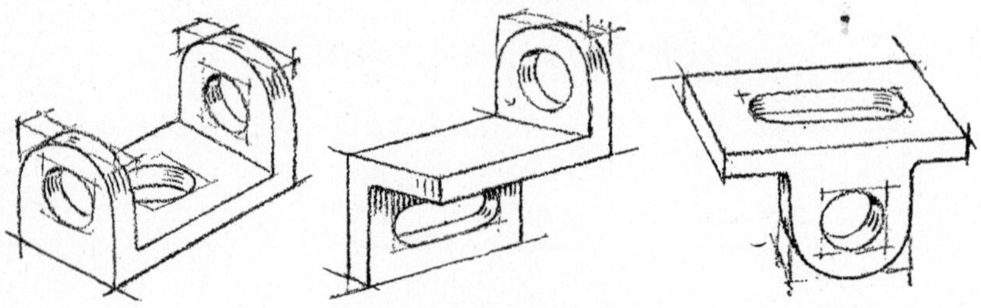

FIG. 23·1—Choice of axes.

draw one of a pair of conjugate diameters of the ellipse and at the other end of this diameter a second tangent parallel to the first. Complete the axonometric square by drawing the other two sides parallel to the diameter.

After setting the axes, the sketch should be blocked in by drawing the principal outlines, boxing in the cylindrical parts in their enclosing square

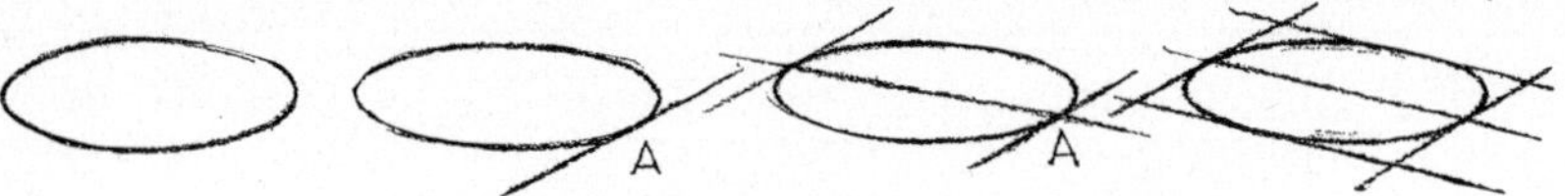

FIG. 23·2—Ellipse method of establishing axes.

prisms. A circle in pictorial drawing is always an ellipse whose major axis is at right angles to the shaft or rotation axis of the circle. Thus its minor axis coincides on the drawing with the picture of the shaft axis, Fig. 23·3. Locate these axes and carry the sketch on as suggested in Fig. 23·4, preserv-

FIG. 23·3—Relation of ellipse axes to axis of rotation.

ing the proportions by completing the main outlines before adding any minor details. Do not use any hidden lines unless necessary for the description of the piece.

Note particularly that by the above rule *all* circles on horizontal planes are drawn as ellipses *with the major axis horizontal,* Fig. 23·5.

Some care must be exercised in adding dimensions to a pictorial sketch. The extension lines must be either in or perpendicular to the plane on which the dimension is being given.

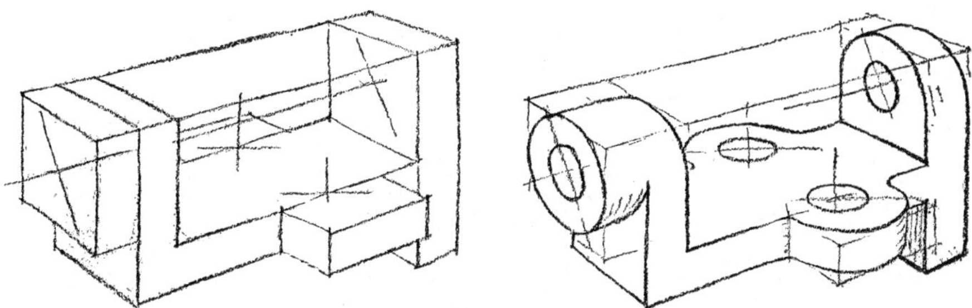

FIG. 23·4—Blocking in a sketch.

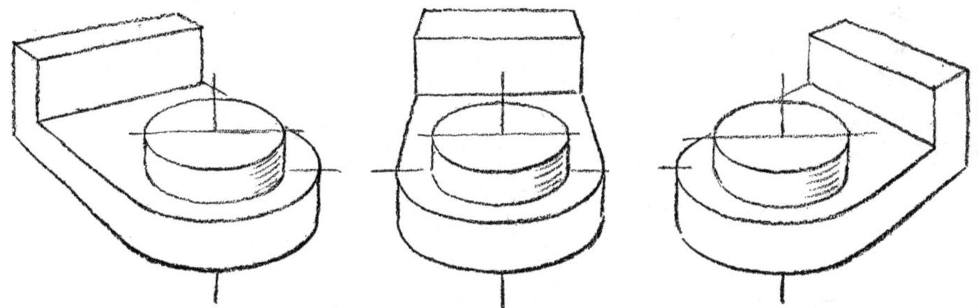

FIG. 23·5—Horizontal circles in axonometric.

23·4 Oblique sketching. The advantage of oblique projection in preserving one face without distortion is of particular value in sketching, and the painful effect of distortion in oblique drawing done mechanically may be greatly lessened in sketching, by foreshortening the cross axis to a pleasing proportion, Fig. 23·6. By converging the lines parallel to the cross axis the effect of parallel perspective is obtained. This converging in either axonometric or oblique is sometimes called "fake perspective."

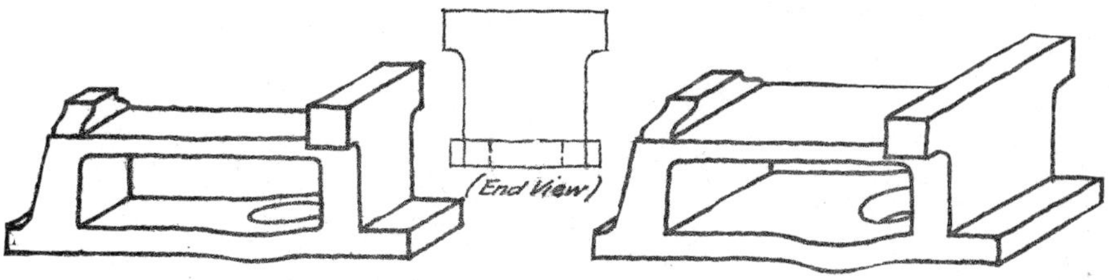

FIG. 23·6—Oblique with and without foreshortening.

23·5 Perspective sketching. A sketch made in perspective gives by far the most pleasing pictorial effect. For constructing a perspective drawing of a proposed structure from its plans and elevations a knowledge of the principles of perspective drawing is required, but for making a perspective sketch from the object one may get along by observing the ordinary phenomena of perspective which affect everything we see: the fact that objects appear smaller in proportion to their distance from the eye, that parallel lines appear to converge as they recede, that horizontal lines and planes appear to "vanish" on the horizon.

In perspective sketching from the model, the drawing is made simply by observation, the directions and proportionate lengths of lines being estimated by sighting and measuring on the pencil held at arm's length, one's knowledge of perspective phenomena being used as a check. With the drawing board or sketch pad held in a comfortable drawing position perpendicular to the line of sight from the eye to the object, the direction of a line is tested by holding the pencil at arm's length parallel to the board and rotating the arm until the pencil appears to coincide with the line on the model, then moving it parallel to this position back to the board. The apparent lengths of lines are estimated in the same way; holding the pencil in a plane perpendicular to the line of sight, one marks with the thumb the length of pencil which covers the line of the model, rotates the arm with the thumb held in position until the pencil coincides with another line, and then estimates the proportion of this measurement to the second line, Fig. 23·7.

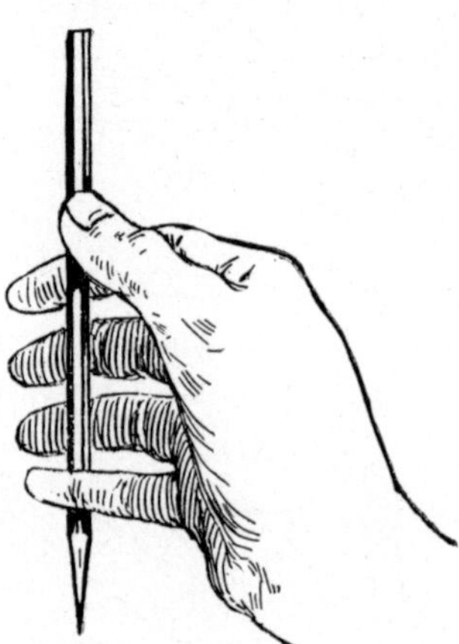

FIG. 23·7—Estimating proportion.

The sketch should be made lightly, with free sketchy lines, and no lines should be erased until the whole sketch has been blocked in. *Do not make the mistake of getting the sketch too small.*

In starting a sketch from the object, set it in a position to give the most advantageous view, and sketch the directions of the principal lines, running them past the limits of the figure toward their vanishing points. Block in the enclosing squares for all circles and circle arcs and proceed with the figure, drawing the main outlines first and adding details later; then brighten the sketch with heavier lines. A good draftsman often adds a few touches of surface shading, but the beginner should be cautious in attempting it. Figure 23·8 shows the general appearance of a "one-point" perspective sketch before the construction lines have been erased. Figure 23·9 is a sketch in angular perspective.

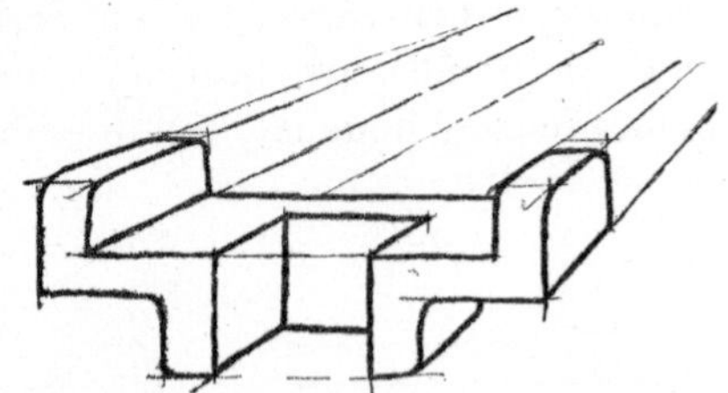

FIG. 23·8—Parallel-perspective sketch.

23·6 Sketching from memory. After one has become proficient in sketching, the memory for form may be strengthened and the capacity for "stored observation" greatly increased by systematic and regular practice in sketching from memory. The order of this study should be graded carefully: first, easy pictorial drawings to be "read" then "copied" exactly from memory; second, orthographic drawings to be read and copied; third, pictorial drawings to be memorized, then drawn in orthographic; fourth, castings and machines to be studied and drawn from memory in orthographic; fifth, orthographic drawings to be studied, then translated from memory into pictorial sketches.

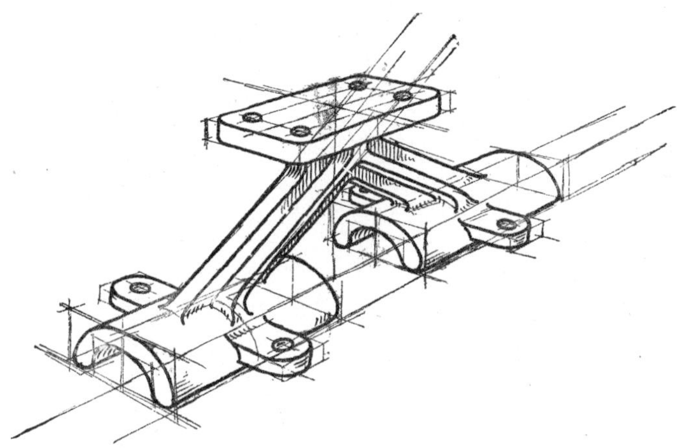

FIG. 23·9—Angular-perspective sketch.

Study the drawing with close concentration until every detail is stored in the memory for future visualization (the time required for this observation should be noted, although it is not the important factor). Then make an accurate sketch of the object from memory. When finished, compare the sketch with the original. The following day make another memory sketch of the same piece without further sight of the original. Carry this practice along, using pieces progressively more difficult. Persevered in for a reasonable time, such practice will give one an ability to remember form and line that will be surprising.

PROBLEMS

Group I. Fig. 23·10. Make pictorial sketches of the pieces shown in this figure.

Group II. Select from Figs. 21·34 to 21·86 some not previously drawn and make freehand sketches in perspective.

Group III. Select one of the objects from Fig. 19·13, study it with concentration for 20 seconds, close the book and reproduce it.

Group IV. Select one of the pieces from Figs. 21·87 to 21·89. Study it for from 10 to 30 seconds, close the book, make a memory sketch of the orthographic projection, and then make a pictorial sketch.

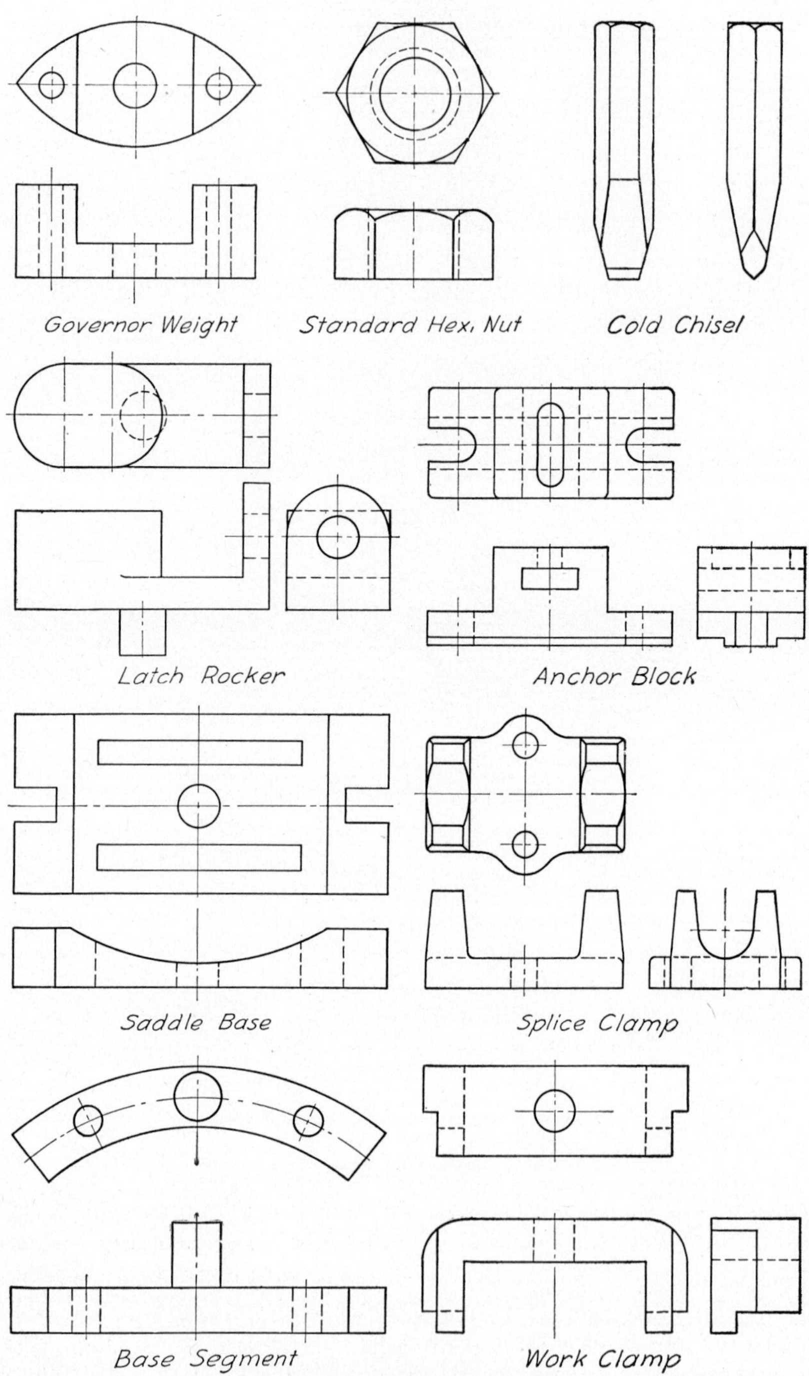

Fig. 23·10—Sketching problems.

Chapter 24

ILLUSTRATION

24·1 As applied to the graphic language, illustration means a clarification in the readability of a drawing through the use of shading and special methods of projection and representation. Often, the drawing may be

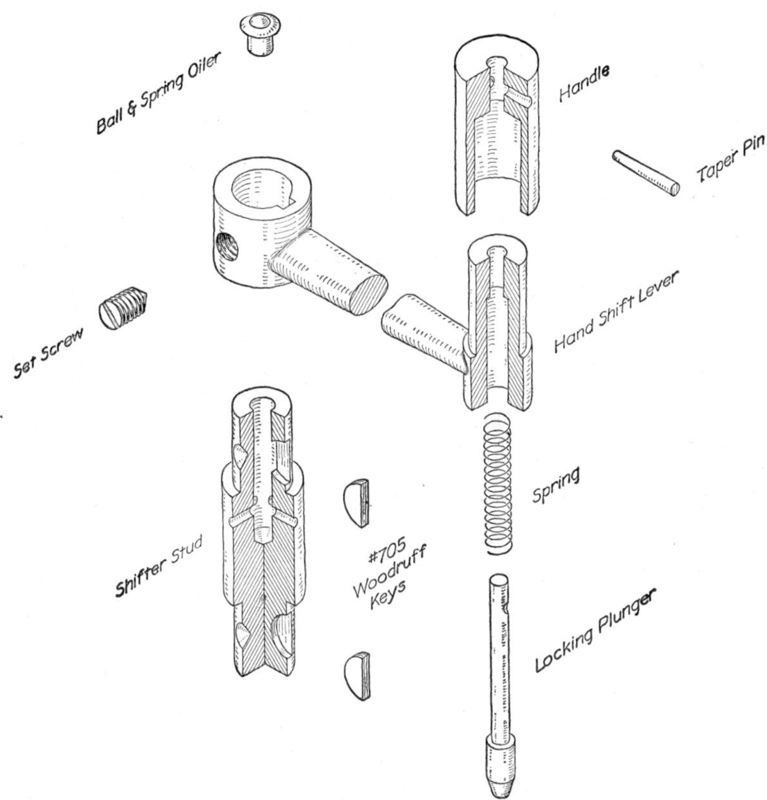

Fig. 24·1—An illustrated drawing.

made so clear that the layman is able to read it quite as readily as one experienced in graphical methods. Any drawing, orthographic, diagrammatic, or pictorial, made either freehand or with instruments in pencil or ink, may be illustrated. Figure 24·1 is an example of an illustrated drawing.

24·2 Types of illustrated drawings. Illustrated drawings are used for many purposes and in many different fields of endeavor. The following examples are typical:

Advertising illustrations are usually rendered pictorial drawings, often having color added to make the presentation as forceful as possible.

Catalogue illustrations, either orthographic or pictorial, are often rendered in pencil, ink, by stippling, air brush, etc.

Operation, service, and repair charts are drawings showing the working parts of a machine with appropriate directions for the purpose intended. These drawings are very effective in shaded pictorial form.

Piping, wiring, and installation diagrams are very easy to read when made in shaded pictorial form.

Architectural and engineering presentation drawings, sometimes rendered in pencil or ink, often in water color, show the building or structure as it will appear when completed.

Textbook illustrations in pictorial form, usually in black and white but sometimes in two colors or full color, add visual clarity and give emphasis not possible by words alone.

Patent drawings are usually shaded to bring out and clarify every feature of the invention.

Production drawings from original design sketches to the final details, subassemblies. and assemblies are frequently made in pictorial form, often shaded. Such drawings are particularly useful when persons not trained in reading orthographic drawings are employed.

24·3 Orthographic illustration. The general practice on working drawings is to use a uniform bold full line for visible outlines. In some special kinds of work, an effective appearance of relief and finish is given, and the legibility of the drawing increased, by using two weights of lines, light and heavy, and by the use of line shading on the surfaces of the object. These methods, singly or together, are used to advantage in technical illustrations, advertising matter, etc., where the definition of *shape* needs emphasis. In any case where an increase in readability is desired the advantage gained will probably justify the increased cost.

24·4 Shade lines. The shade-line system is based on the principle that the object is illuminated by one source of light, with rays coming

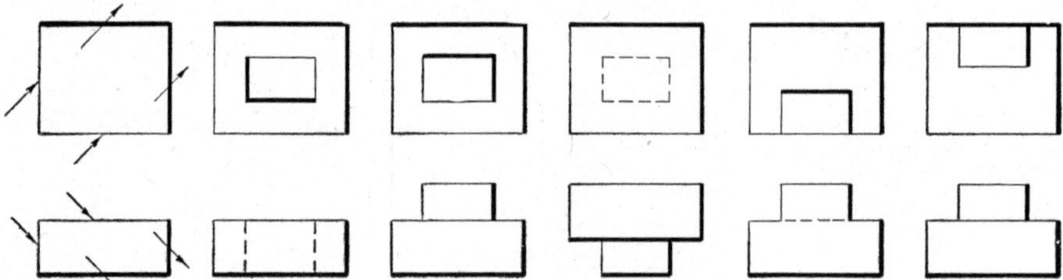

FIG. 24·2—Conventional shade lines.

from the left and downward so that both projections of any ray make an angle of 45° with horizontal-frontal lines. Part of the object is thus illuminated and part is in shade. A *shade line* is a line separating a light face from a dark face, Fig. 24·2. The light lines should be comparatively fine and the shade lines about three times wider. The width of the shade line is added outside the outline of the view. Hidden lines are never shaded.

A circle may be shaded by shifting the center on a 45° line toward the shade line an amount equal to the thickness of the shade line and drawing another semicircular arc with the same radius, Fig. 24·3; or it may be done by keeping the needle in the center and gradually springing the legs out and back to form the shade line, Fig. 24·4.

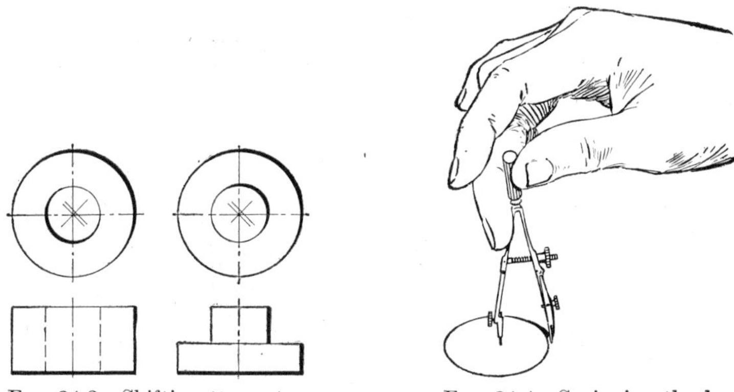

FIG. 24·3—Shifting thecenter.

FIG. 24·4—Springing the legs.

24·5 Line shading. Line shading is a method of representing the effect of light and shade by means of ruled lines. Often the simple shading of a shaft or other round member will add greatly to the effectiveness of a drawing and may even save making another view; or a few lines of "surface shading" on a flat surface will show its position and character.

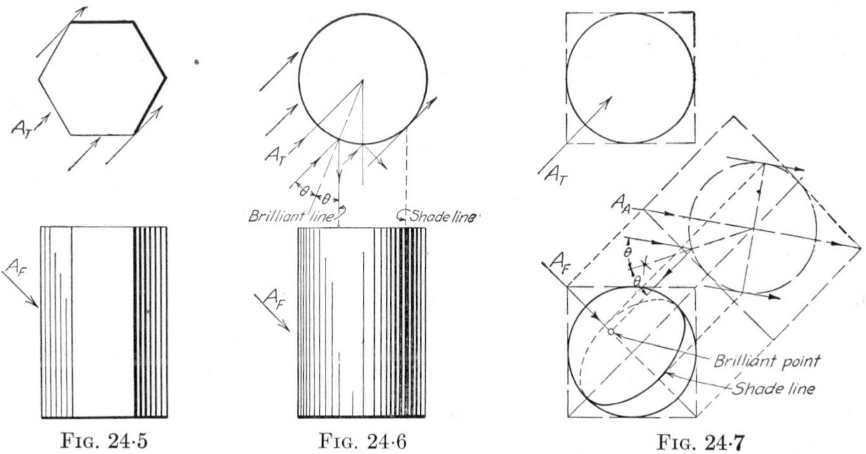

FIG. 24·5 FIG. 24·6 FIG. 24·7
FIGS. 24·5 to 24·7—Theory of line shading.

The theoretical direction of the light is considered to be in the direction of the body diagonal of a cube whose faces are parallel to the planes of projection. Thus the two projections of a ray of light would be as A_T and A_F, Fig. 24·5, and two visible faces of the hexagonal prism would be illuminated while one is in shade. The figure illustrates the rule that *an inclined illuminated surface is lightest nearest the eye and an inclined surface in shade is darkest nearest the eye.*

A cylinder would be illuminated as in Fig. 24·6. The darkest place is at the tangent or "shade line" and the lightest part at the "brilliant line" where the light is reflected directly to the eye.

A method of finding the brilliant point and shade line of a sphere is shown in Fig. 24·7. A right auxiliary view of the sphere and circumscribing

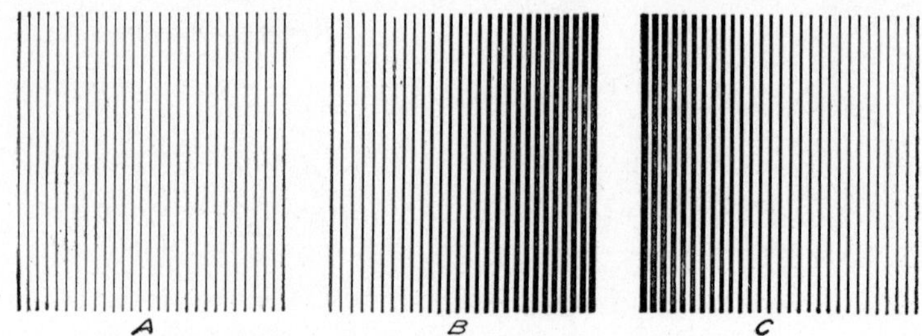

Fig. 24·8—Flat and graded tints.

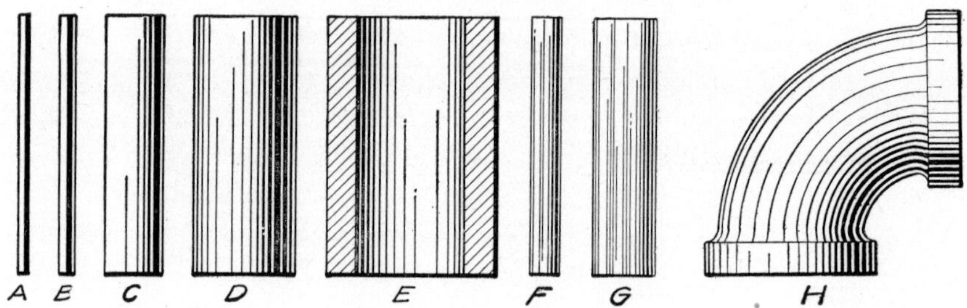

Fig. 24·9—Cylinder shading.

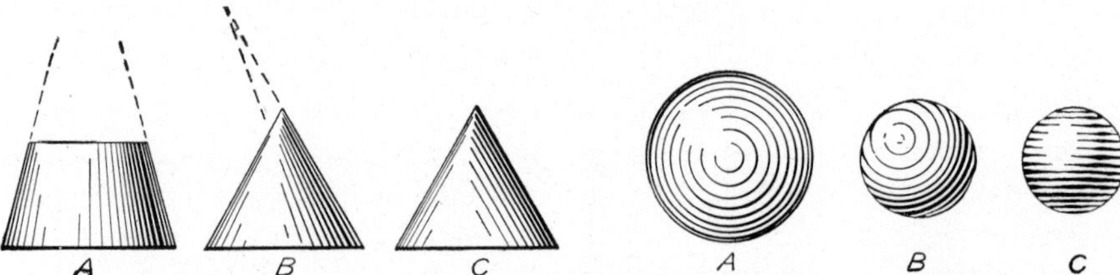

Fig. 24·10—Cone shading.

Fig. 24·11—Sphere shading.

cube is taken on the body diagonal plane of the cube, and the angle (2θ) between the auxiliary view of the ray of light and the auxiliary view of the center line to the eye bisected, giving the brilliant point. Tangents to the auxiliary view of the sphere parallel to the auxiliary view of a ray of light locate the shade line.

Flat and graded tints are shown in Fig. 24·8. In these the pitch, or distance from center to center of lines, is equal. In graded tints, as *B* and *C*, the setting of the pen is not changed for every line, but several lines are drawn, the pen changed, and several more drawn.

Figure 24·9 shows the shading technique for cylinders. A conical surface may be shaded with lines pointing toward the apex A, toward a point on the extension of the side B, or with lines parallel to the sides C, Fig. 24·10. Three methods of shading a sphere are shown in Fig. 24·11.

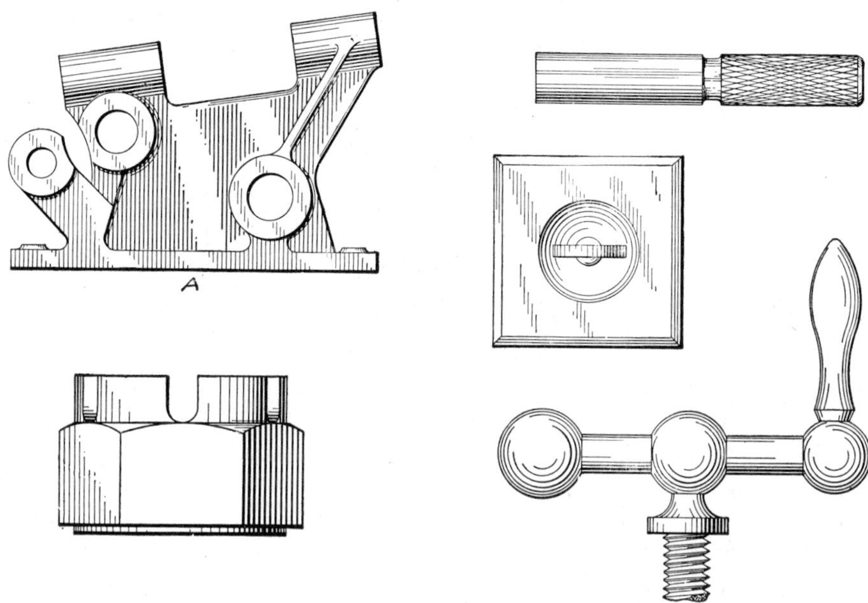

Fig. 24·12—Applications of line shading.

To execute shading rapidly and effectively requires practice, some artistic ability, and, as much as anything else, good judgment in knowing when to stop. Applications of line shading on flat and curved surfaces are shown in Fig. 24·12.

24·6 Pictorial illustration. Pictorial illustration combines any one of the regular pictorial methods with some method of shading or "rendering." In considering a specific problem, the pictorial form—axonometric, oblique, or perspective—should be decided upon, and then a method of shading chosen which is suited to the method of reproduction and the general effect desired. The chapters on pictorial representation, perspective, and sketching are prerequisite to the study of pictorial illustration.

24·7 Light and shade. The conventional position of the light for light-and-shade drawing is the same as that used for orthographic line shading, that is, a position to the left, in front of, and above the object. Any surface or portion of a surface perpendicular to the light direction and directly illuminated by the light would receive the greatest amount of light and be lightest in tone on the drawing; any face not illuminated by the light source would be "in shade" and be darkest on the drawing. Other surfaces, receiving less light than the "high" light but more than a shade portion, would be intermediate in tone.

One must have, at the outset, an understanding of the simple one-light method of illumination and, in addition, have some artistic appreciation for the illumination on various surfaces of the object. Figure 24·13 shows a sphere, cylinder, cone, and cube illuminated as described and shaded accordingly. Study the tone values in this illustration.

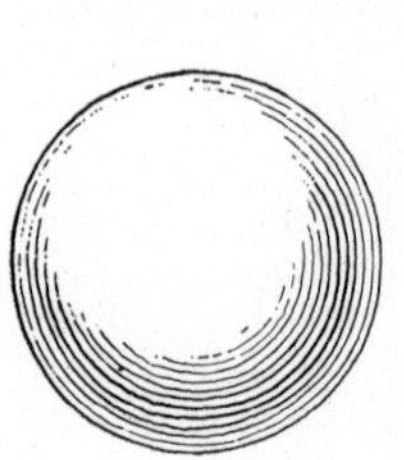
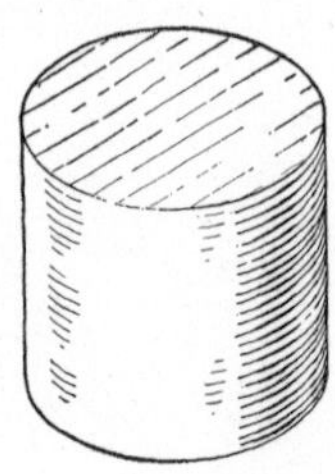
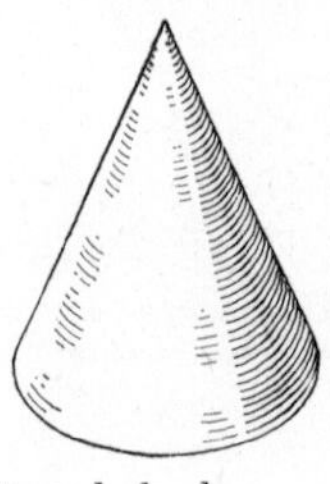
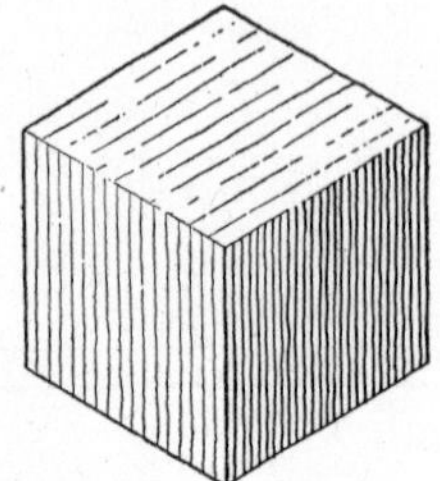

FIG. 24·13—Light and shade.

24·8 Shade lines—pictorial. Shade lines, by their contrast, add some effect of light and shade to the drawing. These lines used alone, without other shading, give the simplest possible shading method. Usually, the best effect is had by using heavy lines for only the left vertical and upper horizontal edges of the dark faces, Fig. 24·14. Holes and other circular features are drawn with heavy lines on the shade side. Shade lines should

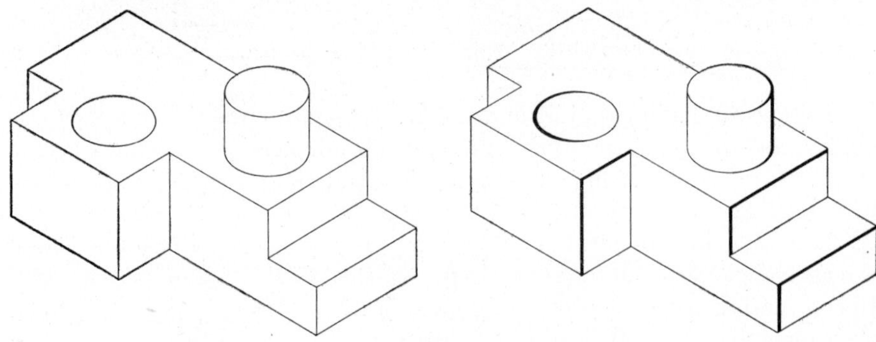

FIG. 24·14—Outline and shade lines.

be used sparingly as the inclusion of too many heavy lines simply adds weight to the drawing and does not give the best effect.

24·9 Pencil rendering. There are two general methods of pencil shading—continuous tone and line tone. Continuous-tone shading is done with a fairly soft pencil with its point flattened. A medium-rough paper is best to use for the purpose. Start with a light over-all tone and then build the middle tones and shade portions gradually. Figure 24·15 is an example. High lights may be cleaned out with an eraser.

Line-tone shading requires a little more skill, as the tones are produced by line spacing and weight. Light lines at wide spacing produce the lightest tone and heavy lines at close spacing make the darkest shade. High lights are left perfectly white, and pure black may be used sparingly for deep shade or shadow. Figure 24·16 is an example, drawn with only a very light outline.

Usually, complete over-all shading is somewhat heavy, and a lighter more "open" treatment is desired. In this method light portions of the object are left with little or no shading, and middle tones and shade are

FIG. 24·15—Continuous-tone shading.

lined sparingly. The few lines used, however, strongly suggest light and shade and surface finish, Fig. 24·17. There are many variations in this type of rendering.

24·10 Pen-and-ink rendering. Pen-and-ink methods follow the same general pattern as work in pencil, with the exception that no continuous tone is possible. There are however, some variations not usually used in pencil work. Figure 15·80 indicates line techniques. As in pencil work, the common, and usually the most pleasing, method is the partially shaded, suggestive system.

24·11 Special shading methods. Several unique methods may be used as occasion demands for the representation of special textures and for rapid work.

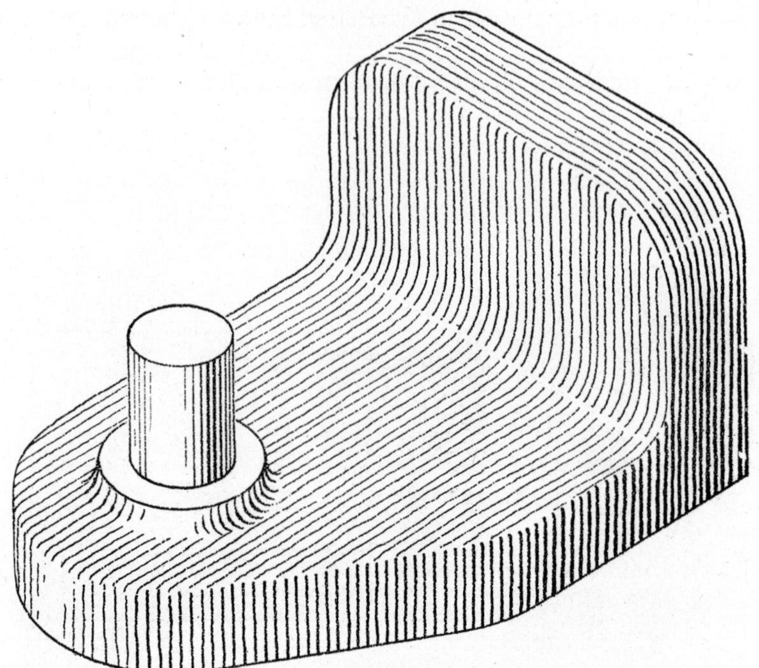

Fig. 24·16—Line-tone shading.

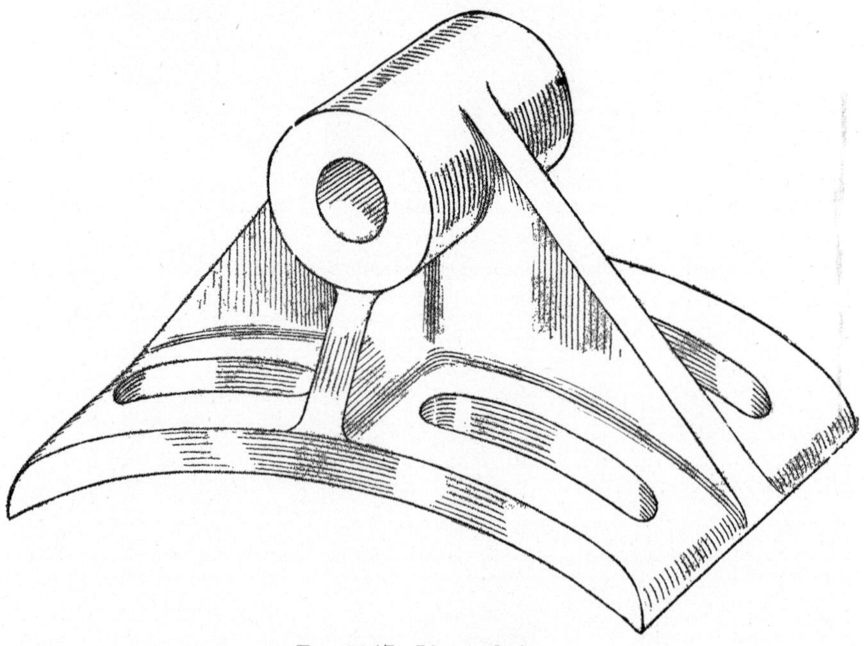

Fig. 24·17—Line technique.

Smudge shading is a rapid method often used for the representation of smooth surfaces, Fig. 24·18. Graphite from a soft pencil, powdered graphite, charcoal, or crayon sauce is rubbed first on a piece of paper, then picked up with a piece of cotton or an artist's stump and applied to the drawing.

High lights are easily cleaned out with a sharpened eraser. Be careful in shading over an erased portion, however, as the abrading of the paper will cause the shading medium to "take" more heavily.

FIG. 24·18—Smudge shading.

Stippling with pen, pencil, brush, or sponge is a very effective method for indicating rough-textured surfaces. With pen or pencil, a multitude of dots widely spaced for light surfaces and closer for dark surfaces give a good effect of light and shade. In brush or sponge stippling, printer's ink or artist's oil color (drier added) is first worked out smoothly on a palette; the medium is then picked up from the palette with a bristle brush or a sponge and applied to the drawing with a dabbing motion. Sharp edges of shaded areas may be maintained by the use of masks.

Small areas are easily cleaned up with a razor blade or "scratcher." High lights may be cleaned out with an eraser after the ink is dry. Figure 24·19 is an example of brush stippling with the smooth surfaces rendered by smudging.

Prepared papers are popular for a wide variety of commercial drawings. Craftint[1] papers are made in two varieties, single-tone and double-tone, and have a shading pattern in the paper that is brought out by a special developer. In using these papers the drawing is penciled and the solid blacks inked in with waterproof drawing ink. The shading tones are then brought out by brushing on the developer in the areas where shading is wanted. These papers are available in a wide variety of shading patterns. Figure 24·21 is drawn on Craftint paper.

[1] Craftint Manufacturing Co., Cleveland, Ohio.

Shading screens of clear cellulose with printed line or dot pattern provide a simple and effective shading method. Craftint shading film is an overlay sheet containing a pattern printed in either black or white. The shading pattern is easily rubbed off with a smooth wood stick wherever the shading is not wanted. Any part of the white pattern may be converted to black with a special developer.

Zip-a-tone screens[1] are clear cellulose printed with a shading pattern and backed with a special adhesive. In use, the screen is applied to the drawing

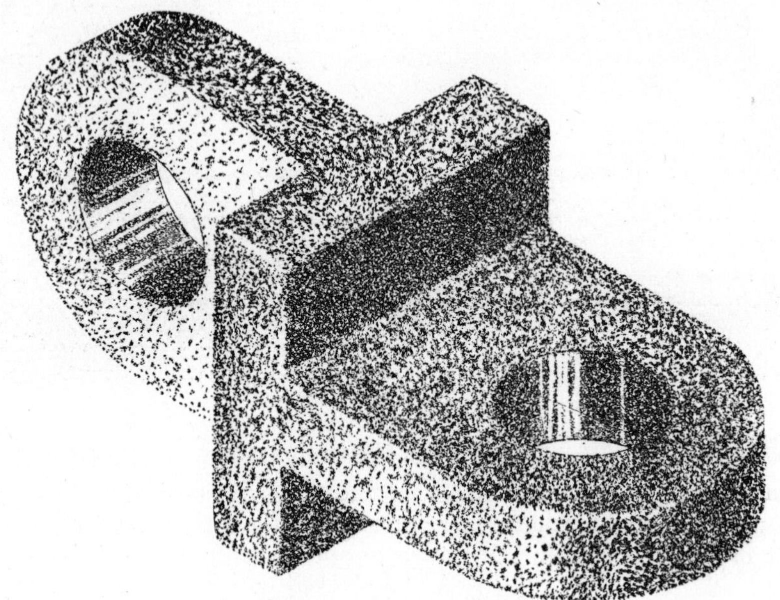

FIG. 24·19—Brush-stipple shading.

and rubbed down lightly wherever shading is wanted. The shaded sections are then outlined with a cutting needle, and the unwanted pieces stripped off. The portions left on the drawing are then rubbed down firmly with a burnisher. High lights may be painted out with opaque white if the area is too small to strip off in the regular way. A variety of shading patterns are available. Figure 3·34 is shaded with a Zip-a-tone screen.

Scratchboard. Drawing paper having a chalky surface is much used for commercial illustrations because of the ease with which white lines may be produced on a black background, as well as black lines on a white background. Ross-board,[2] obtainable in many surface textures for both pencil and ink drawings, is popular among illustrators.

For ink work, the drawing is penciled on the board in the usual way, and then inked in by line-shading the lighter areas, working gradually to the

[1] The Para-tone Company, Chicago, Ill.
[2] The Charles J. Ross Co., Philadelphia, Pa.

darker areas. The darker areas are painted in with a brush, and, when dry, white lines, dots, etc., are easily produced by scratching off the ink with a sharp-pointed knife, sharp stylus, or a needle point. Corrections are easily made by scratching off unwanted ink. Scratched areas may be reinked if necessary. Figure 24·20 is an example of scratchboard technique.

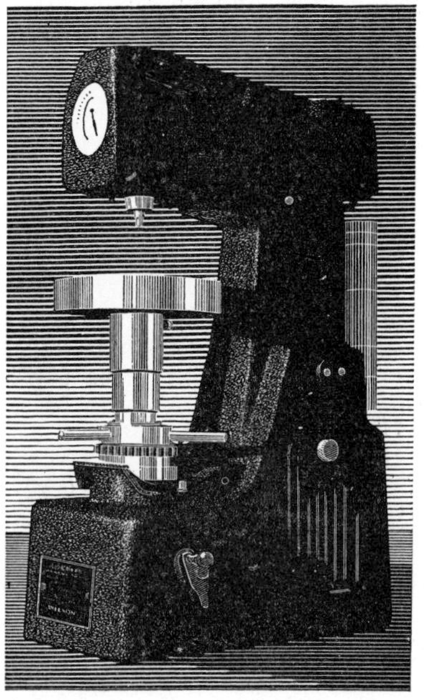

FIG. 24·20—A scratchboard drawing. (*Courtesy of Wilson Mechanical Instrument Co.*)

24·12 Illustrated working drawings. Modern mass-production methods demand simplification and breakdown of the multitude of manufacturing operations. By the use of illustrated drawings, complex and difficult jobs are brought within the grasp of workers not trained in reading complicated orthographic drawings. Illustrated drawings are used in every phase of production, from the original design to the final operating instructions.

Actual practice will vary somewhat within an industry, and vary widely between industries, but in general, illustrated drawings may be classified as (1) *design*, (2) *manufacturing*, and (3) *operation and maintenance.*

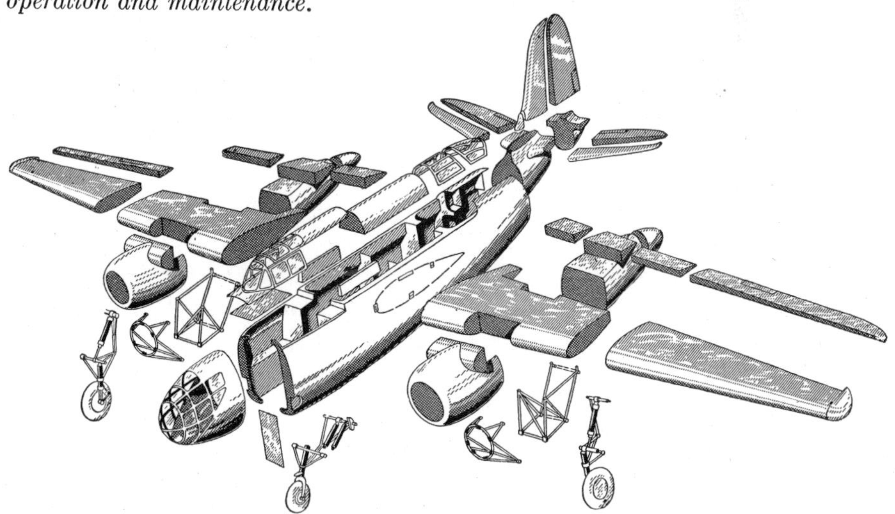

FIG. 24·21—A design drawing. (*Redrawn from Aviation Sketchbook.*)

Design drawings include a variety of pictorial illustrations that first break down the machine or structure into small workable units, and second, give details of construction, location of equipment, structural features, function of parts and equipment, tooling methods, etc. These drawings are used to study the complete production job and to plan and correlate the work. As the design progresses these drawings are altered, corrected, or redrawn.

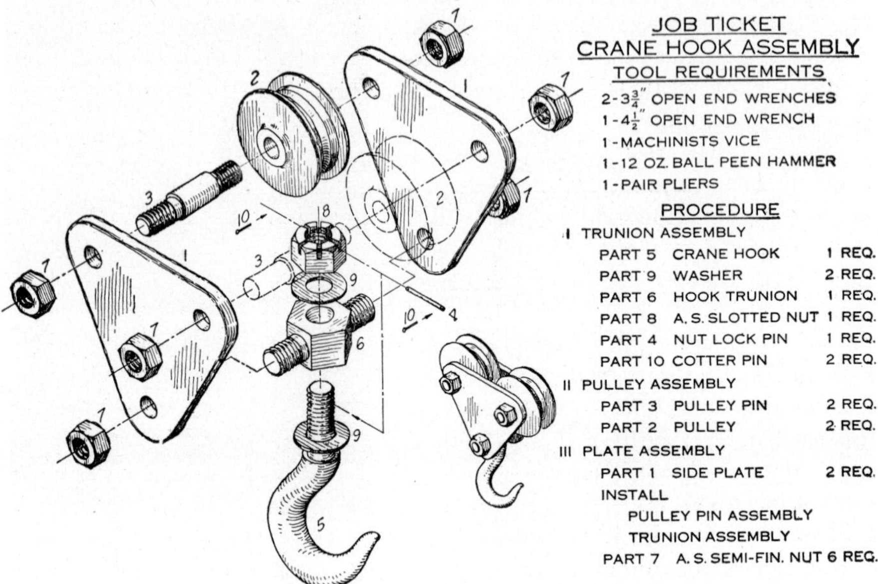

FIG. 24·22—A manufacturing illustration.

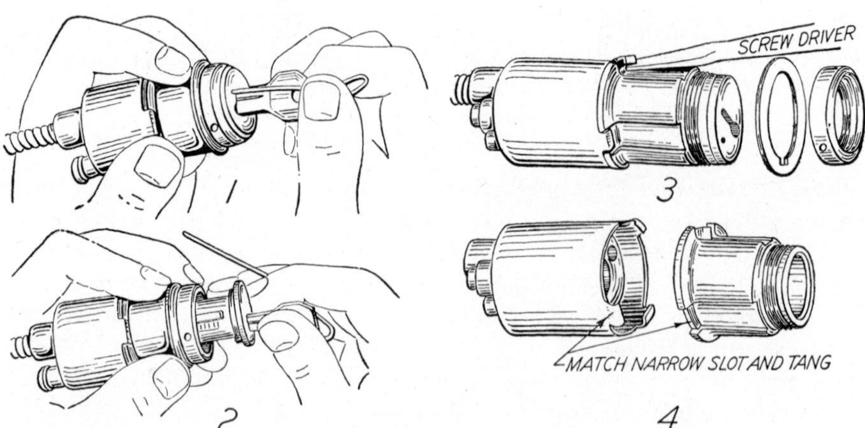

FIG. 24·23—A maintenance illustration. (*Redrawn from Chevrolet Shop Manual.*)

The preliminary production breakdown, Fig. 24·21, is an example of the type of illustration used in the design stage of the work.

Manufacturing illustrations give detailed information regarding the breakdown of the structure or machine from which a multitude of separate illustrations are made to show the location of subassemblies, parts, and equipment, give directions for performing operations, give detailed information for the manufacture of parts, and give directions for assembly. Figure 24·22 is an example of a manufacturing illustration taken from the set of details, Fig. 15·44.

Operation and maintenance illustrations give directions for disassembly, repair and replacement of parts, directions for lubrication, inspection and care of equipment, etc. In many cases the same drawings that were originally made for manufacturing can be used in a service manual. Figure 24·23 is an example.

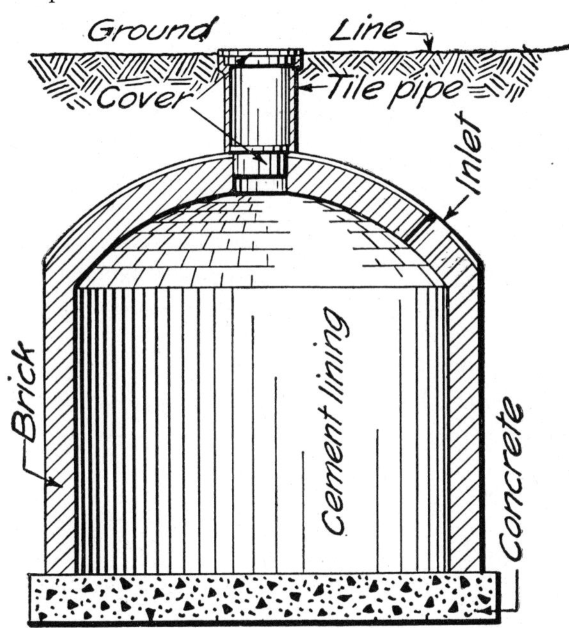

FIG. 24·24—A drawing for one-half reduction.

24·13 Drawing for reproduction. Drawings required for the illustrations in books, periodicals, catalogues, or other printed materials are reproduced by one of the photomechanical processes, that is, by zinc or copper etching, half tone, or one of the methods of photolithography.

The drawings are usually made larger than the final printed size and are reduced photographically in the reproduction process; consequently the work must be done with visualization of the line weights, contrast, size of lettering, and general effect in reduced size.

If it is desired to preserve the hand-drawn character of the original, the reduction should be slight; but if a very smooth effect is wanted, the drawing may be as much as 3 or 4 times larger than the reproduction. The best general size is from 1½ (for one-third reduction) to 2 times (for one-half reduction) the linear size of the cut.

The reduction is usually some even proportion as one-fourth, one-third, one-half, etc., although odd reductions may be used. For a drawing marked "Reduce ⅓″," the reproduction will be two-thirds the linear size of the original. Figure 24·24 illustrates the appearance of an original drawing, and Fig. 24·25 is the same drawing reduced one-half. The coarse appearance, open shading, and lettering size of the original should be noticed. The line work must be kept fairly "open" for if lines are drawn close together the space between them may choke in the reproduction and mar the effect. A reducing glass, a concave lens mounted like a reading glass, is sometimes used to aid in judging the appearance of a drawing on reduction.

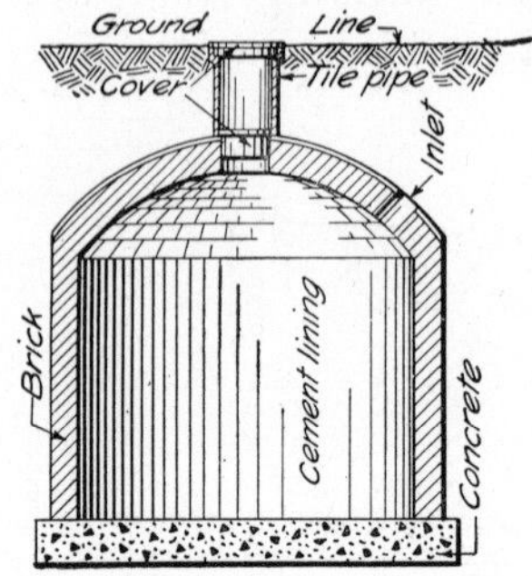

FIG. 24·25—One-half reduction.

Drawings for reproduction may be altered and corrected in ways not permissible in other work. Irregularities may be painted out with opaque white. A sharp blade or "scratcher" may be used to clean off small errors. If it is desired to shift a figure after it has been inked, it may be cut out and pasted on in the required position. A portion of the drawing may be pasted over with a piece of paper for blocking out or for redrawing. Reference letters and numbers, notes, and other lettering are often cut out of a sheet printed from type of proper size and pasted on the drawing. The edges of pasted pieces will not show on the final reproduction as they will be eliminated by the engraver when the plate is finished.

Line drawings are usually reproduced by the process known as "zinc etching" in which the drawing is photographed on a prepared zinc plate (when a particularly fine result is desired, a copper plate is used); then this plate is etched with acid, leaving the lines in relief and giving, when mounted, a block which can be printed along with type in an ordinary printing press. Drawings for zinc etching should be made on smooth white paper or tracing cloth in black drawing ink. The finest lines should be black and definite—weak thin lines will not reproduce well.

Wash drawings and photographs are reproduced in a similar way on copper by the half-tone process in which a ruled screen is placed in front of the plate, that breaks up the tones into a series of dots of varying size. Screens of different fineness are used for different kinds of paper, from the newspaper half tone of 80 to 100 lines to the inch, the ordinary commercial and magazine half tone of 133 lines, to the fine 150- and 175-line half tones for printing on very smooth coated paper.

The photolithographic processes may be used to reproduce line drawings, wash drawings, or photographs. The drawing is photographed on a thin sheet of sensitized zinc and chemically processed to use in a lithographic press in which the zinc plate prints on a rubber blanket, which in turn prints on the paper.

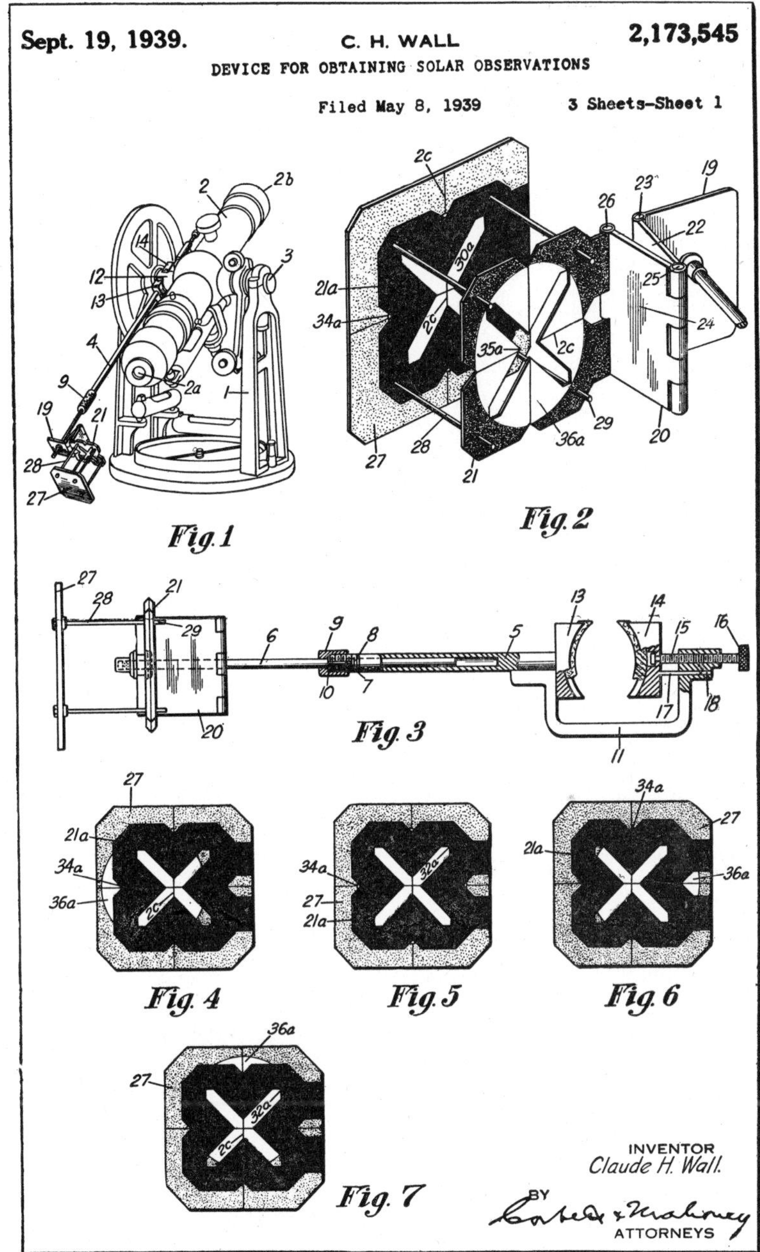

FIG. 24·26—A patent-office drawing (reduced one-half).

24·14 Patent-office drawings. In an application for letters patent on an invention or discovery a written description, called the "specification," is required, and for a machine or device a drawing showing every feature of the invention must also be supplied. A high standard of execution and conformity to the rules of the Patent Office must be observed. A pamphlet called the *Rules of Practice*, giving full information and rules governing Patent-office procedure in applying for a patent, may be had by addressing the *Commissioner of Patents, Washington, D.C.*

The drawings are made on smooth white paper, 10″ × 15″, with a border line 1″ from the edges. A space not less than 1¼″ inside the top border must be left blank for the printed title added by the Patent Office. Drawings must be made in India ink and drawn for reproduction to a reduced size. As many sheets as are necessary may be used.

Patent-office drawings are not working drawings. They are descriptive and pictorial rather than structural; hence they will have no center lines, dimensions, notes, or names of views. The views are lettered with figure numbers and the parts designated by reference numbers through which the invention is described in the specification.

The drawings may be made in orthographic, axonometric, oblique, or perspective. The pictorial system is used extensively, for either all or part of the views. Surface shading is used whenever it will aid legibility.

Figure 24·26 is an example of a Patent-office drawing.

24·15 Axonometric projection from orthographic views. In making pictorial drawings of complicated parts, especially whenever curves must be plotted, projection from orthographic views may give an advantage in speed and ease of drawing. Any position, isometric, dimetric, or trimetric, may be used.

The three axes of an axonometric drawing are *three mutually perpendicular edges* in space. If the angle of rotation and the angle of tilt of the object are known or decided upon, the three axes for the pictorial drawing and the location of the orthographic views for projection to the pictorial may easily be found. Figure 24·27 will illustrate the procedure. At G is shown the three orthographic views of a cube. The three mutually perpendicular edges OA, OB, and OC will be foreshortened differently when the cube is rotated in space for some axonometric position, but the ends of the axes A, B, and C will always lie on the surface of a sphere whose radius is $OA = OB = OC$, as illustrated by G'. At any particular angle of tilt of the cube, the axis ends A and B will describe an ellipse, as shown, if the cube is rotated about the axis OC. The axis OC will appear foreshortened at oc'. Thus, for any particular position of the cube in space, representing some desired axonometric position, the axes may be located and their relative amounts of foreshortening found.

Moreover, if a face of the cube is revolved about a *frontal axis perpendicular to the axis which is at right angles to the face*, an orthographic view of the face, in projection with the axonometric view, will result. Thus, the top and right-side views may be located as at J and projected as at K to give the axonometric drawing.

The drawings at H, J, and K will illustrate the practical use of the theory of rotation just described. The actual size of the sphere is unimportant, as it is used only to establish the direction of the axes. First, the desired angle of rotation R and the angle of tilt T are decided upon and laid out as shown at H. The minor axis for the ellipse upon which A and B will lie is found by projecting vertically from c and drawing the circle as shown. A and B on the major-axis circle of the ellipse will be at a and b; on the minor-axis

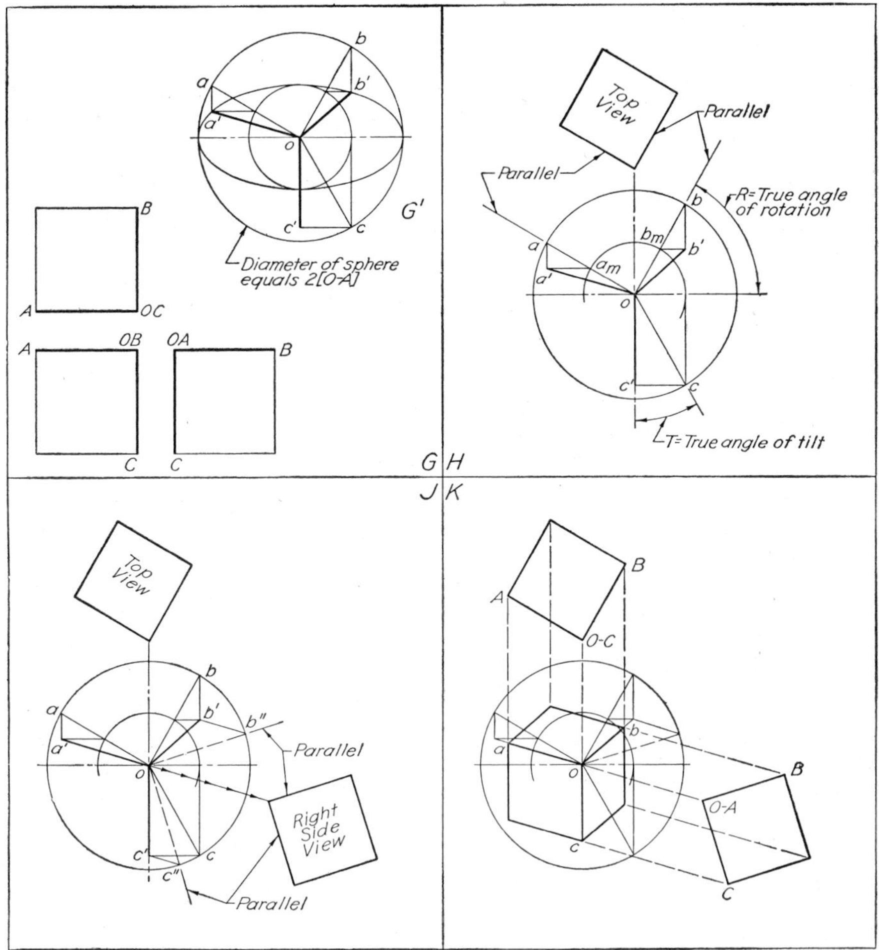

FIG. 24·27—Axonometric projection from orthographic views.

circle they will be at a_m and b_m; and they are found in the axonometric position by projecting as in the concentric-circle ellipse method to a' and b'. The foreshortened position of C is found by projecting horizontally across from c to c'.

The top orthographic view of the cube (or object) will be parallel to oa and ob, and projection from the orthographic view to the axonometric will be vertical (parallel to aa' and bb').

Projection from an orthographic right-side view would be as shown at

J. The right side of the cube, containing axes OC and OB is found by projecting from b' and c', parallel to oa', to locate b'' and c'' on the circle representing the sphere. The sides of the cube (or object) are parallel to ob'' and oc'', as shown at *J*. Projection from the right-side view to the axonometric view is in the direction of oa', as indicated.

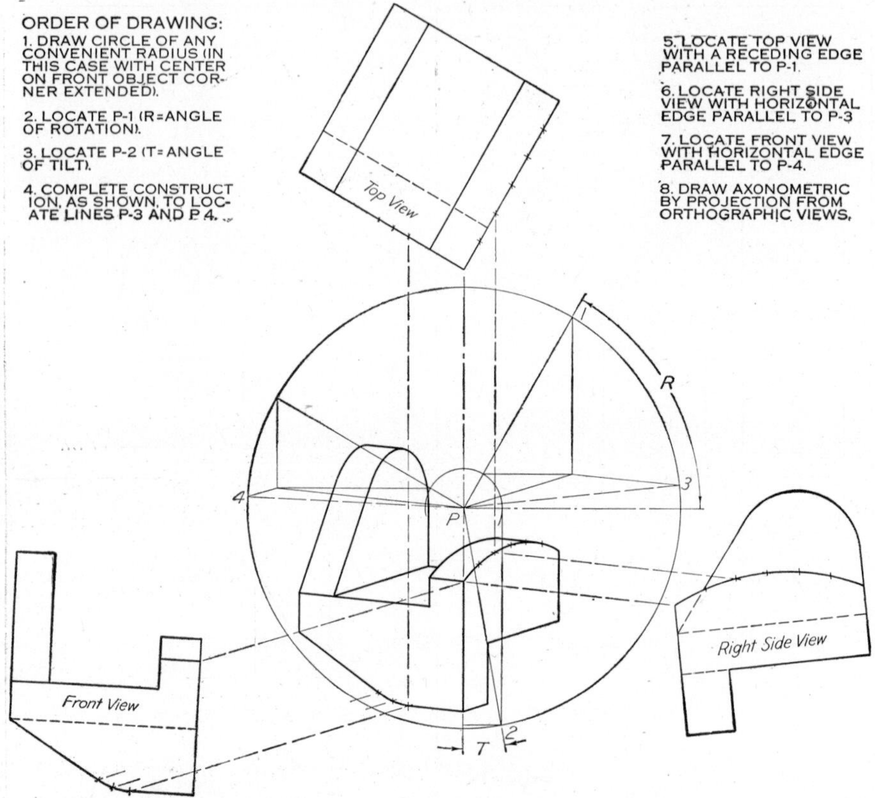

FIG. 24·28—An axonometric drawing by projection.

The axonometric drawing is shown projected at *K*. The dashed lines indicate the actual projectors, and the light solid lines and circles show the necessary construction just described.

One advantage of this method is that the angle of rotation and tilt can be decided upon so that the object may be shown in the best position. Figure 24·28 is an example of an axonometric drawing made by projection. The curved faces are plotted by projecting points as shown.

Isometric is, of course, a special case of axonometric projection in which all three axes are foreshortened equally. The work of finding the axes for isometric projection from orthographic views is reduced if the views are located by angle, as illustrated in Fig. 24·29.

24·16 Oblique projection from orthographic views. In oblique projection the projectors make some oblique angle with the picture plane. The actual angle of the projectors (with horizontal and frontal planes) is not critical, and a variety of angles may be used. The making of an oblique drawing by projection from the views is very simple, as illustrated by Fig. 24·30. The picture plane is located, and one face of the object is made coincident with the picture plane. The front view is located at a convenient place on the paper, as shown. The angle of the projectors in the top view may be assumed (in this case 45°) and projections made to the picture plane as shown. The angle of the projectors in the front view may be then assumed (in this case 30°). Projection from the front view at the assumed angle, and vertically from the picture plane, as shown, will locate the necessary lines and points for the oblique view.

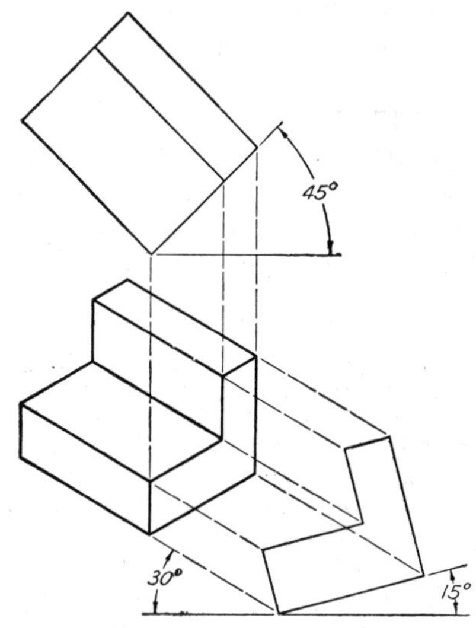

FIG. 24·29—Isometric by projection.

Reversed axes may be obtained by projecting downward from the front view. An axis to the left may be had by changing the direction of the pro-

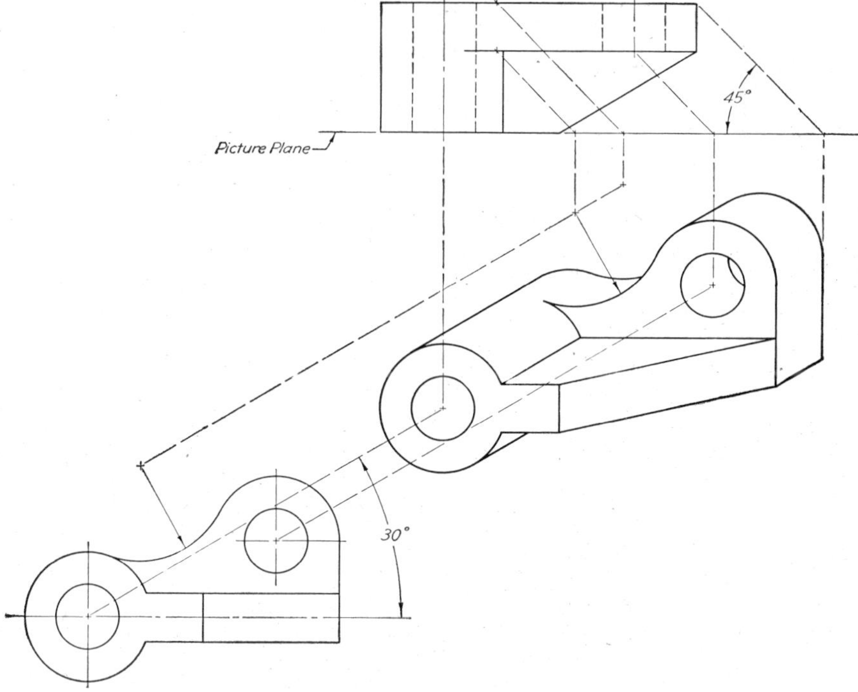

FIG. 24·30—Oblique by projection.

jectors in the top view. Any desired oblique axes may be had by altering the angles (top and front) for the projectors.

PROBLEMS

24·17 The problems in other chapters may be used for problems of illustration as well as their originally assigned purpose. Some previously drawn orthographic problem may be redrawn as an illustration in either orthographic or pictorial, or some problem not previously worked on may be used. The following are suggested:

Group I. Orthographic illustrations

Select one of the pictorial drawings of Chap. 7 and make an orthographic drawing. Use shade lines and line shading to bring out the surface features.

Group II. Isometric illustrations

Select one of the isometric problems of Chap. 21 and make an isometric illustration. Use any appropriate shading method.

Group III. Oblique illustrations

Select one of the oblique problems in Chap. 21 and make an oblique illustration. Use any appropriate shading method.

Group IV. Axonometric illustrations

Select one of the problems in Chap. 21 and make an axonometric illustration by projection from the orthographic views.

Group V. Perspective illustrations

Select one of the problems in Chap. 21 or 22, make a perspective drawing, and shade.

Group VI. Design illustrations

Select one of the problems in Chap. 15, either an assembly or set of details, and redesign for (*a*) different size, (*b*) some different method of manufacture (castings changed to forgings or welded construction, etc.), (*c*) simplification of construction, (*d*) changed appearance. Make first design freehand in pictorial form, then make finished drawings in axonometric or perspective, shaded.

Group VII. Manufacturing illustrations

Select one of the problems in Chap. 15, either an assembly or set of details, and make (*a*) an illustrated detail drawing of a single part, (*b*) a job-sheet illustration for a group of parts, giving directions for assembly, tools used, etc., (*c*) an "exploded" assembly, with piece numbers and parts list.

Group VIII. Operation and maintenance illustrations

Select one of the problems in Chap. 15 and make, (*a*) diagram for oiling, etc., (*b*) exploded assembly with order and directions for assembly.

Group IX. Freehand illustrations

Make any of the illustrations in Groups I to III freehand.

Group X. Illustrations for reduction

Make a shaded pictorial drawing of one of the problems described in Groups I to V for catalogue or advertising illustration.

Chapter 25

AIRCRAFT DRAWING

25·1 In preparation for aircraft drawing, the requisites are a thorough knowledge of orthographic projection and descriptive geometry; an acquaintance with shop practice, including riveted construction and welding; experience in the use of sheet-metal stamped shapes; and, desirably, a facility in using perspective and other pictorial methods. Aircraft drawing differs somewhat from machine drawing because of the type of structure and the material used. In fuselage and wing and in tail and rudder structure the use of stamped metal with standard small angles, etc., to make up the inner construction and permit the application of a perfect outer surface or "skin" presents problems in drawing otherwise rarely encountered. Perhaps in no other branch of engineering is it so necessary that the engineer be a skilled draftsman. Indeed, in some drafting rooms the distinction between designers and draftsmen is not made, as the designers are the draftsmen.

Drawings used in the aircraft industry may be classified under three general divisions: (1) preliminary design drawings, (2) layout drawings, and (3) production drawings.

25·2 Preliminary design drawings. The drawings used in designing may be again classified somewhat in the order in which they are started, although they are carried along concurrently. In the industry these divisions are called (1) *preliminary "three-view" drawing,* (2) *inboard profile,* (3) *wing drawing and details, and* (4) *master diagram.*

Three-view drawing. The three-view drawing is a preliminary drawing with top, front, and side views on one sheet, made for study of the general relationship of fuselage, wings, and tail. This drawing is the basis of all design work. On it the designer studies the placement of the wings, the placement and general design of the landing gear, arrangement of equipment, and the form and blending of the various surfaces. The views are arranged as in Fig. 25·1, although this figure is shown to give the names of the principai parts of an airplane.

Inboard profile. The inboard profile is a section taken longitudinally through the center of the fuselage together with a sectional top view, showing the structure and the arrangement of equipment to larger scale and in greater detail than does the three-view drawing. Several typical cross sections may also be included on this sheet, showing general structure and clearances. Figure 25·2 shows a part of an inboard profile, much reduced.

It is universal practice on all aircraft drawings, both assembly and detail, to have the nose to the left, or pointing west.

Wing drawing and details. This drawing shows in detail the structure of the wings and the method of fastening to the fuselage. The wing shape is described by a top view, front view, and side view, with a number of detail sections to show construction. Figure 25·3 is a portion of a wing drawing.

Master diagram. The master diagram is an accurate center-line skeleton drawing, which shows the locations but omits the details of all major structural parts of the plane, and includes spans, lengths, height, wheel tread, clearances, etc.

The diagram is generally made to small scale, and has on it the lofted or calculated dimensional data. As smaller or auxiliary portions of the plane are designed, the master diagram is consulted in order to get location dimensions correct and to ensure clearances.

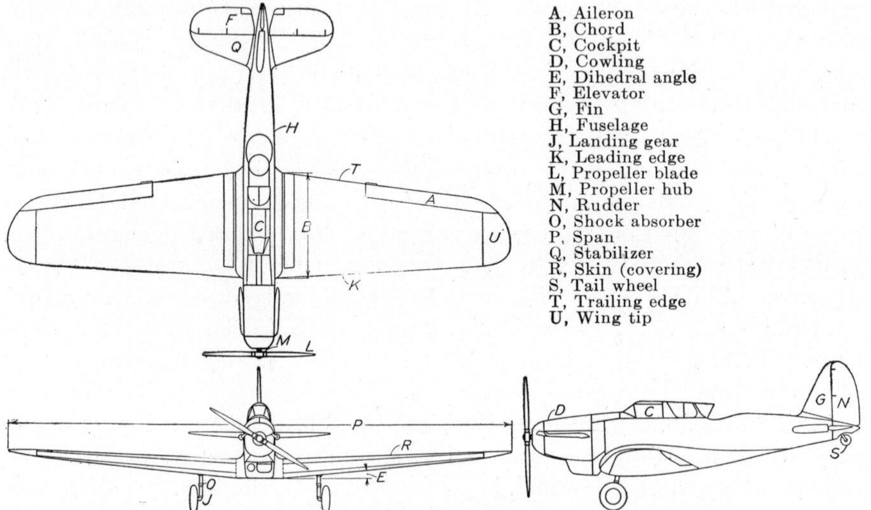

FIG. 25·1—A three-view drawing, with names of parts added.

Weight estimate. An accurate weight estimate of the various parts, obtained by mathematical calculation, is made as the design progresses, with alterations of the master diagram and related drawings as changes in weight or location occur.

25·3 Models. Along with the design drawings, two kinds of models may be made for further study and visualization of the new design.

(1) *Wind-tunnel model.* When the general design of the plane has been decided upon, a wind-tunnel model is made and tested in order to check performance calculations.

(2) *Mock-up.* A mock-up is a full-size model of the plane or, generally, of a portion of it, made for the study of the location of seats, equipment, pilot's controls and instruments, as well as for checking clearances. It is with the mock-up that the "feel" and arrangement of the controls are

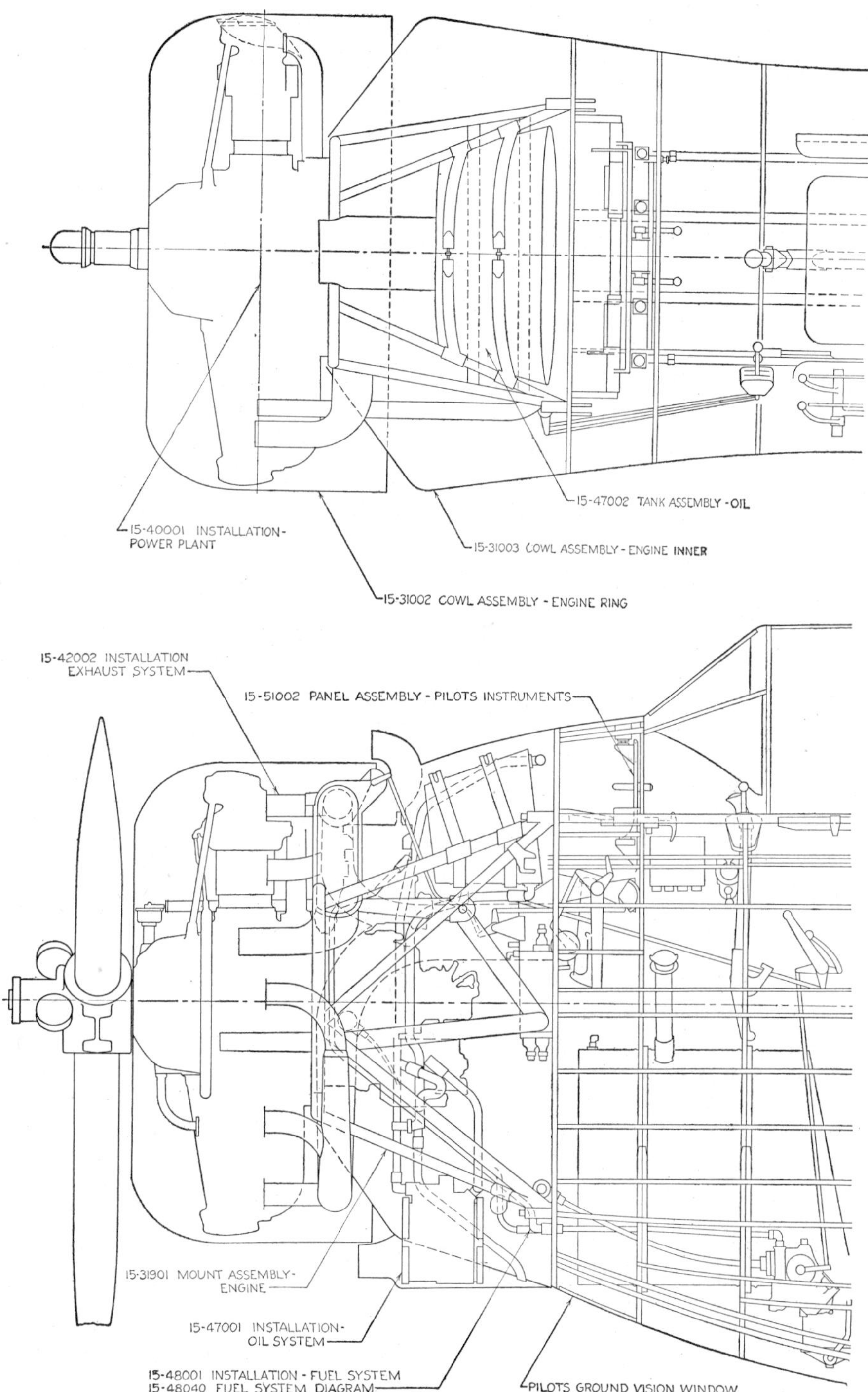

FIG. 25·2—A portion of an inboard profile.

studied, and the location of all equipment for accessibility, convenience, and efficiency is made. When production is actually started, a more nearly complete mock-up is built for final study and checking.

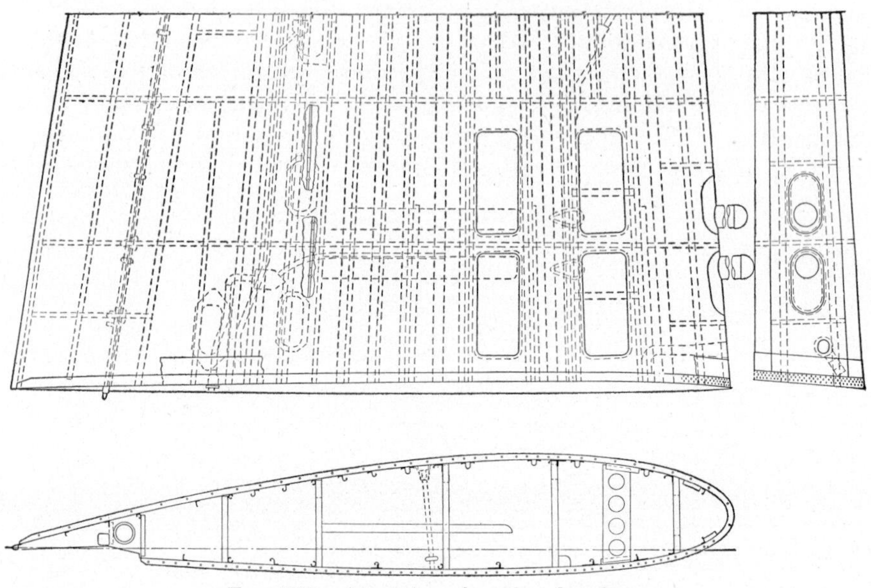

FIG. 25·3—A portion of a wing drawing.

25·4 Layout drawings. Fuselage, wings, tail, landing gear, and auxiliary equipment must be laid out to large scale with great care and accuracy. This work is very important and is done by the more experienced men. All members of the structure must be carefully shown so that connections may be perfect and so that all auxiliary equipment will fit into the main structure. The information that may be needed in making detail drawings is carefully considered when working on the layout, and all special materials, heat-treatments, and fits are noted.

25·5 Production drawings. The meaning of the term "production drawings" is the same as "working drawings," and may be further classified as (*a*) detail, (*b*) assembly, and (*c*) installation drawings. In general the principles of working drawings as given in Chap. 15 are followed in the aircraft industry. One exception to present standard drawing practice is the almost universal aircraft practice of making all dimensions read horizontally, whatever the direction of the dimension line. This method is specified by the U.S. Army Air Corps and is justified by the large average size of airplane drawings.

25·6 Lofting. Detail drawings of sheet-metal parts are sent to the lofting department, where the procedure is to make very accurate full-size layouts, from which templates can be made. Many dimensions, impossible to calculate, are determined for the engineering departments, thereby augmenting mathematical with graphical data. Accuracy is of such prime importance that drawing paper cannot be used because of its expansion and contraction. The first loft drawings were laid out on portions of the shop floor painted white for the purpose. Later they are done on thin laminated-wood drawing boards. Modern practice is to use enameled aluminum sheets with finished edges and rounded corners, which can be handled and stored readily and on which lines as fine as though made by an engraver are drawn with an 8H or 9H pencil sharpened to an extremely sharp point (sometimes the lines *are* engraved with a steel point). Honed plate glass has also

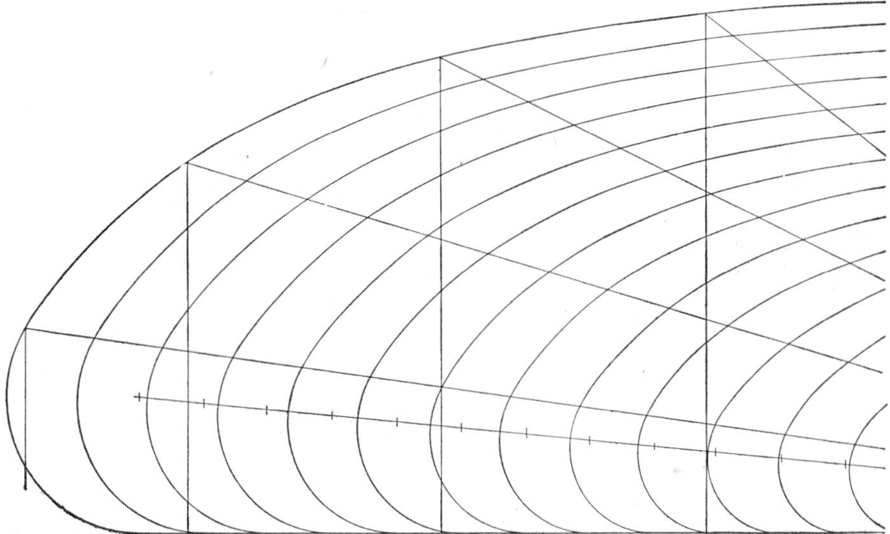

FIG. 25·4—A portion of a loft drawing.

been used for loft drawings. A successful attempt has been made to save lofting time through the use of photographic enlargements made with special lenses and equipment.

No T squares are used in lofting. An accurate datum line is drawn the length of the sheet, and perpendicular offsets are constructed from it. Curves are drawn by first plotting points and then very carefully lining up a spline, held with weights or "ducks," to guide the pencil and pen. After the drawing is satisfactory in pencil it is inked on the aluminum sheet with a very fine line. Colored ink is used to indicate and separate various parts of the work. Figure 25·4 shows a portion of a loft drawing.

25·7 Fairing. To "fair," or streamline, means to make a curve or surface mechancially smooth, with no small reverse curves or humps. When tolerances are given with the statement that the curve or surface must "fair," it may be necessary to work more accurately than the permitted tolerance. Dimensions to plus or minus $\frac{1}{32}$ inch on consecutive points of the curve could produce humps, although a series of points might all be either plus 1/32 or minus 1/32 inch and the surface be smooth. After surfaces have been faired by the loft, alterations of the design and layout drawings may be necessary.

25·8 Naming of drawings. The U.S. Army Air Corps' standard practice is generally followed in the naming of aircraft drawings. The drawing title consists of the simplest basic name, followed by a dash and then further description of the part, for example, "PLATE—RETRACTING SCREW GUIDE." In reading the title the description is read first and then the basic name, thus: "Retracting screw guide plate." The basic name must never be abbreviated, and no commas are used. Basic names of more than one word are allowed in assembly-drawing titles, as: "BRACKET ASSEMBLY—PILOT'S SEAT SUPPORT OUTER."

25·9 Drawing sizes. Drawing sizes in the aircraft industry follow the American Standard sizes, with some additional multiples. The U.S. Army Air Corps specifies 8½″ × 11″, 11″ × 17″, 11″ × 34″, 17″ × 22″, 17″ × 42″, 17″ × 66″, 22″ × 34″, 34″ × 42″, 34″ × 66″, 34″ × 88″, 42″ × 66″, 42″ × 88″, and for larger drawings 36″ or 42″ by a length not to exceed 144″ unless unavoidable. However, drawings as long as 50 feet are sometimes required. Large drawings and Van Dyke negatives are rolled for filing, but blueprints are always "accordion" folded to 8½″ × 11″ size for filing and mailing, as in Fig. 25·5.

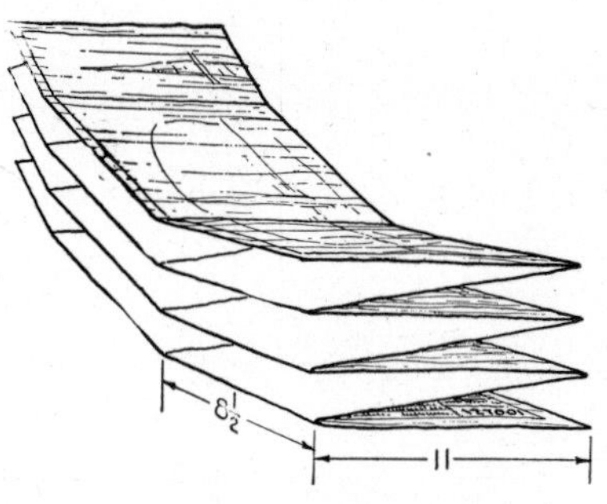

FIG. 25·5—Accordion folding.

25·10 Zone marking. To facilitate the location of sections, dash numbers, or other information on long drawings, the drawing is marked in "zones." The lower border is laid off in zones of 1 foot each, starting from the right-hand border and numbering toward the left. Each foot is marked by the proper numeral in a ½″ square with its base coincident with the border line. Figure 25·6 shows a portion of a zone-marked drawing.

25·11 Scale of drawings. For large-scale drawings of single parts, subassemblies, etc., scales of full size, half size, quarter size, and eighth size are standard. For all smaller scale drawings, such as three-view and proposal drawings, scales of 1/20, 1/30, 1/40, and 1/50 size are used. A civil engineer's scale may be employed for these sizes, reading the scale as 1/20″ = 1″ etc. Architects' scales of ¼″ or ⅛″ to the foot *are not used* in aircraft practice. Full-size drawings are always preferred when possible.

25·12 Title blocks. The variety of general information needed in aircraft work dictates the use of a rather complete title block. One form is illustrated by Fig. 25·7 in which the parts list is started at the top of the block and continued by the draftsman for the number of required items. The change record, at the left, is handled similarly.

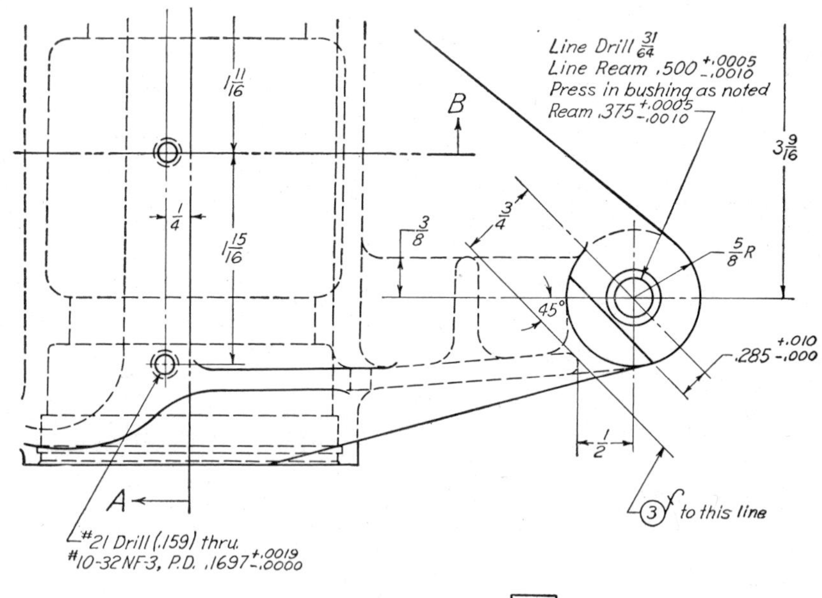

FIG. 25·6—A portion of a zone-marked drawing.

				NO. REQ.	PART NO.	NAME	STOCK	COMM.	ARMY	NAVY
								MATERIAL SPECIFICATION		
				CAL. WT.		LIMITS UNLESS OTHERWISE SPECIFIED	DRAWN			
				ACT. WT.		ANGLES ± 1/2°	TRACED			
LET.	CHANGE	DATE	BY	HEAT TREAT.		FRACTIONAL ± 1/32	CHECKED			
				FINISH		DECIMAL ± .010	CHIEF ENG.			
				SUPERSEDES		③✓ ④✓	CUSTOMER			
NO. REQ.	NEXT ASSEM.	MODEL		SCALE		SMOOTH ROUGH		NAME		DATE
COMPANY NAME										

FIG. 25·7—An aircraft title.

25·13 Dimensioning. In aircraft practice all distances are given in inches and the inch marks (″) are omitted. As one exception to this rule, wing span is sometimes given in feet. Figure 25·6 illustrates the practice, already mentioned, of placing all dimensions so as to read horizontally, or from the bottom of the sheet.

Either vertical or inclined capitals may be used in lettering notes and titles. All notes are placed horizontally.

25·14 Limits and tolerances. The usual tolerances specified in aircraft work are $\pm\frac{1}{32}$ on fractional dimensions for the general run of sheet-metal and fitting work; ± 0.010 on decimal dimensions for the average class of engine work, bolthole locations, and fits where great accuracy is not necessary; and $\pm\frac{1}{2}°$ for angular dimensions. Where very accurate fits are required, the U.S. Army Air Corps' specifications for the determination of limits and tolerances should be followed.

25·15 Sectional views. Sections are treated as projected views wherever space permits (the section should be projected in third angle, never in first angle). On a removed section the correct angle and direction of rotation should be given.

25·16 Line values. For all accurate layout work and in lofting, a fine line must be used, made with a 4, 5, or 6H pencil in layout work, and with an 8H in lofting. For production drawings made on vellum or cloth, for reproduction, the outline must be bold and opaque, made with a pencil

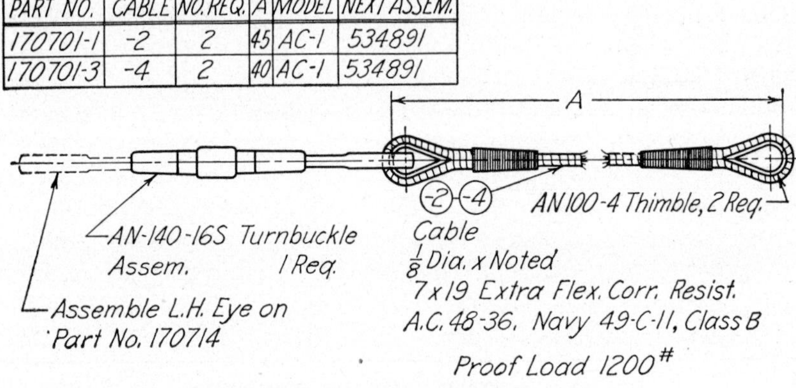

PART NO.	CABLE	NO. REQ.	A	MODEL	NEXT ASSEM.
170701-1	-2	2	45	AC-1	534891
170701-3	-4	2	40	AC-1	534891

Fig. 25·8—A dash-numbered drawing.

chosen from F, H, or 2H to fit the drawing surface, following general engineering practice.

25·17 Dash numbers. In order to identify the great number of parts used in the construction of aircraft, each part is designated by its drawing number, and when further identification is necessary a *dash number* is added after the drawing number. A dash number is simply a numeral prefixed by a dash to distinguish it from other numerals on the sheet, and it is placed in a ⅜″ circle near the piece it identifies, with an arrow touching the outline of the part. It is followed by the name (noun only), material, and number required, see Fig. 25·8. When dash numbers appear on any drawing other than their own, they are given in full with their drawing number, the circle being omitted as, 10127-1. On complicated drawings such as fuselage structures the encircled numbers point out all parts that are to be made from that drawing. The dash-number system, in general, is to be used only when the detailed parts of an assembly can be sufficiently dimensioned in their proper location on the assembly and is used to identify subparts of an assembly, subassemblies of a main assembly, and parts permanently fastened together and used as a unit part.

25·18 Tabulated drawings. When two or more parts are covered by a single drawing and tabulated on that drawing, each piece should have a dash number assigned to it, as the drawing number in this case is not a part number. The coding of parts which are similar but have one or more dimensions different is done by making a single drawing and giving each part a dash number of the basic drawing number.

25·19 Right- and left-hand parts. Where right- and left-hand parts are required, a single drawing is made of the left-hand part and suitable notation placed above the title block as:

LH shown 00156-L
RH opposite 00156-R (Standard Air Corps practice)

Some companies deviate from this system, using even dash numbers for left-hand parts, and odd dash numbers for right-hand parts.

25·20 Standard parts. Wherever possible, standard parts that can be carried in stock should be used. Much unnecessary tooling is thereby saved. *Army-Navy Standard Parts* are those approved by the Standards Committee of both the Army and the Navy. Designation of these parts on assembly drawings requires prefixing the symbol *AN* to the part number, thus, *AN 671*. *Air Corps Standard Parts* (those without the *AN* prefix in the Air Corps Standard Parts book) should have the the symbol *AC* prefixed to the part number. *Navy Standard Parts* (those without the *AN* prefix in the Navy Standard Parts book) should have *NAF* (Naval Aircraft Factory) prefixed to the part number.

Commercial standard parts are any commercial parts usable without reworking. They are designated on assembly drawings by the manufacturer's part numbers or size designations.

25·21 Material and process specifications. In the aircraft industry, materials, heat-treatments, finish, etc., are specified by giving Army, Navy, or commercial specification numbers. The topic is beyond the scope of this chapter, but information is given in *Air Corps Material Specifications* and *Process Specifications*, published by the Government and available to those directly concerned.

25·22 Joggling. For structural shapes of aluminum alloy no joggle whose depth is greater than one-third its length can be made without danger of partially shearing the metal. See Fig. 25·9. Flat sheets, however, may be joggled to the same depth in much shorter distance.

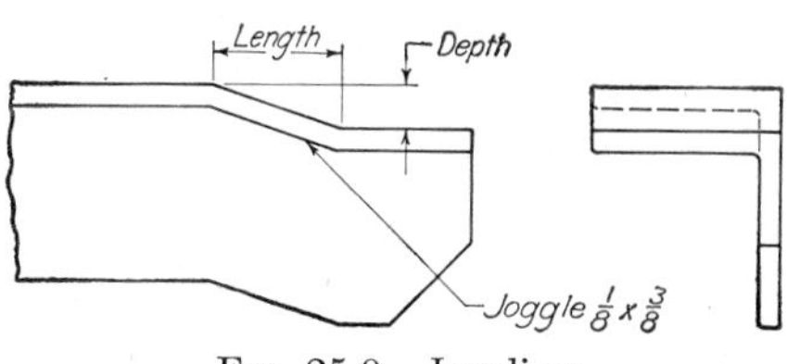

FIG. 25·9—Joggling.

25·23 Bend relief and allowances. Relief at the corners of bent plates is shown in Figure 25·10. In bending any sheet, allowance must be made for the thickness of the metal and its bending characteristics. Shop experience is an important factor, but bend allowance may be computed from the empirical formula $Z = (0.01745R + 0.0078T) \times$ no. of degrees of bend, as given in Fig. 25·11.

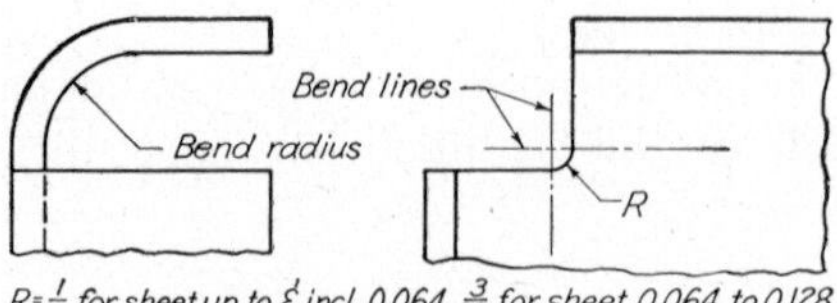

FIG. 25·10—Bend relief.

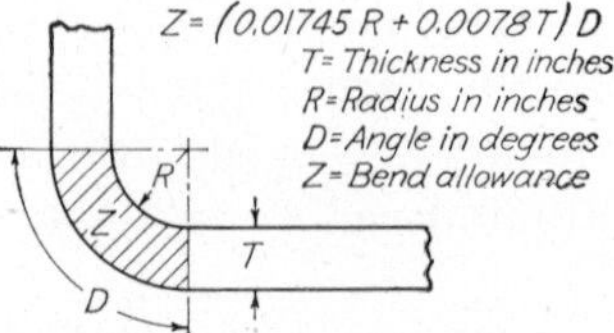

FIG. 25·11—Bend allowance.

25·24 Screw threads. The Army-Navy specifications for aircraft screw threads include the ASA coarse thread series, NC-2 and NC-3; fine thread series, NF-3; and extra-fine, NEF-3; along with the 8-, 12-, and 16-pitch thread series. All these are discussed in Chap. 13, and tables are given in the Appendix.

25·25 In this chapter the essential features of aircraft drawing have been explained. The general principles of engineering drawing all apply to this branch of engineering and may be found in the appropriate chapters of the book by consulting the index. For example, aeronautical maps would be under the chapter on maps and topographic drawings; rivets in the chapter on fastenings; etc.

PROBLEMS

In the following problems, aircraft practices in dimensioning, notation, specification, etc., should be followed.

1. The true fineness ratio of a streamlined shape is L/D where L is the outside length and D the outside width of the section. Draw the cross section of a streamlined tube having a fineness ratio of 2, $L = 10''$, and a wall thickness of 0.10''. Round off the trailing end with a radius so that the actual length is 95 per cent of the 10'' theoretical length. The table below gives coordinate dimensions in percentages of L and D. Use a civil engineer's scale in laying out this problem, full size.

Length, %	Width, %	Length, %	Width, %	Length, %	Width, %
0.0	0.0	20.0	91.1	65.0	80.1
1.25	26.0	25.0	95.9	70.0	73.2
2.5	37.1	30.0	98.6	75.0	65.3
5.0	52.5	35.0	100.0	80.0	56.2
7.5	63.6	40.0	99.5	85.0	46.1
10.0	72.0	45.0	97.9	90.0	33.8
12.5	78.5	50.0	95.0	95.0	19.0
15.0	83.6	55.0	91.0	100.0	0.0
17.5	87.0	60.0	86.1		

2. From the data given for Prob. 1, make a cross-sectional drawing of a streamlined tube, length 15'', fineness ratio 3, wall thickness 0.128.

3. Plot the airfoil shape given in the data following. Chord length, 100''; scale, fifth size. The data give distances from chord line in percentages of chord length.

Chord, %	Upper	Lower	Chord, %	Upper	Lower
0.00	3.50	3.50	40 00	13.00	−1.60
1.25	5.98	1.43	50.00	11.99	−1.48
2.50	7.21	0.76	60.00	10.44	−1.29
5.00	8.86	−0.05	70.00	8.39	−1.04
7.50	10.01	−0.50	80.00	5.95	−0.73
10.00	10.89	−0.87	90.00	3.19	−0.39
15.00	12.17	−1.38	95.00	1.75	−0.25
20.00	12.96	−1.57	100.00	0.14	−0.01
30.00	13.35	−1.65			

4. Make detail drawing of wing-nose rib, Fig. 25·12.

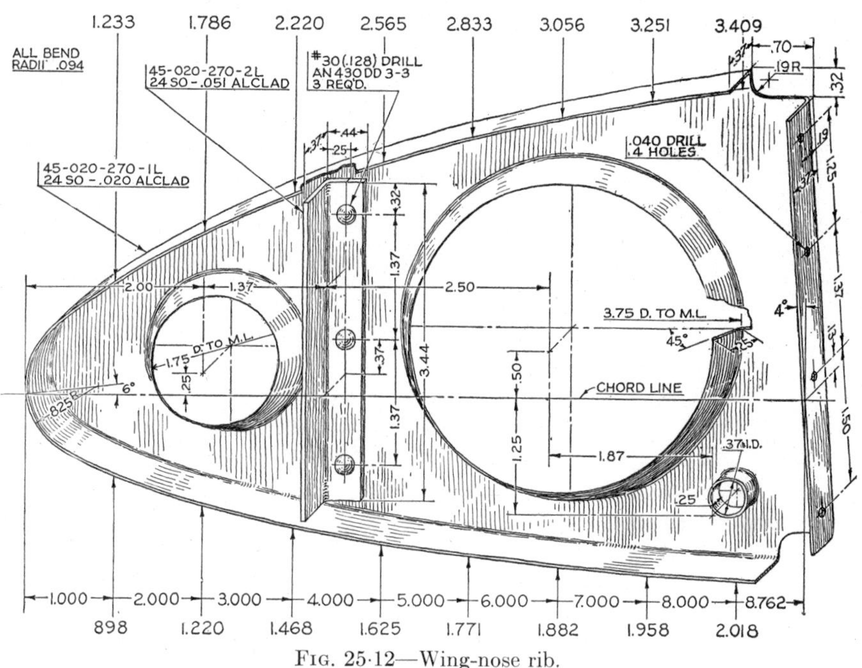

Fig. 25·12—Wing-nose rib.

5. Make detail drawing of rib-stiffener angle, Fig. 25·12.

6. Make unit assembly working drawing of wing-nose rib and rib stiffener, Fig. 25·12. Use dash numbers for rib and stiffener. Add a parts list that includes the rivets.

7. Make detail drawing of retractable-landing-gear link, Fig. 25·13, part No. 45-313-140, 4115 steel drop forging. Drawing is one-half size. Scale for omitted dimensions.

8. Make detail drawing of link bushing, Fig. 25·13, part No. 45-313-163; material is 3230 steel.

9. Make detail drawing of link button, Fig. 25·13, part No. 45-313-164. Drawing is one-half size. Scale for necessary dimensions. Material is 3230 steel.

10. Make unit assembly working drawing of retractable-landing-gear-link assembly, Fig. 25·13. Drawing is one-half size. Scale for omitted dimensions. Assign dash numbers to nonstandard parts; see Probs. 4, 5, and 6 for materials. Add a parts list including all parts.

11. Make detail drawings of each of the nonstandard parts shown in the design drawing of the pulley-bracket and support assembly, Fig. 25·14. Drawing is one-half size.

12. Make a unit assembly working drawing of the pulley-bracket and support assembly shown in the design drawing, Fig. 25·14. Drawing is one-half size. Add a parts list including all parts.

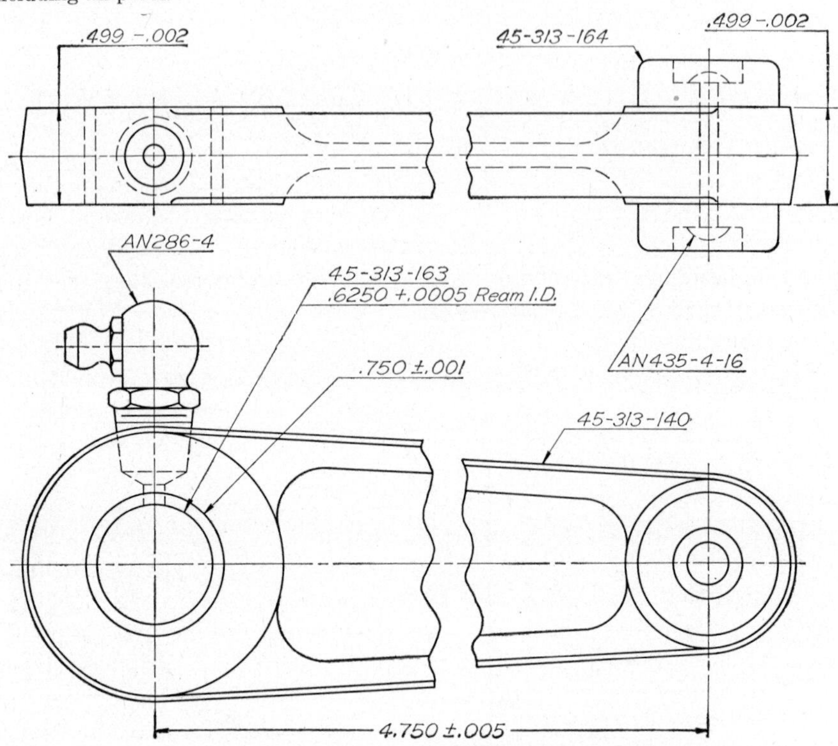

Fig. 25·13—Retractable-landing-gear-link assembly.

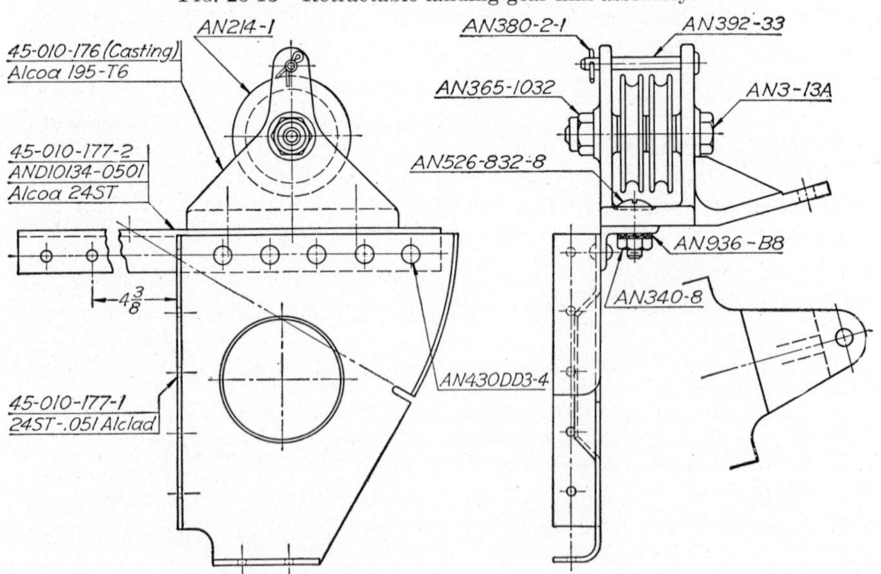

Fig. 25·14—Pulley-bracket and support assembly.

Chapter 26

THE ELEMENTS OF ARCHITECTURAL DRAWING

26·1 Architecture is classed as one of the fine arts, and it is entirely beyond the scope of this book to take up architectural designing. But in applying engineering drawing as a language, to architecture, the architect makes use of idioms and peculiarities of expression with which all engineers should be familiar, for in the interrelation of the professions they are often required to read or work from architects' drawings or to make drawings for special structures.

26·2 Characteristics of architectural drawing. The general principles of drawing are the same for all kinds of technical work, but each profession requires its own special application of these principles and the employment of particular methods, symbols, and conventions. In architectural drawing the necessary smallness of scale requires that the general drawings be made up largely of conventional symbols indicating the various parts. Also so many notes of explanation and information regarding material and finish are required that it is not possible to include all of them on the drawings, hence they are written separately in a document called the *specifications*. These specifications are complementary to the drawings and have equal importance and weight.

In the make-up of an architect's drawings there is evidence of artistic feeling, produced in part by the freehand work and lettering and in part by the use of finer lines, which gives them an entirely different appearance from that of a set of machine drawings. One peculiarity found in many architectural drawings is the overrunning of corners. This artifice in an experienced draftsman's work gives a certain snap and freedom, but this statement must not be taken by the beginner as a license for carelessness.

In arrangement of views, third-angle projection is standard American practice for all branches of drawing, although now and then an architectural detail is seen made in the first angle. Sometimes it is advantageous to use what might be called "second-angle projection," in which one view is superimposed over another. This is often done in stair detailing, as illustrated in Fig. 26·1.

Reflected views. A distinctively architectural feature is the "reflected view," occasionally used, in which the drawing, usually a part view, as of a soffit or ceiling, is made as if reflected in a mirror on the ground.

Profiling. Another architectural drawing feature, shown in Fig. 26·1, is that produced by "profiling" or "silhouetting" the important outline with a heavier line than the other lines of the drawing. This aids the drawing greatly in both appearance and ease of reading. It is of particular value on sectional drawings, to bring out the sectional outline distinctly from the parts beyond the cutting plane.

26·3 Kinds of drawings. Architectural drawings may be divided into three general classes: (1) preliminary studies, (2) presentation drawings, and (3) working drawings.

26·4 Preliminary studies. In an architectural project, the architect, in conference with his client, sets up a program for the required structure. This program includes the essential requirements of the client (owner), *i.e.*, the function of the building, the size and character of the site, the architectural style (if specified), preferred materials of construction, etc. From the program various solutions are developed, usually in rough sketch form on tracing paper with a soft pencil, and a selection of the better solutions is made for further study in plan, elevation, and section. The designer must constantly place himself in the position of a person who will use the building; he must make certain that the final selection of the design scheme allows for the easiest way to accomplish whatever must be done in the completed building.

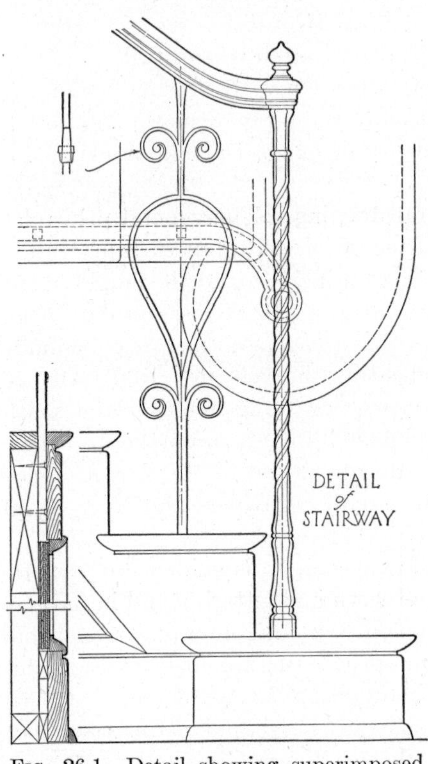

FIG. 26·1—Detail showing superimposed view and profiling.

Throughout this phase of the work the architect will make his sketches relatively small, while still being careful to maintain proper proportions. The smallness of these "thumbnail sketches" force the designer to consider the essential elements only, for a study of detail is impossible at a small scale. In effect, this keeps the drawings free and spontaneous, a necessary requirement in the preparation of early studies.

The preliminary drawings of plans, elevations, sections, and often perspectives, are then developed prior to approval by the owner. For effectiveness these drawings are sometimes rendered in color.

26·5 Presentation drawings. The object of presentation drawings is to give a realistic and effective representation of the design of a proposed building for illustrative or competitive purposes. They may consist of plans and elevations or, to be more thorough, may include perspective drawings, but in either case, they will contain little or no structural information. For legibility and attractiveness they are generally rendered in water color, pen and ink, crayon or pencil, giving the effect of color, light, and shade. Such accessories as human figures, adjacent buildings, foliage, etc., are often introduced in elevations and perspectives not so much for pictorial effect as for *scale*, an idea of the relative size of the building.

In rendering plans for display or competitive purposes, shadows are often used to show the plan in relief. The terms "poché" and "mosaic" are used

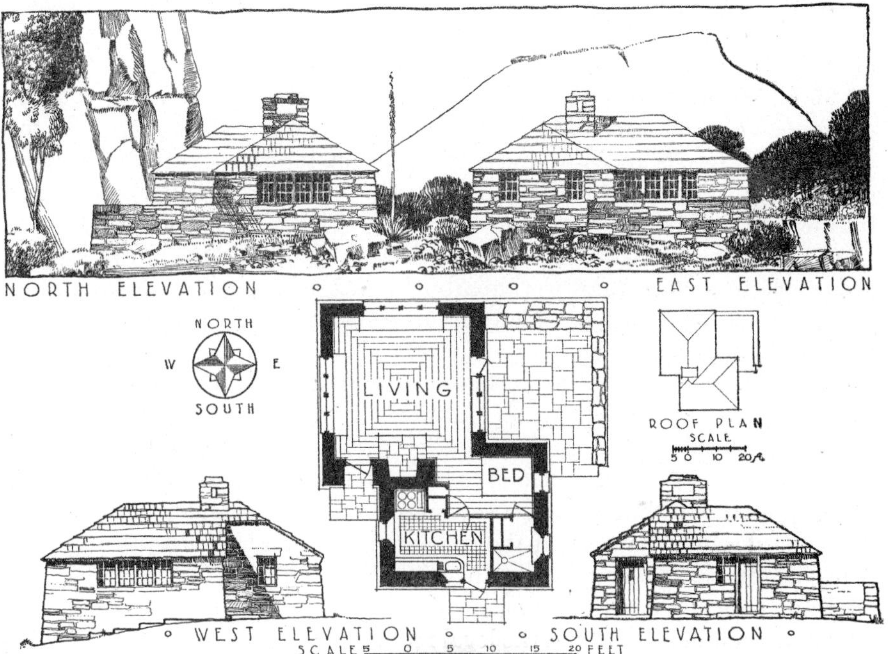

FIG. 26·2—A presentation drawing.

in connection with this type of drawing, poché meaning simply the blackening of the walls to indicate their relative importance in the composition, and mosaic the rendering in light lines and tints of the floor design, furniture, etc., on the interior and the entourage of walks, drives, and planting on the exterior, representing the grounds immediately surrounding the building. Frequently in a symmetrical room one half is shown with a floor mosaic and the other half with the ceiling mosaic as a reflected view. A rendered presentation drawing is shown in Fig. 26·2.

26·6 Models. There is an increasing use of models for proposed buildings. These are made in the drawing room, using drawing paper, cardboard, balsa wood, etc. The advantage of such a model in showing the appearance of the completed building and the perspective effect from any angle is of obvious value both to the designer and to the client. In making paper models the different walls and roofs are laid out in developed form and then rendered, folded, and mounted on a board base. The particularly important point to observe is that all features, such as moldings, railings, planting, etc., be kept to scale. Much artistic ability may be evidenced in their construction, and the ingenuity of the modeler is exhibited in the use of various materials in the entourage. Tinted sponges for trees, rubber sponge for hedges and shrubbery, sawdust and sand in glue (painted green for grass), and various other accessory materials will be thought of. For reproduction purposes, a photograph of the model is used instead of a perspective drawing, sometimes superimposed on one of the site, with adjacent buildings, made at the same angle.

26·7 Working drawings. Under this term are included *plans, elevations, sections,* and *detail drawings,* which, taken with the *specifications* for details of materials and finish, give the working information from which to execute the contract agreement and erect the building. Their first use is by the contractors in estimating for bids.

The general principles of Chap. 15 regarding working drawings are applicable to architectural working drawings. The assembly drawings are usually made with only one plan or elevation on a sheet, in order to keep the drawings to convenient working size. The most frequent scale used on these drawings is ⅛″ = 1′-0″. For small buildings, perhaps up to 60 feet long, ¼″ = 1′-0″ is used.

As a general rule, things which are related should be shown together and information concerning each craft should be grouped, so far as possible. Many present-day buildings are so complicated that it is advantageous to draw special plans for each of the several crafts, in addition to the general plans, as for structural steel, heating, plumbing, and wiring.

In making working drawings, the draftsman must be familiar with local and state building codes, and the legal requirements as to approval, permits, and restrictions.

26·8 Plan of site. Before designing any structure of importance, a site plan is made, giving the property line, contours, available utilities (sewer, electricity, gas, water), location of trees, and other features. The building is then designed to fit the site. This drawing is completed by locating on it the building, approaches, and contours of finished grades. For an ordinary residence, dimensions placed on the basement plan, showing the distances of the building from the lot lines, usually fulfill building-permit requirements.

26·9 Floor plans. Figs. 26·3, 26·4, 26·5. A floor plan is a horizontal section at a distance above the floor varying so as to cut the walls at a height which will best show the construction. The cut will thus evidently cross all openings for that story, no matter at what height they are from the floor. On account of the small scale compared with the actual size of the building, plans are largely made up of conventional symbols, with notes referring to detail drawings of different items. Walls, doors, windows,

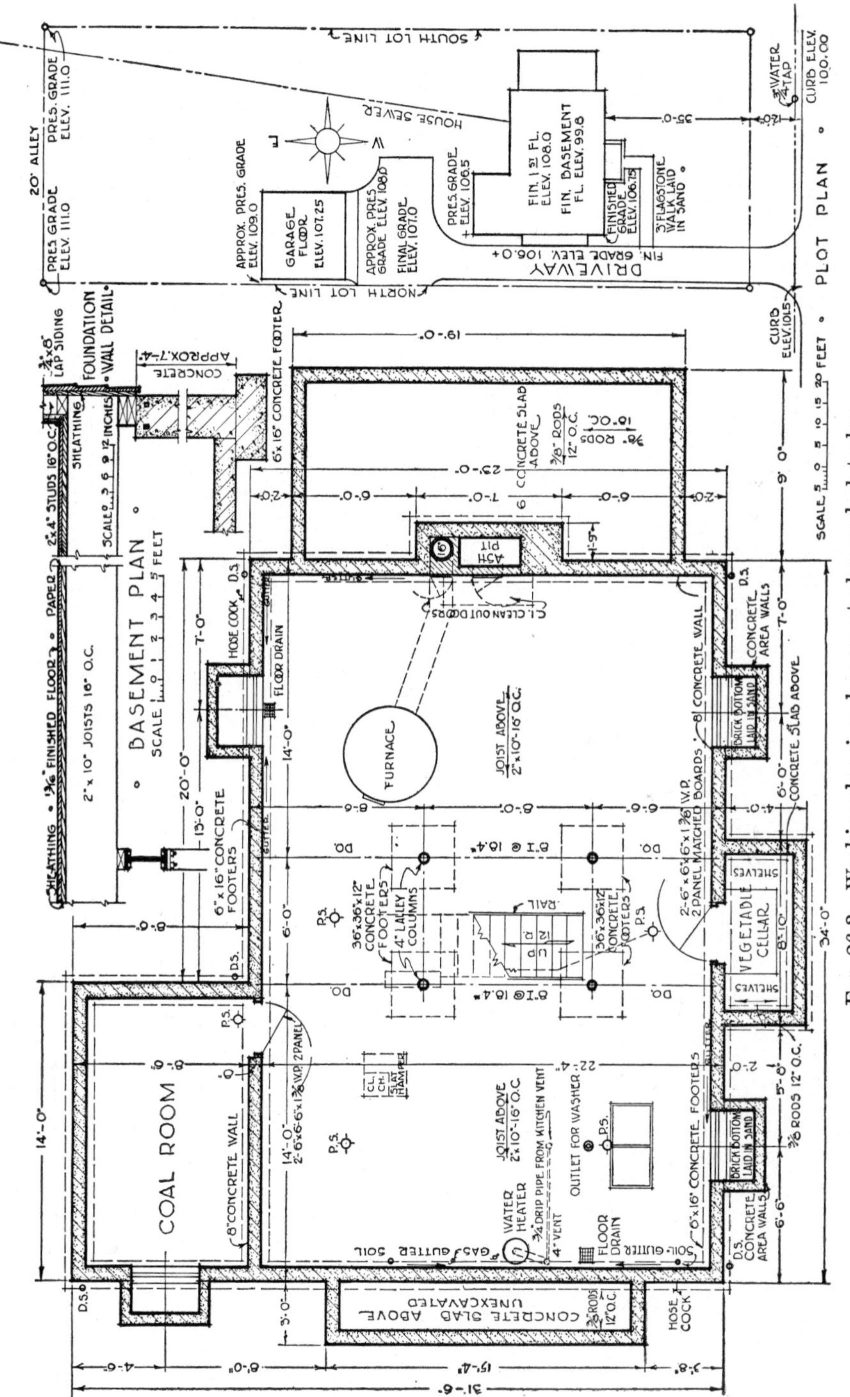

FIG. 26·3—Working drawing; basement plan and plot plan.

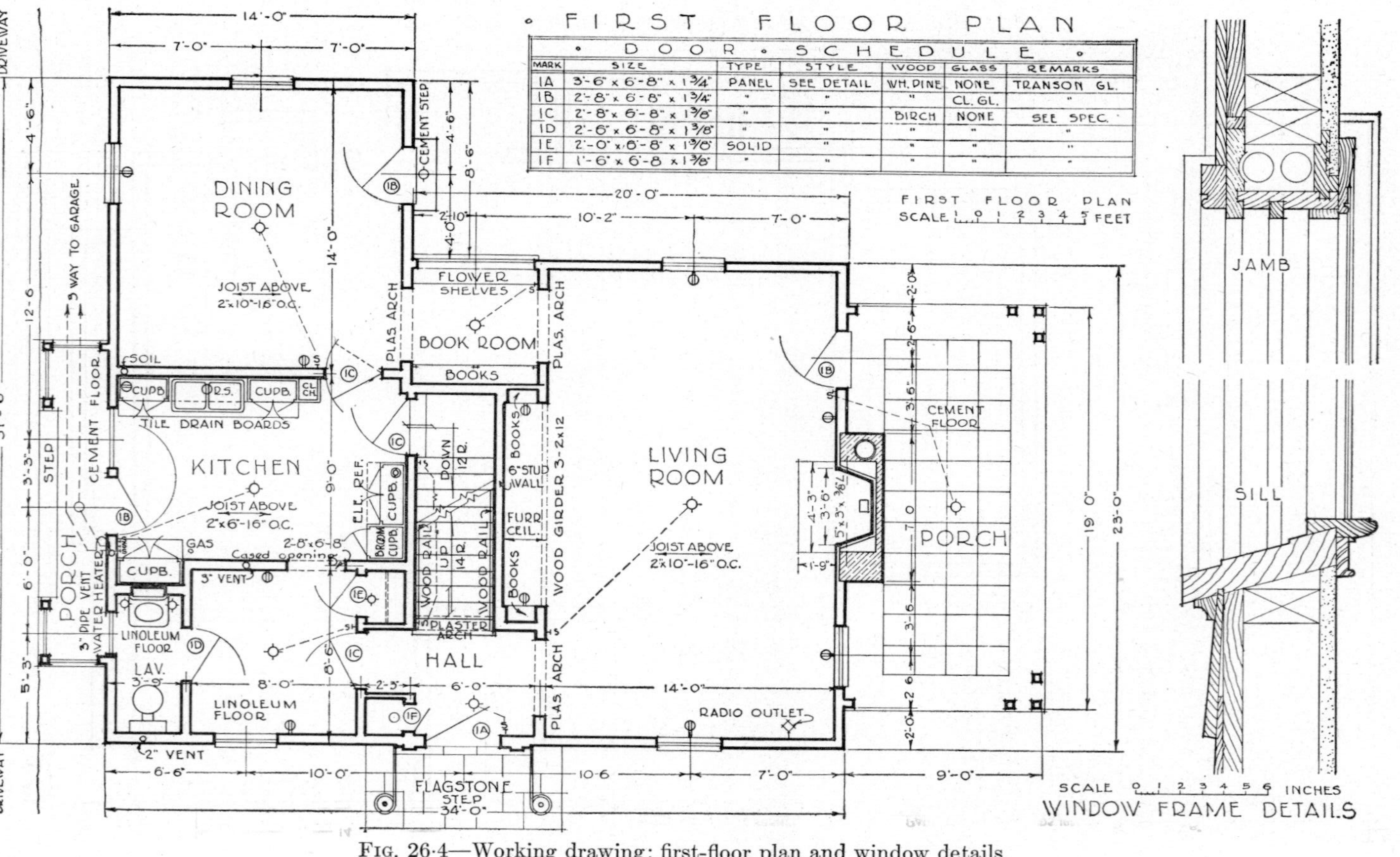

MARK	SIZE	TYPE	STYLE	WOOD	GLASS	REMARKS
1A	3'-6" x 6'-8" x 1 3/4"	PANEL	SEE DETAIL	WH. PINE	NONE	TRANSOM GL.
1B	2'-8" x 6'-8" x 1 3/4"	"	"	"	CL. GL.	"
1C	2'-8" x 6'-8" x 1 3/8"	"	"	BIRCH	NONE	SEE SPEC.
1D	2'-6" x 6'-8" x 1 3/8"	"	"	"	"	"
1E	2'-0" x 6'-8" x 1 3/8"	SOLID	"	"	"	"
1F	1'-6" x 6'-8 x 1 3/8"	"	"	"	"	"

Fig. 26·4—Working drawing; first-floor plan and window details.

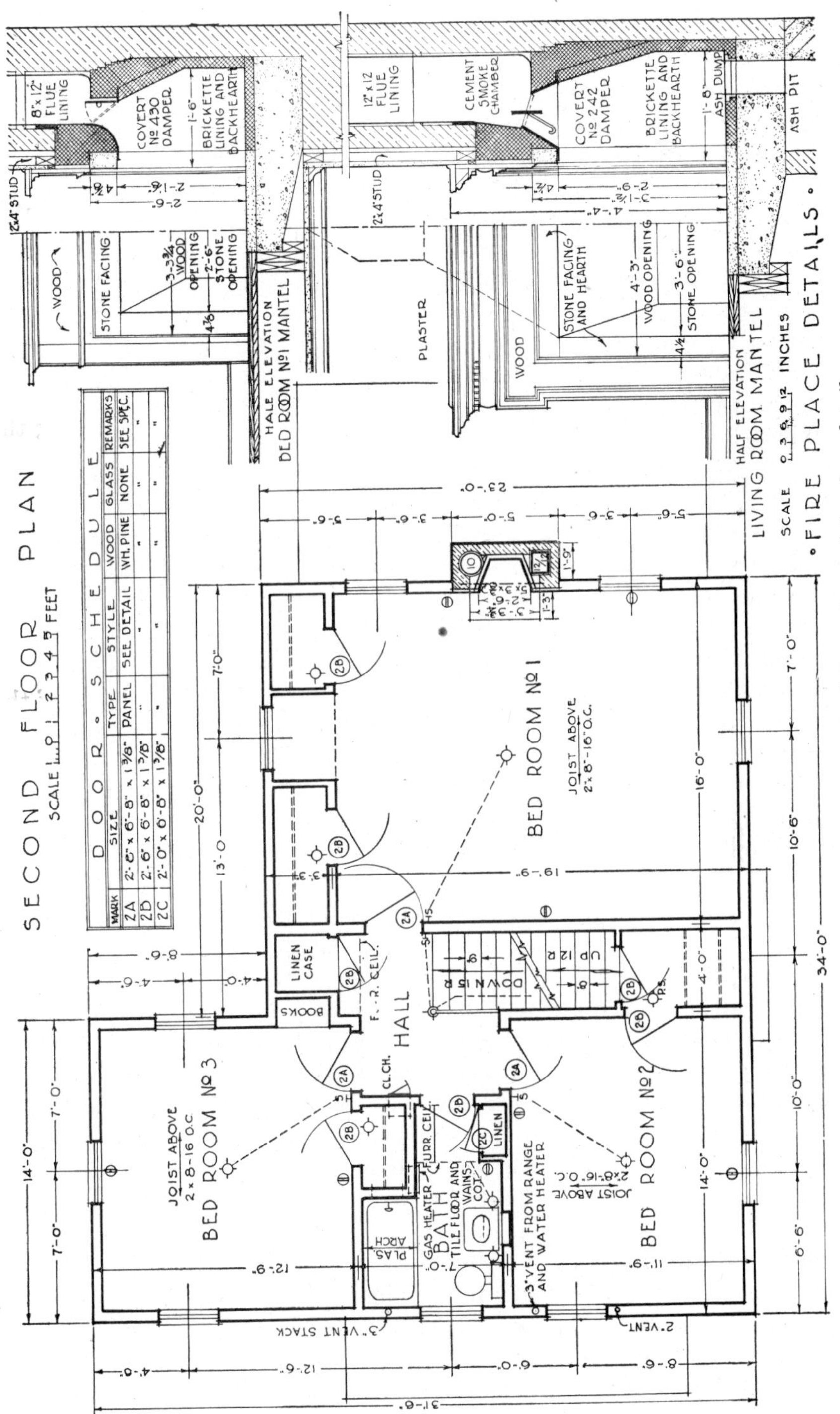

FIG. 26·5—Working drawing; second-floor plan and fireplace details.

fixtures, etc., are all indicated by conventional representation, using symbols which are readily understood by the contractors who read the drawings. A floor plan contains, in general, the information for the space between the floor represented and the floor above, even though some items noted are above the cutting plane. The plan will show the location of all doors, windows, partition walls, radiators, built-in fixtures, ducts and flues, outlets for lighting and heating, material of floor, and information concerning the ceiling above, as beams, light outlets, etc. The joist framing of the floor above is indicated except when separate framing plans are necessary. The framing of a simple building is usually left to the contractor. In the case of special framing for heavy or concentrated loads, such as mill buildings, separate framing plans are drawn showing all the details of construction. A separate plan might be needed also for location of and foundations for machinery.

26·10 Drawing a plan. A plan is always laid out with the front of the building at the bottom of the sheet. After selecting the scale (¼″ = 1′-0″ for ordinary house plans), draw and measure a line representing the outside face of the front wall. If the plan is symmetrical, draw the main axis. The axes of a plan correspond to the center lines of a machine drawing and have a very important place in design. Complete the exterior walls and interior partitions (frame walls are drawn 6″ thick, brick walls 9″, 13″, 17″, etc.), then locate stairways, doors, and other interior construction. In drawing the stairway, first make a diagram to find the number of steps and space required (for this the architect always uses the scale as shown in Fig. 5·3). The rise, or height from one step to the next, will vary in size depending upon the type of building and the position of prominence of the stairway within the building. The lower the rise, the longer the stride will be; and to proportion the tread depth to the riser height, a chart giving the proper relationship is used. Architectural handbooks will give the required information. On the plan, the lines drawn represent the edges of the risers and are as far apart as the width of the tread. The entire flight is not drawn on the plan but is stopped about halfway up so as to show what is under it. Each floor plan thus shows part of the stairways leading both up and down from the floor represented. Always indicate the direction and number of risers in the stairway by an arrow and note, as in Fig. 26·4. The windows are not drawn until the elevations have been designed, but if their position in the wall is known their center lines are indicated. The first-floor plan is usually made first, and the outlines for basement plan, second-floor plan, and roof plan traced or drawn from it.

26·11 Elevations. An elevation is a vertical projection showing the front, side, or rear view of a structure. When a plan is irregular, other elevations parallel to the walls are necessary. The elevation gives the floor heights, openings, and exterior treatment. The visualizing power must be exercised in imagining the actual appearance or perspective of a building

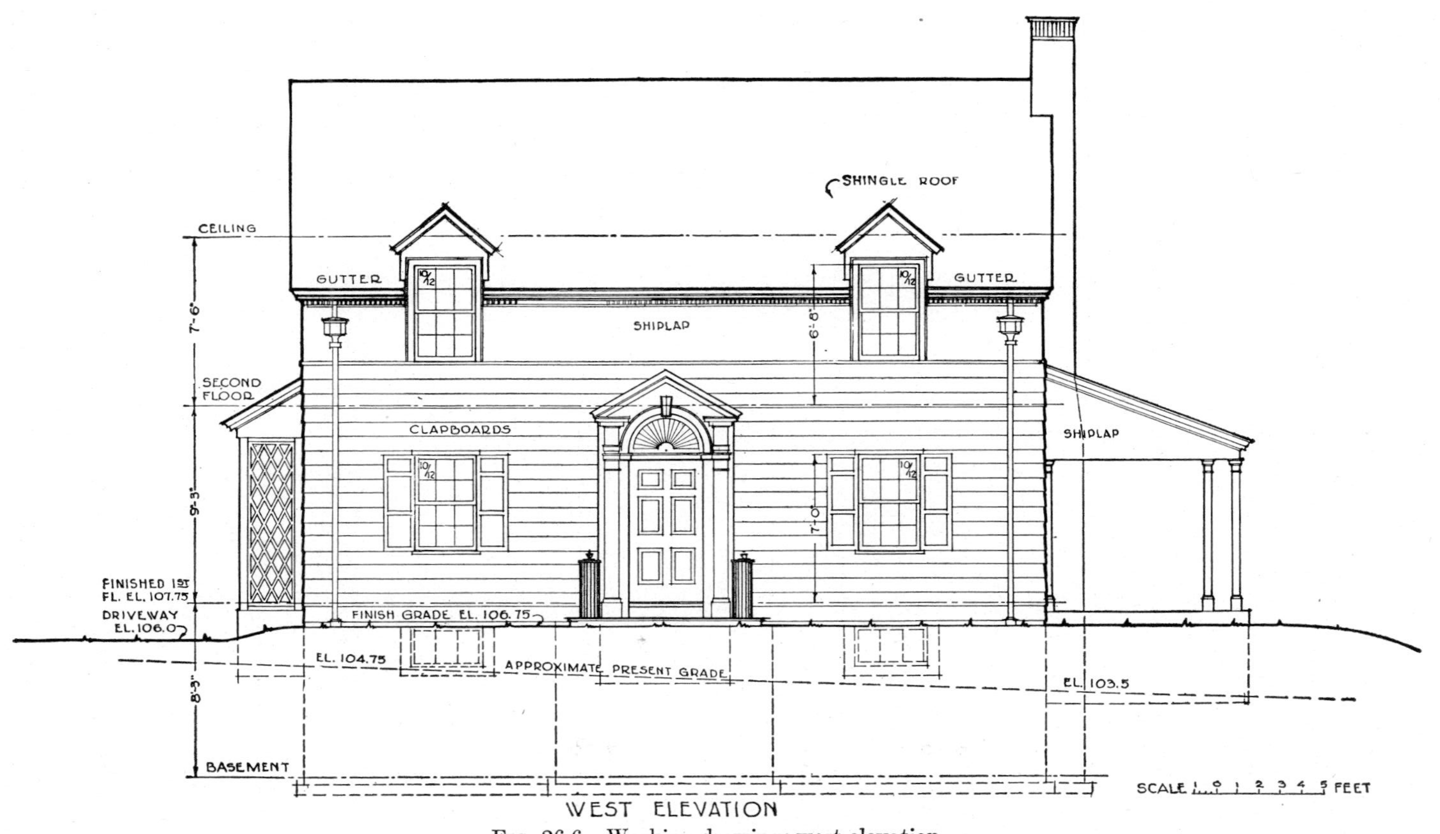

FIG. 26·6—Working drawing; west elevation.

from its elevations. Roofs in elevation are thus often misleading to persons unfamiliar with drawings, as their appearance in projection is so different from their real appearance on the building when finished. Figures 26·6 and 26·7 illustrate what features are shown and what dimensions are given on elevations.

26·12 Drawing an elevation. First draw a wall section at the side of the sheet, starting with the foundation and showing grade line, floor heights, sill and head of windows, cornice and pitch of roof, and thickness of walls. Carry the grade line across the sheet as the working base line. Project the floor and ceiling lines across lightly. With the plan sheet placed above the elevation, project down for widths. Locate the windows and complete the elevations as shown in the figures.

26·13 Sections. A general section is an interior view on a vertical cutting plane to show interior construction and architectural treatment. This cutting plane need not be continuous but, as in the case of the horizontal, may be staggered so as to include as much information as possible. In a simple structure, a part section or "wall section" shown with the elevation, either to the same scale or larger, is often sufficient to give the required vertical dimensions. Part sections to larger scale are often used in connection with drawings, as, for example, in Figs. 26·4, 26·5, and 26·7, the usual cutting-plane line indicating the location and direction of the sectional view.

26·14 Detail drawings. A set of drawings will contain, in addition to the plans, elevations, and sections, larger scale drawings of such parts as are not indicated with sufficient definiteness on the small-scale drawings. Stair details and detail sections of various items, such as footings, windows, framing, etc., may be shown clearly to the scales of ¾″ or 1½″ to 1′-0″. Details are best grouped so that each sheet contains the references made on one sheet of the general drawings.

As the building progresses, the drawings are supplemented by full-size drawings of moldings and millwork details, ornamental iron, etc., usually made in soft pencil on tracing paper and blueprinted, all of which must be checked carefully by measurements on the building. In these drawings, revolved sections are used freely.

Figure 26·1 illustrates a method of combining views, superimposing a plan view on an elevation, that is sometimes used for saving space and for convenience in projecting one view from the other.

26·15 Details of building construction. The engineer and architect are mutually dependent. In building, such questions as strength, mechanical apparatus, and construction are engineering problems, while plan and exterior design are architectural problems.

In the design of a building for engineering or manufacturing purposes, there are many considerations involved which the architect cannot be expected to know. The young engineer should be able to prepare preliminary layouts or to make drawings for simple plant buildings. A few parts of

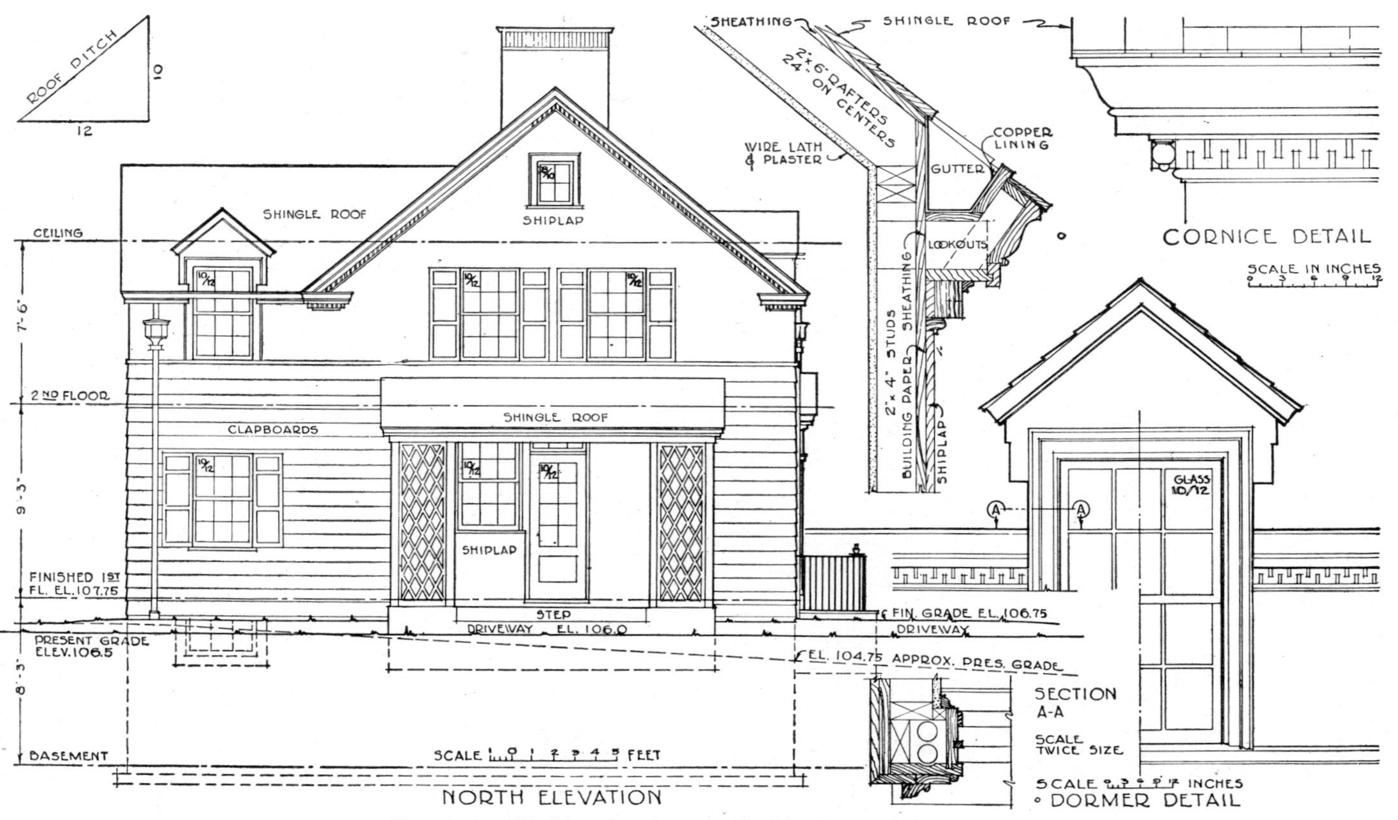

FIG. 26·7—Working drawing; north elevation and details.

such drawings are included here to suggest the method of representation, and the names of the different pieces are given. Column details may be represented as in Fig. 26·8, where the lower and upper end floor connections are illustrated. Parts of the details for large openings in both brick and frame walls are shown pictorially in Fig. 26·9.

26·16 Special features. In modern building construction, many parts are used which are manufactured by firms specializing in one particular item.

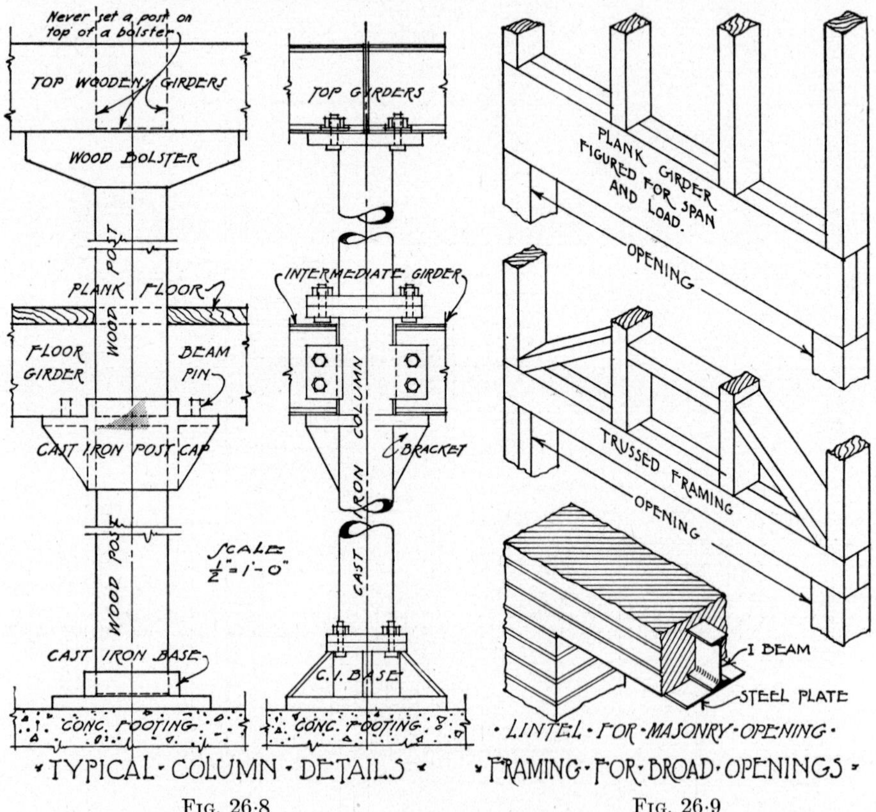

Fig. 26·8

Fig. 26·9

As an example, steel sash details vary with different makes. The architect gets full-size details from the makers and draws his building to conform. Similarly, other items such as ventilating fans, stock stairways, fire doors, and many other special features are always worked out from drawings furnished by the manufacturers of the equipment.

26·17 Symbols. As heretofore stated, plans are made up largely of symbols. Walls are shown by double lines giving their thickness. Symbols for wall materials, in plan and elevation, are shown in Fig. 26·10. The conventional method of representing windows and their derivation from the actual sections are shown in Fig. 26·11. The American Standard symbols for wiring plans, plumbing fixtures, etc., may be found in the Appendix.

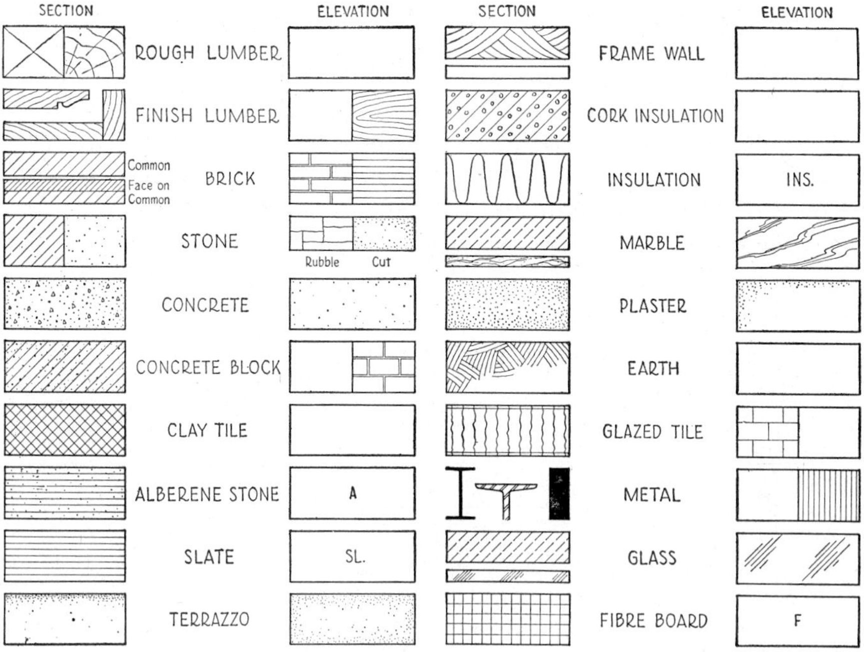

SECTION
ELEVATION
SECTION
ELEVATION
ROUGH LUMBER
FINISH LUMBER
Common
Face on Common
BRICK
STONE
Rubble
Cut
CONCRETE
CONCRETE BLOCK
CLAY TILE
ALBERENE STONE
A
SLATE
SL.
TERRAZZO
FRAME WALL
CORK INSULATION
INSULATION
INS.
MARBLE
PLASTER
EARTH
GLAZED TILE
METAL
GLASS
FIBRE BOARD
F

FIG. 26·10—Symbols for materials.

OUTSIDE
LIMESTONE SILL
BRICK
PLAST.
DETAIL OF BOX FRAME WINDOW IN 9" BRICK WALL
SCALE 1½"=1'-0"
OUTSIDE
LIMESTONE SILL
BRICK
WOOD FRAME
WHITE COAT PLASTER
ANDERSEN NARROLINE DOUBLE HUNG WINDOW IN 9½" BRICK VENEER WALL
SCALE 1½"=1'-0"
OUTSIDE
SHEET COPPER SILL
BRICK
TILE
18 GA. STEEL
SAND FINISH PLASTER
DETAIL OF STEEL CASEMENT WINDOW IN 9" BRICK WALL
SCALE 1½"=1'-0"
SYMBOLS FOR DRAWING AT THE SCALE ¼"=1'-0"
SYMBOLS FOR DRAWING AT THE SCALE ⅛"=1'-0"

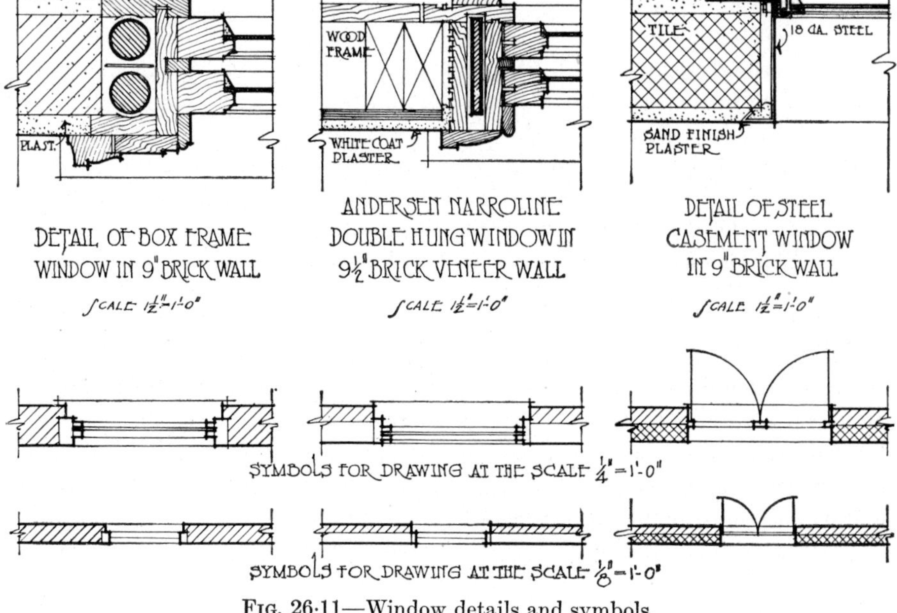

FIG. 26·11—Window details and symbols.

26·18 Dimensioning. The correct dimensioning of an architectural drawing requires first of all a knowledge of the methods of building construction. The dimensions should be placed so as to be most convenient for the workman, should be given to and from accessible points, and should be chosen so that commercial variation in the sizes of materials will not affect the general dimensions. The principles of dimensioning found in Chap. 11 are in general applicable to architectural drawing. A study of the dimensioning on the drawings in this chapter will be of much value.

FINISH SCHEDULE • FIRST FLOOR ROOMS								
ROOM NO.	ROOM NAME	FLOOR	BASE	WALLS & CEILING	WAINSCOT	TRIM	CORNICE	REMARKS
101	HALL	YEL. PINE	BIRCH	PLASTER	———	BIRCH	PICT. MLD.	OAK STAIR TREADS & PLATFORM
102	LIVING RM.	"	"	"	———	"	"	SEE DETAILS
103	DINING RM.	"	"	"	———	"	"	" • "
104	LAVATORY	TILE	4" TILE	"	KEENE'S CEM.	POPLAR	———	OAK STEPS-BIRCH WDW. STOOLS
105	KITCHEN	YEL. PINE	POPLAR	"		"	———	SEE DET'LS- " " "
106	STAIR	Y.P. TREADS	Y. P.	"		Y.P.	———	FINISH TO BOTTOM 1ST FLOOR JOISTS
NOTE - FINISH CLOSETS SAME AS ROOMS FROM WHICH THEY OPEN • • • • •								

FIG. 26·12—Finish schedule.

It will be noted that dimensions are kept outside the plans; that they are given to the outside face of masonry walls; to the center lines of door and window openings, frame partitions, beams, and columns; and to the outside of studs in outside frame walls; and that vertical dimensions and glass sizes are given on elevations.

26·19 Notes and specifications. The statement that the specifications should contain the notes of explanation does not imply that no notes are to be placed on the drawings. On the contrary, there should be on architectural drawings clear, explicit notes in regard to material, construction, and finish even though repeated more fully in the specifications. The builders are apt to overlook a point mentioned only in the specifications but as they are using the drawings constantly will be sure to see a reference or note on the drawing of the part in question. Recent practice has introduced, as an item on the drawings, the "schedule," a systematic method of presenting such notes. This gives in tabular form detailed information taken from the specifications, thus making this required information easily accessible to the craftsmen. Of particular value is the *finish schedule* placed on a plan drawing and giving specifications for all rooms shown on that plan. An example is shown in Fig. 26·12. A door schedule, or door list, the forerunner of other schedules, is on Figs. 26·4 and 26·5.

26·20 Checking. Architectural drawings require careful checking. As the draftsman develops the drawings he checks back and forth continually. Before going to the tracer the design of all structural parts should be checked for strength and fitness, and the drawings should be checked for accuracy of draftsmanship and to see that all special requirements of the client are embodied (these should be on record in writing).

Tracings should be checked by a responsible checker, who should mark all dimensions with a check mark in soft black or in blue pencil and either check mistakes with red pencil or correct them. All checking should be done in a definite order, following each item through separately and systematically. This order will be dictated by the checker's preference or by conditions of the problem. The following is suggested as a guide:

1. Check main over-all dimensions on the plans, seeing that all plans agree.
2. Check location dimensions on plans, seeing that openings line up vertically, and that plan axes (center lines) "carry through" with openings designed to be on axes.
3. See that dimensions of construction and finish on details correspond to those on plans and fit into adjacent features. Large-scale details made as the work progresses must be checked to measurements made at the building.
4. Check stair dimensions carefully, both as to rise and run and to headroom at close places.
5. Check all vertical dimensions on elevations and vertical sections.
6. Check glass sizes of windows and glazed doors.
7. Check all door sizes and see that doors are completely described by note, drawing, or specification.
8. Check design, length, and notation of steel lintels over windows and doors as shown on elevations, and compare with large-scale details.
9. Check sizes and locations of all ducts and flues.
10. Check location and kind of wiring outlets.
11. Check for clearances for all mechanical equipment, including heating, ventilating, plumbing, and wiring.
12. See that all notes are complete and accurate.
13. Check the titles for correctness of statement and spelling.
14. Check specifications for typographical errors.
15. Check the specifications with the drawings. Although the specifications ordinarily take precedence over the drawings, there should be no discrepancy.
16. Check specifications to see that all fixtures and apparatus for plumbing, heating, and lighting systems are specified.
17. Check for conformity with building codes and laws.

26·21 Lettering. There are two distinct divisions in the use of lettering by the architect, the first, *office lettering*, including all the titles and notes put on the drawings for information, and the second, *design lettering*, covering drawings of letters to be executed in stone or bronze or other material in connection with design.

The Old Roman is the architect's one general-purpose letter, which serves him, with few exceptions, for all his work in both divisions. It is a difficult letter to execute properly, and the draftsman should make himself thoroughly familiar with its construction, character, and beauty before attempting to design inscriptions for permanent structures or even titles.

26·22 Titles. Titles on display drawings are usually carefully made in Old Roman in either outline or solid. One alphabet is given in Fig. 4·46. On working drawings a rapid single stroke based on Old Roman, such as Fig. 4·48, is used.

An architectural title should contain part or all of the following items:

1. Name and location of structure.
2. Kind of view, as roof plan (sometimes put elsewhere on sheet).
3. Name and address of client.
4. Date.
5. Scale.
6. Name and address of architect.
7. Number (in set).
8. Key to materials.
9. Office record.
10. For public buildings, space for signed approval of authority.

Three examples of working-drawing titles are given in Fig. 26·13, the first a drawn title, the second a stamp title, such as is made for a large

FIG. 26·13—Working-drawing titles.

project where hundreds of drawings are required, and the third a finished title in roman letters.

PROBLEMS

26·23 The following problems are suggested for practice in architectural drawing. The student should have ready access to information on present-day building materials. Use $\frac{1}{4}''$ scale for plans and elevations, $\frac{3}{4}''$ for wall sections and $\frac{1}{2}''$ for details.

1. Draw the south elevation of the house shown in Figs. 26·3 to 26·7, getting the information from these drawings.

2. Draw the east elevation of foregoing house.

3. Make a complete set of working drawings for a vacation house, developing the presentation drawings shown in Figs. 26·14 and 26·15. Figures 26·16 to 26·20 are given for the detail information concerning materials and construction. At this stage in the progress of a job through an architect's office the chief draftsman will prepare a schedule

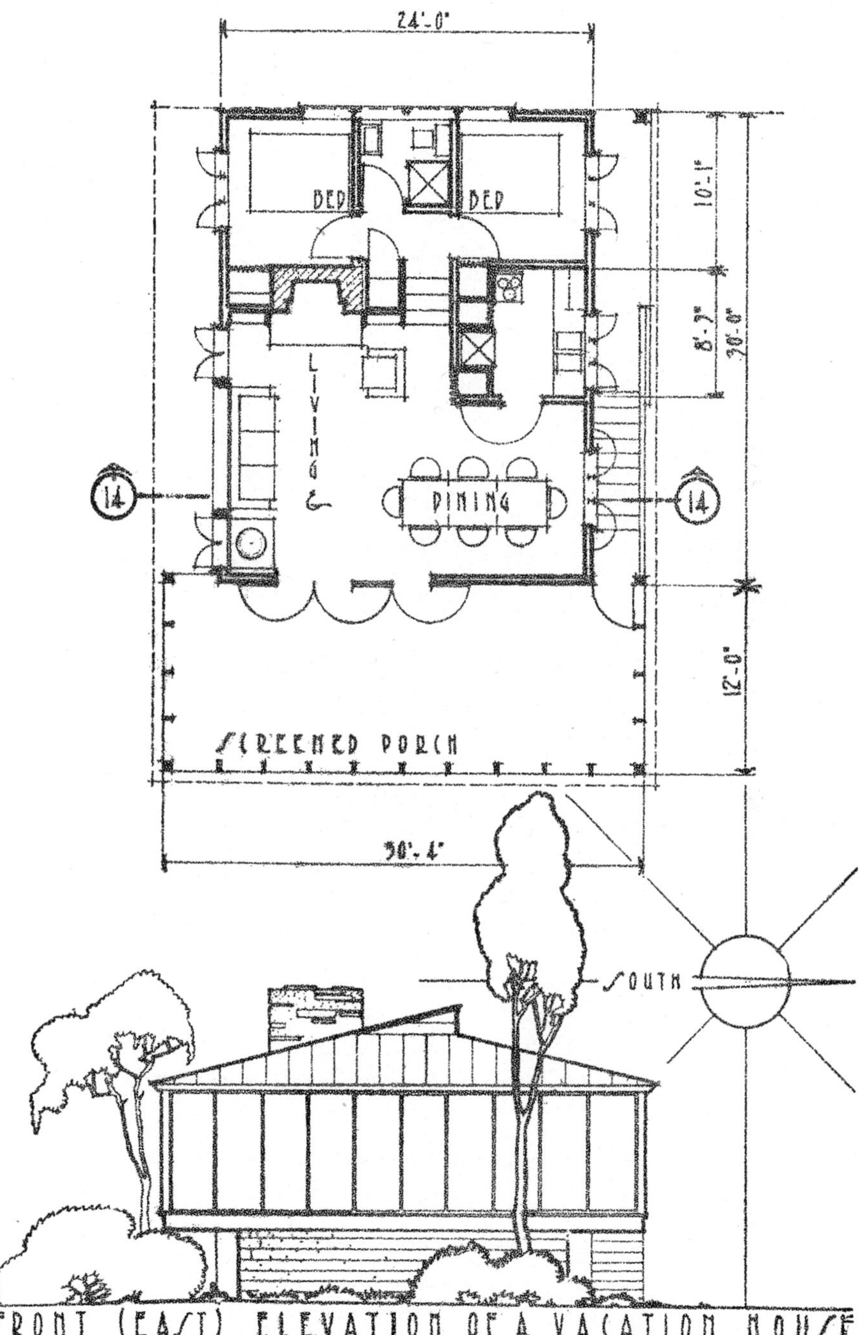

Fig. 26·14—Presentation drawing; vacation house.

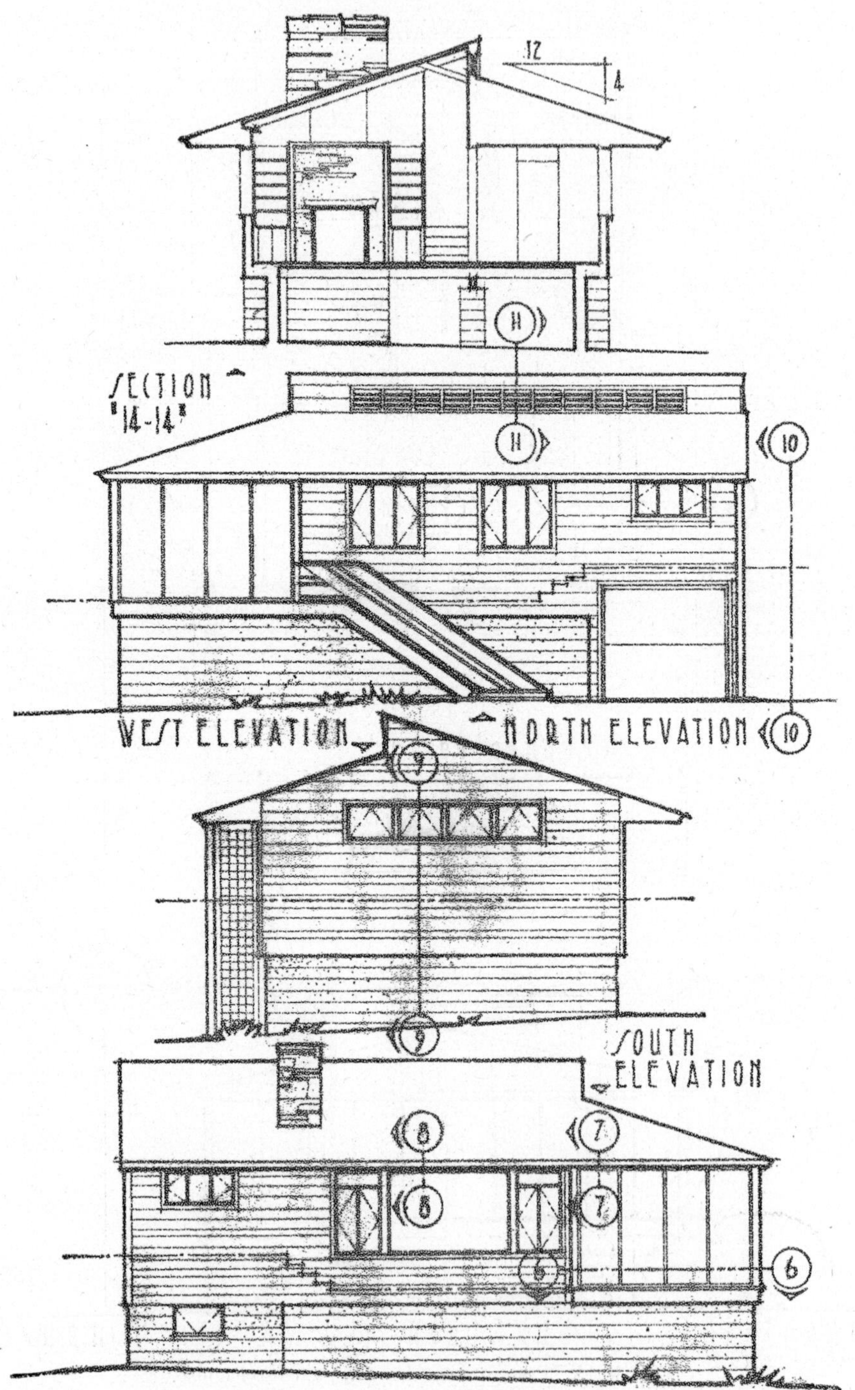

Fig. 26·15—Presentation drawing; vacation house.

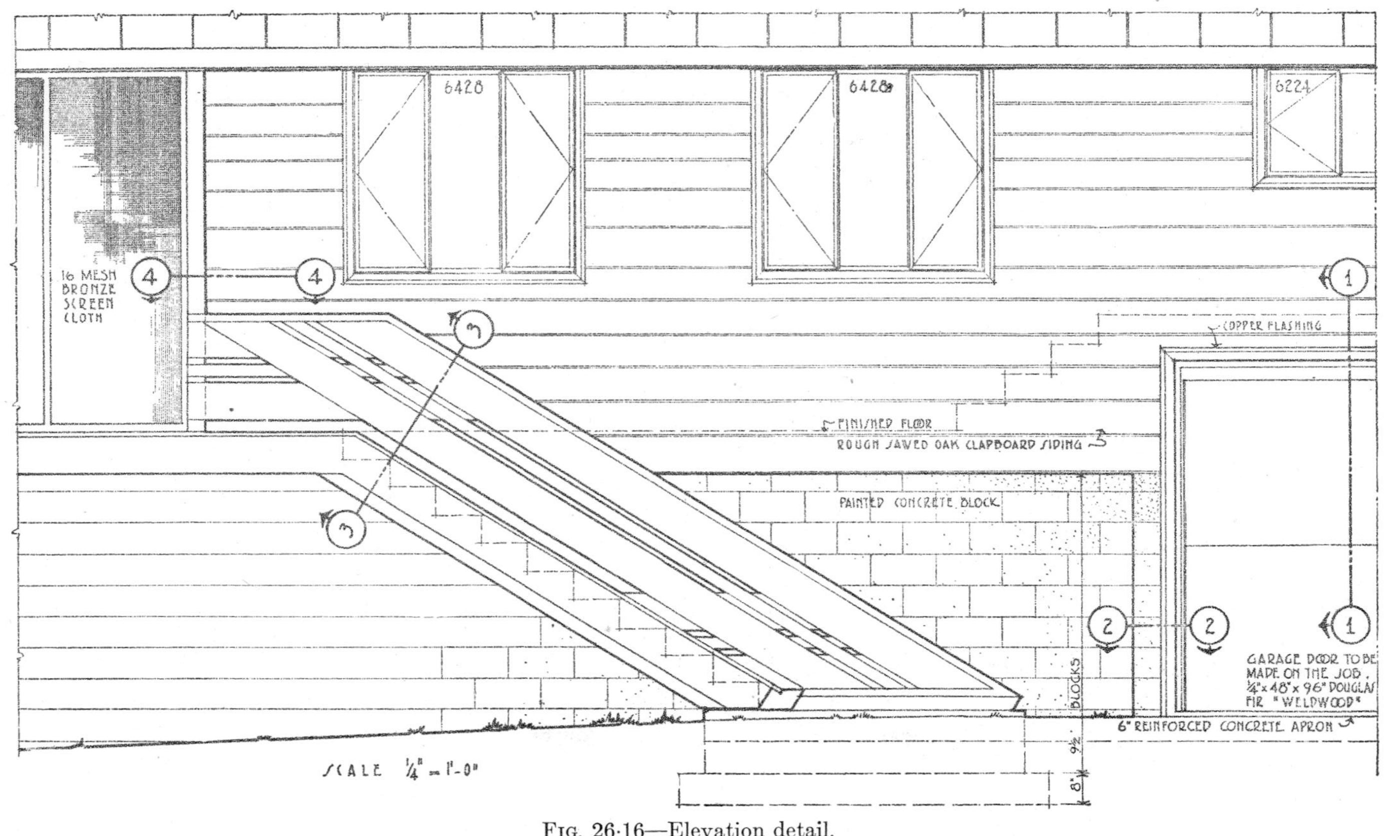

FIG. 26·16—Elevation detail.

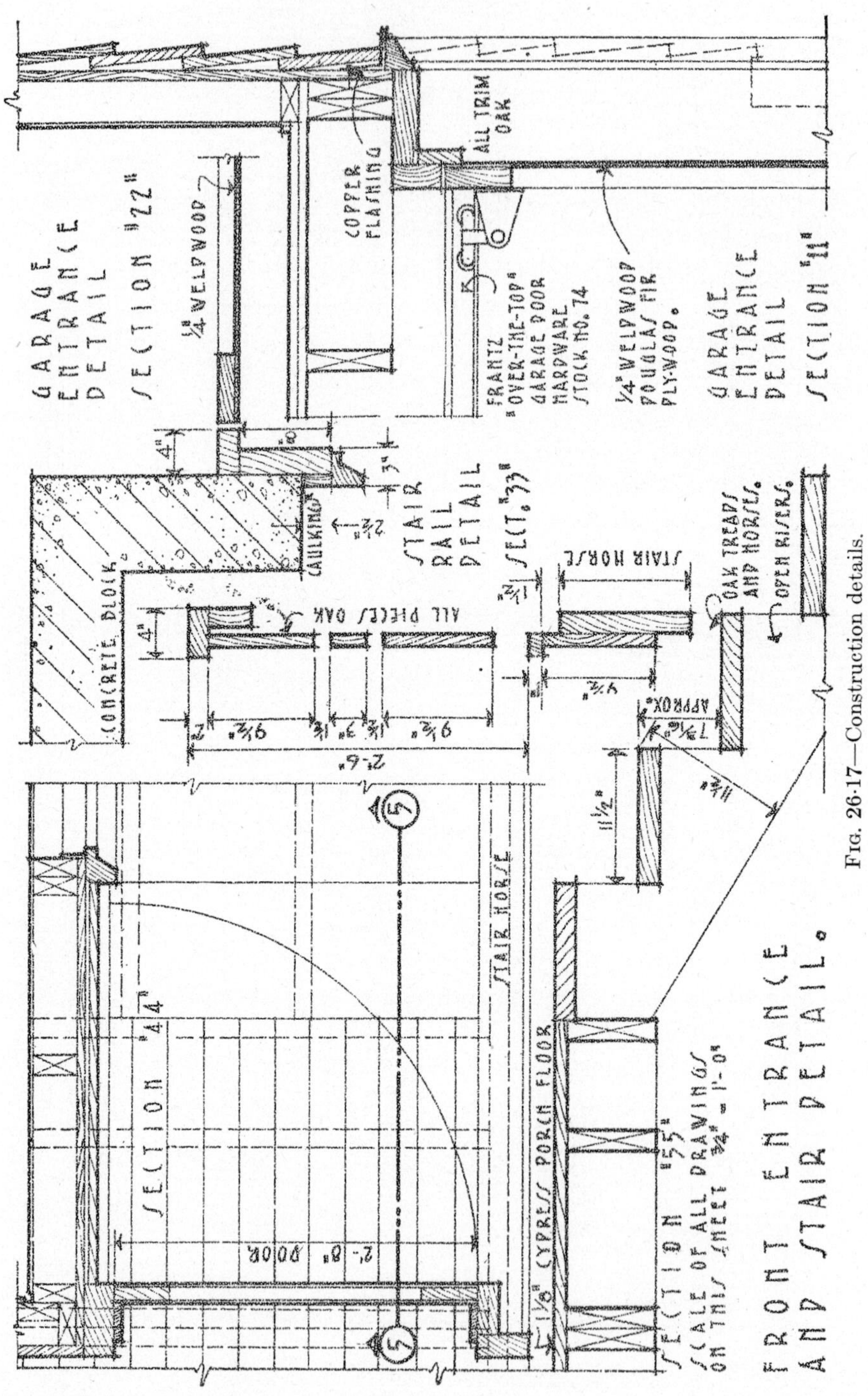

Fig. 26·17—Construction details.

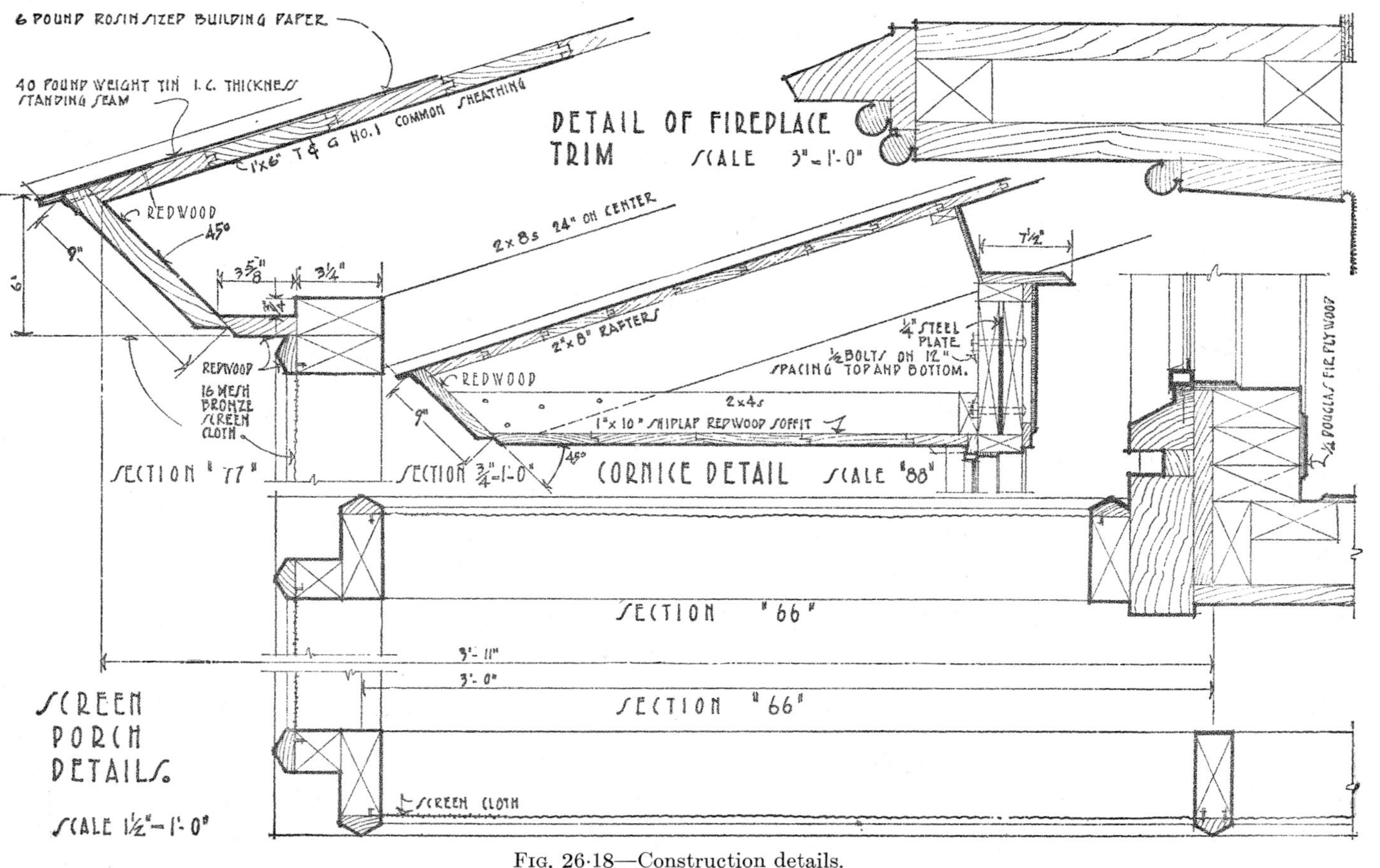

Fig. 26·18—Construction details.

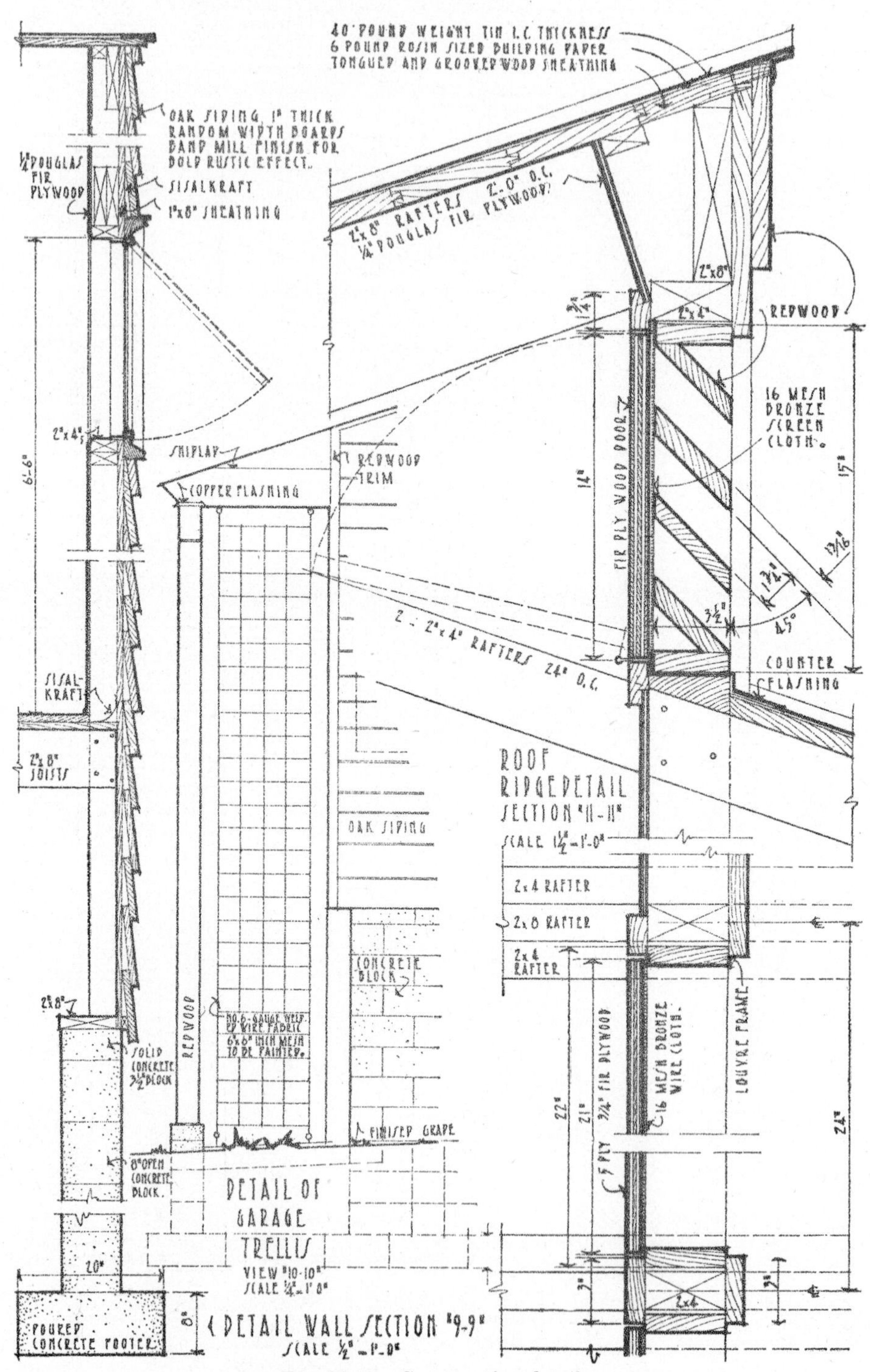

FIG. 26·19—Construction details.

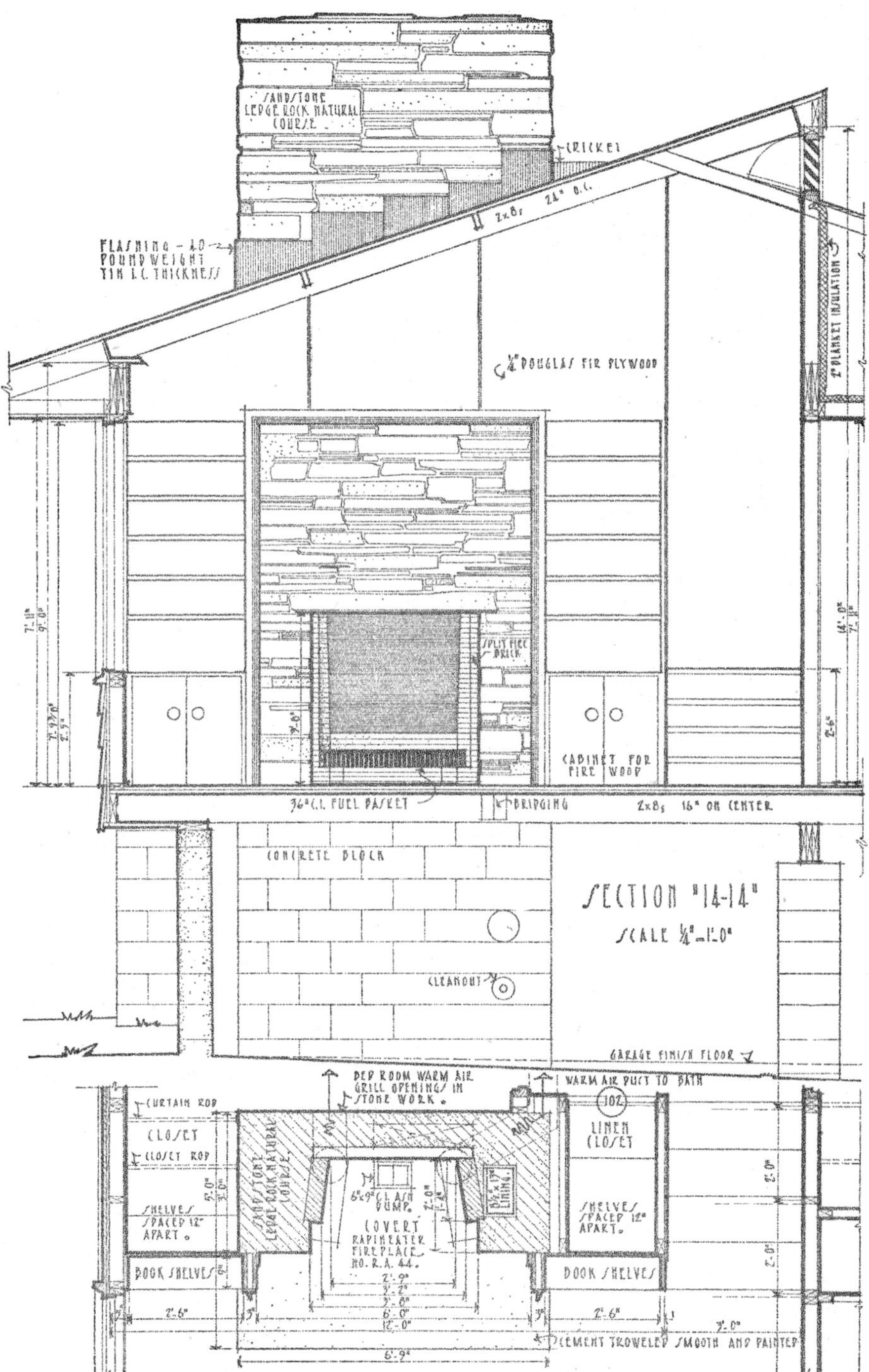

Fig. 26·20—Construction details.

of the principal drawings and details to be shown. The following is a suggested outline for the draftsman to follow:

Sheet No. 1. PLOT PLAN. Scale 1/8″ = 1′-0″. Show septic-tank location and a detail of filter bed.

Sheet No. 2. GROUND-FLOOR PLAN. Scale 1/4″ = 1′-0″. Show first-floor framing plan.

Sheet No. 3. FIRST-FLOOR PLAN. Scale 1/4″ = 1′-0″. Show ceiling framing.

Sheet No. 4. NORTH ELEVATION. Scale 1/4″ = 1′-0″. Show construction details for stairway and garage doorway.

Sheet No. 5. EAST ELEVATION. Scale 1/4″ = 1′-0″. Show construction details for porch-screen frames and cornices.

Sheet No. 6. SOUTH ELEVATION. Scale 1/4″ = 1′-0″. Show construction details for garage window.

Sheet No. 7. WEST ELEVATION. Scale 1/4″ = 1′-0″. Show west-end wall section and trellis details.

Sheet No. 8. CROSS SECTION. Scale 1/4″ = 1′-0″. Show details of fireplace, bookcases, ridge louvers, and cornice.

4. Fig. 26·2. Make floor plan, elevations, and roof framing plan for week-end cottage. In its construction it is suggested that the walls be solid masonry of rough-faced field stone, that roof timbers be of old barn timbers or beams hewed to fit from trees on the site, that the floor be of flagstone with cement joints, that the roof be of heavy slate or large shakes, and that the woodwork be of barn boards or unfinished lumber, stained.

5. Fig. 26·21. Make set of working drawings for vacation cottage. Foundation of field stone.

6. Fig. 26·22. Make working drawings for hunting lodge. Field-stone foundation, hewed-timber construction and sod roof.

7. Fig. 26·23. Make working drawings for house shown. Concrete foundation. Walls of stucco, sheetrock, or metal, backed with insulation. Fireproof construction and steel sash preferred.

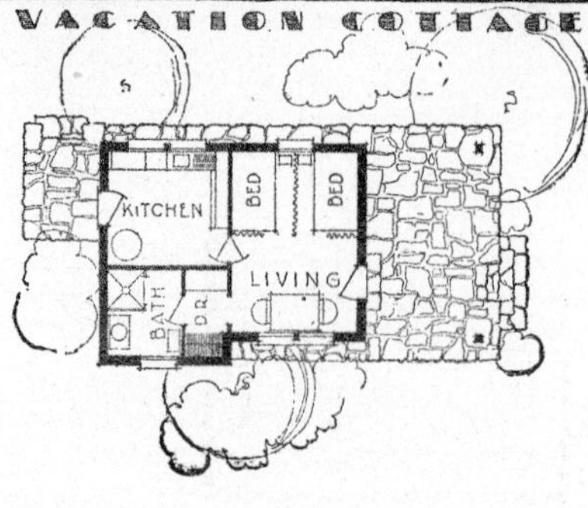

Fig. 26·21—A vacation cottage.

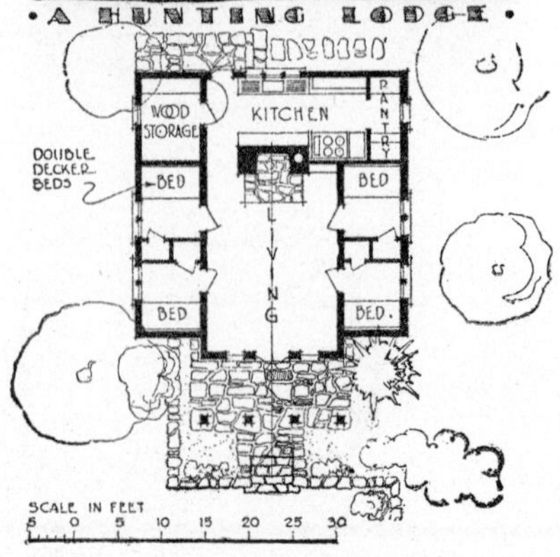

Fig. 26·22—A hunting lodge.

8. Fig. 26·24. Make working drawings for house shown, with choice of building materials.

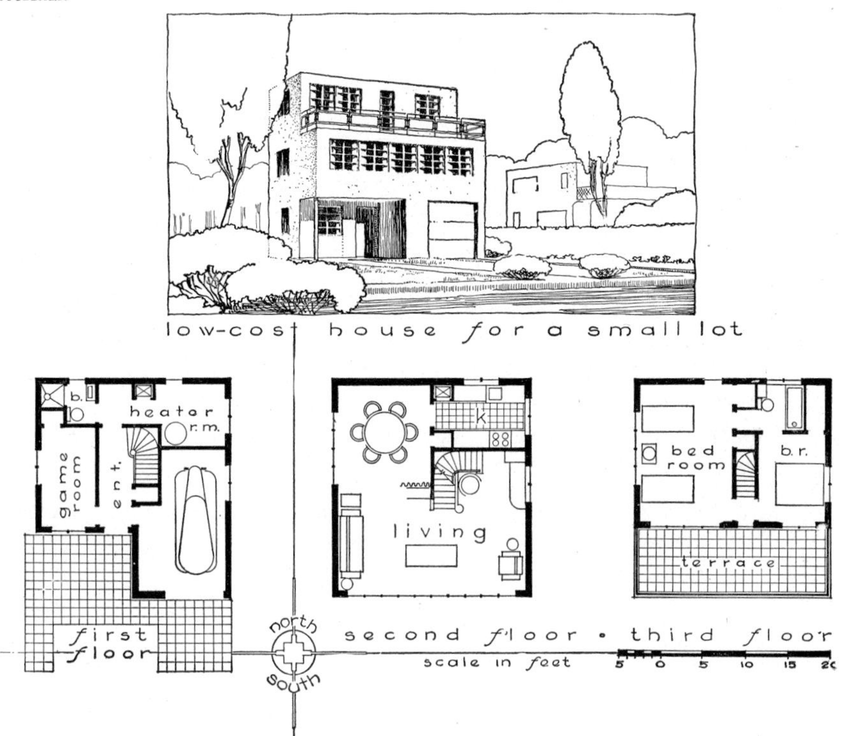

Fig. 26·23—A small house.

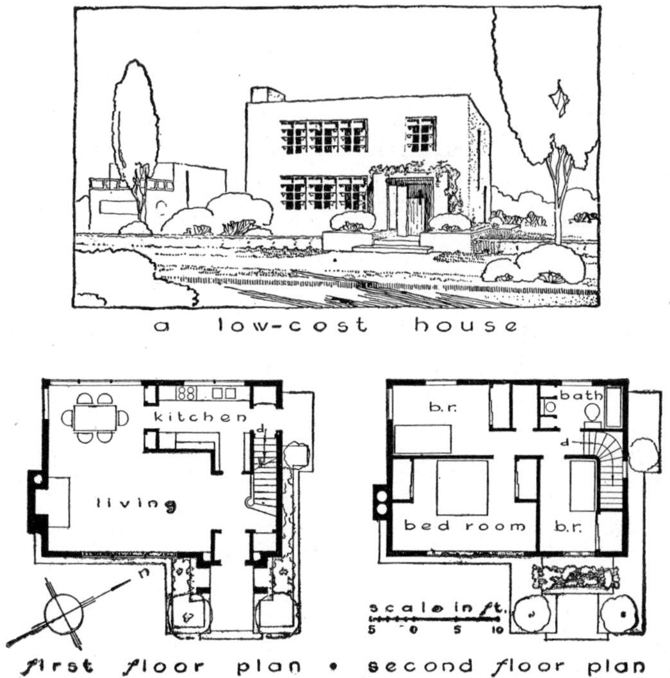

Fig. 26·24—A small house.

Chapter 27

THE ELEMENTS OF STRUCTURAL DRAWING

27·1 Structural drawings differ from other drawings only in certain details and practices which have developed as peculiar to the materials worked with and the method of their fabrication. The differences are so well established that it is essential for any engineer to know something of the methods of representation in use in structural work.

Steel structures are made up of "rolled shapes" put together permanently by riveting or welding. The function of a structural drawing is to show the shapes and sizes used and the details of fastening. Sections of the usual structural shapes are shown in Fig. 27·1.

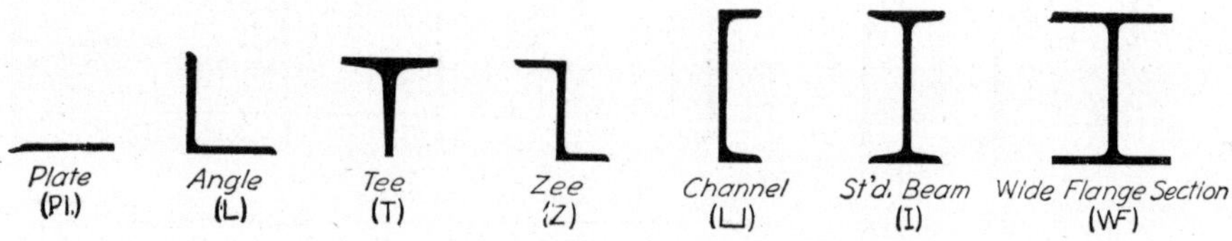

Fig. 27·1—Sections of rolled shapes.

The dimensions of the various sizes of standard steel shapes, together with much other information with which the structural draftsman must be familiar, are given in the various structural-steel handbooks. For wooden structures, where the parts are not so completely standardized, complete details and dimensions of every part are desirable.

A glossary of terms used in structural drawing is given in the Appendix.

27·2 Classification. Professor Ketchum[1] has classified and described the drawings for structures as follows:

(1) *General plan.* This will include a profile of the ground; location of the structure; elevations of ruling points in the structure; clearances; grades; direction of flow, high water, and low water (for a bridge); and all other data necessary for designing the substructure and superstructure.

(2) *Stress diagram.* This will give the main dimensions of the structure, the loading, stresses in all members for the dead loads, live loads, wind loads, etc., itemized separately; the total maximum stresses and minimum stresses; sizes of members; typical sections of all built members showing arrangement of material; and all information necessary for detailing the various parts of the structure.

(3) *Shop drawings.* Shop detail drawings should be made of all steel-and ironwork, and detail drawings should be made of all timber, masonry, and concrete work.

[1] Structural Engineers' Handbook by Milo S. Ketchum.

(4) *Foundation or masonry plan.* The foundation or masonry plan should contain detail drawings of all foundations, walls, piers, etc., that support the structure. The plans should show the loads on the foundations, the depth of footings, the spacing of piles where used, the proportions for the concrete, the quality of masonry and mortar, the allowable bearing on the soil, and all data necessary for accurately locating and constructing the foundations.

(5) *Erection diagram.* The erection diagram should show the relative location of every part of the structure, shipping marks for the various members, all main dimensions, number of pieces in a member, packing of pins, size and grip of pins, and any special feature or information that may assist the erector in the field. The approximate weight of heavy pieces will materially assist the erector in designing his falsework and derricks.

(6) *Falsework plans.* For ordinary structures it is not common to prepare falsework plans in the office, this important detail being left to the erector in the field. For difficult or important work, erection plans should be worked out in the office and should show in detail all members and connections of the falsework and also give instructions for the successive steps in carrying out the work. Falsework plans are especially important for concrete and masonry arches and other concrete structures, and for forms for all walls, piers, etc. Detail plans of travelers, derricks, etc., should also be furnished the erector.

(7) *Bills of material.* Complete bills of material showing the different parts of structure with its mark and the shipping weight should be prepared. This is necessary to permit checking of shipping weights and shipment and arrival of materials.

(8) *Rivet list.* The rivet list should show the dimensions and number of all field rivets, field bolts, spikes, etc., used in the erection of the structure.

(9) *List of drawings.* A list should be made showing the contents of all drawings belonging to the structure.

27·3 General drawings. The general drawings correspond in many respects to the design drawings and assembly drawings of the mechanical engineer and include the general plan, the stress diagram, and the erection diagram. In some cases the design drawing is worked out completely by the engineer, who gives the sizes and weights of members and the number and spacing of all rivets, but in most cases the general dimensions, positions, and sizes of the members and the number of rivets are shown, leaving the details to be worked out in the shop or to be given on separate complete detail shop drawings.

In order to show the details clearly, the structural draftsman often uses two scales in the same view, one for the center lines or skeleton of the structure, showing the shape, and a larger one for the parts composing it. The scale used for the skeleton is determined by the size of the structure as compared with the sheet; ¼″, ⅜″, and ½″ to 1′-0″ are commonly used. Shop details are made ¾″, 1″, or 1½″, and, for small details, 3″ to the foot. Figure 27·2 is a typical drawing of a small roof truss, giving complete details. Such drawings are made about the working lines used in calculating the stresses and sizes of the members. These lines are usually the gravity lines

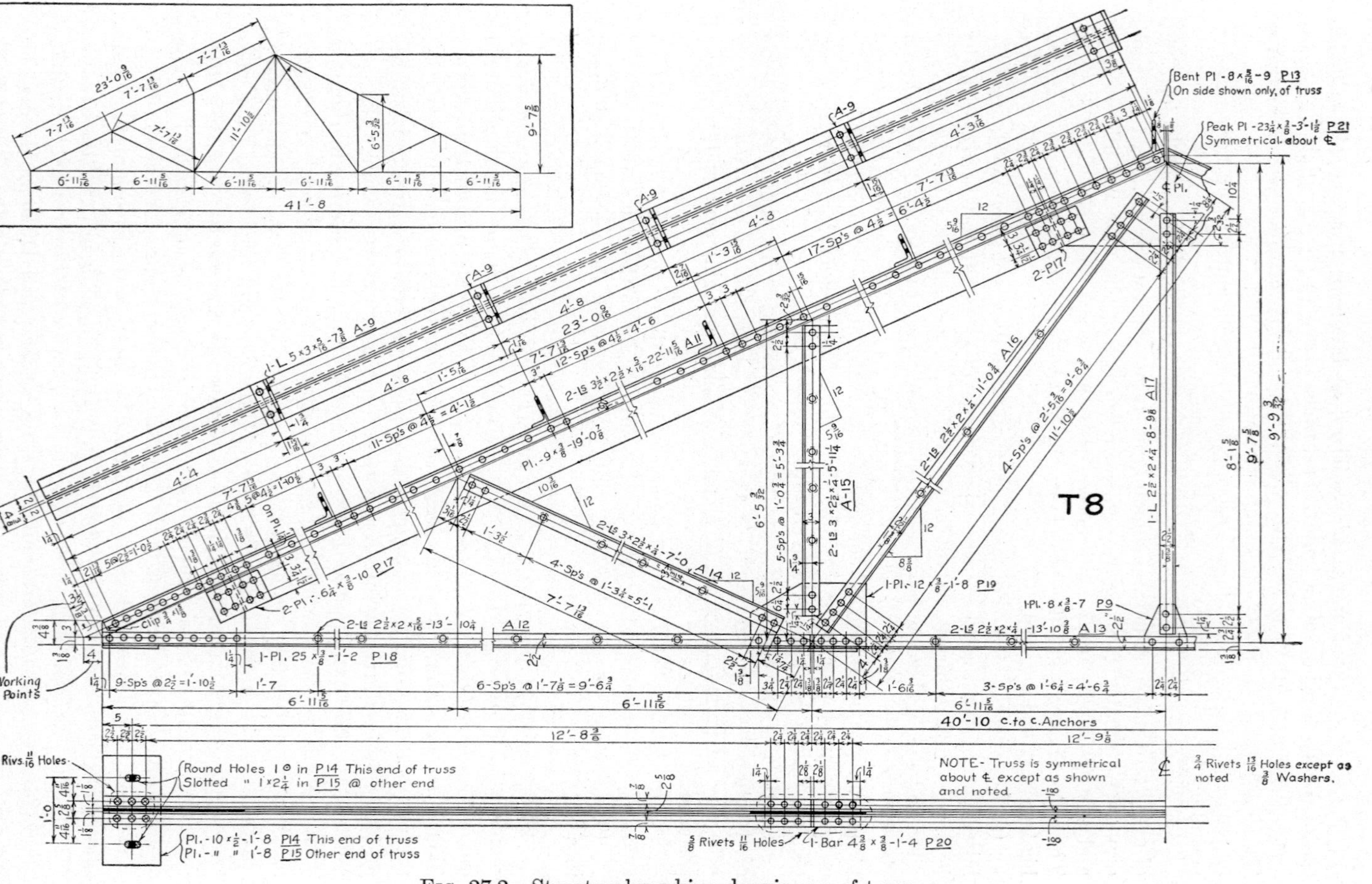

FIG. 27·2—Structural working drawing; roof truss.

of the members and form the skeleton, as illustrated separately to small scale in the box on the figure. The intersections of these lines are called "working points" and are the points from which all distances are figured. The length of each working line is computed accurately, and from it the intermediate dimensions are obtained.

The erection diagram is often put on the same sheet, as with the drawing of the truss.

When one-half of a truss only is shown, it is always the left end, looking toward the side on which the principal connections are made.

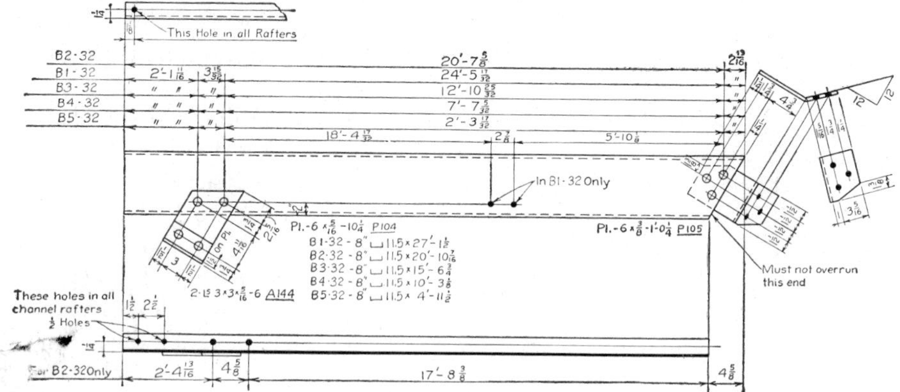

FIG. 27·3—Beam detail.

In building construction a beam schedule and a column schedule, giving the detailed information concerning these members, should be added on the drawings.

27·4 Detail drawings. Separate drawings made to a sufficiently large scale to carry complete information are called "shop detail drawings." All parts are shown to scale, and it should be noted particularly that rivets and rivetheads are drawn accurately to scale. When possible, the drawings of all members are shown in the same relative position which they will occupy in the completed structure: vertical, horizontal, or inclined. Long vertical or inclined members may be drawn in a horizontal position, a vertical member always having its lower end at the left, and an inclined member drawn in the direction it would fall. Except in plain building work, a diagram to small scale showing by a heavy line the relative position of the member in the structure should be drawn on every detail sheet.

Figure 27·3 is a beam detail, giving all the information for five different beams in one drawing and illustrating the method of representing a bent plate. It is obvious that in such a drawing the lengths are not to scale.

As the various members are detailed they are given a mark, such as B1-32 (B for beam; 1, the shop number; and 32, the sheet number of the detail drawing), for identification in assembling.

27·5 Structural drawing practice. All drawings in an office should be made to standard sizes. The American Standard 17″ × 22″, 22″ × 34″, and 34″ × 44″ sheets are common.

Half-inch borders are generally used. Inked outlines should be of sufficient weight to make the main material stand out distinctly, while dimension lines and gage lines are made in very fine full lines in black. Some prefer red ink for dimension and gage lines. This makes the tracing somewhat easier to read, but the prints are not so satisfactory, and it is difficult to get a permanent red ink. When new work is to be attached to old, the old is often drawn in red. Tracing paper or pencil cloth is extensively used for shop details, and occasionally sketches substitute for an instrument drawing. Assemblies in pencil, on vellum, may be used when the permanence of ink is not an essential feature.

Dimensions are always placed above the dimension line and the dimension lines are not broken but are continuous. Length dimensions are expressed in feet and inches. All inch symbols are omitted unless there is the possibility of misunderstanding, thus 1 bolt should be 1″ bolt to distinguish between size and number. Inch symbols are omitted even though the dimensions are in feet and inches, and dimensions should be hyphenated thus, 7′-0, 7′-0½, 7′-4, as shown in Fig. 27·3. Plate widths and section sizes of rolled shapes are given in inches. Care should be taken that dimensions are given to commercial sizes of materials. Sizes of members are specified by figures parallel to them as 2L2½ × 2 × ¼ × 7′-3 which means 2 angles having unequal legs of 2½ and 2, ¼ thick and 7′-3 long. Angular dimensions are indicated by tangents on a 12″ base line, shown on a small triangle adjacent to the inclined member.

The dimensions necessary for the sections of Fig. 27·1 with the abbreviations for sections to be used on drawings, as adopted by the American Institute of Steel Construction, are as follows:

Plates. Width × thickness × length (Pl 18 × ½ × 10′-0).
Equal-leg Angles. Size of legs × thickness × length (L3 × 3 × ¼ × 10′-0).
Unequal-leg Angles. Size of long leg × short leg × thicknessess × length (L7 × 4 × ½ × 10′-0).
Tees. Height × width × weight per foot × length (T3 × 3 × 6.7 × 10′-0).
Zees. Height × thickness × weight per foot × length (Z6 × 3½ × 15.7 × 10′-0).
Standard Channels. Height × weight per foot × length (9⊔ 13.4 × 10′-0).
Standard I Beams. Height × weight per foot × length (15 I 42.9 × 10′-0).
Wide-flange Sections. Height × weight per foot × length (24WF 74 × 10′-0).

Checking is usually indicated by a dot in red ink or pencil placed under the dimension. Elevations, sections, and other views are placed in relation to each other by the rules of third-angle projection, except that when a view is given under a front view, as in Figs. 27·2 and 27·3, it is made as a section taken above the lower flange, looking down, instead of as a regular bottom view looking up. Large sections of materials are shown with uniform cross-hatching. Small-scale sections are blacked-in solid, with white spaces left between adjacent pieces.

Rivets are spaced along "gage lines," measured from the backs of angles and channels and from center to center on I beams. The distance between rivets measured along the gage line is called the "pitch." The gages and pitch for various angles are shown in Fig. 27·4.

The size of most structures prevents their being completed in the shop, so they are "fabricated" as large as transportation facilities allow, and the necessary connections made where the structure is erected. The holes for these "field rivets" are always indicated in solid black to scale on the drawing, while shop rivets are indicated by circles of the diameter of the rivet head. A bill of field rivets is always furnished. In drawing rivets, the drop pen, Fig. 30·5, is a favorite instrument.

A general note is usually added to all detail drawings, giving rivet sizes, size of open holes, and edge distance (unless noted) and painting instructions, as, "Paint one coat of red lead (or black graphite) in shop. Paint all parts in contact before assembly."

Figure 27·5 shows the American Standard symbols for riveting, formerly called the "Osborn symbols," which are so universally used that no key on the drawing is necessary. Figure 27·6 shows rivets to larger scale.

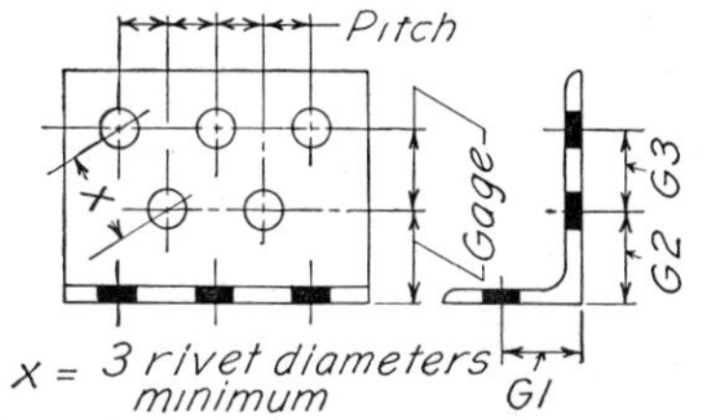

There is a growing use of arc welding instead of riveting for fabricating structural work, see Chap. 16.

Pitch
Gage
G2 G3
X
X = 3 rivet diameters minimum
G1

LEG	G1	G2	G3	MAX RIVET
8	4½	3	3	1⅛
7	4	2½	3	1⅛
6	3½	2¼	2½	1
5	3	2	1¾	1
4	2½			⅞
3½	2			⅞
3	1¾			⅞
2½	1⅜			¾
2	1⅛			⅝
1¾	1			½
1½	⅞			⅜
1⅜	⅞			⅜
1¼	¾			⅜
1	⅝			¼
¾	½			¼

FIG. 27·4—Gage and pitch.

Bent plates should be developed, and the "stretchout" length of bent forged bars given. The length of a bent plate may be taken as the inside length of the bend plus half the thickness of the plate for each bend.

A bill of material always accompanies a structural drawing. This may be put on the drawing, but the best practice is to attach it as a separate "bill sheet," generally on 8½″ × 11″ paper.

Each member of a structure is given a shipping mark, consisting of a capital letter and a number, which appears on the drawings and on the bill sheet. See Figs. 27·2 and 27·3.

Lettering is done in rapid single stroke either inclined or vertical. An example of a printed title form is given in Fig. 27·7.

27·6 Timber structures. The representation of timber-framed structures involves no new principles but requires particular attention to details. Timber members are generally rectangular in section and are specified to

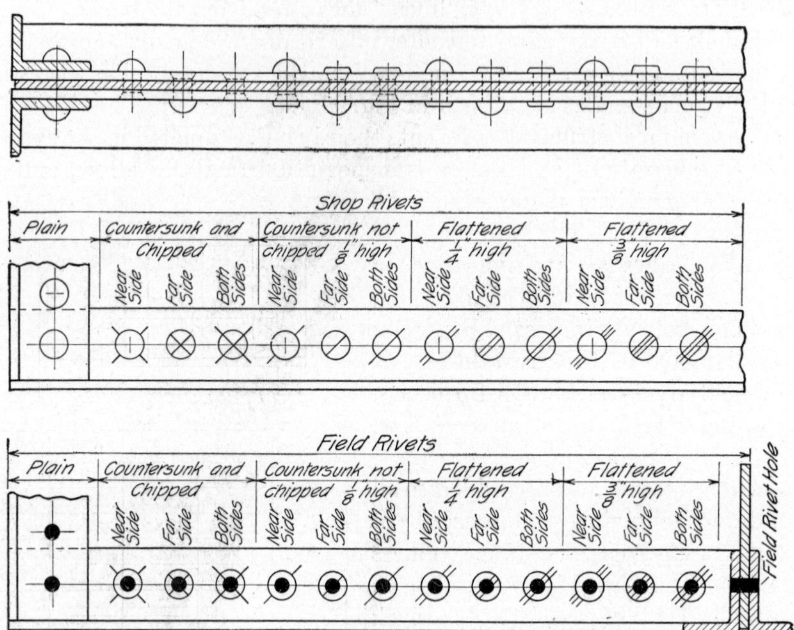

FIG. 27·5—American Standard rivet symbols.

nominal sizes in even inches, as 8″ × 12″. As nominal sizes are generally larger than the actual dimensions, the general drawing must give center and other important distances accurately. Details drawn to larger scale give specific information as to separate parts. Sizes of wood members vary so much that nothing should be left to "guess in" when erecting. The particulars of joints, splices, methods of fastening, etc., should be given in full.

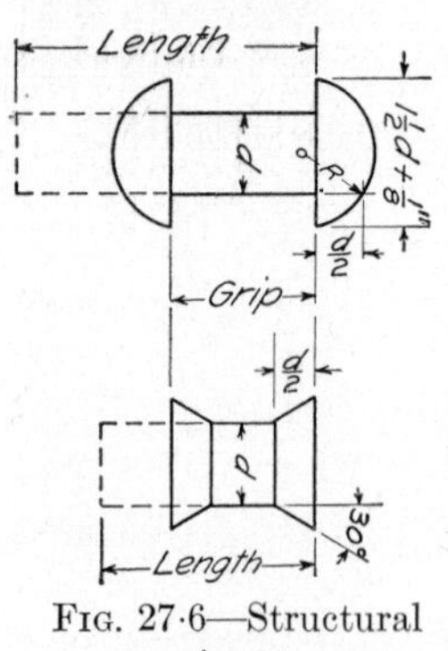

FIG. 27·6—Structural rivets.

Two scales may sometimes be used to advantage on the general drawing, as was done in Fig. 27·8.

Figure 27·9 shows the construction of a wooden trestle on piles. Timbers of the sizes shown are used for heights up to 20 feet. Complete notes are an essential part of such drawings, especially when an attempt at dimensioning the smaller details would result in confusion.

27·7 Timber fastenings. Joints in timber structures may be fastened with nails or spikes, wood screws, bolts, or modern ring-shaped or flat *connectors* in action similar to a dowel or key. Some common types are shown in Fig. 27·10. *A* is a split ring, assembled in grooves in each piece and held together with a bolt, as indicated at *B*. The sharp projections on the alligator connector *C* are forced into the members by pressure. The *claw-plate*

GENERAL NOTES.
WORKMANSHIP
MATERIAL
BILL OF MATERIAL SHEET NO.
RIVETS
OPEN HOLES
REAMING
ASSEMBLING PAINT
SHOP PAINT
FIELD PAINT
INSPECTED BY
ERECTED BY
FIELD CONNECTIONS
F. O. B.
SHIP

APPROVED ______ 194__
BY
CONTRACT ______ OF
SHEET NO. ______ OF
LOCATION
BUILT BY
KING BRIDGE COMPANY
CLEVELAND, OHIO
DRAWINGS FINISHED
FORM NO. 1

FIG. 27·7—A printed title form.

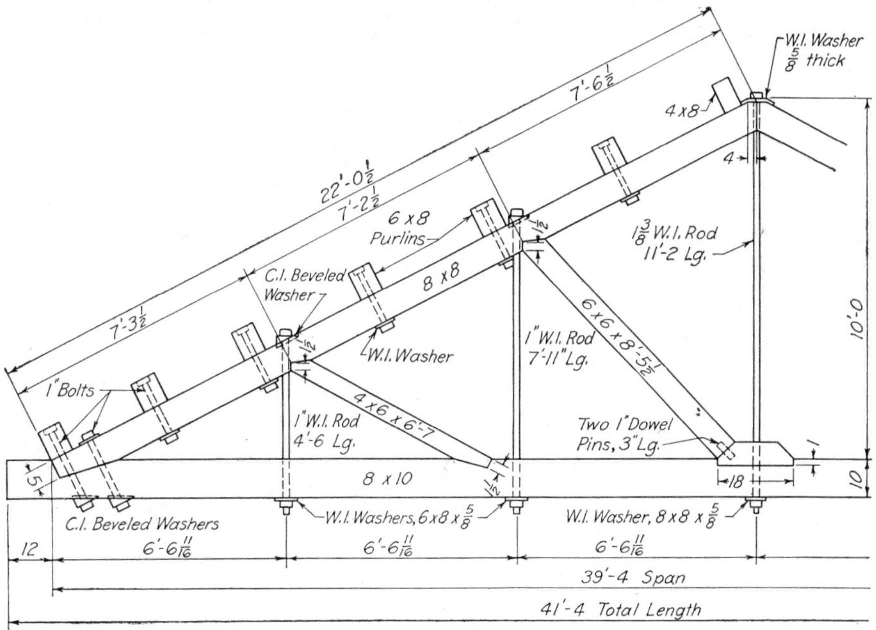

FIG. 27·8—A timber-truss drawing.

connector *D* is used either in pairs, back to back, for timber-to-timber connections, or single for timber to metal. A typical assembly is shown at *E*. The Kubler wood dowel connector *F* fits into a bored hole in each timber face, and a bolt holds the parts together.

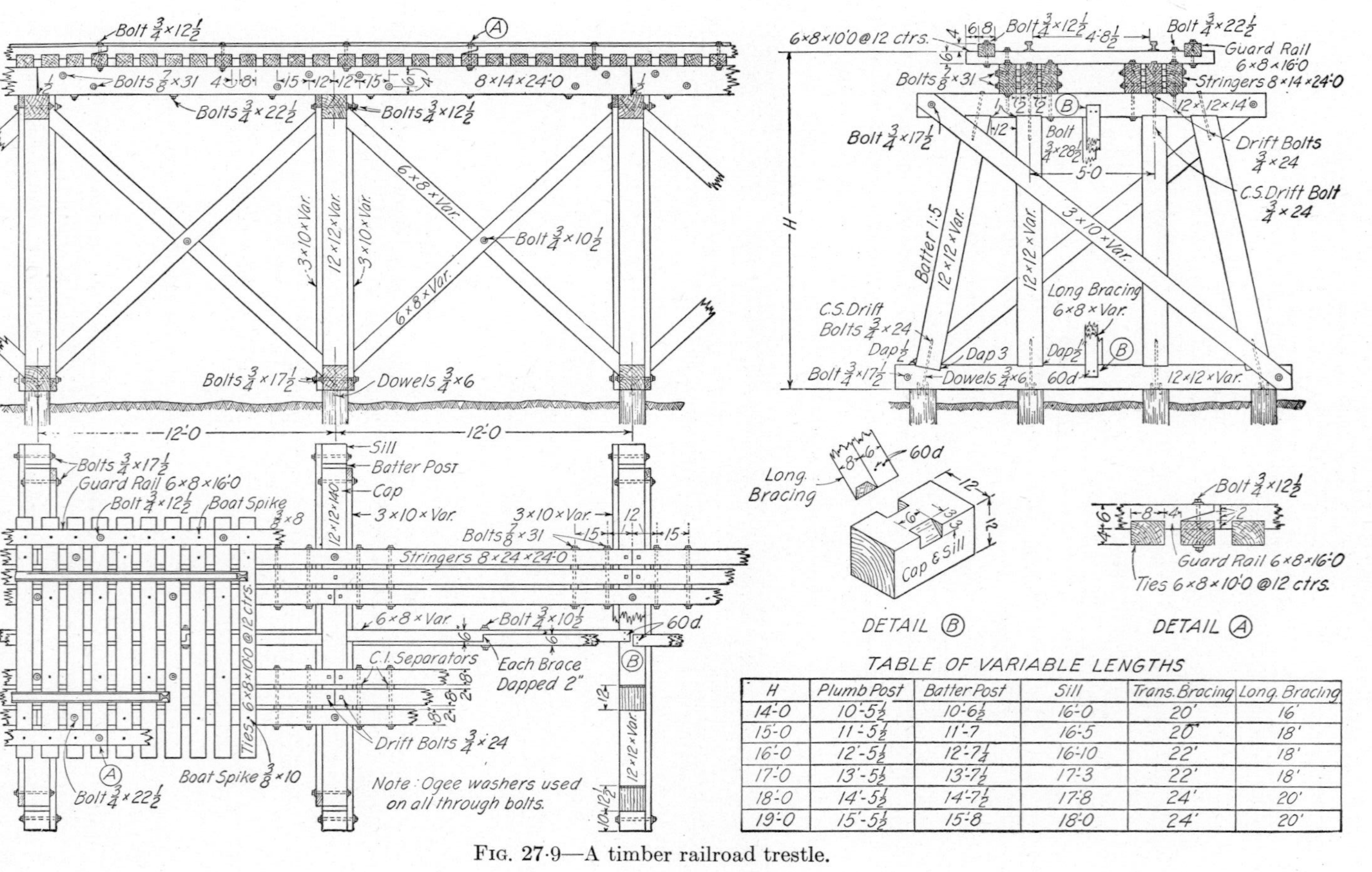

TABLE OF VARIABLE LENGTHS

H	Plumb Post	Batter Post	Sill	Trans. Bracing	Long. Bracing
14'-0	10'-5$\frac{1}{2}$	10'-6$\frac{1}{2}$	16'-0	20'	16'
15'-0	11'-5$\frac{1}{2}$	11'-7	16'-5	20'	18'
16'-0	12'-5$\frac{1}{2}$	12'-7$\frac{1}{4}$	16'-10	22'	18'
17'-0	13'-5$\frac{1}{2}$	13'-7$\frac{1}{2}$	17'-3	22'	18'
18'-0	14'-5$\frac{1}{2}$	14'-7$\frac{1}{2}$	17'-8	24'	20'
19'-0	15'-5$\frac{1}{2}$	15'-8	18'-0	24'	20'

FIG. 27·9—A timber railroad trestle.

The Forest Products Laboratory publication, "Wood Handbook," gives basic information on wood as a material of construction, including the modern connectors, and is available at small cost from the Superintendent of Documents, Washington, D.C.

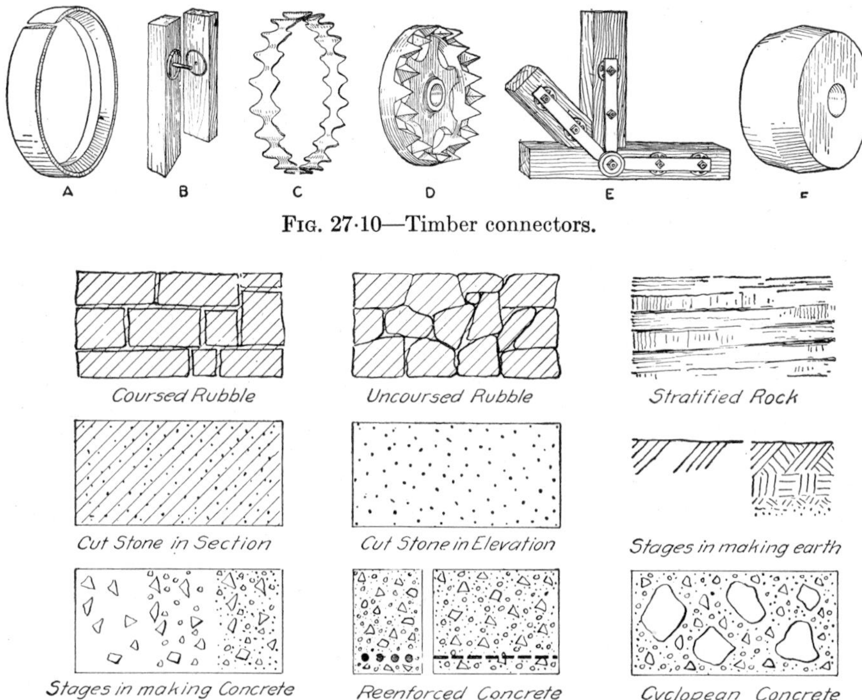

FIG. 27·10—Timber connectors.

FIG. 27·11—Masonry symbols.

27·8 Masonry structures. In drawing masonry the symbols used bear some resemblance to the material represented. Figure 27·11 gives those in common use and shows the stages followed to secure uniformity of effect in rendering earth and concrete. An effective method of crosshatching, leaving a white margin around the edge of the stone is shown in Fig. 27·12. Drawings for piers, foundations for machines, and other structures are met with in all kinds of engineering work. Grade levels, floor levels, and other fixed heights should be given, together with accurate location dimensions for foundation bolts. All materials should be marked plainly with name or notes. A pier is illustrated in Fig. 27·13.

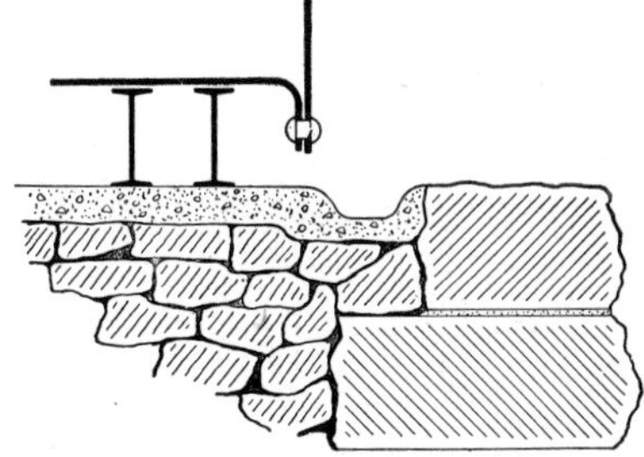

FIG. 27·12—Masonry in section.

27·9 Reinforced concrete is an important division of masonry construction needing careful attention in representation. It is almost impossible to show definitely the shapes of reinforcing bars in concrete by the usual orthographic views, without a systematic scheme of marking. In Fig. 27·14 the various bars are designated by reference letters and numbers on horizontal and vertical center lines. Note the horizontal lines *G* and *F*, and the vertical lines numbered 1, 2, 3, 4, 5. The first bar in the line *G* is called *G*1, the second *G*2, etc., similarly for bars *F*1, *F*2. Each of the bars is marked with its same combination of letter and figure in the other views, and they are detailed in separate bending diagrams, thus completely defining their location and shape. Sometimes the attempt is made to give bending dimensions in the views of the structure but, as this greatly increases the difficulty of reading the drawing, it is not good practice.

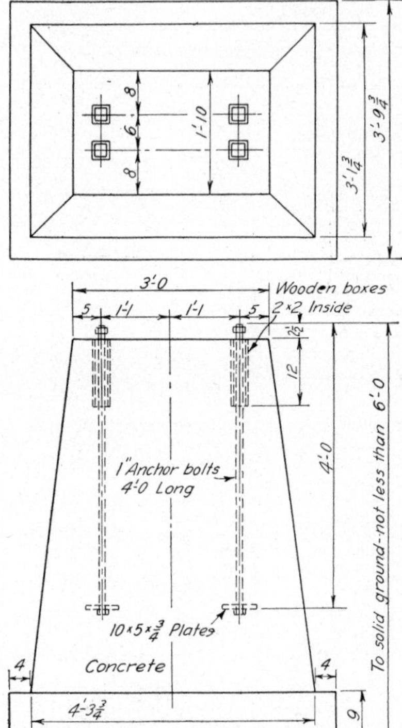

FIG. 27·13—A pier drawing.

The usual symbol for concrete in section is used very commonly for reinforced concrete with the reinforcing-bar sections represented by heavy black dots, and the bars parallel to the section by dashed or full lines. This method, however, gives a very confused appearance. The reinforcing bars can be shown in place much more clearly if the concrete is represented by an even tint instead of the regular symbol. This tint may be made by section lining in colored ink or in very dilute black ink or, if the tracing is made on the smooth side of the cloth or, if pencil drawings on vellum or cloth are employed, by stumping the back with soft pencil. Any one of these methods gives a light blue tint on the blueprint and enables the details of the reinforcing, which is the important item, to be shown clearly. The two methods are shown side by side in Fig. 27·14.

Drawings of reinforced-concrete structures should contain, in tabular form, beam schedules, slab schedules, and column schedules as well as bar schedules.

Certain classes of engineering structures involve much freehand rendering, and the ease of reading (usefulness) depends upon the care with which this rendering is done.

The section of a submerged weir, Fig. 27·15, illustrates a case in which there is comparatively little mechanical execution. Any means of bringing out the construction, such as surface shading or the use of solid black, is legitimate.

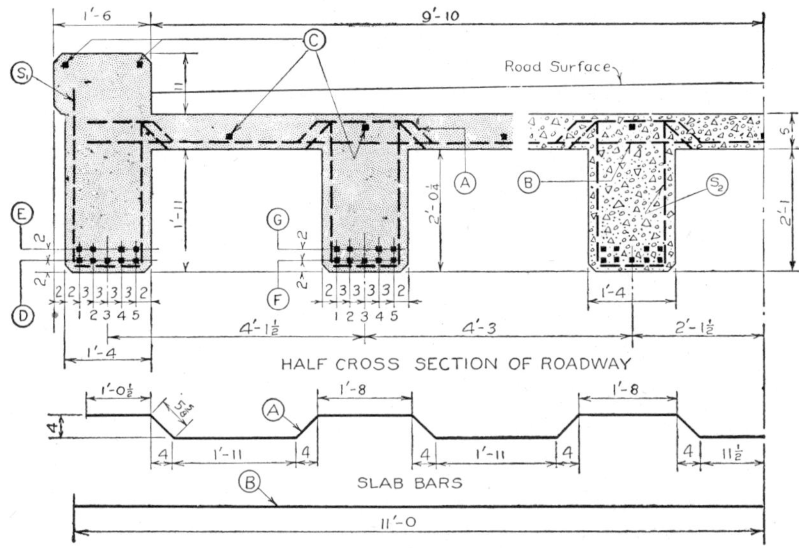

FIG. 27·14—Reinforced concrete in section.

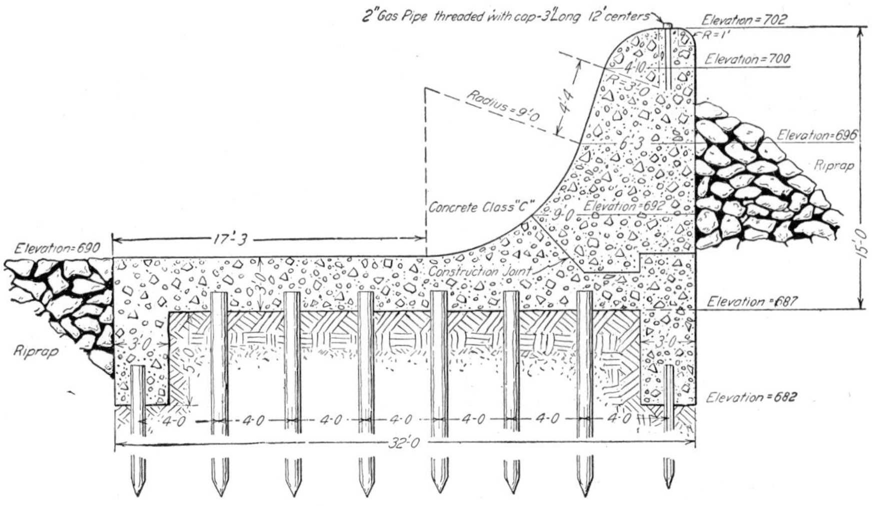

FIG. 27·15—Masonry section; weir dam.

PROBLEMS

The problems following will illustrate the fundamentals of structural drawing. The dimensions of rolled shapes may be obtained from "Steel Construction," the handbook of The American Institute of Steel Construction. Standard beam connections are given on page 662. Refer to Chap. 16 for welding symbols.

1. Make a detail working drawing of the following structural member:

Two L5 × 3 × ¼ × 10′-0 back to back, the 5″ legs outstanding. Five shop rivets on 2′-0 centers in 3″ legs as follows: gage, 1¼″; end of member to first rivet hole, 1′-0. Two field rivet holes in each 5″ outstanding leg as follows: gage, 3″; one rivet hole 3″ from each end of member. Size of rivets ⅝″.

2. Fig. 27·16. Make assembly working drawing of triple-effect evaporator support.

3. Fig. 27·16. Make detail drawings, with bill of material, ⅝″ rivets in 11⁄16″ holes; ¾″ field bolts in 13⁄16″ holes.

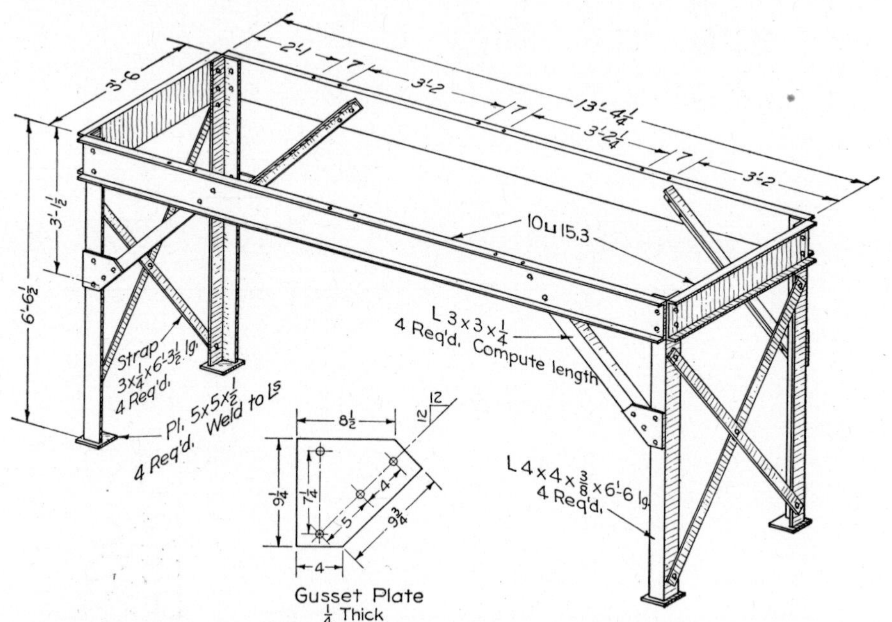

FIG. 27·16—Triple-effect evaporator support.

4. Fig. 27·16. Redesign for welded construction and make welding drawing.

5. Fig. 27·17. Make assembly working drawing of column base.

6. Fig. 27·17. Make detail drawings with bill of material for column base.

7. Fig. 27·18. Make assembly working drawing of crane-trolley-frame support.

8. Fig. 27·18. Make detail drawings with bill of material.

9. Fig. 27·8. Redesign, using modern connectors for fastening members.

10. Make an assembly working drawing of an English roof truss, using span and rise dimensions from Fig. 27·8. Bottom chord: 2 angles 4 × 4 × ⅜ back to back with ⅜ spacers; top chord members: 2 angles 3 × 3 × ⅜, back to back, with ⅜ × 6 plate; compression members: 2 angles 2 × 2 × ¼; tension members: 1 angle 2 × 2 × ¼; ⅝″ rivets throughout. Provide 9⁄16″ holes in top chord for purlins.

11. Fig. 27·2. Make detail drawings with bill of material and rivet list.

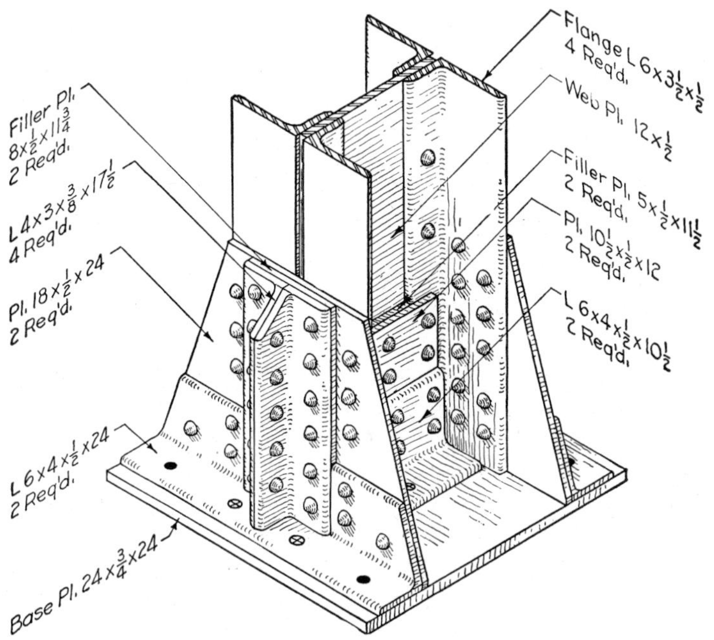

FIG. 27·17—Column base.

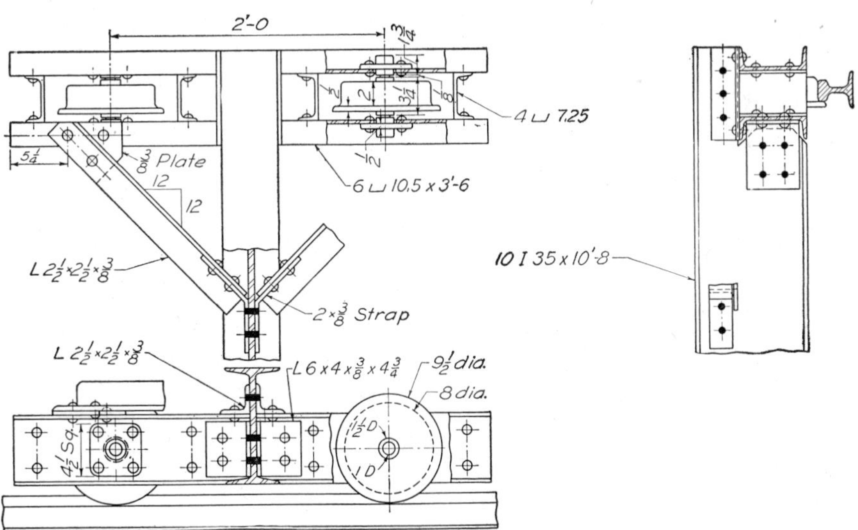

FIG. 27·18—Crane-trolley-frame support.

Chapter 28

MAP AND TOPOGRAPHIC DRAWING

28·1 Thus far in our consideration of drawing as a graphic language we have had to represent the three dimensions of an object either pictorially or, in the usual case, by drawing two or more views of it. In map drawing, that is, the representation of features on parts of the earth's surface, there is the distinct difference that the drawing is complete in one view, the third dimension, the height, being either represented on this view or omitted as not required for the particular purpose for which the map was made.

The surveying and mapping of the site form the first preliminary work in engineering projects, and it is desirable that all engineers should be familiar with the methods and symbols used in this branch of drawing. Without considering the practice of surveying and plotting or the various methods used by the cartographers in projecting the curved surface of the earth on a plane, we are interested in the use and details of execution of plats and topographic maps.

28·2 Classification. The content or information on maps may be classified in general under three divisions:

1. The representation of imaginary lines, such as divisions between areas subject to different authority or ownership, either public or private; or lines indicating geometric measurements on the land, on the sea, and in the air. In this division may be included plats or land maps, farm surveys, city subdivisions, plats of mineral claims, and nautical and aeronautical charts.
2. The representation of real or material features or objects within the limits of the tract, showing their relative location or size and location, depending upon the purpose of the map. When relative location only is required, the scale may be small, and symbols employed to represent objects, as houses, bridges, or even towns. When the size of the objects is an important consideration, the scale must be large and the map becomes a real orthographic top view.
3. The representation of the relative elevations of the surface of the ground. Maps with this feature are called "relief maps" or, if contours are used with elevations marked on them, "contour maps." Hydrographic maps show fathom-line depth curves.

Various combinations of these three divisions are required for different purposes. Classified according to their purpose, maps may be (*a*) geographic, (*b*) topographic, (*c*) hydrographic, (*d*) nautical, (*e*) aeronautical, (*f*) cadastral, (*g*) engineering, (*h*) photogrammetric, and (*i*) military.

a. *Geographic maps* include large areas and consequently must be to small scale. They show important towns and cities, streams and bodies of water, political boundaries, and relief.

b. *Topographic maps* are complete descriptions of certain areas and show to larger scale the geographical positions of the natural features and the works of man. The relief is usually represented by contours.
c. *Hydrographic maps* deal with information concerning bodies of water, as shore lines, sounding depths, subaqueous contours, navigation aids, and water control.
d. *Nautical maps* or charts are designed to show aids to water navigation, as buoys, beacons, lighthouses, lanes of traffic, sounding depths, shoals, and radio compass stations.
e. *Aeronautical maps* or charts provide prominent landmarks of the terrain and accentuate the relief by layer tints, hachures, and 500- or 1,000-foot contours as aids to air navigation.
f. *Cadastral maps* are very accurate control maps for cities and towns, made to large scale with all features drawn to size. They are used to control city development and operation, particularly taxation.
g. *Engineering maps* are working maps for engineering projects and are designed for specific purposes to aid construction. They provide accurate horizontal and vertical control data and show objects on the site or along the right of way.
h. *Photogrammetric maps* represent features on the earth's surface from terrestrial and aerial photographs. These photographs are perspectives from which orthographic views are obtained by stereoscopic instruments. Ground control stations are necessary to bring the photographs to a required datum.
i. *Military maps* are designed to contain information of military importance in the area represented.

28·3 Plats. A map plotted from a plane survey, and having the third dimension omitted, is called a "plat" or "land map." It is used in the description of any tract of land when it is not necessary to show relief, as in such typical examples as a farm survey or a city plat.

The plotting is done from field notes by (1) latitudes and departures, (2) bearings and distances, (3) azimuths and distances, (4) deflection angles and distances, or (5) rectangular coordinates. Or the plotting is done by the total latitude and departure from some fixed origin for each separate point, which method is necessary to distribute plotting errors over the entire survey. Angles are laid off from bearing or azimuth lines by plotting the tangent of the angle or the sine of half the angle, by sine-and-cosine method, or by an accurate protractor.

The first principle to be observed in the execution of this kind of drawings is *simplicity*. Its information should be clear, concise, and direct. The lettering should be done in single stroke, and the north point and border should be of the simplest character. The day of the intricate border corner, elaborate north point, and ornamental title is, happily, past, and all such embellishments are rightly considered not only as a waste of time but as being in very bad taste.

28·4 Plat of a survey. The plat of a survey should give clearly all the information necessary for the legal description of the parcel of land. It should contain

1. Direction and length of each line.
2. Acreage.
3. Location and description of monuments found and set.

4. Location of highways, streams, rights of way, and any appurtenances required.
5. Official division lines within the tract.
6. Names of owners of abutting property.
7. Title, scale, date.
8. North point with certification of horizontal control.
9. Plat certification properly executed.
10. Reference to state plane-coordinate system.

Figure 28·1 illustrates the general treatment of this kind of drawing. It is almost always traced and blueprinted, and no water-lining of streams

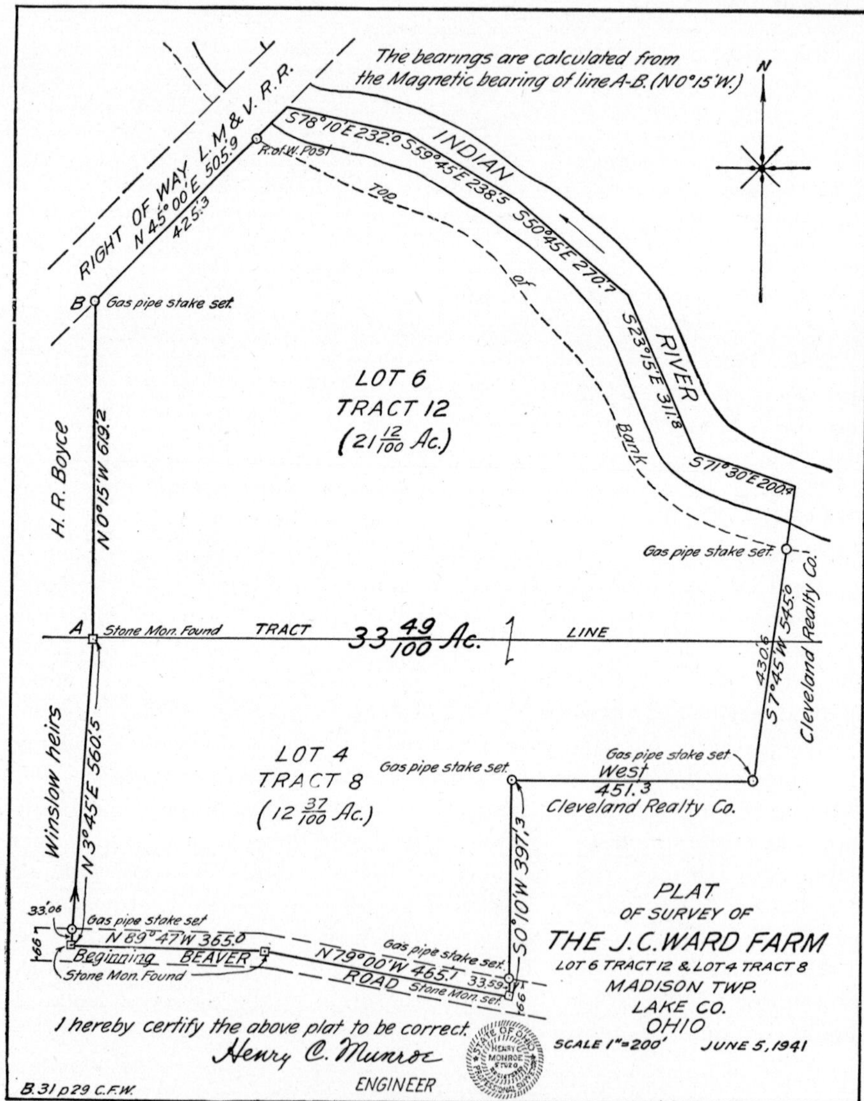

FIG. 28·1—Plat of a survey.

SECTION 11. T.14N. R.17W.
SECTION 14. T.14N. R.17W.
Snider Mfg. Co.
Face Backwall
Thru Girder Bridge
687.7
8" Sewer
#515 - 445'
Platform
516-324
Shop
Platform
#519
#530-311'
529-408'
#520
Valve
1½" Air Line
Driveway

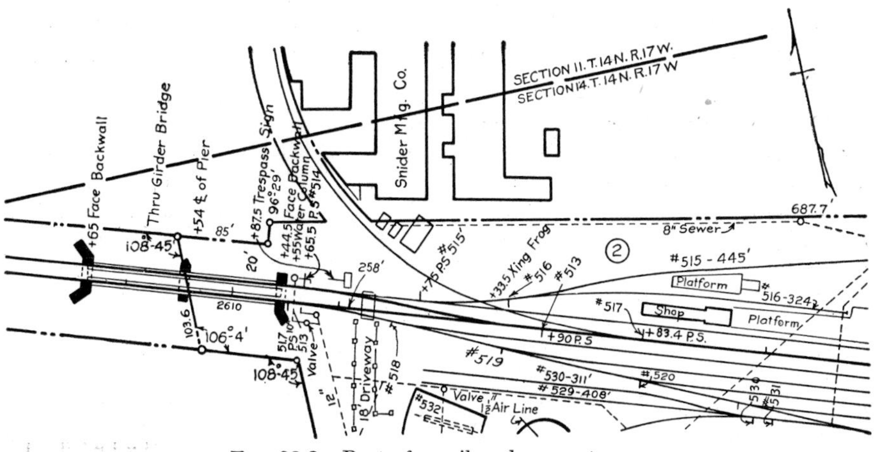

FIG. 28·2—Part of a railroad property map.

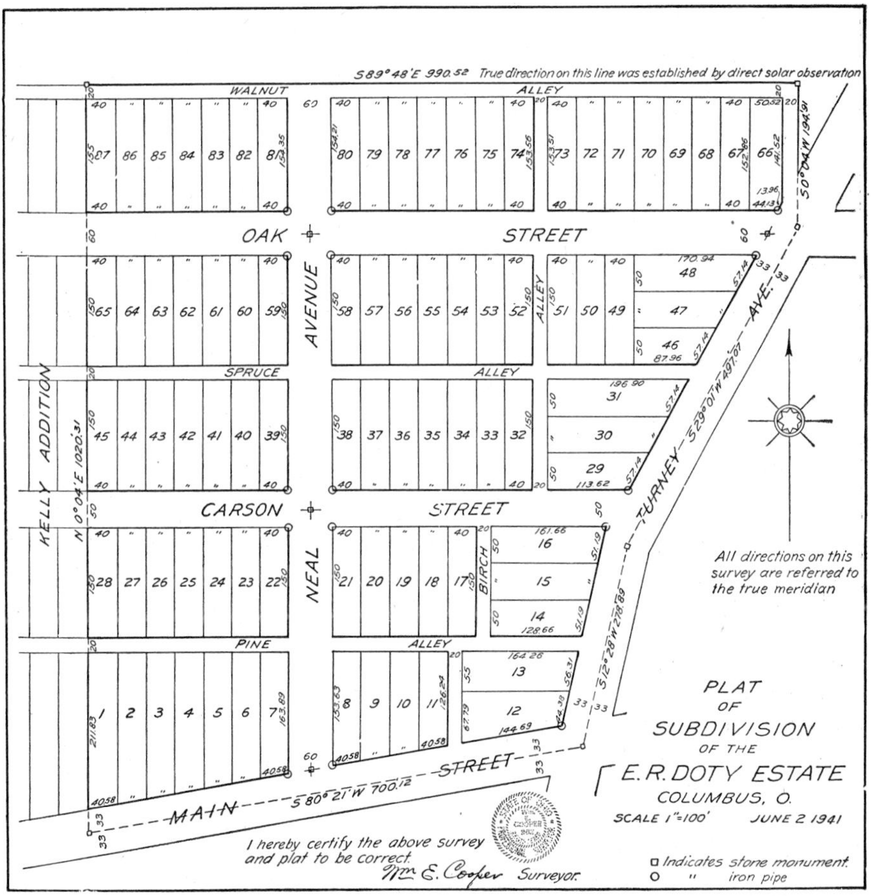

S 89° 48' E 990.52 True direction on this line was established by direct solar observation
WALNUT
ALLEY
OAK
STREET
AVENUE
SPRUCE
ALLEY
KELLY ADDITION
N 0° 04' E 1020.31
CARSON
STREET
NEAL
BIRCH
PINE
ALLEY
MAIN
STREET
S 80° 21' W 700.12
TURNEY
AVE.
S 29° 01' W 497.07
S 12° 28' W 278.89
S 0° 04' W 194.91
All directions on this survey are referred to the true meridian
PLAT
OF
SUBDIVISION
OF THE
E. R. DOTY ESTATE
COLUMBUS, O.
SCALE 1"=100'
JUNE 2 1941
I hereby certify the above survey and plat to be correct.
Wm E. Cooper Surveyor.
□ Indicates stone monument
O " iron pipe

FIG. 28·3—A city subdivision.

or other elaboration should be attempted. It is important to observe that the size of the lettering used for the several features must be in proportion to their importance.

28·5 A railroad property map. Of the many kinds of plats used in industrial work one only is illustrated here, a portion of a railway situation or station map, Fig. 28·2. This might represent also a plant-valuation

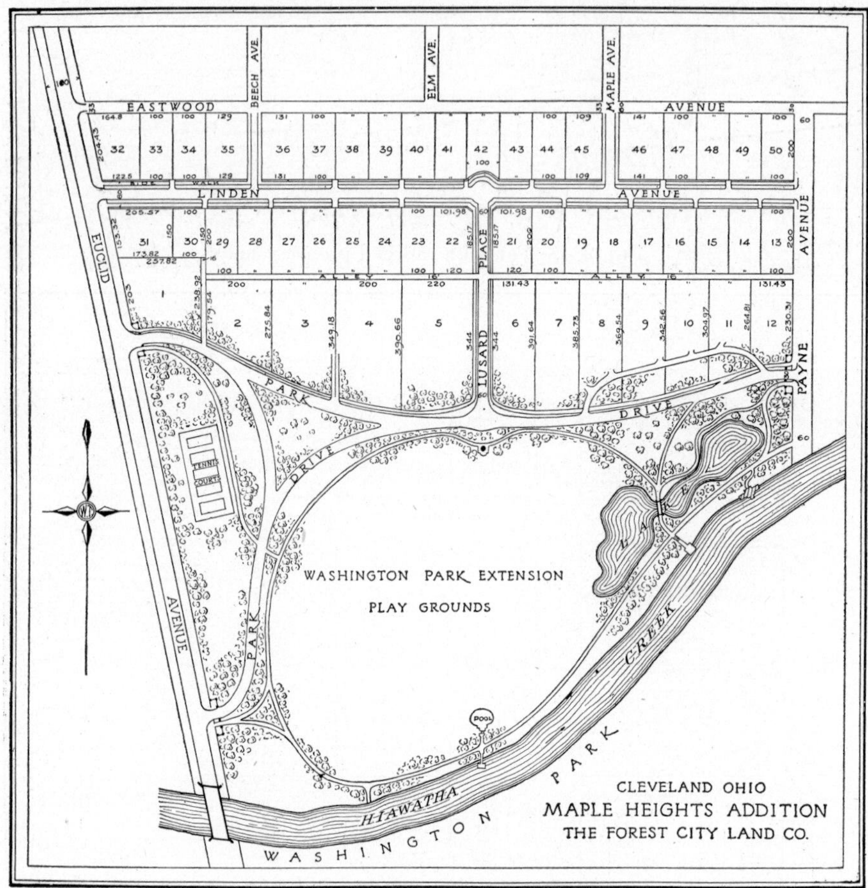

FIG. 28·4—A real-estate display map.

map, a type of plat often required. The information on such maps varies to meet the requirements of particular cases. In addition to the preceding list, it might include such items as pipe lines, fire hydrants, location and description of buildings, railroads and switch points, outdoor-crane runways, etc.

28·6 Plats of subdivisions. The plats of subdivisions and allotments in cities are filed with the county recorder for record and must be very complete in their information concerning the location and size of the various lots and parcels composing the subdivisions, Fig. 28·3. All monuments set should be shown and all directions and distances recorded, so that it will be possible to locate any lot with precision.

Sometimes landowners desire to use these maps in display to prospective buyers and often include a blueprint or black-line print bound with the deed. Some degree of embellishment is allowable, but care must be taken

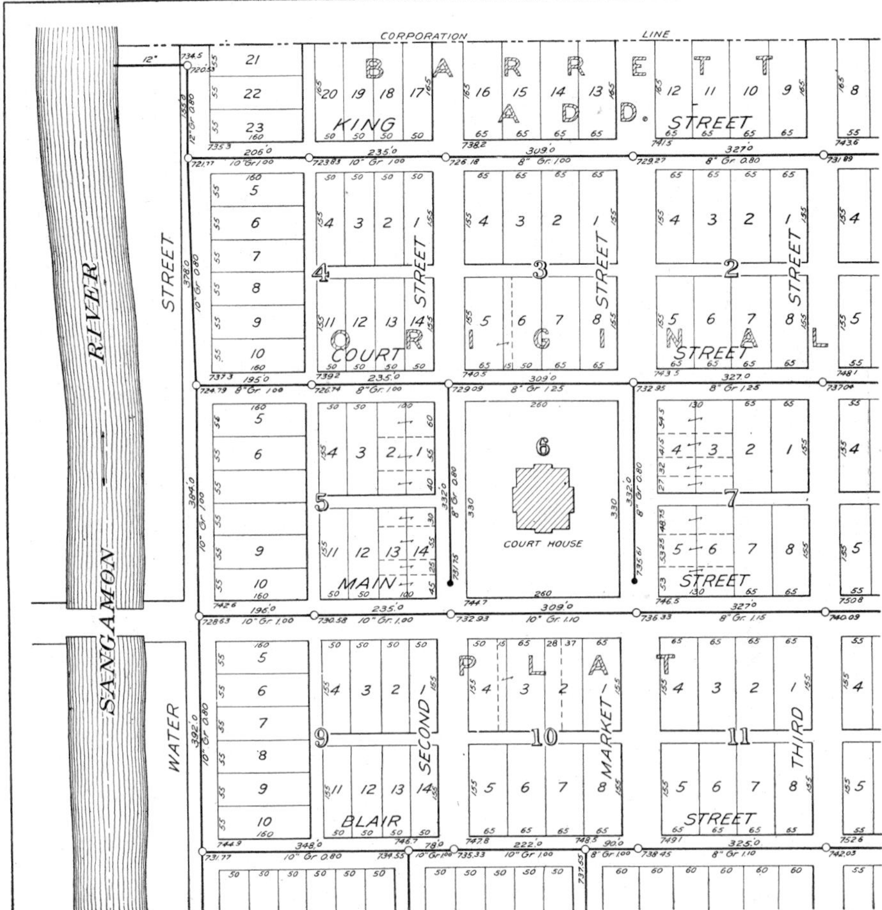

FIG. 28·5—A sewer map.

not to overdo the ornamentation. Figure 28·4 is an example showing an acceptable style of execution and finish.

28·7 City plats. Under this head are included chiefly maps or plats drawn from subdivision plats or other sources for the record of city improvements. These plats are used to record a variety of information, such as the location of sewers, water mains, gas, power and steam lines, telephone installations, and street improvements.

The records maintained on these maps provide valuable data for assessments and constitute progress reports on the growth of a city. As they are made for a definite purpose, they should not contain unnecessary information and hence will not include all the details as to sizes of lots, which are given on subdivision plats, but they should carry both horizontal and vertical control points for proper location of utilities. They are usually made on mounted paper and should be to a scale large enough to show clearly the

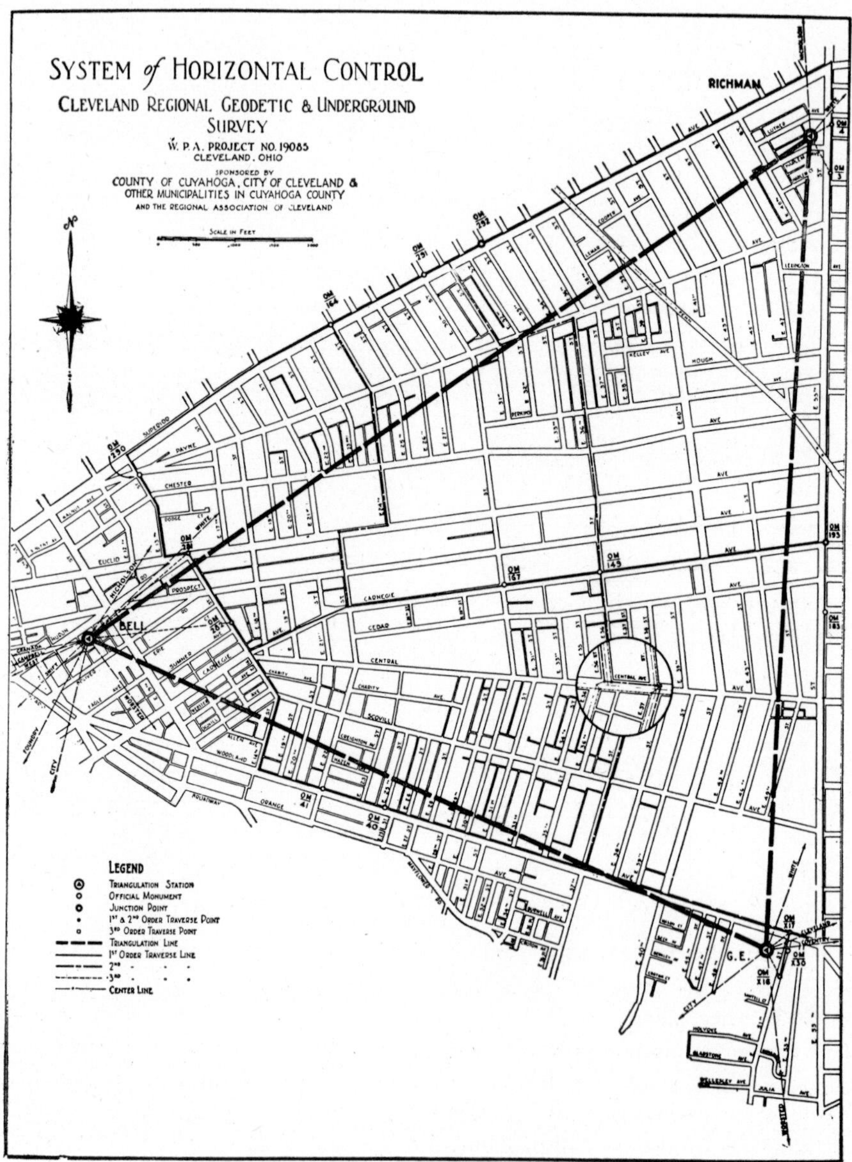

FIG. 28·6—Horizontal control.

features required; 100′ and 200′ to the inch are common scales, and as large as 50′ is sometimes used. For smaller cities the entire area may be covered by one map; for larger cities the maps are made in convenient sections so as to be filed readily.

A study of Fig. 28·5, a sewer map, will show the general treatment of such plats. The appearance of the drawing is improved by adding shade lines on the lower and right-hand side of the blocks, that is, treating the streets and water features as depressions. A few of the more important public buildings are shown, to facilitate reading. The various wards, subdivisions, or districts may be shown by large outline letters or numerals as illustrated in the figure. Contours are often put on these maps in red or brown ink, either on the original or sometimes on a positive print from it. Figure 28·6 shows a modern system of horizontal control used by the city of Cleveland for a geodetic and underground survey.

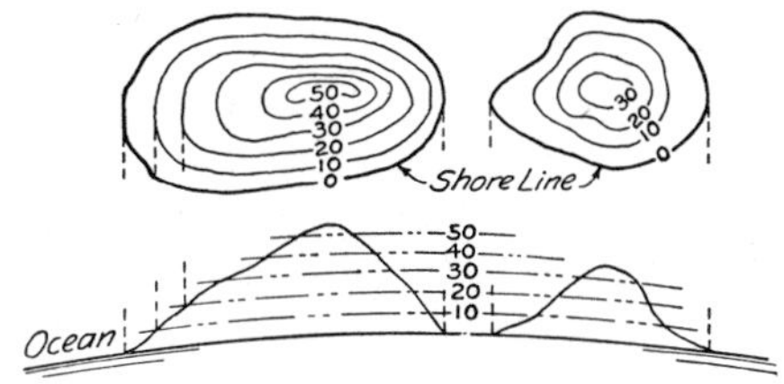

FIG. 28·7—Contours.

28·8 Topographic drawing. As before defined, a complete topographic map would contain

1. The imaginary lines indicating the divisions of authority or ownership.
2. The geographical position of both the natural features and the works of man. They may also include information in regard to the vegetation.
3. The relief, or indication of the relative elevations and depressions. The relief, which is the third dimension, is represented in general either by contours or by hill shading.

28·9 Contours. A contour is an imaginary line on the surface of the ground which, at every point, passes through the same elevation; thus the shore line of a body of water represents a contour. If the water should rise 1 foot the new shore line would be another contour, with 1-foot "contour interval." A series of contours may thus be illustrated approximately as in Fig. 28·7.

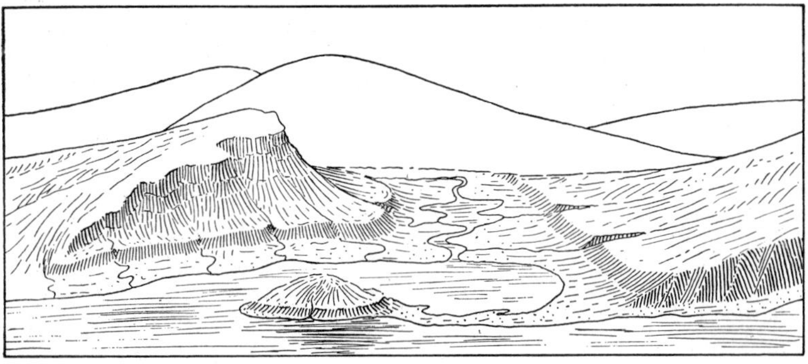

FIG. 28·8—Perspective view.

Figure 28·8 is a perspective view of a tract of land. Figure 28·9 is a contour map of this area, and Fig. 28·10 is the same surface shown with hill shading by hachures. Contours are drawn as fine, full lines, with every fifth one of heavier weight and with the elevations in feet marked on them at intervals, usually with the sea level as datum. They may be drawn with a

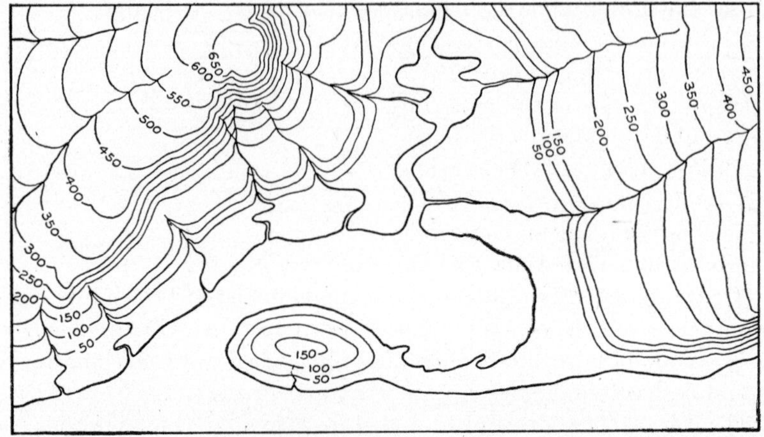

FIG. 28·9—Application of contour lines.

FIG. 28·10—Application of hachures for hill shading.

swivel pen, Fig. 30·7, or a fine pen such as Gillott's 170 or Esterbrook's 356. On paper drawings they are usually made in brown.

Figure 28·11 is a topographic map of the site of a proposed filtration plant and illustrates the use of the contour map as the necessary preliminary drawing for engineering projects. Often on the same drawing there are shown, by lines of different character, both the existing contours and the required finished grades.

28·10 Hill shading. The showing of relief by means of hill shading gives a pleasing effect but is very difficult of execution, does not give exact elevations, and would not be applied on maps to be used for engineering purposes. It may sometimes be used to advantage in reconnaissance maps or in small-scale maps for illustration. There are several systems, of which hachuring, as shown in Fig. 28·10, is the commonest. The contours are sketched lightly in pencil and the hachures drawn perpendicular to them,

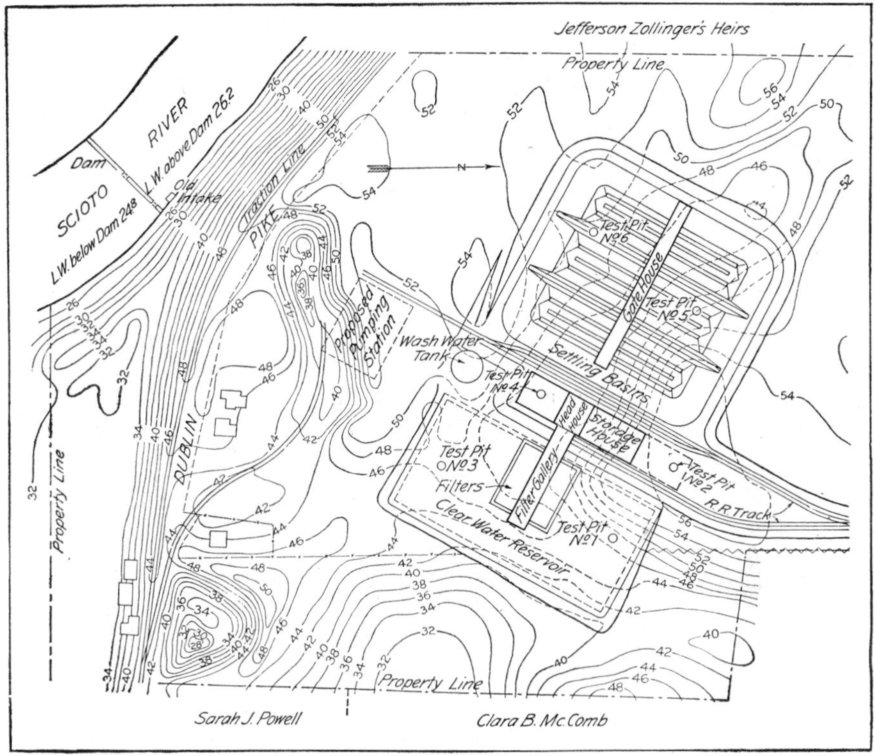

FIG. 28·11—Contour map for an engineering project.

starting at the summit and grading the weight of line to the degree of slope. A scale of hachures to use for reference is often made, graded from black for 45° to white for horizontal. The rows of strokes should touch the pencil line to avoid white streaks along the contours. Two other systems in use are the horizontal, or English system, using graded hachure lines parallel to the contours, and the oblique illumination, or French system, using hachures graded to give sunlight effect as well as the degree of slope.

28·11 Water lining. On topographic maps made for display or reproduction, the water features are usually finished by "water lining," that is, by running a system of fine lines parallel to the shore lines, either in black or in blue (it must be remembered that blue will not photograph for reproduction or print well from a tracing). Poor water lining will ruin the appearance of an otherwise well-executed map, and it is better to omit it rather than do it hastily or carelessly. The shore line is drawn first, and the water lining done with a fine mapping pen, the draftsman always drawing toward his body, with the preceding line to his left. The first line should follow the shore line very closely, and the distances between the succeeding lines should be gradually increased and the irregularities lessened. Sometimes the weight of lines is graded as well as the intervals, but this is a very difficult operation and is not necessary for the effect. A common mistake is to make the lines excessively wavy or rippled.

In water-lining a stream of varying width, the lines are not to be crowded so as to be carried through the narrower portions, but corresponding lines must be brought together in the middle of the stream as illustrated in Fig. 28·10. Care should be taken to avoid spots of sudden increase or decrease in spacing.

28·12 Topographic symbols. The various symbols used in topographic drawing may be grouped under four heads:

1. Culture, or the works of man.
2. Relief—relative elevations and depressions.
3. Water features.
4. Vegetation.

When color is used the culture is done in black, the relief in brown, the water features in blue, and the vegetation in black or green.

These symbols, used to represent characteristics on the earth's surface, are made, when possible, to resemble somewhat the features or objects represented as they would appear either in plan or in elevation. No attempt

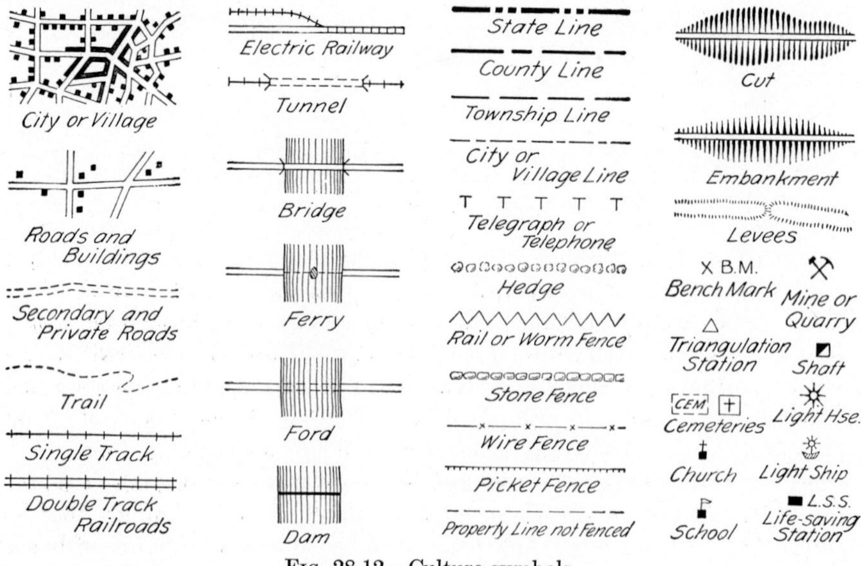

FIG. 28·12—Culture symbols.

is here made to give symbols for all the features that might occur in a map; indeed one may have to invent symbols for some particular locality.

Figure 28·12 illustrates a few of the conventional symbols used for culture, or the works of man, and no suggestion is needed as to the method of their execution. When the scale used is large, houses, bridges, roads,

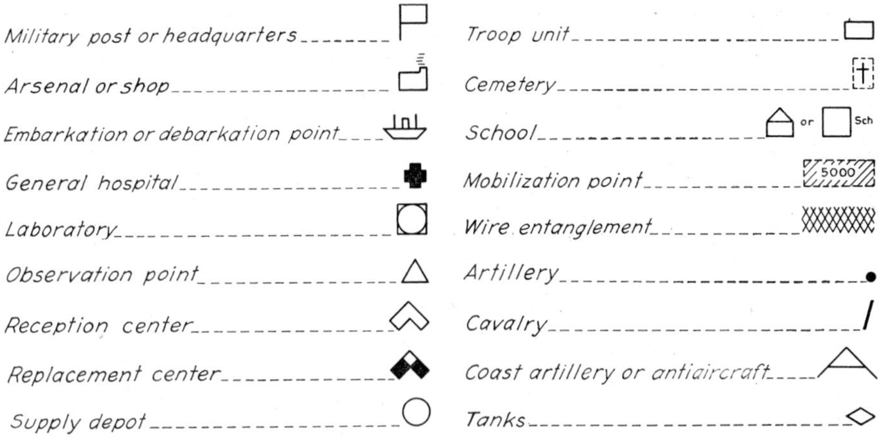

Military post or headquarters
Arsenal or shop
Embarkation or debarkation point
General hospital
Laboratory
Observation point
Reception center
Replacement center
Supply depot
Troop unit
Cemetery
School (or Sch)
Mobilization point (5000)
Wire entanglement
Artillery
Cavalry
Coast artillery or antiaircraft
Tanks

FIG. 28·13—Military symbols.

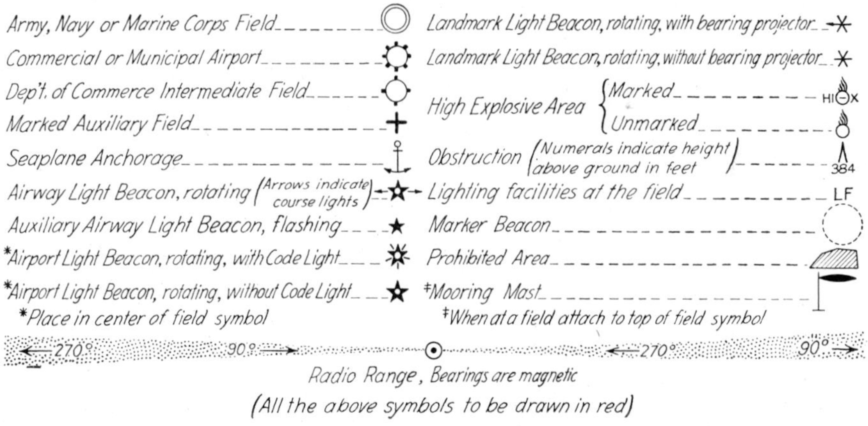

Army, Navy or Marine Corps Field
Commercial or Municipal Airport
Dep't. of Commerce Intermediate Field
Marked Auxiliary Field
Seaplane Anchorage
Airway Light Beacon, rotating (Arrows indicate course lights)
Auxiliary Airway Light Beacon, flashing
*Airport Light Beacon, rotating, with Code Light
*Airport Light Beacon, rotating, without Code Light
*Place in center of field symbol
Landmark Light Beacon, rotating, with bearing projector
Landmark Light Beacon, rotating, without bearing projector
High Explosive Area {Marked (HI X); Unmarked}
Obstruction (Numerals indicate height above ground in feet) (384)
Lighting facilities at the field (LF)
Marker Beacon
Prohibited Area
‡Mooring Mast
‡When at a field attach to top of field symbol
270° 90° 270° 90°
Radio Range, Bearings are magnetic
(All the above symbols to be drawn in red)

FIG. 28·14—Aviation symbols.

and even tree trunks can be plotted so that their principal dimensions can be scaled. The landscape architect is interested not only in the size of the trunk of a tree but also in the spread of its branches. A small-scale map can give by its symbols only the relative locations.

Some military symbols are shown in Fig. 28·13, symbols for aerial navigation in Fig. 28·14, and aids to water navigation in Fig. 28·15, all as adopted by the United States Board of Surveys and Maps. Figure 28·16 gives the standard symbols used in the development of oil and gas fields, Fig. 28·17 the symbols used to show relief, Fig. 28·18 water features, and Fig. 28·19 some of the commoner symbols for vegetation and cultivation.

The draftsman should keep in mind the purpose of the map and in some measure indicate the relative importance of the features, varying their

Wreck (hull above low water)	Life-saving station (in general) L.S.S.
Wreck (depth unknown)	Life-saving station (Coast Guard) C.G.165
Sunken wreck (dangerous to surface navigation)	Lighthouse
Rock under water +	Radio station R.S. ⊙
Rock awash (any tide) *	Radio tower R.T. ⊙
Breakers along shore	Radio beacon R.Bn. ⊙
Beacon ☆, not lighted	Anchorage (any kind)
Buoy of any kind (or red)	Anchorage (small vessels)
Buoy (black)	Dry dock

Fig. 28·15—Symbols for water-navigation aids.

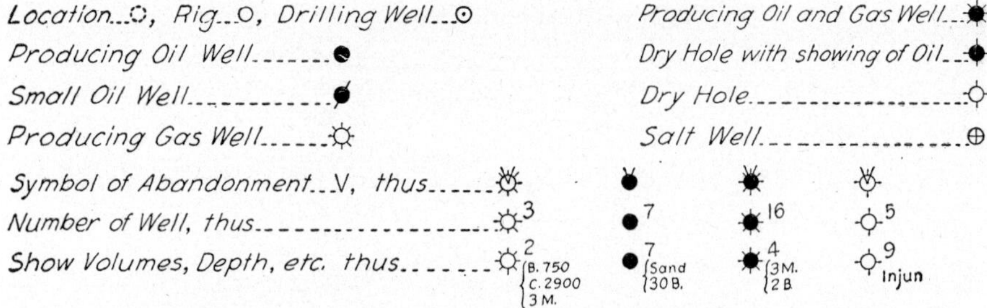

Fig. 28·16—Oil and gas symbols.

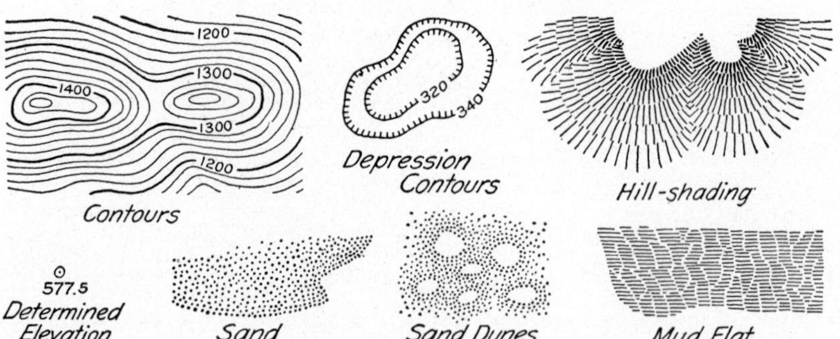

Fig. 28·17—Relief symbols.

prominence by the weights of lines used or sometimes by varying the scale of the symbol. For instance, in a map made for military maneuvering, a cornfield might be an important feature; or in maps made to show the location of special features, such as fire hydrants, these objects would be indicated very plainly. The map of an airport or a golf course would contain emphasized features. This principle calls for some originality to meet various cases.

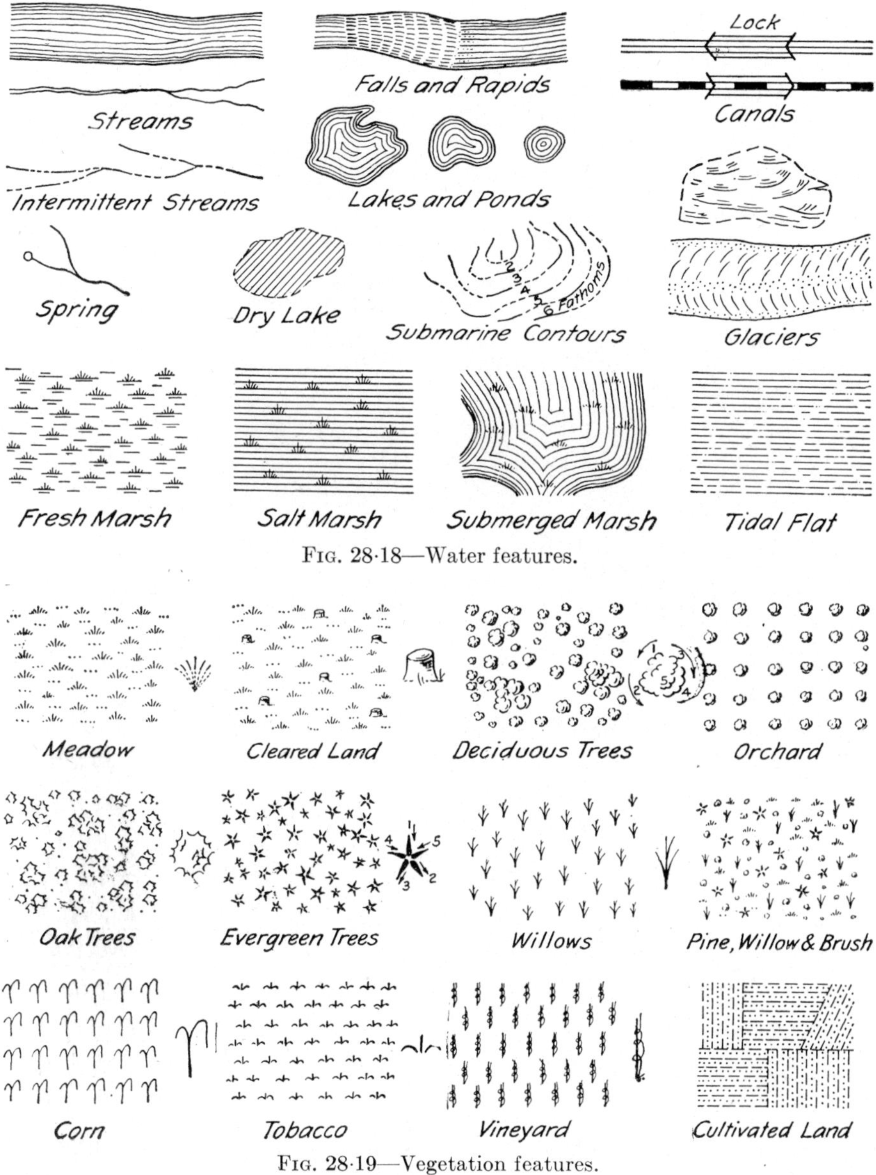

FIG. 28·18—Water features.

FIG. 28·19—Vegetation features.

A common fault of the beginner is to make symbols too large. The symbols for grass, shown under "meadow," Fig. 28·19, if not made and spaced correctly will spoil the entire map. This symbol is composed of from five to seven short strokes radiating from a common center and starting along a horizontal line as shown in the enlarged form, each tuft beginning and ending with a mere dot. Always place the tufts with the bottom parallel to the border and distribute them uniformly over the space, but not in rows. A few incomplete tufts or rows of dots improve the appearance. Grass-tuft symbols should never be as heavy as tree symbols. In

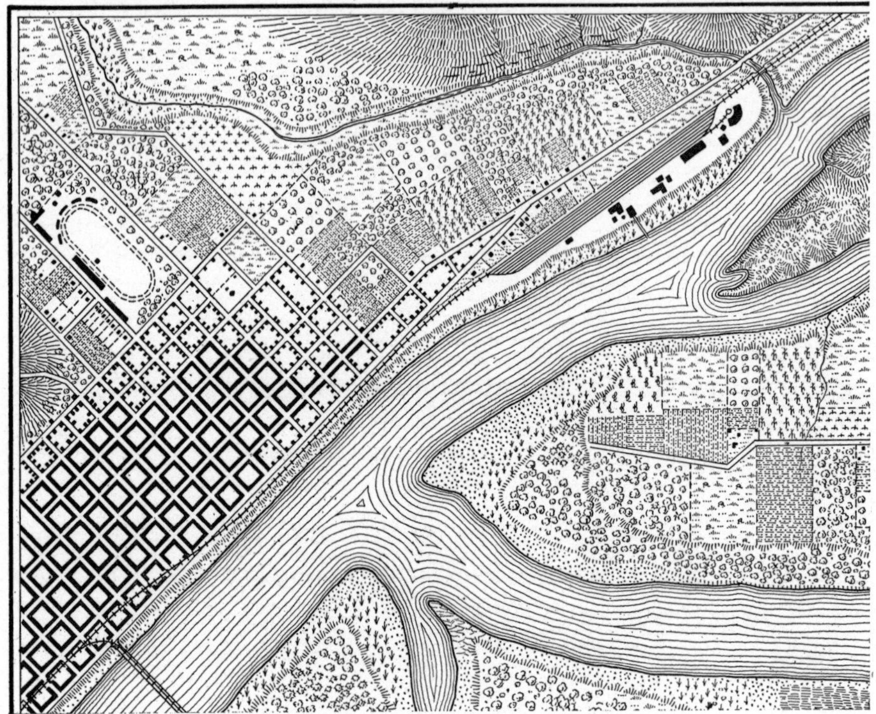

FIG. 28·20—Part of a topographic map.

drawing the symbol for deciduous trees the sequence of strokes shown should be followed.

The topographic map, Fig. 28·20, is given to illustrate the general execution and placing of symbols.

The well-known maps of the U.S. Coast and Geodetic Survey and the Geological Survey illustrate the application of topographic drawing. The *quadrangle sheets* issued by the topographic branch of the U.S. Geological Survey are excellent examples and so easily available that every draftsman should be familiar with them. These sheets represent 15 minutes of latitude and 15 minutes of longitude to the scale of 1:62,500 or approximately 1 inch to the mile. The entire United States is being mapped by the department in cooperation with the different states, and in 1941, with the work of 18 states finished, almost 50 per cent of the country had been completed. This work is now greatly facilitated through the use of aerial photography.

Much territory in the West and South has been mapped ½ inch to the mile, and earlier some in the West was mapped ¼ inch to the mile. These maps may be secured for 10 cents each (not stamps) by addressing The Director, U.S. Geological Survey, Washington, D.C., from whom information as to the completion of any particular locality or the progress in any state may be had.

28·13 Landscape maps. A topographic map made to a relatively large scale and showing all details is called a "landscape map." Such maps are required by architects and landscape gardeners for use in planning buildings to fit the natural topographic features and for landscaping parks, playgrounds, and private estates. These are generally maps of small areas, and a scale of 1″ = 20′ to 1″ = 50′, depending upon the amount of detail, is used.

The contour interval varies from 6 inches to 2 feet according to the ruggedness of the surface. The commonest interval is 1 foot. These maps are often reproduced in black-line prints, upon which contours in different color are drawn to show the landscape treatment proposed. Natural features and culture are added in more detail than on ordinary topographic maps. Trees are designated as to size, species, and sometimes spread of branches and condition. It is often necessary to invent symbols suitable for the particular survey and to include a key or legend on the map. Roads, walks, streams, flower beds, houses, etc., should be plotted carefully to scale, so that measurements can be taken from them.

28·14 Colors. Instead of using colored inks, which are thin and unsatisfactory to handle in the pen and do not photograph or blueprint well, it is much better to use water colors for contours, streams, and other colored features in topographic mapping. For contours, burnt sienna, either straight or darkened with a drop of black, and mixed rather thick; for streams, Prussian blue; and for features in red, alizarin crimson. All work well in either crow-quill or contour pen and make good blueprints. Colors in tubes are more convenient than those in cakes or pans.

28·15 Lettering. The style of lettering on a topographic map will depend upon the purpose for which the map is made. If it is for construction purposes, such as a contour map for the study of municipal problems, street grades, plants, or railroads, the single-stroke Gothic and Reinhardt is to be preferred. For a finished map, vertical Modern Roman letters, as shown on page 58, capitals for important land features, and lower case for less-important features, such as small towns and villages; inclined roman and stump letters, as shown on page 60, for water features, should be used. The scale should always be drawn as well as stated.

28·16 Titles. The standard letter for finished map titles is the Modern Roman. The design should be symmetrical, with the heights of the letters proportioned to the relative importance of the line. A map title should contain as many as are necessary of the following items:

1. Kind—"Map of," etc.
2. Name.
3. Location of tract.
4. Purpose, if special features are represented.
5. For whom made.
6. Engineer in charge.
7. Date (of survey).
8. Scale—stated and drawn; contour interval; datum.
9. Authorities.
10. Legend or key to symbols.
11. North point, with certification of horizontal control.
12. Certification, properly executed.
13. Reference to state plane-coordinate system.

28·17 Profiles. Perhaps no kind of drawing is used more by civil engineers than the ordinary profile, which is simply a vertical section taken

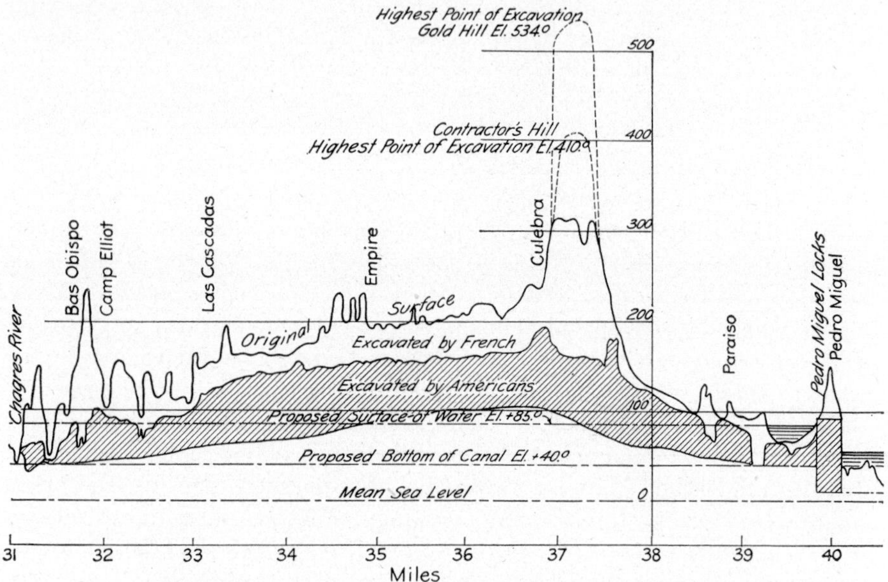

FIG. 28·21—Profile (vertical scale 50 times horizontal).

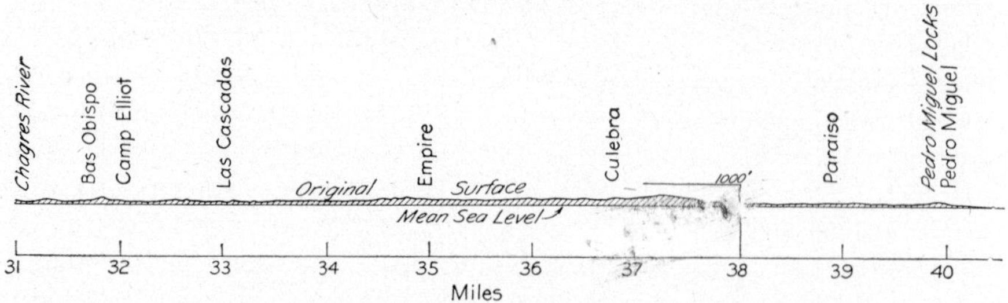

FIG. 28·22—Profile (vertical and horizontal scales equal).

along a given line, either straight or curved. Such drawings are indispensable in problems of railroad construction, highway and street improvements, sewer construction, and many other problems where a study of the surface of the ground is required. Very frequently engineers other than

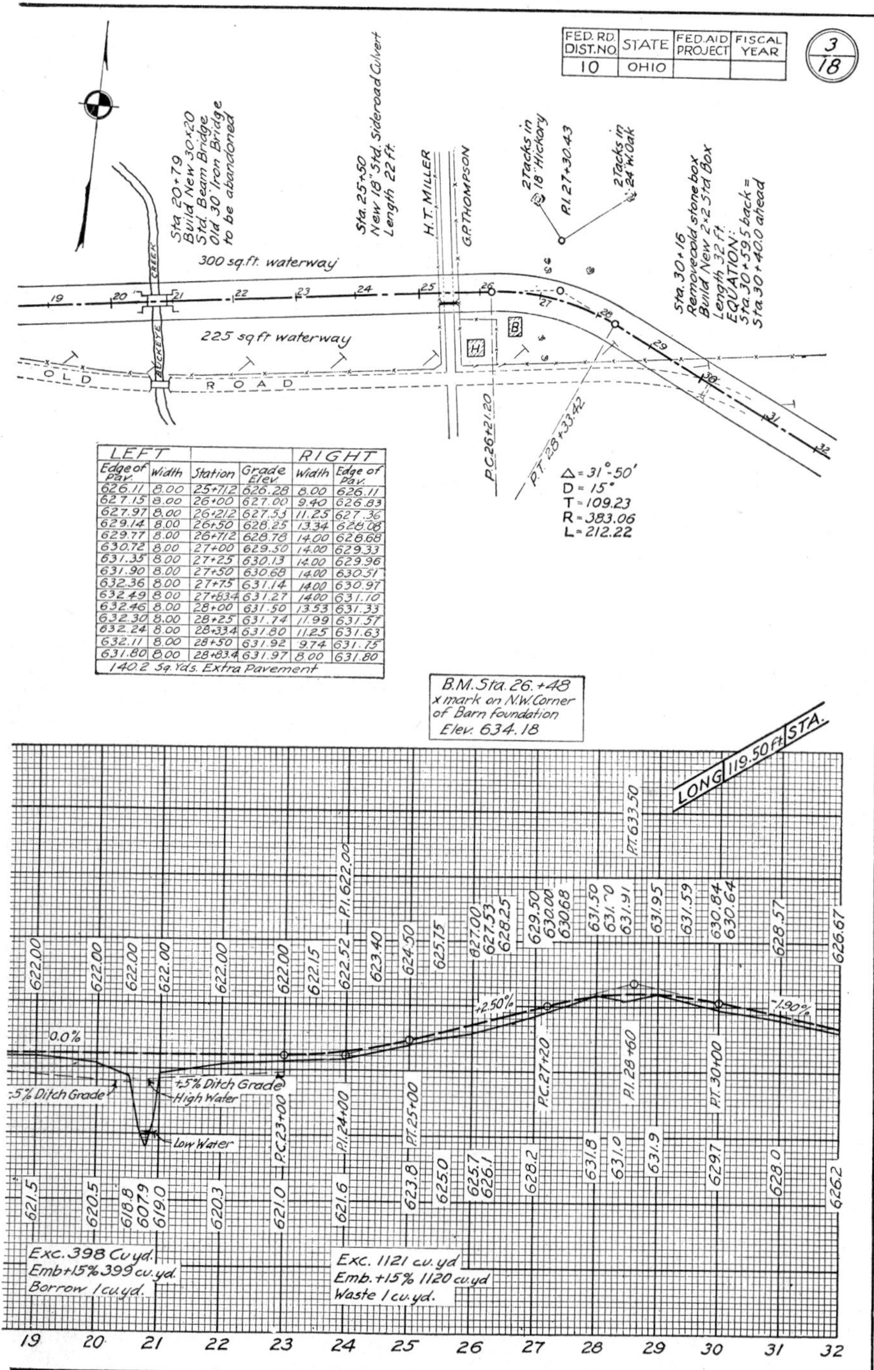

LEFT				RIGHT	
Edge of Pav.	Width	Station	Grade Elev.	Width	Edge of Pav.
626.11	8.00	25+71.2	626.28	8.00	626.11
627.15	8.00	26+00	627.00	9.40	626.83
627.97	8.00	26+21.2	627.53	11.25	627.36
629.14	8.00	26+50	628.25	13.34	628.08
629.77	8.00	26+71.2	628.78	14.00	628.68
630.72	8.00	27+00	629.50	14.00	629.33
631.35	8.00	27+25	630.13	14.00	629.96
631.90	8.00	27+50	630.68	14.00	630.51
632.36	8.00	27+75	631.14	14.00	630.97
632.49	8.00	27+83.4	631.27	14.00	631.10
632.46	8.00	28+00	631.50	13.53	631.33
632.30	8.00	28+25	631.74	11.99	631.57
632.24	8.00	28+33.4	631.80	11.25	631.63
632.11	8.00	28+50	631.92	9.74	631.75
631.80	8.00	28+83.4	631.97	8.00	631.80
140.2 Sq. Yds. Extra Pavement					

FIG. 28·23—Part of a State Highway Alignment and Profile Sheet.

civil engineers are called upon to make these drawings. Several different types of profile and cross-section paper are in use, and their descriptions may be found in the catalogues of the various firms dealing in drawing materials. One type of profile paper in common use is known as "Plate A" and has 4 divisions to the inch horizontally and 20 to the inch vertically. Other divisions in use are 4 × 30 to the inch and 5 × 25 to the inch. At intervals, both horizontally and vertically, somewhat heavier lines are made in order to facilitate reading.

Horizontal distances are plotted as abscissas and elevations as ordinates. Since the vertical distances represent elevations and are plotted to larger scale, a vertical exaggeration is obtained that is very useful in studying profiles that are to be used for establishing grades. The vertical exaggeration is sometimes confusing to the layman or inexperienced engineer, but ordinarily a profile will fail in the purpose for which it was intended if the horizontal and vertical scales are the same. Again, the profile, unless so distorted, would be a very long and unwieldy affair, if not entirely impossible to make. The difference between profiles with and without vertical exaggeration is shown in Figs. 28·21 and 28·22.

Figure 28·23 is a portion of a typical State Highway Alignment and Profile Sheet, plotted to a horizontal scale of 1″ = 100′ and a vertical scale of 1″ = 10′. For this type of drawing, tracing cloth is furnished with the coordinates printed in red on the back so that any changes or erasures on the profile will not damage the coordinate lines. Lettering or other features are sometimes brought out by erasing the lines on the back. This sheet is one of a set of drawings used for estimating cost and, by the contractor, as a working drawing during construction. Other drawings in the set consist of a title sheet showing the location plan with detours provided; a sheet indicating conventional signs; a sheet giving an index to bound sheets; and a sheet with space reserved for declarations of approval and signatures of proper officials.

Also there are sheets of cross sections taken at each 100-foot station and all necessary intermediate stations to estimate earthwork for grading; working drawings for drainage structures; site plans for bridges; specifications for guard rails and other safety devices; standard or typical road sections for cut and fill and various other conditions; and finally summary sheets for separate tables and quantities of materials for roadway, pavement, and structures.

Chapter 29

CHARTS, GRAPHS, AND DIAGRAMS

29·1 This chapter is given as an introduction to the use of graphical methods in tabulating data for analysis, solving problems, and presenting facts. It will indicate to the prospective engineer the uses and value of this application of graphics and suggest his further study of the subject.

For the purpose of presenting a series of quantitative facts quickly, the graphical chart is the one best method. The statement, "it is easier to see than to think," meaning that, with the majority of people, the visual impression is the strongest form of appeal, expresses well the argument for this method of analysis. It is not to be supposed, however, that charts can be substituted for thinking, for really all they can do is to assist clear thinking by eliminating the tiring mental effort necessary to keep in mind an involved series of figures. When properly constructed and thoroughly understood, charts, graphs, and diagrams constitute a powerful tool for computation, analysis of engineering data, and the presentation of statistics for comparison or prediction.

29·2 When classified as to use, charts, graphs, and diagrams may be divided roughly into two classes: those used for purely technical purposes and those for popular appeal in advertising or the presentation of information. The engineer is concerned mainly with the first class, but he should have some acquaintance with the preparation and the influential possibilities of the second class. The aim here is to give a short study of the types with which engineers and those in allied professions should be familiar.

The construction of a graphical chart requires a fair degree of draftsmanship, but in engineering and scientific work the important considerations are judgment in the proper selection of coordinates, accuracy in plotting points and drawing the graph, and an understanding of the functions and limitations of the resulting chart.

It is assumed that the reader is familiar with the use of rectangular coordinates and that the meaning of such terms as "axes," "ordinates," "abscissas," "coordinates," "variables," etc., is understood.

29·3 Titles and notation. The title is a very important part of a chart, and its wording should be studied until it is clear and concise. In every case it should contain sufficient description to tell what the chart is, the source or authority, the name of the observer, and the *date.* Approved practice places the title at the top of the sheet, arranged in phrases symmetrically about a center line. If placed within the ruled space, a border line or box should set it out from the sheet. Each sheet of curves should have a title, and when more than one curve is shown on a sheet, the different curves should be drawn so as to be easily distinguishable, by varying the character of the lines, using full, dotted, and dot-and-dash lines, with a tabular key for identification, or by lettering the names of the curves directly along them. When the charts are not intended for reproduction, inks of different colors may be used.

29·4 Rectilinear charts. The rectilinear chart is made on a sheet ruled with equispaced horizontal lines crossing equispaced vertical lines. The

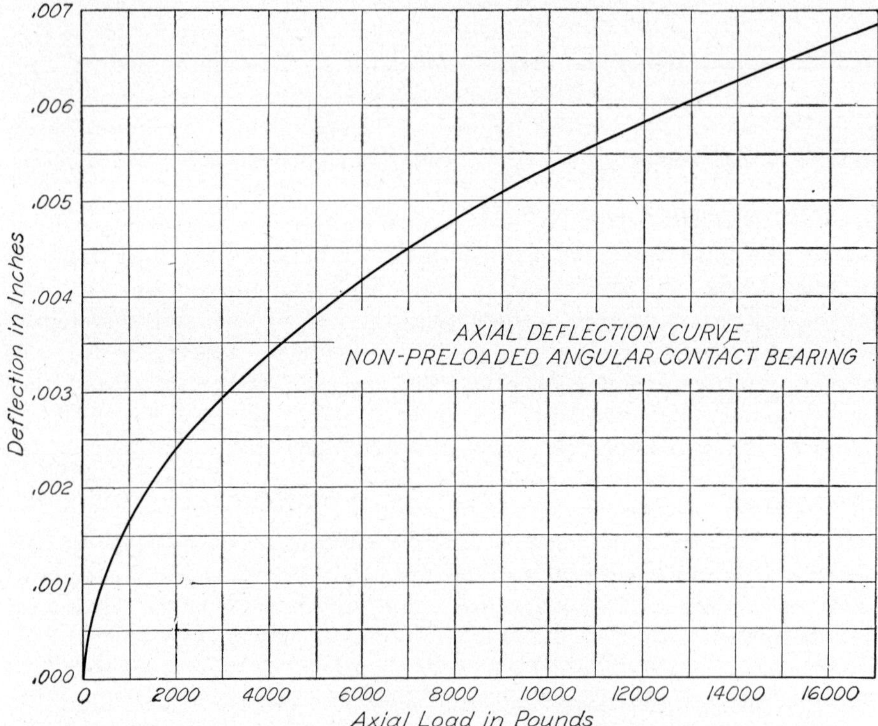

FIG. 29·1—An engineering diagram.

spacing is optional, but it is customary and convenient to use squares of $\frac{1}{20}$ inch with every fifth line heavier, to aid in plotting and reading. Sheets are printed with various other rulings, as 4, 6, 8, 12, and 16 divisions per inch.

As the greater part of chart work in experimental engineering is done on rectilinear graph paper, the student should become familiar with this form of chart early in his course.

It is universal practice to use the upper right-hand quadrant for plotting experimental-data curves, making the lower left-hand corner the origin. In case both positive and negative values of a function are to be plotted, as is the case with many mathematical curves, it is necessary to place the origin so as to include all desired values.

Figure 29·1 shows a usual form of rectilinear chart, such as might be made on 8½″ × 11″ paper for inclusion in a written report.

29·5 Curves. In drawing graphs from experimental data it is often a question whether the curve should pass through all the points plotted or strike a mean between them. In general, observed data not backed up by definite theory or mathematical law are shown by connecting the points plotted with straight lines as at *A*, Fig. 29·2. An empirical relationship between curve and plotted points may be used, as at *B*, when, in the opinion of the engineer, the curve should exactly follow some points, and go to one side of others. Consistency of observation is indicated at *C*, in which case the curve should closely follow a true theoretical curve.

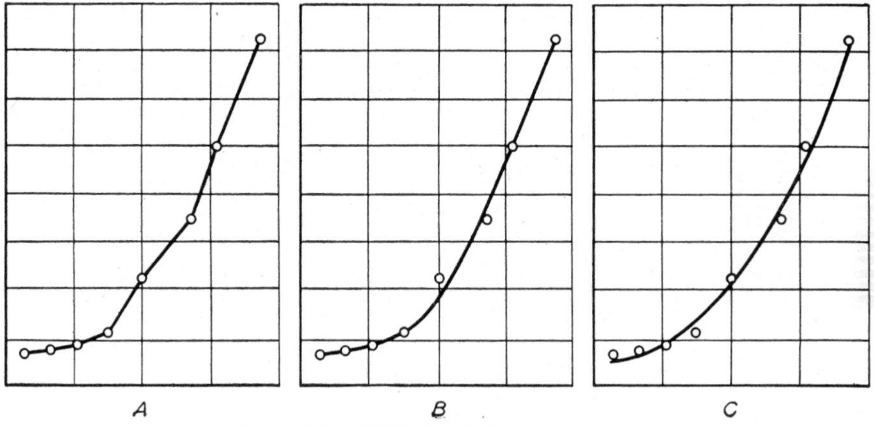

FIG. 29·2—Methods of drawing curves.

29·6 Logarithmic ruling. A very important type of chart is that in which the divisions, instead of being equally spaced, are made proportional to the logarithms of the numbers at the margin instead of to the numbers themselves. When ruled logarithmically in one direction with equal spacing at right angles, it is called "semilogarithmic."

Logarithmic spacing may be done directly from the graduations on one of the scales of a slide rule. Log paper in various combinations of ruling is sold. It may be had in one, two, three, or more cycles, or multiples of 10, also in part-cycle and split-cycle form. In using log paper, interpolations should be made logarithmically, not arithmetically as on rectangular coordinates, for arithmetical interpolation with coarse divisions might lead to considerable error.

29·7 The semilogarithmic chart. This chart has equal spacing on one axis, usually the *X* axis, and logarithmic spacing on the other axis. Owing to a property by virtue of which the slope of the curve at any point is an exact measure of the rate of increase or decrease in the data plotted, it is frequently called a "ratio chart." It is extremely useful in statistical work as it shows at a glance the rate at which a variable changes. Karsten aptly calls it the "rate of change chart" as distinguished from the rectilinear or "amount of change chart." By the use of this chart it is possible to predict a trend, such as the future increase of a business, growth of population, etc.

In choosing between rectilinear ruling and semilog ruling, the important point to consider is whether the chart is to represent *numerical* increases and decreases or *percentage* increases and decreases. In many cases it is desired to emphasize the percentage or rate change, not the numerical change; hence a semilog chart should be used.

An example of the use of the semilog chart is illustrated in Fig. 29·3. This curve was drawn from data compiled for *Automotive Industries* and

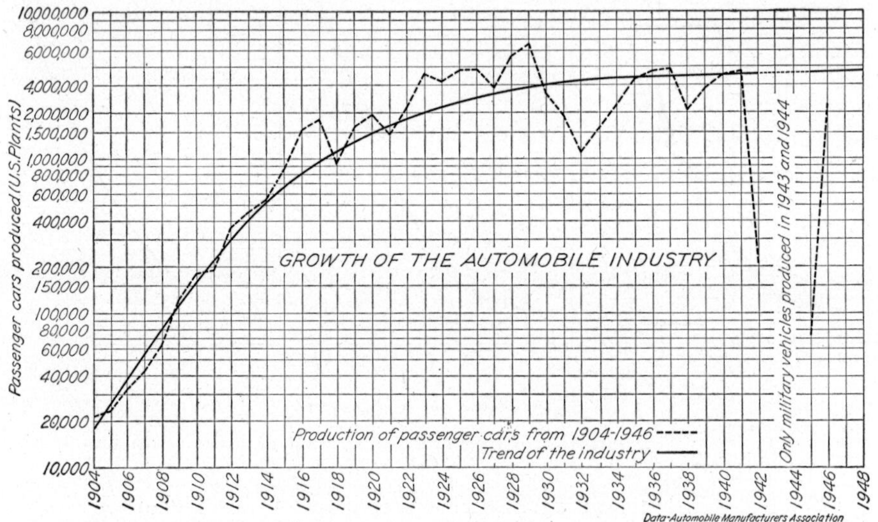

FIG. 29·3—A curve on semilogarithmic paper.

furnished by R. B. Prescott, consulting statistician. The dash line shows the actual production by years, and the full line is the trend curve, the extension of which predicts future production.

29.8 The function of a chart is to reveal facts. It may be entirely misleading if a wrong choice of paper or coordinates is taken. The growth of an operation plotted on a rectilinear chart might, for example, entirely mislead an owner analyzing the trend of his business, while if plotted on a semilog chart it would give a true picture of conditions. Intentionally misleading charts have been used many times in advertising matter, the commonest form being the chart with a greatly exaggerated vertical scale.

29·9 Logarithmic charts with both abscissas and ordinates spaced logarithmically are used more for the solution of problems than for presenting facts. A property which distinguishes the logarithmic chart and accounts for its usefulness in so many cases is that the graphs of all algebraic equations representing multiplication, division, roots, and powers are straight lines.

If the equation $x^2y = 16$ were plotted on ordinary rectangular coordinates, the resulting curve would be a hyperbola of the third degree with the x and y axes as asymptotes. By taking the logarithms of both sides of the given equation it becomes $2 \log x + \log y = \log 16$. The equation now has the slope intercept form $y = mx + b$ and, if so desired, could be plotted on rectangular coordinates by substituting the logarithms of the variables. Obviously, it is easier to use logarithmic coordinates and plot the points directly than to take the logarithms of the variables and plot them on rectangular coordinates.

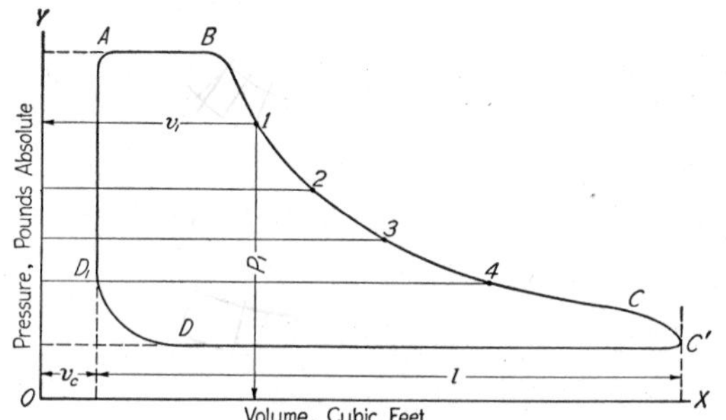

FIG. 29·4—Indicator diagram.

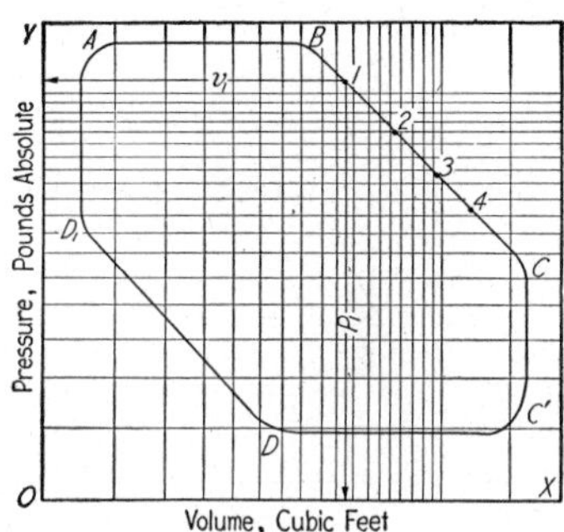

FIG. 29·5—Indicator diagram on log paper.

A feature of the logarithmic chart which makes it valuable for the study of many problems is that the exponent in the equation may be determined by measuring the slope of the graph. An inspection of the foregoing equations will show that the slope m, as given by the slope intercept form, is -2. The value of this exponent may be determined by direct measurement of the slope, using a uniformly graduated scale.

Figures 29·4 and 29·5 show an example of the use of a logarithmic chart in studying steam-engine performance. When the indicator card, Fig. 29·4, is plotted on log paper it takes the form shown in Fig. 29·5. The hyperbolas of a perfect card become straight lines, deviations from which indicate faults.

Figure 29·6 illustrates the use of multiple-cycle paper.

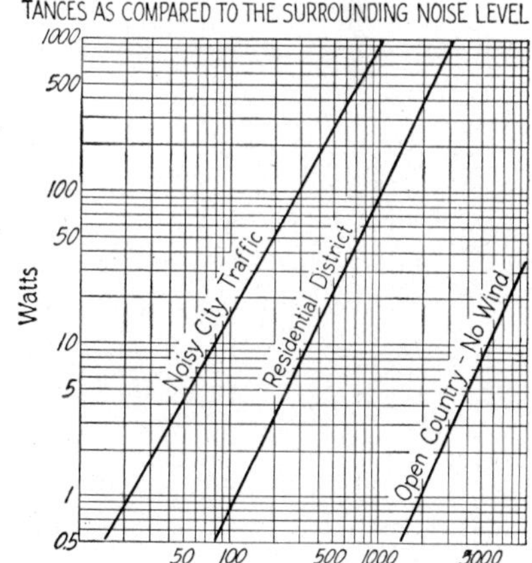

FIG. 29·6—Multiple-cycle ruling.

29·10 The polar chart. The use of polar coordinate paper for representing intensity of illumination, intensity of heat, polar forms of curves, etc., is common. Figure 29·7 shows a candle-power distribution curve for an ordinary Mazda B lamp and Fig. 29·8 the curve for a certain type of reflector. The candle power in any given direction is determined by reading off the distance from the origin to the curve. Use of these curves enables the determination of the foot-candle intensity at any point.

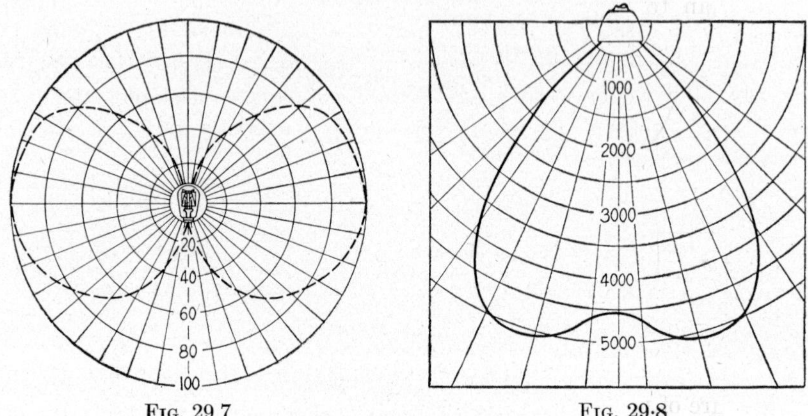

FIG. 29.7 FIG. 29·8

FIGS. 29·7 and 29·8—Polar charts.

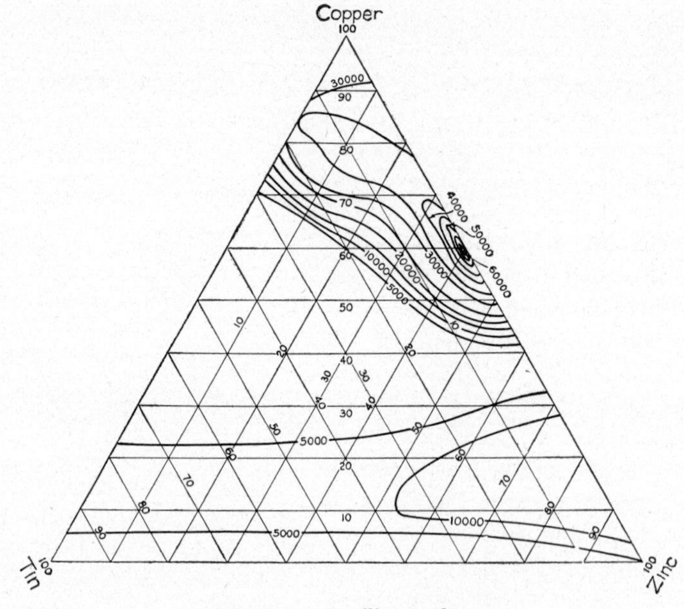

FIG. 29·9—A trilinear chart.

29·11 The trilinear chart. The trilinear chart, or "triaxial diagram" as it is sometimes called, affords a valuable means of studying the properties of chemical compounds consisting of three elements, alloys of three metals or compounds, and mixtures containing three variables. The chart has the form of an equilateral triangle the altitude of which represents 100 per cent of each of the three constituents. Figure 29·9, showing the tensile strength of copper-tin-zinc alloys, is a typical example of its application. The usefulness of such diagrams depends upon the geometrical principle that the sum of the perpendiculars to the sides from any point within an equilateral triangle is a constant and is equal to the altitude.

29·12 Nomographs. The simplest form of nomograph is the *alignment chart,* consisting of three parallel lines graduated and spaced in such a

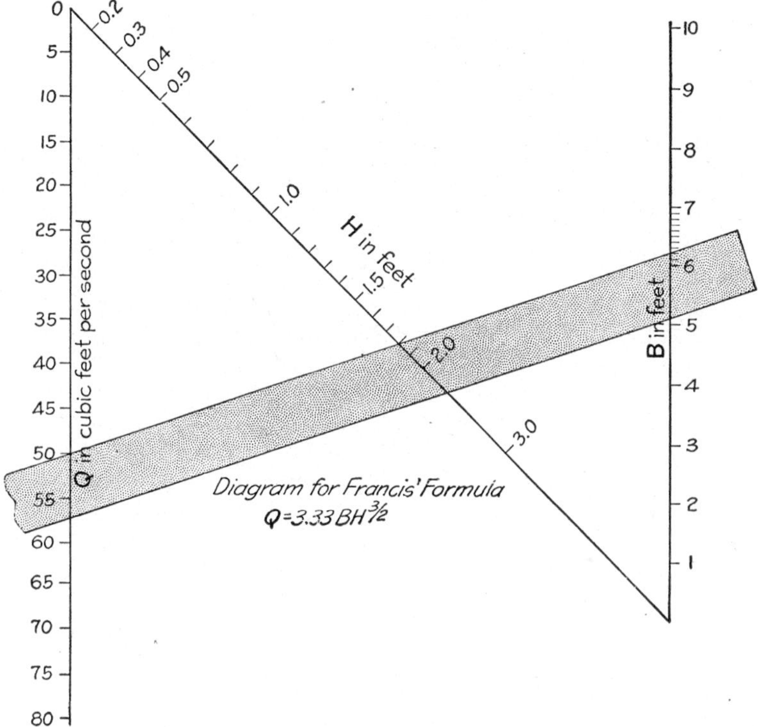

FIG. 29·10—An alignment chart, or nomograph, of an equation. (*Redrawn from Hewes and Seward, "The Design of Diagrams for Engineering Formulas."*)

manner that a straight line passing through known values on two of the scales gives the proper corresponding value at its intersection with the third scale. After an alignment chart is constructed, it is one of the easiest and most accurate means for the solution of the equation for which it is designed. It is beyond our scope here to explain the mathematics underlying the construction of nomographs, as this chapter is only indicating and illustrating the various uses of graphic representation. The graduated lines in a nomograph need not be parallel, and any one or all of them may be either curved or straight, depending upon the equation represented. Figure 29·10 is one form of an alignment chart sometimes called, from its appearance, the "zigzag nomograph." The rectangular chart for the same equation is given for comparison in Fig. 29·11. The simplicity of the alignment chart is obvious.

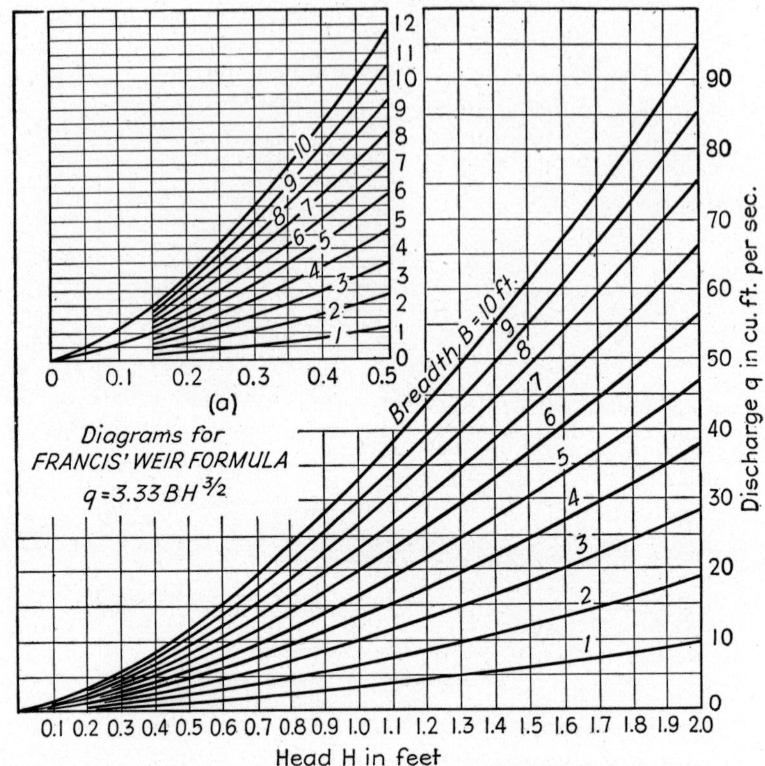

FIG. 29·11—A rectilinear chart of an equation. (*Courtesy of Hewes and Seward "The Design of Diagrams for Engineering Formulas."*)

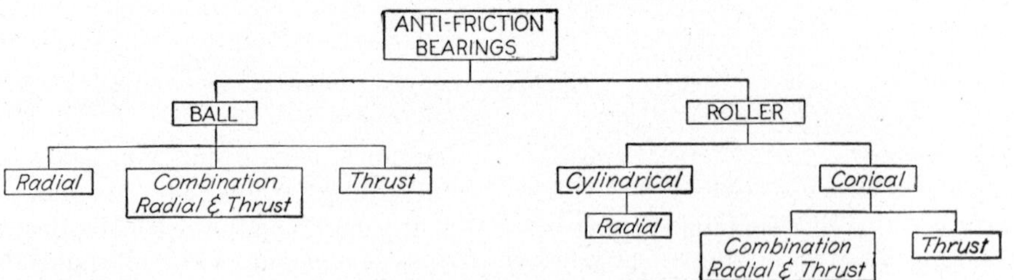

FIG. 29·12—A classification chart.

29·13 Classification charts, route charts, and flow sheets. The uses to which these three classes of charts may be put are widely different, but their underlying principles are similar and they have thus been grouped together for convenience.

A *classification chart*, as illustrated in Fig. 29·12, is intended to show the subdivisions of a whole and the interrelation of its parts to each other.

Such a chart often takes the place of a written outline, since it gives a better visualization of the facts than words alone would convey. A common application is an organization chart of a corporation or business. It is customary to enclose the names of the divisions in rectangles, although circles or other shapes may be used. The rectangle has the advantage of being more convenient for lettering, while the circle may be drawn more

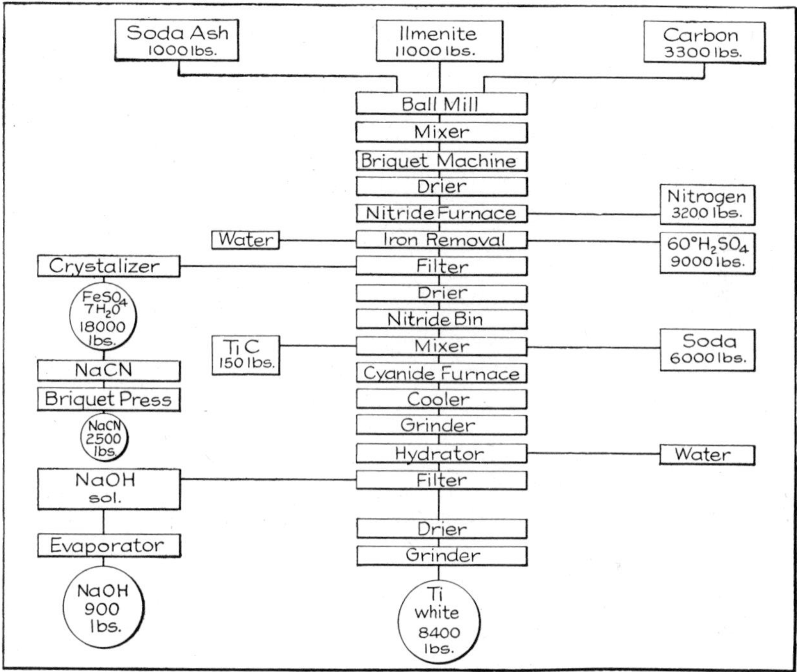

FIG. 29·13—A flow sheet.

quickly and possesses a greater popular appeal. Often a combination of both is used.

The *route chart* is used mainly for the purpose of showing the various steps in a process, either of manufacturing or other business. The *flow sheet* given in Fig. 29·13 is an example of a route chart applied to a chemical process. Charts of this type show in a dynamic way facts which might require considerable study to comprehend from a written description. A different form of route chart is that of Fig. 10·1, showing the course of a drawing through the shops.

29·14 Popular charts. Engineers and draftsmen are frequently called upon to prepare charts and diagrams which will be understood by diversified and nontechnical readers. In many cases it is not advisable to present the facts by means of curves drawn on coordinate paper, although for the sake of greater effectiveness the resulting chart may suffer somewhat in accuracy.

In preparing charts for popular use, particular care must be taken to make them so that the impression produced will be both quick and accurate. It is to be remembered that such charts are seldom studied critically but are taken in at a glance; hence the method of presentation requires the exercise of careful judgment and the application of a certain amount of psychology.

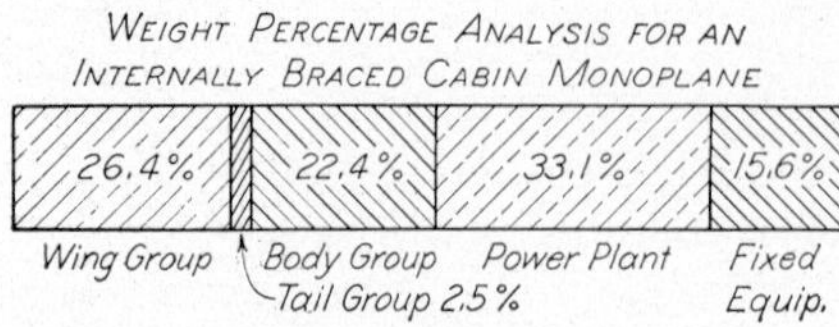

FIG. 29·14—A 100 per cent bar.

29·15 Bar charts. The bar chart is a very easily understood type for the nontechnical reader. One of its simplest forms is the 100 *per cent bar* for showing the relations of the constituents to a given total. Figure 29·14 is an example of this form of chart. The different segments should be crosshatched, shaded, or distinguished in some effective manner, the percentage represented placed on the diagram or directly opposite and the meaning of each segment clearly stated. These bars may be placed either vertically or horizontally, the vertical position giving an advantage for lettering, and the horizontal position an advantage in readability, as the eye judges horizontal distances readily.

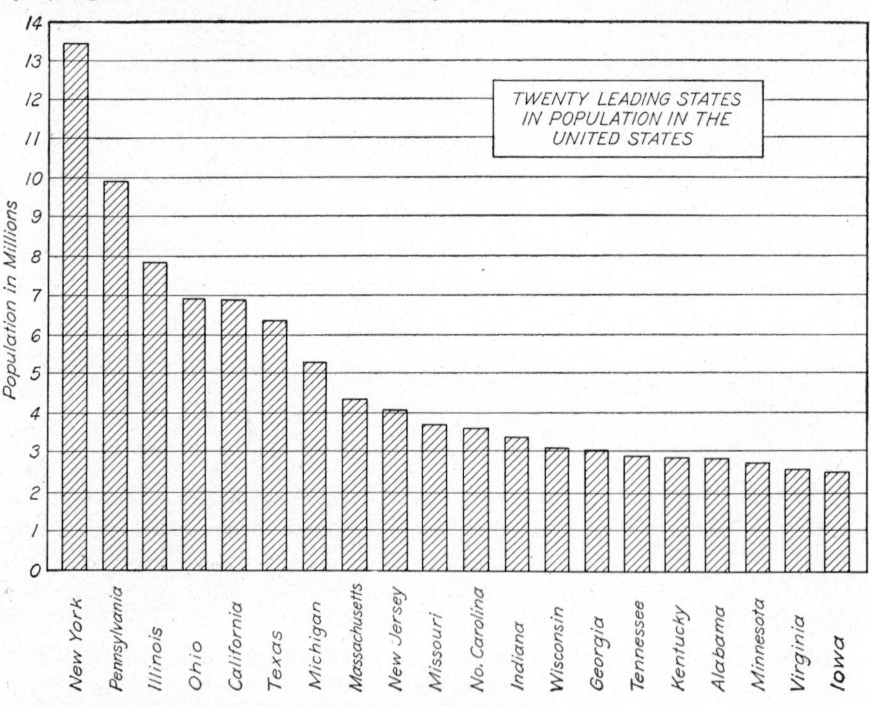

FIG. 29·15—A multiple-bar chart.

Figure 29·15 is an example of a *multiple-bar chart* in which the length of each bar is proportional to the magnitude of the quantity represented.

Means should be provided for reading numerical values represented by the bars. If it is necessary to give the exact value represented by the individual bars, these values should not be lettered at the ends of the bars, since the apparent length would be increased. This type is made both horizontally, with the description at the base, and vertically. The vertical form is sometimes called the "pipe-organ chart." When vertical bars are drawn close together so as to touch along the sides, the diagram is called a "staircase chart." This is made oftener as the "staircase curve," a line plotted on coordinate paper representing the profile of the tops of the bars.

A *compound bar chart* is made when it is desired to show two or more components in each bar. It is really a set of 100 per cent bars of different lengths set together either in pipe-organ or horizontal form.

29·16 Pie charts. The "pie diagram" or 100 per cent circle, Fig. 29·16, is much inferior to the bar chart but is used constantly because of its insistent popular appeal. It is a simple form of chart and, with the exception of the lettering, is easily constructed. It may be regarded as a 100 per cent bar bent into circular form. The circumference of the circle is divided into 100 parts, and sectors are used to represent percentages of the total. To be effective, this diagram must be carefully lettered and the percentages marked on the sectors or at the circumference opposite the sectors. For contrast it is best to crosshatch or shade the individual sectors. If the original drawing is to be displayed, the sectors may be colored and the diagram supplied with a key showing the meaning of each color. In every case the percentage notation should be placed where it can be read without removing the eyes from the diagram.

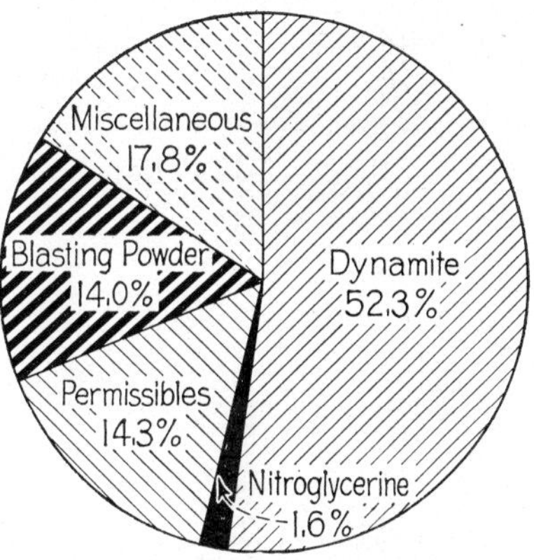

FIG. 29·16—A pie chart.

29·17 Area and volume diagrams. The use of area and volume diagrams has been very common, although they are usually the most deceptive of the graphic methods of representation. Pictorial charts of this type were formerly much used for comparisons, such as of populations, standing armies, livestock, and other products. It was customary to represent the data by human figures, whose heights were proportional to the numerical values, or by silhouettes of the animals or products concerned, whose heights or sometimes areas were proportional. Since volumes vary as the cubes of the linear dimensions, such charts are grossly misleading. For such comparisons bar charts or even pie diagrams should be used.

There are occasions when area diagrams offer the most logical and effective method of presentation, as in Fig. 29·17. Such a chart may be regarded as a series of vertical 100 per cent bars placed side by side.

29·18 To draw a chart. In drawing a coordinate chart the general order is (1) compute and assemble all data, (2) determine size and kind of chart best adapted and whether printed or plain paper should be used, (3) determine, from the limits of the data, the scales for abscissas and ordinates to give the best effect to the resulting curve, (4) lay off the independent variable (often *time*) on the horizontal or X axis, and the dependent variable on the vertical or Y axis, (5) plot points from the data and pencil the curves, (6) ink the curve, and (7) compose and letter title and coordinates.

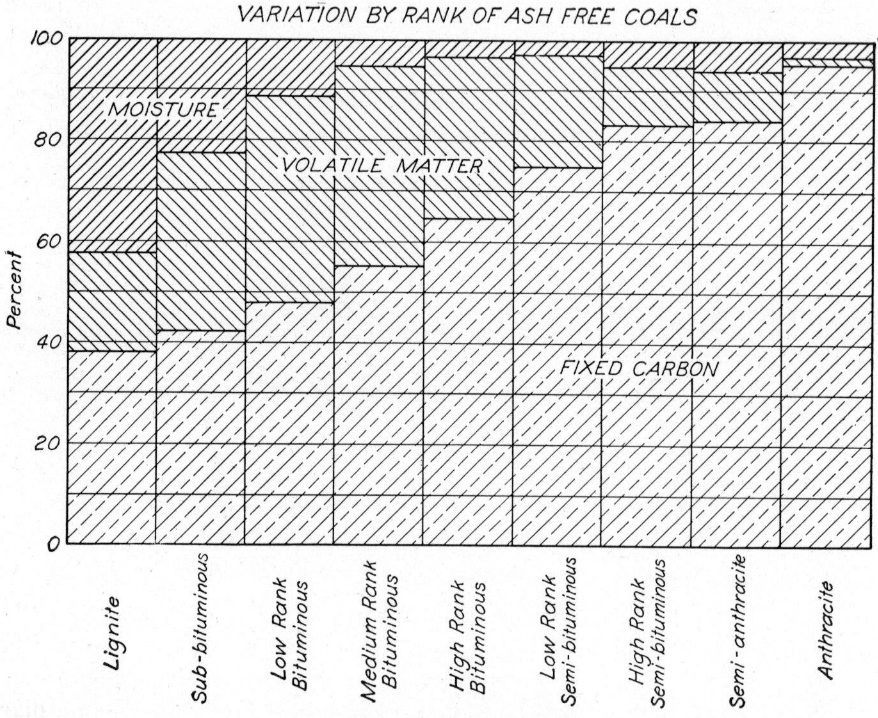

FIG. 29·17—An area diagram.

When the chart is drawn on a printed form, to be blueprinted, the curve may be drawn on the reverse side of the paper, enabling erasures to be made without injuring the ruled surface.

Green is becoming the standard color for printed forms. Blue will not print or photograph and red is trying on the eyes.

If the curve is for purposes of computation, it should be drawn with a fine accurate line. If for demonstration, it should be fairly heavy, for contrast and effect.

The Joint Committee on Standards for Graphic Presentation recommends the following rules:

Standards for Graphic Presentations

1. The general arrangement of a diagram should proceed from left to right.
2. Where possible, represent quantities by linear magnitude, as areas or volumes are likely to be misinterpreted.
3. For a curve the vertical scale, whenever practicable, should be so selected that the zero line will appear in the diagram.
4. If the zero line of the vertical scale will not normally appear in the curve diagram, the zero line should be shown by the use of a horizontal break in the diagram.
5. The zero lines of the scales for a curve should be sharply distinguished from the other coordinate lines.
6. For curves having a scale representing percentages, it is usually desirable to emphasize in some distinctive way the 100 per cent line or other line used as a basis of comparison.
7. When the scale of a diagram refers to dates, and the period represented is not a complete unit, it is better not to emphasize the first and last ordinates, since such a diagram does not represent the beginning and end of time.
8. When the curves are drawn on logarithmic coordinates, the limiting lines of the diagram should each be at some power of 10 on the logarithmic scale.
9. It is advisable not to show any more coordinate lines than necessary to guide the eye in reading the diagram.
10. The curve lines of a diagram should be sharply distinguished from the ruling.
11. In curves representing a series of observations, it is advisable, whenever possible, to indicate clearly on the diagram all the points representing the separate observations.
12. The horizontal scale for curves should usually read from left to right and the vertical scale from bottom to top.
13. Figures for the scale of a diagram should be placed at the left and at the bottom or along the respective axes.
14. It is often desirable to include in the diagram the numerical data or formula represented.
15. If numerical data are not included in the diagram, it is desirable to give the data in tabular form accompanying the diagram.
16. All lettering and all figures in a diagram should be placed so as to be easily read from the base as the bottom or from the right-hand edge of the diagram as the bottom.
17. The title of a diagram should be made as clear and complete as possible. Subtitles or descriptions should be added if necessary to ensure clearness.

29·19 Charts for reproduction. Charts for reproduction by the zinc-etching process should be carefully penciled to about twice the size of the required cut, see Drawing for Reproduction, paragraph 24·13. In inking, first ink circles around plotted points; second, ink the curves with strong lines. A border pen is useful for heavy lines, and a Payzant pen may be used to advantage, particularly with dotted lines. Third, ink the title box and all lettering; fourth, ink the coordinates with fine black lines, putting in only as many as are necessary for easy reading, and breaking them wherever they interfere with title or lettering or where they cross plotted points.

29·20 Charts for display. Large charts for demonstration purposes are sometimes required. These may be drawn on sheets 22″ × 28″ or 28″ × 44″ known as "printer's blanks." The quickest way to make them is with the show-card colors and single-stroke sign-writer's brushes. Large bar charts may be made with strips of black adhesive tape. Lettering may be done with the brush or with gummed letters:

PROBLEMS

29·21 The following problems are given as suggestive of various types for both technical and popular presentation:

1. During a certain chemical process the rise in temperature varied with the time as given in the following data:

Time	Temperature, °C.	Time	Temperature, °C.
0	0	7	136
1	33	8	139
2	66	9	142
3	93	10	143
4	110	11	144
5	123	12	155
6	131		

Using 8½″ × 11″ paper divided into inches and twentieths, show graphically the relation between the time and the corresponding rise in temperature.

2. In a tension test of a machine-steel bar the following data were obtained:

Applied Load, Pounds per Square Inch	Elongation per Inch of Length
0	0
3,000	0.00011
5,000	0.00018
10,000	0.00033
15,000	0.00051
20,000	0.00067
25,000	0.00083
30,000	0.00099
35,000	0.00115
40,000	0.00134
42,000	0.00142

Plot the foregoing data on rectangular coordinates using the elongation as the independent variable and the applied load as the dependent variable.

3. In testing a small 1-kilowatt transformer for efficiency at various loads, the following data were obtained:

Watts Delivered	Losses
948	73
728	62
458	53
252	49
000	47

Plot curves on rectangular coordinate paper showing the relation between percentage of load and efficiency, using watts delivered as the independent variable and remembering that efficiency = output ÷ (output + losses).

4. The following data were obtained from a test of an automobile engine:

Rpm	Length of run, minutes	Fuel per run, pounds	Brake horsepower
1,006	11.08	1.0	5.5
1,001	4.25	0.5	8.5
997	7.53	1.0	13.0
1,000	5.77	1.0	16.3
1,002	2.38	0.5	21.1

Plot curves on rectangular coordinate paper showing the relation between fuel used per brake horsepower-hour and brake horsepower developed. Show also the relation between thermal efficiency and brake horsepower developed assuming the heat value of the gasoline to be 19,000 British thermal units per pound.

5. During a certain year the consumption of bleaching powder by industries was as follows:

Industry	Tons
Pulp and paper	64,000
Textile	16,000
Water purification	9,000
Laundry	4,000
Miscellaneous	7,000

Show these facts by means of a 100 per cent bar, a pie diagram, and a bar chart. After having drawn these three charts, determine which one you would use if you were presenting the information to the president of a manufacturing company; to the general public; to a group of engineers.

6. Make a semilogarithmic chart showing the comparative rate of growth of the five largest American cities during the past 50 years. Data for this chart may be obtained from the U.S. Census Bureau Reports.

7. Make a compound bar chart showing the proportion of men and women students in your school in first, second, third, and fourth years. Data from the registrar.

8. Make a multiple-bar chart showing the minimum distances required to stop a modern automobile by an average driver having normal reflex. Distinguish between "thinking distance" and "braking distance." Source of data: Iowa Motor Vehicle department. Title: Speed and Stopping Distances.

Miles per hour	Feet per second	Thinking distance, feet	Braking distance, feet
20	29	22	18
30	44	33	40
40	59	44	71
50	74	55	111
60	88	66	160
70	103	77	218

9. Make a rectilinear chart showing the fluctuation of one active listed stock during the past month. The data for this may be obtained from the daily papers or from a stockbroker.

10. Draw a chart showing the growth of life insurance in this country in number of policies and in value, from 1900 to date. Data from *World Almanac*.

11. Put the data of Fig. 29·16 into 100 per cent bar form.

12. Make an organization chart of (*a*) your city government, (*b*) the administration of your school, (*c*) a small manufacturing concern.

Chapter 30

NOTES ON COMMERCIAL PRACTICE

30·1 There are many items of practical information of value to the student and draftsman which are not included in the ordinary course in drawing but are learned through experience. A few miscellaneous points are given here as suggestions of kinds of information which are worth collecting and preserving in notebook form.

30·2 Stretching paper. If a drawing is to be tinted the paper should be stretched on the board. First, dampen it on both sides until limp, either with a sponge or under the faucet, then lay it on the drawing board face down, take up the excess water from the edges with a blotter, brush a strip of glue or paste about ½ inch wide around the edge, turn the paper over and rub its edges down on the board until set, and allow to dry horizontally.

Drawings or maps on which much work is to be done, even though not to be tinted, may be made advantageously on stretched paper; but Bristol or calendered paper should not be stretched.

30·3 Tinting is done with washes made with water colors. The drawing may be inked (with waterproof ink) either before or, preferably, after tinting. The drawing should be cleaned and the unnecessary pencil marks removed with a very soft rubber, the tint being mixed in a saucer and applied with a camel-hair or sable brush. Incline the board and flow the color with horizontal strokes, leading the pool of color down over the surface, taking up the surplus at the bottom by wiping the brush out quickly and picking up with it the excess color. Stir the color each time the brush is dipped into the saucer. Tints should be made in light washes, depth of color being obtained if necessary by repeating the wash. To get an even color it is well to go over the surface first with a wash of clear water. Diluted colored inks may be used for washes instead of water color.

30·4 Methods of copying drawings—pricking. Drawings are often copied on opaque paper by laying the drawing over the paper and pricking through with a needle point, turning the upper sheet back frequently and connecting the points. Prickers may be purchased or may be made easily by forcing a fine needle into a softwood handle. They may be used to advantage also in accurate drawing, in transferring measurements from scale to paper.

30·5 Transfer by rubbing. This method, known as *frotté*, is very useful, particularly in architectural drawing, in transferring any kind of sketch or design to the paper on which it is to be rendered.

The original is made on any paper and may be worked over, changed, and marked up until the design is satisfactory. Lay a piece of tracing paper over the original and trace the outline carefully. Turn the tracing over and retrace the outline just as carefully on the other side, using a medium soft pencil with a *sharp* point. Turn back to first position and tack down smoothly over the paper on which the drawing is to be made, registering the tracing to proper position by center or reference lines on both tracing and drawing. Now transfer the drawing by rubbing the tracing with the rounded edge of a knife handle or other instrument (a smooth-edged coin held between thumb and forefinger and scraped back and forth is commonly used), holding a small piece of tracing cloth with smooth side up between the rubbing instrument and the paper, to protect the paper. Do not rub too hard and be sure that neither the cloth nor the paper moves while rubbing. Transfers in ink instead of pencil, useful on wash drawings, may be made by tracing with *encre à poncer*, a rubbing ink made for this purpose.

If the drawing is symmetrical about any axis the reversed tracing need not be made, as the rubbing can be done from the first tracing by reversing it about the axis of symmetry.

Several rubbings can be made from one tracing, and when the same figure or detail must be repeated several times on a drawing, much time can be saved by drawing it on tracing paper and rubbing it in the several positions.

30·6 Glass drawing board. Drawing tables with glass tops and with lights in reflecting boxes underneath are successful devices for copying drawings on opaque paper. Even pencil drawings may be copied readily on the heaviest paper or Bristol board by the use of a transparent drawing board.

30·7 Proportional methods—the pantograph. The principle of the pantograph, used for reducing or enlarging drawings in any proportion, is well known. The instrument consists essentially of four bars, which for any setting must form a parallelogram and have the pivot, tracing point, and marking point in a straight line; and any arrangement of four arms conforming to this requirement will work in true proportion. For reduction the tracing point and marking point are interchanged. A suspended panto-

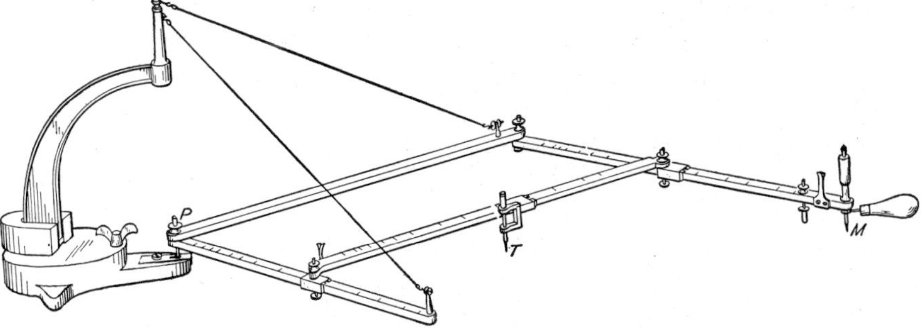

FIG. 30·1—A suspended pantograph.

graph with metal arms, for accurate engineering work, is shown in Fig. 30·1.

Drawings may be copied to reduced or enlarged scale by using the proportional dividers, illustrated in Fig. 30·2. The divisions marked "lines" are linear proportions, those marked "circles" give the setting for dividing a circle into a desired number of equal parts when the large end is opened to the diameter of the circle.

The well-known method of *proportional squares* is often used for reduction or enlargement. The drawing to be copied is ruled in squares of con-

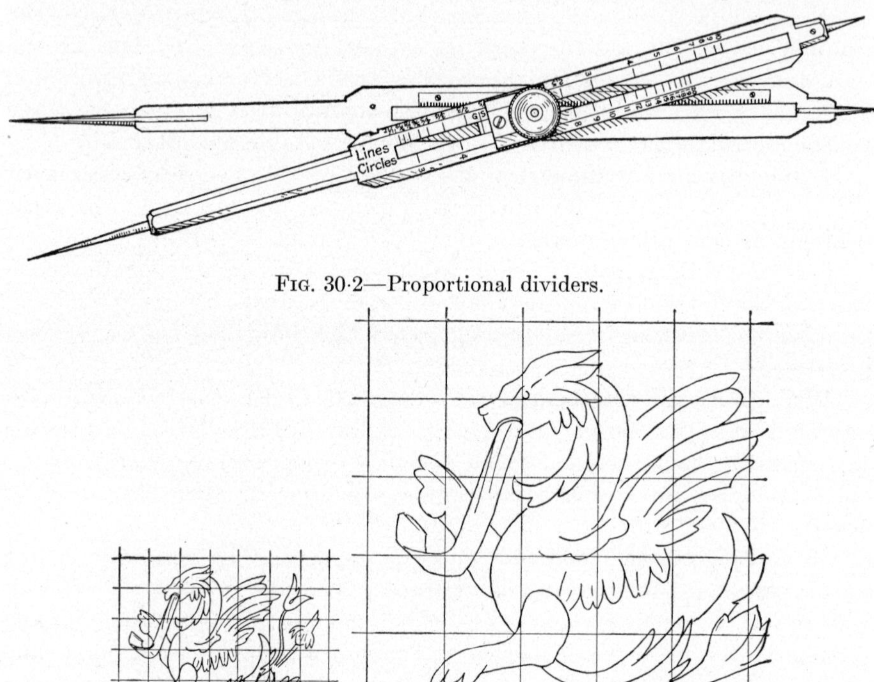

Fig. 30·2—Proportional dividers.

Fig. 30·3—Enlargement by squares (craticulation).

venient size, or, if it is undesirable to mark on the drawing, a sheet of ruled tracing cloth or celluloid is laid over it and the copy made freehand on the paper, which has been ruled in corresponding squares, larger or smaller, Fig. 30·3.

30·8 Special instruments. There are some instruments not in the usual assortment that are occasionally needed. Beam compasses are used for circles larger than the capacity of ordinary compasses with lengthening bar. A good form is illustrated in Fig. 30·4. A tubular beam compass is shown in Fig. 2·8.

With the drop pen or rivet pen, Fig. 30·5, smaller circles can be made much faster than with the bow pen. It is held as shown, the needle point

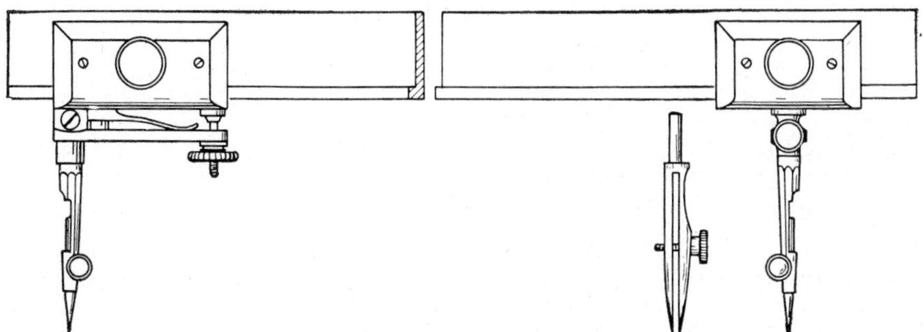

Fig. 30·4—Beam compasses.

is stationary, and the pen is revolved around it. It is of particular convenience in bridge and structural work and in topographic drawing.

Several instruments for drawing ellipses have been made. The ellipsograph, Fig. 30·6, is a very satisfactory one.

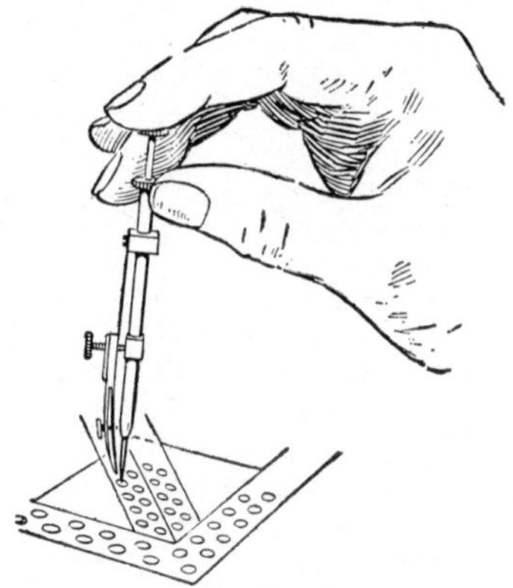

Fig. 30·5—A drop pen.

Three special pens are shown in Fig. 30·7. The *railroad pen A* is used for double lines. A better pen for double lines up to ¼ inch apart is the *border pen B*, as it can be held down to the paper more satisfactorily. It may be used for very wide solid lines by inking the middle space as well as the two pens. The *contour pen* or curve pen *C*, made with a swivel, is used in map work for freehand curves.

A *protractor* is a necessity in map and topographical work. A semicircular brass or nickel-silver one, 6 inches in diameter, will read to half degrees. They may be had with an arm and vernier reading to minutes. Large circular paper protractors 8 and 14

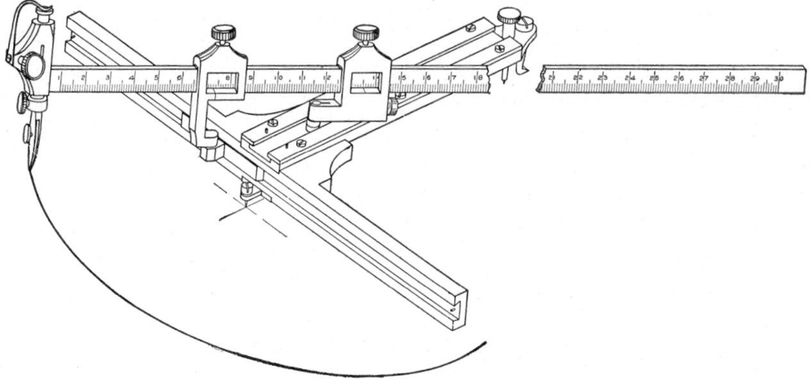

Fig. 30·6—An ellipsograph.

inches in diameter reading to half and quarter degrees are used and preferred by some map draftsmen. Others prefer the Brown and Sharpe protractor, Fig. 30·8, reading to 5 minutes.

A combination of triangle and protractor popular with architects and draftsmen is shown in Fig. 30·9. Numerous different forms of combination

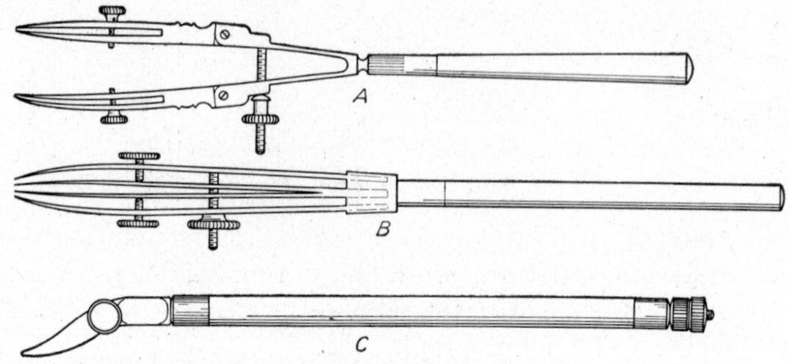

FIG. 30·7—Special pens.

"triangles" have been devised, of which several are usually carried by the dealers.

Drafting machines. Since the expiration of the patent on the Universal drafting machine several makers have come into competition with varied designs of this important instrument, which combines the functions of

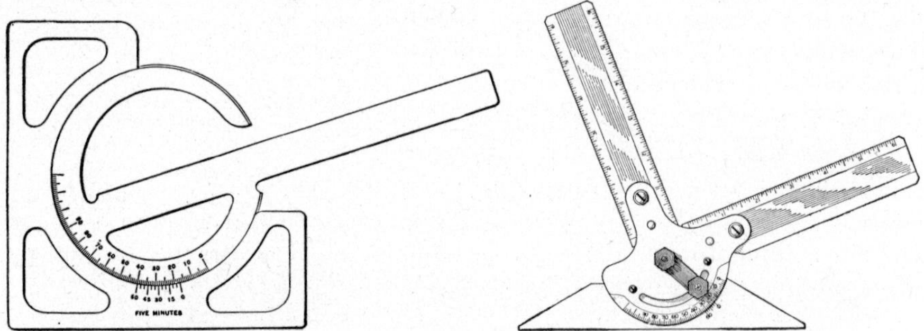

FIG. 30·8—Brown and Sharpe protractor. FIG. 30·9—Tri-Pro-Scale.

T square, triangles, scale, and protractor, and which is used very extensively in commercial drafting rooms (it is estimated that 35 per cent of time in machine drawing and over 50 per cent in structural drawing is saved by its use). Figure 30·10 shows a band-type drafting machine. Special drafting machines are made for left-handed draftsmen.

Vertical drawing boards with sliding parallel straightedges are preferred by some for large work.

Figure 30·11 shows a special *bottleholder* made by the Alteneder Company, with which the pen may be filled with one hand and time saved thereby.

Curves. Some irregular curves were illustrated in Fig. 2·16. Many others are sold. Sometimes for special or recurring curves it is advisable for the draftsman to make his own template. These may be cut out of thin

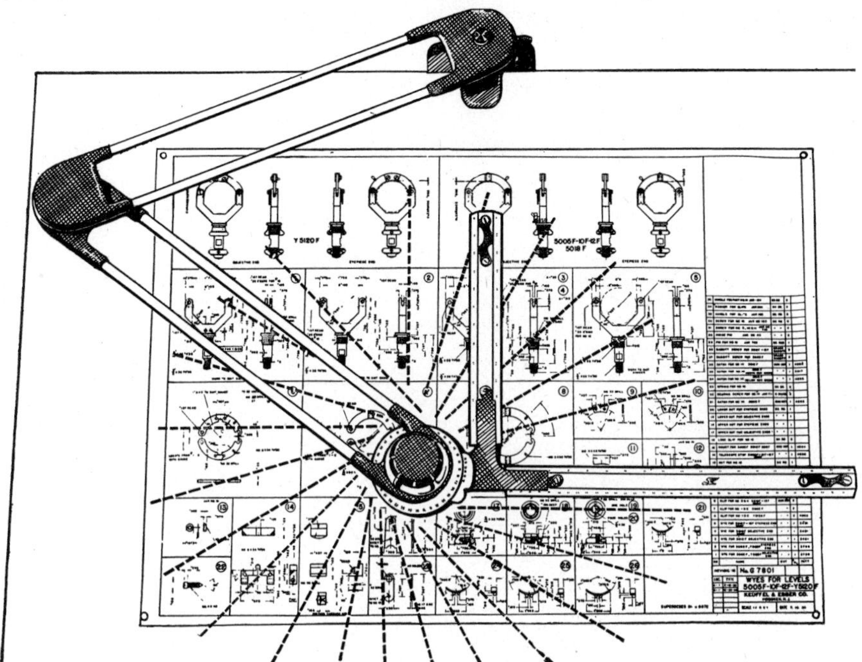

FIG. 30·10—A drafting machine.

nolly or basswood, sheet lead, celluloid, or even cardboard or pressboard. To make a paper curve, sketch the desired shape on the paper, cut out with scissors, and sandpaper the edge. For inking, use it over a triangle or another piece of paper. Flexible curves of different kinds are sold. A copper wire or piece of wire solder can be used as a homemade substitute.

FIG. 30·11—Alteneder bottle-holder.

The curve illustrated in Fig. 30·12 has been found particularly useful for engineering diagrams, steam curves, etc. It is plotted to the polar equation $r = A \sec \theta + K$, in which A may be about $5\frac{1}{2}$ inches and K, 8 inches.

If the glaze is removed from a celluloid irregular curve by rubbing with fine sandpaper, pencil marks that facilitate the drawing of symmetrical curves may be made on it.

Splines are flexible curve rulers, which are adjusted to the points of the curve to be drawn and held in place by lead weights, called by the draftsmen "ducks." They come in various lengths and are part of the regular equipment of all aircraft drawing rooms, Fig. 30·13.

30·9 Various devices. In making a drawing or map so large that it extends over the bottom edge of the board, a piece of half round should be fastened to the board, as in Fig. 30·14, to prevent creasing the paper.

A steel edge for a drawing board may be made of an angle iron planed straight and set flush with the edge. A well-liked adjustable metal edge is made by L. S. Starrett & Company, Fig. 30·15. With a steel edge and steel T square, very accurate plotting may be done. These are often used in bridge offices.

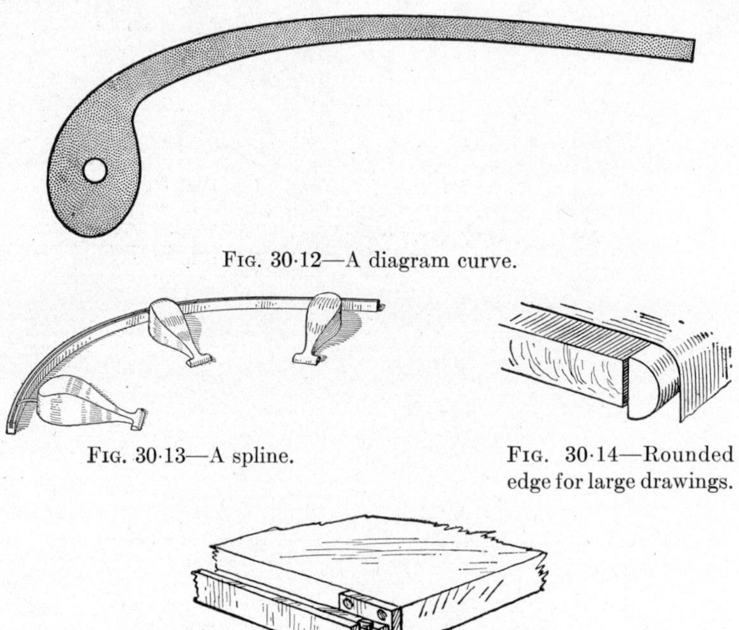

FIG. 30·12—A diagram curve.

FIG. 30·13—A spline.

FIG. 30·14—Rounded edge for large drawings.

FIG. 30·15—Starrett edge.

Section lining or "crosshatching" is a difficult operation for the beginner but is done almost automatically by the experienced draftsman. A number of instruments for mechanical spacing have been devised.

Section liners are mechanical spacers for use in crosshatching or other evenly spaced line work. One type is shown in Fig. 30·16.

Erasing shields of metal or celluloid permit an erasure to be made in a small space. Slots for the same purpose may be cut from sheet celluloid or tough paper.

The *K and E isometric drawing kit*[1] is a set of special triangles with special templates and paper, designed to speed and simplify the making of isometric drawings. Full details may be obtained from the manufacturer.

[1] Keuffel & Esser Co., Hoboken, N.J.

Mechanical lettering devices are being much used in drafting rooms. Several forms are on the market, including the Wrico, Edco, Normograph, and Leroy, all based on the principle of a stylographic pen guided by a sliding master plate. With their use very satisfactory display lettering can be done by unskilled labor. Figures 30·17 and 30·18 illustrate two of these instruments.

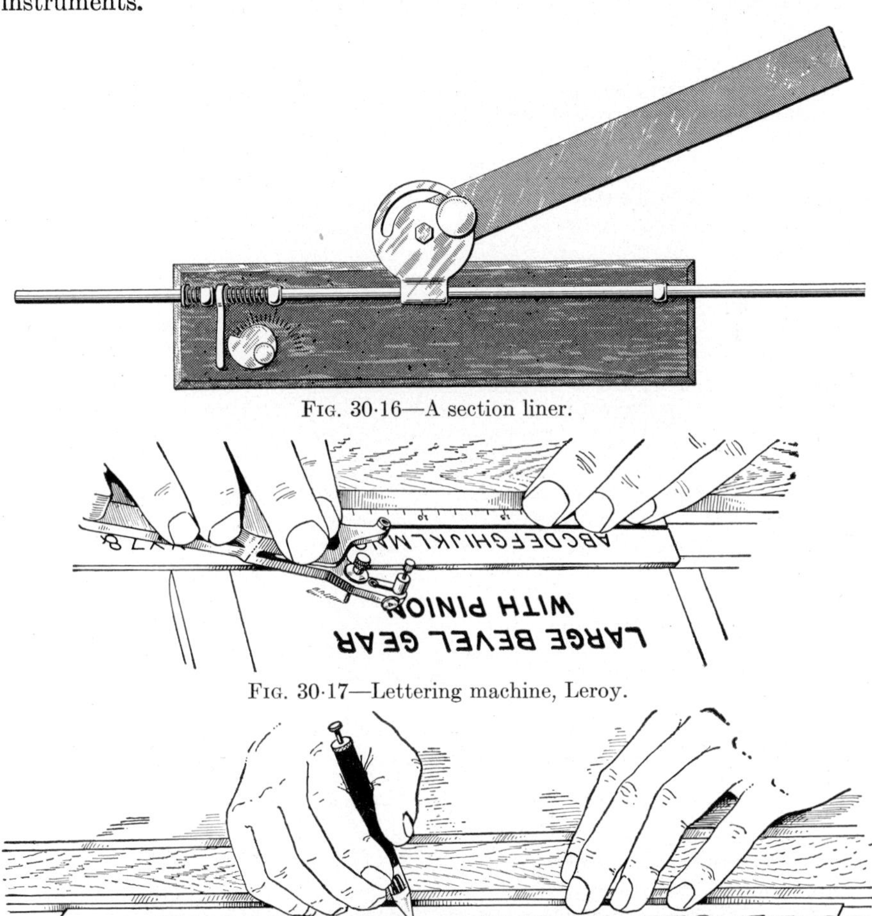

FIG. 30·16—A section liner.

FIG. 30·17—Lettering machine, Leroy.

FIG. 30·18—Lettering machine, Wrico.

There are many other devices designed for labor saving and convenience in drafting rooms. The Bostich tacker is used instead of thumbtacks. Many draftsmen like to fasten paper to the board with scotch tape. For this *drafting tape* should be used in preference to masking tape or other varieties of scotch tape. The Dexter "Draftsmen's Special" pencil sharpener removes the wood only, leaving a long exposure of lead. Electric erasing machines are popular.

Chapter 31

BIBLIOGRAPHY OF ALLIED SUBJECTS

The following short classified list of books is given to supplement this book, whose scope as a general treatise on the language of engineering drawing permits only the mention or brief explanation of some subjects.

Abbreviations used for publishers' names:

Harper—Harper & Brothers, New York.
Int T.—International Textbook Company, Scranton, Pa.
McGH.—McGraw-Hill Book Company, Inc., New York.
Macm.—The Macmillan Company, New York.
PH.—Prentice-Hall, Inc., New York.
PP.—Pencil Points Library (Reinhold Publishing Corporation, New York).
Pitm.—Pitman Publishing Corporation, New York.
Van N.—D. Van Nostrand Company, Inc., New York.
Wiley.—John Wiley & Sons, Inc., New York.

Aeronautical Engineering

ANDERSON, NEWTON.—Aircraft Layout and Detail Design. McGH.
APALATEGUI and ADAMS.—Aircraft Analytic Geometry. McGH.
BRUHN, E. F.—Analysis and Design of Airplane Structures. Tri State Offset Co., Cincinnati.
DAVIS and GOEN.—Aircraft Mechanical Drawing. McGH.
FAULCONER, THOMAS.—Introduction to Aircraft Design. McGH.
LIMING, ROY.—Practical Analytic Geometry with Application to Aircraft. Macm.
MEADOWCROFT, NORMAN.—Aircraft Detail Drafting. McGH.
NILES and NEWELL.—Airplane Structures. 2v. Wiley.
SECHLER and DUNN.—Airplane Structural Analysis and Design. Wiley.
TITTERTON, G. F.—Aircraft Materials and Processes. Pitm.

Architectural Drawing

FIELD, W. B.—An Introduction to Architectural Drawing. McGH.
———.—Architectural Drawing. McGH.
———.—House Planning. McGH.
RAMSEY and SLEEPER.—Architectural Graphic Standards. Wiley.
SLEEPER, H. R.—Architectural Specifications. Wiley.
VOSS and VARNEY.—Architectural Construction. 2v. Wiley.

Cams

FURMAN, F. DER.—Cams, Elementary and Advanced. Wiley.

Charts, Graphs, and Diagrams

DINGMAN, C. F.—Plan Reading and Quantity Surveying. McGH.
HASKELL, A. C.—How to Make and Use Graphic Charts. Codex Book Co., New York.
HEWES and SEWARD.—The Design of Diagrams for Engineering Formulas and the Theory of Nomography. McGH.
KARSTEN, K. G.—Charts and Graphs. PH.

RIGGLEMAN, J. R.—Graphic Methods for Presenting Business Statistics. McGH.
SWETT, G. W.—Construction of Alignment Charts. Wiley.

Descriptive Geometry

BRADLEY and UHLER.—Descriptive Geometry for Engineers. Int T.
CHERRY, F. H.—Descriptive Geometry. Macm.
CHURCH, A. E.—Elements of Descriptive Geometry. American Book Company, New York.
HIGBEE, F. G.—Drawing-board Geometry. Wiley.
HOOD, G. J.—Geometry of Engineering Drawing. McGH.
JORDAN and PORTER.—Descriptive Geometry. Ginn and Company, Boston.
LEVENS and EGGERS.—Descriptive Geometry. Harper.
ROWE, C. E.—Engineering Descriptive Geometry. Van N.
RULE and WATTS.—Descriptive Geometry. PH.
SMITH, W. G.—Practical Descriptive Geometry. McGH.
WARNER, F. M.—Applied Descriptive Geometry. McGH.

Drawing Instruments (Catalogues)

THEO. ALTENEDER AND SONS, Philadelphia.
EUGENE DIETZGEN COMPANY, Chicago.
KEUFFEL & ESSER CO., Hoboken, N.J.
THE FREDERICK POST COMPANY, Chicago.

Engineering Drawing Problem Sheets

FRENCH and MCCULLEY.—Engineering Drawing Sheets, 11″ × 17″. McGH.
HIGBEE and RUSS.—Engineering Drawing Problems, 8½″ × 11″. Wiley.
LEVENS and EDSTROM.—Problems in Engineering Drawing, 8½″ × 11″. McGH.

Gears and Gearing

BEALE, O. J.—Practical Treatise on Gearing. Brown and Sharpe Mfg. Co., Providence, R.I.
BUCKINGHAM, E.—Spur Gears. McGH.
FELLOWS GEAR SHAPER CO.—Treatise on Commercial Gear Cutting. Springfield, Vt.
TRAUTSCHOLD, R. M.—Standard Gear Book. McGH.

Handbooks

A great many handbooks, with tables, formulas, and information, are published for the different branches of the engineering profession, and draftsmen keep the ones pertaining to their particular line at hand for ready reference. Attention is called, however, to the danger of using handbook formulas and figures without understanding the principles upon which they are based. "Handbook designer" is a term of reproach applied not without reason to one who depends wholly upon these aids without knowing their theory or limitations.

Among the best known of these reference books are the following:

American Machinists' Handbook, Colvin and Stanley. McGH.
American Society of Heating and Ventilating Engineers' Guide (annually).
Architects' and Builders' Pocketbook, Kidder-Parker. Wiley.
Aviation Handbook, Warner and Johnson. McGH.
Building Estimator's Reference Book, Walker. F. R. Walker Co., Chicago.
Chemical Engineers' Handbook, J. H. Perry. McGH.
Civil Engineering Handbook, L. C. Urquhart. McGH.
Civil Engineers' Reference Book. Trautwine Co., Ithaca, N.Y.
General Engineering Handbook, C. E. O'Rourke. McGH.

Handbook of Building Construction, Hool and Johnson. McGH.
Handbook of Engineering Fundamentals, O. W. Eshbach. Wiley.
Handbooks of various steel and other material companies, as Bethlehem; Carnegie; Aluminum Co. of America; Portland Cement Assoc., etc.
Machinery's Handbook, Industrial Press, New York.
Mechanical Engineers' Handbook, L. S. Marks. McGH.
Mechanical Engineers' Pocketbook, William Kent. 2v. Wiley.
Pencil Points Data Sheets. PP.
Piping Handbook, Walker and Crocker. McGH.
Standard Handbook for Electrical Engineers. A. E. Knowlton. McGH.
Steel Construction. Am. Inst. of Steel Const., Inc., New York.

Illustration

Hoelscher, Springer, and Pohle.—Industrial Production Illustration. McGH.
Tharratt, George.—Aircraft Production Illustration. McGH.
Treacy, John.—Production Illustration. Wiley.

Lettering

Benson and Carey.—The Elements of Lettering. John Stevens.
French and Meiklejohn.—The Essentials of Lettering. McGH.
French and Turnbull.—Lessons in Lettering. Books I and II. McGH.
Ogg, Oscar.—An Alphabet Source Book. Harper.
Reinhardt, C. W.—Lettering for Draftsmen, etc. Van N.
Svensen, C. L.—The Art of Lettering. Van N.

Machine Drawing and Design

Albert, C. D.—Machine Design Drawing Room Problems. Wiley.
Berard and Waters.—The Elements of Machine Design. Van N.
Bradford and Eaton.—Machine Design. Wiley.
Faires, V. M.—Design of Machine Elements. Macm.
Kimball and Barr.—Elements of Machine Design. Wiley.
Leutwiler, O. A.—Elements of Machine Design. McGH.
Maleev, V. L.—Machine Design. Int T.
Norman, Ault, and Zarobsky.—Fundamentals of Machine Design. Macm.
Tozer and Rising.—Machine Drawing. McGH.
Vallance, A.—Design of Machine Members. McGH.

Map and Topographical Drawing

Deetz, Charles H.—Cartography. U.S. Government Printing Office.
Sloane and Montz.—Elements of Topographic Drawing. McGH.

Mechanism and Kinematics

Guillet, G. L.—Kinematics of Machines. Wiley.
Ham and Crane.—Mechanics of Machinery. McGH.
Keown and Faires.—Mechanism. McGH.
Schwamb, Merrill, and James.—Elements of Mechanism. Wiley.
Vallance and Farris.—Principles of Mechanism. Macm.

Perspective

Freese, E. I.—Perspective Projection. PP.
Lawson, P. J.—Practical Perspective Drawing. McGH.
Lubchez B.—Perspective. Van N.

Piping

CRANE & Co., Chicago; Catalogue.
WALWORTH COMPANY, Boston; Catalogue.
See also Handbooks.

Rendering

GUPTIL, A. L.—Drawing with Pen and Ink. PP.
———.—Sketching and Rendering in Pencil. PP.
KAUTSKY, T.—Pencil Broadsides. PP.
MAGONIGLE, H. V.—Architectural Rendering in Wash. Charles Scribner's Sons, New York.

Sheet-metal Drafting

KIDDER, F. S.—Triangulation Applied to Sheet Metal Pattern Cutting. Sheet Metal Publishing Co., New York.
KITTREDGE, G. W.—The New Metal Worker Pattern Book. Scientific Book Corporation, New York.
LONGFIELD, E. M.—Sheet Metal Drafting McGH.

Shop Practice and Tools

BOSTON, O. W.—Engineering Shop Practice. Wiley.
BURGHARDT, H. D—Machine Tool Operation. 2v. McGH.
CAMPBELL, H. L.—Metal Castings. Wiley.
CINCINNATI MILLING MACHINE CO.—A Treatise on Milling and Milling Machines. Cincinnati.
CLAPP and CLARK.—Engineering Materials and Processes. Int T.
COLVIN and HAAS.—Jigs and Fixtures. McGH.
COLVIN and STANLEY.—Drilling and Surfacing Practice. McGH.
DOWD and CURTIS.—Tool Engineering. 2v. McGH.
STERN, M.—Die-casting Practice. McGH.

Slide Rule

CAJORI, F.—A History of the Logarithmic Slide Rule. Eng. News Pub. Co., N.Y.
COOPER, H. O.—Slide Rule Calculations. Oxford Univ. Press.
MACKEY, C. O.—Graphical Solutions. Wiley.

Structural Drawing and Design

BISHOP, C. T.—Structural Drafting. Wiley.
HOOL and KINNE.—Structural Engineers' Handbook Series. 6v. McGH.
MORRIS, C. T.—The Design of Simple Steel Structures. McGH.
SHEDD and VAWTER.—Theory of Simple Structures. Wiley.
TAYLOR, THOMPSON, and SMULSKI.—Reinforced Concrete Bridges. Wiley.

Welding

FISH, G. D.—Arc Welded Steel Frame Structures. McGH.
FOX and BLOOR.—Welding Technology and Design. J. B. Lippincott Company, Philadelphia.
LINCOLN ELECTRIC CO.—Simple Blueprint Reading with Particular Reference to Welding. Cleveland.
———.—Procedure Handbook of Arc Welding Design and Practice. Cleveland.
MOON, A. R.—Design of Welded Steel Structures. Pitm.

AMERICAN STANDARDS

The American Standards Association is working continually on standardization projects. Of its many publications the following standards having to do with the subjects in this book are available at the time of this printing. A complete list of American Standards will be sent by the association on application to its offices, 29 West Thirty-ninth Street, New York.

Bolt, Nut, and Rivet Proportions

Large Rivets (½-in. Diameter and Larger)	B18.4
Small Rivets—1927 with 1942 Addendum	B18a
Wrench-head Bolts and Nuts and Wrench Openings	B18.2
Round Unslotted Head Bolts	B18.5
Slotted Head Proportions: Machine Screws, Cap Screws, and Wood Screws	B18c
Tinners', Coopers', and Belt Rivets—1928 with 1942 Addendum	B18g
Plow Bolts	B18f
Track Bolts and Nuts	B18d

Pipe and Pipe Fittings

CI Flanges and Flanged Fittings:	
For Class 25	B16b2
For Class 125	B16a
For Class 250	B16b
For Class 800	B16b1
CI Soil Pipe and Fittings	A40.1
Steel Pipe Flanges and Flanged Fittings	B16e
Face-to-face Dimensions of Ferrous Flanged and Welded End Valves	B16.10
CI Screwed Drainage Fittings	B16.12
CI Screwed Fittings	B16d
CI Long Turn Sprinkler Fittings	B16g
Malleable-iron Screwed Fittings, 150 Lb.	B16c
Steel Butt-welded Fittings	B16.9
Brass Fittings for Flared Copper Tubes	A40.2
Soldered-joint Fittings	A40.3
Air Gaps and Back Flow Preventers in Plumbing Systems, 1942	A40.4
Air Gaps and Back Flow Preventers in Plumbing Systems, 1943	A40.6
Threaded Cast-iron Pipe for Drainage, Vent, and Waste Services	A40.5
Wrought-iron and Wrought-steel Pipe	B36.10
Ferrous Plugs, Bushings, Locknuts, and Caps	B16.14
Pipe Threads	B2.1
Scheme for Identification of Piping Systems	A13

Small Tools and Machine-tool Elements

Adjustable Adapters	B5.11
Chucks and Chuck Jaws	B5.8
Circular and Dovetailed Forming Tool Blanks and Holding Elements	B5.7
Involute Splines, Side Bearings	B5.15
Jig Bushings	B5.6
Spindle Noses and Arbors	B5.18
Rotating Air Cylinders and Adapters	B5.5
T Slots, Their Bolts, Nuts, and Cutters	B5.1
Tool Life Tests	B5.19
Twist Drills	B5.12

Tool Shanks and Tool Posts	B5.2
Code for Design of Transmission Shafting	B17c
Shafting and Stock Keys	B17.1
Screw Threads for Bolts, Nuts, Machine Screws, and Threaded Parts	B1.1
Screw Threads for High-strength Bolting	B1.4
Screw Thread Gages and Gaging	B1.2
Acme and Other Translating Threads	B1.3
Tolerances, Allowances, and Gages for Metal Fits	B4a
Woodruff Keys, Keyslots, and Cutters	B17f
Machine Tapers	B5.10
Milling Cutters	B5c
Reamers	B5.14
Taps—Cut and Ground Threads	B5.4
Markings for Grinding Wheels	B5.17
Terminology and Definitions for Single-point Cutting Tools	B5.13

Symbols and Abbreviations

Drawings and Drafting Room Practice	Z14.1
Abbreviations for Scientific and Engineering Terms	Z10.1
Graphical Symbols for Use on Drawings in Mechanical Engineering	Z32.2
Engineering and Scientific Graphs for Publications	Z15.3
Time Series Charts	Z15.2
Engineering and Scientific Charts for Lantern Slides	Z15.1
Letter Symbols for Heat and Thermodynamics, Including Heat Flow	Z10.4
Letter Symbols for Gear Engineering	B6.5
Letter Symbols for Hydraulics	Z10.2
Letter Symbols for Mechanics of Solid Bodies	Z10.3
Illuminating Engineering Nomenclature and Photometric Standards (IES Publication)	Z7.1

Miscellaneous

Fire-hose Coupling Screw Thread	B26
Hose Coupling Screw Threads	B33.1
Indicating Pressure and Vacuum Gages	B40.1
Preferred Thicknesses for Uncoated Thin Flat Metals (under 0.250 in.)	B32.1
Rolled Threads for Screw Shells of Electric Sockets and Lamp Bases	C44
Shaft Couplings	B49
Spur Gear Tooth Form	B6.1
Inspection and Tolerances for Gears	B6
Spring Lock Washers	B27.1

APPENDIX

APPENDIX INDEX

Length of Chord for Circle Arcs of One Inch Radius

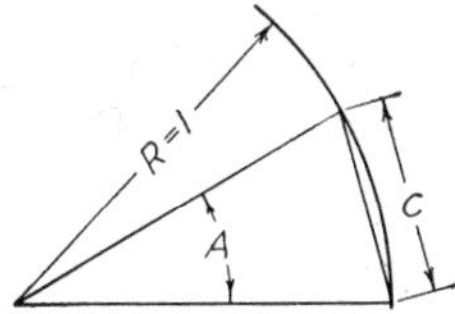

	Minutes					
Deg	0′	10′	20′	30′	40′	50′
0	0.0000	0.0029	0.0058	0.0087	0.0116	0.0145
1	0.0175	0.0204	0.0233	0.0262	0.0291	0.0320
2	0.0349	0.0378	0.0407	0.0436	0.0465	0.0494
3	0.0524	0.0553	0.0582	0.0611	0.0640	0.0669
4	0.0698	0.0727	0.0756	0.0785	0.0814	0.0843
5	0.0872	0.0901	0.0931	0.0960	0.0989	0.1018
6	0.1047	0.1076	0.1105	0.1134	0.1163	0.1192
7	0.1221	0.1250	0.1279	0.1308	0.1337	0.1366
8	0.1395	0.1424	0.1453	0.1482	0.1511	0.1540
9	0.1569	0.1598	0.1627	0.1656	0.1685	0.1714
10	0.1743	0.1772	0.1801	0.1830	0.1859	0.1888
11	0.1917	0.1946	0.1975	0.2004	0.2033	0.2062
12	0.2091	0.2119	0.2148	0.2177	0.2206	0.2235
13	0.2264	0.2293	0.2322	0.2351	0.2380	0.2409
14	0.2437	0.2466	0.2495	0.2524	0.2553	0.2582
15	0.2611	0.2639	0.2668	0.2697	0.2726	0.2755
16	0.2783	0.2812	0.2841	0.2870	0.2899	0.2927
17	0.2956	0.2985	0.3014	0.3042	0.3071	0.3100
18	0.3129	0.3157	0.3186	0.3215	0.3244	0.3272
19	0.3301	0.3330	0.3358	0.3387	0.3416	0.3444
20	0.3473	0.3502	0.3530	0.3559	0.3587	0.3616
21	0.3645	0.3673	0.3702	0.3730	0.3759	0.3788
22	0.3816	0.3845	0.3873	0.3902	0.3930	0.3959
23	0.3987	0.4016	0.4044	0.4073	0.4101	0.4130
24	0.4158	0.4187	0.4215	0.4244	0.4272	0.4300
25	0.4329	0.4357	0.4386	0.4414	0.4442	0.4471
26	0.4499	0.4527	0.4556	0.4584	0.4612	0.4641
27	0.4669	0.4697	0.4725	0.4754	0.4782	0.4810
28	0.4838	0.4867	0.4895	0.4923	0.4951	0.4979
29	0.5008	0.5036	0.5064	0.5092	0.5120	0.5148
30	0.5176	0.5204	0.5233	0.5261	0.5289	0.5317
31	0.5345	0.5373	0.5401	0.5429	0.5457	0.5485
32	0.5513	0.5541	0.5569	0.5597	0.5625	0.5652
33	0.5680	0.5708	0.5736	0.5764	0.5792	0.5820
34	0.5847	0.5875	0.5903	0.5931	0.5959	0.5986
35	0.6014	0.6042	0.6070	0.6097	0.6125	0.6153
36	0.6180	0.6208	0.6236	0.6263	0.6291	0.6319
37	0.6346	0.6374	0.6401	0.6429	0.6456	0.6484
38	0.6511	0.6539	0.6566	0.6594	0.6621	0.6649
39	0.6676	0.6704	0.6731	0.6758	0.6786	0.6813
40	0.6840	0.6868	0.6895	0.6922	0.6950	0.6977
41	0.7004	0.7031	0.7059	0.7086	0.7113	0.7140
42	0.7167	0.7195	0.7222	0.7249	0.7276	0.7303
43	0.7330	0.7357	0.7384	0.7411	0.7438	0.7465
44	0.7492	0.7519	0.7546	0.7573	0.7600	0.7627
45	0.7654	0.7681	0.7707	0.7734	0.7761	0.7788

For angles between 45° and 90°, draw 90° angle and lay off complement from 90° line.

Decimal Equivalents of Fractions of an Inch and of a Foot

Fractions of inch or foot	Decimal equivalents	Inch equivalents of foot fractions	Fractions of inch or foot	Decimal equivalents	Inch equivalents of foot fractions	Fractions of inch or foot	Decimal equivalents	Inch equivalents of foot fractions	Fractions of inch or foot	Decimal equivalents	Inch equivalents of foot fractions
	.0052	1/16		.2552	3 1/16		.5052	6 1/16		.7552	9 1/16
	.0104	1/8		.2604	3 1/8		.5104	6 1/8		.7604	9 1/8
1/64	.015625	3/16	17/64	.265625	3 3/16	33/64	.515625	6 3/16	49/64	.765625	9 3/16
	.0208	1/4		.2708	3 1/4		.5208	6 1/4		.7708	9 1/4
	.0260	5/16		.2760	3 5/16		.5260	6 5/16		.7760	9 5/16
1/32	.03125	3/8	9/32	.28125	3 3/8	17/32	.53125	6 3/8	25/32	.78125	9 3/8
	.0365	7/16		.2865	3 7/16		.5365	6 7/16		.7865	9 7/16
	.0417	1/2		.2917	3 1/2		.5417	6 1/2		.7917	9 1/2
3/64	.046875	9/16	19/64	.296875	3 9/16	35/64	.546875	6 9/16	51/64	.796875	9 9/16
	.0521	5/8		.3021	3 5/8		.5521	6 5/8		.8021	9 5/8
	.0573	11/16		.3073	3 11/16		.5573	6 11/16		.8073	9 11/16
1/16	.0625	3/4	5/16	.3125	3 3/4	9/16	.5625	6 3/4	13/16	.8125	9 3/4
	.0677	13/16		.3177	3 13/16		.5677	6 13/16		.8177	9 13/16
	.0729	7/8		.3229	3 7/8		.5729	6 7/8		.8229	9 7/8
5/64	.078125	15/16	21/64	.328125	3 15/16	37/64	.578125	6 15/16	53/64	.828125	9 15/16
	.0833	1		.3333	4		.5833	7		.8333	10
	.0885	1 1/16		.3385	4 1/16		.5885	7 1/16		.8385	10 1/16
3/32	.09375	1 1/8	11/32	.34375	4 1/8	19/32	.59375	7 1/8	27/32	.84375	10 1/8
	.0990	1 3/16		.3490	4 3/16		.5990	7 3/16		.8490	10 3/16
	.1042	1 1/4		.3542	4 1/4		.6042	7 1/4		.8542	10 1/4
7/64	.109375	1 5/16	23/64	.359375	4 5/16	39/64	.609375	7 5/16	55/64	.859375	10 5/16
	.1146	1 3/8		.3646	4 3/8		.6146	7 3/8		.8646	10 3/8
	.1198	1 7/16		.3698	4 7/16		.6198	7 7/16		.8698	10 7/16
1/8	.1250	1 1/2	3/8	.3750	4 1/2	5/8	.6250	7 1/2	7/8	.8750	10 1/2
	.1302	1 9/16		.3802	4 9/16		.6302	7 9/16		.8802	10 9/16
	.1354	1 5/8		.3854	4 5/8		.6354	7 5/8		.8854	10 5/8
9/64	.140625	1 11/16	25/64	.390625	4 11/16	41/64	.640625	7 11/16	57/64	.890625	10 11/16
	.1458	1 3/4		.3958	4 3/4		.6458	7 3/4		.8958	10 3/4
	.1510	1 13/16		.4010	4 13/16		.6510	7 13/16		.9010	10 13/16
5/32	.15625	1 7/8	13/32	.40625	4 7/8	21/32	.65625	7 7/8	29/32	.90625	10 7/8
	.1615	1 15/16		.4115	4 15/16		.6615	7 15/16		.9115	10 15/16
	.1667	2		.4167	5		.6667	8		.9167	11
11/64	.171875	2 1/16	27/64	.421875	5 1/16	43/64	.671875	8 1/16	59/64	.921875	11 1/16
	.1771	2 1/8		.4271	5 1/8		.6771	8 1/8		.9271	11 1/8
	.1823	2 3/16		.4323	5 3/16		.6823	8 3/16		.9323	11 3/16
3/16	.1875	2 1/4	7/16	.4375	5 1/4	11/16	.6875	8 1/4	15/16	.9375	11 1/4
	.1927	2 5/16		.4427	5 5/16		.6927	8 5/16		.9427	11 5/16
	.1979	2 3/8		.4479	5 3/8		.6979	8 3/8		.9479	11 3/8
13/64	.203125	2 7/16	29/64	.453125	5 7/16	45/64	.703125	8 7/16	61/64	.953125	11 7/16
	.2083	2 1/2		.4583	5 1/2		.7083	8 1/2		.9583	11 1/2
	.2135	2 9/16		.4635	5 9/16		.7135	8 9/16		.9635	11 9/16
7/32	.21875	2 5/8	15/32	.46875	5 5/8	23/32	.71875	8 5/8	31/32	.96875	11 5/8
	.2240	2 11/16		.4740	5 11/16		.7240	8 11/16		.9740	11 11/16
	.2292	2 3/4		.4792	5 3/4		.7292	8 3/4		.9792	11 3/4
15/64	.234375	2 13/16	31/64	.484375	5 13/16	47/64	.734375	8 13/16	63/64	.984375	11 13/16
	.2396	2 7/8		.4896	5 7/8		.7396	8 7/8		.9896	11 7/8
	.2448	2 15/16		.4948	5 15/16		.7448	8 15/16		.9948	11 15/16
1/4	.2500	3	1/2	.5000	6	3/4	.7500	9	1	1.0000	12

Metric Equivalents

In converting inches to millimeters, carry the millimeter equivalent to one *less* decimal place than the number to which the inch value is given.

In converting from millimeters to inches, carry the inch equivalent to two *more* places than the number to which the millimeter value is given.

Millimeters to inches				Inches to millimeters			
Mm	In.	Mm	In.	In.	Mm	In.	Mm
1 =	0.0394	17 =	0.6693	1/32 =	0.79	17/32 =	13.49
2 =	0.0787	18 =	0.7087	1/16 =	1.58	9/16 =	14.28
3 =	0.1181	19 =	0.7480	3/32 =	2.38	19/32 =	15.08
4 =	0.1575	20 =	0.7874	1/8 =	3.17	5/8 =	15.87
5 =	0.1968	21 =	0.8268	5/32 =	3.96	21/32 =	16.66
6 =	0.2362	22 =	0.8661	3/16 =	4.76	11/16 =	17.46
7 =	0.2756	23 =	0.9055	7/32 =	5.55	23/32 =	18.25
8 =	0.3150	24 =	0.9449	1/4 =	6.34	3/4 =	19.04
9 =	0.3543	25 =	0.9843	9/32 =	7.14	25/32 =	19.84
10 =	0.3937	26 =	1.0236	5/16 =	7.93	13/16 =	20.63
11 =	0.4331	27 =	1.0630	11/32 =	8.73	27/32 =	21.43
12 =	0.4724	28 =	1.1024	3/8 =	9.52	7/8 =	22.22
13 =	0.5118	29 =	1.1417	13/32 =	10.31	29/32 =	23.01
14 =	0.5512	30 =	1.1811	7/16 =	11.11	15/16 =	23.81
15 =	0.5906	31 =	1.2205	15/32 =	11.90	31/32 =	24.60
16 =	0.6299	32 =	1.2598	1/2 =	12.69	1 =	25.39

Acme and Square Threads[1]

Nominal size (major diam)	Threads[2] per in.	Basic pitch diam	ID for nut	Nominal size (major diam)	Threads[2] per in.	Basic pitch diam	ID for nut
1/4	16	0.2187	0.1875	1 1/4	5	1.1500	1.0500
5/16	14	0.2768	0.2411	1 3/8	4	1.2500	1.1250
3/8	12	0.3333	0.2917	1 1/2	4	1.3750	1.2500
7/16	12	0.3958	0.3542	1 3/4	4	1.6250	1.5000
1/2	10	0.4500	0.4000	2	4	1.8750	1.7500
5/8	8	0.5625	0.5000	2 1/4	3	2.0833	1.9167
3/4	6	0.6667	0.5833	2 1/2	3	2.3333	2.1667
7/8	6	0.7917	0.7083	2 3/4	3	2.5833	2.4167
1	5	0.9000	0.8000	3	2	2.7500	2.5000
1 1/8	5	1.0250	0.9250	4	2	3.7500	3.5000
				5	2	4.7500	4.5000

All dimensions in inches.

[1] ASA B1.3 1941.

[2] The selection of threads per inch is arbitrary and is intended for the purpose of establishing a standard.

American Standard Screw Threads[1]—National Coarse (NC) and National Fine (NF) Series

TAP-DRILL SIZES FOR APPROXIMATELY 75 PER CENT DEPTH OF THREAD

Nominal size (major diam)	Basic pitch diam	NC series thds per in.	Tap drill	Decimal equiv of tap drill	Basic pitch diam	NF series thds per in.	Tap drill	Decimal equiv of tap drill
0 (0.0600)	......	....	....	......	0.0519	80	3/64	0.0469
1 (0.0730)	0.0629	64	No. 53	0.0595	0.0640	72	No. 53	0.0595
2 (0.0860)	0.0744	56	No. 50	0.0700	0.0759	64	No. 50	0.0700
3 (0.0990)	0.0855	48	No. 47	0.0785	0.0874	56	No. 45	0.0820
4 (0.1120)	0.0958	40	No. 43	0.0890	0.0985	48	No. 42	0.0935
5 (0.1250)	0.1088	40	No. 38	0.1015	0.1102	44	No. 37	0.1040
6 (0.1380)	0.1177	32	No. 36	0.1065	0.1218	40	No. 33	0.1130
8 (0.1640)	0.1437	32	No. 29	0.1360	0.1460	36	No. 29	0.1360
10 (0.1900)	0.1629	24	No. 25	0.1495	0.1697	32	No. 21	0.1590
12 (0.2160)	0.1889	24	No. 16	0.1770	0.1928	28	No. 14	0.1820
1/4	0.2175	20	No. 7	0.2010	0.2268	28	No. 3	0.2130
5/16	0.2764	18	*F*	0.2570	0.2854	24	*I*	0.2720
3/8	0.3344	16	5/16	0.3125	0.3479	24	*Q*	0.3320
7/16	0.3911	14	*U*	0.3680	0.4050	20	25/64	0.3906
1/2	0.4500	13	27/64	0.4219	0.4675	20	29/64	0.4531
9/16	0.5084	12	31/64	0.4844	0.5264	18	33/64	0.5156
5/8	0.5660	11	17/32	0.5312	0.5889	18	37/64	0.5781
3/4	0.6850	10	21/32	0.6562	0.7094	16	11/16	0.6875
7/8	0.8028	9	49/64	0.7656	0.8286	14	13/16	0.8125
1	0.9188	8	7/8	0.8750	0.9536	14	15/16	0.9375
1 1/8	1.0322	7	63/64	0.9844	1.0709	12	1 3/64	1.0469
1 1/4	1.1572	7	1 7/64	1.1094	1.1959	12	1 11/64	1.1719
1 3/8	1.2667	6	1 7/32	1.2187	1.3209	12	1 19/64	1.2969
1 1/2	1.3917	6	1 11/32	1.3437	1.4459	12	1 27/64	1.4219
1 3/4	1.6201	5	1 9/16	1.5625				
2	1.8557	4 1/2	1 25/32	1.7812				
2 1/4	2.1057	4 1/2	2 1/32	2.0312				
2 1/2	2.3376	4	2 1/4	2.2500				
2 3/4	2.5876	4	2 1/2	2.5000				
3	2.8376	4	2 3/4	2.7500				
3 1/4	3.0876	4	3	3.0000				
3 1/2	3.3376	4	3 1/4	3.2500				
3 3/4	3.5876	4	3 1/2	3.5000				
4	3.8376	4	3 3/4	3.7500				

[1] ASA B1.1 1935.

SAE Extra-fine Series[1]

Nominal size (major diam)	Threads per in.	Basic pitch diam	ID for nut	Nominal size (major diam)	Threads per in.	Basic pitch diam	ID for nut
12	32	0.1957	0.1822	1	20	0.9675	0.9459
1/4	32	0.2297	0.2162	1 1/8	18	1.0889	1.0649
5/16	32	0.2922	0.2787	1 1/4	18	1.2139	1.1899
3/8	32	0.3547	0.3412	1 3/8	18	1.3389	1.3149
7/16	28	0.4143	0.3988	1 1/2	18	1.4639	1.4399
1/2	28	0.4768	0.4613	1 3/4	16	1.7094	1.6823
9/16	24	0.5354	0.5174	2	16	1.9594	1.9323
5/8	24	0.5979	0.5799	2 1/4	16	2.2094	2.1823
3/4	20	0.7175	0.6959	2 1/2	16	2.4594	2.4323
7/8	20	0.8425	0.8209	2 3/4	16	2.7094	2.6823
				3	16	2.9594	2.9323

[1] Class 3 fit.

American Standard Screw Threads[1]—8-pitch, 12-pitch, and 16-pitch Thread Series

Nominal size (major diam)	8-pitch series		12-pitch series		16-pitch series	
	Basic pitch diam	ID for nut[2]	Basic pitch diam	ID for nut[2]	Basic pitch diam	ID for nut[3]
1/2	......	......	0.4459	0.4098		
9/16	......	......	0.5048	0.4723		
5/8	......	......	0.5709	0.5348		
11/16	......	......	0.6334	0.5973		
3/4	......	......	0.6959	0.6598	0.7094	0.6823
13/16	......	......	0.7584	0.7223	0.7719	0.7448
7/8	......	......	0.8209	0.7848	0.8344	0.8073
15/16	......	......	0.8834	0.8473	0.8969	0.8698
1	0.9188	0.8647	0.9459	0.9098	0.9594	0.9323
1 1/16	......	......	1.0084	0.9723	1.0219	0.9948
1 1/8	1.0438	0.9897	1.0709	1.0348	1.0844	1.0573
1 3/16	......	......	1.1334	1.0973	1.1469	1.1198
1 1/4	1.1688	1.1147	1.1959	1.1598	1.2094	1.1823
1 5/16	......	......	1.2584	1.2223	1.2719	1.2448
1 3/8	1.2938	1.2397	1.3209	1.2848	1.3344	1.3073
1 7/16	......	......	1.3834	1.3473	1.3969	1.3698
1 1/2	1.4188	1.3647	1.4459	1.4098	1.4594	1.4323
1 9/16	......	......	......	......	1.5219	1.4948
1 5/8	1.5438	1.4897	1.5709	1.5348	1.5844	1.5573
1 11/16	......	......	......	......	1.6469	1.6198
1 3/4	1.6688	1.6147	1.6959	1.6598	1.7094	1.6823
1 13/16	......	......	......	......	1.7719	1.7448
1 7/8	1.7938	1.7397	1.8209	1.7848	1.8344	1.8073
1 15/16	......	......	......	......	1.8969	1.8698
2	1.9188	1.8647	1.9459	1.9098	1.9594	1.9323
2 1/16	......	......	......	......	2.0219	1.9948
2 1/8	2.0438	1.9897	2.0709	2.0348	2.0844	2.0573
2 3/16	......	......	......	......	2.1469	2.1198
2 1/4	2.1688	2.1147	2.1959	2.1598	2.2094	2.1823
2 5/16	......	......	......	......	2.2719	2.2448
2 3/8	......	......	2.3209	2.2848	2.3344	2.3073
2 7/16	......	......	......	......	2.3969	2.3698
2 1/2	2.4188	2.3647	2.4459	2.4098	2.4594	2.4323
2 5/8	......	......	2.5709	2.5348	2.5844	2.5573
2 3/4	2.6688	2.6147	2.6959	2.6598	2.7094	2.6823
2 7/8	......	......	2.8209	2.7848	2.8344	2.8073
3	2.9188	2.8647	2.9459	2.9098	2.9594	2.9323
3 1/8	......	......	3.0709	3.0348	3.0844	3.0573
3 1/4	3.1688	3.1147	3.1959	3.1598	3.2094	3.1823
3 3/8	......	......	3.3209	3.2848	3.3344	3.3073
3 1/2	3.4188	3.3647	3.4459	3.4098	3.4594	3.4323
3 5/8	......	......	3.5709	3.5348	3.5844	3.5573
3 3/4	3.6688	3.6147	3.6959	3.6598	3.7094	3.6823
3 7/8	......	......	3.8209	3.7848	3.8344	3.8073
4	3.9188	3.8647	3.9459	3.9098	3.9594	3.9323
4 1/4	4.1688	4.1147	4.1959	4.1598		
4 1/2	4.4188	4.3647	4.4459	4.4098		
4 3/4	4.6688	4.6147	4.6959	4.6598		
5	4.9188	4.8647	4.9459	4.9098		
5 1/4	5.1688	5.1147	5.1959	5.1598		
5 1/2	5.4188	5.3647	5.4459	5.4098		
5 3/4	5.6688	5.6147	5.6959	5.6598		
6	5.9188	5.8647	5.9459	5.9098		

[1] ASA B1.1 1935.
[2] Class 2 fit } (Recommended for general use).
[3] Class 3 fit }

American Standard Wrench-head Bolts[1]—Regular and Heavy Series

UNFINISHED, SQUARE AND HEXAGON; SEMIFINISHED, HEXAGON ONLY

Diameter	Width			Height (H)	
	Across flats (W) sq and hex	Across corners[2]		Unfin	Semifin
		Sq	Hex		
Regular series					
1/4	3/8	1/2	13/32	11/64	5/32
5/16	1/2	43/64	35/64	13/64	3/16
3/8	9/16	3/4	5/8	1/4	15/64
7/16	5/8	53/64	11/16	19/64	9/32
1/2	3/4	1	53/64	21/64	19/64
9/16	7/8	1 5/32	31/32	3/8	11/32
5/8	15/16	1 1/4	1 1/32	27/64	25/64
3/4	1 1/8	1 1/2	1 15/64	1/2	15/32
7/8	1 5/16	1 47/64	1 29/64	19/32	9/16
1	1 1/2	1 63/64	1 21/32	21/32	19/32
1 1/8	1 11/16	2 15/64	1 55/64	3/4	11/16
1 1/4	1 7/8	2 31/64	2 1/16	27/32	25/32
1 3/8	2 1/16	2 47/64	2 17/64	29/32	27/32
1 1/2	2 1/4	2 63/64	2 31/64	1	15/16
1 5/8	2 7/16	3 15/64	2 11/16	1 3/32	1 1/32
1 3/4	2 5/8	3 31/64	2 57/64	1 5/32	1 3/32
1 7/8	2 13/16	3 47/64	3 3/32	1 1/4	1 3/16
2	3	3 63/64	3 5/16	1 11/32	1 7/32
2 1/4	3 3/8	4 31/64	3 23/32	1 1/2	1 3/8
2 1/2	3 3/4	4 63/64	4 9/64	1 21/32	1 17/32
2 3/4	4 1/8	5 15/32	4 35/64	1 13/16	1 11/16
3	4 1/2	5 31/32	4 61/64	2	1 7/8
Heavy series					
1/4, 5/16, 3/8, 7/16	These sizes not available except on special order				
1/2	7/8	1 11/64	31/32	7/16	13/32
9/16	15/16	1 1/4	1 1/32	15/32	7/16
5/8	1 1/16	1 27/64	1 11/64	17/32	1/2
3/4	1 1/4	1 43/64	1 3/8	5/8	19/32
7/8	1 7/16	1 59/64	1 19/32	23/32	11/16
1	1 5/8	2 5/32	1 51/64	13/16	3/4
1 1/8	1 13/16	2 13/32	2	29/32	27/32
1 1/4	2	2 21/32	2 13/64	1	15/16
1 3/8	2 3/16	2 29/32	2 27/64	1 3/32	1 1/32
1 1/2	2 3/8	3 5/32	2 5/8	1 3/16	1 1/8
1 5/8	2 9/16	3 13/32	2 53/64	1 9/32	1 7/32
1 3/4	2 3/4	3 21/32	3 1/32	1 3/8	1 5/16
1 7/8	2 15/16	3 29/32	3 15/64	1 15/32	1 13/32
2	3 1/8	4 5/32	3 29/64	1 9/16	1 7/16
2 1/4	3 1/2	4 21/32	3 55/64	1 3/4	1 5/8
2 1/2	3 7/8	5 5/32	4 9/32	1 15/16	1 13/16
2 3/4	4 1/4	5 41/64	4 11/16	2 1/8	2
3	4 5/8	6 9/64	5 7/64	2 5/16	2 3/16

All dimensions in inches.

[1] ASA B18.2 1941.

[2] Provides minimum clearance on corner distance.

American Standard Nuts[1]—Regular and Heavy Series

UNFINISHED, SQUARE AND HEXAGON; SEMIFINISHED, HEXAGON ONLY

Diameter	Width: Across flats W sq and hex	Width: Across corners[2] Sq	Width: Across corners[2] Hex	Thickness T: Unfin	Thickness T: Semifin	Thickness, jam nut: Unfin	Thickness, jam nut: Semifin
Regular series							
1/4	7/16	37/64	31/64	7/32	13/64	5/32	9/64
5/16	9/16	3/4	5/8	17/64	1/4	3/16	11/64
3/8	5/8	53/64	11/16	21/64	5/16	7/32	13/64
7/16	3/4	1	53/64	3/8	23/64	1/4	15/64
1/2	13/16	1 5/64	57/64	7/16	27/64	5/16	19/64
9/16	7/8	1 5/32	31/32	1/2	31/64	11/32	21/64
5/8	1	1 21/64	1 7/64	35/64	17/32	3/8	23/64
3/4	1 1/8	1 1/2	1 1/4	21/32	41/64	7/16	27/64
7/8	1 5/16	1 47/64	1 29/64	49/64	3/4	1/2	31/64
1	1 1/2	1 63/64	1 21/32	7/8	55/64	9/16	35/64
1 1/8	1 11/16	2 15/64	1 55/64	1	31/32	5/8	39/64
1 1/4	1 7/8	2 31/64	2 1/16	1 3/32	1 1/16	3/4	23/32
1 3/8	2 1/16	2 47/64	2 17/64	1 13/64	1 11/64	13/16	25/32
1 1/2	2 1/4	2 63/64	2 31/64	1 5/16	1 9/32	7/8	27/32
1 5/8	2 7/16	3 15/64	2 11/16	1 27/64	1 25/64	15/16	29/32
1 3/4	2 5/8	3 31/64	2 57/64	1 17/32	1 1/2	1	31/32
1 7/8	2 13/16	3 47/64	3 3/32	1 41/64	1 39/64	1 1/16	1 1/32
2	3	3 63/64	3 5/16	1 3/4	1 23/32	1 1/8	1 3/32
2 1/4	3 3/8	4 41/64	3 23/32	1 31/32	1 59/64	1 1/4	1 13/64
2 1/2	3 3/4	4 63/64	4 9/64	2 3/16	2 9/64	1 1/2	1 29/64
2 3/4	4 1/8	.....	.....	2 13/32	2 23/64	1 5/8	1 37/64
3	4 1/2	.....	.....	2 5/8	2 37/64	1 3/4	1 45/64
Heavy series							
1/4	1/2	43/64	9/16	1/4	15/64	3/16	11/64
5/16	19/32	51/64	21/32	5/16	19/64	7/32	13/64
3/8	11/16	59/64	49/64	3/8	23/64	1/4	15/64
7/16	25/32	1 3/64	55/64	7/16	27/64	9/32	17/64
1/2	7/8	1 11/64	31/32	1/2	31/64	5/16	19/64
9/16	15/16	1 1/4	1 1/32	9/16	35/64	11/32	21/64
5/8	1 1/16	1 27/64	1 11/64	5/8	39/64	3/8	23/64
3/4	1 1/4	1 43/64	1 3/8	3/4	47/64	7/16	27/64
7/8	1 7/16	1 59/64	1 19/32	7/8	55/64	1/2	31/64
1	1 5/8	2 5/32	1 51/64	1	63/64	9/16	35/64
1 1/8	1 13/16	2 13/32	2	1 1/8	1 7/64	5/8	39/64
1 1/4	2	2 21/32	2 13/64	1 1/4	1 7/32	3/4	23/32
1 3/8	2 3/16	2 29/32	2 27/64	1 3/8	1 11/32	13/16	25/32
1 1/2	2 3/8	3 5/32	2 5/8	1 1/2	1 15/32	7/8	27/32
1 5/8	2 9/16	3 13/32	2 53/64	1 5/8	1 19/32	15/16	29/32
1 3/4	2 3/4	3 21/32	3 1/32	1 3/4	1 23/32	1	31/32
1 7/8	2 15/16	3 29/32	3 15/64	1 7/8	1 27/32	1 1/16	1 1/32
2	3 1/8	4 5/32	3 29/64	2	1 31/32	1 1/8	1 3/32
2 1/4	3 1/2	4 21/32	3 55/64	2 1/4	2 13/64	1 1/4	1 13/64
2 1/2	3 7/8	5 5/32	4 9/32	2 1/2	2 29/64	1 1/2	1 29/64
2 3/4	4 1/4	5 41/64	4 11/16	2 3/4	2 45/64	1 5/8	1 37/64
3	4 5/8	9/64	5 7/64	3	2 61/64	1 3/4	1 45/64

All dimensions in inches.

[1] ASA B18.2 1941.

[2] Provides minimum clearance on corner distance.

American Standard Nuts[1]—Light Series, Semifinished, Hexagon Only

Thread diameter	Width: All light series nuts, Across flats W	Width: All light series nuts, Across corners	Thickness: Castle nuts, T	Thickness: Castle nuts, Height[2] of flats	Thickness: Jam nuts, T	Thickness: Light and light slotted nuts, T	Thickness: Light thick and light thick slotted nuts, T	Slots: All slotted nuts, Width	Slots: All slotted nuts, Depth
1/4	7/16	31/64	9/32	3/16	5/32	7/32	9/32	5/64	3/32
5/16	1/2	9/16	21/64	15/64	3/16	17/16	21/64	3/32	3/32
3/8	9/16	5/8	13/32	9/32	7/32	21/64	13/32	1/8	1/8
7/16	5/8	45/64	29/64	19/64	1/4	3/8	29/64	1/8	5/32
1/2	3/4	27/32	9/16	13/32	5/16	7/16	9/16	5/32	5/32
9/16	7/8	63/64	39/64	27/64	5/16	31/64	39/64	5/32	3/16
5/8	15/16	1 3/64	23/32	1/2	3/8	35/64	23/32	3/16	7/32
3/4	1 1/16	1 3/16	13/16	9/16	3/8	21/32	13/16	3/16	1/4
7/8	1 1/4	1 13/32	29/32	21/32	7/16	49/64	29/32	3/16	1/4
1	1 7/16	1 39/64	1	23/32	1/2	7/8	1	1/4	9/32
1 1/8	1 5/8	1 53/64	1 5/32	13/16	9/16	63/64	1 5/32	1/4	11/32
1 1/4	1 13/16	2 1/32	1 1/4	7/8	5/8	1 3/32	1 1/4	5/16	3/8
1 3/8	2	2 1/4	1 3/8	1	3/4	1 13/64	1 3/8	5/16	3/8
1 1/2	2 3/16	2 15/32	1 1/2	1 1/16	13/16	1 5/16	1 1/2	3/8	7/16

All dimensions in inches.
[1] ASA B18.2 1941.
[2] Height of the hexagon is measured from the bearing surface to the top of arc.

American Standard Nuts[1]—Slotted, Regular and Heavy Series

HEXAGONAL, SEMIFINISHED ONLY

Diameter	Regular series: Across flats W	Regular series: Thickness T	Regular series: Slot Width	Regular series: Slot Depth	Heavy series: Across flats W	Heavy series: Thickness T	Heavy series: Slot Width	Heavy series: Slot Depth
1/4	7/16	13/64	5/64	3/32	1/2	15/64	5/64	3/32
5/16	9/16	1/4	3/32	3/32	19/32	19/64	3/32	3/32
3/8	5/8	5/16	1/8	1/8	11/16	23/64	1/8	1/8
7/16	3/4	23/64	1/8	5/32	25/32	27/64	1/8	5/32
1/2	13/16	27/64	5/32	5/32	7/8	31/64	5/32	5/32
9/16	7/8	31/64	5/32	3/16	15/16	35/64	5/32	3/16
5/8	1	17/32	3/16	7/32	1 1/16	39/64	3/16	7/32
3/4	1 1/8	41/64	3/16	1/4	1 1/4	47/64	3/16	1/4
7/8	1 5/16	3/4	3/16	1/4	1 7/16	55/64	3/16	1/4
1	1 1/2	55/64	1/4	9/32	1 5/8	63/64	1/4	9/32
1 1/8	1 11/16	31/32	1/4	11/32	1 13/16	1 7/64	1/4	11/32
1 1/4	1 7/8	1 1/16	5/16	3/8	2	1 7/32	5/16	3/8
1 3/8	2 1/16	1 11/64	5/16	3/8	2 3/16	1 11/32	5/16	3/8
1 1/2	2 1/4	1 9/32	3/8	7/16	2 3/8	1 15/32	3/8	7/16
1 5/8	2 7/16	1 25/64	3/8	7/16	2 9/16	1 19/32	3/8	7/16
1 3/4	2 5/8	1 1/2	7/16	1/2	2 3/4	1 23/32	7/16	1/2
1 7/8	2 13/16	1 39/64	7/16	9/16	2 15/16	1 27/32	7/16	9/16
2	3	1 23/32	7/16	9/16	3 1/8	1 31/32	7/16	9/16
2 1/4	3 3/8	1 59/64	7/16	9/16	3 1/2	2 13/64	7/16	9/16
2 1/2	3 3/4	2 9/64	9/16	11/16	3 7/8	2 29/64	9/16	11/16
2 3/4	4 1/8	2 23/64	9/16	11/16	4 1/4	2 45/64	9/16	11/16
3	4 1/2	2 37/64	5/8	3/4	4 5/8	2 61/64	5/8	3/4

All dimensions in inches.
[1] ASA B18.2 1941.

American Standard Bolts

BOLT-LENGTH INCREMENTS[1]

Bolt diameter		1/4	5/16	3/8	7/16	1/2	5/8	3/4	7/8	1
Length increments	1/4	3/4–3	3/4–4	3/4–6	1–3	1–6	1–6	1–6	1–4 1/2	
	1/2	3–4	4–5	6–9	3–6	6–13	6–10	6–15	4 1/2–6	3–6
	1	4–5	. . .	9–12	6–8	13–24	10–22	15–24	6–20	6–12
	2	. . .	. . .	. . . .	. . .	. . . . .	22–30	24–30	20–30	12–30

Example: 1/4″ bolt lengths increase by 1/4″ increments from 3/4″ to 3″ length. 1/2″ bolt lengths increase by 1/2″ increments from 6″ to 13″ length. 1″ bolt lengths increase by 2″ increments from 12″ to 30″ length.

Compiled from manufacturers' catalogues.

Recommended Minimum Thread Lengths[1]

Bolt length[2]	No. 10, 1/4	5/16, 3/8	7/16, 1/2	9/16, 5/8	3/4	7/8	1	1 1/8, 1 1/4	1 3/8, 1 1/2	1 5/8, 1 3/4	1 7/8, 2	2 1/4	2 1/2	2 3/4	3
	Minimum thread length														
3/4	1/2	1/2													
1	3/4	3/4	3/4	3/4											
1 1/4	3/4	3/4	1	1	1										
1 1/2	3/4	7/8	1	1 1/8	1 1/8	1 1/8									
1 3/4	3/4	7/8	1	1 3/16	1 3/8	1 3/8	1 3/8								
2	3/4	1	1 1/4	1 1/4	1 3/8	1 9/16	1 5/8	1 5/8							
2 1/2	3/4	1	1 1/4	1 1/2	1 1/2	1 9/16	1 3/4	2	2						
3	7/8	1	1 1/4	1 1/2	1 3/4	1 3/4	1 3/4	2 1/8	2 1/2	2 1/2					
4	7/8	1	1 1/4	1 1/2	1 3/4	2	2 1/4	2 1/4	2 1/2	2 7/8	3 1/4	3 1/4	3 1/4		
5	7/8	1 3/16	1 1/4	1 1/2	1 3/4	2	2 1/4	2 3/4	2 3/4	2 7/8	3 1/4	3 5/8	4	4 1/8	4 1/4
6	7/8	1 3/16	1 1/2	1 1/2	1 3/4	2	2 1/4	2 3/4	3 1/4	3 1/4	3 1/4	3 5/8	4	4 1/8	4 3/4
8	7/8	1 3/16	1 1/2	1 13/16	2	2	2 1/4	2 3/4	3 1/4	3 3/4	4	4	4	4 1/8	4 3/4
10	7/8	1 3/16	1 1/2	1 13/16	2 1/8	2 7/16	2 1/2	2 3/4	3 1/4	3 3/4	4 1/4	4 3/4	4 3/4	4 3/4	4 3/4
12	7/8	1 3/16	1 1/2	1 13/16	2 1/8	2 7/16	2 3/4	2 3/4	3 1/4	3 3/4	4 1/4	4 3/4	5 1/4	5 3/4	6 1/4
16	1	1 3/16	1 1/2	1 13/16	2 1/8	2 7/16	2 3/4	3 1/4	3 1/4	3 3/4	4 1/4	4 3/4	5 1/4	5 3/4	6 1/4
20	1	1 3/8	1 1/2	1 13/16	2 1/8	2 7/16	2 3/4	3 3/8	4	4 5/8	4 3/4	4 3/4	5 1/4	5 3/4	6 1/4
30	. . .	. . . .	1 3/4	1 13/16	2 1/8	2 7/16	2 3/4	3 3/8	4	4 5/8	5 1/4	5 7/8	6 1/2	6 1/2	6 1/2

All dimensions in inches.

Minimum thread length is measured from the end of the bolt to the last complete thread.

For bolts too short for the specified thread lengths, threads shall be cut or rolled to within 1/4 in. of head or neck on sizes up to and including 1/2 in.; 3/8 in. on sizes 9/16 to 1 in., inclusive; 1/2 in. on sizes 1 1/8 to 2 in., inclusive; and 3/4 in. on sizes 2 1/8 to 3 in., inclusive.

Length of incomplete thread shall not exceed 2 1/2 threads.

The thread lengths shown in this table have been inserted as showing the usual practice followed by manufacturers when American Standard bolts are ordered and are applicable to both regular and heavy series.

[1] Recommended by the American Standards Association but not a part of the American Standards.

[2] For intermediate bolt lengths, the minimum thread length shall be the same as that specified in the table for the next shorter length of bolt of the same diameter.

American Standard Cap Screws

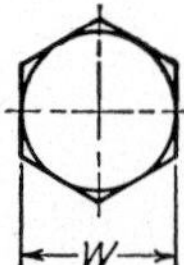

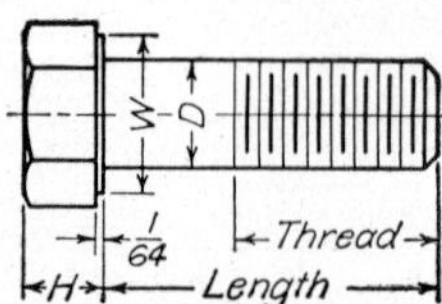

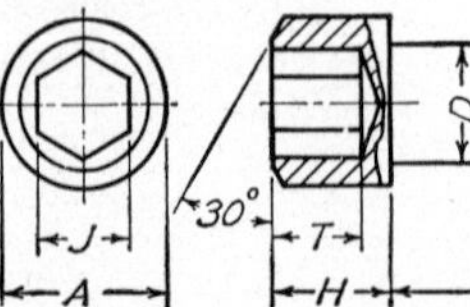

Diameter D	Threads per inch		Hexagon[1]		Socket hexagon[2]			
	Coarse	Fine[3]	Width across flats W	Height of head H	A	H	J	T
1/4	20	28	7/16	3/16	3/8	1/4	3/16	Socket depth is not specified by the standards. Exact depth may be obtained from manufacturers' catalogues. For drawing purposes $T = \frac{3}{4}H$
5/16	18	24	1/2	15/64	7/16	5/16	7/32	
3/8	16	24	9/16	9/32	9/16	3/8	5/16	
7/16	14	20	5/8	21/64	5/8	7/16	5/16	
1/2	13	20	3/4	3/8	3/4	1/2	3/8	
9/16	12	18	13/16	27/64	13/16	9/16	3/8	
5/8	11	18	7/8	15/32	7/8	5/8	1/2	
3/4	10	16	1	9/16	1	3/4	9/16	
7/8	9	14	1 1/8	21/32	1 1/8	7/8	9/16	
1	8	14	1 5/16	3/4	1 5/16	1	5/8	
1 1/8	7	12	1 1/2	27/32	1 1/2	1 1/8	3/4	
1 1/4	7	12	1 11/16	15/16	1 3/4	1 1/4	3/4	

Body-length increments:
- For screw lengths 1/4 to 1 = 1/8″
- For screw lengths 1″ to 4″ = 1/4″
- For screw lengths 4″ to 6″ = 1/2″

Thread length:
- Coarse thread: $2D + \frac{1}{2}''$
- Fine thread: $1\frac{1}{2}D + \frac{1}{2}''$

All dimensions in inches.
[1] ASA B18.2 1940.
[2] ASA B18.3 1936.
[3] Not included in American Standards but in common use.

Dimensions[1] of Slotted-head Cap Screws[2,3]

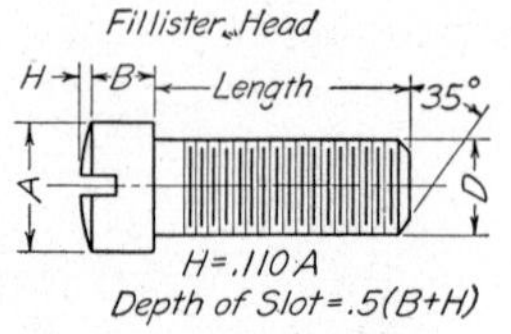

Length of Thread = 2D + 1/4″
Width of Slots = .160D + .024″

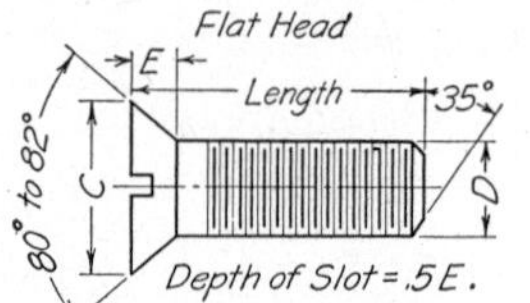

Button Head
G
Length
35°
F
D
Depth of Slot = .66G
Shape of Head is Semi-elliptical

Standard Length Increments:
- for screw lengths 1/4″ to 1″ = 1/8″
- for screw lengths 1″ to 4″ = 1/4″
- for screw lengths 4″ to 6″ = 1/2″

Diameter D of screw	A	B	C	E	F	G
1/4	3/8	11/64	1/2	0.146	7/16	3/16
5/16	7/16	13/64	5/8	0.183	9/16	15/64
3/8	9/16	1/4	3/4	0.220	5/8	1/4
7/16	5/8	19/64	13/16	0.220	3/4	5/16
1/2	3/4	21/64	7/8	0.220	13/16	21/64
9/16	13/16	3/8	1	0.256	15/16	25/64
5/8	7/8	27/64	1 1/8	0.293	1	7/16
3/4	1	1/2	1 3/8	0.366	1 1/4	17/32
7/8	1 1/8	19/32				
1	1 5/16	21/32				

All dimensions in inches.
[1] Nominal.
[2] ASA B18c 1930.
[3] Compiled from American Standards.

Dimensions of Machine Screws and Machine-screw and Stove-bolt Nuts[1]

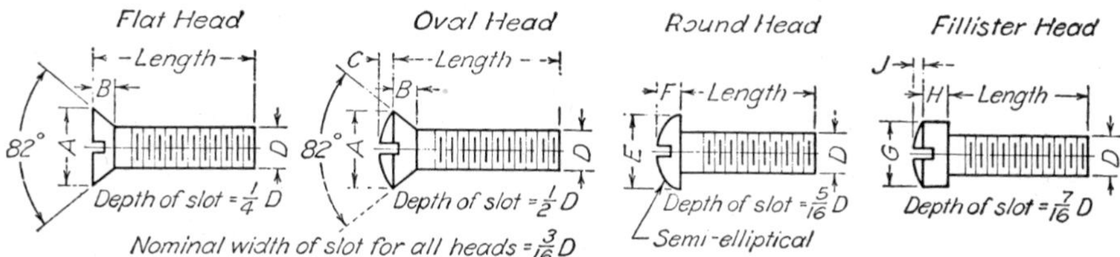

Nominal size	Diameter D	Threads per in. (coarse)	Threads per in. (fine)	A	B	C	E	F	G	H	J
2	0.086	56	64	0.164	0.046	0.041	0.154	0.065	0.132	0.050	0.023
3	0.099	48	56	0.190	0.054	0.048	0.178	0.073	0.153	0.058	0.027
4	0.112	40	48	0.216	0.061	0.054	0.202	0.081	0.175	0.066	0.030
5	0.125	40	..	0.242	0.069	0.061	0.227	0.089	0.198	0.075	0.033
6	0.138	32	40	0.268	0.076	0.067	0.250	0.097	0.217	0.083	0.037
8	0.164	32	36	0.320	0.092	0.080	0.298	0.113	0.260	0.099	0.043
10	0.190	24	32	0.372	0.107	0.094	0.346	0.130	0.303	0.115	0.049
12	0.216	24	28	0.424	0.122	0.107	0.395	0.146	0.344	0.132	0.056
1/4	0.250	20	28	0.492	0.142	0.124	0.458	0.168	0.402	0.153	0.064
5/16	0.3125	18	24	0.618	0.179	0.156	0.574	0.207	0.505	0.193	0.080
3/8	0.375	16	24	0.742	0.215	0.186	0.689	0.247	0.606	0.232	0.096

Nominal size		2	3	4	5	6	8	10	12	1/4	5/16	3/8
Machine-screw[2] and stove-bolt[3] nuts	W	3/16	3/16	1/4	5/16	5/16	11/32	3/8	7/16	7/16	9/16	5/8
	T	1/16	1/16	3/32	7/64	7/64	1/8	1/8	5/32	3/16	7/32	1/4

Dimensions in inches.
[1] Compiled from formulas of American Standards.
[2] Machine-screw nuts are hexagonal.
[3] Stove-bolt nuts are square.

American Phillips-head Machine Screws

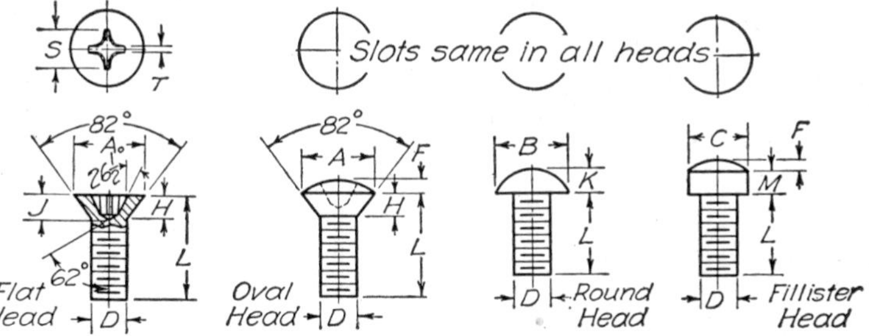

Nominal size[1]	Diameter D	Head major diam A	Head major diam B	Head major diam C	Head height (max) H	Head height (max) K	Head height (max) M	Oval height (max) F	Recess spread (max) S	Recess depth (max) J	Wing thick (max) T
2	0.086	0.172	0.162	0.140	0.051	0.070	0.055	0.029	0.111	0.089	0.020
3	0.099	0.199	0.187	0.161	0.059	0.078	0.063	0.033	0.119	0.097	0.020
4	0.112	0.225	0.211	0.183	0.067	0.086	0.072	0.037	0.127	0.105	0.020
5	0.125	0.232	0.236	0.204	0.075	0.095	0.081	0.041	0.151	0.104	0.027
6	0.138	0.279	0.260	0.226	0.083	0.103	0.089	0.045	0.159	0.112	0.027
8	0.164	0.332	0.309	0.270	0.100	0.119	0.106	0.053	0.175	0.128	0.027
10	0.190	0.385	0.359	0.313	0.116	0.136	0.123	0.061	0.192	0.145	0.027
12	0.216	0.438	0.408	0.357	0.132	0.152	0.141	0.069	0.246	0.165	0.032
1/4	0.250	0.507	0.472	0.414	0.153	0.174	0.163	0.079	0.265	0.187	0.032
5/16	0.3125	0.636	0.591	0.519	0.192	0.214	0.205	0.098	0.305	0.227	0.032
3/8	0.375	0.762	0.708	0.622	0.230	0.254	0.246	0.117	0.384	0.281	0.045

Dimensions in inches.
[1] See machine screw table above for threads per inch.

American Standard Hexagonal Socket Setscrews[1]

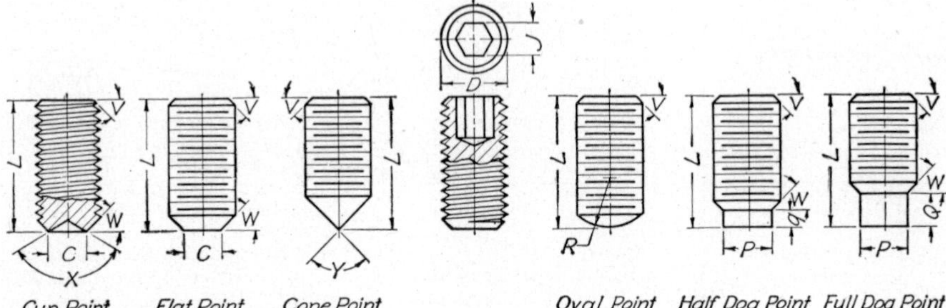

Diameter D	Cup and flat-point diameter C	Oval-point radius R	Cone-point angle Y for these lengths and		Full and half dog points			Socket width J
			Under	Over	Diameter P	Length		
			118° ± 2°	90° ± 2°		Full Q	Half q	
5	1/16	3/32	1/8	3/16	0.083	0.06	0.03	1/16
6	0.069	7/64	1/8	3/16	0.092	0.07	0.03	1/16
8	5/64	1/8	3/16	1/4	0.109	0.08	0.04	5/64
10	3/32	9/64	3/16	1/4	0.127	0.09	0.04	3/32
12	7/64	5/32	3/16	1/4	0.144	0.11	0.06	3/32
1/4	1/8	3/16	1/4	5/16	5/32	1/8	1/16	1/8
5/16	11/64	15/64	5/16	3/8	13/64	5/32	5/64	5/32
3/8	13/64	9/32	3/8	7/16	1/4	3/16	3/32	3/16
7/16	15/64	21/64	7/16	1/2	19/64	7/32	7/64	7/32
1/2	9/32	3/8	1/2	9/16	11/32	1/4	1/8	1/4
9/16	5/16	27/64	9/16	5/8	25/64	9/32	9/64	1/4
5/8	23/64	15/32	5/8	3/4	15/32	5/16	5/32	5/16
3/4	7/16	9/16	3/4	7/8	9/16	3/8	3/16	3/8
7/8	33/64	21/32	7/8	1	21/32	7/16	7/32	1/2
1	19/32	3/4	1	1 1/8	3/4	1/2	1/4	9/16
1 1/8	43/64	27/32	1 1/8	1 1/4	27/32	9/16	9/32	9/16
1 1/4	3/4	15/16	1 1/4	1 1/2	15/16	5/8	5/16	5/8
1 3/8	53/64	1 1/32	1 3/8	1 5/8	1 1/32	11/16	11/32	5/8
1 1/2	29/32	1 1/8	1 1/2	1 3/4	1 1/8	3/4	3/8	3/4
1 3/4	1 1/16	1 5/16	1 3/4	2	1 5/16	7/8	7/16	1
2	1 7/32	1 1/2	2	2 1/4	1 1/2	1	1/2	1

All dimensions in inches.
Chamfer and point angle.
$W = 45°, +5°, -0°$; draw 45°.
$X = 118° \pm 5°$; draw 120°.
V and $Z = 35° + 5°, -0°$; draw 45°.
Standard length increments: 1/4″ to 5/8″ by (1/16″); 5/8″ to 1″ by (1/8″); 1″ to 4″ by (1/4″); 4″ to 6″ by (1/2″). Fractions in parentheses show length increments; for example, 5/8″ to 1″ by (1/8″) includes the lengths 5/8″, 3/4″, 7/8″, and 1″.

[1] Compiled from ASA B18.3 1936.

American Standard Square-headed Setscrews

THREADS ARE AMERICAN STANDARD[1]

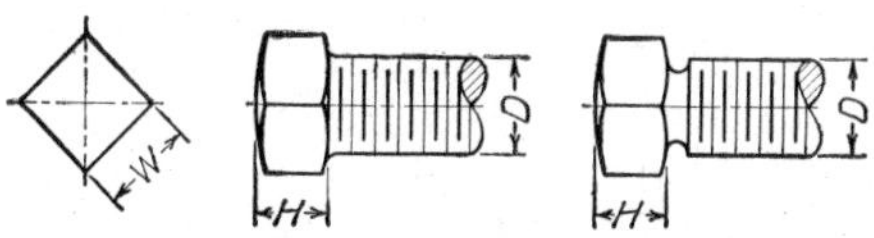

Diameter	1/4	5/16	3/8	7/16	1/2	9/16	5/8	3/4	7/8	1	1 1/8	1 1/4	1 3/8	1 1/2
Width across flats W	1/4	5/16	3/8	7/16	1/2	9/16	5/8	3/4	7/8	1	1 1/8	1 1/4	1 3/8	1 1/2
Height of head H	3/16	15/64	9/32	21/64	3/8	27/64	15/32	9/16	21/32	3/4	27/32	15/16	1 1/32	1 1/8

[1] ASA B18.2 1940.

Dimensions of Wood Screws[1]

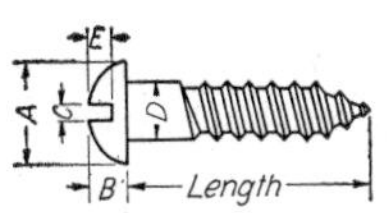

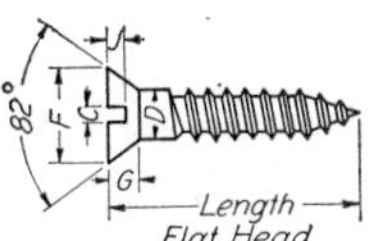

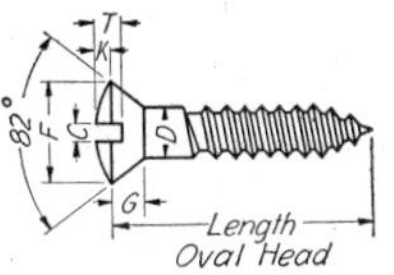

Screw No.	Diameter D	A	B	C	E	F	G	J	K	T
0	0.060	0.106	0.047	0.025	0.034	0.112	0.030	0.012	0.018	0.027
1	0.073	0.130	0.056	0.027	0.038	0.138	0.038	0.015	0.022	0.034
2	0.086	0.154	0.064	0.030	0.042	0.164	0.045	0.019	0.025	0.041
3	0.099	0.178	0.072	0.032	0.046	0.190	0.053	0.022	0.029	0.047
4	0.112	0.202	0.080	0.034	0.050	0.216	0.061	0.025	0.033	0.054
5	0.125	0.228	0.089	0.037	0.054	0.242	0.068	0.028	0.037	0.061
6	0.138	0.250	0.097	0.039	0.058	0.268	0.076	0.031	0.040	0.067
7	0.151	0.274	0.105	0.041	0.062	0.294	0.083	0.034	0.044	0.073
8	0.164	0.298	0.113	0.043	0.066	0.320	0.092	0.037	0.048	0.080
9	0.177	0.322	0.121	0.045	0.070	0.346	0.100	0.040	0.051	0.086
10	0.190	0.346	0.130	0.048	0.075	0.371	0.107	0.043	0.055	0.093
11	0.203	0.370	0.138	0.050	0.078	0.398	0.114	0.046	0.059	0.100
12	0.216	0.395	0.146	0.052	0.083	0.424	0.123	0.049	0.063	0.116
14	0.242	0.443	0.162	0.057	0.091	0.476	0.137	0.056	0.069	0.120
16	0.268	0.491	0.178	0.061	0.099	0.528	0.152	0.062	0.077	0.133
18	0.294	0.539	0.195	0.066	0.107	0.580	0.167	0.068	0.085	0.146

Dimensions in inches. [1] Compiled from ASA B18c 1930.

Parker-Kalon Self-tapping Cap Screws[1]

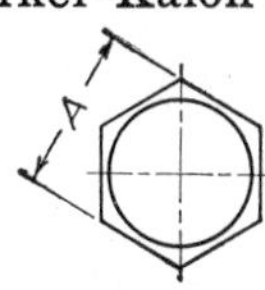

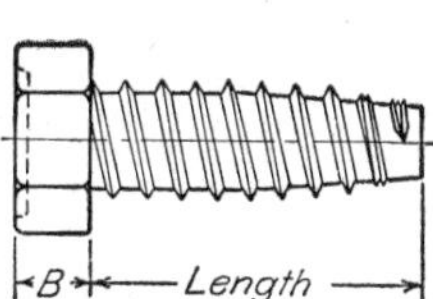

Diameter	A	B	Length L[2]	Drill size: Aluminum die castings, etc.	Drill size: Slate, ebony, asbestos, etc.
6	1/4	5/64	3/16, 3/8, 1/4, 5/16	No. 30	No. 31
8	1/4	7/64	1/4″ to 1″ by (1/8″)	No. 24	No. 26
10	9/32	1/4	3/8″ to 1″ by (1/8″)	No. 16	No. 19
14	3/8	11/64	3/8″ to 1 1/2″ by (1/8″)	15/64	No. 1
5/16	1/2	13/64	1/2″ to 1″ by (1/8″) 1 1/4, 1 1/2	L	9/32
3/8	9/16	9/32	5/8″ to 1″ by (1/8″) 1″ to 2″ by (1/4″)	S	21/64
7/16	5/8	5/16	3/4″ to 1″ by (1/8″) 1″ to 2″ by (1/4″)	Z	X
1/2	3/4	3/8	3/4″ to 1″ by (1/8″) 1″ to 2 1/2″ by (1/4″)	15/32	29/64

[1] Compiled from Parker-Kalon catalogue. [2] Fractions in parentheses show length increments; for example, 1/4″ to 1″ by (1/8″) included the lengths 1/4″, 3/8″, 1/2″, 5/8″, 3/4″, 7/8″, and 1″.

American Standard Round Unslotted-head Bolts[1]

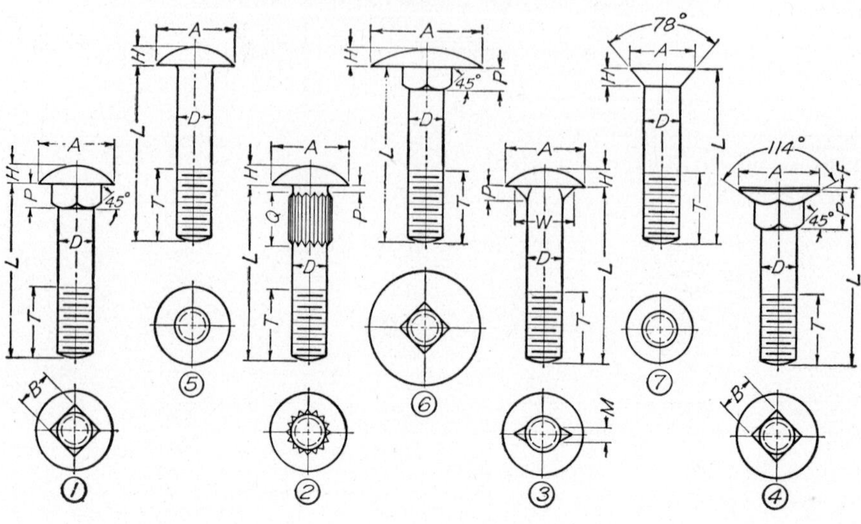

Fastening		Nominal diameter[2]	A	H	P and M	B	F	W	Q Rib neck only
Carriage bolts	① Square neck	No. 10, ¼″ to ⅝″ by (1/16″); ⅝″ to 1″ by (⅛″)	$2D + \frac{1}{16}$	$\frac{D}{2}$	$\frac{D}{2} + \frac{1}{16}$	D			3/16″ for bolt lengths ⅞″ or less; 5/16″ for bolt lengths 1″ and 1⅛″; ½″ for bolt lengths 1¼″ and more
	② Rib neck	No. 10, ¼″ to ⅝″ by (1/16″); ⅝″ and ¾″	$2D + \frac{1}{16}$	$\frac{D}{2}$	$\frac{1}{16}$				
	③ Fin neck	No. 10, ¼″ to ½″ by (1/16″)	$2D + \frac{3}{32}$	$\frac{D}{2} - \frac{1}{64}$	$\frac{3}{8}D$			$1\frac{1}{2} + \frac{1}{16}$	
	④ Counter sunk	No. 10, ¾″; ¼″ to ⅝″ by (1/16″)	$2D + \frac{1}{8}$	......	$D + \frac{1}{32}$	D	$\frac{1}{32}$		
⑤ Button-head bolt		No. 10, ¼″ to ⅝″ by (1/16″) ⅝″ to 1″ by (⅛″)	$2D + \frac{1}{16}$	$\frac{D}{2}$					
⑥ Step bolt		No. 10, ¼″ to ½″ by (1/16″)	$3D + \frac{1}{16}$	$\frac{D}{2}$	$\frac{D}{2} + \frac{1}{16}$	D			
⑦ Counter-sunk bolt		½″ by ⅝″ by (1/16″); ⅝″ to 2″ by (⅛″)	Obtain by projection	$\frac{D}{2}$					

NOTE.—The proportions in this table are for drawing purposes. Thread lengths for drawing are $2D + \frac{1}{4}$.

For exact dimensions see ASA B18.5 1939.

[1] Compiled from ASA B18.5 1939.

[2] Fractions in parentheses show diameter increments, for example, ¼″ to ⅝″ by (1/16″) includes the diameters ¼″, 5/16″, ⅜″, 7/16″, ½″, 9/16″ and ⅝″.

Stripper Bolts or Shoulder Screws

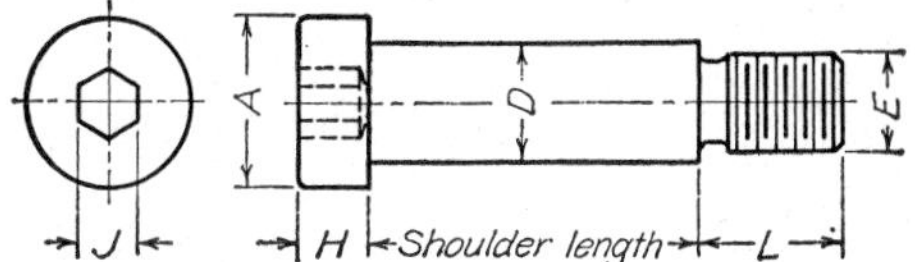

Shoulder diameter D		Head			Thread[1]		Shoulder lengths[2]
Nominal	Limits	Diameter A	Height H	Hexagon J	Diameter E	Length L	
3/8	0.373 / 0.370	9/16	1/4	3/16	5/16	1/2	1″–4″ by (1/4″)
1/2	0.498 / 0.494	3/4	5/16	1/4	3/8	5/8	1″–5″ by (1/4″)
5/8	0.623 / 0.619	7/8	3/8	5/16	1/2	3/4	1″–5″ by (1/4″); 5″–6″ by (1/2″)
3/4	0.748 / 0.744	1	1/2	3/8	5/8	7/8	1″–5″ by (1/4″); 5″–7″ by (1/2″)

Dimensions in inches.
[1] Threads are American Standard Coarse.
[2] Fractions in parentheses show shoulder-length increments; for example, 1″ to 4″ by (1/4″) includes the lengths 1″, 1 1/4″, 1 1/2″, 1 3/4″, 2″, 2 1/4″, 2 1/2″, 2 3/4″, 3″, 3 1/4″, 3 1/2″, 3 3/4″, and 4″.

Sizes of Numbered and Lettered Drills

Number	Size	Number	Size	Number	Size	Letter	Size
80	0.0135	53	0.0595	26	0.1470	*A*	0.2340
79	0.0145	52	0.0635	25	0.1495	*B*	0.2380
78	0.0160	51	0.0670	24	0.1520	*C*	0.2420
77	0.0180	50	0.0700	23	0.1540	*D*	0.2460
76	0.0200	49	0.0730	22	0.1570	*E*	0.2500
75	0.0210	48	0.0760	21	0.1590	*F*	0.2570
74	0.0225	47	0.0785	20	0.1610	*G*	0.2610
73	0.0240	46	0.0810	19	0.1660	*H*	0.2660
72	0.0250	45	0.0820	18	0.1695	*I*	0.2720
71	0.0260	44	0.0860	17	0.1730	*J*	0.2770
70	0.0280	43	0.0890	16	0.1770	*K*	0.2810
69	0.0292	42	0.0935	15	0.1800	*L*	0.2900
68	0.0310	41	0.0960	14	0.1820	*M*	0.2950
67	0.0320	40	0.0980	13	0.1850	*N*	0.3020
66	0.0330	39	0.0995	12	0.1890	*O*	0.3160
65	0.0350	38	0.1015	11	0.1910	*P*	0.3230
64	0.0360	37	0.1040	10	0.1935	*Q*	0.3320
63	0.0370	36	0.1065	9	0.1960	*R*	0.3390
62	0.0380	35	0.1100	8	0.1990	*S*	0.3480
61	0.0390	34	0.1110	7	0.2010	*T*	0.3580
60	0.0400	33	0.1130	6	0.2040	*U*	0.3680
59	0.0410	32	0.1160	5	0.2055	*V*	0.3770
58	0.0420	31	0.1200	4	0.2090	*W*	0.3860
57	0.0430	30	0.1285	3	0.2130	*X*	0.3970
56	0.0465	29	0.1360	2	0.2210	*Y*	0.4040
55	0.0520	28	0.1405	1	0.2280	*Z*	0.4130
54	0.0550	27	0.1440				

Recommended[1] SAE Standard Lock Washers

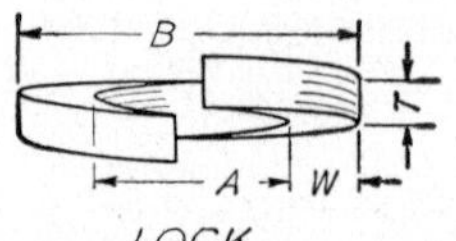

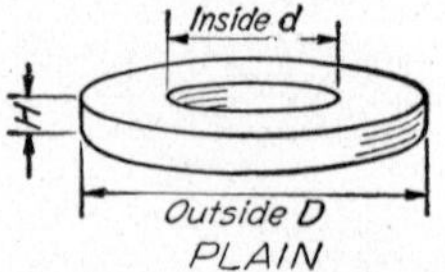

Screw or bolt size, nominal	SAE standard sizes			Lock washers for use with					
	SAE light W × T	SAE standard[2] W × T	SAE heavy W × T	All regular boltheads and nuts, series A W × T	Cap screws, series B W × T	Round-head mach. screws, series C W × T	Fillister-head mach. screws, series D W × T	Mach.-screw and stovebolt nuts, series E W × T	Socket-head cap screws W × T
2*	0.022 × 0.022	1/32 × 0.022	1/32 × 1/32	…	…	…	1/32 × 0.022		
2†	1/32 × 0.022	1/32 × 1/32	3/64 × 1/32	…	…	1/32 × 1/32			
4*	1/32 × 0.022	1/32 × 1/32	3/64 × 1/32	…	…	…	1/32 × 1/32	…	0.022 × 0.022
4†	3/64 × 1/32	1/16 × 1/32	5/64 × 1/32	…	…	3/64 × 1/32			
6*	1/32 × 1/32	3/64 × 1/32	3/64 × 3/64	…	…	…	3/64 × 1/32	…	1/32 × 1/32
6†	1/16 × 1/32	5/64 × 1/32	5/64 × 3/64	…	…	1/16 × 3/64	…	3/32 × 3/64	
8*	3/64 × 1/32	3/64 × 3/64	1/16 × 3/64	…	…	…	1/16 × 3/64	…	3/64 × 3/64
8†	5/64 × 1/32	5/64 × 3/64	3/32 × 3/64	…	…	5/64 × 3/64	…	7/64 × 1/16	
10*	3/64 × 3/64	1/16 × 3/64	1/16 × 1/16	…	…	…	1/16 × 3/64	…	3/64 × 3/64
10†	5/64 × 3/64	3/32 × 3/64	3/32 × 1/16	…	…	3/32 × 1/16	…	7/64 × 1/16	
1/4	3/32 × 3/64	3/32 × 1/16	3/32 × 5/64	9/64 × 5/64	1/8 × 1/16	1/8 × 1/16	5/64 × 1/16	9/64 × 5/64	3/64 × 5/64
5/16	1/8 × 3/64	1/8 × 1/16	1/8 × 3/32	5/32 × 3/32	9/64 × 5/64	9/64 × 5/64	7/64 × 1/16	5/32 × 3/32	3/64 × 5/64
3/8	1/8 × 1/16	1/8 × 3/32	1/8 × 1/8	11/64 × 7/64	5/32 × 3/32	5/32 × 3/32	1/8 × 3/32	11/64 × 7/64	5/64 × 1/8
7/16	5/32 × 1/16	5/32 × 1/8	5/32 × 5/32	13/64 × 1/8	11/64 × 7/64	…	…	…	5/64 × 1/8
1/2	11/64 × 1/16	11/64 × 1/8	11/64 × 11/64	7/32 × 5/32	3/16 × 1/8	…	…	…	7/64 × 11/64
9/16	3/16 × 3/32	3/16 × 1/8	3/16 × 3/16	1/4 × 3/16	13/64 × 1/8				
5/8	13/64 × 3/32	13/64 × 5/32	13/64 × 13/64	17/64 × 3/16	7/32 × 5/32	…	…	…	7/64 × 11/64
3/4	1/4 × 1/8	1/4 × 3/16	1/4 × 1/4	5/16 × 7/32	1/4 × 3/16	…	…	…	7/64 × 3/16
7/8	17/64 × 5/32	17/64 × 3/16	17/64 × 17/64	11/32 × 1/4	5/16 × 7/32	…	…	…	7/64 × 3/16
1	5/16 × 3/16	5/16 × 1/4	5/16 × 5/16	13/32 × 9/32	5/16 × 1/4	…	…	…	1/8 × 13/64
1 1/8	3/8 × 3/16	3/8 × 1/4	3/8 × 3/8	7/16 × 5/16	11/32 × 1/4	…	…	…	5/32 × 5/16
1 1/4	7/16 × 3/16	7/16 × 1/4	7/16 × 5/16	1/2 × 3/8	3/8 × 5/16	…	…	…	7/32 × 5/16
1 3/8	7/16 × 1/4	7/16 × 5/16	7/16 × 3/8	1/2 × 3/8	3/8 × 5/16	…	…	…	
1 1/2	1/2 × 1/4	1/2 × 5/16	1/2 × 3/8	1/2 × 3/8	3/8 × 5/16	…	…	…	7/32 × 5/16

Dimensions in inches. * For fillister-head machine screws. † For round-head machine screws. [1] By Spring Washer Industry. [2] Also called "Regular."

SAE Standard Plain Washers

Nominal size	1/4	5/16	3/8	7/16	1/2	9/16	5/8	11/16	3/4	7/8	1	1 1/8	1 1/4	1 3/8	1 1/2
Inside diameter d	9/32	11/32	13/32	15/32	17/32	19/32	21/32	23/32	13/16	15/16	1 1/16	1 3/16	1 5/16	1 7/16	1 9/16
Outside diameter D	5/8	11/16	13/16	15/16	1 1/16	1 3/16	1 5/16	1 3/8	1 1/2	1 3/4	2	2 1/4	2 1/2	2 3/4	3
Thickness H	1/16	1/16	1/16	1/16	3/32	3/32	3/32	3/32	1/8	1/8	1/8	1/8	5/32	5/32	5/32

Dimensions in inches.

Small Rivets[1]

Tinner's	Cooper's	Belt
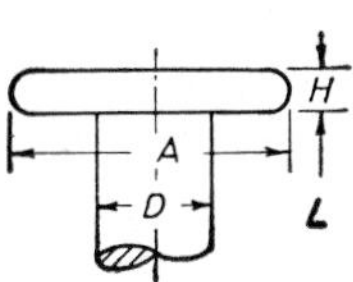	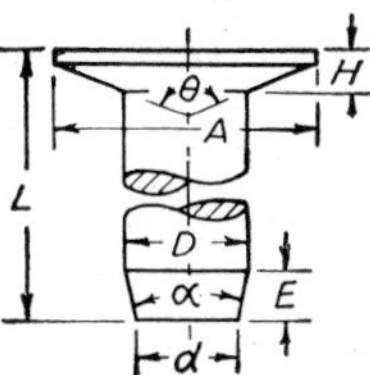	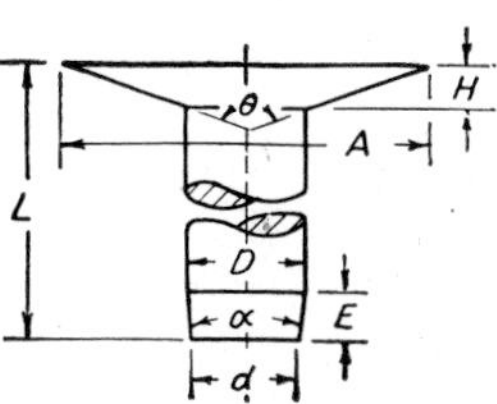

Tinner's			Cooper's			Belt		
Size No.[2]	*D* Diam body	*L* Length	Size No.[2]	*D* Diam body	*L* Length	Size No.[3]	*D* Diam body	*L* Length
8 oz	0.089	0.16	1 lb	0.109	0.219	7	0.180	From 3/8 to 3/4 by 1/8" increments
12	0.105	0.19	1½	0.127	0.256	8	0.165	
1 lb	0.111	0.20	2	0.141	0.292	9	0.148	
1½	0.130	0.23	2½	0.148	0.325	10	0.134	
2	0.144	0.27	3	0.156	0.358	11	0.120	
2½	0.148	0.28	4	0.165	0.392	12	0.109	
3	0.160	0.31	6	0.203	0.466	13	0.095	
4	0.176	0.34	8	0.238	0.571			
6	0.203	0.39	10	0.250	0.606			
8	0.224	0.44	12	0.259	0.608			
10	0.238	0.47	14	0.271	0.643			
12	0.259	0.50	16	0.281	0.677			
14	0.284	0.52						
16	0.300	0.53						

Tinner's — Approximate proportions:
$A = 2.25 \times D,\ H = 0.30 \times D$

Cooper's — Approximate proportions:
$A = 2.25 \times D,\ d = 0.90 \times D$
$E = 0.40 \times D,\ H = 0.30 \times D$
Included $\angle\theta = 144°$
$\angle\alpha = 18°$

Belt — Approximate proportions:
$A = 2.8 \times D,\ d = 0.9 \times D$
$E = 0.4 \times D,\ H = 0.3 \times D$

Tolerances on the nominal diameter:
+0.002
−0.004

Finished rivets shall be free from injurious defects.

All dimensions given in inches.

[1] ASA B18gl 1942.

[2] Size numbers refer to the "Trade Name" or weight of 1,000 rivets.

[3] Size number refers to the Stubs iron wire gage number of the stock used in the body of the rivet.

Widths and Heights of Standard Square- and Flat-stock Keys with Corresponding Shaft Diameters

APPROVED BY AMERICAN STANDARDS ASSOCIATION[1]

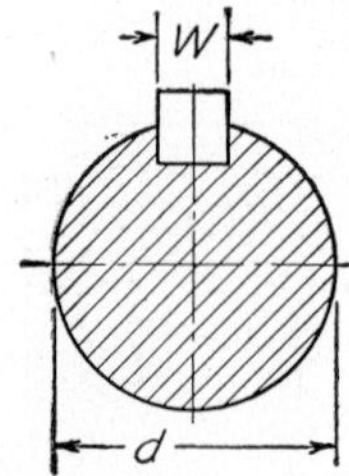

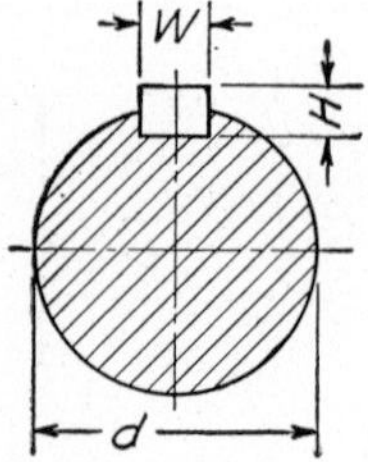

Shaft diameter d (inclusive)	Square-stock keys W	Flat-stock keys, $W \times H$	Shaft diameter d (inclusive)	Square-stock keys W	Flat-stock keys, $W \times H$
1/2 – 9/16	1/8	1/8 × 3/32	2 7/8–3 1/4	3/4	3/4 × 1/2
5/8 – 7/8	3/16	3/16 × 1/8	3 3/8–3 3/4	7/8	7/8 × 5/8
15/16–1 1/4	1/4	1/4 × 3/16	3 7/8–4 1/2	1	1 × 3/4
1 5/16–1 3/8	5/16	5/16 × 1/4			
1 7/16–1 3/4	3/8	3/8 × 1/4	4 3/4–5 1/2	1 1/4	1 1/4 × 7/8
1 13/16–2 1/4	1/2	1/2 × 3/8	5 3/4–6	1 1/2	1 1/2 × 1
2 5/16–2 3/4	5/8	5/8 × 7/16			

Dimensions in inches.
[1] ASA B17.1 1934.

Dimensions of Standard Gib-head Keys, Square and Flat

APPROVED BY AMERICAN STANDARDS ASSOCIATION[1]

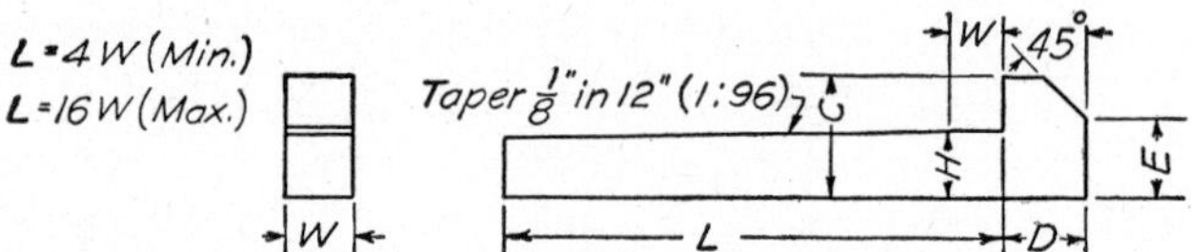

Diameters of shafts	Square type					Flat type				
	Key		Gib head			Key		Gib head		
	W	H	C	D	E	W	H	C	D	E
1/2 – 9/16	1/8	1/8	1/4	7/32	5/32	1/8	3/32	3/16	1/8	1/8
5/8 – 7/8	3/16	3/16	5/16	9/32	7/32	3/16	1/8	1/4	3/16	5/32
15/16–1 1/4	1/4	1/4	7/16	11/32	11/32	1/4	3/16	5/16	1/4	3/16
1 5/16–1 3/8	5/16	5/16	9/16	13/32	13/32	5/16	1/4	3/8	5/16	1/4
1 7/16–1 3/4	3/8	3/8	11/16	15/32	15/32	3/8	1/4	7/16	3/8	5/16
1 13/16–2 1/4	1/2	1/2	7/8	19/32	5/8	1/2	3/8	5/8	1/2	7/16
2 5/16–2 3/4	5/8	5/8	1 1/16	23/32	3/4	5/8	7/16	3/4	5/8	1/2
2 7/8 –3 1/4	3/4	3/4	1 1/4	7/8	7/8	3/4	1/2	7/8	3/4	5/8
3 3/8 –3 3/4	7/8	7/8	1 1/2	1	1	7/8	5/8	1 1/16	7/8	3/4
3 7/8 –4 1/2	1	1	1 3/4	1 3/16	1 3/16	1	3/4	1 1/4	1	1 3/16
4 3/4 –5 1/2	1 1/4	1 1/4	2	1 7/16	1 7/16	1 1/4	7/8	1 1/2	1 1/4	1
5 3/4 –6	1 1/2	1 1/2	2 1/2	1 3/4	1 3/4	1 1/2	1	1 3/4	1 1/2	1 1/4

Dimensions in inches.
[1] ASA B17.1 1934

Dimensions of Pratt and Whitney Keys

PRATT AND WHITNEY ROUND-END FEATHER KEYS ARE IN EXTENSIVE USE. THE LENGTH L MAY VARY BUT SHOULD NEVER BE LESS THAN $2W$.

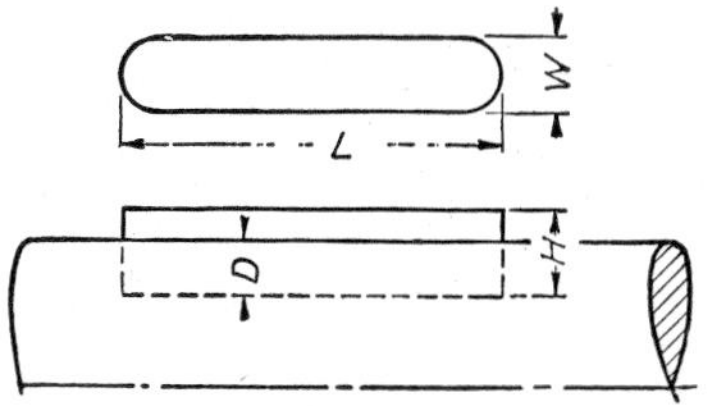

Key No.	L	W	H	D	Key No.	L	W	H	D
1	1/2	1/16	3/32	1/16	22	1 3/8	1/4	3/8	1/4
2	1/2	3/32	9/64	3/32	23	1 3/8	5/16	15/32	5/16
3	1/2	1/8	3/16	1/8	F	1 3/8	3/8	9/16	3/8
4	5/8	3/32	9/64	3/32	24	1 1/2	1/4	3/8	1/4
5	5/8	1/8	3/16	1/8	25	1 1/2	5/16	15/32	5/16
6	5/8	5/32	15/64	5/32	G	1 1/2	3/8	9/16	3/8
7	3/4	1/8	3/16	1/8	51	1 3/4	1/4	3/8	1/4
8	3/4	5/32	15/64	5/32	52	1 3/4	5/16	15/32	5/16
9	3/4	3/16	9/32	3/16	53	1 3/4	3/8	9/16	3/8
10	7/8	5/32	15/64	5/32	26	2	3/16	9/32	3/16
11	7/8	3/16	9/32	3/16	27	2	1/4	3/8	1/4
12	7/8	7/32	21/64	7/32	28	2	5/16	15/32	5/16
A	7/8	1/4	3/8	1/4	29	2	3/8	9/16	3/8
13	1	3/16	9/32	3/16	54	2 1/4	1/4	3/8	1/4
14	1	7/32	21/64	7/32	55	2 1/4	5/16	15/16	5/16
15	1	1/4	3/8	1/4	56	2 1/4	3/8	9/16	3/8
B	1	5/16	15/32	5/16	57	2 1/4	7/16	21/32	7/16
16	1 1/8	3/16	9/32	3/16	58	2 1/2	5/16	15/32	5/16
17	1 1/8	7/32	21/64	7/32	59	2 1/2	3/8	9/16	3/8
18	1 1/8	1/4	3/8	1/4	60	2 1/2	7/16	21/32	7/16
C	1 1/8	5/16	15/32	5/16	61	2 1/2	1/2	3/4	1/2
19	1 1/4	3/16	9/32	3/16	30	3	3/8	9/16	3/8
20	1 1/4	7/32	21/64	7/32	31	3	7/16	21/32	7/16
21	1 1/4	1/4	3/8	1/4	32	3	1/2	3/4	1/2
D	1 1/4	5/16	15/32	5/16	33	3	9/16	27/32	9/16
E	1 1/4	3/8	9/16	3/8	34	3	5/8	15/16	5/8

Dimensions in inches.
Key is 2/3 in shaft; 1/3 in hub.
Keys are 0.001 inch oversize in width to ensure proper fitting in keyway.
Keyway size: width = W; depth = $H - D$.

Woodruff Key Dimensions

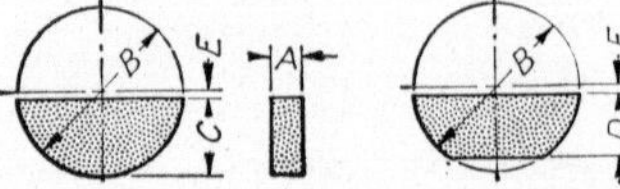

Key[1] No.	Nominal size $A \times B$	Maximum width of key A	Maximum diameter of key B	Maximum height of key		Distance below center E
				C	D	
204	1/16 × 1/2	0.0635	0.500	0.203	0.194	3/64
304	3/32 × 1/2	0.0948	0.500	0.203	0.194	3/64
305	3/32 × 5/8	0.0948	0.625	0.250	0.240	1/16
404	1/8 × 1/2	0.1260	0.500	0.203	0.194	3/64
405	1/8 × 5/8	0.1260	0.625	0.250	0.240	1/16
406	1/8 × 3/4	0.1260	0.750	0.313	0.303	1/16
505	5/32 × 5/8	0.1573	0.625	0.250	0.240	1/16
506	5/32 × 3/4	0.1573	0.750	0.313	0.303	1/16
507	5/32 × 7/8	0.1573	0.875	0.375	0.365	1/16
606	3/16 × 3/4	0.1885	0.750	0.313	0.303	1/16
607	3/16 × 7/8	0.1885	0.875	0.375	0.365	1/16
608	3/16 × 1	0.1885	1.000	0.438	0.428	1/16
609	3/16 × 1 1/8	0.1885	1.125	0.484	0.475	5/64
807	1/4 × 7/8	0.2510	0.875	0.375	0.365	1/16
808	1/4 × 1	0.2510	1.000	0.438	0.428	1/16
809	1/4 × 1 1/8	0.2510	1.125	0.484	0.475	5/64
810	1/4 × 1 1/4	0.2510	1.250	0.547	0.537	5/64
811	1/4 × 1 3/8	0.2510	1.375	0.594	0.584	3/32
812	1/4 × 1 1/2	0.2510	1.500	0.641	0.631	7/64
1008	5/16 × 1	0.3135	1.000	0.438	0.428	1/16
1009	5/16 × 1 1/8	0.3135	1.125	0.484	0.475	5/64
1010	5/16 × 1 1/4	0.3135	1.250	0.547	0.537	5/64
1011	5/16 × 1 3/8	0.3135	1.375	0.594	0.584	3/32
1012	5/16 × 1 1/2	0.3135	1.500	0.641	0.631	7/64
1210	3/8 × 1 1/4	0.3760	1.250	0.547	0.537	5/64
1211	3/8 × 1 3/8	0.3760	1.375	0.594	0.584	3/32
1212	3/8 × 1 1/2	0.3760	1.500	0.641	0.631	7/64

Dimensions in inches.

[1] Key numbers indicate the nominal key dimensions. The last two digits give the nominal diameter B in eighths of an inch and the digits preceding the last two give the nominal width A in thirty-seconds of an inch. Thus, 204 indicates a key 2/32 by 4/8, or 1/16 by 1/2 inch.

Woodruff Key-slot Dimensions

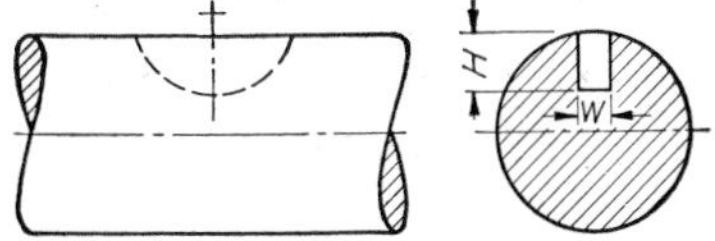

Key[1] No.	Nominal size	Key slot			
		Width W		Depth H	
		Maximum	Minimum	Maximum	Minimum
204	1/16 × 1/2	0.0630	0.0615	0.1718	0.1668
304	3/32 × 1/2	0.0943	0.0928	0.1561	0.1511
305	3/32 × 5/8	0.0943	0.0928	0.2031	0.1981
404	1/8 × 1/2	0.1255	0.1240	0.1405	0.1355
405	1/8 × 5/8	0.1255	0.1240	0.1875	0.1825
406	1/8 × 3/4	0.1255	0.1240	0.2505	0.2455
505	5/32 × 5/8	0.1568	0.1553	0.1719	0.1669
506	5/32 × 3/4	0.1568	0.1553	0.2349	0.2299
507	5/32 × 7/8	0.1568	0.1553	0.2969	0.2919
606	3/16 × 3/4	0.1880	0.1863	0.2193	0.2143
607	3/16 × 7/8	0.1880	0.1863	0.2813	0.2763
608	3/16 × 1	0.1880	0.1863	0.3443	0.3393
609	3/16 × 1 1/8	0.1880	0.1863	0.3903	0.3853
807	1/4 × 7/8	0.2505	0.2487	0.2500	0.2450
808	1/4 × 1	0.2505	0.2487	0.3130	0.3080
809	1/4 × 1 1/8	0.2505	0.2487	0.3590	0.3540
810	1/4 × 1 1/4	0.2505	0.2487	0.4220	0.4170
811	1/4 × 1 3/8	0.2505	0.2487	0.4690	0.4640
812	1/4 × 1 1/2	0.2505	0.2487	0.5160	0.5110
1008	5/16 × 1	0.3130	0.3111	0.2818	0.2768
1009	5/16 × 1 1/8	0.3130	0.3111	0.3278	0.3228
1010	5/16 × 1 1/4	0.3130	0.3111	0.3908	0.3858
1011	5/16 × 1 3/8	0.3130	0.3111	0.4378	0.4328
1012	5/16 × 1 1/2	0.3130	0.3111	0.4848	0.4798
1210	3/8 × 1 1/4	0.3755	0.3735	0.3595	0.3545
1211	3/8 × 1 3/8	0.3755	0.3735	0.4060	0.4015
1212	3/8 × 1 1/2	0.3755	0.3735	0.4535	0.4485

Dimensions in inches.

[1] Key numbers indicate the nominal key dimensions. The last two digits give the nominal diameter B in eighths of an inch and the digits preceding the last two give the nominal width A in thirty-seconds of an inch. Thus, 204 indicates a key 2/32 by 4/8, or 1/16 by 1/2 inch.

Key-slot Cutters. Two series of key-slot cutters, fine and coarse teeth, are standard. Both have a shank diameter of 1/2″ for all sizes. They are designated by the key numbers used to designate the size of the key It will be noted that the depth H is measured from the sharp edge of the slot, not from the shaft circumference on the center line of the key, and therefore does not indicate the depth to which the cutter should be fed into the shaft. The shaft is brought against the cutter until a flat the same width as the thickness of the cutter is formed; the cutter is then fed into the shaft the required depth.

Table of Limits for Cylindrical Fits[1]

Size of hole or external member, inclusive	Clearance fits							
	Class 1 Loose fit				Class 2 Free fit			
	Hole or external member		Shaft or internal member		Hole or external member		Shaft or internal member	
	+		−	−	+		−	−
0–3/16	0.001	0.000	0.001	0.002	0.0007	0.0000	0.0004	0.0011
3/16–5/16	0.002	0.000	0.001	0.003	0.0008	0.0000	0.0006	0.0014
5/16–7/16	0.002	0.000	0.001	0.003	0.0009	0.0000	0.0007	0.0016
7/16–9/16	0.002	0.000	0.002	0.004	0.0010	0.0000	0.0009	0.0019
9/16–11/16	0.002	0.000	0.002	0.004	0.0011	0.0000	0.0010	0.0021
11/16–13/16	0.002	0.000	0.002	0.004	0.0012	0.0000	0.0012	0.0024
13/16–15/16	0.002	0.000	0.002	0.004	0.0012	0.0000	0.0013	0.0025
15/16–1 1/16	0.003	0.000	0.003	0.006	0.0013	0.0000	0.0014	0.0027
1 1/16–1 3/16	0.003	0.000	0.003	0.006	0.0014	0.0000	0.0015	0.0029
1 3/16–1 3/8	0.003	0.000	0.003	0.006	0.0014	0.0000	0.0016	0.0030
1 3/8–1 5/8	0.003	0.000	0.003	0.006	0.0015	0.0000	0.0018	0.0033
1 5/8–1 7/8	0.003	0.000	0.004	0.007	0.0016	0.0000	0.0020	0.0036
1 7/8–2 1/8	0.003	0.000	0.004	0.007	0.0016	0.0000	0.0022	0.0038
2 1/8–2 3/8	0.003	0.000	0.004	0.007	0.0017	0.0000	0.0024	0.0041
2 3/8–2 3/4	0.003	0.000	0.005	0.008	0.0018	0.0000	0.0026	0.0044
2 3/4–3 1/4	0.004	0.000	0.005	0.009	0.0019	0.0000	0.0029	0.0048
3 1/4–3 3/4	0.004	0.000	0.006	0.010	0.0020	0.0000	0.0032	0.0052
3 3/4–4 1/4	0.004	0.000	0.006	0.010	0.0021	0.0000	0.0035	0.0056
4 1/4–4 3/4	0.004	0.000	0.007	0.011	0.0021	0.0000	0.0038	0.0059
4 3/4–5 1/2	0.004	0.000	0.007	0.011	0.0022	0.0000	0.0041	0.0063
5 1/2–6 1/2	0.005	0.000	0.008	0.013	0.0024	0.0000	0.0046	0.0070
6 1/2–7 1/2	0.005	0.000	0.009	0.014	0.0025	0.0000	0.0051	0.0076
7 1/2–8 1/2	0.005	0.000	0.010	0.015	0.0026	0.0000	0.0056	0.0082

Size of hole or external member, inclusive	Class 3 Medium fit				Class 4 Snug fit			
	Hole or external member		Shaft or internal member		Hole or external member		Shaft or internal member	
	+		−	−	+			−
0–3/16	0.0004	0.0000	0.0002	0.0006	0.0003	0.0000	0.0000	0.0002
3/16–5/16	0.0005	0.0000	0.0004	0.0009	0.0004	0.0000	0.0000	0.0003
5/16–7/16	0.0006	0.0000	0.0005	0.0011	0.0004	0.0000	0.0000	0.0003
7/16–9/16	0.0006	0.0000	0.0006	0.0012	0.0005	0.0000	0.0000	0.0003
9/16–11/16	0.0007	0.0000	0.0007	0.0014	0.0005	0.0000	0.0000	0.0003
11/16–13/16	0.0007	0.0000	0.0007	0.0014	0.0005	0.0000	0.0000	0.0004
13/16–15/16	0.0008	0.0000	0.0008	0.0016	0.0006	0.0000	0.0000	0.0004
15/16–1 1/16	0.0008	0.0000	0.0009	0.0017	0.0006	0.0000	0.0000	0.0004
1 1/16–1 3/16	0.0008	0.0000	0.0010	0.0018	0.0006	0.0000	0.0000	0.0004
1 3/16–1 3/8	0.0009	0.0000	0.0010	0.0019	0.0006	0.0000	0.0000	0.0004
1 3/8–1 5/8	0.0009	0.0000	0.0012	0.0021	0.0007	0.0000	0.0000	0.0005
1 5/8–1 7/8	0.0010	0.0000	0.0013	0.0023	0.0007	0.0000	0.0000	0.0005
1 7/8–2 1/8	0.0010	0.0000	0.0014	0.0024	0.0008	0.0000	0.0000	0.0005
2 1/8–2 3/8	0.0010	0.0000	0.0015	0.0025	0.0008	0.0000	0.0000	0.0005
2 3/8–2 3/4	0.0011	0.0000	0.0017	0.0028	0.0008	0.0000	0.0000	0.0005
2 3/4–3 1/4	0.0012	0.0000	0.0019	0.0031	0.0009	0.0000	0.0000	0.0006
3 1/4–3 3/4	0.0012	0.0000	0.0021	0.0033	0.0009	0.0000	0.0000	0.0006
3 3/4–4 1/4	0.0013	0.0000	0.0023	0.0036	0.0010	0.0000	0.0000	0.0006
4 1/4–4 3/4	0.0013	0.0000	0.0025	0.0038	0.0010	0.0000	0.0000	0.0007
4 3/4–5 1/2	0.0014	0.0000	0.0026	0.0040	0.0010	0.0000	0.0000	0.0007
5 1/2–6 1/2	0.0015	0.0000	0.0030	0.0045	0.0011	0.0000	0.0000	0.0007
6 1/2–7 1/2	0.0015	0.0000	0.0033	0.0048	0.0011	0.0000	0.0000	0.0008
7 1/2–8 1/2	0.0016	0.0000	0.0036	0.0052	0.0012	0.0000	0.0000	0.0008

All dimensions in inches.

[1] Compiled from American Standard ASA B4a 1925.

Table of Limits for Cylindrical Fits[1]—(*Continued*)

Size of hole or external member, inclusive	Interference fits							
	Class 5 Wringing fit				Class 6 Tight fit			
	Hole or external member		Shaft or internal member		Hole or external member		Shaft or internal member	
	+		+		+		+	+
0–3/16	0.0003	0.0000	0.0002	0.0000	0.0003	0.0000	0.0003	0.0000
3/16–5/16	0.0004	0.0000	0.0003	0.0000	0.0004	0.0000	0.0005	0.0001
5/16–7/16	0.0004	0.0000	0.0003	0.0000	0.0004	0.0000	0.0005	0.0001
7/16–9/16	0.0005	0.0000	0.0003	0.0000	0.0005	0.0000	0.0006	0.0001
9/16–11/16	0.0005	0.0000	0.0003	0.0000	0.0005	0.0000	0.0007	0.0002
11/16–13/16	0.0005	0.0000	0.0004	0.0000	0.0005	0.0000	0.0007	0.0002
13/16–15/16	0.0006	0.0000	0.0004	0.0000	0.0006	0.0000	0.0008	0.0002
15/16–1 1/16	0.0006	0.0000	0.0004	0.0000	0.0006	0.0000	0.0009	0.0003
1 1/16–1 3/16	0.0006	0.0000	0.0004	0.0000	0.0006	0.0000	0.0009	0.0003
1 3/16–1 3/8	0.0006	0.0000	0.0004	0.0000	0.0006	0.0000	0.0009	0.0003
1 3/8 –1 5/8	0.0007	0.0000	0.0005	0.0000	0.0007	0.0000	0.0011	0.0004
1 5/8 –1 7/8	0.0007	0.0000	0.0005	0.0000	0.0007	0.0000	0.0011	0.0004
1 7/8–2 1/8	0.0008	0.0000	0.0005	0.0000	0.0008	0.0000	0.0013	0.0005
2 1/8 –2 3/8	0.0008	0.0000	0.0005	0.0000	0.0008	0.0000	0.0014	0.0006
2 3/8 –2 3/4	0.0008	0.0000	0.0005	0.0000	0.0008	0.0000	0.0014	0.0006
2 3/4 –3 1/4	0.0009	0.0000	0.0006	0.0000	0.0009	0.0000	0.0017	0.0008
3 1/4 –3 3/4	0.0009	0.0000	0.0006	0.0000	0.0009	0.0000	0.0018	0.0009
3 3/4 –4 1/4	0.0010	0.0000	0.0006	0.0000	0.0010	0.0000	0.0020	0.0010
4 1/4 –4 3/4	0.0010	0.0000	0.0007	0.0000	0.0010	0.0000	0.0021	0.0011
4 3/4 –5 1/2	0.0010	0.0000	0.0007	0.0000	0.0010	0.0000	0.0023	0.0013
5 1/2 –6 1/2	0.0011	0.0000	0.0007	0.0000	0.0011	0.0000	0.0026	0.0015
6 1/2 –7 1/2	0.0011	0.0000	0.0008	0.0000	0.0011	0.0000	0.0029	0.0018
7 1/2 –8 1/2	0.0012	0.0000	0.0008	0.0000	0.0012	0.0000	0.0032	0.0020

	Class 7 Medium force fit				Class 8 Heavy force and shrink fit			
	Hole or external member		Shaft or internal member		Hole or external member		Shaft or internal member	
	+		+	+	+		+	+
0–3/16	0.0003	0.0000	0.0004	0.0001	0.0003	0.0000	0.0004	0.0001
3/16–5/16	0.0004	0.0000	0.0005	0.0001	0.0004	0.0000	0.0007	0.0003
5/16–7/16	0.0004	0.0000	0.0006	0.0002	0.0004	0.0000	0.0008	0.0004
7/16–9/16	0.0005	0.0000	0.0008	0.0003	0.0005	0.0000	0.0010	0.0005
9/16–11/16	0.0005	0.0000	0.0008	0.0003	0.0005	0.0000	0.0011	0.0006
11/16–13/16	0.0005	0.0000	0.0009	0.0004	0.0005	0.0000	0.0013	0.0008
13/16–15/16	0.0006	0.0000	0.0010	0.0004	0.0006	0.0000	0.0015	0.0009
15/16–1 1/16	0.0006	0.0000	0.0010	0.0005	0.0006	0.0000	0.0016	0.0010
1 1/16–1 3/16	0.0006	0.0000	0.0012	0.0006	0.0006	0.0000	0.0017	0.0011
1 3/16–1 3/8	0.0006	0.0000	0.0012	0.0006	0.0006	0.0000	0.0019	0.0013
1 3/8–1 5/8	0.0007	0.0000	0.0015	0.0008	0.0007	0.0000	0.0022	0.0015
1 5/8–1 7/8	0.0007	0.0000	0.0016	0.0009	0.0007	0.0000	0.0025	0.0018
1 7/8–2 1/8	0.0008	0.0000	0.0018	0.0010	0.0008	0.0000	0.0028	0.0020
2 1/8–2 3/8	0.0008	0.0000	0.0019	0.0011	0.0008	0.0000	0.0031	0.0023
2 3/8–2 3/4	0.0008	0.0000	0.0021	0.0013	0.0008	0.0000	0.0033	0.0025
2 3/4–3 1/4	0.0009	0.0000	0.0024	0.0015	0.0009	0.0000	0.0039	0.0030
3 1/4–3 3/4	0.0009	0.0000	0.0027	0.0018	0.0009	0.0000	0.0044	0.0035
3 3/4–4 1/4	0.0010	0.0000	0.0030	0.0020	0.0010	0.0000	0.0050	0.0040
4 1/4–4 3/4	0.0010	0.0000	0.0033	0.0023	0.0010	0.0000	0.0055	0.0045
4 3/4–5 1/2	0.0010	0.0000	0.0035	0.0025	0.0010	0.0000	0.0060	0.0050
5 1/2–6 1/2	0.0011	0.0000	0.0041	0.0030	0.0011	0.0000	0.0071	0.0060
6 1/2–7 1/2	0.0011	0.0000	0.0046	0.0035	0.0011	0.0000	0.0081	0.0070
7 1/2–8 1/2	0.0012	0.0000	0.0052	0.0040	0.0012	0.0000	0.0092	0.0080

All dimensions in inches.

[1] Compiled from American Standard ASA B4a 1925.

Standard Jig

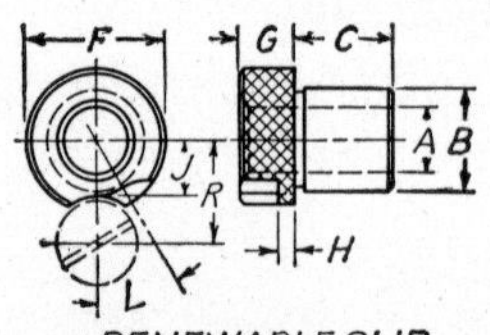

RENEWABLE SLIP

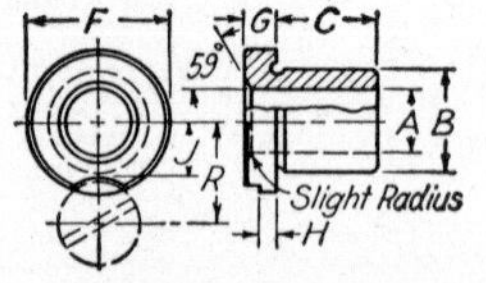

RENEWABLE FIXED

RENEWABLE SLIP TYPE AND RENEWABLE FIXED TYPE

Slip type Hole size *A*	Fixed type Hole size *A*	Tolerance on hole	Body diameter limits *B*	Lengths available *C*	Head dimensions *F*	*G* Slip type	*G* Fixed type	*H*	*J*	*L*	*R*	Lock screw No.
0.052 to 0.089	0.055 to 0.089	+0.0004 +0.0001	0.3125 0.3123	5/16, 1/2; 3/4, 1	35/64	3/8	1/4	1/8	11/64	65°	1/2	1
0.0935 to 0.1562	0.0935 to 0.1562			5/16, 1/2; 3/4, 1								
0.1406 to 0.3437	0.1570 to 0.3125	Incl 1/4 +0.0004 +0.0001 Over 1/4 +0.0005 +0.0001	0.5000 0.4998	5/16, 1/2, 3/4; 1, 1 3/8, 1 3/4	51/64	7/16	1/4	1/8	19/64	65°	5/8	
0.2812 to 0.5312	0.3160 to 0.5000	+0.0005 +0.0001	0.7500 0.7498	1/2, 3/4, 1; 1 3/8, 1 3/4, 2 1/8	1 3/64	7/16	1/4	1/8	27/64	50°	3/4	
0.4687 to 0.7812	0.5156 to 0.750		1.0000 0.9998	3/4, 1, 1 3/8; 1 3/4, 2 1/8, 2 1/2	1 27/64	7/16	3/8	3/16	19/32	35°	59/64	2
0.7817 to 1.0312	0.7656 to 1.0000	+0.0006 +0.0002	1.3750 1.3747	3/4, 1, 1 3/8; 1 3/4, 2 1/8, 2 1/2	1 51/64	7/16	3/8	3/16	25/32	30°	1 7/64	
0.9687 to 1.4062	1.0156 to 1.3750		1.7500 1.7497	1, 1 3/8, 1 3/4; 2 1/8, 2 1/2, 3	2 19/64	5/8	3/8	3/16	1	30°	1 25/64	3
1.3437 to 1.7812	1.3906 to 1.750	Incl. 1 1/2 +0.0006 +0.0002 Over 1 1/2 +0.0007 +0.0003	2.2500 2.2496	1, 1 3/8, 1 3/4; 2 1/8, 2 1/2, 3	2 51/64	5/8	3/8	3/16	1 1/4	25°	1 41/64	

Dimensions in inches.
[1] ASA B5.6 1941.
Head design in accordance with manufacturer's practice; slip type usually knurled.

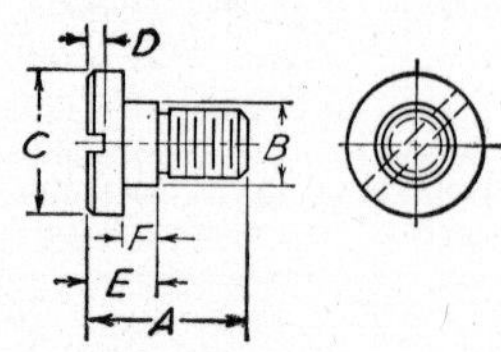

LOCK SCREWS

Screw No.	*A*	*B*	*C*	*D*	*E*	*F*	ASA thd
1	5/8	3/8	5/8	1/16	1/4	.138 .132	5/16–18
2	7/8	3/8	5/8	3/32	3/8	.200 .194	5/16–18
3	1	7/16	3/4	1/8	3/8	.200 .194	3/8–16

Bushings[1]

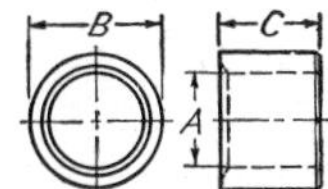

LINER (used with Renewable Type bushings)

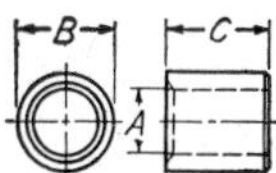

PRESS FIT HEADLESS TYPE

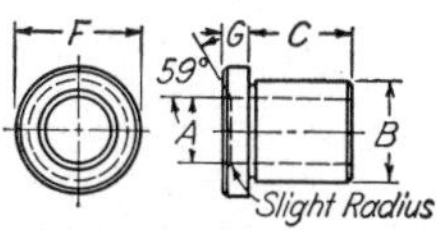

PRESS FIT HEAD TYPE

LINERS		
Hole limits A	OD limits B	Lengths
0.3126 / 0.3129	0.5017 / 0.5014	Same as the bushing
0.5002 / 0.5005	0.7518 / 0.7515	
0.7503 / 0.7506	1.0015 / 1.0018	
1.0004 / 1.0007	1.3772 / 1.3768	
1.3756 / 1.3760	1.7523 / 1.7519	
1.7508 / 1.7512	2.2521 / 2.2525	
2.2510 / 2.2515	2.7526 / 2.7522	

PRESS FIT HEADLESS AND PRESS FIT HEAD TYPES					
Hole size A	Tolerance on hole	OD limits B	Lengths available C	Head type dimension F	Head type dimension G
0.055 to 0.0995	+0.0004 +0.0001	0.2046 / 0.2043	5/16, 1/2	19/64	3/32
0.1015 to 0.1360		0.2516 / 0.2513	5/16, 1/2	23/64	3/32
0.1405 to 0.1875		0.3141 / 0.3138	5/16, 1/2, 3/4, 1	27/64	1/8
0.1890 to 0.2500		0.4078 / 0.4075	5/16, 1/2, 3/4, 1, 1 3/8, 1 3/4	1/2	5/32
0.2570 to 0.3125	+0.0005 +0.0001	0.5017 / 0.5014		39/64	7/32
0.316 to 0.4219		0.6267 / 0.6264	1/2, 3/4, 1, 1 3/8, 1 3/4, 2 1/8	51/64	7/32
0.4375 to 0.500		0.7518 / 0.7515		59/64	7/32
0.5156 to 0.625		0.8768 / 0.8765	3/4, 1	1 7/64	1/4
0.6406 to 0.7500		1.0018 / 1.0015	1 3/8, 1 3/4	1 15/64	5/16
0.7656 to 1.0000	+0.0006 +0.0002	1.3772 / 1.3768	2 1/8, 2 1/2	1 39/64	3/8
1.0156 to 1.3750		1.7523 / 1.7519	1, 1 3/8, 1 3/4, 2 1/8, 2 1/2, 3	1 63/64	3/8
1.3906 to 1.7500	Incl. 1 1/2 +0.0006 +0.0002 Over 1 1/2 +0.0007 +0.0003	2.2525 / 2.2521		2 31/64	3/8

Tapers. Taper means the difference in diameter or width in 1 foot of length, see figure below. *Taper pins*, much used for fastening cylindrical parts and for doweling, have a standard taper of ¼″ per foot.

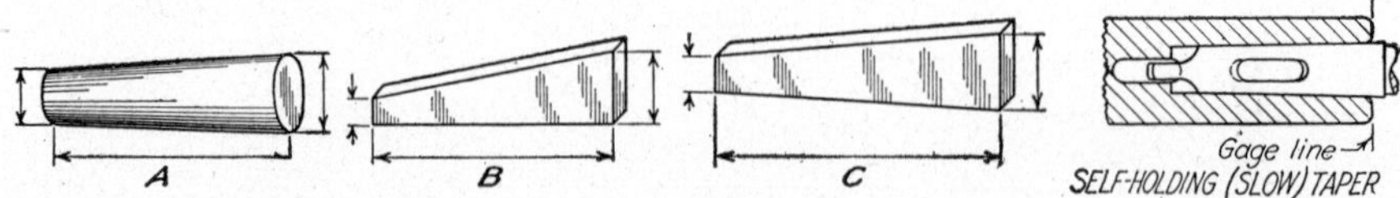

Machine tapers. The American Standard for self-holding (slow) machine tapers is designed to replace the various former standards. The table below shows its derivation. Detailed dimensions and tolerances for taper tool shanks and taper sockets will be found in ASA B5.10 1937.

Dimensions of Taper Pins

TAPER ¼″ PER FOOT

Size No.	Diameter, large end	Drill size for reamer	Max length
000000	0.072	53	⅝
00000	0.092	47	⅝
0000	0.108	42	¾
000	0.125	37	¾
00	0.147	31	1
0	0.156	28	1
1	0.172	25	1¼
2	0.193	19	1½
3	0.219	12	1¾
4	0.250	3	2
5	0.289	¼	2¼
6	0.341	9/32	3¼
7	0.409	11/32	3¾
8	0.492	13/32	4½
9	0.591	31/64	5¼
10	0.706	19/32	6
11	0.857	23/32	7¼
12	1.013	55/64	8¾
13	1.233	1 1/64	10¾

All dimensions in inches.

American Standard Machine Tapers[1] Self-holding (Slow) Taper Series

BASIC DIMENSIONS

Origin of series	No. of taper	Taper per foot	Diameter at gage line	Means of driving and holding
Brown and Sharpe taper series	0.239	0.500	0.239	Tongue drive with shank held in by friction
	0.299	0.500	0.299	
	0.375	0.500	0.375	
Morse taper series	1	0.600	0.475	Tongue drive with shank held in by friction; Tongue drive with shank held in by key
	2	0.600	0.700	
	3	0.602	0.938	
	4	0.623	1.231	
	4½	0.623	1.500	
	5	0.630	1.748	
¾″ per foot taper series	200	0.750	2.000	Tongue drive with shank held in by friction; Tongue drive with shank held in by key; Key drive with shank held in by key; Key drive with shank held in by drawbolt
	250	0.750	2.500	
	300	0.750	3.000	
	350	0.750	3.500	
	400	0.750	4.000	Key drive with shank held in by key; Key drive with shank held in by drawbolt
	500	0.750	5.000	
	600	0.750	6.000	
	800	0.750	8.000	
	1,000	0.750	10.000	
	1,200	0.750	12.000	

All dimensions in inches

[1] ASA B5.10 1937.

American Standard Pipe[1,5]

WELDED WROUGHT IRON

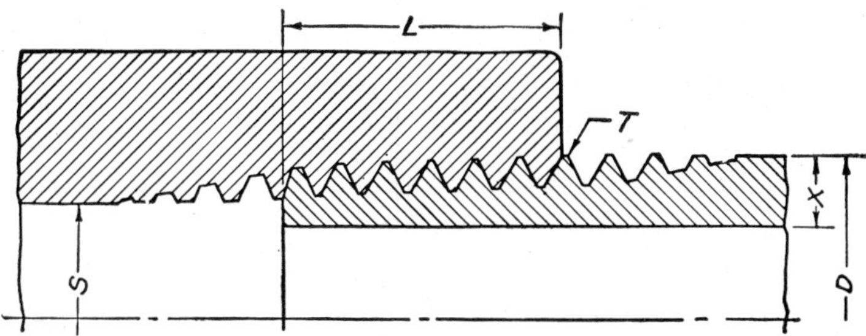

Nominal pipe size	Actual outside diam D	Tap-drill size S	Thds per in. T	Distance pipe enters fittings L	Wall thickness X			Weight—pounds per foot[6]		
					Standard 40[2]	Extra strong 80[3]	Double extra strong[4]	Standard 40[2]	Extra strong 80[3]	Double extra strong[4]
1/8	0.405	11/32	27	3/16	0.070	0.098	.....	0.25	0.32	
1/4	0.540	7/16	18	9/32	0.090	0.122	.....	0.43	0.54	
3/8	0.675	37/64	18	19/64	0.093	0.129	.....	0.57	0.74	
1/2	0.840	23/32	14	3/8	0.111	0.151	0.307	0.86	1.09	1.714
3/4	1.050	59/64	14	13/32	0.115	0.157	0.318	1.14	1.48	2.440
1	1.315	1 5/32	11 1/2	1/2	0.136	0.183	0.369	1.68	2.18	3.659
1 1/4	1.660	1 1/2	11 1/2	35/64	0.143	0.195	0.393	2.28	3.00	5.214
1 1/2	1.900	1 47/64	11 1/2	9/16	0.148	0.204	0.411	2.72	3.64	6.408
2	2.375	2 7/32	11 1/2	37/64	0.158	0.223	0.447	3.66	5.03	9.029
2 1/2	2.875	2 5/8	8	7/8	0.208	0.282	0.565	5.80	7.67	13.695
3	3.5	3 1/4	8	15/16	0.221	0.306	0.615	7.58	10.3	18.583
3 1/2	4.0	3 3/4	8	1	0.231	0.325	.....	9.11	12.5	......
4	4.5	4 1/4	8	1 1/16	0.242	0.344	0.690	10.8	15.0	27.451
5	5.563	5 5/16	8	1 5/32	0.263	0.383	0.768	14.7	20.8	38.552
6	6.625	6 5/16	8	1 1/4	0.286	0.441	0.884	19.0	28.6	53.160
8	8.625	.....	8	1 15/32	0.329	0.510	0.895	28.6	43.4	72.424
10	10.75	.....	8	1 43/64	0.372	0.606	.....	40.5	64.4	
12	12.75	.....	8	1 7/8	0.414	0.702	.....	53.6	88.6	
14 OD	14.0	.....	8	2	0.437	0.750	.....	62.2	104.	
16 OD	16.0	.....	8	2 13/64	0.500	.....	.....	81.2		
18 OD	18.0	.....	8	2 13/32	0.562	.....	.....	103.		
20 OD	20.0	.....	8	2 19/32	0.562	.....	.....	115.		
24 OD	24.0	.....	8	3						

Dimensions in inches.

[1] For welded and seamless steel pipe—see ASA B36.10 1939.

[2] Refers to American Standard schedule numbers, approximate values for the expression 1,000 × P/S. Schedule 40—standard weight.

[3] Schedule 80—extra strong.

[4] Not American Standard, but commercially available in both wrought iron and steel.

[5] A pipe size may be designated by giving the nominal pipe size and wall thickness, or by giving the nominal pipe size and weight per linear foot.

[6] Plain ends.

American 150-lb Malleable-iron Screwed-fitting Standard[1]

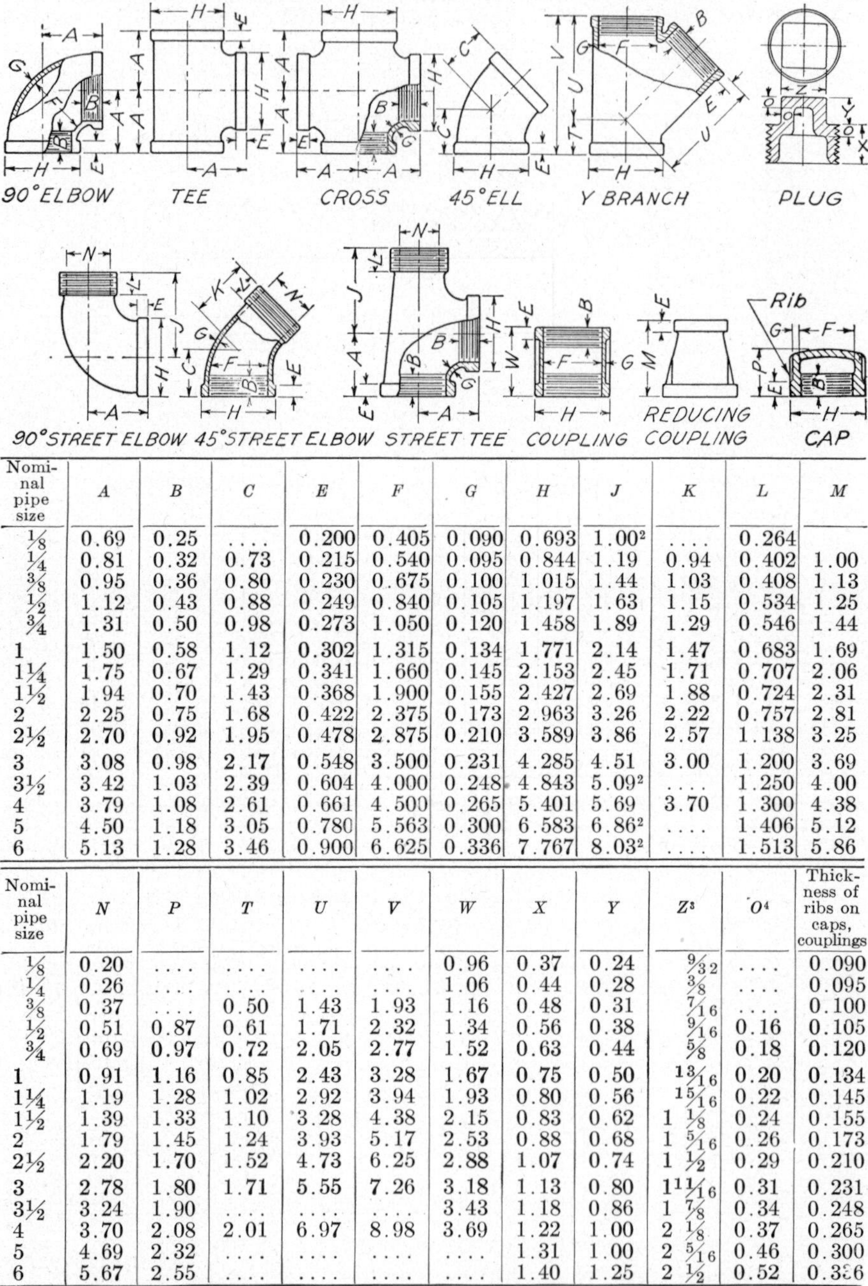

Nominal pipe size	A	B	C	E	F	G	H	J	K	L	M
⅛	0.69	0.25	....	0.200	0.405	0.090	0.693	1.00[2]	....	0.264	
¼	0.81	0.32	0.73	0.215	0.540	0.095	0.844	1.19	0.94	0.402	1.00
⅜	0.95	0.36	0.80	0.230	0.675	0.100	1.015	1.44	1.03	0.408	1.13
½	1.12	0.43	0.88	0.249	0.840	0.105	1.197	1.63	1.15	0.534	1.25
¾	1.31	0.50	0.98	0.273	1.050	0.120	1.458	1.89	1.29	0.546	1.44
1	1.50	0.58	1.12	0.302	1.315	0.134	1.771	2.14	1.47	0.683	1.69
1¼	1.75	0.67	1.29	0.341	1.660	0.145	2.153	2.45	1.71	0.707	2.06
1½	1.94	0.70	1.43	0.368	1.900	0.155	2.427	2.69	1.88	0.724	2.31
2	2.25	0.75	1.68	0.422	2.375	0.173	2.963	3.26	2.22	0.757	2.81
2½	2.70	0.92	1.95	0.478	2.875	0.210	3.589	3.86	2.57	1.138	3.25
3	3.08	0.98	2.17	0.548	3.500	0.231	4.285	4.51	3.00	1.200	3.69
3½	3.42	1.03	2.39	0.604	4.000	0.248	4.843	5.09[2]	....	1.250	4.00
4	3.79	1.08	2.61	0.661	4.500	0.265	5.401	5.69	3.70	1.300	4.38
5	4.50	1.18	3.05	0.780	5.563	0.300	6.583	6.86[2]	....	1.406	5.12
6	5.13	1.28	3.46	0.900	6.625	0.336	7.767	8.03[2]	....	1.513	5.86

Nominal pipe size	N	P	T	U	V	W	X	Y	Z[3]	O[4]	Thickness of ribs on caps, couplings
⅛	0.20	....	....	....	....	0.96	0.37	0.24	9/32	....	0.090
¼	0.26	....	....	....	....	1.06	0.44	0.28	⅜	....	0.095
⅜	0.37	....	0.50	1.43	1.93	1.16	0.48	0.31	7/16	....	0.100
½	0.51	0.87	0.61	1.71	2.32	1.34	0.56	0.38	9/16	0.16	0.105
¾	0.69	0.97	0.72	2.05	2.77	1.52	0.63	0.44	⅝	0.18	0.120
1	0.91	1.16	0.85	2.43	3.28	1.67	0.75	0.50	13/16	0.20	0.134
1¼	1.19	1.28	1.02	2.92	3.94	1.93	0.80	0.56	15/16	0.22	0.145
1½	1.39	1.33	1.10	3.28	4.38	2.15	0.83	0.62	1 ⅛	0.24	0.155
2	1.79	1.45	1.24	3.93	5.17	2.53	0.88	0.68	1 5/16	0.26	0.173
2½	2.20	1.70	1.52	4.73	6.25	2.88	1.07	0.74	1 ½	0.29	0.210
3	2.78	1.80	1.71	5.55	7.26	3.18	1.13	0.80	1 11/16	0.31	0.231
3½	3.24	1.90	....	....	....	3.43	1.18	0.86	1 ⅞	0.34	0.248
4	3.70	2.08	2.01	6.97	8.98	3.69	1.22	1.00	2 ⅛	0.37	0.265
5	4.69	2.32	....	....	....	....	1.31	1.00	2 5/16	0.46	0.300
6	5.67	2.55	....	....	....	....	1.40	1.25	2 ½	0.52	0.336

Dimensions in inches. Left-hand couplings have four or more ribs. Right-hand couplings have two ribs.
[1] ASA B16c 1939. Street tee not made in ⅛″ size. [2] Street ell only. [3] These dimensions are the nominal size of wrench (ASA B18.2 1941). Square-head plugs are designed to fit these wrenches. [4] Solid plugs are provided in sizes ⅛ to 3½ in. incl.; cored plugs ½ to 3½ in., inclusive. Cored plugs have minimum metal thickness at all points equal to dimension *O* except at the end of the thread.

American Standard Cast-iron Screwed Fittings[1]

FOR MAXIMUM WORKING SATURATED STEAM PRESSURE OF 125 AND 250 PSI

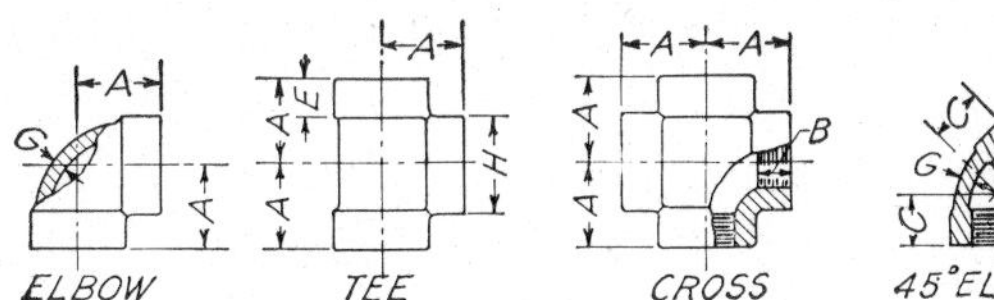

Nominal pipe size	A	B min	C	E min	F Min	F Max	G min	H min
¼	0.81	0.32	0.73	0.38	0.540	0.584	0.110	0.93
⅜	0.95	0.36	0.80	0.44	0.675	0.719	0.120	1.12
½	1.12	0.43	0.88	0.50	0.840	0.897	0.130	1.34
¾	1.31	0.50	0.98	0.56	1.050	1.107	0.155	1.63
1	1.50	0.58	1.12	0.62	1.315	1.385	0.170	1.95
1¼	1.75	0.67	1.29	0.69	1.660	1.730	0.185	2.39
1½	1.94	0.70	1.43	0.75	1.900	1.970	0.200	2.68
2	2.25	0.75	1.68	0.84	2.375	2.445	0.220	3.28
2½	2.70	0.92	1.95	0.94	2.875	2.975	0.240	3.86
3	3.08	0.98	2.17	1.00	3.500	3.600	0.260	4.62
3½	3.42	1.03	2.39	1.06	4.000	4.100	0.280	5.20
4	3.79	1.08	2.61	1.12	4.500	4.600	0.310	5.79
5	4.50	1.18	3.05	1.18	5.563	5.663	0.380	7.05
6	5.13	1.28	3.46	1.28	6.625	6.725	0.430	8.28
8	6.56	1.47	4.28	1.47	8.625	8.725	0.550	10.63
10	8.08	1.68	5.16	1.68	10.750	10.850	0.690	13.12
12	9.50	1.88	5.97	1.88	12.750	12.850	0.800	15.47

Dimensions in inches.
[1] ASA B16d 1941.

Globe, Angle-globe, and Gate Valves[1]

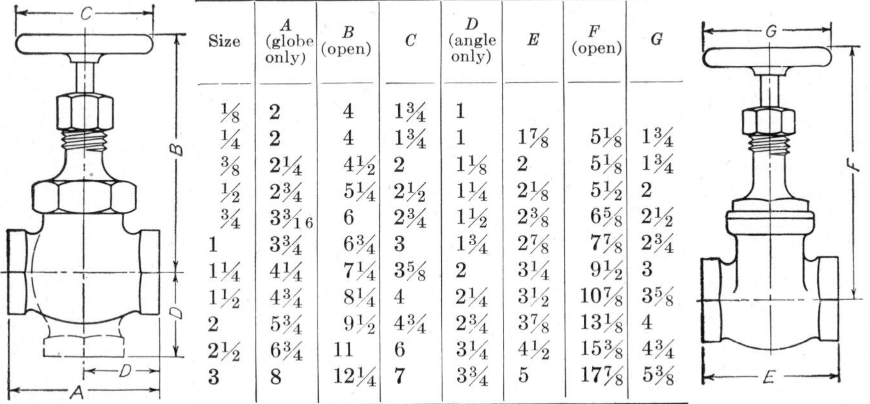

Size	A (globe only)	B (open)	C	D (angle only)	E	F (open)	G
⅛	2	4	1¾	1			
¼	2	4	1¾	1	1⅞	5⅛	1¾
⅜	2¼	4½	2	1⅛	2	5⅛	1¾
½	2¾	5¼	2½	1¼	2⅛	5½	2
¾	3 3/16	6	2¾	1½	2⅜	6⅝	2½
1	3¾	6¾	3	1¾	2⅞	7⅞	2¾
1¼	4¼	7¼	3⅝	2	3¼	9½	3
1½	4¾	8¼	4	2¼	3½	10⅞	3⅝
2	5¾	9½	4¾	2¾	3⅞	13⅛	4
2½	6¾	11	6	3¼	4½	15⅜	4¾
3	8	12¼	7	3¾	5	17⅞	5⅜

Dimensions in inches.
[1] Dimensions compiled from manufacturers' catalogues for drawing purposes.

American Standard Cast-iron Pipe Flanges and Flanged Fittings[1]

FOR MAXIMUM WORKING SATURATED STEAM PRESSURE OF 125 PSI (GAGE)
APPROVED BY AMERICAN STANDARDS ASSOCIATION, 1939

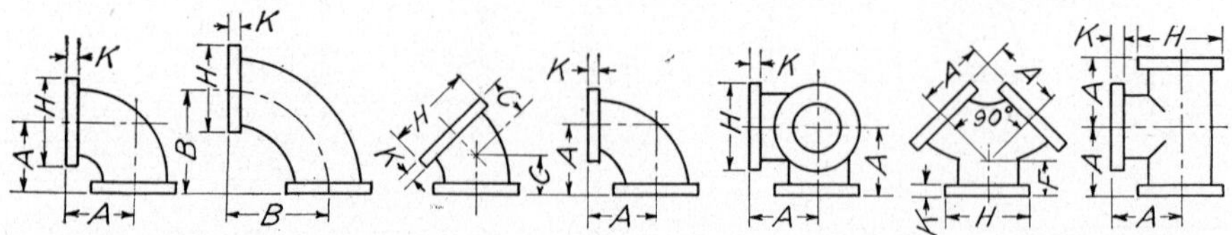

90°ELL LONG RAD.ELL 45°ELL REDUCING ELL SIDE OUTLET ELL TRUE"Y" TEE

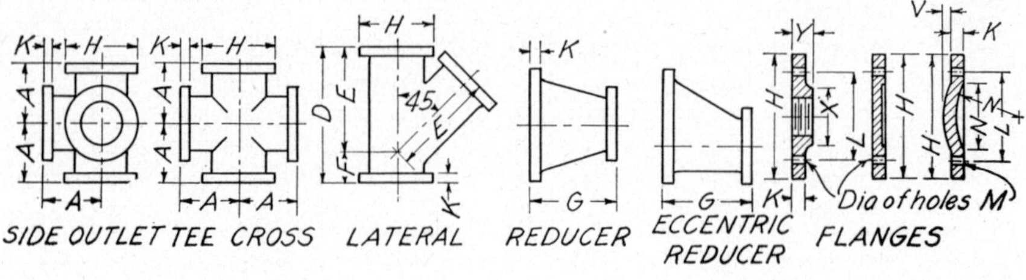

SIDE OUTLET TEE CROSS LATERAL REDUCER ECCENTRIC REDUCER FLANGES

Nominal pipe size N	A	B	C	D	E	F	G	H	K min
1	3 1/2	5	1 3/4	7 1/2	5 3/4	1 3/4	....	4 1/4	7/16
1 1/4	3 3/4	5 1/2	2	8	6 1/4	1 3/4	....	4 5/8	1/2
1 1/2	4	6	2 1/4	9	7	2	....	5	9/16
2	4 1/2	6 1/2	2 1/2	10 1/2	8	2 1/2	5	6	5/8
2 1/2	5	7	3	12	9 1/2	2 1/2	5 1/2	7	11/16
3	5 1/2	7 3/4	3	13	10	3	6	7 1/2	3/4
3 1/2	6	8 1/2	3 1/2	14 1/2	11 1/2	3	6 1/2	8 1/2	13/16
4	6 1/2	9	4	15	12	3	7	9	15/16
5	7 1/2	10 1/4	4 1/2	17	13 1/2	3 1/2	8	10	15/16
6	8	11 1/2	5	18	14 1/2	3 1/2	9	11	1
8	9	14	5 1/2	22	17 1/2	4 1/2	11	13 1/2	1 1/8
10	11	16 1/2	6 1/2	25 1/2	20 1/2	5	12	16	1 3/16
12	12	19	7 1/2	30	24 1/2	5 1/2	14	19	1 1/4

Nominal pipe size N	L	M	Number of bolts	Diam of bolts	Length of bolts	X min	Y min	Wall thickness	V
1	3 1/8	5/8	4	1/2	1 3/4	1 15/16	11/16	5/16	3/8
1 1/4	3 1/2	5/8	4	1/2	2	2 5/16	13/16	5/16	7/16
1 1/2	3 7/8	5/8	4	1/2	2	2 9/16	7/8	5/16	1/2
2	4 3/4	3/4	4	5/8	2 1/4	3 1/16	1	5/16	9/16
2 1/2	5 1/2	3/4	4	5/8	2 1/2	3 9/16	1 1/8	5/16	5/8
3	6	3/4	4	5/8	2 1/2	4 1/4	1 3/16	3/8	11/16
3 1/2	7	3/4	8	5/8	2 3/4	4 13/16	1 1/4	7/16	3/4
4	7 1/2	3/4	8	5/8	3	5 5/16	1 5/16	1/2	7/8
5	8 1/2	7/8	8	3/4	3	6 7/16	1 7/16	1/2	7/8
6	9 1/2	7/8	8	3/4	3 1/4	7 9/16	1 9/16	9/16	15/16
8	11 3/4	7/8	8	3/4	3 1/2	9 11/16	1 3/4	5/8	1 1/16
10	14 1/4	1	12	7/8	3 3/4	11 15/16	1 15/16	3/4	1 1/8
12	17	1	12	7/8	3 3/4	14 1/16	2 3/16	13/16	

Dimensions in inches.
[1] ASA B16a 1939.

American Standard Steel Butt-welding Fittings[1,2]

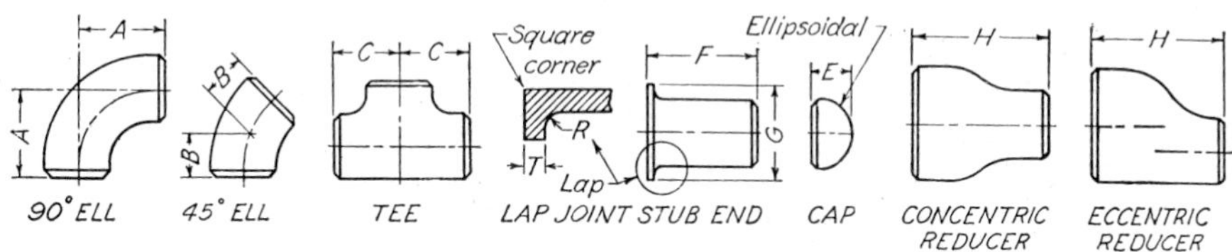

ELBOWS, TEES, CAPS, AND STUB ENDS

Nominal pipe size	Outside diameter at bevel	Center to end: 90-deg welding elbow A	Center to end: 45-deg welding elbow B	Center to end: of run, welding tee C	Welding caps E	Lapped-joint stub ends: Lengths F	Lapped-joint stub ends: Radius of fillet R	Lapped-joint stub ends: Diameter of lap G
1	1.310	1½	⅞	1½	1½	4	⅛	2
1¼	1.660	1⅞	1	1⅞	1½	4	3/16	2½
1½	1.900	2¼	1⅛	2¼	1½	4	¼	2⅞
2	2.375	3	1⅜	2½	1½	6	5/16	3⅝
2½	2.875	3¾	1¾	3	1½	6	5/16	4⅛
3	3.500	4½	2	3⅜	2	6	⅜	5
3½	4.000	5¼	2¼	3¾	2½	6	⅜	5½
4	4.500	6	2½	4⅛	2½	6	7/16	6 3/16

BUTT-WELDING REDUCERS

Nominal pipe size	Outside diameter at bevel: Large end	Outside diameter at bevel: Small end	End to end H
1 × ¾	1.315	1.050	2
1 × ½		0.840	
1 × ⅜		0.675	
1¼ × 1	1.660	1.315	2
1¼ × ¾		1.050	
1¼ × ½		0.840	
1½ × 1¼	1.900	1.660	2½
1½ × 1		1.315	
1½ × ¾		1.050	
1½ × ½		0.840	
2 × 1½	2.375	1.900	3
2 × 1¼		1.660	
2 × 1		1.315	
2 × ¾		1.050	
2½ × 2	2.875	2.375	3½
2½ × 1½		1.900	
2½ × 1¼		1 660	
2½ × 1		1.315	
3 × 2½	3.500	2.875	3½
3 × 2		2.375	
3 × 1½		1.900	
3 × 1¼		1.660	
3½ × 3	4.000	3.500	4
3½ × 2½		2.875	
3½ × 2		2.375	
3½ × 1½		1.900	
3½ × 1¼		1.660	
4 × 3½	4.500	4.000	4
4 × 3		3.500	
4 × 2½		2.875	
4 × 2		2.375	
4 × 1½		1.900	
5 × 4	5.563	4.500	5
5 × 3½		4.000	
5 × 3		3.500	
5 × 2½		2.875	

Dimensions in inches.
[1] For larger sizes see ASA B16.
[2] ASA B16.9 1940.

Threaded Cast-iron Pipe[1]

DIMENSION OF PIPE AND DRAINAGE HUBS

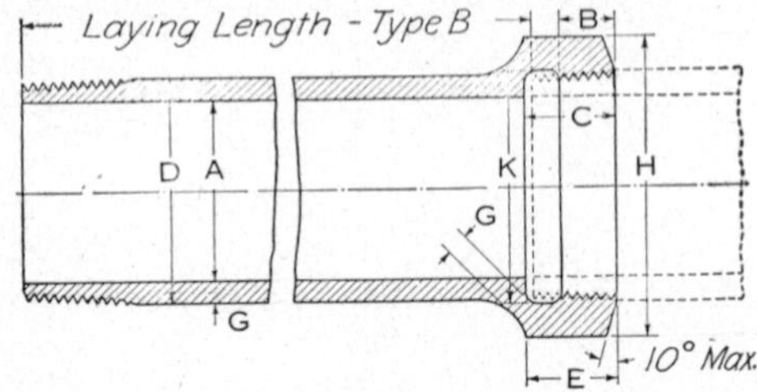

Pipe size	Pipe			Drainage hubs					Nominal weights	
	Nominal diameter		Wall thick-ness min	Thread length[1]	Diameter of groove max	End to shoulder[2]	Minimum band		Type *A* and barrel of type *B* per ft	Additional wt of hubs for type *B*
	Outside *D*	Inside *A*	*G*	*B*	*K*	*C*	Diameter *H*	Length *E*		
1¼	1.66	1.23	0.187	0.42	1.73	0.71	2.39	0.71	3.033	0.60
1½	1.90	1.45	0.195	0.42	1.97	0.72	2.68	0.72	3.666	0.90
2	2.38	1.89	0.211	0.43	2.44	0.76	3.28	0.76	5.041	1.00
2½	2.88	2.32	0.241	0.68	2.97	1.14	3.86	1.14	7.032	1.35
3	3.50	2.90	0.263	0.76	3.60	1.20	4.62	1.20	9.410	2.80
4	4.50	3.83	0.294	0.84	4.60	1.30	5.79	1.30	13.751	3.48
5	5.56	4.81	0.328	0.93	5.66	1.41	7.05	1.41	19.069	5.00
6	6.63	5.76	0.378	0.95	6.72	1.51	8.28	1.51	26.223	6.60
8	8.63	7.63	0.438	1.06	8.72	1.71	10.63	1.71	39.820	10.00
10	10.75	9.75	0.438	1.21	10.85	1.92	13.12	1.93	50.234	
12	12.75	11.75	0.438	1.36	12.85	2.12	15.47	2.13	60.036	

All dimensions are given in inches, except where otherwise stated. Type *A* has external threads both ends. Type *B* as shown. [1] ASA A40.5 1943. [2] The length of thread *B* and the end to shoulder *C* shall not vary from the dimensions shown by more than plus or minus the equivalent of the pitch of one thread.

Beam connections

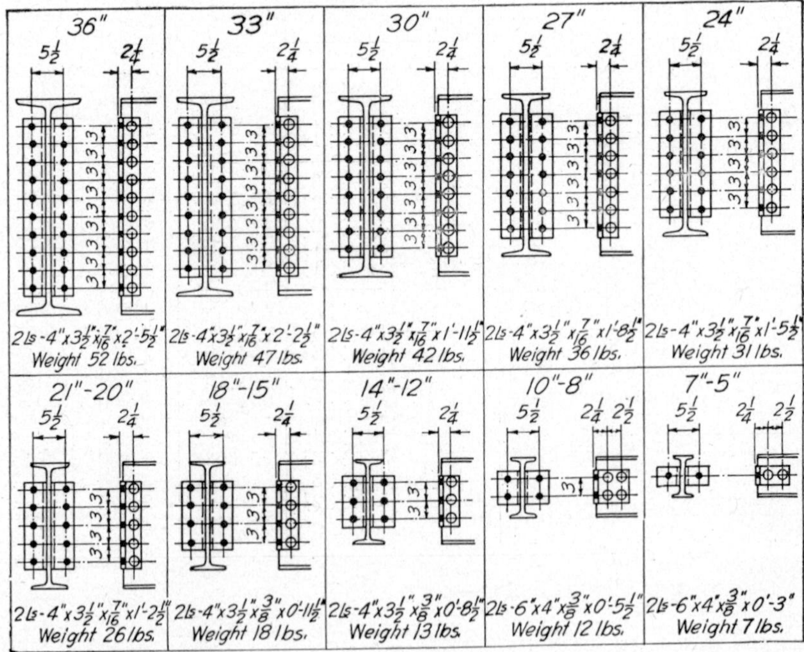

Wire and Sheet-metal Gages

DIMENSIONS IN DECIMAL PARTS OF AN INCH

Number of gage	American or Brown and Sharpe[1]	Washburn & Moen or American Steel & Wire Co.[2]	Birmingham or Stubs iron wire[3]	Music wire[4]	Imperial wire gage[5]	U.S. Std. for plate[6]
0000000	......	0.4900	.....	.....	0.5000	0.5000
000000	0.5800	0.4615	.....	0.004	0.4640	0.4688
00000	0.5165	0.4305	0.500	0.005	0.4320	0.4375
0000	0.4600	0.3938	0.454	0.006	0.4000	0.4063
000	0.4096	0.3625	0.425	0.007	0.3720	0.3750
00	0.3648	0.3310	0.380	0.008	0.3480	0.3438
0	0.3249	0.3065	0.340	0.009	0.3240	0.3125
1	0.2893	0.2830	0.300	0.010	0.3000	0.2813
2	0.2576	0.2625	0.284	0.011	0.2760	0.2656
3	0.2294	0.2437	0.259	0.012	0.2520	0.2500
4	0.2043	0.2253	0.238	0.013	0.2320	0.2344
5	0.1819	0.2070	0.220	0.014	0.2120	0.2188
6	0.1620	0.1920	0.203	0.016	0.1920	0.2031
7	0.1443	0.1770	0.180	0.018	0.1760	0.1875
8	0.1285	0.1620	0.165	0.020	0.1600	0.1719
9	0.1144	0.1483	0.148	0.022	0.1440	0.1563
10	0.1019	0.1350	0.134	0.024	0.1280	0.1406
11	0.0907	0.1205	0.120	0.026	0.1160	0.1250
12	0.0808	0.1055	0.109	0.029	0.1040	0.1094
13	0.0720	0.0915	0.095	0.031	0.0920	0.0938
14	0.0641	0.0800	0.083	0.033	0.0800	0.0781
15	0.0571	0.0720	0.072	0.035	0.0720	0.0703
16	0.0508	0.0625	0.065	0.037	0.0640	0.0625
17	0.0453	0.0540	0.058	0.039	0.0560	0.0563
18	0.0403	0.0475	0.049	0.041	0.0480	0.0500
19	0.0359	0.0410	0.042	0.043	0.0400	0.0438
20	0.0320	0.0348	0.035	0.045	0.0360	0.0375
21	0.0285	0.0317	0.032	0.047	0.0320	0.0344
22	0.0253	0.0286	0.028	0.049	0.0280	0.0313
23	0.0226	0.0258	0.025	0.051	0.0240	0.0281
24	0.0201	0.0230	0.022	0.055	0.0220	0.0250
25	0.0179	0.0204	0.020	0.059	0.0200	0.0219
26	0.0159	0.0181	0.018	0.063	0.0180	0.0188
27	0.0142	0.0173	0.016	0.067	0.0164	0.0172
28	0.0126	0.0162	0.014	0.071	0.0148	0.0156
29	0.0113	0.0150	0.013	0.075	0.0136	0.0141
30	0.0100	0.0140	0.012	0.080	0.0124	0.0125
31	0.0089	0.0132	0.010	0.085	0.0116	0.0109
32	0.0080	0.0128	0.009	0.090	0.0108	0.0102
33	0.0071	0.0118	0.008	0.095	0.0100	0.0094
34	0.0063	0.0104	0.007	0.100	0.0092	0.0086
35	0.0056	0.0095	0.005	0.106	0.0084	0.0078
36	0.0050	0.0090	0.004	0.112	0.0076	0.0070
37	0.0045	0.0085	.....	0.118	0.0068	0.0066
38	0.0040	0.0080	.....	0.124	0.0060	0.0063
39	0.0035	0.0075	.....	0.130	0.0052	
40	0.0031	0.0070	.....	0.138	0.0048	

[1] Recognized standard in the United States for wire and sheet metal of copper and other metals except steel and iron.

[2] Recognized standard for steel and iron wire. Called the "U.S. steel wire gage."

[3] Formerly much used, now nearly obsolete.

[4] American Steel & Wire Company's music or piano wire gage. Recommended by U.S. Bureau of Standards.

[5] Official British Standard.

[6] Legalized U.S. Standard for iron and steel plate, although plate is now always specified by its thickness in decimals of an inch.

Preferred thicknesses for uncoated thin flats metals (under 0.250 in.), ASA B32 1941, gives recommended sizes for sheets.

American Standard graphical symbols[1]

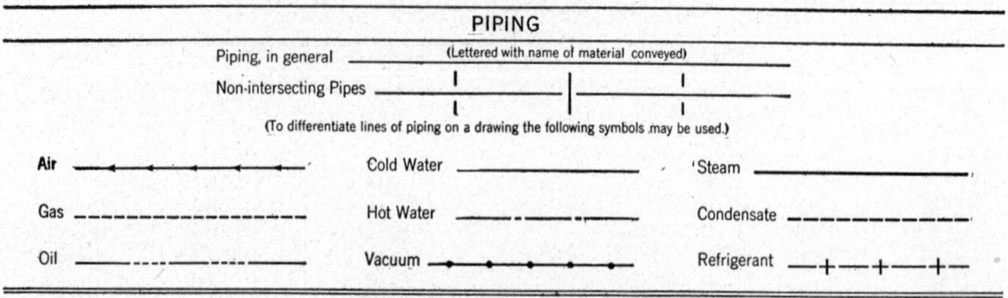

PIPING

Piping, in general (Lettered with name of material conveyed)

Non-intersecting Pipes

(To differentiate lines of piping on a drawing the following symbols may be used.)

Air	Cold Water	Steam
Gas	Hot Water	Condensate
Oil	Vacuum	Refrigerant

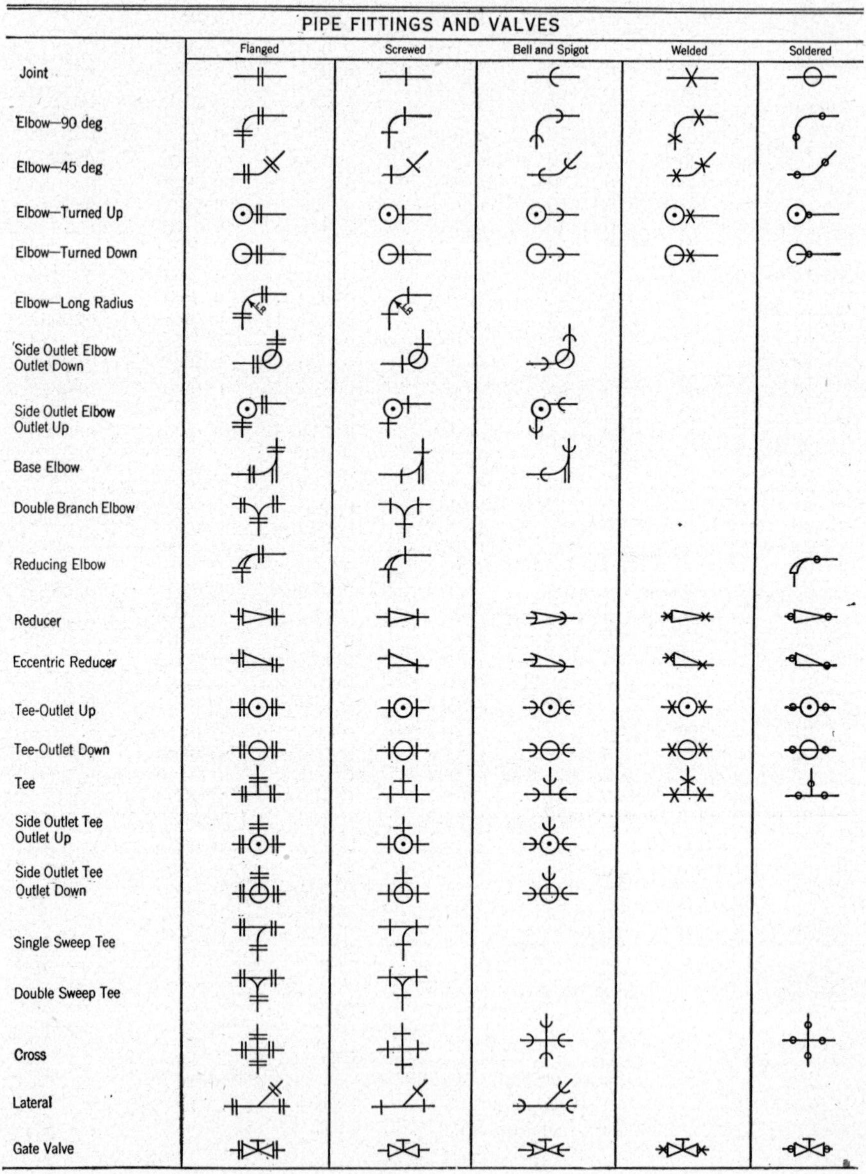

PIPE FITTINGS AND VALVES

	Flanged	Screwed	Bell and Spigot	Welded	Soldered
Joint					
Elbow—90 deg					
Elbow—45 deg					
Elbow—Turned Up					
Elbow—Turned Down					
Elbow—Long Radius					
Side Outlet Elbow Outlet Down					
Side Outlet Elbow Outlet Up					
Base Elbow					
Double Branch Elbow					
Reducing Elbow					
Reducer					
Eccentric Reducer					
Tee-Outlet Up					
Tee-Outlet Down					
Tee					
Side Outlet Tee Outlet Up					
Side Outlet Tee Outlet Down					
Single Sweep Tee					
Double Sweep Tee					
Cross					
Lateral					
Gate Valve					

[1] ASA Z14.2 1935.

American Standard graphical symbols[1]

PIPING

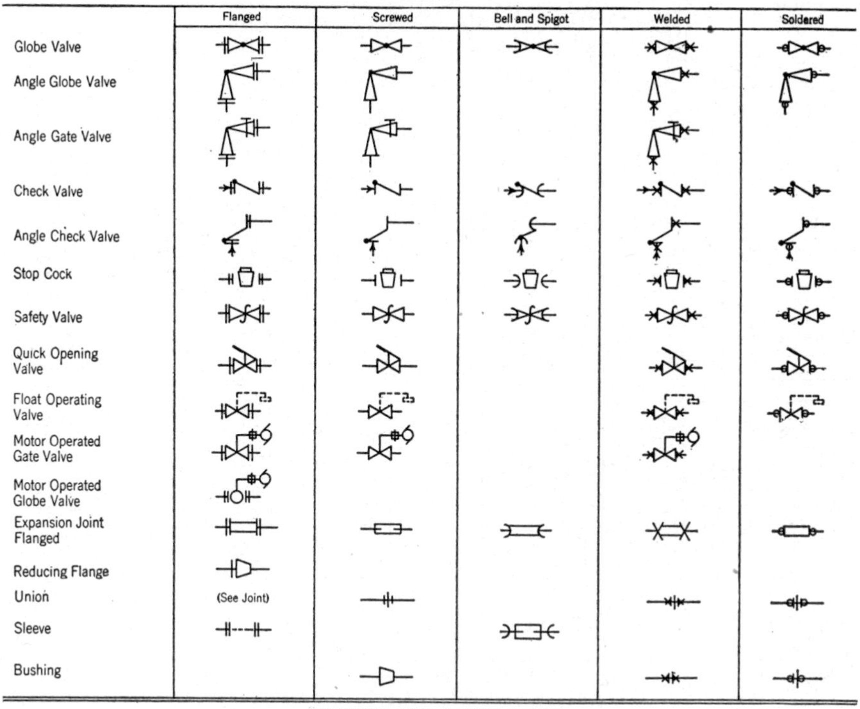

	Flanged	Screwed	Bell and Spigot	Welded	Soldered
Globe Valve					
Angle Globe Valve					
Angle Gate Valve					
Check Valve					
Angle Check Valve					
Stop Cock					
Safety Valve					
Quick Opening Valve					
Float Operating Valve					
Motor Operated Gate Valve					
Motor Operated Globe Valve					
Expansion Joint Flanged					
Reducing Flange					
Union	(See Joint)				
Sleeve					
Bushing					

HEATING AND VENTILATING

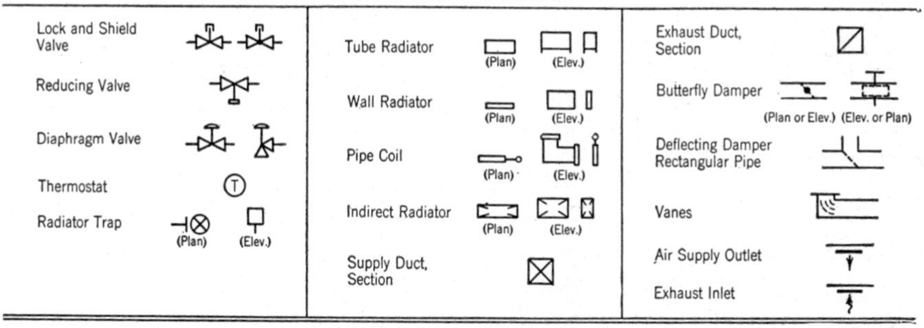

Lock and Shield Valve

Reducing Valve

Diaphragm Valve

Thermostat

Radiator Trap (Plan) (Elev.)

Tube Radiator (Plan) (Elev.)

Wall Radiator (Plan) (Elev.)

Pipe Coil (Plan) (Elev.)

Indirect Radiator (Plan) (Elev.)

Supply Duct, Section

Exhaust Duct, Section

Butterfly Damper (Plan or Elev.) (Elev. or Plan)

Deflecting Damper Rectangular Pipe

Vanes

Air Supply Outlet

Exhaust Inlet

HEAT-POWER APPARATUS

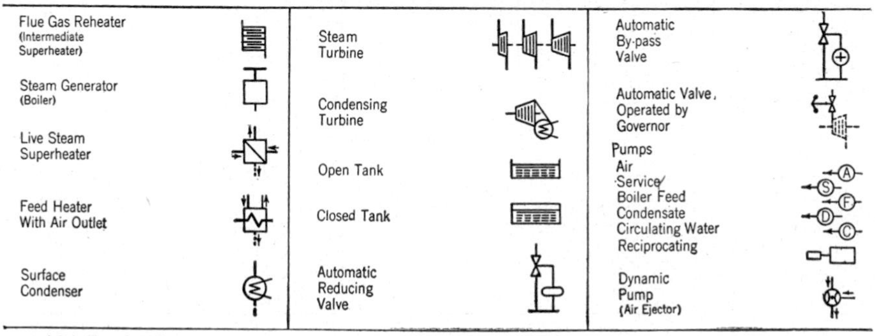

Flue Gas Reheater (Intermediate Superheater)

Steam Generator (Boiler)

Live Steam Superheater

Feed Heater With Air Outlet

Surface Condenser

Steam Turbine

Condensing Turbine

Open Tank

Closed Tank

Automatic Reducing Valve

Automatic By-pass Valve

Automatic Valve, Operated by Governor

Pumps
Air
Service
Boiler Feed
Condensate
Circulating Water
Reciprocating

Dynamic Pump (Air Ejector)

[1] ASA Z14.2 1935.

Plumbing symbols[1]

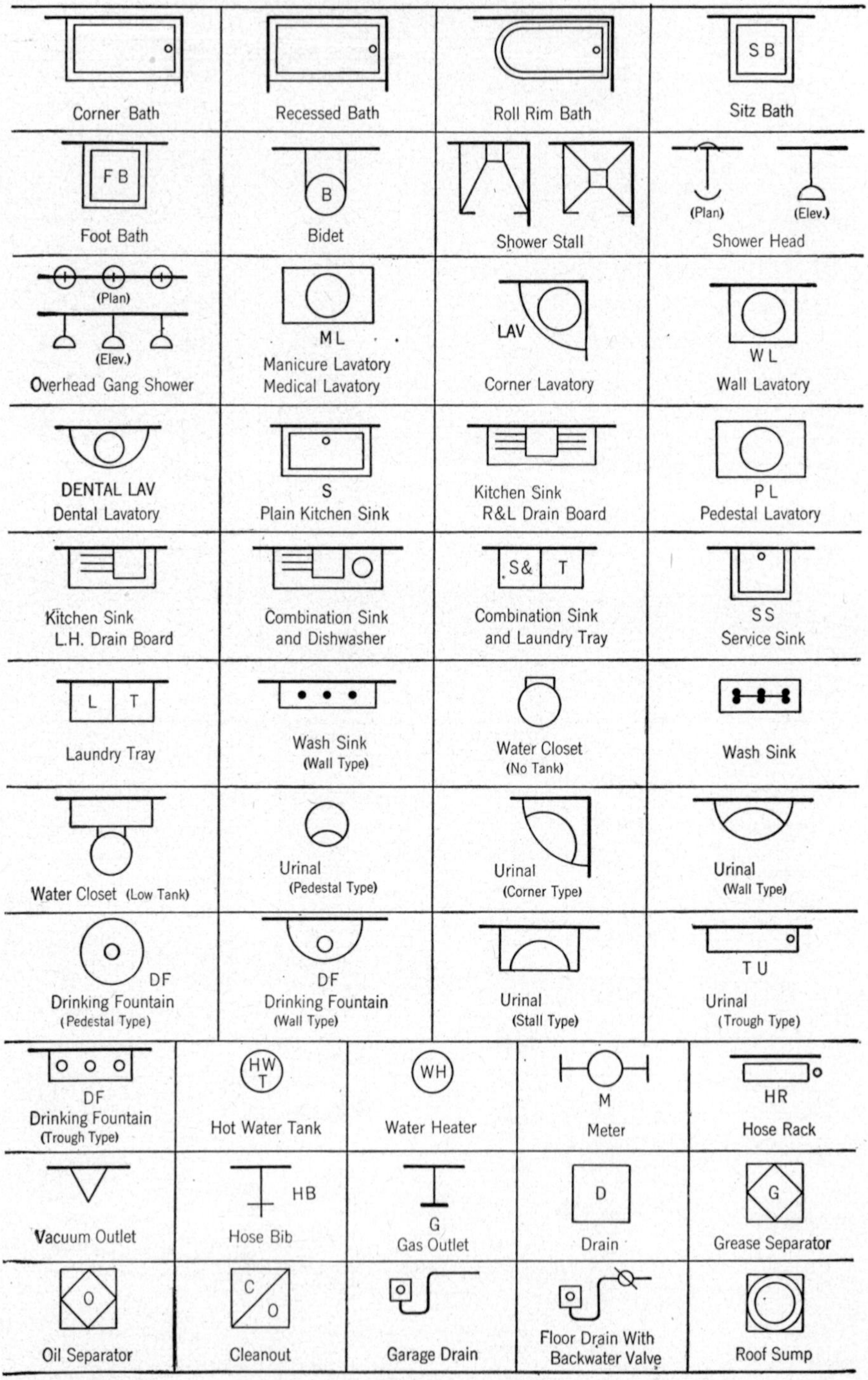

Corner Bath	Recessed Bath	Roll Rim Bath	S B Sitz Bath
F B Foot Bath	B Bidet	Shower Stall	(Plan) (Elev.) Shower Head
(Plan) (Elev.) Overhead Gang Shower	M L Manicure Lavatory Medical Lavatory	LAV Corner Lavatory	W L Wall Lavatory
DENTAL LAV Dental Lavatory	S Plain Kitchen Sink	Kitchen Sink R&L Drain Board	P L Pedestal Lavatory
Kitchen Sink L.H. Drain Board	Combination Sink and Dishwasher	S& T Combination Sink and Laundry Tray	S S Service Sink
L T Laundry Tray	Wash Sink (Wall Type)	Water Closet (No Tank)	Wash Sink
Water Closet (Low Tank)	Urinal (Pedestal Type)	Urinal (Corner Type)	Urinal (Wall Type)
DF Drinking Fountain (Pedestal Type)	DF Drinking Fountain (Wall Type)	Urinal (Stall Type)	T U Urinal (Trough Type)

DF Drinking Fountain (Trough Type)	HW T Hot Water Tank	WH Water Heater	M Meter	HR Hose Rack
Vacuum Outlet	HB Hose Bib	G Gas Outlet	D Drain	G Grease Separator
O Oil Separator	C O Cleanout	Garage Drain	Floor Drain With Backwater Valve	Roof Sump

A Z14.2 1935.

American Standard wiring symbols[1]

- Ceiling Outlet
- " " for Extensions
- " Lamp Receptacle, Specifications to describe type, as Key, Keyless or Pull Chain
- Ceiling Fan Outlet
- Pull Switch — PS
- Drop Cord
- Wall Bracket
- " Outlet for Extensions
- " Lamp Receptacle, as specified
- " Fan Outlet
- Single Convenience Outlet
- Double " " "
- Junction Box
- Special Purpose Outlets Lighting, Heating and Power as described in specifications
- Exit Light
- Floor Outlet
- Floor Elbow, Floor Tee
- Local Switch, Single Pole — S^1
- Double Pole — S^2, 3-Way — S^3, 4-Way — S^4
- Automatic Door Switch — S^D
- Key Push Button Switch — S^K
- Electrolier Switch — S^E
- Push Button Switch and Pilot — S^P
- Remote Control Push Button Switch — S^R
- Tank Switch — T.S.
- Motor, Motor Controller — M.C.
- Lighting Panel
- Power Panel
- Heating Panel
- Pull Box
- Cable Supporting Box
- Meter
- Transformer
- Push Button
- Pole Line
- Buzzer, Bell
- Annunciator

- Branch Circuit, Run Exposed
- Run Concealed Under Floor
- " " " Floor Above
- Feeder Run Exposed
- " Run Concealed Under Floor
- " " " Floor Above
- Telephone, Interior, Public
- Clock, Secondary, Master
- Time Stamp
- Electric Door Opener
- Local Fire Alarm Gong — F
- City Fire Alarm Station
- Local " " " — F
- Fire Alarm Central Station — FA
- Speaking Tube
- Nurse's Signal Plug — N
- Maid's Plug — M
- Horn Outlet
- District Messenger Call
- Watchman Station — W
- Watchman Central Station Detector — W
- Public Telephone-P.B.X. Switchboard — PBX
- Interior Telephone Central Switchboard — IX
- Interconnection Cabinet
- Telephone Cabinet
- Telegraph "
- Special Outlet for Signal System as Specified
- Battery
- Signal Wires in Conduit Under Floor
- " " " " " Floor Above

This Character Marked on Tap Circuits Indicates

2 No. 14 Conductors in	$\frac{1}{2}$" Conduit		II
3 " 14 "	" $\frac{1}{2}$" "		III
4 " 14 "	" $\frac{3}{4}$" "	(Unless Marked $\frac{1}{2}$")	IIII
5 " 14 "	" $\frac{3}{4}$" "		IIIII
6 " 14 "	" 1" "	(Unless Marked $\frac{3}{4}$")	IIIIII
7 " 14 "	" 1" "		IIIIIII
8 " 14 "	" 1" "		IIIIIIII

- (Radio Outlet)
- (Public Speaker Outlet)

[1] ASA C10

Electric symbols[1]

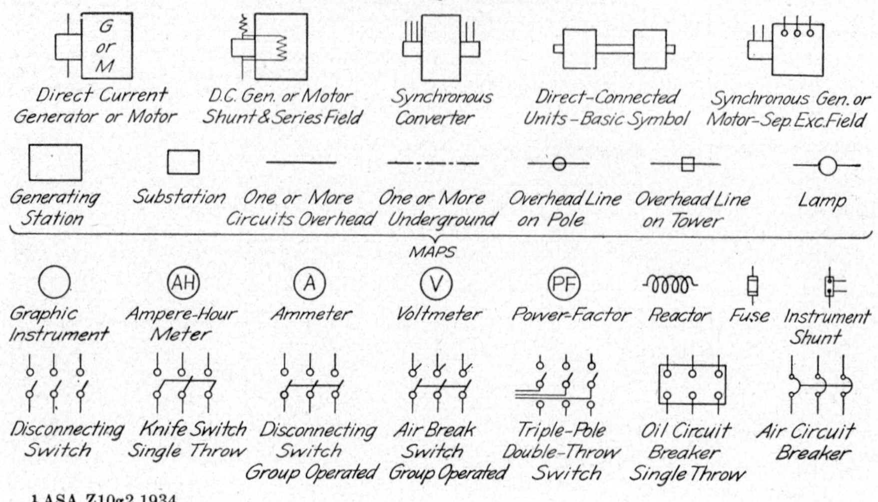

[1] ASA Z10g2 1934.

Radio symbols[2]

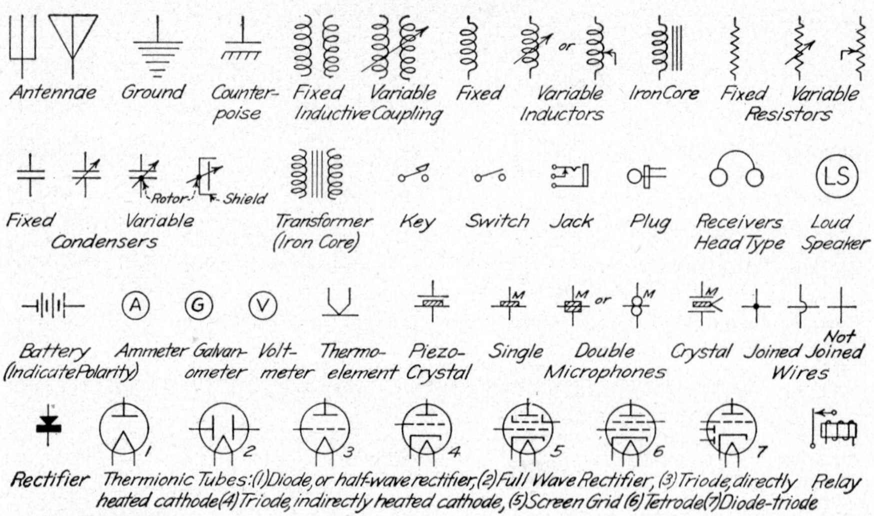

[2] ASA Z10g3 1933.

Symbols for materials (exterior)

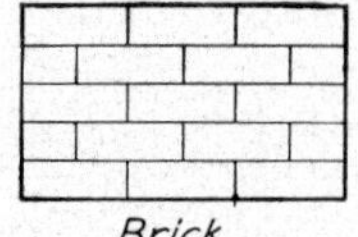

Brick

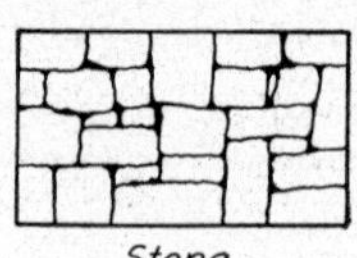

Stone

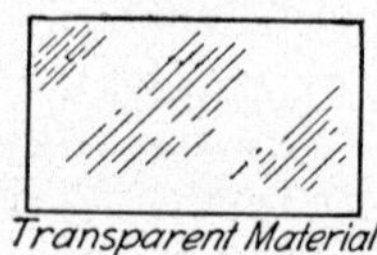

Transparent Material Glass, Celluloid, Etc.

Wood

Symbols for materials (section)

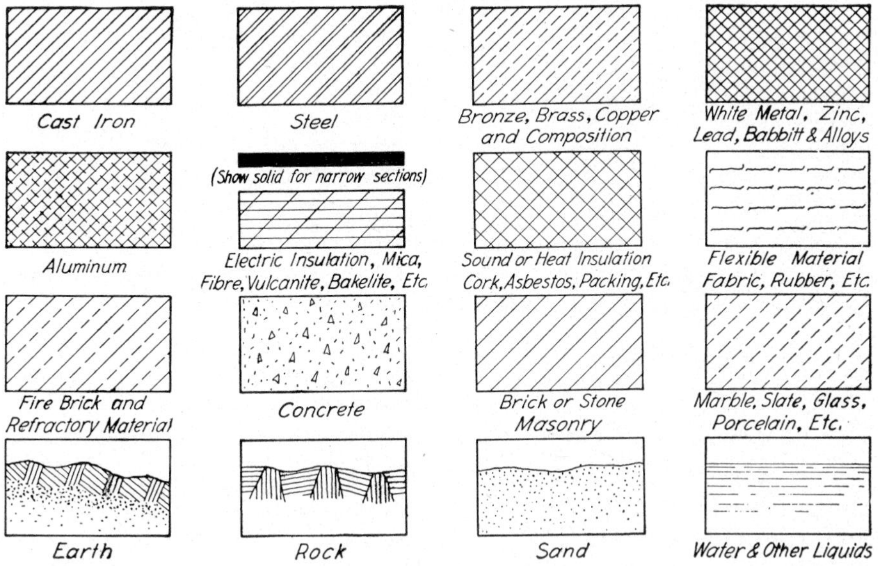

Cast Iron	Steel	Bronze, Brass, Copper and Composition	White Metal, Zinc, Lead, Babbitt & Alloys
Aluminum	(Show solid for narrow sections) Electric Insulation, Mica, Fibre, Vulcanite, Bakelite, Etc.	Sound or Heat Insulation Cork, Asbestos, Packing, Etc.	Flexible Material Fabric, Rubber, Etc.
Fire Brick and Refractory Material	Concrete	Brick or Stone Masonry	Marble, Slate, Glass, Porcelain, Etc.
Earth	Rock	Sand	Water & Other Liquids

Weights of Materials

METALS

	lb/cu in.
Aluminum alloy, cast	0.099
Aluminum, cast	0.094
Aluminum, wrought	0.097
Babbitt metal	0.267
Brass, cast or rolled	0.303–0.313
Brass, drawn	0.323
Bronze, aluminum cast	0.277
Bronze, phosphor	0.315–0.321
Chromium	0.256
Copper, cast	0.311
Copper, rolled, drawn or wire	0.322
Dowmetal *A*	0.065
Duralumin	0.101

	lb/cu in.
Gold	0.697
Iron, cast	0.260
Iron, wrought	0.283
Lead	0.411
Magnesium	0.063
Mercury	0.491
Monel metal	0.323
Silver	0.379
Steel, cast or rolled	0.274–0.281
Steel, tool	0.272
Tin	0.263
Zinc	0.258

WOOD

	lb/cu in.
Ash	0.024
Balsa	0.0058
Cedar	0.017
Cork	0.009
Hickory	0.0295
Maple	0.025
Oak (white)	0.028
Pine (white)	0.015
Pine (yellow)	0.025
Poplar	0.018
Walnut (black)	0.023

MISCELLANEOUS MATERIALS

	lb/cu ft
Asbestos	175
Bakelite	79.5
Brick, common	112
Brick, fire	144
Celluloid	86.4
Earth, packed	100
Fiber	89.9
Glass	163
Gravel	109
Limestone	163
Plexiglass	74.3
Sandstone	144
Water	62.4

ABBREVIATIONS AND WORD SYMBOLS TO BE USED ON DRAWINGS

Alternating current	a-c
Angle (structural shape)	∟
American Standard	Am Std
American Standards Association	ASA
American wire gage (B & S gage)	Awg
Approved (by)	App
Birmingham wire gage	Bwg
Brown & Sharpe gage	B & S
Babbitt metal (specified by number)	bab #——
Brass, SAE (specified by number)	br #——
Bronze, SAE (specified by number)	bro #——
Brinell hardness number	Bhn
Cast iron	CI
Center line	℄ or CL
Center to center	c to c
Centimeter (s)	cm
Chamfer	chfr
Channel	⊔
Checked (by)	Ch
Circular	cir
Circular pitch (gear drawings)	CP
Copper	cop
Cold rolled steel	CRS
Counterbore	c'bore
Countersink	csk
Cubic inches (feet; yards)	cu in. (ft; yd)
Cylinder, cylindrical	cyl
Degree (s) (angular measurement)	° or deg
Diameter	D
Direct current	d-c
Diagonal	diag
Diametral pitch (gear drawings)	DP
Drawing (s)	Dwg, Dwgs
Drawn (by)	Dr
Drop forging	D forg
Detail drawing	Dtl dwg
Die casting	D cast
Die stamping	D st
External	ext
Extra fine (Am Std fine thread)	EF
Fabricate	fab

Fillister	fil
Foot, Feet	ft or ′
Finish	V or fin or f
Gage	ga
Gallon	gal
Galvanized iron	GI
Grind	gr
H Beam	H
Head	hd
Hexagonal	hex
Harden	hdn
Horsepower	hp or HP
Heat-treatment, SAE (specified by number)	htr #——
I beam	I
Impregnate	impreg
Inside diameter	ID
Inch (es)	″ or in.
Insulate, insulated	insl
Kilowatt	kw
Kip	k
Left hand	LH
Laminate	lam
Lateral	lat
Longitudinal	long
Lubricate, lubrication	lub
Machine	mach
Magnetic	mag
Malleable iron	Mal I
Maximum	max
Meter (s)	m
Millimeter (s)	mm
Minute (s), (time)	′ or min
Minute (s) (angular measure)	′
Minimum	min
National form (screw threads)	N
National Coarse (screw threads)	NC
National Fine (screw threads)	NF
National Electrical Code	NEC
Number	# or no.
On center—(center to center)	oc
Outside diameter	OD
Oxidize	ox
Parallel to	‖
Patent	pat

Pattern	patt
Perforate	perf
Perpendicular to	⊥
Phosphor bronze	phos bro
Piece (s)	pc, pcs
Pitch	P
Pitch diameter	PD
Plate	pl
Pound	# or lb
Pratt and Whitney (key)	P & W
Propeller	prop
Quart	qt
Radius	R
Required	req
Revolutions per minute	rpm
Revolutions per second	rps
Right hand	RH
Round	rd
Round bar	⌀
Round bar deformed	∮
Screw	sc
Section	sec
Society of Automotive Engineers	SAE
Square	□ or sq
Square bar	⊡
Square bar, deformed	⊡ (deformed)
Square foot, feet	sq ft or □′
Square inch (es)	sq in. or □″
Standard	Std
Steel	Stl
Steel casting	Stl C
Tee (structural shape)	T
Teeth (on gear drawings)	T
Thread (s)	thd, thds
Traced (by)	Tr
United States form (old)	USF
United States Standard (old)	USS
Wide flange section (structural)	WF
Woodruff (key)	spell out or Wdrf
Wrought iron	WI
Yard (s)	yd, yds
Zee (structural shape)	Z

THE GREEK ALPHABET

While Greek is not a required study in most engineering curricula, the engineer often uses letters of the Greek alphabet, both capitals and lower case, as symbols and reference letters. He should therefore be able to draw them readily and to read them without hesitation when encountered in equations or formulas.

There is a variety in Greek alphabets, just as there is in Roman alphabets. The one given below is a legible form with accented and unaccented strokes in the capitals that follow closely the rules for shading Roman letters. The lower case has good historical precedent in form, shading, and comparative size.

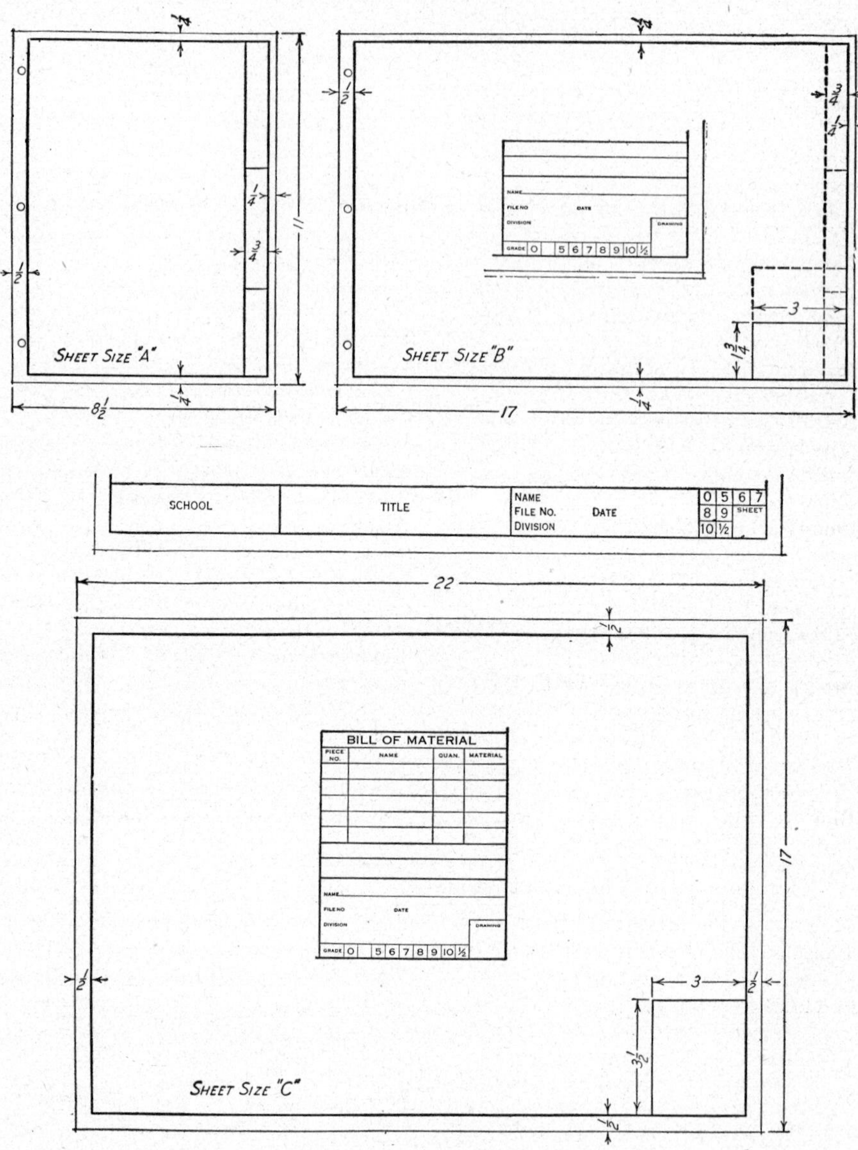

American Standard sheet sizes.

The above are suggested border and title dimensions for American Standard trimmed sheet sizes *A*, *B*, and *C*. The title blocks shown are convenient forms for classroom use. The grading strip at the bottom of the title block gives a method of grading in increments of 5 per cent; thus a mark over the eight and the one-half blocks will indicate a grade of 85 per cent. The strip title shown may be used in place of the block title on the *B* size sheet, as indicated by the dotted lines.

GLOSSARY OF SHOP TERMS FOR DRAFTSMEN

Anneal (*v*)—To soften a metal piece and remove internal stresses by heating to its critical temperature and allowing to cool very slowly.

Arc-weld (*v*)—To weld by electric-arc process.

Bore (*v*)—To enlarge a hole with a boring tool as in a lathe or boring mill. Distinguished from *drill*.

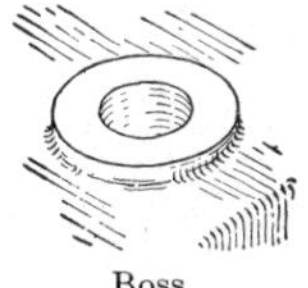
Boss.

Boss (*n*)—A projection of circular cross section, as on a casting or forging.

Braze (*v*)—To join by the use of hard solder.

Broach (*v*)—To finish the inside of a hole to a shape usually other than round. (*n*) A tool with serrated edges, pushed or pulled through a hole to enlarge it to a required shape.

Buff (*v*)—To polish with abrasive on a cloth wheel or other soft carrier.

Burnish (*v*)—To smooth or polish by a rolling or sliding tool under pressure.

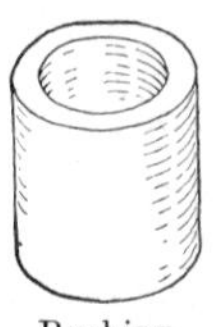
Bushing.

Bushing (*n*)—A removable sleeve or liner for a bearing; also a guide for a tool in a jig or fixture.

Carburize (*v*)—To prepare a low-carbon steel for heat-treatment by packing in a box with carbonizing material, such as wood charcoal, and heating to about 2000° F. for several hours, then allowing to cool slowly.

Caseharden (*v*)—To harden the surface of carburized steel by heating to critical temperature and quenching, as in an oil or lead bath.

Castellate (*v*)—To form into a shape resembling a castle battlement, as castellated nut. Often applied to a shaft with multiple integral keys milled on it.

Chamfer (*v*)—To bevel a sharp external edge. (*n*) A beveled edge.

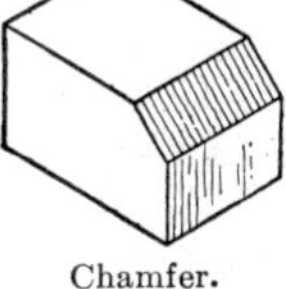
Chamfer.

Chase (*v*)—To cut threads in a lathe, as distinguished from cutting threads with a die. (*n*) A slot or groove.

Chill (*v*)—To harden the surface of cast iron by sudden cooling against a metal mold.

Chip (*v*)—To cut or clean with a chisel.

Coin (*v*)—To stamp and form a metal piece in one operation, usually with a surface design.

Cold-work (*v*)—To deform metal stock by hammering, forming, drawing, etc., while the metal is at ordinary room temperature.

Color-harden (*v*)—To caseharden to a very shallow depth, chiefly for appearance.

Core (*v*)—To form the hollow part of a casting, using a solid form made of sand, shaped in a core box, baked and placed in the mold. After cooling the core is easily broken up leaving the casting hollow.

Counterbore (*v*)—To enlarge a hole to a given depth. (*n*) 1. The cylindrical enlargement of the end of a drilled or bored hole. 2. A cutting tool for counterboring, having a piloted end of the size of the drilled hole.

Counterbore.

Countersink (*v*)—To form a depression to fit the conical head of a screw, or the thickness of a plate, so the face will be level with the surface. (*n*) A conical tool for counter-sinking.

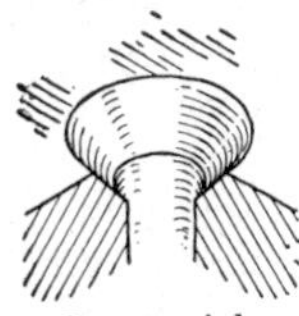
Countersink.

Crown (*n*)—Angular or rounded contour, as on the face of a pulley.

Die (*n*)—1. One of a pair of hardened metal blocks for forming, impressing, or cutting out a desired shape. 2 (thread). A tool for cutting external threads. Opposite of *tap*.

Die casting (*n*)—A very accurate and smooth casting made by pouring a molten alloy (or composition, as Bakelite) usually under pressure into a metal mold or die. Distinguished from a casting made in sand.

Die stamping (*n*)—A piece, usually of sheet metal, formed or cut out by a die.

Draw (*v*)—1. To form by a distorting or stretching process. 2. To temper steel by gradual or intermittent quenching.

Drill (*v*)—To sink a hole with a drill, usually a twist drill. (*n*) A pointed cutting tool rotated under pressure.

Drop forging (*n*)—A wrought piece formed hot between dies under a drop hammer, or by pressure.

Face (*v*)—To machine a flat surface perpendicular to the axis of rotation on a lathe. Distinguished from *turn*.

Feather (*n*)—A flat sliding key, usually fastened to the hub.

Fettle (*v*)—To remove fins and smooth the corners on unfired ceramic products.

File (*v*)—To finish or trim with a file.

Fillet (*n*)—A rounded filling of the internal angle between two surfaces.

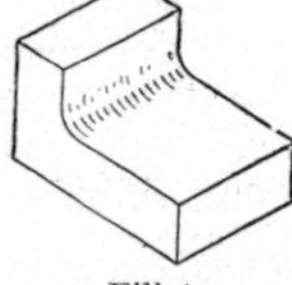

Fillet.

Fin (*n*)—A thin projecting rib. Also, excess ridge of material.

Fit (*n*)—The kind of contact between two machined surfaces, as (1) *drive, force*, or *press*—when the shaft is slightly larger than the hole and must be forced in with sledge or power press.

(2) *shrink*—when the shaft is slightly larger than the hole, the piece containing the hole is heated, thereby expanding the hole sufficiently to slip over the shaft. On cooling, the shaft will be seized firmly if the fit allowances have been correctly proportioned.

(3) *running* or *sliding*—when sufficient allowance has been made between sizes of shaft and hole to allow free running without seizing or heating.

(4) *wringing*—when the allowance is smaller than a running fit and the shaft will enter the hole by twisting it by hand.

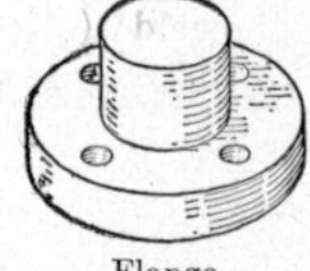

Flange.

Flange (*n*)—A projecting rim or edge for fastening or stiffening.

Forge (*v*)—To shape metal while hot and plastic by a hammering or forcing process either by hand or by machine.

Galvanize (*v*)—To treat with a bath of lead and zinc to prevent rusting.

Graduate (*v*)—To divide a scale or dial into regular spaces.

Grind (*v*)—To finish or polish a surface by means of an abrasive wheel.

Harden (*v*)—To heat hardenable steel above the critical temperature and quench in a bath.

Hot-work (*v*)—To deform metal stock by hammering, forming, drawing, etc., while the metal is heated to a plastic state.

Kerf (*n*)—The channel or groove cut by a saw or other tool.

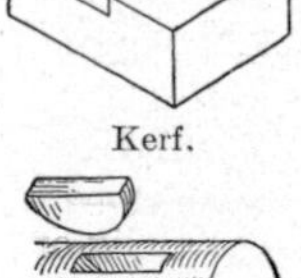

Kerf.

Key (*n*)—A small block or wedge inserted between shaft and hub to prevent circumferential movement.

Key and Seat.

Keyway, or key seat (*n*) A groove or slot cut to fit a key. A key fits into a key seat and slides in a keyway.

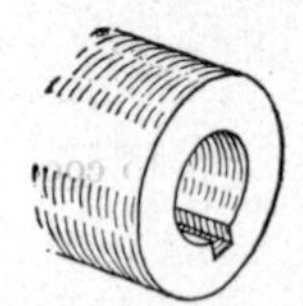

Keyway.

Knurl (*v*)—To roughen or indent a turned surface, as a knob or handle.

Lap (*n*)—A piece of soft metal, wood, or leather charged with abrasive material, used for obtaining an accurate finish. (*v*) To finish by lapping.

Lug (*n*)—A projecting "ear" usually rectangular in cross section. Distinguished from *boss*.

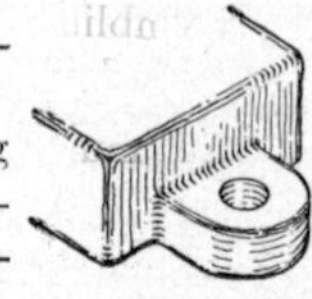

Lug.

Malleable casting (*n*)—An ordinary casting toughened by annealing. Applicable to small castings with uniform metal thicknesses.

Mill (*v*)—To machine with rotating toothed cutters on a milling machine.

Neck (*v*)—To cut a groove around a shaft, usually near the end or at a change in diameter. (*n*) A portion reduced in diameter between the ends of a shaft.

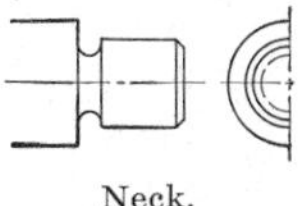
Neck.

Normalize (*v*)—To remove internal stresses by heating a metal piece to its critical temperature and allowing to cool very slowly.

Pack-harden (*v*)—To carburize and caseharden.

Pad (*n*)—A shallow projection. Distinguished from *boss* by shape or size.

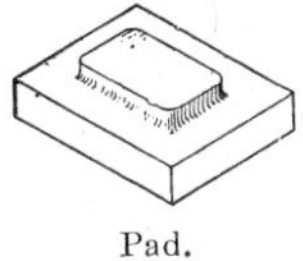
Pad.

Peen (*v*)—To stretch, rivet, or clinch over by strokes with the peen of a hammer. (*n*) The end of a hammer head opposite the face, as *ball peen.*

Pickle (*v*)—To clean castings or forgings in a hot weak sulphuric acid bath.

Plane (*v*)—To machine work on a planer having a fixed tool and reciprocating bed.

Planish (*v*)—To finish sheet metal by hammering with polished-faced hammers.

Plate (*v*)—The electrochemical coating of a metal piece with a different metal.

Polish (*v*)—To make smooth or lustrous by friction with a very fine abrasive.

Profile (*v*)—To machine an outline with a rotary cutter usually controlled by a master cam or die.

Punch (*v*)—To perforate by pressing a nonrotating tool through the work.

Ream (*v*)—To finish a drilled or punched hole very accurately with a rotating fluted tool of the required diameter.

Relief (*n*)—The amount one plane surface of a piece is set below or above another plane, usually for clearance or for economy in machining.

Rivet (*v*)—1. To fasten with rivets. 2. To batter or upset the headless end of a pin used as a permanent fastening.

Round (*n*)—A rounded exterior corner between two surfaces. Compare with *Fillet.*

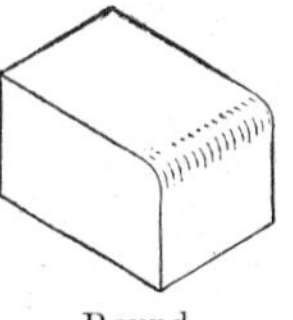
Round.

Sandblast (*v*)—To clean castings or forgings by means of sand driven through a nozzle by compressed air.

Shape (*v*)—To machine with a shaper, a machine tool differing from a planer in that the work is stationary and the tool reciprocating.

Shear (*v*)—To cut off sheet or bar metal between two blades.

Sherardize (*v*)—To galvanize with zinc by a dry heating process.

Shim (*n*)—A thin spacer of sheet metal used for adjusting.

Spin (*v*)—To shape sheet metal by forcing it against a form as it revolves.

Spline (*n*)—A long keyway. Sometimes also a flat key.

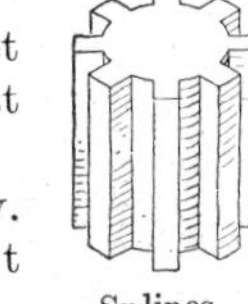
Splines.

Spot-face (*v*)—To finish a round spot on a rough surface, usually around a drilled hole, to give a good seat to a screw or bolthead. Cut, usually $\frac{1}{16}''$ deep, by a rotating milling cutter.

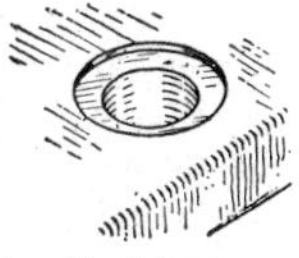
Spot-face.

Spot-weld (*v*)—To weld in spots by means of the heat of resistance to an electric current. Not applicable to sheet copper or brass.

Steel casting (*n*)—Material used in machine construction. It is ordinary cast iron into which varying amounts of scrap steel have been added in the melting.

Swage (*v*)—To shape metal by hammering or pressure with the aid of a form or anvil called a "swage block."

Sweat (*v*)—To join metal pieces by clamping together with solder between and applying heat.

Tack-weld (*v*)—To join at the edge by welding in short intermittent sections.

Tap (*v*)—To cut threads in a hole with a tapered tool called a "tap," having threads on it and fluted to give cutting edges.

Temper (*v*)—To change the physical characteristics of hardened steel by reheating to a temperature below the critical point and allowing to cool.

Template, templet (*n*)—A flat pattern for laying out shapes, location of holes, etc.

Trepan (*v*)—To cut an outside annular groove around a hole.

Trepan.

Tumble (*v*)—To clean, smooth, or polish castings or forgings in a rotating barrel or drum by friction with each other, assisted by added mediums, as scraps, "jacks," balls, sawdust, etc.

Turn (*v*)—To machine on a lathe. Distinguished from *face*.

Undercut (*v*)—To cut, leaving an overhanging edge. (*n*) A cut having inwardly sloping sides.

Undercut.

Upset (*v*)—To forge a larger diameter or shoulder on a bar.

Weld (*v*)—To join two pieces by heating them to the fusing point and pressing or hammering together.

GLOSSARY OF STRUCTURAL TERMS FOR DRAFTSMEN

Batten plate—A small plate used to hold two parts in their proper position when made up as one member.

Batter—A deviation from the vertical in upright members.

Bar—Square or round rod; also flat steel up to 6 inches in width.

Bay—The distance between two trusses or transverse bents.

Beam—A horizontal member forming part of the frame of a building or structure.

Bearing plate—Flat steel over 6 inches in width and over 2 inches in thickness.

Bent—A vertical framework usually consisting of a truss or beam supported at the ends on columns.

Brace—A diagonal member used to stiffen a framework.

Buckle plate—A flat plate with dished depression pressed into it to give transverse strength.

Built-up member—A member built from standard shapes to give one single stronger member.

Camber—Slight upward curve given to trusses and girders to avoid effect of sag.

Cantilever—A beam, girder, or truss overhanging one or both supports.

Chord—The principal member of a truss on either the top or bottom.

Clearance—Rivet driving clearance is distance from center of rivet to obstruction. Erection clearance is amount of space left between members for ease in assembly.

Clevis—U-shaped shackle for connecting a rod to a pin.

Clip angle—A small angle used for fastening various members together.

Column—A vertical compression member.

Cope—To cut out top or bottom of flanges and web so that one member will frame into another.

Coping—A projecting top course of concrete or stone.

Counters—Diagonal members in a truss to provide for reversal of shear due to live load.

Cover plate—A plate used in building up flanges in a built-up member to give greater strength and area, or for protection.

Crimp—To offset the end of a stiffener to fit over the leg of an angle.

Diagonals—Diagonal members used for stiffening and wind bracing.

Dowel—An iron or wooden pin extending into but not through two timbers to connect them.

Driftpin—A tapered steel pin used to bring rivet holes fair in assembling steel work.

Edge distance—The distance from center of rivet to edge of plate or flange.

Fabricate—To cut, punch, and subassemble members in the shop.

Fillers—Either plate or ring fills used to take up space in riveting two members where a gusset is not used.

Flange—The projecting portion of a beam, channel, or column.

Gage line—The center line for rivet holes.

Gin pole—A guyed mast with block at the top for hoisting.

Girder—A horizontal member, either single or built up, acting as a principal beam.

Girt—A beam usually bolted to columns to support the side covering or serve as window lintels.

Gusset plate—A plate used to connect various members, such as in a truss.

Hip—The intersection between two sloping surfaces forming an exterior angle.

Knee brace—A corner brace used to prevent angular movement.

Lacing or lattice bars—Bars used diagonally to space and stiffen two parallel members, such as in a built-up column.

Laterals—Members used to prevent lateral deflection.

Lintel—A horizontal member used to carry a wall over an opening.

Louvers—Metal slats either movable or fixed, as in a monitor ventilator.

Monitor ventilator—A framework that carries fixed or movable louvers at the top of the roof.

Muntin—Parting strip in sash.

Panel—The space between adjacent floor supports, or purlins in a roof.

Pitch—Center distance between rivets parallel to axis of member. Also for roofs, the ratio of rise to span.

Plate—Flat steel over 6 inches in width and ¼ inch or more in thickness.

Purlins—Horizontal members extending between trusses, used as beams for supporting the roof.

Rafters—Beams or truss members supporting the purlins.

Sag ties—Tie rods between purlins in the plane of the roof to carry the component of the roof load parallel to the roof.

Separator—Either a cast-iron spacer or wrought-iron pipe on a bolt for the purpose of holding members a fixed distance apart.

Sheet—Flat steel over 6 inches in width and less than ¼ inch in thickness.

Shim—A thin piece of wood or steel placed under a member to bring it to a desired elevation.

Sleeve nut—A long nut with right and left threads for connecting two rods to make an adjustable member.

Span—Distance between centers of supports of a truss, beam, or girder.

Splice—A longitudinal connection between the parts of a continuous member.

Stiffener—Angle, plate, or channel riveted to a member to prevent buckling.

Stringer—A longitudinal member used to support loads directly.

Strut—A compression member in a framework.

Truss—A rigid framework for carrying loads, formed in a series of triangles.

Turnbuckle—A coupling, threaded right and left or swiveled on one end, for adjustably connecting two rods.

Valley—The intersection between two sloping surfaces, forming a reentrant angle.

Web—The part of a channel, I beam, or girder between the flanges.

SUPPLEMENTARY VISUAL MATERIALS

In addition to the McGraw-Hill Text-Films that are specifically correlated with certain chapters in this book and are listed at the end of these chapters, the following list of visual aids may be used to supplement some of the material in the book. It is suggested that each film and filmstrip be previewed before using as some may contain information that is too advanced while others may contain information that is too elementary.

These films and filmstrips can be obtained from the producer or distributor listed with each title. (The addresses of these producers and distributors are given at the end of this listing.) In many cases these films can also be obtained from your local film library or distributor; also, many universities have large film libraries from which they can be borrowed.

The running time (min), whether it is silent (si) or sound (sd), and whether it is a motion picture (MP) or filmstrip (FS) are listed with each title. All the motion pictures are 16mm; filmstrips are 35mm.

All the U.S. Office of Education films have coordinated silent filmstrips and instructor's manuals. In many cases other films also have accompanying instructor's manuals.

Each film and filmstrip has been listed only once in connection with the chapter to which it is most applicable. However, many of them can be used advantageously in connection with other chapters.

CHAPTER 1—INTRODUCTORY

The Draftsman (VGF 11min sd MP). A vocational guidance film showing the work of the draftsman as related to the various types of constructional and mechanical work; indicates the multitude of jobs available for draftsmen in industry.

Behind the Shop Drawing (JH 20min sd MP). Provides an excellent introduction to drafting nomenclature; explains isometric and orthographic engineering drawing.

Industrial Design (Knaus 10min si MP). Shows step-by-step procedure in designing a radio cabinet from the first "thumbnail" sketch to the finished drawing.

Modes and Motors (GM 10min sd MP). Describes complete process in designing products from the artist's first rough sketch to the finished product.

CHAPTER 2—THE SELECTION OF INSTRUMENTS
and
CHAPTER 3—THE USE OF INSTRUMENTS

T Squares and Triangles, Part 1 (JH FS). Fundamental uses of a T Square and the 45-degree and 30–60-degree triangles; tools and equipment needed; correct care and usage.

T Squares and Triangles, Part 2 (JH FS). Manipulation of triangle to obtain angular lines.

Use of T Square and Triangles (Purdue 11min sd MP). Demonstrates the basic principles governing the proper use of the T square and triangles; shows how a variety of angular lines may be constructed using these tools.

Testing of T Square and Triangles (Purdue 13min si MP). Shows the proper procedure to follow in checking these tools for accuracy.

Instruments and Materials (IIT 18min si MP). Shows mechanical drawing with properly arranged table; use of drawings and blueprints.

Drafting Tips (PSC 28min sd MP). Shows procedures in developing a drawing; use and care of drafting equipment.

The Steel Rule (USOE 14min sd MP). Explains proper methods for reading various types of metal rules, depth gages, squares, and inside and outside calipers.

Layout Work, Part 1 (JH FS). Techniques used in layout work.

Layout Work, Part 2 (JH FS). Special layout problems on actual work examples.

Layout Work and Measuring Instruments (JH FS). Explains what layout work is; tools used; use and care of measuring instruments.

Ink Work and Tracing (Purdue 30min si MP). Shows various steps in preparing tracings on cloth; explains procedure to follow, with emphasis on use of instruments and the order of inking in producing a desirable tracing.

CHAPTER 4—LETTERING

Capital Letters (Purdue 20min sd MP). Shows the construction of single-stroke inclined commercial gothic capital letters, ampersand, and numerals on ruled grid.

Lower Case Letters (Purdue 13min sd MP). Demonstrates construction of each lower-case letter.

Basic Standards in Mechanical Drafting (Eberhard Faber 16 by 24″ wall chart). Shows lettering, alphabet of lines, dimensioning standards, and sectioning practices.

CHAPTER 5—APPLIED GEOMETRY

Applied Geometry (Purdue 16min si MP). Explains geometric construction for mechanical drafting showing how to bisect a line and how to draw tangents and figures with the use of the T square, triangles, and compasses.

Geometric Construction, Part 1 (JH FS). Describes method of applying simple geometric construction principles to drawing problems.

Geometric Construction, Part 2 (JH FS). Presents more advanced geometric construction principles applied to drawing problems.

Angles (Kansas 11min sd MP). Illustrates how angles occur around us in common designs and constructions; defines the simple angle and its variations.

Lines and Angles (Knowledge 12min sd MP). Depicts the geometry of straight, right, acute, obtuse, and reflex angles.

Angular Measurement (JH FS). Shows systems of angular measurements, degrees, and radians as they are related to each other.

CHAPTER 6—THE THEORY OF PROJECTION DRAWING
and
CHAPTER 7—ORTHOGRAPHIC PROJECTION

Orthographic Projection (Purdue 30min si MP). Demonstrates proper methods for representing objects on paper with three orthographic views; shows how to transfer dimensions and use the instruments.

Introduction to Mechanical Drawing (Cocking 20min si MP). Shows preparation of materials and methods of procedure for making drawings of objects requiring one, two, and three views.

CHAPTER 8—AUXILIARY VIEWS

Auxiliary Views (Purdue 15min si MP). Demonstrates principles of sectioning and of transparent cutting planes; shows full, half, and offset sectional drawings.

CHAPTER 9—SECTIONS AND CONVENTIONS

Sectional Views, Projections, Finish Marks (USOE 15min sd MP). Shows alphabet of lines and their uses, location and use of finish marks, and standard cross-section lines denoting types of materials.

Shop Drawing, Part 1 (IIT 11min sd MP). An introduction to the elements of engineering drawing practice including conventional methods in use; shows dimensioning, sectioning, and crosshatching of drawings.

CHAPTER 10—THE DRAWINGS AND THE SHOP

Shop Drawing, Part 2 (IIT 11min sd MP). Illustrates recognized procedures used in drawing various types of curves and contours; emphasizes the importance of the draftsman's responsibility to produce accurate and legible drawings.

Basic Machines: The Lathe (USOE 15min sd MP). Explains that the lathe is used to shape cylindrical work; shows how the workpiece is supported between centers; how power is applied to rotate the workpiece; how the spindle speed, the position of the cutting tool, and the rate of feed may be varied to fit the job.

Machine Tools: The Lathe (Army sd FS). Gives nomenclature, practical uses, and illustrates the operation of the lathe.

The Turret Lathe: An Introduction (USOE 17min sd MP). Shows the functions of the head, hexagon turret, square turret, and bed; how to determine the sequence of operations; how to take a multiple cut; how to combine cuts from the hexagon and square turrets.

Turret Lathes (Gisholt 45min sd MP). Shows operations that can be performed on turret lathe; method of setting up machine for different types of cuts.

Specialized Machines: Turret Lathe (JH FS). Tells what turret lathe is and what can be done with it; shows the automatic screw and its functions; illustrates its relationship to lathe work.

Basic Machines: The Milling Machine (USOE 15min sd MP). Explains that the milling machine is used with formed cutters to cut an infinite variety of shapes in metal; shows how the cutter is supported on the arbor; how power is applied to rotate the cutter; how the workpiece is fed to the cutter; how the spindle speed, the position of the workpiece, and the rate of feed may be varied to fit the job.

Machine Tools: The Milling Machine (Army sd FS). Gives nomenclature, practical uses, and operation of the milling machine.

The Milling Machine (USOE 18min sd MP). Illustrates the basic operating principle of the milling machine; how to set up cutters on the arbor; how to control movements of the table by power traverse and by hand; demonstrates the various types of jobs that can be done on the milling machine.

Basic Machines: The Shaper (USOE 15min sd MP). Explains that the shaper is used to produce flat surfaces on metal; shows how the cutting tool is mounted and positioned; how the workpiece is mounted; how the length of stroke, cutting speed, and table feed are adjusted to fit the job.

Machine Tools: The Shaper (Army sd FS). Gives nomenclature, practical uses, and operation of the shaper.

Machine Tools: Planers (Army sd FS). Gives nomenclature, practical uses, and operation of the planer.

Planer and Shaper Operations (FiPr 10min sd MP). Shows machine operations; portrays construction, holding of work and tool, and use of machinery.

Basic Machines: The Drill Press (USOE 10min sd MP). Explains that the drill press is used to produce round holes in metal; shows briefly the principal steps in operating a drill press; identifies the parts of a drill press and explains their functions; shows different types of drill presses.

In addition to the above, there are many U.S. Office of Education and industrial motion pictures that can be used to show practices in machine, patternmaking, foundry, and various other shops.

CHAPTER 11—DIMENSIONS AND NOTES
and
CHAPTER 12—THE DIMENSIONING OF MACHINE DRAWINGS

Principal Dimensions, Reference Surfaces and Tolerances (USOE 12min sd MP). Shows the use and theory of dimensions.

Visualizing an Object (USOE 9min sd MP). Shows how a blueprint is developed; how dimensions are shown by different views; how various kinds of lines are shown on a blueprint; how special information is indicated on a blueprint.

Reading a Three-view Drawing (USOE 10min sd MP). Shows how to use a blueprint to visualize the object; how to interpret a blueprint; how to make a tool block according to specifications.

Reading a Drawing of a Valve Bonnet (USOE 20min sd MP). Explains significance of conventional symbols as applicable to mechanical drawings; how to use the blueprint as a guide in planning machine operations; how to determine dimensions not directly denoted on a drawing.

Drawing an Anchor Plate (JH FS). Explains the drawing-board setup and the tools required; follows through with layout of lines, holes, arcs, and dimensions; illustrates and defines the various lines in use, also arrowheads and lettering applications.

CHAPTER 13—BOLTS, SCREWS, KEYS, RIVETS, AND SPRINGS

Screw Threads (Purdue 23min si MP). Defines important terms associated with screw threads; shows step-by-step construction of National and square threads; explains meaning of each line of the drawing.

CHAPTER 19—TECHNICAL SKETCHING

The Micrometer (USOE 15min sd MP). Describes different types of micrometers; how to apply them to practice; the use and care they should receive.

Verniers (USOE 19min sd MP). A detailed study of the principles and applications of the vernier scale as used for precision measurements.

Fixed Gages (USOE 17min sd MP). Demonstrates the use of numerous types of gages used for production work in modern manufacturing.

The Bevel Protractor (USOE 15min sd MP). Shows how to use, set, and read the bevel protractor.

Height Gages and Test Indicators (USOE 12min sd MP). Shows vernier measure as applied to height gages; also shows the use of standard indicators for checking finished work.

Measurements and Measuring, Part 1 (JH FS). Illustrates standards of measurement and work accuracy; discussion of the steel scale and its variations, dividers, and calipers.

Measurements and Measuring, Part 2 (JH FS). Explains the micrometer, vernier-scale principle, gages, and gage blocks.

Precision Layout and Measuring (PSC 11min sd MP). Shows basic methods used in jig boring, milling machining, and lathe boring; illustrates principles of measuring instruments and gives examples of each.

CHAPTER 20—DEVELOPED SURFACES AND INTERSECTIONS

Development of Surfaces (Purdue 15min si MP). Shows the construction of patterns of surfaces; describes methods for right and oplique prisms, right cylinders, pyramids and cones, oblique cones.

Intersection of Surfaces (Purdue 15min si MP). Demonstrates procedures for finding intersections of right. oblique, and curved surfaces.

How to Develop an Intersection: Part 1 (Castle si FS). Shows how to make a true layout for a flat pattern of a cylinder.

How to Develop an Intersection: Part 2 (Castle si FS). Demonstrates steps in laying out, forming, and assembling a filler neck and collar to a metal tank.

CHAPTER 23—PICTORIAL SKETCHING

Pictorial Drawing (Purdue 30min si MP). Illustrates the principles of isometric and oblique drawing.

Freehand Drawing (Purdue 13min si MP). Shows sketching as an antecedent in drawing; illustrates use of pencil, strokes, horizontal, vertical, and inclined lines in forming figures, circles, and ellipses.

CHAPTER 24—ILLUSTRATION

Broad Stroke Drawing (Ideal 10min sd MP). Demonstrates the art of broad stroke drawing; shows variety of strokes that can be obtained by using various surfaces of the drawing implement.

CHAPTER 25—AIRCRAFT DRAWING

Airplane Sheet Metal Work (Vesco 30min si MP). Shows use of drafting instruments; reading of blueprints necessary; procedures and techniques of work.

The Making of an Airplane Fitting (Vesco 30min si MP). Demonstrates drawing of design; transfer of blueprint to metal; fitting part into plane; tools and machinery.

Fabricating Metal Aircraft (Castle 14min sd MP). Describes different manufacturing processes utilized in manufacturing metal aircraft.

CHAPTER 26—THE ELEMENTS OF ARCHITECTURAL DRAWING

Basic Standards for Architectural Drawing (Eberhard Faber 16 by 24″ wall chart). Shows architectural details.

Architectural and Engineering Symbols (Fredrick Post 23 by 35″ wall chart).

Standard Woodworking Joints (Eberhard Faber 16 by 24″ wall chart). Shows isometric views of common wood joints.

CHAPTER 27—THE ELEMENTS OF STRUCTURAL DRAWING

Structural Drawing (Purdue 20min si MP). Explains procedure for making pencil drawings on tracing paper for blueprinting; work is related to structural construction.

CHAPTER 29—CHARTS, GRAPHS, AND DIAGRAMS

Plotting Graphs (JH FS). Describes visualizing the equation; constants and how they change the picture; simultaneous equations and their solutions.

Graph Uses (JH FS). Shows how to develop and use graphs in everyday activities; gives their relationship to formulas and equations and indicates their use as a device for giving the facts at a glance.

Analytic Geometry (JH FS). Illustrates quadratic equations, writing the equation for easy graphing; drawing board methods in graphing.

Rectilinear Co-ordinates (United 12min sd MP). Demonstrates Descartes' theorem, point, line, plane, and solid; number-scale, coordinates, plus and minus, axes, and three-dimensional locations and relationships.

Frequency Curves (Wisconsin 11min sd MP). Explains the nature of statistical frequency distribution; depicts why frequency curves must be regarded as limits of an area; analyzes properties of natural objects to show facts supporting theory.

GENERAL

Shop Terms and Methods (NYU 30min si MP). Defines the mechanical nomenclature used in industry and its application to drawing instruments.

Scales and Models (JH FS). The story behind scales and models; bringing "too big" and "too small" into easy focus; how to plan, use, and understand these valuable aids.

Geometry in Action (Illinois 11min sd MP). Explains the practical applications of geometry to answer the question, "What good will geometry do me?"

Geometry Brought to Life (Wisconsin 11min sd MP). Shows that everyday life is concerned with applications of geometry.

Locus (Knowledge 12min sd MP). Visual explanation of locus.

The Slide Rule: Multiplication and Division (USOE 24min sd MP). Explains in detail the *C* and *D* scales; the parts and markings of the rule; shows how to use these scales for multiplication, division, and combinations of these two operations.

The Slide Rule: Percentage, Proportion, Squares and Square Roots (USOE 21min sd MP). Shows how to use the *B* and *C* scales to calculate proportions and percentages; how to calculate squares and square roots; how to determine placing of decimals after the square root is extracted.

An Introduction to Vectors: Coplanar Concurrent Forces (USOE 22min sd MP). Explains the meaning of scalar and vector quantities; the various methods of vector composition and vector resolution; shows how vectors may be employed to solve engineering problems.

Vectors (JH FS). A simple means for graphic visualization of the three force properties; concurrent and resultant forces analyzed.

SOURCES OF FILMS LISTED ABOVE

Army—U.S. Army (obtainable from Castel Films, Inc.).
Castle Films, 30 Rockefeller Plaza, New York 20.
Cocking, Floyd W., 4757 Constance Dr., San Diego, Calif.
Eberhard Faber Co., Education Department, 37 Greenpoint Ave., Brooklyn 27, N.Y.
FiPr—Film Production Co., 3650 N. Fremont Ave., Minneapolis, Minn.
Gisholt Machine Co., 1245 E. Washington Ave., Madison 3, Wis.
GM—General Motors Corp., Department of Public Relations, 1775 Broadway, New York 19.
Ideal Pictures Corp., 28 E. Eighth St., Chicago 5.
IIT—Illinois Institute of Technology, 3300 Federal St., Chicago.
Illinois, University of, Visual Aids Service, Champaign, Ill.
JH—Jam Handy Organization, 2900 E. Grand Blvd., Detroit 11, Mich.
Kansas, University of, Visual Instruction Bureau, Lawrence, Kan.
Knaus, Frank, 2113 Parkside Ave., Los Angeles, Calif.
Knowledge Builders, 625 Madison Ave., New York 22.
NYU—New York University Film Library, 26 Washington Sq., New York 3.
PSC—Pennsylvania State College, Film Library, State College, Pa.
Post Co., Fredrick, 3635 N. Hamilton Ave., Chicago.
Purdue University, General Engineering Dept., Lafayette, Ind.
United World Films, Inc., 1250 Sixth Ave., New York 20.
USOE—U.S. Office of Education (obtainable from Castle Films, Inc.).
Vesco Film Library, Audio-Visual Corp., 116 Newbury St., Boston 16.
VGF—Vocational Guidance Films, 2708 Beaver Ave., Des Moines 10, Iowa.
Wisconsin, University of, Bureau of Visual Instruction, Madison 6, Wis.

INDEX

D

E

F

G

H

I

J

K

L

M

N

Q

R

CHARLES Spielman...